PFAFF'S PROBLEM
AND ITS
GENERALIZATIONS

PFAFF'S PROBLEM
AND ITS
GENERALIZATIONS

BY

J. A. SCHOUTEN

PROFESSOR OF MATHEMATICS AT
AMSTERDAM UNIVERSITY

AND

W. v. d. KULK

ASSISTANT PROFESSOR AT BROWN UNIVERSITY
PROVIDENCE (R.I.), U.S.A.

CHELSEA PUBLISHING COMPANY
NEW YORK, N. Y.

THE PRESENT WORK IS A REPRINT, TEXTUALLY UNALTERED EXCEPT FOR THE CORRECTION OF ERRATA, OF A TREATISE FIRST PUBLISHED IN 1949 AT OXFORD. ITS PUBLICATION IS BY ARRANGEMENT WITH OXFORD UNIVERSITY PRESS

PUBLISHED, NEW YORK, N. Y., 1969 (ALKALINE PAPER)

LIBRARY OF CONGRESS CATALOGUE CARD NO. 75-77340

STANDARD BOOK NUMBER 8284-0221-3

PRINTED IN THE UNITED STATES OF AMERICA

PREFACE

We dedicate this book to PROFESSOR E. CARTAN, whose valuable investigations have thrown so much light on all fields of differential geometry.

IN olden times there was a slave, packing valuable leaves for his king. But he packed the leaves at random and the leaves came out badly damaged and the king was very angry and the head of the slave was cut off. Many other slaves came and went and the story was very sad. But at last there came one more intelligent than his predecessors, who packed the leaves nicely in layers, and they came out in a way that pleased the king. That slave not only saved his own life but he was the first man who faced and solved a Pfaff's problem.

Now let us take the leaves very small and very thin, say, infinitesimal 'facets', and let us pack them so closely that there is one facet in every point of the occupied space. Then they may be arranged in such a way that they form a system of ∞^1 surfaces in space. That is the nice packing. But if the packing is at random, though continuous, no such surfaces can be built. That is the packing to be condemned if valuable leaves are concerned. But mathematically it is not less interesting. To handle all kinds of packing we need an exact mathematical formulation and this will be given at once for an n-dimensional space.

A Pfaffian equation

$$w_\lambda d\xi^\lambda = 0 \quad (\lambda = 1,..., n) \tag{1}$$

represents an E_{n-1}-field in an X_n, that is, an $(n-1)$-direction in every point. If we write

$$W_{\mu\lambda} \stackrel{\text{def}}{=} \partial_\mu w_\lambda - \partial_\lambda w_\mu, \tag{2}$$

it may happen that

$$W_{\mu\lambda} w_\nu + W_{\lambda\nu} w_\mu + W_{\nu\mu} w_\lambda = 0. \tag{3}$$

In that case the equation (1) is called completely integrable or complete, and its E_{n-1}'s are tangent to a system of ∞^1 X_{n-1}'s in X_n. If (1) is not complete we may ask for the X_m's in X_n such that the tangent E_m in every point lies in the E_{n-1} of the field in this point. If 2ρ is the rank of the matrix of $W_{\mu\lambda}$ and $2\rho+2\epsilon$ ($\epsilon = 1$ or 0) the rank of the matrix

$$\overset{\longleftarrow n \longrightarrow \longleftarrow 1 \longrightarrow}{\left\| \begin{matrix} W_{\mu\lambda} & w_\mu \\ -w_\lambda & 0 \end{matrix} \right\|} \begin{matrix} \updownarrow n \\ \updownarrow 1 \end{matrix}$$

in the region of X_n considered, the maximum value of m is $\nu = n-\rho-\epsilon$.

The problem of the determination of all 'enveloped' X_m's we call the *simple Pfaff's problem.* It was formulated and partly solved by J. F. Pfaff in 1814.† Its complete solution is due to the collaboration of a great number of authors. We mention here only the names of Gauss, Jacobi, Natani, Clebsch, Grassmann, Frobenius, Lie, Darboux, Engel, v. Weber, Cartan, and Goursat and refer for full historical details to Forsyth,‡ Cartan,§ v. Weber,|| and Engel and Faber.††

A system of $n-p$ linearly independent Pfaffian equations represents an E_p-field in X_n. Here we have two problems. The *inner* problem requires the determination of the X_m's $(m \leqslant p)$ enveloped by E_p's of the field for the *maximum* value of m. The *outer* problem requires the determination, for the *minimum* value of m, of the 'enveloping' X_m's $(m \geqslant p)$, which are the X_m's whose tangent E_m in every point contains the E_p of the field. In this form the outer problem is equivalent to the problem of the solution of a system of p linearly independent homogeneous linear partial differential equations of the first order with one unknown variable.

We may formulate the inner and outer problem in another way, suitable for generalization. The E_p-field determines in every point, for $m \leqslant p$, a system of $\infty^{p(m-p)}$ E_m's and, for $m \geqslant p$, a system of $\infty^{(n-m)(m-p)}$ E_m's. From these E_m's a system of ∞^m E_m's, tangent to an X_m, has to be singled out. Now the generalization is obvious. Let a system of ∞^d geometric objects, all of the same kind, e.g. E_m's or vectors or tensors, be given in every local E_n in the points of X_n. We call these ∞^{n+d} objects the field A. Now let a class B of fields of the same objects be defined, whose field region does not necessarily have the dimension n, e.g. the E_m's tangent to some X_q in X_n. Then we may ask if A contains fields of class B, or, in other words, if there exist fields of class B whose objects all belong to A.

Naturally it is not our aim to give the solution of the problem in this most general form. For that we would need to develop the whole theory of differential equations and much more. This book contains in Chapters III, IV, V, VI, and VIII a detailed survey of well-known theories on Pfaff's problem and its known generalizations. The results of the investigations of the authors on some further generalizations will be found for the most part in Chapters VII and IX.

In Chapter I we give some algebraic preliminaries necessary for the sequel. In § 9 special attention is paid to the theory of the two

† 1814. 1.
‡ 1890. 2, ch. iii.
§ 1899. 1, pp. 239–41.
|| 1900. 1, ch. xv.
†† 1932. 1.

connecting quantities of an E_m in E_n, belonging to the null form and the parametric form respectively of the E_m, and to the section and reduction of quantities of E_n with respect to an E_m in E_n.

Chapter II contains analytical preliminaries. In §§ 1–6, 8 a number of theorems concerning the theory of an X_m in X_n, given by its null form or by its parametric form (§ 4), are dealt with. Here the notion of minimal regular systems, introduced in §§ 3 and 4, proves to be very useful. The theory of supernumerary coordinates, used in all domains of differential geometry, is developed in § 9. It is proved that a regular system remains regular if supernumerary coordinates are introduced. §§ 7 and 10 are devoted to the theory of section and reduction of quantities in X_n with respect to an X_m or X_n^m in X_n in close connexion with I, § 9. The remaining sections deal with the theory of differential comitants, the Lie derivative, invariant fields, and integral invariants.

In Chapter III the theory of linear partial differential equations of first order with one unknown variable is developed. This is an outer problem. § 1 contains a survey of the formulae for the outer and the inner problem in its simplest form. The theory of non-homogeneous systems is dealt with in §§ 7 and 14. By means of the canonical form of a contravariant vector field deduced in § 7 it is possible to prove in § 8 a theorem concerning the construction of absolutely invariant fields from relatively invariant ones, postponed in II, § 18. Special attention is paid to the theory of integrating factors in §§ 9 and 17. The hydrodynamical illustration in § 10 will be welcome to readers with a geometrical attitude of mind. The method of Mayer is expounded in § 16 in a form suitable as well for Mayer systems as for Jacobian systems and for their adjoint systems. § 19 deals with the facilitation of the integrating process if some solutions and some admitted infinitesimal transformations are known.

Chapter IV deals with the simple Pfaff's problem. In § 1 we give the definitions of general representation, normal representation, and canonical representation of general sets of objects and of isomorphy of fields. The classification of Pfaffians is based on the four associated complete systems S_1, S_2, S_3, and S_4, dealt with in §§ 3 and 4. Here three arithmetic invariants come in, the class K, the rotation class 2ρ, and the similarity class k. The canonical forms (§§ 5, 6) can be deduced in the easiest way by making use of the theory of conjugate and semi-conjugate sets of functions, expounded in § 4. In view of later developments the principal theorem IV.2 on the necessary and sufficient conditions for a set of S functions with index κ is most important.

The properties of similarity transformations and gradient transformations and the transformation of the arithmetic invariants with them are to be found in § 7. In § 8 a theorem concerning canonical forms with given initial conditions is proved.

The simplest arithmetic invariants of covariant q-vector fields are deduced in Chapter V, § 2, by methods similar to those used in Chapter IV. Similarity transformations of covariant q-vector fields are dealt with in § 4. In § 5 we show the use of the absolutely invariant fields, introduced in III, § 18, for integrating purposes. If the q-vector field is simple it is useful to introduce a fifth system S_5 next to the complete systems S_1, S_2, S_3, and S_4. Using these five systems we get the preliminary classification of Grynaeus. There are eight cases, and normal forms can be given for the cases A_1, A_2, B_1, B_2, C_1, and C_2.

Contact transformations of various kinds are dealt with under different names by a great number of authors. In Chapter VI we have introduced the following classification. If a Pfaffian of class $2\rho+\epsilon$ ($\epsilon = 1$ or 0) is written in a canonical form $\epsilon\, d\xi^0 + w_1 d\xi^1 + \ldots + w_\rho d\xi^\rho$, there are three kinds of special transformations of the $2\rho+\epsilon$ variables $\epsilon\xi^0$, $\xi^1, \ldots, \xi^\rho$, $w_1, \ldots, w_\rho$. The first leaves the Pfaffian invariant to within a scalar factor, the second leaves it invariant to within an additive gradient, and for the third the Pfaffian is invariant without any restrictions. If $w_1, \ldots, w_\rho$ are looked upon as components of a covariant vector or an E_ρ for $\epsilon = 0$ or $\epsilon = 1$ respectively in the $X_{\rho+\epsilon}$ of $\epsilon\xi^0$, $\xi^1, \ldots, \xi^\rho$, three kinds of transformations of elements (element = vector or E_ρ respectively in a point) arise, C_1-, C_2-, and C_3-transformations. Since $\epsilon = 1$ or 0, there are six cases and these represent just the six different kinds of contact transformations occurring in literature.

If a Pfaffian is given in a canonical form, enveloped X_ν's can be found without integration, and from this it follows that for this simple case the inner problem can be solved by means of C_3-transformations without integration, provided that a canonical form be known. Conversely, if a rule for the construction of all enveloped X_ν's of a Pfaffian is established, this rule immediately gives a rule for the construction of all possible C_3-transformations and the rules for the construction of all possible C_1- and C_2-transformations can easily be deduced. In § 2 it is shown that there are two different rules for the construction of the enveloped X_ν's, and this leads to two different rules for the construction of the most general C_1-, C_2-, and C_3-transformation in §§ 4, 6, and 5. Infinitesimal transformations leaving a Pfaffian invariant, or invariant to within a scalar factor or an additive gradient, are dealt with in

§ 7. This leads in § 8 to the most general forms of infinitesimal C_1-, C_2-, and C_3-transformations.

The properties of Poisson brackets (F, G) are most easily deduced if next to them Lagrange brackets $\{F, G\}$ are used. This is done in § 9. The next section is devoted to the transformation of the expressions (F, G) and $(F) = w_\lambda \frac{\partial F}{\partial w_\lambda}$ with C_1-, C_2-, and C_3-transformations.

Lie has shown that the integration of a system of partial differential equations can be effected with the smallest possible number of operations using function groups. In §§ 11 and 12 we give a new exposition of the theory of function groups based upon the construction of the canonical form of a bivector field.

If w_λ denotes a covariant vector in the X_n of ξ^κ, a system of $2n-m$ independent equations in ξ^κ, w_λ represents a vector manifold $\mathfrak{N}_m$, that is, a system ∞^m vector elements. In §§ 1–3 of Chapter VII we discuss the principal arithmetic invariants of an $\mathfrak{N}_m$, the w_λ-rank r, the field dimension t, the class K, the rotation class 2ρ, the similarity class k, the index l, and the invariants $\bar{K}$, $2\bar{\rho}$, and $\bar{k}$, connected with the vector field U_b in parametric space. The transformation of these invariants for C_1-, C_2-, and C_3-transformations is discussed in § 3.

An $\mathfrak{N}_m$ of class K and field dimension t is said to be totally integrable with respect to integral-$\mathfrak{N}_{m'}$'s of class K' and field dimension t' if each vector element of $\mathfrak{N}_m$ belongs to at least one $\mathfrak{N}_{m'}$ of this kind, whose vector elements all belong to $\mathfrak{N}_m$. The problem of the integrability of a given $\mathfrak{N}_m$ with respect to $\mathfrak{N}_{m'}$'s of a certain kind is one of the generalizations of Pfaff's problem mentioned above. Here the field A is the given $\mathfrak{N}_m$ and the class B is the set of all $\mathfrak{N}_{m'}$'s of the kind in question. In § 4 the principal theorem, giving the necessary and sufficient conditions for total integrability, is established by applying the principal theorem IV.2 of systems with index κ to the field U_b. It is interesting that, if total integrability exists for special values of K' and m' and if $n \leqslant m' < m$ and not simultaneously $K' = K$ and $m' = n$, the $\mathfrak{N}_{m'}$ containing a given vector element can always be chosen in such a way that it has the same field dimension as $\mathfrak{N}_m$ (Theorem VII.8). As special cases of an $\mathfrak{N}_m$ the $\mathfrak{V}_{m-n}$-fields, consisting of ∞^{m-n} vectors in every point of X_n and the $\mathfrak{S}_d^{n-1}$-fields, consisting of ∞^d E_{n-1}'s in every point, are treated.

The determination of all $\mathfrak{N}_{m'}$'s with respect to which total integrability exists is effected in § 5 by means of the construction of conjugate or semiconjugate sets of functions with respect to the field U_b in parametric space. Translated into terms of the null form this means that the set of $2n-m$ functions appearing in the null form has to be extended by adding new functions, satisfying certain conditions. These conditions are represented first in the form of congruences, but it is always possible to replace these congruences by equations.

In § 6 it is shown that the solution of a system of $2n-m$ partial differential equations of first order, known as the second method of Jacobi, forms a special case with $K = 1$ or 0, $K' = 1$, and $m' = n$. Lie's method of integration by means of function groups is expounded in detail in this section.

If $K' < K$ there is no total integrability, but nevertheless it may be possible that integral-$\mathfrak{N}_{m'}$'s of class K' exist. It is proved in § 7 that, if integral $\mathfrak{N}_{m'}$'s of class K' exist, it is always possible to construct an $\mathfrak{N}_{m^*}$ without integrations, which has the same integral-$\mathfrak{N}_{m'}$'s of class K' as the given $\mathfrak{N}_m$, and which is totally integrable with respect to these integral-$\mathfrak{N}_{m'}$'s.

By means of the theory of the $\mathfrak{N}_m$ it is now possible to complete the considerations of Chapter V and to give in § 8 a complete classification of simple q-vector fields and to construct normal forms for these fields in § 9. In § 10 it is proved that by means of C_3-transformations every $\mathfrak{N}_m$ can be brought into a canonical form.

In Chapter VIII we treat the inner problem, first for a Cartan system (§§ 1–4) and then for a Goursat system (§§ 5–9). § 10 gives the relations between the arithmetic invariants r_i, the characters s_i, the genus g, and the reduced genus g'. § 11 deals with the s-number ζ of a Goursat system and the simplification of the integration for $\zeta < g+1$. In this section we show that Mayer's method of integration of a complete system loses its artificial appearance if it is looked upon as a special case of Cartan's method of integration of a Cartan system. The determination of the invariant σ of a scalar-free Cartan system (the species of J. M. Thomas) can in some cases be reduced to the integration of a Goursat system, as is shown in § 12. For the testing of chains of integral elements two methods are developed in § 13. The special Cartan systems occurring in the theory of the integration of systems of partial differential equations are treated in § 14.

An $\mathfrak{S}_d^m$ is a system of ∞^d E_m's in a point of an X_n. An $\mathfrak{S}_d^m$-field is said to be completely integrable if every E_m of the field belongs to an X_m whose tangent E_m's belong all to the field. Using the parametric form (IX, § 2) of the field it is possible by means of the adjoint $'E_{m+d}$-field (IX, § 3) to deduce a necessary condition for complete integrability:

the field has to be 'preferred'. Sufficient conditions for preferred fields are given in § 5 for three special cases connected with the cases A, B, and C of Grynaeus (Ch. V). To every $\mathfrak{S}_d^m$-field belongs a set of $\mathfrak{S}_{d_p}^p$-fields ($p \leqslant m$) called the induced $\mathfrak{S}_{d_p}^p$-fields. In §§ 7 and 8 it is proved that every preferred $\mathfrak{S}_d^m$-field whose induced $\mathfrak{S}_{d_p}^p$-fields are 'stationary' is completely integrable (principal theorem of complete integrability of $\mathfrak{S}_d^m$-fields). The connexion between Goursat systems and $\mathfrak{S}_d^m$-fields is dealt with in § 9. § 10 contains the relations between the arithmetic invariants d_p, τ_p, ρ_p, and σ_p of an $\mathfrak{S}_d^m$-field. Complete integrability being established, it can be asked how the integral-X_m's can be uniquely determined by certain initial conditions. The two theorems of uniqueness solving this problem are proved in § 11. The formulae of the $\mathfrak{S}_d^m$-field are much more complicated if the null form is used instead of the parametric form. This is shown in § 12.

In X, § 1 we show that the solution of a system of partial differential equations can always be reduced to the determination of the integral-X_m's of a reduced special Cartan system. If $m \leqslant g$ these integral-X_m's can be determined by the methods developed in VIII, § 9. If $m > g$ the Cartan system has to be prolonged. The prolongation of a general Goursat system is dealt with in § 2. It is shown that the first prolongation always leads to a finite number of special Cartan systems. § 3 deals with the methods of prolongation of special Cartan systems. Total prolongation always leads to a finite number of reduced special Cartan systems, partial prolongation in general only to a finite number of not necessarily special Cartan systems. If the original system has a genus $< m$ the process of prolongation has to be repeated till we have got only systems with a genus $\geqslant m$. The theorem of prolongation of Cartan asserts that this process is finite. In §§ 4 and 5 the proof of this theorem is prepared by transforming the Cartan system into a normalized Cartan system by means of sets of polynomials of auxiliary variables. The properties of the prolongations of these normalized systems, dealt with in § 6, enable us in § 7 to give an exposition of Cartan's proof of 1904 of the theorem of prolongation. Special attention is paid to the extraordinary integral-X_m's for which Cartan's proof is not valid. If these extraordinary integral-X_m's are taken into consideration the finiteness of the integration process is not yet wholly established. This section closes with some remarks on Cartan's proof of 1945 for the case $m = 2$ and on another proof for that case that will become possible if the proof of a certain theorem of the theory of linear complexes can be found. In § 8 a short exposition is given of Riquier's treatment of systems of partial differential equations and a comparison of the advantages and disadvantages of both methods.

Throughout this book we use the kernel-index method of tensor calculus and in many cases an abbreviated notation allied to Cartan's ω-symbolism.

A table of operations necessary for integrating purposes at the end of the book will be welcome to many readers.

We owe many thanks to Mrs. J. Rooth in Epe, to Prof. E. T. Davies in Southampton, and to Mrs. A. M. Wood in Oxford who did much to improve our English, and to Dr. A. Urban, who during his stay in Epe gave valuable help with the correction of proofs.

Our collaboration with the Clarendon Press has been most agreeable and we wish to express our thanks for all they did to make the book what it should be. Continental authors are often accustomed to begin the real writing of the book when the first proofs come in. From the first the Press made the strict condition that this method should not be followed and accordingly we did our very best to deliver the manuscript in such a form that no avoidable corrections had to be made in the proofs. As a matter of fact the more we worked with this method the more we appreciated it, and we should like to advise other continental authors to give it full consideration.

EPE, HOLLAND — J. A .S.
PROVIDENCE (R.I.), U.S.A. — W. v. d. K.

CONTENTS

I

ALGEBRAIC PRELIMINARIES†

1. Affine transformations of coordinates and of points

WE consider an n-dimensional space with coordinates x^κ, subjected to the transformations of the affine group‡

$$x^{\kappa'} = a^{\kappa'} + A^{\kappa'}_{\kappa} x^\kappa; \quad \Delta \stackrel{\text{def}}{=} \operatorname{Det}(A^{\kappa'}_{\kappa}) \neq 0 \quad (\kappa = 1,..., n;\ \kappa' = 1',..., n')\S \tag{1.1}$$

with constant coefficients $a^{\kappa'}$, $A^{\kappa'}_{\kappa}$. Because $\Delta \neq 0$ there exists an inverse transformation

$$x^\kappa = a^\kappa + A^\kappa_{\kappa'} x^{\kappa'}; \quad \operatorname{Det}(A^\kappa_{\kappa'}) = \Delta^{-1} \quad (\kappa' = 1',..., n'). \tag{1.2}$$

Every coordinate system $x^{\kappa'}$ which can be formed from the x^κ by means of (1.1) is called an *allowable coordinate system*. In this chapter we use only allowable coordinate systems. A space equipped with all these allowable coordinate systems is called an *affine space* or an E_n.

Instead of the affine group we could use the special affine group with $a^{\kappa'} = 0$. In this case the centre O has the coordinates zero with respect to every allowable coordinate system. A space equipped only with these special coordinate systems is called a *centred* E_n.

In all formulae we have *kernel-letters* like A, x, *running indices* like κ, κ', and *fixed indices* like $1,..., n, 1',..., n'$. Every set of running indices belongs to one definite coordinate system, and to each such system belongs one definite set of fixed indices. A coordinate system is indicated by one of its running indices in parentheses, e.g. (κ), (κ'). Points and kernel-letters do not change with coordinate transformations, but the coordinates change, and a new set of running indices and of fixed indices has to be introduced for the new coordinate system.

There exists another kind of transformation called a point-transformation. With a point-transformation the points and the kernel-letters change but not the coordinate system, the running indices, or the fixed indices. So an affine transformation of points can be written in the form

$$y^\kappa = p^\kappa + P^\kappa_\lambda x^\lambda; \quad \operatorname{Det}(P^\kappa_\lambda) \neq 0. \tag{1.3}$$

† General references: v. Weber 1900. 1; Veblen 1927. 1; Schouten and v. Kampen 1930. 1; Veblen and Whitehead 1932. 2; Kähler 1934. 1; Schouten and Struik 1935. 1; Schouten 1938. 1; Schouten and v. Dantzig 1940. 1.

‡ We adopt the summation convention: if the same index appears in a term once as a subscript and once as a superscript, summation has to be effected.

§ Apart from a few exceptional cases the *five* indices $\kappa, \lambda, \mu, \nu, \omega$ always take the values $1,..., n$, and the five indices $\kappa', \lambda', \mu', \nu', \omega'$ always take the values $1',..., n'$.

A change of the kernel-letters will be effected by

(1) a change of the letter itself;

(2) adjoining an accent or another sign, e.g. *;

(3) adjoining an index *over* or *under* the kernel-letter. The upper and lower places to the right of the kernel-letter are reserved for running indices and fixed indices.

2. The geometry of the E_n

In this paragraph we give a brief account of the most important properties of affine space.

All points whose coordinates are solutions of a system of $n-p$ linearly independent linear equations, in any allowable system of coordinates, form the *null space* of this system. We can always choose the coordinates in such a way that $n-p$ of these coordinates vanish in this null space. All transformations of the affine group which leave invariant these $n-p$ coordinates form the affine group in the other p coordinates. Hence the null space is an E_p. Such an E_p is called *a linear manifold in* E_n or *an* E_p *in* E_n. We call an E_0 a *point*, an E_1 a *straight line*, an E_2 a *plane* and an E_{n-1} a *hyperplane*. To every allowable coordinate system belong n *coordinate-*E_1's, the *coordinate axes*, $\binom{n}{2}$ *coordinate-*E_2's, and $\binom{n}{p}$ *coordinate-*E_p's.

If every point of an E_q belongs to an E_p $(p > q)$, we say that the E_q *lies in* E_p or the E_p *contains* E_q.

A *translation* is a point-transformation of the form

$$'x^\kappa = x^\kappa + p^\kappa \tag{2.1}$$

with respect to some allowable coordinate system and thus with respect to all other allowable coordinate systems also. Two E_p's are called *parallel* if they can be transformed into each other by means of a translation. The set of all E_p's parallel to a given E_p is called a p-*direction* or an $\vec{E}_p$ or an *improper* E_{p-1}. In a centred E_n there exists a one-to-one correspondence between all $\vec{E}_p$'s and all E_p's through O. A *1*-direction or improper E_0 is called shortly a *direction*.† If one of the E_q's belonging to an $\vec{E}_q$ lies in an E_p belonging to an $\vec{E}_p$, we say that the $\vec{E}_q$ *lies in* the $\vec{E}_p$ and in the E_p, or that the $\vec{E}_p$ and E_p *contain* the E_q.

The following properties are valid both for proper and improper linear manifolds. An E_p and an E_q $(p \leqslant q,\ p > 0)$ are called $\frac{t}{p}$-*parallel* and,

† A direction in everyday language is a direction according to our definition with a sense (arrow).

for $t = p$, *parallel* if they contain the same $\vec{E}_t$ but no common $\vec{E}_{t+1}$. The *section* of an E_p and an E_q consists of all common E_0's. They form an E_s ($s \geqslant n-p-q$, $s \leqslant p$, $s \leqslant q$). An E_p and an E_q *span* an E_r if they are both contained in this E_r and if there exists no E_{r-1} containing E_p and E_q. For r and s the following equation holds

$$r = p+q-s. \tag{2.2}$$

E_r is called the *junction* of E_p and E_q.

To fix a proper E_p in E_n we need $(p+1)(n-p)$ numbers, e.g. the coordinates of the $p+1$ sections with $p+1$ of the $\binom{n}{p}$ coordinate-E_{n-p}'s with respect to a suitably chosen coordinate system. If an E_s in the E_p is already given, we need only $(p-s)(n-p)$ numbers.

If a p-direction $\vec{E}_p$ is given in E_n, we may consider all E_p's with this p-direction as points of an E_{n-p}. This process is called the *reduction* of the E_n with respect to $\vec{E}_p$. It can also be interpreted as an identification of all points in every E_p with this p-direction.

If any geometrical figure is given in E_n and if there is given an E_p and an $\vec{E}_q$ ($q = n-p$) having no $\vec{E}_1$ in common with E_p the following processes can be carried out:

(*a*) *Section with* E_p: all points of the figure, not belonging to E_p are omitted. Only the E_p is used.

(*b*) *Reduction with respect to* $\vec{E}_q$: all points of the figure lying in the same E_q with the q-direction $\vec{E}_q$ are identified. The resulting figure is contained in the E_p which is obtained from the E_n by reduction with respect to $\vec{E}_q$. Only the $\vec{E}_q$ is used.

(*c*) *Projection on the* E_p *in the q-direction* $\vec{E}_q$: through every point of the figure an E_q is laid with the q-direction $\vec{E}_q$. The section of this E_q with the E_p is the projection of the point. Both the E_p and the $\vec{E}_q$ are used.

An n-dimensional screw-sense is determined by n directions with sense (arrow), which are not contained in an $\vec{E}_{n-1}$ and are given in a definite order.† Two such systems determine the same screw-sense if they can be transformed into each other by an affine transformation with $\Delta > 0$. From this it follows that every coordinate system defines a definite screw-sense by its n axes, their $+$-senses, and the order $1,..., n$. This screw-sense changes with coordinate transformations if

† A part of a curve with a sense (arrow), not contained in E_n, can be used instead of n directions. If $\frac{1}{2}n(n+1)$ is even the sense can be omitted.

and only if $\Delta < 0$. If a p-dimensional screw-sense is given in an E_p in E_n, this screw-sense induces a definite screw-sense in every parallel E_p. Hence we can speak of an E_p or $\vec{E}_p$ with a screw-sense. An E_p or $\vec{E}_p$ with a screw-sense is said to be *oriented with inner orientation*. If a q-dimensional screw-sense is given in an E_q ($q = n-p$), having no direction in common with the E_p, this screw-sense induces a definite screw-sense in every E_q with this property. Hence we can speak of an E_p or $\vec{E}_p$ with a screw-sense outside the $\vec{E}_p$. An E_p or $\vec{E}_p$ with such a screw-sense is said to be *oriented with outer orientation*.

3. Quantities in E_n

A *quantity* in E_n is a correspondence between the allowable coordinate systems and the ordered sets of N numbers, subject to the following conditions:

(1) to every coordinate system corresponds one, and only one, ordered set of N numbers;

(2) if Φ_Λ ($\Lambda = 1,..., N$), and $\Phi_{\Lambda'}$ ($\Lambda' = 1',..., N'$) correspond to (κ) and (κ') respectively, the $\Phi_{\Lambda'}$ are functions of the Φ_Λ and the $A_\kappa^{\kappa'}$, linear in Φ_Λ and homogeneous algebraical in $A_\kappa^{\kappa'}$.

The Φ_Λ are called the *components* of the quantity *with respect to the coordinate system* (κ). Quantities are distinguished by the manner of transformation of their components. The most important quantities in E_n are the following:

(*a*) A *scalar* is a quantity with only one component, which is invariant with the transformation (1.1).

(*b*) A contravariant vector is a quantity with n components v^κ, and the law of transformation

$$v^{\kappa'} = A_\kappa^{\kappa'} v^\kappa. \tag{3.1}$$

A vector v^κ is represented by two points, x^κ and $y^\kappa = x^\kappa + v^\kappa$, fixed to within a translation and having a sense (arrow) from x^κ to y^κ. In a centred E_n the point with coordinates v^κ can be used instead.

A contravariant *pseudo-vector* is a contravariant vector, determined to within an arbitrary scalar factor. It is generally denoted by $\lfloor v^\kappa \rfloor$ and sometimes by v^κ. Its geometrical representation is a 1-direction and in a centred E_n it is an E_1 through O.

p linearly independent contravariant vectors determine an $\vec{E}_p$, and the directions of all contravariant vectors linearly dependent on these p are contained in this $\vec{E}_p$. Such a system of contravariant vectors is called a *contravariant domain* and the $\vec{E}_p$ its *support*. In a centred E_n, an E_p through O can be used as support instead. p is called the *dimension of the domain*. The contravariant domain is said to be *spanned* by the p vectors. If the vectors are given in a definite order, they determine an *inner* orientation of the $\vec{E}_p$. A contravariant domain and its support determine each other mutually.

To every coordinate system (κ) there belongs a system of contravariant vectors $\underset{\lambda}{e}^{\kappa}$ with the components†

$$\underset{\lambda}{e}^{\kappa} \overset{*}{=} \delta_{\lambda}^{\kappa} \overset{\text{def}}{=} \begin{cases} 1 & (\kappa = \lambda), \\ 0 & (\kappa \neq \lambda). \end{cases} \tag{3.2}$$

These are called the *contravariant measuring vectors of* (κ). The components $\underset{\lambda}{e}^{\kappa'}$ of these vectors with respect to another coordinate system (κ') are in general not 1 or 0 because

$$\underset{\lambda}{e}^{\kappa'} = A_{\kappa}^{\kappa'} \underset{\lambda}{e}^{\kappa} \overset{*}{=} A_{\lambda}^{\kappa'}. \tag{3.3}$$

The index λ in $\underset{\lambda}{e}^{\kappa}$, belonging to the central letter, is an example of an index which is not subject to transformations of coordinates. Such indices are said to be *dead* in contradistinction to indices like κ, which are called *living*. The symbol $\delta_{\lambda}^{\kappa}$ is the well-known *Kronecker symbol.* It stands for n^2 scalars and contains two dead indices. For historical reasons we write $\delta_{\lambda}^{\kappa}$ instead of $\overset{\kappa}{\underset{\lambda}{\delta}}$, which would be the logical notation. To another coordinate system (κ') belong n other measuring vectors $\underset{\lambda'}{e}^{\kappa'}$ whose components with respect to (κ') are 1 or 0. A coordinate system is determined by its measuring vectors to within a translation.

(c) A *covariant vector* is a quantity with n components w_{λ} and the law of transformation

$$w_{\lambda'} = A_{\lambda'}^{\lambda} w_{\lambda}. \tag{3.4}$$

A vector w_{λ} is represented by two hyperplanes,‡

$$u_{\lambda} x^{\lambda} = 1, \quad v_{\lambda} x^{\lambda} = 1, \quad u_{\lambda} :: v_{\lambda},$$
$$\frac{1}{w_{\lambda}} = \frac{1}{u_{\lambda}} - \frac{1}{v_{\lambda}}, \tag{3.5}$$

fixed to within translations and having a sign, e.g. a curved arrow, fixing a direction from the first to the second hyperplane. In a centred E_n the hyperplane $w_{\lambda} x^{\lambda} = 1$ can be used instead.

† The symbol $\overset{*}{=}$ denotes that an equation is only valid, or at least that the validity is only ascertained, for the coordinate system or systems used in the equation. Hence for every equation with $\overset{*}{=}$ there may be transformations of coordinates for which the equation is not invariant.

‡ :: denotes 'proportional to'.

A *covariant pseudo-vector* is a covariant vector, determined to within an arbitrary scalar factor. It is usually denoted by $\lfloor w_\lambda \rfloor$, but sometimes by w_λ. Its geometrical representation is an $(n-1)$-direction, and in a centred E_n, an E_{n-1} through O.

p linearly independent covariant vectors determine an $\vec{E}_{n-p}$, and the $(n-1)$-directions of all covariant vectors, linearly dependent on these p, all contain this $\vec{E}_{n-p}$. Such a system of covariant vectors is called a *covariant domain* and the $\vec{E}_{n-p}$ its support. In a centred E_n an E_{n-p} through O can be used as its support. p is called the *dimension of the domain.* The covariant domain is said to be *spanned* by the p vectors. If the vectors are given in a definite order, they determine an *outer* orientation of the $\vec{E}_{n-p}$. A covariant domain and its support determine each other mutually.

To every coordinate system (κ) belongs a system of covariant vectors $\overset{\kappa}{e}_\lambda$ with the components

$$\overset{\kappa}{e}_\lambda \overset{*}{=} \delta^\kappa_\lambda. \tag{3.6}$$

These are called the *covariant measuring vectors of* (κ).

All that was said about contravariant measuring vectors holds *mutatis mutandis* for covariant measuring vectors.

A contravariant vector v^κ and a covariant one w_λ can be combined so as to form a scalar

$$v^\lambda w_\lambda = p. \tag{3.7}$$

This combination is called the *transvection* of v^κ and w_λ. p can be found geometrically by measuring the vector v^κ, using as a unit the line-segment cut out on v^κ by the hyperplanes of w_λ. The sign is to be taken $+$ if the orientation of v^κ and w_λ correspond and $-$ in the other case. Hence, if $v^\lambda w_\lambda = +1$ or -1, this means that the vector v^κ just fits between the hyperplanes of w_λ. For the measuring vectors $\underset{\lambda}{e}^\kappa$, $\overset{\kappa}{e}_\lambda$ belonging to the same coordinate system, it is evident that the following equation holds:

$$\underset{\lambda}{e}^\mu \overset{\kappa}{e}_\mu = \delta^\kappa_\lambda. \tag{3.8}$$

If a vector v^κ is transvected with the measuring vectors $\overset{\kappa}{e}_\lambda$, n scalars arise:

$$\overset{\kappa}{v} = v^\lambda \overset{\kappa}{e}_\lambda; \tag{3.9}$$

and from these the vector can be rebuilt:

$$v^\kappa = \overset{\lambda}{v} \underset{\lambda}{e}^\kappa. \tag{3.10}$$

The equations (3.9) and (3.10) are numerically equivalent but their geometrical meanings are quite different. (3.9) describes how the components can be deduced from the vector by means of the covariant measuring vectors, and (3.10) how the vector can be formed from its components by means of the contravariant measuring vectors. If we introduce another coordinate system (κ') the equations transform into

$$\overset{\kappa}{v} = v^{\lambda'}\overset{\kappa}{e}_{\lambda'} \tag{3.11}$$

and

$$v^{\kappa'} = \underset{\lambda}{\overset{\lambda}{v}} e^{\kappa'}, \tag{3.12}$$

respectively, with the same geometrical meaning. But these equations are no longer numerically equivalent. The transition of a living to a dead index in (3.9) we call the *strangling of an index.*

(*d*) An *affinor* with the *contravariant valence p*, the *covariant valence q*, and the *valence p+q* is a quantity with n^{p+q} components and the following transformation

$$P^{\kappa'_1...\kappa'_p}{}_{\lambda'_1...\lambda'_q} = A^{\kappa'_1}_{\kappa_1}...A^{\kappa'_p}_{\kappa_p} A^{\lambda_1}_{\lambda'_1}...A^{\lambda_q}_{\lambda'_q} P^{\kappa_1...\kappa_p}{}_{\lambda_1...\lambda_q}. \tag{3.13}$$

If $q = 0$ the affinor is called *contravariant*, if $p = 0$ *covariant*, and in the general case *mixed*. $p = 0$, $q = 0$ gives a scalar, $p = 1$, $q = 0$ a contravariant, and $p = 0$, $q = 1$ a covariant vector. The place of the indices is important, so the same quantity cannot at one time be written $P^{\kappa}{}_{\cdot\mu\lambda}$, and at another, $P_{\mu\lambda}{}^{\cdot\cdot\kappa}$.

A *pseudo-affinor* is an affinor determined to within a scalar factor. If necessary it can be distinguished from an affinor by the sign $\lfloor\,\rfloor$.

The components of an affinor of valence *2* with respect to (κ) can be written in a quadratic table, called the *matrix* of the affinor *with respect* to (κ). If for the components A^{κ}_{λ} of an affinor with respect to (κ) the equation

$$A^{\kappa}_{\lambda} \overset{*}{=} \delta^{\kappa}_{\lambda} \tag{3.14}$$

holds, then with respect to every other coordinate system the following equation holds:†

$$A^{\kappa'}_{\lambda'} \overset{*}{=} \delta^{\kappa'}_{\lambda'}. \tag{3.15}$$

This affinor is called the *unity affinor*. For every choice of v^{κ} and w_{λ}, we have

$$v^{\kappa} = A^{\kappa}_{\lambda} v^{\lambda}, \qquad w_{\lambda} = A^{\kappa}_{\lambda} w_{\kappa}. \tag{3.16}$$

If all the $(r+1)$-rowed determinants, which can be formed from a matrix by omitting all but $r+1$ rows and all but $r+1$ columns, are

† Nevertheless we use the sign $\overset{*}{=}$ in (3.14) and (3.15). This will become clear after the introduction of intermediary components.

zero, but at least one r-rowed determinant is not, the matrix is said to be of *rank* r. To every affinor of valence 2 whose matrix has rank n, belongs another affinor, called its *inverse*, by whose transvection with the first affinor the unity affinor arises:

$$P^{\kappa}_{\cdot\mu}\overset{-1}{P}{}^{\mu}_{\cdot\lambda} = A^{\kappa}_{\lambda},$$
$$Q^{\kappa\mu}\overset{-1}{Q}_{\mu\lambda} = A^{\kappa}_{\lambda}, \tag{3.17}$$
$$R_{\lambda\mu}\overset{-1}{R}{}^{\mu\kappa} = A^{\kappa}_{\lambda}.$$

The element in the pth row and qth column of the matrix of the inverse is equal to the determinant resulting from the matrix of the affinor by omitting the pth column and the qth row, multiplying by $(-1)^{p+q}$, and dividing by the determinant of this matrix. We call the matrices of an affinor and its inverse the inverse of each other.

An affinor of valence > 1 has, besides the components already mentioned, components belonging to two or more coordinate systems simultaneously, e.g.

$$P^{\kappa}_{\cdot\lambda'}{}^{\mu\nu'} = A^{\lambda}_{\lambda'}A^{\nu'}_{\nu}P^{\kappa}_{\cdot\lambda}{}^{\mu\nu} = A^{\kappa}_{\kappa'}A^{\mu}_{\mu'}P^{\kappa'}_{\cdot\lambda'}{}^{\mu'\nu'}. \tag{3.18}$$

These components are called *intermediary*. They are used very often. $A^{\kappa'}_{\lambda}$ and $A^{\kappa}_{\lambda'}$ in (1.1) and (1.2) are intermediary components of the unity affinor.

4. Invariant processes

The following processes are invariant with transformations of coordinates:

(*a*) The *addition* of two affinors with the same valences and the same location of indices, e.g.

$$R_{\mu\lambda}{}^{\cdot\cdot\kappa} = P_{\mu\lambda}{}^{\cdot\cdot\kappa} + Q_{\mu\lambda}{}^{\cdot\cdot\kappa}. \tag{4.1}$$

(*b*) The *construction* of an *isomer* by interchanging the upper or the lower indices, e.g.

$$Q_{\mu\lambda}{}^{\cdot\cdot\kappa} = P_{\lambda\mu}{}^{\cdot\cdot\kappa}. \tag{4.2}$$

(*c*) The *multiplication* of two or more affinors, e.g.

$$R_{\mu\lambda\cdot\cdot\rho}{}^{\cdot\cdot\kappa\nu\cdot\sigma} = P_{\mu\rho}{}^{\cdot\cdot\kappa}Q^{\nu\cdot\sigma}_{\cdot\lambda}. \tag{4.3}$$

(*d*) The *contraction*† of an affinor with respect to an upper and a lower index or with respect to several such pairs of indices, e.g.

$$Q^{\kappa}_{\cdot\rho} = P^{\lambda\cdot\cdot\mu\cdot\kappa}_{\cdot\mu\rho\cdot\lambda}. \tag{4.4}$$

† In the theory of invariants this process was originally called 'faltung' (folding up). Physicists have introduced the name 'verjüngung' (rejuvenation).

The following processes may now be carried out by combination of the four independent processes (*a*), (*b*), (*c*), and (*d*).

(*e*) The *transvection* of two affinors, resulting from the application of the process of contraction to the product of two affinors, e.g.

$$R_{\rho}{}^{\cdot\kappa} = P_{\mu\lambda}{}^{\cdot\cdot\kappa} Q^{\lambda}{}_{\cdot\rho}{}^{\cdot\mu}. \tag{4.5}$$

The processes (*b*), (*c*), (*d*), and (*e*) have the properties of a multiplication, i.e. they are distributive with respect to addition. The indices which are used for the summation in contractions and transvections are called *saturated*, the others, *free indices*.

(*f*) The process of *mixing*, over p upper or p lower indices, is effected by constructing all $p!$ isomers that can be obtained by writing these indices in all possible permutations, addition of these isomers and division by $p!$. We denote this process by putting these indices between parentheses ( ). If indices have to be singled out, the sign | | is used, e.g.

$$P_{(\dot{\kappa}\lambda|\omega|\dot{\mu})}{}^{\nu} = \tfrac{1}{6}(P_{\dot{\kappa}\lambda\omega\dot{\mu}}{}^{\nu} + P_{\dot{\lambda}\mu\omega\dot{\kappa}}{}^{\nu} + P_{\dot{\mu}\kappa\omega\dot{\lambda}}{}^{\nu} + P_{\dot{\lambda}\kappa\omega\dot{\mu}}{}^{\nu} + P_{\dot{\mu}\lambda\omega\dot{\kappa}}{}^{\nu} + P_{\dot{\kappa}\mu\omega\dot{\lambda}}{}^{\nu}). \tag{4.6}$$

A quantity is called *symmetric* with respect to p upper or p lower indices if it is invariant with mixing over these indices. Then it does not change if any two of these indices are interchanged.

(*g*) The process of *alternation*, over p upper or p lower indices, is effected by constructing all $p!$ isomers obtained by writing these indices in all possible permutations, adding these isomers after changing the sign of the odd permutations, and dividing by $p!$. We denote this process by putting these indices between brackets [ ]. If indices have to be singled out, the sign | | is used, e.g.

$$P_{[\dot{\kappa}\dot{\lambda}|\dot{\omega}|\dot{\mu}]}{}^{\nu} = \tfrac{1}{6}(P_{\dot{\kappa}\dot{\lambda}\dot{\omega}\dot{\mu}}{}^{\nu} + P_{\dot{\lambda}\dot{\mu}\dot{\omega}\dot{\kappa}}{}^{\nu} + P_{\dot{\mu}\dot{\kappa}\dot{\omega}\dot{\lambda}}{}^{\nu} - P_{\dot{\lambda}\dot{\kappa}\dot{\omega}\dot{\mu}}{}^{\nu} - P_{\dot{\mu}\dot{\lambda}\dot{\omega}\dot{\kappa}}{}^{\nu} - P_{\dot{\kappa}\dot{\mu}\dot{\omega}\dot{\lambda}}{}^{\nu}). \tag{4.7}$$

A quantity is called *alternating* with respect to p upper or p lower indices if it is invariant with alternation over these indices. Then only the sign changes if any two of these indices are interchanged.

Alternation over more than n indices always leads to zero.

5. Strangling; rank

Transvection with the measuring vectors leads to strangling of one or more indices. So we may obtain, for example, from an affinor $P^{\kappa\lambda}{}_{\cdot\cdot\mu\nu}$ with valence *4*, a system of n^2 affinors of valence *2*:

$$P^{(\kappa)\lambda}{}_{\cdot\cdot\mu(\nu)} = \overset{\kappa}{e}_{\rho} \underset{\nu}{e}^{\sigma} P^{\rho\lambda}{}_{\cdot\cdot\mu\sigma} \quad (\rho, \sigma = 1,\ldots, n). \tag{5.1}$$

If several indices are strangled it is recommended that these indices should not be put over or under the kernel-letters but should be marked by parentheses in their present position.

If the same indices are strangled on both sides of an invariant equation the equation remains invariant. If the strangled indices are not the same, the equation remains valid with respect to the coordinate system or systems used, but as there is no longer invariance, the sign $\overset{*}{=}$ has to be introduced. We have, for example,

$$P^{(\kappa)\lambda}{}_{\cdot\cdot\mu(\nu)} \overset{*}{=} P^{\kappa\lambda}{}_{\cdot\cdot\mu\nu} \tag{5.2}$$

and

$$A^{\kappa}_{\lambda} \overset{*}{=} A^{(\kappa)}_{\lambda} = \overset{\kappa}{e}_{\lambda} \overset{*}{=} A^{(\kappa)}_{(\lambda)} = \delta^{\kappa}_{\lambda} \overset{*}{=} A^{\kappa}_{(\lambda)} = \underset{\lambda}{e}^{\kappa}. \tag{5.3}$$

The *rank* of an affinor with respect to some of its indices is the number of linearly independent quantities obtained if all *other* indices are strangled. It is not necessary that the indices concerned should be all upper or lower or that they should belong to the same system of coordinates. *The rank is invariant with all allowable transformations of coordinates.* From the definition, it follows immediately that the rank with respect to some indices is equal to the rank with respect to the other indices, and that the rank with respect to all indices is one.† An affinor with valence *2* has therefore only one rank, and this is equal to the rank of its matrix.

If r is the rank of an affinor with respect to the index μ, by strangling of all other indices just r linearly independent co- or contravariant vectors are obtained. The domain of these vectors is called the μ-*domain* of the affinor. The domain with respect to several indices is defined in the same way.

As an example we consider an $\vec{E}_p$ and an $\vec{E}_q$ $(q = n-p)$ having no direction in common. We wish to determine an affinor B^{κ}_{λ} of rank p having $\vec{E}_p$ for support of the domain of κ and $\vec{E}_q$ for support of the domain of λ and satisfying the equation

$$B^{\kappa}_{\mu} B^{\mu}_{\lambda} = B^{\kappa}_{\lambda}. \tag{5.4}$$

We choose the coordinate system in such a way that $\underset{1}{e}^{\kappa},\ldots, \underset{p}{e}^{\kappa}$ span $\vec{E}_p$ and the other contravariant measuring vectors $\vec{E}_q$. Then B^{κ}_{λ} must take the form

$$B^{\kappa}_{\lambda} = \overset{\alpha}{\underset{\beta}{w}} \overset{\beta}{e}_{\lambda} \underset{\alpha}{e}^{\kappa} \quad (\alpha, \beta = 1,\ldots, p). \tag{5.5}$$

† Cf. Alexander 1925. 1; Rice 1928. 1.

The matrix of the still unknown numbers $\overset{\alpha}{\underset{\beta}{w}}$ cannot have a rank $<p$ because the rank of B_λ^κ has to be p. From (5.4) we get

$$\overset{\alpha}{\underset{\beta}{w}}\,\overset{\beta}{e}_\mu\,\underset{\alpha}{e}^\kappa\,\overset{\gamma}{\underset{\delta}{w}}\,\overset{\delta}{e}_\lambda\,\underset{\gamma}{e}^\mu = \overset{\epsilon}{\underset{\eta}{w}}\,\overset{\eta}{e}_\lambda\,\underset{\epsilon}{e}^\kappa \quad (\alpha,\beta,\gamma,\delta,\epsilon,\eta = 1,\dots,p) \tag{5.6}$$

or

$$\overset{\alpha}{\underset{\beta}{w}}\,\overset{\beta}{\underset{\gamma}{w}} = \overset{\alpha}{\underset{\gamma}{w}} \quad (\alpha,\beta,\gamma = 1,\dots,p), \tag{5.7}$$

and this is only possible if $\overset{\alpha}{\underset{\beta}{w}} = \delta_\beta^\alpha$ or

$$B_\lambda^\kappa = \overset{\gamma}{e}_\lambda\,\underset{\gamma}{e}^\kappa \quad (\gamma = 1,\dots,p). \tag{5.8}$$

In the same way we obtain an affinor C_λ^κ of rank $n-p$ having $\vec{E}_q$ for support of the domain of κ and $\vec{E}_p$ for support of the domain of λ:

$$C_\lambda^\kappa = \overset{\zeta}{e}_\lambda\,\underset{\zeta}{e}^\kappa \quad (\zeta = p+1,\dots,n). \tag{5.9}$$

For B_λ^κ and C_λ^κ the following identities may readily be proved

$$\begin{gathered} B_\lambda^\kappa + C_\lambda^\kappa = A_\lambda^\kappa, \\ B_\mu^\mu = p, \quad C_\mu^\mu = n-p, \quad A_\mu^\mu = n, \\ B_\mu^\kappa C_\lambda^\mu = 0, \quad B_\lambda^\mu C_\mu^\kappa = 0. \end{gathered} \tag{5.10}$$

The affinors B_λ^κ and C_λ^κ are often used. With the aid of them a contravariant vector v^κ can be resolved into two components in $\vec{E}_p$ and $\vec{E}_q$ respectively,

$$v^\kappa = B_\mu^\kappa v^\mu + C_\mu^\kappa v^\mu, \tag{5.11}$$

and a covariant vector w_λ into two components, whose $(n-1)$-direction contains $\vec{E}_p$ and $\vec{E}_q$ respectively,

$$w_\lambda = B_\lambda^\mu w_\mu + C_\lambda^\mu w_\mu. \tag{5.12}$$

If any system of affinors is given, and if we choose for all of them a definite upper (lower) index place we may write the same index, e.g. μ in all these places. If now all *other* indices are strangled, we obtain a system of contravariant (covariant) vectors. The number of linearly independent vectors among them is called the *rank of the system* of affinors *with respect to the index* μ and the domain of these vectors the *μ-domain of the system*. For instance, n is the κ-rank and also the λ-rank of the system B_λ^κ, C_λ^κ.

The *rank and the domain of a system* of affinors *with respect to several indices* may be defined in the same way. For instance, *2* is the rank of the system B_λ^κ, C_λ^κ with respect to κ, λ.

6. Tensors

A tensor is a contra- or covariant affinor, symmetrical in all indices. Hence a tensor is invariant with every interchange of its indices and with mixing over any number of these indices. The number of the mutually independent components of a tensor of valence p is $\binom{n+p-1}{p}$. If a tensor is determined to within an arbitrary scalar factor it is called a *pseudotensor*.

In a centred E_n, a covariant tensor (pseudotensor) $P_{\lambda_1 ... \lambda_p}$, is represented by the hypersurface (hypercone) with the equation

$$P_{\lambda_1 ... \lambda_p} x^{\lambda_1} ... x^{\lambda_p} = 1 \quad (0) \tag{6.1}$$

and a contravariant tensor (pseudotensor) $Q^{\kappa_1 ... \kappa_q}$, by the hypersurface (hypercone) with the equation

$$Q^{\kappa_1 ... \kappa_q} u_{\kappa_1} ... u_{\kappa_q} = 1 \quad (0) \tag{6.2}$$

in the hyperplane-coordinates u_λ.

From two contra- or covariant tensors (pseudotensors) of valences p and q a tensor (pseudotensor) of valence $p+q$ may be obtained by multiplication and mixing over all $p+q$ indices:

$$R_{\lambda_1 ... \lambda_q \kappa_1 ... \kappa_q} = P_{(\lambda_1 ... \lambda_p} Q_{\kappa_1 ... \kappa_q)}. \tag{6.3}$$

This process is called the *symmetric multiplication of tensors (pseudotensors)*. The symmetric multiplication of tensors is distributive with respect to addition, commutative and associative.

If we multiply pseudotensors in this way, the polynomial on the left-hand side of the equation of the cone of the product is the product of the polynomials on the left-hand sides of the equations of the cones of the factors. Hence the notions division and divisor from the theory of homogeneous polynomials may be extended to tensors. A tensor Q is called a divisor of P if there exists a tensor R such that P is the symmetric product of Q and R. A tensor without any tensor divisor is called *irreducible*. From the theorem of factorization in the theory of homogeneous polynomials it follows immediately that:

Every tensor is the symmetric product of a finite number of irreducible tensors. These factors are uniquely determined to within a scalar factor.

If all divisors of a contra- or a covariant pseudotensor have the valence *1*, the cone consists of p hyperplanes or p straight lines respectively through O.

The rank of a tensor is the same with respect to all indices. The support of the domain of a covariant tensor $w_{\lambda_1 ... \lambda_p}$ of rank r is an $\vec{E}_{n-r}$.

The hypersurface of $w_{\lambda_1...\lambda_p}$ is a cylinder consisting of ∞^{r-1} E_{n-r}'s with the $(n-r)$-direction $\vec{E}_{n-r}$. The cone of $\lfloor w_{\lambda_1...\lambda_p}\rfloor$ consists of ∞^{r-2} E_{n-r+1}'s, all of them containing the E_{n-r} with the equation

$$w_{\lambda_1...\lambda_p} x^{\lambda_p} = 0 \tag{6.4}$$

and with the $(n-r)$-direction $\vec{E}_{n-r}$.

7. p-vectors

A *p-vector* ($p \leqslant n$) is a contra- or covariant affinor, which is alternating in all indices. Hence a p-vector is invariant with alternation over any number of these indices and changes its sign if two of the indices change places. It is usual to call a *1*-vector, vector, a *2*-vector, bivector, a *3*-vector, trivector, and a *4*-vector, quadrivector. If a p-vector is determined to within a scalar factor, it is called a *pseudo-p-vector*. The number of mutually independent components of a p-vector is $\binom{n}{p}$. An n-vector has only one independent component, e.g. $w_{1...n}$, all the other components being equal to zero, $+w_{1...n}$, or $-w_{1...n}$. This component is *not a scalar*. For $w_{1'...n'}$ we have

$$w_{1'...n'} = A_{1'}^{\kappa_1}...A_{n'}^{\kappa_n} w_{\kappa_1...\kappa_n} = n!\, A_{1'}^{[1}...A_{n'}^{n]} w_{1...n}. \tag{7.1}$$

Now
$$A_{1'}^{[1}...A_{n'}^{n]} = A_{[1'}^{1}...A_{n']}^{n} = A_{[1'}^{[1}...A_{n']}^{n]} = \frac{1}{n!}\Delta^{-1}; \tag{7.2}$$

hence
$$w_{1'...n'} = \Delta^{-1} w_{1...n}. \tag{7.3}$$

In the same way we deduce for a contravariant n-vector $v^{\kappa_1...\kappa_n}$

$$v^{1'...n'} = \Delta v^{1...n}. \tag{7.4}$$

From these transformation formulae it follows that two contra- or two covariant n-vectors differ only by a scalar factor.

From a co-(contra-)variant p-vector (pseudo-p-vector) P and a co-(contra-)variant q-vector (pseudo-q-vector) Q ($p+q \leqslant n$), a $(p+q)$-vector (pseudo-$(p+q)$-vector) may be obtained by multiplication and alternation over all $p+q$ indices, e.g.

$$R_{\lambda_1...\lambda_p\,\kappa_1...\kappa_q} = P_{[\lambda_1...\lambda_p} Q_{\kappa_1...\kappa_q]}. \tag{7.5}$$

This process is called *alternated multiplication*. For this multiplication we often use the abbreviated notation

$$R = PQ. \tag{7.6}$$

The alternated multiplication of a p-vector and a q-vector is distributive with respect to addition, and associative but not always commutative, because
$$PQ = (-1)^{pq} QP. \tag{7.7}$$

A q-vector Q is called a *divisor* of a p-vector P, if there exists a $(p-q)$-vector R such that P is the alternated product of Q and R. If a p-vector has no divisors it is called *irreducible*. If it has p linearly independent factors of valence *1* it is called *simple* and in the other case *compound*. The rank of a p-vector is the same with respect to all indices. The rank of a simple p-vector is p.

A complete theory of divisors of p-vectors does not yet exist. We need only the following theorem, which will be formulated here for contravariant p-vectors.

THEOREM I.1. *v^κ is a divisor of $v^{\kappa_1\ldots\kappa_p}$ if and only if*

$$v^{[\kappa_1\ldots\kappa_p}v^{\kappa]} = 0. \tag{7.8}$$

PROOF. If v^κ is a divisor of $v^{\kappa_1\ldots\kappa_p}$, it is immediately clear that the left-hand side of (7.8) vanishes. Now take any vector w_λ satisfying the equation

$$v^\kappa w_\kappa = 1. \tag{7.9}$$

It follows that

$$v^{\kappa_1\ldots\kappa_p} = p w_\kappa v^{\kappa[\kappa_2\ldots\kappa_p}v^{\kappa_1]}, \tag{7.10}$$

which proves the theorem.

If a p-vector has q $(<p)$ linearly independent vector factors it is easily proved that it is the alternating product of these vectors and a $(p-q)$-vector. *Hence a simple p-vector is always the alternated product of p vectors.* But these factors are not uniquely determined. In order to decide if a p-vector is simple we use the following theorem, formulated here for contravariant p-vectors.

THEOREM I.2. *A p-vector $v^{\kappa_1\ldots\kappa_p}$ is simple if and only if*

$$v^{[\kappa_1\ldots\kappa_p}v^{\lambda_1]\ldots\lambda_p} = 0. \tag{7.11}$$

PROOF. It is trivial that the condition is necessary. By interchanging indices we can always arrange that $v^{1\ldots p} \neq 0$. Then (7.11) states that the p vectors $v^{2\ldots p\,\kappa}$, $v^{1\,3\ldots p\,\kappa},\ldots,$ $v^{1\,2\ldots(p-1)\kappa}$ are divisors of $v^{\kappa_1\ldots\kappa_p}$. These vectors cannot be linearly dependent because the first component $v^{2\ldots p\,1}$ of the first vector is $\neq 0$, and the first components of all other vectors are zero. The same holds for the second component of the second vector, etc. Hence $v^{\kappa_1\ldots\kappa_p}$ has p linearly independent vector factors.

From this theorem it follows immediately that *every n-vector is simple.* But *every $(n-1)$-vector is also simple.* To prove this we suppose that

$$v^{[\kappa_1\ldots\kappa_{n-1}}v^{\lambda_1]\ldots\lambda_{n-1}} \neq 0. \tag{7.12}$$

From this inequality it follows that at least one of the vectors obtained by replacing $\lambda_2\ldots\lambda_{n-1}$ in $v^{\lambda_1\ldots\lambda_{n-1}}$ by $n-2$ of the indices $1,\ldots,n$, is not zero. By interchanging indices we can always arrange that this is $v^{\kappa\, 2\ldots n-1}$. Then (7.12) gives

$$v^{1\ldots n-1}v^{n\,2\ldots n-1} - v^{n\,2\ldots n-1}v^{1\ldots n-1} \neq 0, \tag{7.13}$$

which is impossible.

To every allowable coordinate system (κ) there belongs, for every value of p from 1 to n, a system of $\binom{n}{p}$ simple contravariant p-vectors and also a system of $\binom{n}{p}$ simple covariant p-vectors uniquely determined for $p = 1$ or n and for $n > p > 1$ uniquely determined to within the sign. These p-vectors are the alternating products of the measuring vectors. Their p-directions and $(n-p)$-directions are the $\binom{n}{p}$ coordinate-E_p's and coordinate-E_{n-p}'s respectively (cf. I, § 2). For the much-used n-vectors belonging to (κ) we use the notation

$$\overset{(\kappa)}{E}{}^{\kappa_1\ldots\kappa_n} = n!\, \underset{1}{e}{}^{[\kappa_1}\ldots\underset{n}{e}{}^{\kappa_n]},$$

$$\overset{(\kappa)}{e}_{\lambda_1\ldots\lambda_n} = n!\, \overset{1}{e}_{[\lambda_1}\ldots\overset{n}{e}_{\lambda_n]}. \tag{7.14}$$

The following identities may easily be verified:

$$(a) \qquad \overset{(\kappa)}{E}{}^{1\ldots n} = \overset{(\kappa)}{e}_{1\ldots n} = 1;$$

$$(b) \qquad \overset{(\kappa)}{E}{}^{\mu_1\ldots\mu_n}\overset{(\kappa)}{e}_{\mu_1\ldots\mu_n} = n!; \tag{7.15}$$

$$(c) \qquad \overset{(\kappa)}{E}{}^{\mu_1\ldots\mu_m\,\kappa_{m+1}\ldots\kappa_n}\overset{(\kappa)}{e}_{\mu_1\ldots\mu_m\,\lambda_{m+1}\ldots\lambda_n} = m!(n-m)!\,A^{[\kappa_{m+1}}_{[\lambda_{m+1}}\ldots A^{\kappa_n]}_{\lambda_n]}.$$

Since
$$v^{\kappa_1\ldots\kappa_p} = v^{(\lambda_1)\ldots(\lambda_p)}\underset{\lambda_1}{e}{}^{[\kappa_1}\ldots\underset{\lambda_p}{e}{}^{\kappa_p]} \tag{7.16}$$

and a similar equation holds for covariant p-vectors, every p-vector is the sum of a finite number of simple p-vectors. This decomposition is called the decomposition into *blades*. The minimal number of blades C in any decomposition is an invariant of the p-vector. There exist several relations between p, C and the rank, but for $p > 2$ the theory of these relations is almost completely undeveloped.

Here we investigate only the case $p = 2$ which is very important for the following chapters. We take a covariant bivector $F_{\lambda\kappa}$; the contravariant case can be treated in the same way. The rank of $F_{\lambda\kappa}$ has to be even because, as is well known, the rank of every antisymmetric matrix is even. If this rank is r we have

$$\overset{s}{G}_{\lambda_1\ldots\lambda_s\,\kappa_1\ldots\kappa_s} \overset{\text{def}}{=} F_{[\lambda_1[\kappa_1}\ldots F_{\lambda_s]\kappa_s]} \begin{cases} \neq 0 & (s \leqslant r), \\ = 0 & (s > r), \end{cases} \tag{7.17}$$

because the $\binom{n}{s}^2$ components of $\overset{s}{G}$ are, to within a non-vanishing scalar factor, equal to the s-rowed sub-determinants of the matrix of $F_{\lambda\kappa}$. Now we can prove the theorem

Theorem I.3. *A bivector of rank r is always the sum of $\frac{1}{2}r$ simple bivectors but never the sum of $\frac{1}{2}r-1$ simple bivectors.*

Proof. Let x^κ and y^κ be two vectors such that

$$x^\kappa y^\lambda F_{\lambda\kappa} = 1. \tag{7.18}$$

Then if

$$w_{\lambda\kappa} \stackrel{\text{def}}{=} 2F_{[\lambda|\mu|}\, x^\mu F_{\kappa]\nu}\, y^\nu \tag{7.19}$$

we prove that the rank of

$$'F_{\lambda\kappa} \stackrel{\text{def}}{=} F_{\lambda\kappa} - w_{\lambda\kappa} \tag{7.20}$$

is $< r$. There exist $n-r$ linearly independent contravariant vectors whose transvections with $F_{\lambda\kappa}$ are zero. From (7.19, 20) it follows that the transvections of these vectors with $'F_{\lambda\kappa}$ are also zero. Now

$$\begin{aligned} x^\lambda\, 'F_{\lambda\kappa} &= x^\lambda F_{\lambda\kappa} + F_{\kappa\mu}\, x^\mu x^\lambda F_{\lambda\nu}\, y^\nu \\ &= x^\lambda F_{\lambda\kappa} - x^\lambda F_{\lambda\kappa} = 0, \end{aligned} \tag{7.21}$$

and in the same way it is proved that

$$y^\lambda\, 'F_{\lambda\kappa} = 0. \tag{7.22}$$

Now in consequence of (7.18) x^κ and y^κ are linearly independent of each other and of the $n-r$ contravariant vectors mentioned above. Hence the rank of $'F_{\lambda\kappa}$ is $\leqslant r-2$. But, since

$$F_{[\lambda_1[\kappa_1}\ldots F_{\lambda_r]\kappa_r]} = {'F}_{[\lambda_1[\kappa_1}\ldots {'F}_{\lambda_r]\kappa_r]} + r w_{[\lambda_1[\kappa_1}\, {'F}_{\lambda_2\kappa_2}\ldots {'F}_{\lambda_r]\kappa_r]} \tag{7.23}$$

the rank of $F_{\lambda\kappa}$ could not be r if the rank of $'F_{\lambda\kappa}$ were $< r-2$. Hence the rank of $'F_{\lambda\kappa}$ is just $r-2$. If the described process is carried out $\frac{1}{2}r-1$ times we get a simple bivector, and $F_{\lambda\kappa}$ is thus decomposed into $\frac{1}{2}r$ simple bivectors. On the other hand, $F_{\lambda\kappa}$ cannot be decomposed into $\frac{1}{2}r-1$ simple bivectors because, if this were possible, $F_{[\lambda_1[\kappa_1}\ldots F_{\lambda_r]\kappa_r]}$ would vanish.

From Theorem I.3 we deduce a more simple form for the condition (7.17). If

$$F_{\lambda\kappa} = \overset{1}{f}_{\lambda\kappa} + \ldots + \overset{\rho}{f}_{\lambda\kappa} \quad (\rho = \tfrac{1}{2}r) \tag{7.24}$$

is one of the possible decompositions into $\frac{1}{2}r$ simple bivectors, the r-dimensional domain of $F_{\lambda\kappa}$ is spanned by the 2-dimensional domains of $\overset{1}{f}_{\lambda\kappa},\ldots,\overset{\rho}{f}_{\lambda\kappa}$. Hence these domains can have no vector in common and from this we may conclude that

$$F_{[\lambda_1\kappa_1}\ldots F_{\lambda_\rho\kappa_\rho]} \neq 0 \quad (\rho = \tfrac{1}{2}r). \tag{7.25}$$

Hence the necessary and sufficient conditions for $F_{\lambda\kappa}$ to be of rank r are

$$F_{[\lambda_1\kappa_1}\cdots F_{\lambda_\sigma\kappa_\sigma]}\begin{cases}\neq 0 & (\sigma \leqslant \tfrac{1}{2}r),\\ = 0 & (\sigma > \tfrac{1}{2}r).\end{cases} \tag{7.26}$$

The geometrical representation of simple pseudo-p-vectors is much more simple than that of simple p-vectors. A simple contravariant pseudo-p-vector is represented by an $\vec{E}_p$, and in a centred E_n, by an E_p through O, and a covariant pseudo-p-vector by an $\vec{E}_{n-p}$ or E_{n-p} through O respectively. Hence a simple contravariant pseudo-p-vector has the same geometrical representation as a simple covariant pseudo-$(n-p)$-vector. This is also clear from an algebraic point of view because there exists only one contravariant pseudo-n-vector $\lfloor E^{\kappa_1\ldots\kappa_n}\rfloor$, and only one covariant pseudo-n-vector $\lfloor e_{\lambda_1\ldots\lambda_n}\rfloor$, and these quantities establish for every value of p a one-to-one correspondence between contravariant pseudo-p-vectors and covariant pseudo-$(n-p)$-vectors by means of the equations

$$\begin{aligned}\lfloor v^{\kappa_1\ldots\kappa_p}\rfloor &= \lfloor w_{\lambda_1\ldots\lambda_q}\rfloor\lfloor E^{\lambda_1\ldots\lambda_q\kappa_1\ldots\kappa_p}\rfloor\\ \lfloor w_{\lambda_1\ldots\lambda_q}\rfloor &= \lfloor e_{\lambda_1\ldots\lambda_q\kappa_1\ldots\kappa_p}\rfloor\lfloor v^{\kappa_1\ldots\kappa_p}\rfloor\end{aligned}\quad (q = n-p). \tag{7.27}$$

To obtain a geometrical representation of a simple contravariant p-vector $v^{\kappa_1\ldots\kappa_p}$, we take an arbitrary E_p with the p-direction of $v^{\kappa_1\ldots\kappa_p}$, and in this E_p, a p-dimensional region whose projection in the direction of $\underset{p+1}{e}^{[\kappa_{p+1}}\ldots\underset{n}{e}^{\kappa_n]}$ on the E_p of $\underset{1}{e}^{[\kappa_1}\ldots\underset{p}{e}^{\kappa_p]}$, measured by the parallelotop of this latter p-vector, has just the volume $|v^{1\ldots p}|$. If this region is equipped with a screw-sense corresponding to the screw-sense of $\underset{1}{e}^{\kappa},\ldots,\underset{p}{e}^{\kappa}$ for $v^{1\ldots p} > 0$ and opposite for $v^{1\ldots p} < 0$ we obtain the geometrical representation of $v^{\kappa_1\ldots\kappa_p}$. If $v^{1\ldots p} = 0$ another set of p measuring vectors has to be chosen from the $\underset{\lambda}{e}^{\kappa}$. Obviously the result is independent of the choice of the set of p measuring vectors. We see that every contravariant p-vector provides its $\vec{E}_p$ with an *inner* orientation.

The geometrical representation of a simple covariant p-vector $w_{\lambda_1\ldots\lambda_p}$ is obtained in the following way. We take an arbitrary n-dimensional cylinder, whose $(n-1)$-dimensional hypersurface consists of ∞^{p-1} E_{n-p}'s having the $(n-p)$-direction of $w_{\lambda_1\ldots\lambda_p}$ and whose section with the E_p of $\underset{1}{e}^{[\kappa_1}\ldots\underset{p}{e}^{\kappa_p]}$ has the volume $1:|w_{1\ldots p}|$ if measured with the parallelotop of this latter p-vector. If this cylinder is equipped with a screw-sense corresponding to the screw-sense of $\underset{1}{e}^{\kappa_1},\ldots,\underset{p}{e}^{\kappa_p}$ for $w_{1\ldots p} > 0$ and opposite for $w_{1\ldots p} < 0$ we obtain the geometrical representation of $w_{\lambda_1\ldots\lambda_p}$. If $w_{1\ldots p} = 0$ we have to take another set of p measuring vectors from the

$\underset{\lambda}{e^{\kappa}}$. The result is independent of the choice of the set of p measuring vectors. We see that every covariant p-vector provides its $\vec{E}_{n-p}$ with an *outer* orientation.

An E_{p-1} in E_{n-1} is determined by $p(n-p)$ numbers. Now every E_p through O can be fixed by giving an E_{p-1} in an arbitrarily but definitely chosen E_{n-1}. Hence an E_p through O is determined by $p(n-p)$ numbers and the same holds for a simple contravariant pseudo-p-vector and for a simple covariant pseudo-p-vector. For a p-vector one more number is needed, so the total amount is $p(n-p)+1$. From this it follows that among the equations (7.11) there are just $\binom{n}{p}-p(n-p)-1$ which are mutually independent.

In order to obtain a convenient system of $p(n-p)$ independent components of a pseudo-p-vector from the $v^{\kappa_1 \dots \kappa_p}$ (or $w_{\lambda_1 \dots \lambda_p}$) we interchange the indices in such a way that $v^{1 \dots p} \neq 0$ and put†

$$B^{\kappa}_{\beta} \overset{\text{def}}{=} \frac{v^{1 \dots (\beta-1)\kappa(\beta+1) \dots p}}{v^{1 \dots p}} \quad (\beta = 1,\dots,p). \tag{7.28}$$

Then

$$\frac{v^{\kappa_1 \dots \kappa_p}}{v^{1 \dots p}} = p!\, B^{[\kappa_1}_{1} \dots B^{\kappa_p]}_{p}, \tag{7.29}$$

$$B^{\alpha}_{\beta} = \delta^{\alpha}_{\beta}. \tag{7.30}$$

(7.29) is proved in the following way. Obviously the p vectors $B^{\kappa}_{1},\dots, B^{\kappa}_{p}$ are independent divisors of $v^{\kappa_1 \dots \kappa_p}$. Hence $v^{\kappa_1 \dots \kappa_p}$ is the alternated product of these vectors to within a scalar factor. If we put $\kappa_1 = 1,\dots, \kappa_p = p$ it follows that this factor is just $p!\, v^{1 \dots p}$. If in (7.29) the B^{α}_{β} are replaced by their values (7.30) we obtain the quotients on the left-hand side of (7.29) as rational homogeneous functions of the B^{ζ}_{β} ($\beta = 1,\dots, p$; $\zeta = p+1,\dots, n$):

$$\frac{v^{\zeta_1 \dots \zeta_s \alpha_{s+1} \dots \alpha_p}}{v^{1 \dots p}} = s!\, B^{[\zeta_1}_{\alpha_1} \dots B^{\zeta_s]}_{\alpha_s} \quad (\zeta_1,\dots, \zeta_s = p+1,\dots,n;$$

$$\alpha_1,\dots, \alpha_p = \text{even permutation of } 1,\dots, p). \tag{7.31}$$

The degree of these functions is equal to the number of indices with a value $> p$. The B^{ζ}_{α} are the $p(n-p)$ components we looked for.

The simple pseudo-p-vectors can be used to get a geometrical representation of compound pseudo-p-vectors. Let $x^{\kappa_1 \dots \kappa_p}$ be the symbol of a general simple contravariant pseudo-p-vector or of an E_p through O

† Kähler 1934. 1, p. 17.

in a centred E_n, and $w_{\lambda_1...\lambda_p}$ some given covariant pseudo-p-vector. Then the equation

$$w_{\lambda_1...\lambda_p} x^{\lambda_1...\lambda_p} = 0 \tag{7.32}$$

represents a system of $\infty^{p(n-p)-1}$ E_p's through O. If the straight lines through O are looked upon as points of an E_{n-1} this system corresponds to a system of $\infty^{p(n-p)-1}$ E_{p-1}'s in this E_{n-1}. Such a system is well known from ordinary projective geometry and is called a *linear E_{p-1}-complex.* Hence the geometrical representations of covariant pseudo-p-vectors and contravariant pseudo-$(n-p)$-vectors in E_n are the linear E_{p-1}-complexes in the E_{n-1} of all straight lines through O.

8. Densities†

An affinor-density of weight $\mathfrak{k}$, contravariant valence p, covariant valence q, and valence $p+q$, is defined by its law of transformation:

$$\mathfrak{P}^{\kappa'_1...\kappa'_p}{}_{\lambda'_1...\lambda'_q} = \Delta^{-\mathfrak{k}} A^{\kappa'_1}_{\kappa_1}...A^{\kappa'_p}_{\kappa_p} A^{\lambda_1}_{\lambda'_1}...A^{\lambda_q}_{\lambda'_q} \mathfrak{P}^{\kappa_1...\kappa_p}{}_{\lambda_1...\lambda_q}$$

$$(\kappa'_1,..., \kappa'_p, \lambda'_1,..., \lambda'_q = 1',..., n'). \tag{8.1}$$

A Gothic letter is generally used for the kernel-letter of a density.

All that has been said about indices, addition, isomers, multiplication, contraction, transvection, mixing, alternation, strangling, rank, region, and support holds *mutatis mutandis* for affinor-densities. Symmetric affinor-densities are called *tensor-densities* and alternating ones *p-vector-densities* ($p = 1,..., n$). Affinor-densities with valence zero are called *scalar-densities* and sometimes *densities* if no ambiguity can arise.

Addition is only possible if the quantities have the same weight.

From the alternating affinor-densities we use in the sequel only contravariant p-vector-densities of weight $+1$ and covariant ones of weight -1. *A priori* there exists a contravariant n-vector-density of weight $+1$ and a covariant n-vector-density of weight -1, defined by the equations

$$\begin{aligned} \mathfrak{E}^{1...n} &= 1, \\ \mathfrak{e}_{1...n} &= 1, \end{aligned} \tag{8.2}$$

holding with respect to *every* coordinate system. From this it follows that there must be a one-to-one correspondence between contravariant p-vectors and covariant $(n-p)$-vector-densities of weight -1 and similarly between covariant p-vectors and contravariant $(n-p)$-vector-

† Cf. Schouten and Struik 1935. 1, pp. 8, 29; Schouten 1938. 1; Schouten and v. Dantzig 1940. 1.

densities of weight $+1$. This correspondence we establish by the equations

$$\begin{aligned} p!\,\mathfrak{v}_{\lambda_1\ldots\lambda_q} &= \mathfrak{e}_{\lambda_1\ldots\lambda_q\kappa_1\ldots\kappa_p} v^{\kappa_1\ldots\kappa_p}, \\ (n-p)!\,v^{\kappa_1\ldots\kappa_p} &= \mathfrak{v}_{\lambda_1\ldots\lambda_q} \mathfrak{E}^{\lambda_1\ldots\lambda_q\kappa_1\ldots\kappa_p}, \\ p!\,\mathfrak{w}^{\kappa_1\ldots\kappa_q} &= w_{\lambda_1\ldots\lambda_p} \mathfrak{E}^{\lambda_1\ldots\lambda_p\kappa_1\ldots\kappa_q}, \\ (n-p)!\,w_{\lambda_1\ldots\lambda_p} &= \mathfrak{e}_{\lambda_1\ldots\lambda_p\kappa_1\ldots\kappa_p} \mathfrak{w}^{\kappa_1\ldots\kappa_q}. \end{aligned} \tag{8.3}$$

From a contra- or covariant n-vector we get in this way a scalar-density of weight -1 or $+1$ respectively. This is in accordance with the fact that the one component of this n-vector transforms just like a scalar-density, as we have proved in § 7. It follows that the geometrical representation of a co-(contra)-variant p-vector-density of weight -1 ($+1$) is the same as that of a contra-(co)-variant $(n-p)$-vector.

There exists still another kind of density, called *Weyl-density*, in whose transformation formulae $|\Delta|$ replaces Δ. From the geometrical point of view the only difference between Weyl-densities and ordinary densities is that an inner orientation is changed into an outer orientation and vice versa.† Weyl-densities are very important for physical investigations but appear in the following only a few times.

9. Connecting quantities‡

If several affine spaces are considered simultaneously, quantities may occur with different sorts of indices. Such quantities are called *connecting quantities*. For example, an E_m in E_n can be given by m linear equations in x^κ with constant coefficients b^κ and B^κ_a and m parameters x^a ($a = 1,\ldots,\mathrm{m}$) which can be looked upon as coordinates in E_m:

$$x^\kappa = b^\kappa + B^\kappa_a x^a \quad (a = 1,\ldots,\mathrm{m}). \tag{9.1}$$

The quantity

$$B^\kappa_b = \frac{\partial x^\kappa}{\partial x^b} \quad (b = 1,\ldots,\mathrm{m}) \tag{9.2}$$

of rank m is called the *contravariant connecting quantity* of the E_m in E_n. B^κ_b determines uniquely the m-direction of E_m. Every contravariant vector v^a in E_m is also a contravariant vector in E_n and has in E_n the components

$$v^\kappa = B^\kappa_b v^b \quad (b = 1,\ldots,\mathrm{m}). \tag{9.3}$$

† Cf. Schouten and v. Kampen 1930. 1; Schouten and Struik 1935. 1, pp. 9, 90; Schouten 1938. 1, 1938. 2; Schouten and v. Dantzig 1940. 1.

‡ Cf. Schouten 1938. 1, 1938. 2.

The same cannot be said for a covariant vector of E_m, but to every covariant vector w_λ of E_n belongs one and only one covariant vector $'w_b$ of E_m

$$'w_b = w_\lambda B_b^\lambda \quad (b = 1,..., m). \tag{9.4}$$

Geometrically, $'w_b$ is obtained from w_λ by section with E_m. Accordingly we call $'w_b$ the *section* of w_λ *with* E_m. If $\underset{b}{e^a}$, $\overset{b}{e_a}$ are the measuring vectors in E_m with respect to the coordinate system (a) and $\underset{b}{e^\kappa}$ the components of the $\underset{b}{e^a}$, considered as vectors of E_n, we have

$$B_b^\kappa = \underset{c}{e^\kappa} \overset{c}{e_b} \quad (b, c = 1,..., m). \tag{9.5}$$

If $v^{\kappa_1 \dots \kappa_m}$ is a simple p-vector in E_n and $v^{1\dots m} \neq 0$, the coordinates $x^1,..., x^m$ can be used as coordinates in the E_m through O with the m-direction of $v^{\kappa_1 \dots \kappa_m}$. For this E_m the equations (9.1) then take the form

$$x^\kappa = B_\beta^\kappa x^\beta, \tag{9.6}$$

where

$$B_\beta^\alpha = \delta_\beta^\alpha \quad (\alpha, \beta = 1,..., m), \tag{9.7}$$

and where the x^β $(\beta = 1,..., m)$ play the role of parameters. Now x^κ is a vector of E_m, hence

$$0 = (m+1)x^{[\zeta}v^{1\dots m]} = x^\zeta v^{1\dots m} - x^1 v^{\zeta 2\dots m} - \dots x^m v^{1\dots(m-1)\zeta} \quad (\zeta = m+1,..., n) \tag{9.8}$$

or

$$x^\zeta = x^1 \frac{v^{\zeta 2\dots m}}{v^{1\dots m}} + \dots + x^m \frac{v^{1\dots(m-1)\zeta}}{v^{1\dots m}} \quad (\zeta = m+1,..., n), \tag{9.9}$$

and thus

$$B_\beta^\zeta = \frac{v^{1\dots(\beta-1)\zeta(\beta+1)\dots m}}{v^{1\dots m}} \quad (\beta = 1,..., m;\ \zeta = m+1,..., n). \tag{9.10}$$

From this it follows that the quantity B_β^κ, already mentioned in § 7, is a special form of the contravariant connecting quantity of the E_m.

An E_m in E_n can also be given by means of $n-m$ independent linear equations in x^κ:

$$C_\lambda^x x^\lambda = c^x \quad (x = m+1,..., n) \tag{9.11}$$

with constant coefficients C_λ^x, c^x. Every E_m parallel to this E_m has equations of the form

$$C_\lambda^x x^\lambda = x^x \quad (x = m+1,..., n) \tag{9.12}$$

with the $n-m$ parameters x^x which pass into c^x if the E_m coincides with the E_m given first. Hence the x^x can be used as coordinates in the E_{n-m} which is obtained by reducing the E_n with respect to the m-direction of the E_m (cf. § 2). The quantity C_λ^x of rank $n-m$ is called the *covariant connecting quantity* of the E_m in E_n. C_λ^x determines uniquely the m-direction of E_m. Every covariant vector w_y in the E_{n-m} mentioned above may be considered also as a covariant vector of E_n, because its two parallel E_{n-m-1}'s and the m-direction of E_m determine two parallel E_{n-1}'s. Its components in E_n are

$$w_\lambda = w_y C^y_\lambda \quad (y = \mathrm{m}+1,\dots,\mathrm{n}). \tag{9.13}$$

The same cannot be said of the contravariant vector of E_{n-m}, but to every contravariant vector v^κ of E_n belongs one and only one contravariant vector $'v^x$ of E_{n-m}

$$'v^x = v^\kappa C^x_\kappa \quad (x = \mathrm{m}+1,\dots,\mathrm{n}). \tag{9.14}$$

Geometrically, $'v^x$ is obtained from v^κ by reducing with respect to the m-direction of E_m. Accordingly we call $'v^x$ the *reduction* of v^κ *with respect to* E_m. If $\underset{x}{e^y}$, $\overset{y}{e_x}$ are the measuring vectors in E_{n-m} with respect to the coordinate system (x) and $\overset{x}{e_\lambda}$ the components of the $\overset{x}{e_y}$, considered as vectors of E_n, we have

$$C^x_\lambda = \underset{y}{e^x}\overset{y}{e_\lambda} \quad (x, y = \mathrm{m}+1,\dots,\mathrm{n}). \tag{9.15}$$

Now the directions of the $\underset{b}{e^\kappa}$ all lie in the m-direction of E_m and the $(n-1)$-directions of the $\overset{y}{e_\lambda}$ all contain this m-direction. Hence all transvections $\underset{b}{e^\mu}\overset{x}{e_\mu}$ are zero, and in consequence of (9.5) and (9.15) we have

$$B^\mu_b C^x_\mu = \underset{c}{e^\mu}\overset{c}{e_b}\,\underset{y}{e^x}\overset{y}{e_\mu} = 0 \quad (b, c = 1,\dots,\mathrm{m};\ x, y = \mathrm{m}+1,\dots,\mathrm{n}). \tag{9.16}$$

This may be seen also by substituting (9.1) in (9.11) and observing that this equation must hold for all values of the parameters x^c:

$$C^x_\lambda b^\lambda + C^x_\lambda B^\lambda_c x^c = c^x \quad (c = 1,\dots,\mathrm{m};\ x = \mathrm{m}+1,\dots,\mathrm{n}). \tag{9.17}$$

If $v^{\kappa_1\dots\kappa_m}$ is a simple p-vector in E_n and $v^{1\dots m} \neq 0$, the coordinates $x^{m+1},\dots, x^n$ can be used as coordinates in the E_{n-m} arising from E_n by reduction with respect to the m-direction of $v^{\kappa_1\dots\kappa_m}$. For the E_m through O with the m-direction of $v^{\kappa_1\dots\kappa_m}$ the equations (9.12) then take the form

$$C^\zeta_\lambda x^\lambda = 0 \quad (\zeta = m+1,\dots,n), \tag{9.18}$$

where
$$C^\zeta_\eta = \delta^\zeta_\eta \quad (\zeta, \eta = m+1,\dots,n). \tag{9.19}$$

Now x^μ being any vector of E_m we have

$$0 = C^\zeta_{\lambda_1} v^{\lambda_1\dots\lambda_m} = v^{\zeta\lambda_2\dots\lambda_m} + C^\zeta_\beta v^{\beta\lambda_2\dots\lambda_m} \quad (\beta = 1,\dots,m;\ \zeta = m+1,\dots,n),$$

(9.20

and from this it follows that

$$v^{1\ldots(\beta-1)\zeta(\beta+1)\ldots m} = -C^{\zeta}_{\beta}\, v^{1\ldots m} \quad (\beta = 1,\ldots,m;\ \zeta = m+1,\ldots,n). \tag{9.21}$$

Comparing this result with (9.10) we get

$$C^{\zeta}_{\beta} = -B^{\zeta}_{\beta} \quad (\beta = 1,\ldots,m;\ \zeta = m+1,\ldots,n). \tag{9.22}$$

The quantity C^{ζ}_{λ} is a special form of the covariant connecting quantity of the E_m. These special forms of the connecting quantities will be useful in dealing with Jacobi systems and their conjugate systems in III, § 12.

If an E_m and an $E_{m'}$ are given in E_n with the connecting quantities R^{κ}_{b}, $S^{\mathfrak{x}}_{\lambda}$ $(b = 1,\ldots,\mathrm{m};\ \mathfrak{x} = (\mathrm{m}'+1)',\ldots,\mathrm{n}';\ m \leqslant m')$, respectively, the equation

$$R^{\mu}_{b}\, S^{\mathfrak{x}}_{\mu} = 0 \tag{9.23}$$

expresses that the m-direction of E_m is contained in the m'-direction of $E_{m'}$.

If an E_m in E_n be given, identification, section, and reduction can be defined for covariant and contravariant affinors in the same way as for vectors. As an example we give here a detailed description for p-vectors, this being the most important case:

(*a*) Every contravariant p-vector $v^{a_1\ldots a_p}$ $(p \leqslant m)$ of E_m may be identified with the contravariant p-vector of E_n

$$v^{\kappa_1\ldots\kappa_p} = B^{\kappa_1}_{a_1}\ldots B^{\kappa_p}_{a_p}\, v^{a_1\ldots a_p} \quad (a_1,\ldots,a_p = 1,\ldots,\mathrm{m}). \tag{9.24}$$

(*b*) The *section* of a covariant p-vector $w_{\lambda_1\ldots\lambda_p}$ $(p \leqslant m)$ of E_n with E_m is

$$'w_{b_1\ldots b_p} = B^{\lambda_1}_{b_1}\ldots B^{\lambda_p}_{b_p}\, w_{\lambda_1\ldots\lambda_p} \quad (b_1,\ldots,b_p = 1,\ldots,\mathrm{n}). \tag{9.25}$$

(*c*) Every covariant vector $w_{y_1\ldots y_p}$ $(p \leqslant n-m)$ of the E_{n-m} arising from E_n by reduction with respect to the m-direction of E_m, may be identified with the p-vector of E_n

$$w_{\lambda_1\ldots\lambda_p} = C^{y_1}_{\lambda_1}\ldots C^{y_p}_{\lambda_p} w_{y_1\ldots y_p} \quad (y_1,\ldots,y_p = \mathrm{m}+1,\ldots,\mathrm{n}). \tag{9.26}$$

(*d*) The *reduction* of a contravariant p-vector $v^{\kappa_1\ldots\kappa_p}$ $(p \leqslant n-m)$ of E_n with respect to the p-direction of E_p is

$$'v^{x_1\ldots x_p} = C^{x_1}_{\kappa_1}\ldots C^{x_p}_{\kappa_p}\, v^{\kappa_1\ldots\kappa_p} \quad (x_1,\ldots,x_p = \mathrm{m}+1,\ldots,\mathrm{n}). \tag{9.27}$$

If an E_m with the connecting quantities B^{κ}_{b}, C^{x}_{λ} be given, it is sometimes convenient to add an E_{n-m}, having no direction in common with the E_m. Then the E_m is called *rigged*.† Of course the E_{n-m} is rigged as well. The rigging of an E_m can be carried out most conveniently in the following way. The B^{κ}_{b} $(b = 1,\ldots,\mathrm{m})$ fix m E_1's in the E_m and the C^{x}_{λ}

† Weyl uses the expression 'eingespannt'.

(x = m+1,..., n) fix $n-m$ E_{n-1}'s through the E_m. Every set of $m-1$ of these E_1's span together with the E_{n-m}, an E_{n-1}. In the m E_{n-1}'s through the E_{n-m} obtained in this way we lay m covariant vectors and denote them by B^a_λ (a = 1,..., m), choosing the magnitude and the order in such a way that

$$B^\kappa_b B^a_\kappa = B^a_b \overset{\text{def}}{=} \delta^a_b \quad (a, b = 1,\ldots,\mathrm{m}). \tag{9.28}$$

Similarly every set of $n-m-1$ of the E_{n-1}'s intersects the E_{n-m} in an E_1. In the $n-m$ E_1's obtained in this way we lay $n-m$ contravariant vectors and denote them by C^κ_y (y = m+1,..., n), choosing the magnitude and the order in such a way that

$$C^\kappa_y C^x_\kappa = C^x_y \overset{\text{def}}{=} \delta^x_y \quad (x, y = \mathrm{m}+1,\ldots,\mathrm{n}). \tag{9.29}$$

Obviously C^κ_y is the contravariant and B^a_λ the covariant connecting quantity of the E_{n-m}. Hence

$$C^\kappa_y B^a_\kappa = 0 \quad (a = 1,\ldots,\mathrm{m};\ y = \mathrm{m}+1,\ldots,\mathrm{n}). \tag{9.30}$$

Introducing the quantities

$$\begin{aligned} B^\kappa_\lambda &\overset{\text{def}}{=} B^\kappa_b B^b_\lambda \\ C^\kappa_\lambda &\overset{\text{def}}{=} C^\kappa_x C^x_\lambda \end{aligned} \quad (b = 1,\ldots,\mathrm{m};\ x = m+1,\ldots,\mathrm{n}), \tag{9.31}$$

we get from (9.28, 29, 30)

$$\begin{aligned} (B^\kappa_\lambda + C^\kappa_\lambda) B^\lambda_b &= B^\kappa_b + 0 \\ (B^\kappa_\lambda + C^\kappa_\lambda) C^\lambda_y &= 0 + C^\kappa_y \end{aligned} \quad (b = 1,\ldots,\mathrm{m};\ y = \mathrm{m}+1,\ldots,\mathrm{n}), \tag{9.32}$$

and from this it follows that

$$A^\kappa_\lambda = B^\kappa_\lambda + C^\kappa_\lambda = B^\kappa_b B^b_\lambda + C^\kappa_x C^x_\lambda \quad (b = 1,\ldots,\mathrm{m};\ x = \mathrm{m}+1,\ldots,\mathrm{n}). \tag{9.33}$$

Now let w_λ be an arbitrary vector. Then we know that

$$'w_b \overset{\text{def}}{=} B^\lambda_b w_\lambda, \qquad ''w_y \overset{\text{def}}{=} C^\lambda_y w_\lambda \tag{9.34}$$

are the sections of w_λ with E_m and E_{n-m} respectively. But according to (9.32) these sections can also be considered as the sections of the two component parts of w_λ

$$'w_\lambda \overset{\text{def}}{=} B^\kappa_\lambda w_\kappa, \qquad ''w_\lambda \overset{\text{def}}{=} C^\kappa_\lambda w_\kappa, \qquad w_\lambda = {}'w_\lambda + {}''w_\lambda. \tag{9.35}$$

$'w_\lambda$ is entirely determined by $'w_b$, its E_{n-1} being spanned by the E_{m-1} of $'w_b$ and E_{n-m}. Hence these quantities can be identified and $'w_\lambda$ and $'w_b$ can be looked upon as two different kinds of components of a covariant vector through E_{n-m}. The same holds *mutatis mutandis* for $''w_y$ and $''w_\lambda$. In the same way, if v^κ is an arbitrary vector, the vectors

$$'v^a \overset{\text{def}}{=} B^a_\lambda v^\lambda, \qquad ''v^x \overset{\text{def}}{=} C^x_\lambda v^\lambda \tag{9.36}$$

are the reductions of v^κ with respect to the E_{n-m} and E_m respectively. These vectors are also the reductions of the two component parts of v^κ

$$'v^\kappa \overset{\text{def}}{=} B^\kappa_\lambda v^\lambda, \qquad ''v^\kappa \overset{\text{def}}{=} C^\kappa_\lambda v^\lambda. \tag{9.37}$$

$'v^a$ and $'v^\kappa$ can be looked upon as two different kinds of components of a contravariant vector in E_m. The same holds *mutatis mutandis* for $''v^x$ and $''v^\kappa$.

10. Sections of a covariant bivector

Let $w_{\mu\lambda}$ be a covariant bivector of rank 2ρ in E_n and $2\rho'$ the rank of the section of $w_{\mu\lambda}$ with the hyperplane

$$u_\lambda x^\lambda = 0. \tag{10.1}$$

We will prove that $\rho - 1 \leqslant \rho' \leqslant \rho$. For that purpose we choose the coordinate system in such a way that $u_\lambda = \overset{1}{e}_\lambda$ and that the hyperplane is spanned by the $\underset{2}{e}^\kappa, \ldots, \underset{n}{e}^\kappa$. Then $w_{\mu\lambda}$ can always be written as follows

$$w_{\mu\lambda} = 'w_{\mu\lambda} + p_{[\mu}\overset{1}{e}_{\lambda]}, \tag{10.2}$$

where $'w_{\mu\lambda}$ only depends on $\overset{2}{e}_\lambda, \ldots, \overset{n}{e}_\lambda$. The rank of $'w_{\mu\lambda}$ is $2\rho'$. If we write now

$$\begin{aligned} \overset{2}{I} &= w, & '\overset{2}{I} &= 'w; \\ \overset{4}{I} &= ww, & '\overset{4}{I} &= 'w\,'w; \quad \text{etc.,} \end{aligned} \tag{10.3}$$

making use of the abbreviated notation of I, § 7, according to our suppositions we have

$$\overset{2\rho}{I} \neq 0, \qquad \overset{2\rho+2}{I} = 0. \tag{10.4}$$

Now

$$\begin{aligned} &(a) & 0 = \overset{2\rho+2}{I} &= '\overset{2\rho+2}{I} + (\rho+1)\,'\overset{2\rho}{I} p \overset{1}{e}, \\ &(b) & \overset{2\rho}{I} &= '\overset{2\rho}{I} + \rho\, '\overset{2\rho-2}{I} p \overset{1}{e}, \\ &(c) & \overset{2\rho-2}{I} &= '\overset{2\rho-2}{I} + (\rho-1)\, '\overset{2\rho-4}{I} p \overset{1}{e}, \end{aligned} \tag{10.5}$$

and from (10.5 a) it follows that $'\overset{2\rho+2}{I}\overset{1}{e} = 0$. But, since $'\overset{2\rho+2}{I}$ does not contain $\overset{1}{e}$ this is only possible if $'\overset{2\rho+2}{I} = 0$. Hence $\rho' \leqslant \rho$. From (10.5 b) it follows that $'\overset{2\rho-2}{I}$ cannot vanish because from $'\overset{2\rho-2}{I} = 0$ would follow $'\overset{2\rho}{I} = 0$ and consequently $\overset{2\rho}{I} = 0$. Hence $\rho - 1 \leqslant \rho'$. We call $2\rho - 2\rho'$ the *reduction number* of u_λ with respect to $w_{\mu\lambda}$. If $\rho' = \rho$ we get from (10.5 b)

$$\overset{2\rho}{I}\overset{1}{e} = '\overset{2\rho}{I}\overset{1}{e} \neq 0 \tag{10.6}$$

because $\overset{2\rho}{'I}$ does not contain $\overset{1}{e}$. If $\rho' = \rho-1$ we get from (10.5 b, c)

$$\overset{2\rho}{I}\overset{1}{e} = 0, \qquad \overset{2\rho-2}{I}\ \overset{1}{e} = \overset{2\rho-2}{'I}\ \overset{1}{e} \neq 0. \tag{10.7}$$

Similarly we call $2\rho-2\rho'$ the *reduction number* of the system of vectors $\overset{1}{u}_\lambda,\dots,\overset{\sigma}{u}_\lambda$ with respect to $w_{\mu\lambda}$ if the rank of the section of $w_{\mu\lambda}$ with the $E_{n-\sigma}$

$$\overset{1}{u}_\lambda x^\lambda = 0, \quad \dots, \quad \overset{\sigma}{u}_\lambda x^\lambda = 0 \tag{10.8}$$

is $2\rho'$. If these vectors are introduced successively the diminishing of the rank is, at every step, $\leqslant 2$, hence

$$0 \leqslant 2\rho-2\rho' \leqslant 2\sigma. \tag{10.9}$$

According to our suppositions we have

$$\overset{2\rho'}{I}\ \overset{1}{u}\dots\overset{\sigma}{u} \neq 0, \qquad \overset{2\rho'+2}{I}\ \overset{1}{u}\dots\overset{\sigma}{u} = 0. \tag{10.10}$$

Now consider the matrix

$$\begin{array}{c} \overbrace{\hphantom{w_{\mu\lambda}}}^{n}\ \overbrace{\hphantom{\overset{1}{u}_\mu \ \dots\ \overset{\sigma}{u}_\mu}}^{\sigma} \end{array}$$

$$\left\| \begin{array}{cccc} w_{\mu\lambda} & \overset{1}{u}_\mu & \dots & \overset{\sigma}{u}_\mu \\ -\overset{1}{u}_\lambda & 0 & \dots & 0 \\ \vdots & \vdots & & \vdots \\ -\overset{\sigma}{u}_\lambda & 0 & \dots & 0 \end{array} \right\| \begin{array}{l} \}\, n \\ \\ \}\, \sigma \\ \\ \end{array} . \tag{10.11}$$

If $2R$ is the rank of this matrix it is readily shown that

$$(a) \quad \left.\begin{array}{l} \overset{2R}{I} \\ \overset{2R-2}{I}\ \overset{a_1}{u} \\ \overset{2R-4}{I}\ \overset{a_1}{u}\overset{a_2}{u} \\ \vdots \\ \overset{2R-2\sigma}{I}\ \overset{a_1}{u}\dots\overset{a_\sigma}{u} \end{array}\right\} \text{not all} = 0, \qquad (b) \quad \left.\begin{array}{l} \overset{2R+2}{I} \\ \overset{2R}{I}\ \overset{a_1}{u} \\ \overset{2R-2}{I}\ \overset{a_1}{u}\overset{a_2}{u} \\ \vdots \\ \overset{2R-2\sigma+2}{I}\ \overset{a_1}{u}\dots\overset{a_\sigma}{u} \end{array}\right\} = 0$$

$$(a_1,\dots,a_\sigma = 1,\dots,\sigma). \tag{10.12}$$

The easiest way to prove this is to write $w_{\mu,n+1},\dots, w_{\mu,n+\sigma}$ instead of $\overset{1}{u}_\mu,\dots,\overset{\sigma}{u}_\mu$ (cf. Ex. 9).

We will now prove that

$$\overset{2R-2\sigma}{I}\ \overset{1}{u}\dots\overset{\sigma}{u} \neq 0. \tag{10.13}$$

If this were not true, the reduction number κ of $\overset{1}{u}_\lambda,\dots,\overset{\sigma}{u}_\lambda$ would satisfy the inequality

$$\kappa \geqslant 2\rho-2R+2\sigma+2 \tag{10.14}$$

according to (10.10). Now if one of the other expressions in (10.12a) were $\neq 0$, for instance,

$$\overset{2R-4}{I}\ \overset{1}{u}\overset{2}{u} \neq 0, \tag{10.15}$$

the reduction number κ_{12} of $\overset{1}{u}_\lambda$, $\overset{2}{u}_\lambda$ would satisfy the inequality

$$\kappa_{12} \leqslant 2\rho - 2R + 4. \tag{10.16}$$

From this it would follow that the vectors $\overset{3}{u}_\lambda,\dots,\overset{\sigma}{u}_\lambda$, introduced after $\overset{1}{u}_\lambda$, $\overset{2}{u}_\lambda$ would have to diminish the rank by at least $2\sigma - 2$. The reduction number of $\sigma - 2$ vectors being at most $2\sigma - 4$ the supposition (10.15) cannot be true. From this it follows that (10.13) must hold, because all expressions (10.12a) cannot vanish simultaneously. We collect these results in the following theorem:

THEOREM I.4. *The reduction number of σ vectors $\overset{1}{u}_\lambda,\dots,\overset{\sigma}{u}_\lambda$ with respect to the covariant bivector $w_{\mu\lambda}$ of rank 2ρ is equal to κ if and only if*

$$\overset{2\rho-\kappa}{I}\ \overset{1}{u}\dots\overset{\sigma}{u} \neq 0, \qquad \overset{2\rho-\kappa+2}{I}\ \overset{1}{u}\dots\overset{\sigma}{u} = 0 \tag{10.17}$$

or, in another form, if and only if the matrix

$$\begin{array}{cc} & \begin{array}{cc} \longleftarrow n \longrightarrow & \longleftarrow\qquad \sigma \qquad\longrightarrow \end{array} \\ \begin{array}{c} n\updownarrow \\ \\ \sigma\updownarrow \\ \\ \end{array} & \left\| \begin{array}{cccc} w_{\mu\lambda} & \overset{1}{u}_\mu & \dots & \overset{\sigma}{u}_\mu \\ -\overset{1}{u}_\lambda & 0 & \dots & 0 \\ \vdots & \vdots & & \vdots \\ -\overset{\sigma}{u}_\lambda & 0 & \dots & 0 \end{array} \right\| \end{array}$$

has rank $2\rho + 2\sigma - \kappa$.

EXERCISES†

1. An $(n-2)$-vector in E_n is always the sum of two simple $(n-2)$-vectors.

2. If

$$u^{\kappa_1\dots\kappa_p} = \underset{1}{e}{}^{[\kappa_1}\dots\underset{p}{e}{}^{\kappa_p]} \tag{2α}$$

and if $v^{\kappa_1\dots\kappa_q}$ is a simple q-vector $(p+q-n = r)$ such that

$$v^{1\dots r(p+1)\dots n} \neq 0, \tag{2β}$$

the E_p of $u^{\kappa_1\dots\kappa_p}$ and the E_q of $v^{\kappa_1\dots\kappa_q}$ have just an E_r in common.

3. If $P^{\kappa\lambda}$ is an affinor of rank n and if Δ is the determinant of its matrix, prove that

$$\Delta E^{\kappa_1\dots\kappa_n} E^{\lambda_1\dots\lambda_n} = n!\, P^{[\kappa_1[\lambda_1}\dots P^{\kappa_n]\lambda_n]} = n!\, P^{\kappa_1[\lambda_1}\dots P^{|\kappa_n|\lambda_n]} \tag{3α}$$

and

$$\Delta = n!\, P^{[1[1}\dots P^{n]n]} = n!\, P^{1[1}\dots P^{|n|n]}. \tag{3β}$$

The same holds *mutatis mutandis* for an affinor $P^{\kappa}_{\cdot\lambda}$ or $P_{\kappa\lambda}$.

† Cf. the suggestions at the end of the book.

4. If $P^{\kappa\lambda}$ is an affinor of rank n and if Δ is the determinant of its matrix, prove that

$$\Delta \overset{-1}{P}_{\lambda\kappa} = nn!\, A^{[1}_{\kappa} A^{[1}_{\lambda} P^{22} \ldots P^{n]n]}. \tag{4 α}$$

The same holds *mutatis mutandis* for an affinor $P^{\kappa}_{.\lambda}$ or $P_{\lambda\kappa}$ of rank n.

5. If $v^{\kappa\lambda}$ is a bivector of rank $2\rho = n$ and if Δ is the determinant of its matrix, prove that

$$\Delta = \left\{ \frac{(2\rho)!}{2^{\rho}.\rho!} v^{[12} \ldots v^{n-1 n]} \right\}^2. \tag{5 α}$$

The same holds *mutatis mutandis* for a bivector $v_{\lambda\kappa}$.

6. If $v^{\kappa\lambda}$ is a bivector of rank 2ρ, prove that†

$$(2\rho)!\, v^{[\kappa_1 [\lambda_1} \ldots v^{\kappa_{2\rho}] \lambda_{2\rho}]} = \left(\frac{(2\rho)!}{2^{\rho}.\rho!} \right)^2 v^{[\kappa_1 \kappa_2} \ldots v^{\kappa_{2\rho-1} \kappa_{2\rho}]} v^{[\lambda_1 \lambda_2} \ldots v^{\lambda_{2\rho-1} \lambda_{2\rho}]}. \tag{6 α}$$

For any choice of $\kappa_1, \ldots, \kappa_\rho, \lambda_1, \ldots, \lambda_\rho$ the left-hand side is the value of a 2ρ-rowed sub-determinant of the matrix $v^{\kappa\lambda}$, arising by striking out $n-2\rho$ rows and $n-2\rho$ columns. The same holds *mutatis mutandis* for a bivector $v_{\lambda\kappa}$.

7. A main sub-determinant of a quadratic matrix is a sub-determinant symmetrical about the main diagonal. If the bivector $v^{\kappa\lambda}$ or $v_{\lambda\kappa}$ has the rank 2ρ, at least one 2ρ-rowed main sub-determinant of its matrix does not vanish.

8. If $P_{\lambda\kappa}$ is an affinor of rank n and Δ the determinant of its matrix, prove that

$$\overset{\leftarrow n \rightarrow \leftarrow 1 \rightarrow}{\begin{vmatrix} P_{\lambda\kappa} & u_\kappa \\ v_\lambda & 0 \end{vmatrix}} \begin{matrix} \updownarrow n \\ \updownarrow 1 \end{matrix} = -\Delta \overset{-1}{P}{}^{\kappa\lambda} u_\kappa v_\lambda. \tag{8 α}$$

9. Let $w_{\mu\lambda}$ be a bivector of rank 2ρ and $\overset{1}{u}_\lambda, \ldots, \overset{\sigma}{u}_\lambda$ a set of σ linearly independent vectors. Let κ_ν be the lowest value of the reduction number of $\nu \leqslant \sigma$ arbitrary vectors among $\overset{1}{u}_\lambda, \ldots, \overset{\sigma}{u}_\lambda$. Determine the 2τ-rowed sub-determinants of the matrix

$$\left\| \begin{matrix} w_{\mu\lambda} & \overset{1}{u}_\mu & \ldots & \overset{\sigma}{u}_\mu \\ -\overset{1}{u}_\lambda & 0 & \ldots & 0 \\ \vdots & \vdots & & \vdots \\ -\overset{\sigma}{u}_\lambda & 0 & \ldots & 0 \end{matrix} \right\| \tag{9 α}$$

(2τ=rank of (9 α)) that necessarily vanish.

10. If $v_{\lambda_1 \ldots \lambda_m}$ is a general m-vector and $w_{\lambda_1 \ldots \lambda_q}$ a simple q-vector, the section of $v_{\lambda_1 \ldots \lambda_m}$ with the E_{n-q} of $w_{\lambda_1 \ldots \lambda_q}$ vanishes if and only if

$$v_{[\lambda_1 \ldots \lambda_m} w_{\kappa_1 \ldots \kappa_q]} = 0. \tag{10 α}$$

11. The reduction number of u_λ with respect to the bivector $w_{\mu\lambda}$ is equal to 2 if and only if u_λ is contained in the domain of $w_{\mu\lambda}$.

† The expression $(2\rho)!\, 2^{-\rho}.(\rho!)^{-1} v^{[\kappa_1 \kappa_2} \ldots v^{\kappa_{2\rho-1} \kappa_{2\rho}]}$ is called a 'Pfaff aggregate' of order 2ρ, cf. v. Weber 1900. 1, p. 21, and is the sum of $(2\rho)!\, 2^{-\rho}(\rho!)^{-1}$ terms of the form $v^{\nu_1 \nu_2} \ldots v^{\nu_{2\rho-1} \nu_{2\rho}}$; $\nu_1, \ldots, \nu_{2\rho}$ being an even permutation of $\kappa_1, \ldots, \kappa_{2\rho}$.

II

ANALYTICAL PRELIMINARIES

1. The arithmetic n-dimensional manifold $\mathfrak{A}_n$†

EVERY ordered set of n real or complex values of n variables $\overset{\kappa}{\xi}$ is called an *arithmetic point* and the totality of all these points an *arithmetic manifold* or $\mathfrak{A}_n$. The $\overset{\kappa}{\xi}$ are called the *components of the arithmetic point*. For 'point with components $\overset{\kappa}{\xi}$' we write 'point $\overset{\kappa}{\xi}$' for brevity.

If $\underset{0}{\overset{\kappa}{\xi}}$ are n arbitrary numbers and $\overset{\kappa}{\beta}$ n arbitrary *positive* numbers, the set of all arithmetic points satisfying the inequalities

$$|\overset{\kappa}{\xi}-\underset{0}{\overset{\kappa}{\xi}}| < \overset{\kappa}{\beta} \tag{1.1}$$

is called a *polycylinder* in $\mathfrak{A}_n$. A set of arithmetic points is called a *region* of $\mathfrak{A}_n$ if the following conditions are satisfied:

1. The set is open, i.e. every point of the set belongs to at least one polycylinder consisting only of points of the region.

2. For every choice of two points of the region there exists a finite chain of polycylinders each consisting only of points of the region, such that the first point lies in the first and the second point in the last polycylinder and consecutive polycylinders have at least one point in common.

It is evident that every polycylinder is a region. Also the whole $\mathfrak{A}_n$ is a region. Every polycylinder given by equations of the form (1.1) is called a *neighbourhood* of the point $\underset{0}{\overset{\kappa}{\xi}}$. For 'neighbourhood of $\underset{0}{\overset{\kappa}{\xi}}$' we write $\mathfrak{N}(\underset{0}{\overset{\kappa}{\xi}})$ for brevity.

2. The geometric n-dimensional manifold X_n

We consider a set M whose elements are in one-to-one correspondence with the points of a region $\underset{0}{\mathfrak{R}}$ of $\mathfrak{A}_n$. With respect to the elements of M we only presume that they are not points of $\mathfrak{A}_n$. They may be, for instance, homogeneous linear forms in n variables or polynomials of degree $n-1$ in one variable, or points of an arithmetic manifold $\mathfrak{A}'_n$ different from $\mathfrak{A}_n$. The one-to-one correspondence between the elements

† For § 1 and § 2 of this chapter cf. Veblen and Whitehead 1932. 2; Behnke and Thullen 1934. 2.

of M and the points of $\underset{0}{\mathfrak{R}}$ is called a *coordinate system defined over M.* If the point $\overset{\kappa}{\xi}$ corresponds to a certain element of M, we call the numbers $\overset{\kappa}{\xi}$ the *coordinates of this element with respect to the coordinate system* (κ). We shall write ξ^κ instead of $\overset{\kappa}{\xi}$ if these numbers are looked upon as coordinates of an element of M and not as components of a point of $\mathfrak{A}_n$. Referring to I, § 3, we point out that for an arithmetic point the kernel-letter is $\overset{\kappa}{\xi}$ and κ is a dead index, whilst for the elements of M the kernel-letter is ξ and κ is a living index.

The following theorem is proved in every reliable advanced text-book of analysis:

THEOREM II.1. (*Theorem of inversion.*) *If in the system of equations*

$$\overset{\kappa'}{\xi} = \overset{\kappa'}{f}(\overset{\kappa}{\xi}) \quad (\kappa' = 1',..., n') \tag{2.1}$$

the functions $\overset{\kappa'}{f}$ are analytic† *in an $\mathfrak{R}(\underset{0}{\overset{\kappa}{\xi}})$ and if the functional determinant of these functions*

$$\Delta \overset{\text{def}}{=} \operatorname{Det}(\partial\overset{\kappa'}{\xi}/\partial\overset{\kappa}{\xi}) \quad (\kappa' = 1',..., n') \tag{2.2}$$

is $\neq 0$ for $\overset{\kappa}{\xi} = \underset{0}{\overset{\kappa}{\xi}}$, the $\overset{\kappa}{\xi}$ can be solved from (2.1) *and in this solution*

$$\overset{\kappa}{\xi} = \overset{\kappa}{f}(\overset{\kappa'}{\xi}) \quad (\kappa' = 1',..., n') \tag{2.3}$$

the functions $\overset{\kappa}{f}$ are analytic in an $\mathfrak{R}(\underset{0}{\overset{\kappa'}{\xi}})$, $\underset{0}{\overset{\kappa'}{\xi}}$ being defined by

$$\underset{0}{\overset{\kappa'}{\xi}} = \overset{\kappa'}{f}(\underset{0}{\overset{\kappa}{\xi}}). \tag{2.4}$$

The functional determinant of the $\overset{\kappa}{f}$ is equal to $1/\Delta$ for $\overset{\kappa'}{\xi} = \underset{0}{\overset{\kappa'}{\xi}}$.

As a consequence of this theorem there exists in $\mathfrak{R}(\underset{0}{\overset{\kappa}{\xi}})$ a neighbourhood $\mathfrak{R}$ of $\underset{0}{\overset{\kappa}{\xi}}$ and in $\mathfrak{R}(\underset{0}{\overset{\kappa'}{\xi}})$ a neighbourhood $\mathfrak{R}'$ of $\underset{0}{\overset{\kappa'}{\xi}}$ for the points of which equations (2.1) and (2.3) establish a one-to-one correspondence.

We now presume that $\underset{0}{\overset{\kappa}{\xi}}$ is a point of $\underset{0}{\mathfrak{R}}$ and that $\mathfrak{R}$ lies in $\underset{0}{\mathfrak{R}}$. Then

† A function, defined in an $\mathfrak{R}(\underset{0}{\overset{\kappa}{\xi}})$ is said to be analytic in $\underset{0}{\overset{\kappa}{\xi}}$ if there exists an $\mathfrak{R}(\underset{0}{\overset{\kappa}{\xi}})$ where the function can be expanded into a power series in $\overset{\kappa}{\xi} - \underset{0}{\overset{\kappa}{\xi}}$, convergent in this latter $\mathfrak{R}(\underset{0}{\overset{\kappa}{\xi}})$.

there exists in M a subset R whose points are in one-to-one correspondence with the points of $\mathfrak{R}$ and hence by (2.1) also with the points of $\mathfrak{R}'$. This latter correspondence is, according to our definition, another coordinate system over R.

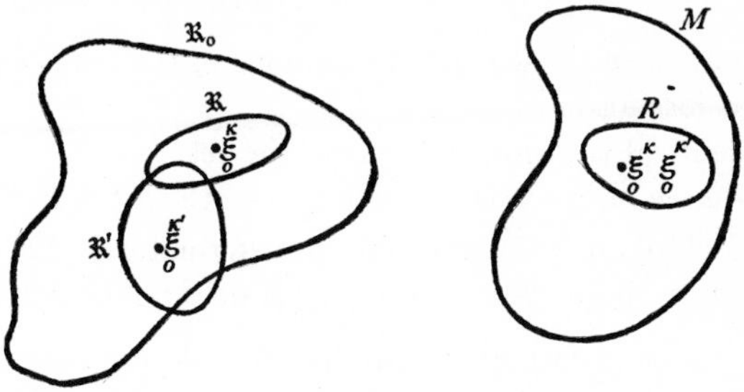

FIG. 1.

We denote this coordinate system by (κ') and write $\xi^{\kappa'}$ for the $\overset{\kappa'}{\xi}$ if they are considered as coordinates of points M. The equations (2.1, 4) are point transformations in $\mathfrak{A}_n$. If in these equations we replace $\overset{\kappa}{\xi}$, $\overset{\kappa'}{\xi}$ by ξ^{κ}, $\xi^{\kappa'}$ the resulting equations

$$\begin{aligned} &(a) \qquad \xi^{\kappa'} = \overset{\kappa'}{f}(\xi^{\kappa}) \\ &(b) \qquad \xi^{\kappa} = \overset{\kappa}{f}(\xi^{\kappa'}) \end{aligned} \qquad (\kappa = 1',\ldots, n') \tag{2.5}$$

are *transformations of coordinates* in R in M. In contradistinction to a transformation of the coordinates of M a *transformation of the elements* of M has the form

$$\eta^{\kappa} = F^{\kappa}(\xi^{\lambda}) \tag{2.6}$$

if the coordinate system κ is used; and this transformation takes another form

$$\eta^{\kappa'} = F^{\kappa'}(\xi^{\lambda'}) \quad (\kappa', \lambda' = 1',\ldots, n') \tag{2.7}$$

with respect to another coordinate system (κ').

According to this a coordinate system over a set of elements R, is a one-to-one correspondence between the elements of R and the points of a region of $\mathfrak{A}_n$; and transformation of coordinates in R means passing to another one-to-one correspondence between these elements and the points of another region of $\mathfrak{A}_n$.†

If we allow only analytic transformations chosen in such a way that

† Veblen and Whitehead 1932. 2, p. 22. We consider only ordinary coordinates in this section. Supernumerary coordinates are dealt with in II, § 9.

$\mathfrak{R} = \mathfrak{R}' = \underset{0}{\mathfrak{R}}$, all allowable transformations interchange the points of $\underset{0}{\mathfrak{R}}$ among each other. An example of such a transformation is the much used process of interchanging the variables $\overset{\kappa}{\xi}$. The set of all transformations which interchange the points of $\underset{0}{\mathfrak{R}}$ constitute a *group* $\mathfrak{G}_0$ because

(1) the succession of two transformations of the set is equivalent to a transformation of the set;
(2) the identical transformation is in the set;
(3) the inverse of every transformation of the set is in the set.

The set $\mathfrak{P}$ of all analytic invertible transformations of the form (2.1) with a definitely chosen $\underset{0}{\mathfrak{R}}$ but arbitrary $\mathfrak{R}$ does not constitute a group, because the two transformations can be effected after each other only if the last region of the first, and the first region of the second, have some region in common. $\mathfrak{P}$ is called a *pseudo-group*.†

The set of elements M, with the pseudo-group $\mathfrak{P}$ and with all allowable coordinate systems, viz. all coordinate systems which can be derived from the system (κ) originally given, by the transformations of $\mathfrak{P}$, is called a *geometric n-dimensional manifold* or an X_n. The elements of M are called *geometric points* or *points of* X_n. If we use the expression 'points' in the following we always mean geometric points. For 'point with the coordinates ξ^κ' we write 'point ξ^κ' for brevity.

$\mathfrak{R}_0$ is chosen arbitrarily. Often $\underset{0}{\mathfrak{R}} = \mathfrak{A}_n$, but in many cases another choice of $\underset{0}{\mathfrak{R}}$ is advantageous. If a sub-group or sub-pseudo-group of $\mathfrak{P}$ is used instead of $\mathfrak{P}$ we get an n-dimensional manifold with another geometry. For instance, we get the E_n, the space of ordinary affine geometry, if $\underset{0}{\mathfrak{R}} = \mathfrak{A}_n$ and if $\mathfrak{P}$ is replaced by the group of all affine transformations. The allowable coordinate systems are then all systems derivable from the one originally given by any affine transformation.‡

In an X_n the notion of polycylinder is of no use because there is no preferred coordinate system. Instead of polycylinders we use cells; a *cell* being defined as a set of points given by

$$|\xi^\kappa| < 1 \tag{2.8}$$

in some allowable coordinate system. A point set R in X_n is called a region, if there exists an allowable coordinate system (κ), determining a one-to-one correspondence between the points of R and the arithmetic

† Veblen and Whitehead 1932. 2, p. 38.
‡ This is briefly the foundation of affine geometry.

points of a region $\mathfrak{R}$ in $\mathfrak{A}_n$. Evidently then every allowable coordinate system determines such a correspondence. $\mathfrak{R}$ is called the *fundamental region of R with respect to* (κ).† Evidently every cell is a region. But every region need not be a cell. Also, the X_n itself is a region, and every region in X_n is itself an X_n. Every X_n which is a region of another X_n is said to be *imbedded* in the latter. Every region in X_n is called a neighbourhood of every one of its points. For 'neighbourhood of $\underset{0}{\xi^\kappa}$' we write $\mathfrak{N}(\underset{0}{\xi^\kappa})$ for brevity.

p is said to be *analytic in the region R*, if for any choice of the coordinate system (κ), p is a function of ξ^κ,

$$p = f(\xi^\kappa), \tag{2.9}$$

and if $f(\overset{\kappa}{\xi})$ is analytic in every arithmetic point of the fundamental region $\mathfrak{R}$ of R with respect to (κ). If this condition is satisfied and if (κ') is another allowable coordinate system and

$$\overset{\kappa}{\xi} = \overset{\kappa}{f}(\overset{\kappa'}{\xi}) \quad (\kappa' = 1',..., n'), \tag{2.10}$$

it is well known from the theory of functions of several variables that

$$f\{\overset{\kappa}{f}(\overset{\kappa'}{\xi})\} \quad (\kappa' = 1',..., n') \tag{2.11}$$

is analytic in the fundamental region $\mathfrak{R}'$ of R with respect to (κ'). Hence the choice of the coordinate system is not important.

3. The null form of the equations of an X_m in X_n‡

Let N functions $F^\mathfrak{a}(\xi^\kappa)$ ($\mathfrak{a} = 1,..., \mathrm{N}$) be analytic in an $\mathfrak{N}(\underset{0}{\xi^\kappa})$. The matrix of the nN derivatives of the $F^\mathfrak{a}$ with n rows and N columns is called the *functional matrix of the system $F^\mathfrak{a}$*, and its rank r in $\underset{0}{\xi^\kappa}$ the *rank of the system* in that point. Evidently $r \leqslant n$ and $r \leqslant N$. r is the maximum number of linearly independent differentials among the $dF^\mathfrak{a}$. If we form the matrix of the MN derivatives of the $F^\mathfrak{a}$ with respect to M of the variables ξ^κ, the rank of this matrix in $\underset{0}{\xi^\kappa}$ is called the *rank of the system $F^\mathfrak{a}$ with respect to these variables* in that point.

The functions $F^\mathfrak{a}$ are said to be (functionally) *independent* in $\mathfrak{N}(\underset{0}{\xi^\kappa})$ if none of them can be expressed as a function of the others in that neighbourhood and (functionally) *dependent* in the opposite case.

† A region in an X_n can also be defined in the same way as a region in $\mathfrak{A}_n$ by using cells instead of polycylinders.

‡ Cf. Kähler 1934. 1.

We have the theorem

THEOREM II.2. (*Theorem of independence.*) *The functions* $F^{\mathfrak{a}}(\xi^{\kappa})$ $(\mathfrak{a} = 1,\ldots,\mathrm{N})$, *analytic in* $\mathfrak{N}(\overset{}{\underset{0}{\xi^{\kappa}}})$, *are independent in* $\mathfrak{N}(\underset{0}{\xi^{\kappa}})$ *if and only if the rank of the system* $F^{\mathfrak{a}}$ *is equal to N in at least one point of* $\mathfrak{N}(\underset{0}{\xi^{\kappa}})$.

The proof of this theorem will be found in text-books on analysis.

According to this theorem the $F^{\mathfrak{a}}$ are always dependent for $N > n$.

If the $F^{\mathfrak{a}}$ are independent and the rank r is equal to N the following theorem holds.

THEOREM II.3. (*Theorem of adaption.*) *If the functions* $F^{\mathfrak{a}}(\xi^{\kappa})$ $(\mathfrak{a} = 1,\ldots,\mathrm{N};\ N \leqslant n)$ *are analytic in* $\mathfrak{N}(\underset{0}{\xi^{\kappa}})$, *and if* $r = N$ *in every point of* $\mathfrak{N}(\underset{0}{\xi^{\kappa}})$, *there exists a coordinate system* ξ^{h} $(h = 1,\ldots,\mathrm{n})$ *in some* $\mathfrak{N}(\underset{0}{\xi^{\kappa}})$, *such that*

$$F^{\mathfrak{a}} = \xi^{\mathfrak{a}} \quad (\mathfrak{a} = 1,\ldots,\mathrm{N}). \tag{3.1}$$

PROOF. We take $n-N$ functions

$$F^{\mathrm{N}+1}(\xi^{\kappa}),\quad \ldots,\quad F^{\mathrm{n}}(\xi^{\kappa}) \tag{3.2}$$

analytic in $\mathfrak{N}(\underset{0}{\xi^{\kappa}})$, such that the rank of the system F^{h} $(h = 1,\ldots,\mathrm{n})$ is n in each point of $\mathfrak{N}(\underset{0}{\xi^{\kappa}})$. Then the transformation

$$\xi^{h} = F^{h}(\xi^{\kappa}) \quad (h = 1,\ldots,\mathrm{n}) \tag{3.3}$$

is an allowable transformation of coordinates and thus the ξ^{h} form an allowable coordinate system in $\mathfrak{N}(\underset{0}{\xi^{\kappa}})$.

Now we consider a system of N equations

$$F^{\mathfrak{a}}(\xi^{\kappa}) = 0 \quad (\mathfrak{a} = 1,\ldots,\mathrm{N}), \tag{3.4}$$

the $F^{\mathfrak{a}}$ being analytic in $\mathfrak{N}(\underset{0}{\xi^{\kappa}})$. Every point ξ^{κ} of $\mathfrak{N}(\underset{0}{\xi^{\kappa}})$ satisfying (3.4) is called a *null point* and the set M of all these points the *null manifold* of (3.4). The system (3.4) is called the *null form* of M. The rank of the system $F^{\mathfrak{a}}$ in the null points of (3.4) is called the *rank* of (3.4); and the rank of the system $F^{\mathfrak{a}}$ with respect to some of the variables ξ^{κ} in the null points of (3.4), the *rank* of (3.4) *with respect to these variables*. Thus the rank of (3.4) in a null point is the maximum number of independent differentials among the $dF^{\mathfrak{a}}$ in that point.

Two systems of equations having the same null points in $\mathfrak{N}(\underset{0}{\xi^{\kappa}})$ are said to be *equivalent in that region. Two equivalent systems need not have the same rank in all null points.*

Let $\underset{0}{\xi^{\kappa}}$ be a null point of (3.4). If the rank of (3.4) is N in $\underset{0}{\xi^{\kappa}}$ and consequently also N in every point of an $\mathfrak{N}(\overset{}{\underset{0}{\xi}}{}^{\kappa})$, (3.4) is said to be *minimal regular of dimension* $n-N$ in $\underset{0}{\xi}{}^{\kappa}$. The number $n-N$ is called the *dimension* of the null manifold in $\underset{0}{\xi}{}^{\kappa}$ and the null manifold is said to be $(n-N)$-dimensional in $\underset{0}{\xi}{}^{\kappa}$. Evidently $0 \leqslant n-N \leqslant n$. From the definition it follows immediately that *every sub-system*† *of a system minimal regular in* $\underset{0}{\xi}{}^{\kappa}$ *is also minimal regular in* $\underset{0}{\xi}{}^{\kappa}$. If a system is minimal regular in $\underset{0}{\xi}{}^{\kappa}$ there exists an $\mathfrak{N}(\underset{0}{\xi}{}^{\kappa})$ such that the system is minimal regular and the null manifold $(n-N)$-dimensional in all null points in $\mathfrak{N}(\underset{0}{\xi}{}^{\kappa})$. The notions 'minimal regular' and 'dimension' are obviously invariant for transformations of coordinates.

If $\underset{0}{\xi}{}^{\kappa}$ is a null point of a system of equations and if there exists no $\mathfrak{N}(\underset{0}{\xi}{}^{\kappa})$ such that the system is, in this $\mathfrak{N}(\underset{0}{\xi}{}^{\kappa})$, equivalent to a minimal regular system of some dimension m, the system is said to be *irregular* in $\underset{0}{\xi}{}^{\kappa}$. The null manifold has in this case no dimension in $\underset{0}{\xi}{}^{\kappa}$. If there exists such an $\mathfrak{N}(\underset{0}{\xi}{}^{\kappa})$ there are only three possible cases:

1. Among the N differentials $dF^{\mathfrak{a}}$ in $\underset{0}{\xi}{}^{\kappa}$ there exist no $n-m$ that are linearly independent. In this case the system is said to be *semi-regular* of dimension m in $\underset{0}{\xi}{}^{\kappa}$.

2. Among the N differentials $dF^{\mathfrak{a}}$ in $\underset{0}{\xi}{}^{\kappa}$ there exist just $n-m$ that are linearly independent and $n-m < N$. In this case the system is called *regular of dimension* m in $\underset{0}{\xi}{}^{\kappa}$‡. If we wish to distinguish a regular system from a minimal regular one, we call it *supernumerary regular*.

3. Among the N differentials $dF^{\mathfrak{a}}$ in $\underset{0}{\xi}{}^{\kappa}$ there exist just $n-m$ that are linearly independent and $n-m = N$. According to our definition the system is then *minimal regular of dimension* m in $\underset{0}{\xi}{}^{\kappa}$.

A sub-system of a system regular in $\underset{0}{\xi}{}^{\kappa}$ need not be regular in $\underset{0}{\xi}{}^{\kappa}$. If a system is regular of dimension m in $\underset{0}{\xi}{}^{\kappa}$ there always exists an $\mathfrak{N}(\underset{0}{\xi}{}^{\kappa})$

† A sub-system consists of some of the equations of the given system.

‡ We adopt here the definition of Kähler 1934. 1, p. 12. Other authors, e.g. v. Weber 1900. 1, p. 48, call regular what we call minimal regular. Our exposition differs from that given by Kähler mainly in the introduction of the notions 'semi-regular' and 'minimal regular' and in its form, which is a little more adapted to geometrical applications.

such that the system is regular of dimension m in every null point in $\mathfrak{N}(\underset{0}{\xi}^{\kappa})$.

If a system has a sub-system of $n-m$ equations, equivalent to the given system in $\mathfrak{N}(\underset{0}{\xi}^{\kappa})$ and minimal regular in $\underset{0}{\xi}^{\kappa}$, it is evident that the system is regular of dimension m in $\underset{0}{\xi}^{\kappa}$. Conversely, a system regular of dimension m in $\underset{0}{\xi}^{\kappa}$ always contains an equivalent sub-system of $n-m$ equations, minimal regular in $\underset{0}{\xi}^{\kappa}$. This will not be proved until we can make use of the first basis theorem II.4.

Here follow some examples:

$$\begin{array}{lll} (1) & xy = 0;\ xz = 0; & \text{irregular in } x = 0,\ y = 0,\ z = 0; \\ (2) & x^2 = 0;\ \ y = 0; & \text{semi-regular in } x = 0,\ y = 0; \\ (3) & x^2 = 0;\ \ x = 0;\ y = 0; & \text{regular in } x = 0,\ y = 0; \\ (4) & x = 0;\ \ y = 0; & \text{minimal regular in } x = 0,\ y = 0. \end{array} \tag{3.5}$$

Though a supernumerary regular system differs from a minimal regular one only by containing some superfluous equations, it is not always convenient to drop these equations because the remaining system is often not invariant.

A null form of an m-dimensional manifold, minimal regular in $\underset{0}{\xi}^{\kappa}$, is often written in the form

$$C^x(\xi^\kappa) = 0 \quad (x = \mathrm{m}+1,\ldots,\mathrm{n}), \tag{3.6}$$

the C^x being analytic in $\mathfrak{N}(\underset{0}{\xi}^{\kappa})$ and the rank having the value $n-m$ in this region. Then the rank of the quantity

$$C^x_\lambda \overset{\text{def}}{=} \partial_\lambda C^x \quad (x = \mathrm{m}+1,\ldots,\mathrm{n}) \tag{3.7}$$

is $n-m$ in $\mathfrak{N}(\underset{0}{\xi}^{\kappa})$. If we introduce another coordinate system (κ'), (3.6) becomes

$$C^x(\xi^{\kappa'}) = 0 \quad (x = \mathrm{m}+1,\ldots,\mathrm{n};\ \kappa' = 1',\ldots,n'), \tag{3.8}$$

the functions $C^x(\xi^{\kappa'})$ being defined by the equations

$$C^x(\xi^{\kappa'}) \overset{\text{def}}{=} C^x\{f^\kappa(\xi^{\kappa'})\} \quad (x = \mathrm{m}+1,\ldots,\mathrm{n};\ \kappa' = 1',\ldots,n'). \tag{3.9}$$

If then

$$C^x_{\lambda'} \overset{\text{def}}{=} \partial_{\lambda'} C^x(\xi^{\kappa'}) \quad (x = \mathrm{m}+1,\ldots,\mathrm{n};\ \kappa',\lambda' = 1',\ldots,n';\ \partial_{\lambda'} = \partial/\partial\xi^{\lambda'}) \tag{3.10}$$

we have

$$C^x_{\lambda'} = A^\lambda_{\lambda'} C^x_\lambda \quad (A^\lambda_{\lambda'} \overset{\text{def}}{=} \partial_{\lambda'}\xi^\lambda;\ x = \mathrm{m}+1,\ldots,\mathrm{n};\ \lambda' = 1',\ldots,n'). \tag{3.11}$$

From this it follows that the rank of $C^{x}_{\lambda'}$ is also $n-m$ and that (3.8) is also a null form of the manifold, minimal regular in $\underset{0}{\xi}^{\kappa'}$. Accordingly the notion of 'dimension' is really invariant for coordinate transformations.

We will now prove the theorem

THEOREM II.4. (*First basis theorem.*) *If a function* $s(\xi^\kappa)$ *is analytic in* $\mathfrak{N}(\underset{0}{\xi}^\kappa)$ *and zero in all points in* $\mathfrak{N}(\underset{0}{\xi}^\kappa)$ *of an m-dimensional manifold with the null form* (3.6), *minimal regular in* $\mathfrak{N}(\underset{0}{\xi}^\kappa)$, *there always exists an* $\mathfrak{N}(\underset{0}{\xi}^\kappa)$ *such that s satisfies in this* $\mathfrak{N}(\underset{0}{\xi}^\kappa)$ *an equation of the form*

$$s = \phi_x(\xi^\kappa)C^x \quad (x = \mathrm{m}+1,\ldots,\mathrm{n}) \tag{3.12}$$

where the functions ϕ_x *are analytic in this* $\mathfrak{N}(\underset{0}{\xi}^\kappa)$.

PROOF. According to the theorem of adaption II.3 there exists a coordinate system ξ^h $(h = 1,\ldots,\mathrm{n})$ such that the equations (3.6) take the form

$$\xi^x = 0 \quad (x = \mathrm{m}+1,\ldots,\mathrm{n}) \tag{3.13}$$

with respect to (h). We may choose the ξ^a $(a = 1,\ldots,\mathrm{m})$ in such a way that $\underset{0}{\xi}^h = 0$ $(h = 1,\ldots,\mathrm{n})$. Now since s is analytic in $\mathfrak{N}(\underset{0}{\xi}^h)$, there exists an $\mathfrak{N}(\underset{0}{\xi}^h)$ where s can be expanded into a convergent series in the ξ^h. In every point of the manifold s vanishes, so all terms of this series which do not contain one of the variables ξ^x $(x = \mathrm{m}+1,\ldots,\mathrm{n})$ as a factor must vanish. Consequently in this latter $\mathfrak{N}(\underset{0}{\xi}^\kappa)$ s can be written in the form

$$s = \psi_x(\xi^h)\xi^x = \phi_x(\xi^\kappa)C^x(\xi^\nu) \quad (x = \mathrm{m}+1,\ldots,\mathrm{n};\ h = 1,\ldots,\mathrm{n}), \tag{3.14}$$

where the ϕ_x are analytic in an $\mathfrak{N}(\underset{0}{\xi}^\kappa)$.

$n-m$ functions $C^{x'}$ $\{x' = (\mathrm{m}+1)',\ldots,\mathrm{n}'\}$ taking the value zero in every point of the manifold with the equations (3.6), and whose differentials $dC^{x'}$ are linearly independent in $\underset{0}{\xi}^\kappa$ are said to constitute a *basis* of the manifold in $\underset{0}{\xi}^\kappa$.† Hence the C^x in (3.6) constitute a basis. As a consequence of the first basis theorem II.4 we have in $\mathfrak{N}(\underset{0}{\xi}^\kappa)$, equations of the form

$$C^{x'} = C^{x'}_{x}\,C^x \quad \{x = \mathrm{m}+1,\ldots,\mathrm{n};\ x' = (\mathrm{m}+1)',\ldots,\mathrm{n}'\} \tag{3.15}$$

† We define a basis in a different way from Kähler, who also allows systems of more than $n-m$ functions. Cf. 1934. 1, p. 13.

with coefficients $C_x^{x'}$ analytic in $\mathfrak{N}(\underset{0}{\xi^\kappa})$. By differentiation we get in $\underset{0}{\xi^\kappa}$

$$dC^{x'} = C_x^{x'} dC^x \quad \{x = \mathrm{m}+1,\dots,\mathrm{n};\ x' = (\mathrm{m}+1)',\dots,\mathrm{n}'\}. \tag{3.16}$$

From this it follows, that $C_x^{x'}$ has the rank $n-m$ in $\mathfrak{N}(\underset{0}{\xi^\kappa})$ and that consequently the system

$$C^{x'} = 0 \tag{3.17}$$

is a null form of the manifold, minimal regular in $\underset{0}{\xi^\kappa}$. We collect these results in the following theorem:

THEOREM II.5. (*Second basis theorem.*) *If $n-m$ functions*

$$C^{x'} \quad \{x' = (\mathrm{m}+1)',\dots,\mathrm{n}'\}$$

constitute a basis in $\underset{0}{\xi^\kappa}$ of a manifold m-dimensional in $\underset{0}{\xi^\kappa}$ the equations

$$C^{x'} = 0 \quad \{x' = (\mathrm{m}+1)',\dots,\mathrm{n}'\} \tag{3.18}$$

constitute a minimal regular null form of this manifold in an $\mathfrak{N}(\underset{0}{\xi^\kappa})$.

If the C^x $(x = \mathrm{m}+1,\dots,\mathrm{n})$ and the $C^{x'}$ $\{x = (\mathrm{m}+1)',\dots, \mathrm{n}'\}$ each constitute a basis of a manifold in $\underset{0}{\xi^\kappa}$, there exist $(n-m)^2$ functions $C_x^{x'}(\xi^\kappa)$ analytic in an $\mathfrak{N}(\underset{0}{\xi^\kappa})$, such that

$$C^{x'} = C_x^{x'} C^x \quad \{x = \mathrm{m}+1,\dots,\mathrm{n};\ x' = (\mathrm{m}+1)',\dots,\mathrm{n}'\}, \tag{3.19}$$

and

$$\mathrm{Det}(C_x^{x'}) \neq 0 \tag{3.20}$$

in that region.

From this second basis theorem it follows that the index x in (3.6) is subject to linear homogeneous transformations with coefficients analytic in an $\mathfrak{N}(\underset{0}{\xi^\kappa})$ and a non-vanishing determinant. We call these transformations *basis transformations*. From (3.19) we have

$$C_\lambda^{x'} = C_x^{x'} C_\lambda^x + C^x \partial_\lambda C_x^{x'} \quad \{x = \mathrm{m}+1,\dots,\mathrm{n};\ x' = (\mathrm{m}+1)',\dots,\mathrm{n}'\}; \tag{3.21}$$

hence in the null points

$$C_\lambda^{x'} = C_x^{x'} C_\lambda^x \quad \{x = \mathrm{m}+1,\dots,\mathrm{n};\ x' = (\mathrm{m}+1)',\dots,\mathrm{n}'\}. \tag{3.22}$$

If a coordinate transformation and a basis transformation are effected simultaneously, a null form becomes a null form. The transformation of C_λ^x is

$$C_{\lambda'}^{x'} = C_x^{x'} A_{\lambda'}^\lambda C_\lambda^x \quad \{x = \mathrm{m}+1,\dots,\mathrm{n};\ x' = (\mathrm{m}+1)',\dots,\mathrm{n}';\ \lambda' = 1',\dots,n'\} \tag{3.23}$$

in all null points. We call C_λ^x the *covariant connecting quantity of the manifold in X_n.*

According to the theorem of adaption II.3 it is always possible to choose the coordinates ξ^κ in such a way, that the minimal regular null form takes the form

$$\xi^\zeta = 0 \quad (\zeta = m+1,..., n). \tag{3.24}$$

The ξ^α $(\alpha = 1,..., m)$ can be used as coordinates in the manifold. Now the pseudo-group $\mathfrak{P}$ of all analytic and invertible transformations of the ξ^κ in $\mathfrak{N}(\underset{0}{\xi^\kappa})$ contains as a sub-group the pseudo-group $\mathfrak{P}'$ of all analytic and invertible transformations of the ξ^α $(\alpha = 1,..., m)$ in $\mathfrak{N}(\underset{0}{\xi^\kappa})$, the ξ^ζ $(\zeta = m+1,..., n)$ being left invariant. Hence the pseudo-group of all allowable coordinate transformations in X_n induces in the manifold a pseudo-group of allowable coordinate transformations that makes this manifold an X_m. Hence every manifold, m-dimensional in $\underset{0}{\xi^\kappa}$ is an X_m in an $\mathfrak{N}(\underset{0}{\xi^\kappa})$. Such an X_m is called an X_m *in* X_n, (3.6) a *minimal regular null form of the* X_m and C^x_λ the *covariant connecting quantity of the* X_m *in* X_n. An X_m in X_n is often called an *m-dimensional surface.* For $m = 1$, 2 and $n-1$ the expressions *curve, surface,* and *hypersurface* are also used.†

Using the first basis theorem II.4 we can now give the proof delayed on p. 36. Let

$$F^{\mathfrak{a}}(\xi^\kappa) = 0 \quad (\mathfrak{a} = 1,..., \mathrm{N}) \tag{3.25}$$

be a system, regular of dimension m, in $\underset{0}{\xi^\kappa}$. We choose a sub-system of $n-m$ equations having the rank $n-m$ in $\underset{0}{\xi^\kappa}$. This sub-system is minimal regular in $\underset{0}{\xi^\kappa}$ and we have to prove that it is equivalent to (3.25) in an $\mathfrak{N}(\underset{0}{\xi^\kappa})$. By interchanging the indices $\mathfrak{a}$ it can always be arranged that the sub-system is

$$F^{\mathfrak{a}'}(\xi^\kappa) = 0 \quad (\mathfrak{a}' = 1,..., \mathrm{n}-\mathrm{m}). \tag{3.26}$$

The system (3.25) represents in $\mathfrak{N}(\underset{0}{\xi^\kappa})$ an X_m in X_n and the $F^{\mathfrak{a}'}$ constitute a basis for this X_m in $\underset{0}{\xi^\kappa}$. In consequence of the first basis theorem II.4 all functions $F^{\mathfrak{a}}$ $(\mathfrak{a} = 1,..., \mathrm{N})$ can be expressed linearly in the $F^{\mathfrak{a}'}$ $(\mathfrak{a}' = 1,..., \mathrm{n}-\mathrm{m})$ in an $\mathfrak{N}(\underset{0}{\xi^\kappa})$; hence (3.25) follows from (3.26), and (3.25) and (3.26) are equivalent in an $\mathfrak{N}(\underset{0}{\xi^\kappa})$.

† It has to be remarked that in consequence of this definition an X_m in X_n never has any singularities. For example, an X_2 or surface in ordinary space in our sense is never a surface in the ordinary sense with singular points or curves, but it can be a part of such a surface free from singularities.

4. The parametric form of the equations of an X_m in X_n

In the preceding section we introduced the X_m in X_n starting from the minimal regular null form (3.6). In this section we proceed in another way. We consider an X_m with the coordinates η^a ($a = 1,\ldots, \mathrm{m}$) having no point in common with the X_n of the ξ^κ, and a system of equations

$$\xi^\kappa = B^\kappa(\eta^a) \quad (a = 1,\ldots,\mathrm{m}), \tag{4.1}$$

where the B^κ are analytic in an $\mathfrak{N}(\underset{0}{\eta^a})$. If the matrix of

$$B_b^\kappa = \partial_b B^\kappa \quad (b = 1,\ldots,\mathrm{m}) \tag{4.2}$$

has the rank m in all points of this region, (4.1) establishes a one-to-one correspondence between the points of X_m in a sufficiently small $\mathfrak{N}(\underset{0}{\eta^a})$ and certain points of X_n in an $\mathfrak{N}(\underset{0}{\xi^\kappa})$, $\underset{0}{\xi^\kappa}$ being given by

$$\underset{0}{\xi^\kappa} = B^\kappa(\underset{0}{\eta^a}) \quad (a = 1,\ldots,\mathrm{m}). \tag{4.3}$$

Consequently every point of this $\mathfrak{N}(\underset{0}{\eta^a})$ may be identified with its corresponding point in the $\mathfrak{N}(\underset{0}{\xi^\kappa})$. This process we call the *imbedding of an X_m into X_n*. We call (4.1) a *parametric form* of the X_m in X_n, *minimal regular of dimension m* in $\underset{0}{\eta^a}$, and B_b^κ the *contravariant connecting quantity* of the X_m in X_n.

In order to prove that this definition of an X_m in X_n is in accordance with the definition of II, § 3, we write the system (3.24) in the form

$$\begin{aligned} \xi^\alpha &= \xi^\alpha \\ \xi^\zeta &= 0 \end{aligned} \quad (\alpha = 1,\ldots, m;\ \zeta = m+1,\ldots, n) \tag{4.4}$$

and look upon the ξ^α as parameters. Then this system has the parametric form.

In (4.1) the ξ^κ and η^a can be transformed simultaneously. The conditions imposed on the B^κ are invariant for coordinate transformations and so we get another parametric form

$$\xi^{\kappa'} = B^{\kappa'}(\eta^{a'}) \tag{4.5}$$

minimal regular with dimension m in $\mathfrak{N}(\underset{0}{\eta^{a'}})$. The B_b^κ transform in the following way:

$$B_{b'}^{\kappa'} = B_{b'}^{b} A_\kappa^{\kappa'} B_b^\kappa, \quad \text{where } A_\kappa^{\kappa'} \overset{\text{def}}{=} \partial_\kappa \xi^{\kappa'} \quad \text{and} \quad B_{b'}^{b} \overset{\text{def}}{=} \partial_{b'} \eta^b$$
$$(b = 1,\ldots,\mathrm{m};\ b' = 1',\ldots,\mathrm{m}';\ \kappa' = 1',\ldots,n'). \tag{4.6}$$

If (3.6) and (4.1) are a minimal regular null form and a minimal regular parametric form respectively of the same X_m in X_n we have

$$C^x\{B^\kappa(\eta^a)\} = 0 \quad (a = 1,\ldots,\mathrm{m};\ x = \mathrm{m}+1,\ldots,\mathrm{n}) \tag{4.7}$$

identically in the η^a; and from this, by differentiation, we get the identity

$$B_b^\kappa C_\kappa^x = 0 \quad (b = 1,\dots,m;\ x = m+1,\dots,n) \tag{4.8}$$

identically in the η^a.

We have seen that it is possible to derive a minimal regular parametric form of an X_m from a minimal regular null form by means of a transformation of coordinates. The converse is also true. Since B_b^κ has the rank m in $\mathfrak{N}(\underset{0}{\eta^a})$, by interchanging the indices κ, it can always be arranged that the determinant of B_b^α ($\alpha = 1,\dots,m$; $b = 1,\dots,m$) does not vanish. Then the transformation

$$\xi^\kappa = B^\kappa(\xi^a) + \delta_x^\kappa \xi^x \quad (a = 1,\dots,m;\ x = m+1,\dots,n) \tag{4.9}$$

is an allowable coordinate transformation. When we carry out this transformation we get from (4.1)

$$\begin{aligned} &(a) \quad B^\alpha(\xi^a) = B^\alpha(\eta^a), \quad (a = 1,\dots,m;\ x = m+1,\dots,n;\\ &(b) \quad B^\zeta(\xi^a) + \delta_x^\zeta \xi^x = B^\zeta(\eta^a) \quad \alpha = 1,\dots,m;\ \zeta = m+1,\dots,n). \end{aligned} \tag{4.10}$$

The determinant of B_b^α does not vanish in $\underset{0}{\eta^a}$. Hence, according to the theorem of inversion II.1 the η^a can be solved uniquely from (4.10 *a*), as functions of the ξ^a in an $\mathfrak{N}(\underset{0}{\xi^a})$. Now obviously $\xi^a = \eta^a$ is a solution, so these equations form the only solution of (4.10 *a*). Hence we may conclude that (4.10 *b*) is equivalent to the system

$$\xi^x = 0, \tag{4.11}$$

and that this system is a minimal regular null form of the X_m.

It is also possible to derive a parametric form of an X_m in X_n from a null form, and vice versa, without transformation of coordinates. In order to prove the first assertion we need the theorem

THEOREM II.6. (*Existence theorem for implicit functions.*) *If the system*

$$F^{\mathfrak{a}}(\xi^\kappa) = 0 \quad (\mathfrak{a} = 1,\dots,N) \tag{4.12}$$

is regular of dimension m in the null point $\underset{0}{\xi^\kappa}$, *the system contains an equivalent sub-system of n—m equations with a rank n—m with respect to n—m of the variables* ξ^κ. *By interchanging the equations, and also the* ξ^κ, *it can always be arranged that this sub-system is*

$$F^{\mathfrak{a}'}(\xi^\kappa) = 0 \quad (\mathfrak{a}' = 1,\dots,n-m) \tag{4.13}$$

and that the n—m variables are ξ^ζ ($\zeta = m+1,\dots,n$). *Then an* $\mathfrak{N}(\underset{0}{\xi^\kappa})$ *exists in which the* ξ^ζ *can be solved from* (4.13)

$$\xi^\zeta = f^\zeta(\xi^\alpha) \quad (\alpha = 1,..., m;\ \zeta = m+1,..., n), \tag{4.14}$$

and the following equations hold for the $\underset{0}{\xi}{}^\kappa$:†

$$\underset{0}{\xi}{}^\zeta = f^\zeta(\underset{0}{\xi}{}^\alpha) \quad (\alpha = 1,..., m;\ \zeta = m+1,..., n). \tag{4.15}$$

The proof of this theorem will be found in text-books on analysis.

Now, if we complete the system (4.14) with the identities

$$\xi^\alpha = \xi^\alpha \quad (\alpha = 1,..., m) \tag{4.16}$$

we have a parametric form of the X_m with the null form (4.12).

Conversely, to derive a null form from a parametric form we need the theorem

THEOREM II.7. (*Theorem of elimination.*)‡ *If a system of N equations is given, regular of dimension m in* $\underset{0}{\xi}{}^\kappa$, *and if the rank with respect to* M $(< n)$ *of the* ξ^κ *is* R $(< n-m)$ *in an* $\mathfrak{N}(\underset{0}{\xi}{}^\kappa)$, *from these equations a system of* $n-m-R$ *and not more equations can be derived, valid in an* $\mathfrak{N}(\underset{0}{\xi}{}^\kappa)$ *and minimal regular in* $\underset{0}{\xi}{}^\kappa$, *which does not contain these M variables. The converse is also true.*

PROOF. From the given system we choose an equivalent sub-system of $n-m$ equations, minimal regular in $\underset{0}{\xi}{}^\kappa$. The other equations are ignored. Since the differentials of the left-hand sides of these other equations are linearly dependent on the differentials of the left-hand sides of the chosen equations, the rank of the sub-system with respect to the M variables is also R. Now we interchange the ξ^κ and the equations in such a way that the M variables are $\xi^1,..., \xi^M$ and that the rank of the first R equations of the sub-system with respect to $\xi^1,..., \xi^M$ is just R. Then the sub-system takes the form

$$\begin{aligned} &(a) \quad F^\alpha(\xi^\kappa) = 0, \qquad \mathrm{Det}(\partial_\beta F^\alpha) \neq 0 \ \text{ in } \ \mathfrak{N}(\underset{0}{\xi}{}^\kappa) \quad (\alpha, \beta = 1,..., R), \\ &(b) \quad F^{\mathfrak{x}}(\xi^\kappa) = 0 \quad (\mathfrak{x} = R+1,..., n-m). \end{aligned} \tag{4.17}$$

According to the existence theorem for implicit functions II. 6, the variables $\xi^1,..., \xi^M$ can be interchanged in such a way that the ξ^α $(\alpha = 1,..., R)$ can be solved from (4.17*a*) in $\mathfrak{N}(\underset{0}{\xi}{}^\kappa)$, and consequently

† The theorem of inversion II.1 is a special case of this theorem. In fact the system (2.1) in the $2n$ variables ξ^κ, $\xi^{\kappa'}$ is minimal regular of dimension n in $\underset{0}{\xi}{}^\kappa$, $\underset{0}{\xi}{}^{\kappa'}$.

‡ Cf. e.g. v. Weber 1900. 1, p. 50. Though very important, this theorem is not always stated explicitly in its most general form.

(4.17 a) is equivalent in $\mathfrak{N}(\underset{0}{\xi}^{\kappa})$ to a minimal regular system of the form

$$G^{\alpha}(\xi^{\kappa}) \overset{\text{def}}{=} \xi^{\alpha}-f^{\alpha}(\xi^{\zeta}) = 0 \quad (\alpha = 1,..., R;\ \zeta = R+1,..., n). \tag{4.18}$$

From this it follows that

$$\begin{array}{lll} (a) & G^{\alpha} = 0 & \\ & & (\alpha = 1,..., R;\ \mathfrak{x} = R+1,..., n-m) \\ (b) & F^{\mathfrak{x}}(\xi^{\kappa}) = 0 & \end{array} \tag{4.19}$$

is equivalent to (4.17) in $\mathfrak{N}(\underset{0}{\xi}^{\kappa})$ and minimal regular in $\underset{0}{\xi}^{\kappa}$. If we now replace ξ^{α} by $f^{\alpha}(\xi^{\zeta})$ in (4.19 b), we get equations of the form

$$G^{\mathfrak{x}}(\xi^{\kappa}) \overset{\text{def}}{=} F^{\mathfrak{x}}\{f^{\alpha}(\xi^{\eta}), \xi^{\zeta}\} \quad (\alpha = 1,..., R); \tag{4.20}$$

and the system (4.19) takes the form

$$\begin{array}{lll} (a) & G^{\alpha} = 0 & \\ & & (\alpha = 1,..., R;\ \mathfrak{x} = R+1,..., n-m). \\ (b) & G^{\mathfrak{x}} = 0 & \end{array} \tag{4.21}$$

We still have to prove that (4.21) is minimal regular in $\underset{0}{\xi}^{\kappa}$. So we have to show that the matrix

$$\begin{array}{rl} & \ \ \longleftarrow R \longrightarrow\longleftarrow n-R \longrightarrow \\ \begin{array}{r} R \updownarrow \\[3ex] n-m-R \updownarrow \end{array} & \left\| \begin{array}{cc} \partial_{\beta} G^{\alpha} & \partial_{\zeta} G^{\alpha} \\[3ex] \partial_{\beta} G^{\mathfrak{x}} & \partial_{\zeta} G^{\mathfrak{x}} \end{array} \right\| \end{array} \quad \begin{array}{r} (\alpha, \beta = 1,..., R;\ \zeta = R+1,..., n; \\ \mathfrak{x} = R+1,..., n-m) \end{array} \tag{4.22}$$

is of rank $n-m$ in $\underset{0}{\xi}^{\kappa}$. Since

$$\begin{array}{lll} (a) & \partial_{\beta} G^{\alpha} = \delta^{\alpha}_{\beta} & \\ & & (\alpha, \beta = 1,..., R;\ \mathfrak{x} = R+1,..., n-m), \\ (b) & \partial_{\beta} G^{\mathfrak{x}} = 0 & \end{array} \tag{4.23}$$

we have only to prove that $\partial_{\zeta} G^{\mathfrak{x}}$ is of rank $n-m-R$ in $\underset{0}{\xi}^{\kappa}$, i.e. that no relation of the form

$$\mu_{\mathfrak{x}} \partial_{\zeta} G^{\mathfrak{x}} = 0 \quad (\zeta = R+1,..., n;\ \mathfrak{x} = R+1,..., n-m) \tag{4.24}$$

can exist with coefficients $\mu_{\mathfrak{x}}$ which do not all vanish. According to (4.20), (4.24) is equivalent to

$$-\mu_{\mathfrak{x}}(\partial_{\alpha} F^{\mathfrak{x}})\partial_{\zeta} G^{\alpha}+\mu_{\mathfrak{x}}(\partial_{\zeta} F^{\mathfrak{x}}) = 0 \quad \begin{array}{r} (\alpha = 1,..., R;\ \zeta = R+1,..., n; \\ \mathfrak{x} = R+1,..., n-m), \end{array} \tag{4.25}$$

and from (4.23 a) follows the identity

$$-\mu_{\mathfrak{x}}(\partial_{\alpha} F^{\mathfrak{x}})\partial_{\beta} G^{\alpha}+\mu_{\mathfrak{x}}(\partial_{\beta} F^{\mathfrak{x}}) = 0 \quad (\alpha, \beta = 1,..., R;\ \mathfrak{x} = R+1,..., n-m). \tag{4.26}$$

Now in consequence of (4.25) and (4.26) the matrix

$$\left\| \begin{array}{cc} \partial_{\beta} G^{\alpha} & \partial_{\zeta} G^{\alpha} \\[2ex] \partial_{\beta} F^{\mathfrak{x}} & \partial_{\zeta} F^{\mathfrak{x}} \end{array} \right\| \quad \begin{array}{r} (\alpha, \beta = 1,..., R;\ \zeta = R+1,..., n; \\ \mathfrak{x} = R+1,..., n-m) \end{array} \tag{4.27}$$

would have a rank $< n-m$. But this is impossible, because (4.19) is minimal regular. Hence (4.21) is minimal regular in $\overset{}{\underset{0}{\xi^\kappa}}$. F^α, F^x as well as G^α, G^x, constitute a basis of the X_m represented by (4.17). According to the second basis theorem II.5 every basis can be transformed into every other basis by a homogeneous linear transformation, and this implies that the rank of F^α, F^x with respect to M $(< n)$ of the variables ξ^κ, is equal to the rank of G^α, G^x with respect to these same variables (cf. (3.19) and (3.20)). The matrix of the derivatives of G^α, G^x with respect to $\xi^1,\ldots, \xi^M$ has the form

$$\begin{array}{c} \\ R\left\{ \begin{array}{c} \\ \\ \\ \end{array} \right. \\ n-m-R\left\{ \begin{array}{c} \\ \\ \\ \end{array} \right. \end{array} \overbrace{}^{R}\overbrace{\phantom{-\partial_{R+1}f^1 \ldots -\partial_M f^1}}^{M-R} \left\| \begin{array}{cccccc} 1 & \ldots & 0 & -\partial_{R+1}f^1 & \ldots & -\partial_M f^1 \\ \vdots & & \vdots & \vdots & & \vdots \\ 0 & \ldots & 1 & -\partial_{R+1}f^R & \ldots & -\partial_M f^R \\ 0 & \ldots & 0 & \partial_{R+1}G^{R+1} & \ldots & \partial_M G^{R+1} \\ \vdots & & \vdots & \vdots & & \vdots \\ 0 & \ldots & 0 & \partial_{R+1}G^{n-m} & \ldots & \partial_M G^{n-m} \end{array} \right\| . \tag{4.28}$$

Now if one of the derivatives of the G^x with respect to $\xi^{R+1},\ldots, \xi^M$ were $\neq 0$, this matrix would have a rank $> R$. Consequently all these derivatives have to vanish and the G^x contain only the variables $\xi^{M+1},\ldots, \xi^n$. Hence the equations (4.21 b) do not contain $\xi^1,\ldots, \xi^M$ and the rank of this system has to be $n-m-R$, because otherwise the rank of (4.22) could not be $n-m$. The first part of the theorem is thus proved. The converse is trivial.

Now let

$$\xi^\kappa = B^\kappa(\eta^a) \quad (a = 1,\ldots, \mathrm{m}) \tag{4.29}$$

be a parametric form of an X_m in X_n in $\mathfrak{N}(\underset{0}{\xi^\kappa})$. The equations

$$\xi^\kappa - B^\kappa(\eta^a) = 0 \quad (a = 1,\ldots, \mathrm{m}) \tag{4.30}$$

constitute a system, minimal regular of dimension m in $\underset{0}{\xi^\kappa}$, $\underset{0}{\eta^a}$, in the $n+m$ variables ξ^κ, η^a. The rank with respect to the η^a is m. According to the theorem of elimination II.7 there exists a system of $n-m$ equations, minimal regular in $\underset{0}{\xi^\kappa}$, which does not contain the η^a. This system is the required null form of the X_m.

The simplest example of an X_m in X_n is given by equations of the form

$$\xi^\zeta = c^\zeta \quad (\zeta = m+1,\ldots, n), \tag{4.31}$$

where the c^ζ are constants. If the c^ζ are brought to the left-hand side, we get a minimal regular null form of the X_m, and if we complete the system with the equations

$$\xi^\alpha = \xi^\alpha \quad (\alpha = 1,\ldots, m) \tag{4.32}$$

we get a minimal regular parametric form of the X_m. If the c^ζ are allowed to vary we get the system

$$\xi^\zeta = \text{const.} \quad (\zeta = m+1,\ldots, n) \tag{4.33}$$

representing a system of ∞^{n-m} X_m's, one through every point of X_n. These X_m's are called the coordinate-X_m's of the coordinate system (κ). Every system of ∞^{n-m} X_m's, which is a system of coordinate-X_m's of some system of coordinates, is called a *normal system of* X_m's.

If a normal system of X_m's in X_n is given, the ∞^{n-m} X_m's constitute an $(n-m)$-dimensional manifold. If the equations of the normal system have the form (4.33) the ξ^ζ can be used as coordinates in this manifold. Now the pseudo-group $\mathfrak{P}$ of all analytic invertible transformations of the ξ^κ contains as a sub-pseudo-group the pseudo-group of all analytic invertible transformations of the ξ^ζ, the ξ^α $(\alpha = 1,\ldots, m)$ remaining constant. Hence the manifold of the ∞^{n-m} X_m's is an X_{n-m}. The process of forming this X_{n-m} from the X_n is called the *reduction of* X_n *with respect to the normal system of* X_m's. The simplest way to carry out this process is to write the equations of the normal system in the form (4.33) and to drop the ξ^α $(\alpha = 1,\ldots, m)$. From the theorem of adaption II.3 it follows that a system of equations of the form

$$C^x(\xi^\kappa) = \text{const.} \quad (x = \text{m}+1,\ldots, \text{n}) \tag{4.34}$$

represents a normal system of X_m's in some $\mathfrak{N}(\overset{}{\underset{0}{\xi^\kappa}})$, if the C^x are analytic in some $\mathfrak{N}(\underset{0}{\xi^\kappa})$, and the rank of the C^x is $n-m$ in all points thereof.

We are now able to give a geometrical interpretation of the theorem of elimination II.7. If the X_n is reduced with respect to the normal system of X_M's with the equations

$$\xi^{M+1} = \text{const.}, \quad \ldots, \quad \xi^n = \text{const.} \tag{4.35}$$

and if the given X_m has an X_s in common with every X_M of this normal system, reduction of this X_m leads to an X_{m-s}. Now the equations (4.21 *b*) represent an X_{m-M+R} in the X_{n-M} of the variables $\xi^{M+1},\ldots, \xi^n$. Hence $s = M-R$.

There exists still another kind of parametric form of an X_m in X_n containing more than m parameters. Let a system of n equations of the form

$$\xi^\kappa = \bar{B}^\kappa(\eta^{\mathfrak{a}}) \quad (\mathfrak{a} = 1,\ldots, \text{M}) \tag{4.36}$$

be given with functions $\bar{B}^\kappa$ analytic in $\underset{0}{\mathfrak{N}}(\eta^{\mathfrak{a}})$ and such that the matrix of the derivatives

$$\bar{B}^\kappa_{\mathfrak{b}} \overset{\text{def}}{=} \partial_{\mathfrak{b}} \bar{B}^\kappa \quad (\mathfrak{b} = 1,..., \mathrm{M}) \tag{4.37}$$

has a rank m ($< M$) in that region. According to the theorem of independence II.2, among the $\bar{B}^\kappa$ there exist just m mutually independent functions. By interchanging the indices κ it may be arranged that these functions are $\bar{B}^\alpha$ ($\alpha = 1,..., m$). Then there exist equations of the form

$$\xi^\zeta = \psi^\zeta(\xi^\alpha) \quad (\alpha = 1,..., m;\ \zeta = m+1,..., n). \tag{4.38}$$

To prove this we solve the $\eta^1,..., \eta^{\mathrm{m}}$ from the first m equations (4.36) as functions of $\xi^1,..., \xi^m, \eta^{\mathrm{m}+1},..., \eta^{\mathrm{M}}$, making use of the existence theorem for implicit functions II.6, and substitute these solutions in the remaining $n-m$ equations (4.36). According to the theorem of elimination II.7 the right members of these equations then only contain the ξ^α ($\alpha = 1,..., m$), and consequently they take the form (4.38). Now the system (4.38) is a minimal regular parametric form of an X_m in X_n. Therefore we call a system of the form (4.36), with $\bar{B}^\kappa$ analytic in $\underset{0}{\mathfrak{N}}(\eta^{\mathfrak{a}})$ and $\bar{B}^\kappa_{\mathfrak{b}}$ of the rank m ($\leqslant M$) in that region, a *regular parametric form of dimension* m. To distinguish the case $m < M$ we may use the term *supernumerary regular parametric form.* If a supernumerary regular parametric form is given, a minimal regular parametric form can always be obtained by replacing $M-m$ well-chosen parameters by constants.

Since there are just m independent functions among the $\bar{B}^\kappa$, the equations

$$\bar{B}^\kappa(\eta^{\mathfrak{a}}) = \text{const.} \quad (\mathfrak{a} = 1,..., \mathrm{M}) \tag{4.39}$$

represent a normal system of ∞^m X_{M-m}'s in the X_M of the variables $\eta^{\mathfrak{a}}$. If the X_{M} is reduced with respect to this normal system we get an X_m whose points are in one-to-one correspondence with the points of the X_m in X_n. Hence the equations (4.36) represent a one-to-one correspondence between the X_m in X_n and the X_m arising from a reduction of the X_M.

5. The local E_n†

From (2.5 *a*) we get by differentiation

$$d\xi^{\kappa'} = A^{\kappa'}_{\kappa}\, d\xi^\kappa \quad (A^{\kappa'}_{\kappa} \overset{\text{def}}{=} \partial_\kappa \xi^{\kappa'}), \tag{5.1}$$

and from this equation it follows that every allowable coordinate transformation induces in every point of the region where it is defined a homogeneous linear transformation of the differentials $d\xi^\kappa$. If any system

† Cf. e.g. Schouten and Struik 1935. 1, p. 65.

of n^2 values with a non-vanishing determinant be given in any point of X_n, there always exists an allowable coordinate transformation such that the $A_\kappa^{\kappa'}$ just take these values in that point. Hence the pseudogroup $\mathfrak{P}$ of all allowable coordinate transformations in X_n induces in every point the whole special affine group (cf. I, § 1). Hence from the results of Chapter I it follows that to every point of an X_n there belongs a centred E_n. The E_n belonging to a point $\underset{0}{\xi}^\kappa$ is called the *local* E_n *of* $\underset{0}{\xi}^\kappa$. We identify the centre of this E_n with $\underset{0}{\xi}^\kappa$ and call it the *contact-point*.†

All definitions of Chapter I are valid in every local E_n. Hence all quantities defined in that chapter may occur in every local E_n. But it must be remarked, that the quantities belonging to different local E_n's have nothing to do with each other, neither addition nor multiplication nor any other kind of combination of them is allowed. This follows from the fact that the special affine transformation induced in one local E_n is wholly independent of that induced in another local E_n. If a quantity is defined in all local E_n's of the points of a region of an X_m $(m \leqslant n)$ in an $\mathfrak{N}(\underset{0}{\xi}^\kappa)$ it is said to constitute a *field*. So we speak of scalar fields, vector fields, affinor fields, etc. The region of X_m where the field is defined is called the *field region* and m is called the *field dimension*. But often the appendix 'field' is dropped and we speak, for example, of a vector defined in some region.

A field with components with respect to any coordinate system, analytic in some region, is called *analytic* in that region. The components of an analytic field with respect to every other allowable coordinate system are also analytic.

For analytic fields the following propositions hold. If a set of affinors is defined in an $\mathfrak{N}(\underset{0}{\xi}^\kappa)$ and if r is the rank of this set with respect to one or more indices (cf. I, § 5) there always exists a region in $\mathfrak{N}(\underset{0}{\xi}^\kappa)$ where r is constant. Such a region is called a *region of constant rank* with respect to the quantities and indices concerned. r has the same value in all regions of constant rank and this value is the highest value of the rank occurring in $\mathfrak{N}(\underset{0}{\xi}^\kappa)$. These propositions are an immediate consequence of the well-known fact that an analytic function is equal to zero if it has the value zero in all points of some region.

† If an X_n is imbedded in an E_N $(N > n)$, the local E_n of a point of X_n may be identified with the tangent E_n. But a difficulty arises here. Two tangent E_n's in different points may have common points, and these have to be neglected because the local E_n's of two different points have nothing in common and are wholly independent.

The linear element $d\xi^\kappa$ is the simplest example of a contravariant vector of X_n. A *direction* or an E_1 of X_n in any point $\overset{0}{\xi}{}^\kappa$ is a linear element in $\overset{0}{\xi}{}^\kappa$ determined to within a scalar factor. A *p-direction* or an E_p of X_n in $\overset{0}{\xi}{}^\kappa$ is a system of p linearly independent linear elements, determined to within a homogeneous linear transformation. So there exists a one-to-one correspondence between the E_p's of X_n in $\overset{0}{\xi}{}^\kappa$ and the p-directions or E_p's through the contact point in the local E_n of $\overset{0}{\xi}{}^\kappa$. We use this correspondence to identify these E_p's. Often an 'infinitesimal neighbourhood' of a point $\overset{0}{\xi}{}^\kappa$ of X_n is identified with an 'infinitesimal neighbourhood' of the contact point in the local E_n of $\overset{0}{\xi}{}^\kappa$. By this is meant that the end point of the vector $v^\kappa dt$ in the local E_n is identified with the point of X_n with the coordinates $\xi^\kappa + v^\kappa dt$. This identification, though quite incorrect, may have some heuristic value as it leads sometimes to a geometrical illustration of analytical facts, but it has to be used very carefully if mistakes are to be avoided.

If a scalar field s is analytic in $\mathfrak{N}(\overset{0}{\xi}{}^\kappa)$ and $\partial_\lambda s \neq 0$ in that region, the equations

$$s = \text{const.} \tag{5.2}$$

represent a normal system of X_{n-1}'s. These X_{n-1}'s are called the *equiscalar hypersurfaces* of the field. The $\partial_\lambda s$ are transformed in the following way:

$$\partial_{\lambda'} s = A^\lambda_{\lambda'} \partial_\lambda s. \tag{5.3}$$

Hence the $\partial_\lambda s$ are the components of a covariant vector field in $\mathfrak{N}(\overset{0}{\xi}{}^\kappa)$. Every linear element $d\xi^\kappa$ in $\overset{0}{\xi}{}^\kappa$ lying in the X_{n-1} through $\overset{0}{\xi}{}^\kappa$ satisfies the equation

$$d\xi^\lambda \partial_\lambda s = 0 \tag{5.4}$$

and from this it follows that all these linear elements span an E_{n-1} in $\overset{0}{\xi}{}^\kappa$ with the $(n-1)$-direction of $\partial_\lambda s$. Every vector field that can be written in the form $\partial_\lambda s$ in any region is called a *gradient field* in that region. $\partial_\lambda s$ is said to be the *gradient* or *natural derivative* of s and is written grad s, or Ds or $\bar{s}$ if the abbreviated notation of I, § 7, is used. The $(n-1)$-directions of a gradient field fit together in such a way that they form ∞^1 X_{n-1}'s. A covariant vector field, whose $(n-1)$-directions fit together in this way is said to be *X_{n-1}-forming*. Every gradient field is X_{n-1}-forming but not every X_{n-1}-forming field is a gradient field, e.g. the field $\sigma\partial_\lambda s$. A gradient field has still another property which can be illustrated easily by using the above-mentioned identification of 'infinitesimal neighbourhoods' of the X_n and the local E_n. Consider the hypersurfaces $s = s_0$, $s = s_0+\epsilon$, $s = s_0+2\epsilon$, etc. If ϵ is sufficiently small, to every point there belongs a system of two 'infinitesimal' parallel hyperplanes in the 'infinitesimal neighbourhood' of this point, one through the contact point and one on the side of s increasing. This figure represents the covariant vector $\frac{1}{\epsilon}\partial_\lambda s$ at this point. Hence a gradient field is characterized by the property that not only its $(n-1)$-directions fit together and form a system of X_{n-1}'s, but that for $\epsilon \to 0$ the two 'infinitesimal' hyperplanes fit together and form a system of X_{n-1}-pairs. From this it may be seen that as successively smaller values of ϵ are chosen, so the representation of the field $\frac{1}{\epsilon}\partial_\lambda s$ by a system of hypersurfaces improves.

Associated with every allowable coordinate system (κ) in a region R there are n scalar fields, analytic in $\mathfrak{R}$, i.e. the fields $\overset{\kappa}{\xi}$. Their gradients

$$\overset{\kappa}{e}_\lambda = \partial_\lambda \overset{\kappa}{\xi} \overset{*}{=} \delta^\kappa_\lambda, \qquad \overset{\kappa}{e}_{\lambda'} = \partial_{\lambda'} \overset{\kappa}{\xi} \tag{5.5}$$

are in the local E_n's the covariant measuring vectors belonging to (κ) (cf. I, § 3). Conversely we may look upon the ξ^κ and $\xi^{\kappa'}$ as functions in the arithmetic manifold $\mathfrak{A}_n$, i.e. functions of the $\overset{\kappa}{\xi}$ in the region $\mathfrak{R}$. The derivatives

$$\underset{\lambda}{e^\kappa} = \partial\xi^\kappa/\partial\overset{\lambda}{\xi} \overset{*}{=} \delta^\kappa_\lambda, \qquad \underset{\lambda}{e^{\kappa'}} = \partial\xi^{\kappa'}/\partial\overset{\lambda}{\xi} \tag{5.6}$$

are, in the local E_n's, the components of the contravariant measuring vectors belonging to (κ) (cf. I, § 3). If the ξ^κ and $\xi^{\kappa'}$ are looked upon as functions in the X_n, i.e. functions of the ξ^κ, we get the components of the unit affinor

$$A^\kappa_\lambda = \partial_\lambda \xi^\kappa, \qquad A^{\kappa'}_\lambda = \partial_\lambda \xi^{\kappa'}. \tag{5.7}$$

Finally, if we look upon the $\overset{\kappa}{\xi}$ as functions in the $\mathfrak{A}_n$, the derivatives

$$\delta^\kappa_\lambda = \partial\overset{\kappa}{\xi}/\partial\overset{\lambda}{\xi} \tag{5.8}$$

are the n^2 scalars 1 or 0 of the Kronecker symbol.

We prove the following theorem:

THEOREM II.8. *To every analytic covariant vector field $w_{\lambda_1\ldots\lambda_q}$, which does not vanish in any point $\underset{0}{\xi^\kappa}$ of a region $\mathfrak{R}(\underset{0}{\xi^\kappa})$, there exists, among every set of n arbitrarily chosen linearly independent covariant vectors defined in*

$\mathfrak{N}(\overset{}{\underset{0}{\xi}}{}^{\kappa})$ at least one set of $n-q$ vectors whose alternating product with $w_{\lambda_1 \dots \lambda_q}$ does not vanish anywhere in some $\mathfrak{N}(\underset{0}{\xi}{}^{\kappa})$.

PROOF. The coordinate system κ may be chosen in such a way that in some arbitrarily chosen point $\underset{0}{\xi}{}^{\kappa}$ in R the n vectors are the covariant measuring vectors $\overset{\kappa}{e}_{\lambda}$. If then

$$w_{[\lambda_1 \dots \lambda_q} \overset{q+1}{e}_{\lambda_{q+1}} \dots \overset{n}{e}_{\lambda_n]} = 0 \tag{5.9}$$

it follows that

$$w_{\lambda_1 \dots \lambda_q} \underset{1}{e}{}^{\lambda_1} \dots \underset{q}{e}{}^{\lambda_q} = 0 \tag{5.10}$$

and this means that $w_{1 \dots q}$ is zero. Hence if every set of $n-q$ of the measuring vectors $\overset{\kappa}{e}_{\lambda}$ when multiplied by $w_{\lambda_1 \dots \lambda_q}$ leads to zero, every component of $w_{\lambda_1 \dots \lambda_q}$ would vanish in $\underset{0}{\xi}{}^{\kappa}$, which is contrary to our supposition.

For an X_n we often make use of geometric things which are more general than fields of quantities. In order to get an exact definition of these things we consider a set of manifolds $M_1, \dots, M_t$, each with a given set of allowable coordinate systems $(\kappa_1), \dots, (\kappa_t)$ and the group of transformations transforming these systems into each other

$$\underset{1}{\xi}{}^{\kappa_1'} = f^{\kappa_1'}(\underset{1}{\xi}{}^{\kappa_1}), \quad \dots, \quad \underset{t}{\xi}{}^{\kappa_t'} = f^{\kappa_t'}(\underset{t}{\xi}{}^{\kappa_t}) \quad (\kappa_1 = 1, \dots, n_1; \ \dots; \ \kappa_t = 1, \dots, n_t). \tag{5.11}$$

Then we define a *geometric object* as a set of N functions

$$\gamma^1(\underset{1}{\xi}{}^{\kappa_1}, \dots, \underset{t}{\xi}{}^{\kappa_t}), \quad \dots, \quad \gamma^N(\underset{1}{\xi}{}^{\kappa_1}, \dots, \underset{t}{\xi}{}^{\kappa_t}) \quad (\kappa_1 = 1, \dots, n_1; \ \dots; \ \kappa_t = 1, \dots, n_t), \tag{5.12}$$

called the *components of the object*, analytic in an $\mathfrak{N}(\underset{1}{\xi}{}^{\kappa_1}, \dots, \underset{t}{\xi}{}^{\kappa_t})$ and transforming with (5.11) in such a way that the new components $\gamma^{A'}$ $(A' = 1', \dots, N')$ are functionals† of the old components and the functions $f^{\kappa_1'}, \dots, f^{\kappa_t'}$:

$$\gamma^{A'} = F^{A'}[\gamma^A, f^{\kappa_1'}, \dots, f^{\kappa_t'}] \quad (A = 1, \dots, N; \ A' = 1', \dots, N'; \quad \kappa_1' = 1', \dots, n_1'; \ \dots; \ \kappa_t' = 1', \dots, n_t'). \tag{5.13}$$

Quantities and fields of quantities are special geometric objects. But

† Here we call a function $g(\xi^{\kappa})$, a functional of a function $f(\xi^{\kappa})$, analytic in $\mathfrak{N}(\underset{0}{\xi}{}^{\kappa})$, if there exists a rule for the determination of the coefficients of the power series of g in $\xi^{\kappa} - \underset{0}{\xi}{}^{\kappa}$ from the coefficients of the power series of f, and if this rule satisfies the condition that g is analytic in an $\mathfrak{N}(\underset{0}{\xi}{}^{\kappa})$ if f is analytic in an $\mathfrak{N}(\underset{0}{\xi}{}^{\kappa})$ and the coefficients of the power series of f satisfy certain inequalities. The functional equation $g = F[f]$ represents a point-transformation in functional space (cf. e.g. Courant and Hilbert 1924. 1, p. 149).

a point and a vector v^κ together with $\partial_\lambda v^\kappa$ form also a geometric object. If an X_m in X_n is given by a parametric form

$$\xi^\kappa = F^\kappa(\eta^a) \quad (a = 1,\ldots, \mathrm{m}), \tag{5.14}$$

and if the ξ^κ and the η^a are transformed, we get

$$\xi^{\kappa'} = {}'F^{\kappa'}(\eta^{a'}) \quad (a' = 1',\ldots, \mathrm{m}'), \tag{5.15}$$

and the ${}'F^{\kappa'}$ depend only on the functions $F^\kappa(\eta^a)$, $\xi^{\kappa'}(\xi^\kappa)$, and $\eta^{a'}(\eta^a)$. Hence an X_m in X_n is a geometric object according to our definition. Geometric objects are distinguished by their law of transformation.

6. Anholonomic systems of coordinates†

If in any region R of X_n we have n arbitrary linearly independent contravariant vector fields $\underset{i}{e}^\kappa$ $(i = 1,\ldots,\mathrm{n})$ analytic in R, these vector fields determine in every local E_n a system of coordinates whose contravariant measuring vectors are the $\underset{i}{e}^\kappa$. From the $\underset{i}{e}^\kappa$ n covariant vector fields can be derived uniquely from the equations

$$\overset{h}{e}_\mu \underset{i}{e}^\mu = \delta_i^h \quad (h, i = 1,\ldots,\mathrm{n})$$

and these vectors are the covariant measuring vectors of the local coordinate systems. The $\overset{h}{e}_\lambda$ are also analytic in R. Such systems of measuring vectors do not in general belong to any allowable coordinate system because the $\overset{h}{e}_\lambda$ are in general not gradient vectors. We call them *anholonomic coordinate systems* in X_n. A coordinate system is anholonomic if and only if its covariant measuring vectors are not all gradient vectors. Anholonomic coordinate systems are often used to simplify the equations.

7. Section and reduction with respect to an X_m in X_n‡

Let
$$C^x(\xi^\kappa) = 0 \quad (x = \mathrm{m}+1,\ldots,\mathrm{n}) \tag{7.1}$$

be a minimal regular null form of an X_m in X_n and

$$\xi^\kappa = B^\kappa(\eta^a) \quad (a = 1,\ldots,\mathrm{m}) \tag{7.2}$$

a minimal regular parametric form of the same X_m. Then there exist in every point of X_m three centred affine spaces:

(1) the local E_n of X_n;

(2) the a-space, viz. the local E_m of X_m;

(3) the x-space, a local E_{n-m} with the special affine transformations (3.15).

† For references to literature cf. Schouten and Struik 1935. 1, p. 94.
‡ Cf. Schouten 1938. 1, 1938. 2; Schouten and v. Dantzig 1940. 1.

These spaces are related by the connecting quantities B_b^κ and C_λ^x already defined in II, § 4, and II, § 3, respectively.

By strangling (cf. I, §§ 3, 5) the index b in B_b^κ we get the m contravariant vectors of X_n

$$\underset{b}{e}^\kappa = \underset{b}{e}^a B_a^\kappa \overset{*}{=} B_b^\kappa \quad (a, b, = 1, \ldots, \mathrm{m}). \tag{7.3}$$

These vectors span a central E_m in the local E_n. (7.3) establishes a one-to-one correspondence between the contravariant vectors of this E_m and the contravariant vectors of the local E_m of X_m

$$v^\kappa = v^a B_a^\kappa \quad (a = 1, \ldots, \mathrm{m}). \tag{7.4}$$

We use this correspondence to identify these E_m's, identifying also the centre of the first with the contact point of the other. By this process the local E_m of X_m is imbedded in the local E_n of X_n and from now on we call this E_m the *tangent-E_m* or *tangent space* of the X_m and its m-direction the *tangent m-direction* of X_m at the point considered. After the identification v^κ and v^a are two different sets of components of one and the same vector and this afterwards justifies the choice of the same kernel-letter $\underset{b}{e}$ in (7.3) and v in (7.4). On the other hand,

$$'w_b = B_b^\lambda w_\lambda \quad (b = 1, \ldots, \mathrm{m}) \tag{7.5}$$

is a covariant vector of X_m, different from w_λ. We call $'w_b$ the *section* of w_λ *with the* X_m.

Similarly by strangling the index x in C_λ^x we get the $n-m$ covariant vectors of X_n

$$\overset{x}{e}_\lambda = \overset{x}{e}_y C_\lambda^y \overset{*}{=} C_\lambda^x \quad (x, y = \mathrm{m}+1, \ldots, \mathrm{n}). \tag{7.6}$$

The support of the domain of these vectors is the E_m in the local E_n already identified with the local E_m of X_m. By reduction of the E_n with respect to this E_m (cf. I, § 2) we get a centred E_{n-m}. The equation (7.6) establishes a one-to-one correspondence between the covariant vectors of this E_{n-m} and the covariant vectors of the x-space:

$$w_\lambda = w_x C_\lambda^x \quad (x = \mathrm{m}+1, \ldots, \mathrm{n}). \tag{7.7}$$

We use this correspondence to identify the x-space with this E_{n-m}, identifying also their centres. After this identification w_λ and w_x are two different sets of components of one and the same vector and this afterwards justifies the choice of the same kernel-letter $\overset{x}{e}$ in (7.6) and w in (7.7). On the other hand,

$$'v^x = C_\lambda^x v^\lambda \quad (x = \mathrm{m}+1, \ldots, \mathrm{n}) \tag{7.8}$$

is a contravariant vector of the E_{n-m} different from v^κ. We call $'v^x$ the *reduction* of v^κ *with respect to the* X_m.

Comparing these results with I, § 9, we see that they are in full agreement. This is due to the fact that in the local E_n all processes are linear. For the identification of p-vectors of X_n and X_m and the definition of section and reduction of these quantities it will be sufficient to refer to I, § 9.

8. Decomposition of a regular system according to Kähler

We prove the following theorem due to Kähler.†

THEOREM II.9. (*Theorem of decomposition of regular systems.*) *Let a system of N equations*

$$F^{\mathfrak{a}}(\xi^\kappa) = 0 \quad (\mathfrak{a} = 1,\dots,\mathrm{N}), \tag{8.1}$$

where the functions $F^{\mathfrak{a}}$ are analytic in $\mathfrak{N}(\underset{0}{\xi^\kappa})$, contain a system of N' equations which is regular of dimension $m' \geqslant n-N'$ in $\underset{0}{\xi^\kappa}$. Using the existence theorem for implicit functions II.6, *let us solve $n-m'$ of the ξ^κ as functions of the remaining m' (which are here called ξ^α). If we now introduce these solutions into the remaining $N-N'$ equations of the set* (8.1), *then the $N-N'$ equations in ξ^α so obtained will constitute a regular system of dimension m in $\underset{0}{\xi^\alpha}$ if and only if the system* (8.1) *is regular and of dimension m in $\underset{0}{\xi^\kappa}$.*

PROOF. By interchanging the indices $\mathfrak{a}$ it can always be arranged that the equations

$$F^{\mathfrak{b}}(\xi^\kappa) = 0 \quad (\mathfrak{b} = 1,\dots,\mathrm{N'}) \tag{8.2}$$

constitute the regular system of dimension m' in $\underset{0}{\xi^\kappa}$ and that the equations

$$F^{\mathfrak{b}'}(\xi^\kappa) = 0 \quad (\mathfrak{b}' = 1,\dots,\mathrm{n-m'}) \tag{8.3}$$

constitute an equivalent sub-system of (8.2), minimal regular in $\underset{0}{\xi^\kappa}$. By interchanging the indices κ it can always be arranged that $\xi^{m'+1},\dots,\xi^n$ can be solved from (8.3) as functions of the ξ^α ($\alpha = 1,\dots,m'$):

$$G^\zeta(\xi^\kappa) \overset{\text{def}}{=} \xi^\zeta - f^\zeta(\xi^\alpha) = 0 \quad (\alpha = 1,\dots,m';\ \zeta = m'+1,\dots,n). \tag{8.4}$$

The equations (8.3) and also (8.4) represent an $X_{m'}$ in X_n in which the ξ^α ($\alpha = 1,\dots,m'$) can be used as coordinates. Substituting these solutions into (8.1) we get a system of the form

$$H^{\mathfrak{a}}(\xi^\alpha) \overset{\text{def}}{=} F^{\mathfrak{a}}(\xi^\alpha, f^\zeta(\xi^\alpha)) = 0 \quad (\mathfrak{a} = 1,\dots,\mathrm{N};\ \alpha = 1,\dots,m';\ \zeta = m'+1,\dots,n), \tag{8.5}$$

† Kähler, 1934. 1, p. 13, without proof.

which reduces to a system of $N-N'$ equations

$$H^{\mathfrak{c}}(\xi^{\alpha}) = 0 \quad (\mathfrak{c} = \mathrm{N}'+1,\dots,\mathrm{N}), \tag{8.6}$$

because the $H^{\mathfrak{b}}$ ($\mathfrak{b} = 1,\dots,\mathrm{N}'$) vanish identically in the ξ^{α}. Now we have

$$\partial_{\alpha} H^{\mathfrak{a}} = \partial_{\alpha} F^{\mathfrak{a}} + (\partial_{\zeta} F^{\mathfrak{a}})\partial_{\alpha} f^{\zeta} = \partial_{\lambda} F^{\mathfrak{a}}(A^{\lambda}_{\alpha} + A^{\lambda}_{\zeta}\,\partial_{\alpha} f^{\zeta})$$
$$(\mathfrak{a} = 1,\dots,\mathrm{N};\ \alpha = 1,\dots,m';\ \zeta = m'+1,\dots,n), \tag{8.7}$$

and from this it follows that for every choice of $\mathfrak{a}$ the covariant vector $\partial_{\alpha} H^{\mathfrak{a}}$ of the $X_{m'}$ is the section of the covariant vector $\partial_{\lambda} F^{\mathfrak{a}}$ of X_n with the tangent $E_{m'}$ of $X_{m'}$. In fact this $E_{m'}$ is spanned by the vectors

$$\underset{\alpha}{e}^{\kappa} + \underset{\zeta}{e}^{\kappa}\partial_{\alpha} f^{\zeta} \quad (\alpha = 1,\dots,m';\ \zeta = m'+1,\dots,n) \tag{8.8}$$

according to (8.4). Now (8.3) is a sub-system of (8.1) and consequently *the support of the λ-domain of $\partial_{\lambda} F^{\mathfrak{a}}$ lies in the tangent $E_{m'}$ and coincides with the support of the α-domain of $\partial_{\alpha} H^{\mathfrak{c}}$.*

Now suppose that (8.1) is regular and of dimension m in $\underset{0}{\xi}^{\kappa}$. Then the support of the λ-domain of $\partial_{\lambda} F^{\mathfrak{a}}$ in $\underset{0}{\xi}^{\kappa}$ is the tangent E_m of the X_m with the equations (8.1). (8.2), and (8.3) also, represent an $X_{m'}$ in X_n in which the ξ^{α} ($\alpha = 1,\dots,m'$) can be used as coordinates, and in this $X_{m'}$ (8.5) represents the X_m. In $\underset{0}{\xi}^{\kappa}$ the support of the α-domain of $\partial_{\alpha} H^{\mathfrak{c}}$ coincides with the support of the λ-domain of $\partial_{\lambda} F^{\mathfrak{a}}$, and from this it follows that the rank of $\partial_{\alpha} H^{\mathfrak{c}}$ in $\underset{0}{\xi}^{\kappa}$ is $m'-m$ and that consequently (8.5) is regular of dimension m in $\underset{0}{\xi}^{\alpha}$.

Conversely, suppose that (8.5) is regular of dimension m in $\underset{0}{\xi}^{\alpha}$. Then the support of the α-domain of $\partial_{\alpha} H^{\mathfrak{c}}$ in $\underset{0}{\xi}^{\alpha}$ is the tangent E_m of the X_m represented in $X_{m'}$ by (8.5) and in X_n by the equations (8.2) and (8.5). Now (8.1) is equivalent to the system constituted by (8.2) and (8.5) and consequently represents the same X_m. Since the support of the λ-domain of $\partial_{\lambda} F^{\mathfrak{a}}$ coincides in $\underset{0}{\xi}^{\kappa}$ with the support of the α-domain of $\partial_{\alpha} H^{\mathfrak{c}}$, the rank of $\partial_{\lambda} F^{\mathfrak{a}}$ in $\underset{0}{\xi}^{\kappa}$ is $n-m$, and from this it follows that (8.1) is regular of dimension m in $\underset{0}{\xi}^{\kappa}$.

9. Supernumerary coordinates†

The ξ^{κ} can be used as *supernumerary coordinates* in an X_m in X_n. Then there exist $n-m$ relations between the ξ^{κ}, viz. the equations of a minimal regular null form of the X_m, and the points of the X_m are

† Cf. Schouten and v. Dantzig 1935. 2, p. 33.

in one-to-one correspondence with the sets of values ξ^κ satisfying these relations.

If an X_m in X_n is given by the supernumerary parametric form

$$\xi^\kappa = \bar{B}^\kappa(\eta^{\mathfrak{a}}) \quad (\mathfrak{a} = 1,\ldots, \mathrm{M}) \tag{9.1}$$

the $\eta^{\mathfrak{a}}$ can also be used as supernumerary coordinates in the X_m. No relation exists between these $\eta^{\mathfrak{a}}$. Every set of values $\eta^{\mathfrak{a}}$ corresponds to one, and only one, point of X_m, but conversely every point of X_m corresponds to ∞^{M-m} sets of value of the $\eta^{\mathfrak{a}}$.

From these examples we see that there are different kinds of supernumerary coordinates. The most general supernumerary coordinates in an $\mathfrak{N}(\underset{0}{\xi^\kappa})$ of an X_n are defined by the equations

$$\begin{array}{lll} (a) & \xi^\kappa = \phi^\kappa(\eta^a) & (a = 1,\ldots, n+\epsilon_1+\epsilon_2;\ \epsilon_1 \geqslant 0;\ \epsilon_2 \geqslant 0; \\ (b) & \psi^{\mathfrak{x}}(\eta^a) = 0 & \qquad \epsilon_1+\epsilon_2 \geqslant 1;\ \mathfrak{x} = 1,\ldots, \mathrm{N}') \end{array} \tag{9.2}$$

subject to the conditions that:

(1) $\underset{0}{\eta^a}$ is a definitely chosen arbitrary solution of the equations

$$\begin{array}{ll} (a) & \underset{0}{\xi^\kappa} = \phi^\kappa(\underset{0}{\eta^a}) \\ (b) & \psi^{\mathfrak{x}}(\underset{0}{\eta^a}) = 0 \end{array} \quad (a = 1,\ldots, n+\epsilon_1+\epsilon_2;\ \mathfrak{x} = 1,\ldots, \mathrm{N}'), \tag{9.3}$$

where the ϕ^κ are analytic in an $\mathfrak{N}(\underset{0}{\eta^a})$ and the rank of $\partial_b \phi^\kappa$ is n in that region;

(2) the system (9.2 b) is regular and of dimension $n+\epsilon_2$ in $\underset{0}{\eta^a}$;

(3) among the $n+N'$ differentials $d\phi^\kappa$, $d\psi^{\mathfrak{x}}$ there are exactly $n+\epsilon_1$ which are linearly independent in every point of $\mathfrak{N}(\underset{0}{\eta^a})$.

If $\epsilon_2 = 0$ the $\underset{0}{\eta^a}$ are uniquely determined by (9.3). This is not true if $\epsilon_2 \neq 0$. But from the form of our conditions it follows that, if $\underset{*}{\eta^a}$ is another solution of (9.3) in $\mathfrak{N}(\underset{0}{\eta^a})$, by choosing $\mathfrak{N}(\underset{0}{\eta^a})$ sufficiently small it can always be arranged that the conditions hold for $\underset{*}{\eta^a}$ as well. Hence $\underset{0}{\eta^a}$ is not in any way specially chosen.

Every set of values η^a satisfying (9.2 b) corresponds to one, and only one, point of X_n; but conversely every point of X_n corresponds to ∞^{ϵ_2} ($\infty^0 = 1$) sets of values η^a satisfying (9.2 b).

The ξ^κ, looked upon as coordinates in an X_m in X_n, afford an example with $\epsilon_1 = n-m$, $\epsilon_2 = 0$. An example with $\epsilon_1 = 0$, $\epsilon_2 = M-m$, is provided by the η^a in (9.1). The $n+1$ projective coordinates in an ordinary n-dimensional projective space provide an example with $\epsilon_1 = 0$, $\epsilon_2 = 1$.

As another example, we consider the $X_{p(n-p)}$ of all E_p's through the origin in a centred E_n having only one point in common with the E_{n-p} spanned by the vectors $\underset{p+1}{e^\kappa},\dots,\underset{n}{e^\kappa}$. If $v^{\kappa_1\dots\kappa_p}$ is a simple p-vector in this E_p we know that $v^{1\dots p}\neq 0$. We may therefore assume $v^{1\dots p}=1$ and look upon the remaining $\binom{n}{p}-1$ components of $v^{\kappa_1\dots\kappa_p}$ as coordinates in $X_{p(n-p)}$. But it is also possible to introduce the B^ζ_β (cf. I, § 7) by the equations

$$B^\zeta_\beta = v^{1\dots(\beta-1)\,\zeta\,(\beta+1)\dots p} \quad (\beta = 1,\dots,p;\ \zeta = p+1,\dots,n). \tag{9.4}$$

Then we have the relations (cf. I (7.31))

$$v^{\zeta_1\dots\zeta_s\,\alpha_{s+1}\dots\alpha_p} - s!\,B^{[\zeta_1}_{\alpha_1}\dots B^{\zeta_s]}_{\alpha_s} = 0 \quad (\zeta_1,\dots,\zeta_s = p+1,\dots,n;$$
$$\alpha_1,\dots,\alpha_p = \text{even permutation of } 1,\dots,p;\ s = 1,\dots,p) \tag{9.5}$$

by means of which all components $v^{\zeta_1\dots\zeta_s\,\alpha_{s+1}\dots\alpha_p}$ can be expressed in terms of the variables $v^{\kappa_1\dots\kappa_p}$ occurring in (9.4). For this (9.4) has to be substituted in (9.5). Now the B^ζ_β constitute a system of non-supernumerary coordinates in $X_{p(n-p)}$ and we will prove that the $v^{\kappa_1\dots\kappa_p}$ except $v^{1\dots p}=1$ constitute a system of supernumerary coordinates with

$$\epsilon_1 = \binom{n}{p} - p(n-p) - 1, \qquad \epsilon_2 = 0,$$

in this manifold in the sense of our definition.

From the form of the equations (9.4, 5) it follows that the first condition is satisfied. We show now that the conditions

$$v^{[\kappa_1\dots\kappa_p}\,v^{\lambda_1]\dots\lambda_m} = 0 \tag{9.6}$$

constitute a system, regular of dimension $p(n-p)+1$ in all its null points. (9.5) is a consequence of (9.6), and if we substitute the values (9.5) into (9.6) these equations are satisfied identically. Consequently (9.5) and (9.6) are equivalent. Now from (9.6) at least $\binom{n}{p}-p(n-p)-1$ of the $v^{\kappa_1\dots\kappa_p}$ can be solved as functions of the remaining ones, and this proves that (9.6) has a rank $\geqslant \binom{n}{p}-p(n-p)-1$ in all its null points. Since the differentials of the members of the left-hand side of (9.5) are all linearly independent it follows that (9.5) is minimal regular in all its null points and represents an $X_{p(n-p)}$ in the $X_{\binom{n}{p}-1}$ of all the $v^{\kappa_1\dots\kappa_p}$ except

$v^{1\dots p}$. Because (9.6) represents the same $X_{p(n-p)}$, and its rank is $\geqslant \binom{n}{p} - p(n-p) - 1$ in all its null points, this rank has to be exactly $\binom{n}{p} - p(n-p) - 1$, which proves that (9.6) is regular of dimension $p(n-p)+1$ in all its null points. Hence the second condition is also satisfied.

In order to show that the third condition is also satisfied it is sufficient to remark that among the differentials $dv^{1\dots(\beta-1)\,\zeta\,(\beta+1)\dots p}$ and the differentials of the left-hand side of (9.5) there exist exactly $\binom{n}{p} - 1$ which are linearly independent.

In the same way it can be proved that the $v^{\kappa_1\dots\kappa_p}$ including $v^{1\dots p}$ constitute a system of supernumerary coordinates with

$$\epsilon_1 = \binom{n}{p} - p(n-p) - 1, \qquad \epsilon_2 = 1,$$

in the $X_{p(n-p)}$.

The B^{κ}_{β} ($\beta = 1,\dots,p$; $\kappa = 1,\dots,n$) (cf. I, § 7) constitute a system of supernumerary coordinates with $\epsilon_1 = p^2$, $\epsilon_2 = 0$, in the $X_{p(n-p)}$ because the first and third conditions are satisfied and the second condition is trivial. Instead of the B^{κ}_{β} the pn components of p arbitrary contravariant vector factors $\underset{1}{v}^{\kappa},\dots,\underset{p}{v}^{\kappa}$ of $v^{\kappa_1\dots\kappa_p}$ can also be taken ($\epsilon_1 = 0$, $\epsilon_2 = p^2$).

In the $X_{p(n-p)+1}$ of all simple contravariant p-vectors in E_n, the $v^{\kappa_1\dots\kappa_p}$ are supernumerary coordinates with

$$\epsilon_1 = \binom{n}{p} - p(n-p) - 1, \qquad \epsilon_2 = 0,$$

and the $\underset{1}{v}^{\kappa},\dots,\underset{p}{v}^{\kappa}$ are such coordinates with $\epsilon_1 = 0$, $\epsilon_2 = p^2 - 1$.

We will give one final example. The equations

$$F^{\mathfrak{a}}(\xi^{\kappa}) = c^{\mathfrak{a}} \quad (\mathfrak{a} = 1,\dots,\mathrm{N}) \tag{9.7}$$

represent a normal system of X_m's in X_n if and only if the $F^{\mathfrak{a}}$ are analytic in an $\mathfrak{N}(\underset{0}{\xi}^{\kappa})$, the number of independent functions among the $F^{\mathfrak{a}}$ is exactly $n-m$ and the $c^{\mathfrak{a}}$ are variable. If the X_n is reduced with respect to this normal system, in the resulting X_{n-m}, the $c^{\mathfrak{a}}$ are supernumerary coordinates with $\epsilon_1 = N-n+m$, $\epsilon_2 = 0$. Between them there are exactly $N-n+m$ relations and the sets of values $c^{\mathfrak{a}}$ satisfying these relations are in one-to-one correspondence with the points of the X_{n-m}. Also the ξ^{κ} may be used as supernumerary coordinates with $\epsilon_1 = 0$, $\epsilon_2 = m$ in this X_{n-m}. There is no relation between them.

Supernumerary coordinates are very often used. They are important because, in many cases, only by their use is the invariance of the equations retained.

Here a very important point arises. As we have seen, the regularity of a system of equations is invariant for ordinary coordinate transformations. It is shown in the following theorem that this invariance holds also when supernumerary coordinates are introduced.

THEOREM II.10.† *Let*

$$F^{\mathfrak{a}}(\xi^\kappa) = 0 \quad (\mathfrak{a} = 1,\ldots, \mathrm{N}) \tag{9.8}$$

be a given system of N equations with the functions $F^{\mathfrak{a}}$ analytic in $\mathfrak{N}(\underset{0}{\xi}{}^\kappa)$. Let a system of supernumerary coordinates η^a be introduced by means of the equations (9.2, 3), *viz.*

$$\begin{aligned} &\xi^\kappa = \phi^\kappa(\eta^a),\ \underset{0}{\xi}{}^\kappa = \phi^\kappa(\underset{0}{\eta}{}^a) && (a = 1,\ldots, n+\epsilon_1+\epsilon_2;\ \epsilon_1 \geqslant 0;\ \epsilon_2 \geqslant 0; \\ &\psi^{\mathfrak{x}}(\eta^a) = 0,\ \psi^{\mathfrak{x}}(\underset{0}{\eta}{}^a) = 0 && \epsilon_1+\epsilon_2 \geqslant 1;\ \mathfrak{x} = 1,\ldots, \mathrm{N}') \end{aligned} \tag{9.9}$$

subject to the three conditions imposed on p. 55. *Then the system* (9.8) *is regular of dimension M in $\underset{0}{\xi}{}^\kappa$ if and only if the system*

$$\begin{aligned} &(a)\quad G^{\mathfrak{a}}(\eta^a) \overset{\mathrm{def}}{=} F^{\mathfrak{a}}\{\phi^\kappa(\eta^a)\} = 0 && (\mathfrak{a} = 1,\ldots, \mathrm{N};\ a = 1,\ldots, n+\epsilon_1+\epsilon_2; \\ &(b)\quad \psi^{\mathfrak{x}}(\eta^a) = 0 && \mathfrak{x} = 1,\ldots, \mathrm{N}') \end{aligned} \tag{9.10}$$

is regular of dimension $M+\epsilon_2$ in $\underset{0}{\eta}{}^a$; and this is the case if and only if the equations (9.10 *a*) *constitute by themselves a system regular of dimension $M+\epsilon_1+\epsilon_2$ in $\underset{0}{\eta}{}^a$.*

PROOF. To prove the second part of the theorem we suppose first that (9.10) is regular of dimension $M+\epsilon_2$ in $\underset{0}{\eta}{}^a$. According to our conditions (9.10 *b*) is regular of dimension $n+\epsilon_2$ in $\underset{0}{\eta}{}^a$, so by interchanging the indices $\mathfrak{x}$ it can always be arranged that the equations

$$\psi^{\mathfrak{x}'}(\eta^a) = 0 \quad (\mathfrak{x}' = 1,\ldots, \epsilon_1;\ a = 1,\ldots, n+\epsilon_1+\epsilon_2) \tag{9.11}$$

form an equivalent sub-system of (9.10 *b*), minimal regular in $\underset{0}{\eta}{}^a$. From (9.10 *a*) $n-M$ equations can be chosen constituting together with (9.11) an equivalent sub-system of (9.10), minimal regular in $\underset{0}{\eta}{}^a$. By interchanging the indices $\mathfrak{a}$ it can always be arranged that these $n-M$ equations are

$$G^{\mathfrak{a}'}(\eta^a) = 0 \quad (\mathfrak{a}' = 1,\ldots, \mathrm{n-M};\ a = 1,\ldots, n+\epsilon_1+\epsilon_2). \tag{9.12}$$

† Kähler 1934. 1, p. 35, for a special case.

Now every sub-system of a minimal regular system is minimal regular, hence (9.12) is minimal regular in $\underset{0}{\eta}^a$. Since (9.11) and (9.12) are together equivalent to (9.10) they are also equivalent to the combination of (9.10a) and (9.11). Hence, if the remaining equations of (9.10a) are

$$G^{\mathfrak{a}''}(\eta^a) = 0 \quad (\mathfrak{a}'' = \mathrm{n}-\mathrm{M}+1,\dots,\mathrm{N};\ a = 1,\dots,n+\epsilon_1+\epsilon_2), \tag{9.13}$$

from the first basis theorem II.4 it follows that there has to exist in $\mathfrak{N}(\underset{0}{\eta}^a)$ a relation of the form

$$G^{\mathfrak{a}''} = \alpha_{\mathfrak{a}'}^{\mathfrak{a}''} G^{\mathfrak{a}'} + \beta_{\mathfrak{x}'}^{\mathfrak{a}''} \psi^{\mathfrak{x}'} \quad (\mathfrak{a}' = 1,\dots,\mathrm{n}-\mathrm{M};\ \mathfrak{a}'' = \mathrm{n}-\mathrm{M}+1,\dots,\mathrm{N};$$
$$\mathfrak{x}' = 1,\dots,\epsilon_1). \tag{9.14}$$

Now according to Theorem II. 6, $n+\epsilon_1$ of the η^a can be solved from (9.2) as functions of the ξ^κ and the remaining η^a. Hence after rearranging the η^a we have in some $\mathfrak{N}(\underset{0}{\xi}^\kappa, \underset{0}{\eta}^a)$

$$\eta^\alpha = H^\alpha(\xi^\kappa, \eta^\theta) \quad (\alpha = 1,\dots, n+\epsilon_1;$$
$$\theta = n+\epsilon_1+1,\dots, n+\epsilon_1+\epsilon_2). \tag{9.15}$$

If (9.15) is substituted into (9.14) we get equations of the form

$$F^{\mathfrak{a}''}(\xi^\kappa) = \bar{\alpha}_{\mathfrak{a}'}^{\mathfrak{a}''}(\xi^\kappa, \eta^\theta) F^{\mathfrak{a}'}(\xi^\kappa) \tag{9.16}$$

and if in these equations the ξ^κ are replaced by $\phi^\kappa(\eta^a)$ we get equations of the form (9.14) with vanishing $\beta_{\mathfrak{x}'}^{\mathfrak{a}''}$. Hence the system (9.10$a$) containing an equivalent sub-system, minimal regular of dimension $M+\epsilon_1+\epsilon_2$ in $\underset{0}{\eta}^a$, is regular of dimension $M+\epsilon_1+\epsilon_2$ in $\underset{0}{\eta}^a$.

Conversely, suppose that (9.10a) is regular of dimension $M+\epsilon_1+\epsilon_2$ in $\underset{0}{\eta}^a$. Then by interchanging the indices $\mathfrak{a}$ it can always be arranged that the system

$$G^{\mathfrak{a}'}(\eta^a) = 0 \quad (\mathfrak{a}' = 1,\dots,\mathrm{n}-\mathrm{M};\ a = 1,\dots,n+\epsilon_1+\epsilon_2) \tag{9.17}$$

is an equivalent sub-system of (9.10a), minimal regular in $\underset{0}{\eta}^a$. The system (9.10) is then equivalent to its sub-system consisting of (9.11) and (9.17), both systems being minimal regular in $\underset{0}{\eta}^a$. So we have only to show that the whole system (9.11, 17) is minimal regular in $\underset{0}{\eta}^a$, i.e. that its rank in $\underset{0}{\eta}^a$ is $n-M+\epsilon_1$. If this rank were $\neq n-M+\epsilon_1$ it would have to be $< n - M + \epsilon_1$ and in $\underset{0}{\eta^a}$ there would have to exist a relation of the form

$$\alpha_{\mathfrak{a}'}\partial_b G^{\mathfrak{a}'} + \beta_{\mathfrak{x}'}\partial_b \psi^{\mathfrak{x}'} = 0 \quad (\mathfrak{a}' = 1,\ldots,\mathrm{n}-\mathrm{M};\ \mathfrak{x}' = 1,\ldots,\epsilon_1;$$
$$b = 1,\ldots,n+\epsilon_1+\epsilon_2), \qquad (9.18)$$

of whose coefficients neither all the α nor all the β could vanish simultaneously. From (9.18) there would follow in $\underset{0}{\eta^a}$

$$\alpha_{\mathfrak{a}'}(\partial_\kappa F^{\mathfrak{a}'})\partial_b \phi^\kappa + \beta_{\mathfrak{x}'}\partial_b \psi^{\mathfrak{x}'} = 0 \quad (\mathfrak{a}' = 1,\ldots,\mathrm{n}-\mathrm{M};\ \mathfrak{x}' = 1,\ldots,\epsilon_1;$$
$$b = 1,\ldots,n+\epsilon_1+\epsilon_2) \qquad (9.19)$$

and a relation of this form cannot exist because the differentials $d\phi^\kappa$ and $d\psi^{\mathfrak{x}'}$ are linearly independent in $\underset{0}{\eta^a}$. This proves the second part of the theorem.

To prove the first part of the theorem we first suppose (9.8) to be regular of dimension M in $\underset{0}{\xi^\kappa}$. Then, by interchanging the indices $\mathfrak{a}$ it can always be arranged that the equations

$$F^{\mathfrak{a}'}(\xi^\kappa) = 0 \quad (\mathfrak{a}' = 1,\ldots,\mathrm{n}-\mathrm{M}) \qquad (9.20)$$

constitute an equivalent sub-system, minimal regular in $\underset{0}{\xi^\kappa}$. From (9.10a) we consider the equations corresponding to (9.20):

$$G^{\mathfrak{a}'}(\eta^a) = 0 \quad (\mathfrak{a}' = 1,\ldots,\mathrm{n}-\mathrm{M};\ a = 1,\ldots,n+\epsilon_1+\epsilon_2). \qquad (9.21)$$

We now have

$$\partial_b G^{\mathfrak{a}'} = (\partial_\kappa F^{\mathfrak{a}'})\partial_b \phi^\kappa \quad (\mathfrak{a}' = 1,\ldots,\mathrm{n}-\mathrm{M};\ b = 1,\ldots,n+\epsilon_1+\epsilon_2) \quad (9.22)$$

and $\partial_\kappa F^{\mathfrak{a}'}$ has the rank $n-M$ in all points of $\mathfrak{N}(\underset{0}{\xi^\kappa})$ and $\partial_b \phi^\kappa$ has the rank n in all points of $\mathfrak{N}(\underset{0}{\eta^a})$. Hence $\partial_b G^{\mathfrak{a}'}$ has the rank $n-M$ in all points of $\mathfrak{N}(\underset{0}{\eta^a})$ and consequently (9.21) is minimal regular in $\underset{0}{\eta^a}$. The remaining equations of (9.8)

$$F^{\mathfrak{a}''}(\xi^\kappa) = 0 \quad (\mathfrak{a}'' = \mathrm{n}-\mathrm{M}+1,\ldots,\mathrm{N}) \qquad (9.23)$$

are dependent on (9.20). Therefore, if the ξ^κ in (9.23) are replaced by $\phi^\kappa(\eta^a)$, the resulting equations

$$G^{\mathfrak{a}''}(\eta^\alpha) = 0 \quad (\mathfrak{a}'' = \mathrm{n}-\mathrm{M}+1,\ldots,\mathrm{n};\ a = 1,\ldots,n+\epsilon_1+\epsilon_2) \qquad (9.24)$$

depend on (9.21). Hence (9.10a) is regular of dimension $M+\epsilon_1+\epsilon_2$ in $\underset{0}{\eta^a}$ and consequently as we have proved already, (9.10) is regular of dimension $M+\epsilon_2$ in $\underset{0}{\eta^a}$.

Finally, let us assume again that (9.10) is regular and of dimension $M+\epsilon_2$ in $\underset{0}{\eta}^a$. We have proved already that the indices $\mathfrak{a}$ can be interchanged in such a way that

$$G^{\mathfrak{a}'}(\eta^a) = 0 \quad (\mathfrak{a}' = 1,..., n-M;\ a = 1,..., n+\epsilon_1+\epsilon_2) \tag{9.25}$$

is an equivalent sub-system of (9.10 a) minimal regular in $\underset{0}{\eta}^a$. Now we consider the equations (9.8) corresponding to (9.25)

$$F^{\mathfrak{a}'}(\xi^\kappa) = 0 \quad (\mathfrak{a}' = 1,..., n-M). \tag{9.26}$$

We have

$$\partial_b G^{\mathfrak{a}'} = (\partial_\kappa F^{\mathfrak{a}'})\partial_b \phi^\kappa \quad (\mathfrak{a}' = 1,..., n-M;\ b = 1,..., n+\epsilon_1+\epsilon_2) \tag{9.27}$$

and $\partial_b G^{\mathfrak{a}'}$ has the rank $n-M$, and $\partial_b \phi^\kappa$ the rank n, in all points of $\mathfrak{N}(\underset{0}{\eta}^a)$. Hence $\partial_\kappa F^{\mathfrak{a}'}$ has the rank $n-M$ in all points of $\mathfrak{N}(\underset{0}{\xi}^\kappa)$, and consequently (9.26) is minimal regular in $\underset{0}{\xi}^\kappa$. Now we have only to prove that (9.26) is equivalent to (9.8). If this were not true there would exist at least one point of $\mathfrak{N}(\underset{0}{\xi}^\kappa)$ where the number of linearly independent differentials among the $dF^{\mathfrak{a}}$ would be $> n-M$. Consequently, since $\partial_b \phi^\kappa$ has the rank n in all points of $\mathfrak{N}(\underset{0}{\eta}^a)$, there would have to exist at least one point of $\mathfrak{N}(\underset{0}{\eta}^a)$ where the rank of

$$\partial_b G^{\mathfrak{a}} = (\partial_\lambda F^{\mathfrak{a}})\partial_b \phi^\lambda \quad (\mathfrak{a} = 1,..., N;\ b = 1,..., n+\epsilon_1+\epsilon_2) \tag{9.28}$$

would be $> n-M$. But this is impossible because (9.10 a) is regular of dimension $M+\epsilon_1+\epsilon_2$ in $\underset{0}{\eta}^a$. This proves the first part of the theorem.

10. Fields of m-directions; the X_n^m†

When in every point of some region of X_n an m-direction is given, we get a field of m-directions or E_m-field. Such a field is called an X_n^m in X_n. An X_n^m can be given by a simple contravariant pseudo-m-vector field $\lfloor v^{\kappa_1...\kappa_m}\rfloor$ or by a simple covariant pseudo-$(n-m)$-vector field $\lfloor w_{\lambda_1...\lambda_{n-m}}\rfloor$. We have the relations

$$\begin{aligned} &(a) \qquad v^{[\kappa_1...\kappa_m} v^{\lambda_1]...\lambda_m} = 0, \\ &(b) \qquad w_{[\lambda_1...\lambda_{n-m}} w_{\mu_1]...\mu_{n-m}} = 0, \\ &(c) \qquad v^{\mu\kappa_2...\kappa_m} w_{\mu\lambda_2...\lambda_{n-m}} = 0, \end{aligned} \tag{10.1}$$

each of which expresses the fact that v and w are simple.

† Cf. Schouten and v. Kampen, 1930. 1. References to literature are to be found there and in Schouten and Struik, 1935. 1, p. 194.

In the $X_{n+m(n-m)}$ of all E_m's through the contact point in all local E_n's of X_n, the ξ^κ, $v^{\kappa_1 \dots \kappa_m}$, and the ξ^κ, $w_{\lambda_1 \dots \lambda_{n-m}}$ are supernumerary coordinates with $\epsilon_1 = \binom{n}{m} - m(n-m) - 1$, and $\epsilon_2 = 1$.

Often it is convenient to proceed in the following way. m linearly independent contravariant vectors $\underset{b}{e}^\kappa$ ($b = 1,\dots, \mathrm{m}$) and $n-m$ linearly independent covariant vectors $\overset{x}{e}_\lambda$ ($x = \mathrm{m}+1,\dots, \mathrm{n}$) are chosen, analytic in the region considered and such that the $\underset{b}{e}^\kappa$ span the local E_m of X_n^m at each point and the $\overset{x}{e}_\lambda$ span a domain with the m-direction of this E_m. Then the $\underset{b}{e}^\kappa$ are looked upon as contravariant measuring vectors $\underset{b}{e}^a$ in their own domain. Let the covariant measuring vectors belonging to them be written $\overset{a}{e}_b$. Similarly the $\overset{x}{e}_\lambda$ are looked upon as covariant measuring vectors $\overset{x}{e}_y$ in their own domain, and the associated contravariant measuring vectors are written $\underset{y}{e}^x$. Then $\underset{b}{e}^a$ and $\overset{a}{e}_b$ are measuring vectors in the E_m in the local E_n, and $\underset{y}{e}^x$ and $\overset{x}{e}_y$ are measuring vectors in the E_{n-m} resulting from the local E_n by reducing with respect to E_m (cf. I, § 9). Now the connecting quantities

$$B_b^\kappa \overset{\text{def}}{=} \underset{c}{e}^\kappa \overset{c}{e}_b \qquad (b, c = 1,\dots, \mathrm{m};\ x, z = \mathrm{m}+1,\dots, \mathrm{n}) \qquad (10.2)$$
$$C_\lambda^x \overset{\text{def}}{=} \overset{z}{e}_\lambda \underset{z}{e}^x$$

can be formed. We call them the *contra-* and *covariant connecting quantity* of the X_n^m in X_n respectively. They are analytic in the region considered. ξ^κ, B_b^κ are supernumerary coordinates with $\epsilon_1 = 0$, $\epsilon_2 = m^2$ and ξ^κ, C_λ^x are such coordinates with $\epsilon_1 = 0$, $\epsilon_2 = (n-m)^2$ in the $X_{n+m(n-m)}$ mentioned above. It is evident that

$$B_b^\mu C_\mu^x = 0. \qquad (10.3)$$

Transformations of the B_b^κ and C_λ^x have to be considered with respect to transformations $\xi^\kappa \to \xi^{\kappa'}$, to linear homogeneous transformations $\underset{b}{e}^\kappa \to \underset{b'}{e}^\kappa$, and to linear homogeneous transformations $\overset{x}{e}_\lambda \to \overset{x'}{e}_\lambda$. We will always assume that the coefficients of these linear transformations are analytic in the region considered. Then the new components $B_{b'}^{\kappa'}$, $C_{\lambda'}^{x'}$ are also analytic in this region and their ranks are always m and $n-m$ respectively.

In accordance with the results in I, § 9, and II, § 7, the identification, section, and reduction of vectors with respect to an X_n^m in X_n have to be defined in the following way:

(*a*) Every contravariant vector v^a of the b-domain of B_b^κ can be identified with the contravariant vector $v^\kappa = v^a B_a^\kappa$ of X_n in the local E_m.

(*b*) The *section* of a covariant vector w_λ of X_n with the X_n^m, is the covariant vector $'w_b = w_\lambda B_b^\lambda$ of the b-domain of B_b^κ. On the other hand, w_λ is not uniquely determined by $'w_b$.

(*c*) Every covariant vector w_y of the x-domain of C_λ^x can be identified with the covariant vector $w_y C_\lambda^y$ of X_n. The $(n-1)$-direction of this latter vector contains the m-direction of the local E_m.

(*d*) The *reduction* of a contravariant vector v^κ of X_n with respect to the X_n^m is the contravariant vector $'v^x = v^\kappa C_\kappa^x$ of the x-domain of C_λ^x. On the other hand, v^κ is not uniquely determined by $'v^x$.

Identification, section, and reduction of p-vectors with respect to an X_n^m in X_n have to be defined in the same way. As there is full agreement with I, § 9, it will be sufficient to refer to that section.

An X_n^m is called X_m-forming if there exists a normal system of ∞^{n-m} X_m's whose tangent E_m coincides with the local E_m of X_n^m at each point. In this special case the $\underset{b}{e}^a$ are the measuring vectors of a generally anholonomic coordinate system in each X_m, but they can be chosen in such a way that these coordinate systems are all holonomic.

11. Differential comitants I: Rot and Div†

A *differential comitant* of a system of quantities in X_n is a quantity whose components, for every choice of the coordinates, can be derived from the components of these quantities by the same algebraic and differentiating processes.

The derivatives of an affinor, e.g. $P^{\kappa\lambda}{}_{\cdot\cdot\nu}$, are transformed in the following way:

$$\partial_{\mu'} P^{\kappa'\lambda'}{}_{\cdot\cdot\nu'} = A^{\mu}_{\mu'} \partial_\mu A^{\kappa'\lambda'\nu}_{\kappa\lambda\nu'} P^{\kappa\lambda}{}_{\cdot\cdot\nu} = A^{\mu\kappa'\lambda'\nu}_{\mu'\kappa\lambda\nu'} \partial_\mu P^{\kappa\lambda}{}_{\cdot\cdot\nu} + P^{\kappa\lambda}{}_{\cdot\cdot\nu} A^{\mu}_{\mu'} \partial_\mu A^{\kappa'\lambda'\nu}_{\kappa\lambda\nu'}, \tag{11.1}$$

and according to this equation they do not behave like the components of an affinor. But the alternated derivation of a covariant q-vector transforms as follows:

$$\partial_{[\mu'} w_{\lambda'_1\ldots\lambda'_q]} = A^{\mu\lambda_1\ldots\lambda_q}_{\mu'\lambda'_1\ldots\lambda'_q} \partial_{[\mu} w_{\lambda_1\ldots\lambda_q]} + w_{\lambda_1\ldots\lambda_q} \partial_{[\mu'} A^{\lambda_1\ldots\lambda_q}_{\lambda'_1\ldots\lambda'_q]} = A^{\mu\lambda_1\ldots\lambda_q}_{\mu'\lambda'_1\ldots\lambda'_q} \partial_{[\mu} w_{\lambda_1\ldots\lambda_q]} \tag{11.2}$$

since

$$\partial_{[\mu'} A^{\lambda}_{\lambda']} = \partial_{[\mu'} \partial_{\lambda']} \xi^\lambda = 0. \tag{11.3}$$

† Cf. Goursat 1922. 1, ch. iii.

Hence this derivation is zero for $q = n$ and a covariant $(q+1)$-vector for $q < n$. We call this differential comitant multiplied by $q+1$ the *natural derivative* or *rotation* of $w_{\lambda_1 \dots \lambda_q}$ and we will often use the abbreviated notation Rot w, and $(q+1)Dw$ with the abbreviated notation of I, § 7. It follows from the definition that the process of natural derivation, applied twice in succession to a scalar or a covariant q-vector always leads to zero (cf. II, § 5):

$$\begin{aligned} \operatorname{Rot} \operatorname{Grad} p &= 2DDp = 0, \\ \operatorname{Rot} \operatorname{Rot} w &= (q+2)(q+1)DDw = 0. \end{aligned} \tag{11.4}$$

If from w the corresponding contravariant p-vector density of weight $+1$, $p = n-q$ is formed (cf. I, § 8)

$$\mathfrak{w}^{\kappa_1 \dots \kappa_p} = \frac{1}{q!} w_{\lambda_1 \dots \lambda_q} \mathfrak{E}^{\lambda_1 \dots \lambda_q \, \kappa_1 \dots \kappa_p}, \tag{11.5}$$

it follows that

$$\partial_\mu \mathfrak{w}^{\mu \kappa_2 \dots \kappa_p} = (-1)^q \frac{q+1}{(q+1)!} \partial_{[\mu} w_{\lambda_1 \dots \lambda_q]} \mathfrak{E}^{\mu \lambda_1 \dots \lambda_q \, \kappa_2 \dots \kappa_p}. \tag{11.6}$$

Hence the contravariant $(p-1)$-vector density $\partial_\mu \mathfrak{w}^{\mu \kappa_2 \dots \kappa_p}$ of weight $+1$ is a differential comitant of $\mathfrak{w}$ and therefore of w. We call $\partial_\mu \mathfrak{w}^{\mu \kappa_2 \dots \kappa_p}$ the *natural derivative* or *divergence* of $\mathfrak{w}$ and we will often use the notations Div $\mathfrak{w}$ and $D\mathfrak{w}$. From the definition it follows that the process of natural derivation applied twice in succession to a q-vector density of weight $+1$ always leads to zero:

$$\operatorname{Div} \operatorname{Div} \mathfrak{w} = 0. \tag{11.7}$$

If $\mathfrak{w}$ corresponds to w, it follows from (11.6) that $(-1)^q \operatorname{Div} \mathfrak{w}$ corresponds to Rot w.

We will prove the theorem

THEOREM II.11. (*Principal theorem on covariant $(q+1)$-vector fields.*) *If $W_{\lambda_1 \dots \lambda_{q+1}}$ is a covariant $(q+1)$-vector, $1 \leqslant q+1 \leqslant n$, whose components depend on the ξ^κ and on z parameters $\theta^\mathfrak{a}$ ($\mathfrak{a} = 1, \dots, z$) and are analytic in an $\mathfrak{N}(\overset{0}{\xi^\kappa}, \overset{0}{\theta^\mathfrak{a}})$, this $(q+1)$-vector can be written as the gradient of a scalar (depending on the ξ^κ and the $\theta^\mathfrak{a}$) for $q = 0$, and as the rotation of a q-vector (depending on the ξ^κ and the $\theta^\mathfrak{a}$) for $q > 0$, in some $\mathfrak{N}(\overset{0}{\xi^\kappa}, \overset{0}{\theta^\mathfrak{a}})$, if and only if there exists an $\mathfrak{N}(\overset{0}{\xi^\kappa}, \overset{0}{\theta^\mathfrak{a}})$ where* Rot $W = 0$.

PROOF. We first take the case $q+1 = n$. Then Rot $W = 0$. Since all covariant n-vectors differ only by a scalar factor, there exists a scalar τ, analytic in an $\mathfrak{N}(\overset{0}{\xi^\kappa}, \overset{0}{\theta^\mathfrak{a}})$ such that

$$W_{\lambda_1 \cdots \lambda_n} = \tau \overset{1}{e}_{[\lambda_1} \cdots \overset{n}{e}_{\lambda_n]}. \tag{11.8}$$

We consider the integral

$$T(\xi^\kappa, \theta^\alpha) = \int_{\overset{\xi^1}{0}}^{\xi^1} \tau(t, \xi^2, ..., \xi^n, \theta^\alpha)\, dt, \tag{11.9}$$

in which the $\xi^2,..., \xi^n$ and the θ^α play the role of parameters. There exists an $\mathfrak{N}(\overset{0}{\xi^\kappa}, \overset{0}{\theta^\alpha})$ where T is analytic. In this region we have

$$\partial_\lambda T \overset{*}{=} \overset{\kappa}{e}_\lambda \partial_\kappa T \tag{11.10}$$

$$\overset{*}{=} \tau \overset{1}{e}_\lambda + \overset{2}{e}_\lambda \partial_2 T + ... + \overset{n}{e}_\lambda \partial_n T; \tag{11.11}$$

hence, by using (11.8) we obtain

$$W_{\lambda_1...\lambda_n} = (\partial_{[\lambda_1} T)\overset{2}{e}_{\lambda_2}...\overset{n}{e}_{\lambda_n]} = \partial_{[\lambda_1}(T\overset{2}{e}_{\lambda_2}...\overset{n}{e}_{\lambda_n]}). \tag{11.12}$$

This proves the theorem for $q+1 = n$. Incidentally, we have also proved that every covariant n-vector is a *gradient product*, i.e. the alternating product of gradients.

For $q+1 < n$ we proceed by induction. Suppose the theorem is proved for every value of q $(1 \leqslant q+1 \leqslant n-1)$ in an X_{n-1}. Then it has to be shown that the theorem is true in an X_n.

First suppose that $q > 0$. From

$$\partial_{[\nu} W_{\mu\lambda_1...\lambda_q]} = 0 \tag{11.13}$$

it follows that

$$\partial_{[\delta} W_{\gamma\beta_1...\beta_q]} = 0 \quad (\beta_1,..., \beta_q, \gamma, \delta = 1,..., n-1). \tag{11.14}$$

This is an equation in the X_{n-1} of $\xi^1,..., \xi^{n-1}$, involving the parameters ξ^n and θ^α. Since the theorem is assumed proved in an X_{n-1}, we know that there exists a q-vector $w_{\beta_1...\beta_q}$ of X_{n-1}, analytic in an $\mathfrak{N}(\overset{0}{\xi^\kappa}, \overset{0}{\eta^\alpha})$ such that

$$W_{\gamma\beta_1...\beta_q} = (q+1)\partial_{[\gamma} w_{\beta_1...\beta_q]} \quad (\beta_1,..., \beta_q, \gamma = 1,..., n-1). \tag{11.15}$$

So it remains to prove that there exists for $q > 1$ a $(q-1)$-vector $w_{n\,\beta_2...\beta_q}$, analytic in an $\mathfrak{N}(\overset{0}{\xi^\kappa}, \overset{0}{\eta^\alpha})$, such that

$$W_{n\beta_1...\beta_q} = \partial_n w_{\beta_1...\beta_q} - q\partial_{[\beta_1} w_{|n|\beta_2...\beta_q]} \quad (\beta_1,..., \beta_q = 1,..., n-1) \tag{11.16}$$

and for $q = 1$, a scalar w_n analytic in an $\mathfrak{N}(\overset{0}{\xi^\kappa}, \overset{0}{\eta^\alpha})$ such that

$$W_{n\beta} = \partial_n w_\beta - \partial_\beta w_n \quad (\beta = 1,..., n-1). \tag{11.17}$$

In these equations ξ^n and the θ^α are to be regarded as parameters.

The necessary and sufficient conditions follow from the theorem already proved in X_{n-1}, i.e.

$$\partial_{[\gamma} W_{|n|\beta_1...\beta_q]} - \partial_{[\gamma} \partial_{|n|} w_{\beta_1...\beta_q]} = 0 \quad (\beta_1,..., \beta_q, \gamma = 1,..., n-1) \tag{11.18}$$

for $q > 1$ and

$$\partial_{[\gamma} W_{|n|\beta]} - \partial_{[\gamma} \partial_{|n|} w_{\beta]} = 0 \quad (\beta, \gamma = 1,..., n-1) \tag{11.19}$$

for $q = 1$. From (11.15), these are equivalent to the conditions

$$\partial_{[\gamma} W_{|n|\beta_1...\beta_q]} - \frac{1}{q+1} \partial_n W_{\gamma\beta_1...\beta_q} = 0 \quad (\beta_1,..., \beta_q, \gamma = 1,..., n-1) \tag{11.20}$$

and

$$\partial_{[\gamma} W_{|n|\beta]} - \tfrac{1}{2} \partial_n W_{\gamma\beta} = 0 \quad (\beta, \gamma = 1,..., n-1) \tag{11.21}$$

respectively, which are really satisfied as they result from (11.13).

If $q = 0$, from

$$\partial_{[\nu} W_{\mu]} = 0 \tag{11.22}$$

we get the equation in the X_{n-1} of $\xi^1,..., \xi^{n-1}$

$$\partial_{[\gamma} W_{\beta]} = 0 \quad (\beta, \gamma = 1,..., n-1) \tag{11.23}$$

with the parameters ξ^n and θ^a, from which we may conclude that there exists a scalar p, analytic in an $\mathfrak{N}(\overset{}{\underset{0}{\xi^\kappa}}, \underset{0}{\theta^a})$, such that

$$W_\beta = \partial_\beta p \quad (\beta, \gamma = 1,..., n-1). \tag{11.24}$$

p is determined to within an additional term p', depending only on ξ^n and θ^a. It remains to be proved that p' can be chosen in such a way that

$$W_n = \partial_n(p+p'). \tag{11.25}$$

Now from (11.22) and (11.24) it follows that $W_n - \partial_n p$ is really independent of the $\xi^1,..., \xi^{n-1}$. Hence the differential equation

$$\frac{dp'}{d\xi^n} = W_n - \partial_n p \tag{11.26}$$

can be integrated in an $\mathfrak{N}(\underset{0}{\xi^\kappa}, \underset{0}{\theta^a})$. This proves the theorem for $q = 0$.

Collecting these results, we have proved the theorem for an X_n if it is true for an X_{n-1}, and, moreover, that it is true for $q = n-1$ in an X_n. Hence it is true for an X_1, and by induction for every value of n.

It is remarkable that the theory of homogeneous linear partial differential equations, which will be treated in Chapter III, is not used in the proof of this theorem. This is due to the fact that the determination of w and p from W can be effected by quadratures. On the other hand, the theory of partial differential equations is needed if we wish to prove that every *simple* covariant q-vector ($q \leqslant n-1$) whose rotation vanishes, is a gradient product (cf. III, § 18).

It is possible to prove the theorem for contravariant ($p-1$)-vector densities instead of covariant ($q+1$)-vectors. It then takes the form

THEOREM II.12. (*Principal theorem on contravariant ($p-1$)-vector densities.*) *If* $\mathfrak{W}^{\kappa_1\ldots\kappa_{p-1}}$ *is a contravariant ($p-1$)-vector density of weight $+1$ ($0 \leqslant p-1 \leqslant n-1$), whose components depend on the* ξ^κ *and on z parameters* $\theta^{\mathfrak{a}}$ ($\mathfrak{a} = 1,\ldots, z$) *and are analytic in an* $\mathfrak{N}(\underset{0}{\xi^\kappa}, \underset{0}{\theta^{\mathfrak{a}}})$, *this ($p-1$)-vector density can be written as the divergence of a p-vector density of weight $+1$ (depending on the* ξ^κ *and the* $\theta^{\mathfrak{a}}$) *in some* $\mathfrak{N}(\underset{0}{\xi^\kappa}, \underset{0}{\theta^{\mathfrak{a}}})$, *if and only if there exists an* $\mathfrak{N}(\underset{0}{\xi^\kappa}, \underset{0}{\theta^{\mathfrak{a}}})$, *where* Div $\mathfrak{W} = 0$.

To the property that every covariant n-vector is a gradient product (cf. (11.12)) corresponds the property that every scalar density of weight $+1$ is the divergence of a vector density of weight $+1$.

12. Differential comitants II: the theorem of Stokes†

In an $\mathfrak{N}(\underset{0}{\xi^\kappa})$ let a covariant q-vector $w_{\lambda_1\ldots\lambda_q}$ be given and an X_q through $\underset{0}{\xi^\kappa}$ with the parametric form

$$\xi^\kappa = f^\kappa(\xi^a) \quad (a = 1,\ldots, \mathrm{q}). \tag{12.1}$$

In $\underset{0}{\xi^\kappa}$, we consider the parallelotop of the q vectors

$$\underset{1}{d\xi^1 e^a}, \quad \ldots, \quad \underset{\mathrm{q}}{d\xi^{\mathrm{q}} e^a} \quad (a = 1,\ldots, \mathrm{q}) \tag{12.2}$$

with the screw-sense determined by the sequence $\underset{1}{e^a},\ldots, \underset{\mathrm{q}}{e^a}$. This parallelotop with its screw-sense, is the geometrical representation of the contravariant q-vector of X_q

$$\underset{q}{dF^{a_1\ldots a_q}} \overset{\text{def}}{=} q!\, d\xi^1\ldots d\xi^{\mathrm{q}} \underset{1}{e}^{[a_1}\ldots \underset{\mathrm{q}}{e}^{a_q]} \quad (a_1,\ldots, a_q = 1,\ldots, \mathrm{q}) \tag{12.3}$$

which can be looked upon as a q-vector of X_n

$$\underset{q}{dF^{\kappa_1\ldots\kappa_q}} = B^{\kappa_1}_{b_1}\ldots B^{\kappa_q}_{b_q} \underset{q}{dF^{b_1\ldots b_q}} = q!\, d\xi^1\ldots d\xi^{\mathrm{q}} \underset{1}{e}^{[\kappa_1}\ldots \underset{\mathrm{q}}{e}^{\kappa_q]} \quad (b_1,\ldots, b_q = 1,\ldots, \mathrm{q}). \tag{12.4}$$

From w and $\underset{q}{dF}$ we get by transvection the scalar

$$w_{\lambda_1\ldots\lambda_q} \underset{q}{dF^{\lambda_1\ldots\lambda_q}} = q!\, d\xi^1\ldots d\xi^{\mathrm{q}} \underset{1}{e}^{\lambda_1}\ldots \underset{\mathrm{q}}{e}^{\lambda_q} w_{\lambda_1\ldots\lambda_q} = q!\, d\xi^1\ldots d\xi^{\mathrm{q}}\, 'w_{1\ldots\mathrm{q}}, \tag{12.5}$$

† Cf. Goursat 1922. 1, ch. v; Schouten and v. Dantzig 40. 1, § 9, also for references to literature.

where $'w_{b_1\ldots b_q}$ is the section of $w_{\lambda_1\ldots\lambda_q}$ with the X_q (cf. II, § 7):

$$'w_{b_1\ldots b_q} = B^{\lambda_1}_{b_1}\ldots B^{\lambda_q}_{b_q} w_{\lambda_1\ldots\lambda_q} \quad (b_1,\ldots, b_q = 1,\ldots, \mathrm{q}). \tag{12.6}$$

Now if in the X_q a finite region τ_q is enclosed by a closed X_{q-1}, denoted by τ_{q-1}, the integral

$$\int_{\tau_q} w_{\lambda_1\ldots\lambda_q} \underset{q}{dF}^{\lambda_1\ldots\lambda_q} = q! \int_{\tau_q} d\xi^1 \ldots d\xi^{\mathrm{q}}\, 'w_{1\ldots\mathrm{q}} \tag{12.7}$$

is called the *integral of* $w_{\lambda_1\ldots\lambda_q}$ *over* τ_q. Note that the sign of this integral depends on the choice of the screw-sense of $\underset{q}{dF}^{a_1\ldots a_q}$.

If the following conditions are satisfied:

(1) $w_{\lambda_1\ldots\lambda_q}$ is the rotation of a $(q-1)$-vector $u_{\lambda_2\ldots\lambda_q}$;

(2) $u_{\lambda_2\ldots\lambda_q}$ is continuous in τ_q and τ_{q-1};

(3) the derivatives of $u_{\lambda_2\ldots\lambda_q}$ occurring in $w_{\lambda_1\ldots\lambda_q}$ exist in all points of τ_q;

(4) these derivatives are continuous in all points of τ_q with the exception of the points of a finite number of X_{q-1}'s;

the integral (12.7) can be transformed into an integral of $u_{\lambda_2\ldots\lambda_q}$ over the enclosing X_{q-1} of τ_q. We will prove this theorem first for the case where the coordinate system can be chosen in such a way that τ_q is given by the inequalities

$$\alpha^a > \xi^a > \beta^a \quad (a = 1,\ldots, \mathrm{q}), \tag{12.8}$$

α^a and β^a being positive numbers and $\alpha^a > \beta^a$ $(a = 1,\ldots, \mathrm{q})$. From

$$w_{\lambda_1\ldots\lambda_q} = q\partial_{[\lambda_1} u_{\lambda_2\ldots\lambda_q]} \tag{12.9}$$

we get by transvection

$$\begin{aligned} 'w_{b_1\ldots b_q} &= qB^{\lambda_1}_{[b_1}\ldots B^{\lambda_q}_{b_q]} \partial_{\lambda_1} u_{\lambda_2\ldots\lambda_q} \\ &= q\partial_{[b_1}\, 'u_{b_2\ldots b_q]} - qu_{\lambda_2\ldots\lambda_q} B^{\lambda_1}_{[b_1} \partial_{|\lambda_1|} B^{\lambda_2}_{b_2}\ldots B^{\lambda_q}_{b_q]} \quad (b_1,\ldots, b_q = 1,\ldots, \mathrm{q}), \end{aligned} \tag{12.10}$$

$'u_{b_2\ldots b_q}$ being the section of $u_{\lambda_2\ldots\lambda_q}$ with X_q. Now from the identity

$$B^{\mu}_{[c} \partial_{|\mu|} B^{\kappa}_{b]} = \partial_{[c} \partial_{b]} \xi^\kappa = 0 \quad (b, c = 1,\ldots, \mathrm{q}) \tag{12.11}$$

the last term in (12.10) vanishes, which proves that $'w_{b_1\ldots b_q}$ is the rotation of $'u_{b_2\ldots b_q}$. Consequently

$$\begin{aligned} &\int_{\tau_q} w_{\lambda_1\ldots\lambda_q} \underset{q}{dF}^{\lambda_1\ldots\lambda_q} \\ &= qq! \int_{\tau_q} d\xi^1\ldots d\xi^{\mathrm{q}}\, \partial_{[1}\, 'u_{2\ldots \mathrm{q}]} \\ &= q! \sum_{\mathrm{a}=1}^{\mathrm{a}=\mathrm{q}} \int_{\beta^1}^{\alpha^1} d\xi^1 \ldots \int_{\beta^{\mathrm{a}-1}}^{\alpha^{\mathrm{a}-1}} d\xi^{\mathrm{a}-1} \int_{\beta^{\mathrm{a}+1}}^{\alpha^{\mathrm{a}+1}} d\xi^{\mathrm{a}+1} \ldots \int_{\beta^{\mathrm{q}}}^{\alpha^{\mathrm{q}}} d\xi^{\mathrm{q}} \int_{\beta^{\mathrm{a}}}^{\alpha^{\mathrm{a}}} d\xi^{\mathrm{a}} \partial_{\mathrm{a}}\, 'u_{1\ldots(\mathrm{a}-1)\,(\mathrm{a}+1)\ldots\mathrm{q}}. \end{aligned} \tag{12.12}$$

Since the f^k in (12.1) are analytic in τ_q it follows from our conditions that the derivatives of $'u_{b_2...b_q}$ occurring in $\partial_{[b_1}\,'u_{b_2...b_q]}$ exist in all points of τ_q and are continuous in all these points with the exception of the points of a finite number of X_{q-1}'s. Hence in each of the q terms on the right-hand side of (12.12) the last integration, involving only derivatives of this sort, can be carried out, and we get an expression of the form

$$q!\sum_{\mathfrak{a}=1}^{\mathfrak{a}=\mathfrak{q}}\int_{\beta^1}^{\alpha^1} d\xi^1 \ldots \int_{\beta^{\mathfrak{a}-1}}^{\alpha^{\mathfrak{a}-1}} d\xi^{\mathfrak{a}-1}\int_{\beta^{\mathfrak{a}+1}}^{\alpha^{\mathfrak{a}+1}} d\xi^{\mathfrak{a}+1}\ldots\int_{\beta^{\mathfrak{q}}}^{\alpha^{\mathfrak{q}}} d\xi^{\mathfrak{q}}\left('u_{1\ldots\mathfrak{a}-1\,\mathfrak{a}+1\ldots\mathfrak{q}}\Big|_{\beta^{\mathfrak{a}}}^{\alpha^{\mathfrak{a}}}\right). \qquad (12.13)$$

Now we define in the τ_{q-1} enclosing τ_q, a screw-sense in such a way that the sense from τ_q to the part of X_n outside τ_q followed by this screw-sense, determines the screw-sense of $\underset{q}{F}{}^{\kappa_1\ldots\kappa_q}$, and we denote an infinitesimal part of τ_{q-1} with this screw-sense by $d\underset{q-1}{F}{}^{\kappa_2\ldots\kappa_q}$. Then the term of (12.13)

$$q!\int_{\beta^2}^{\alpha^2} d\xi^2 \ldots \int_{\beta^{\mathfrak{q}}}^{\alpha^{\mathfrak{q}}} d\xi^{\mathfrak{q}}\,'u_{2\ldots\mathfrak{q}}(\alpha^1,\xi^2,\ldots,\xi^{\mathfrak{q}}) \qquad (12.14)$$

is just equal to q times the part of the integral

$$\int_{\tau_{q-1}} u_{\lambda_2\ldots\lambda_q}\, d\underset{q-1}{F}{}^{\lambda_2\ldots\lambda_q} \qquad (12.15)$$

belonging to the facet $\xi^1 = \alpha^1$ of τ_{q-1}. Hence we have

$$\int_{\tau_q} (\partial_{[\lambda_1} u_{\lambda_2\ldots\lambda_q]})\, d\underset{q}{F}{}^{\lambda_1\ldots\lambda_q} = \int_{\tau_{q-1}} u_{\lambda_2\ldots\lambda_q}\, d\underset{q-1}{F}{}^{\lambda_2\ldots\lambda_q}. \qquad (12.16)$$

If τ_q does not have the special form (12.8) but is a region which can be built up from a finite number of regions, each having this special form with respect to some coordinate system, (12.16) is also true because in the process of integration, every boundary common to two neighbouring sub-regions occurs twice with opposite signs, leaving only the integral over τ_{q-1} in the result. This proves the theorem which we will formulate now as follows:

THEOREM II.13. (*Theorem of Stokes.*) *Let τ_q be a q-dimensional region of an X_q in X_n which can be built up from a finite number of sub-regions, each having the special form* (12.8) *with respect to some coordinate system, and let τ_{q-1} be its (q—1)-dimensional boundary. If $u_{\lambda_2\ldots\lambda_q}$ is a covariant (q—1)-vector of X_n, continuous in τ_q and τ_{q-1}, and if its rotation $w_{\lambda_1\ldots\lambda_q}$ is continuous at all points of τ_q with the exception of the points of a finite number of X_{q-1}'s in τ_q, the integral of $w_{\lambda_1\ldots\lambda_q}$ over τ_q is equal to the integral* *of* $qu_{\lambda_2...\lambda_q}$ *over* τ_{q-1}, *provided the screw-senses in* τ_q *and* τ_{q-1} *are chosen in such a way that the sense from within* τ_q *to without followed by the screw-sense in* τ_{q-1} *determines the screw-sense in* τ_q.

The theorem of Stokes can also be stated for a contravariant p-vector density of weight 1 ($p = n-q$), instead of a covariant q-vector. It then takes the form

$$\binom{n}{q}\int\limits_{\tau_q} (\partial_\mu \mathfrak{u}^{\mu[\kappa_1...\kappa_p})\, d\underset{q}{F}^{\lambda_1...\lambda_q]} = \binom{n}{q-1}\int\limits_{\tau_{q-1}} \mathfrak{w}^{[\lambda_1\kappa_1...\kappa_p}\, d\underset{q-1}{F}^{\lambda_2...\lambda_q} \tag{12.17}$$

which is readily derived from (12.16) by means of (11.5) and (11.6).

13. Differential comitants III: the Lie derivative†

Let the points of a region R of X_n be subject to the point transformation

$$\eta^\kappa \overset{*}{=} f^\kappa(\xi^\lambda). \tag{13.1}$$

The functions f^κ are supposed to be analytic in R with a non-vanishing functional determinant and chosen in such a way that they determine a one-to-one correspondence between the points of R and the points of another region R'. Now we introduce another coordinate system (κ') such that each point in R has the same coordinates with respect to (κ) as its image in R' has with respect to (κ'). Hence if

$$\xi^\kappa \overset{*}{=} \phi^\kappa(\eta^\lambda) \tag{13.2}$$

is the inversion of (13.1) the transformation of (κ) into (κ') and vice versa is given by

$$\xi^{\kappa'} = \delta^{\kappa'}_\kappa \phi^\kappa(\xi^\lambda), \qquad \xi^\kappa = f^\kappa(\xi^{\lambda'}). \tag{13.3}$$

This process is called the *dragging along*‡ of (κ), and (κ') is the *system dragged along*.

Now let a field $\underset{1}{P}^{\kappa_1...\kappa_p}{}_{\lambda_1...\lambda_q}$ be defined in R. In R', we form another field, whose components $\underset{2}{P}^{\kappa'_1...\kappa'_p}{}_{\lambda'_1...\lambda'_q}$ with respect to (κ') in any point of R' are equal to the components of $\underset{1}{P}^{\kappa_1...\kappa_p}{}_{\lambda_1...\lambda_q}$ with respect to (κ) in the corresponding point of R. This process is called the *dragging along*‡ of the field $\underset{1}{P}$ *by the transformation* (13.1) and $\underset{2}{P}$ is the *field dragged along*. If R and R' have some region in common the fields $\underset{1}{P}$ and $\underset{2}{P}$

† Cf. Slebodzinski 1931. 1; Schouten and v. Kampen 1933. 2; Schouten and Struik 1935. 1, i. 142, ii. 161.

‡ 'Mitschleppen' in 1933. 2 and 1935. 1.

can be compared. If in that case $\underset{1}{P} = \underset{2}{P}$, the field $\underset{1}{P}$ is said to be *invariant with the dragging along.*

If the solution of a system of n ordinary differential equations

$$\frac{d\eta^\kappa}{dt} = v^\kappa = \psi^\kappa(\eta^\nu), \tag{13.4}$$

with functions ψ^κ analytic in R and with the initial conditions

$$\eta^\kappa = \xi^\kappa \quad \text{for} \quad t = 0, \tag{13.5}$$

is expanded into a power series of t, we get a point transformation of the form

$$\eta^\kappa = \xi^\kappa + v^\kappa(\xi^\nu)t + \dots. \tag{13.6}$$

For this point transformation the system dragged along (κ') is given by the equations

$$\begin{aligned} \xi^\kappa &= \delta^\kappa_{\kappa'}\xi^{\kappa'} + \psi^\kappa(\xi^{\lambda'})t + \dots, \\ \xi^{\kappa'} &= \delta^{\kappa'}_\kappa \xi^\kappa - \delta^{\kappa'}_\kappa \psi^\kappa(\xi^\lambda)t + \dots. \end{aligned} \tag{13.7}$$

Differentiation gives

$$\begin{aligned} A^\kappa_{\kappa'} &= \delta^\lambda_{\kappa'}(A^\kappa_\lambda + t\partial_\lambda v^\kappa + \dots), \\ A^{\lambda'}_\lambda &= \delta^{\lambda'}_\kappa(A^\kappa_\lambda - t\partial_\lambda v^\kappa + \dots). \end{aligned} \tag{13.8}$$

Now we neglect all higher powers of t, and accordingly write dt instead of t. Then we get what is called an '*infinitesimal point transformation* $v^\kappa\,dt$'. It is usual to say that the one-parameter group of transformations whose equations are the solutions of (13.4) is *generated by the infinitesimal transformation* $v^\kappa\,dt$.

The dragging along belonging to the infinitesimal transformation $v^\kappa\,dt$ is called the *dragging along over* $v^\kappa\,dt$. The system dragged along (κ') is given by the equations

$$\begin{aligned} \xi^\kappa &= \delta^\kappa_{\kappa'}\xi^{\kappa'} + v^\kappa\,dt, \\ \xi^{\kappa'} &= \delta^{\kappa'}_\kappa(\xi^\kappa - v^\kappa\,dt). \end{aligned} \tag{13.9}$$

Now if v^κ and any field $P^{\kappa_1 \dots \kappa_p}{}_{\lambda_1 \dots \lambda_q}$ are given we may wish to calculate the components with respect to (κ) of the field resulting from P by dragging along over $v^\kappa\,dt$. For the sake of simplicity we take the case of an affinor field $P^\kappa_{.\lambda}$ of valence two. From the calculations it will be sufficiently clear that the results hold for quantities of any valence. The components of the field dragged along in $\xi^\kappa + v^\kappa\,dt$ with respect to (κ') are equal to the values of $P^\kappa_{.\lambda}$ in ξ^κ and, therefore, the components of the field dragged along in $\xi^\kappa + v^\kappa\,dt$ with respect to (κ) are

$$\begin{aligned} A^{\rho'\kappa}_{\lambda\sigma'}\delta^\rho_{\rho'}\delta^{\sigma'}_\sigma P^\sigma_{.\rho} &= (A^\rho_\lambda - \partial_\lambda v^\rho\,dt)(A^\kappa_\sigma + \partial_\sigma v^\kappa\,dt)P^\sigma_{.\rho} \\ &= P^\kappa_{.\lambda} - P^\kappa_{.\rho}\partial_\lambda v^\rho\,dt + P^\sigma_{.\lambda}\partial_\sigma v^\kappa\,dt. \end{aligned} \tag{13.10}$$

To get the components of the field dragged along in ξ^κ with respect to (κ) we have to subtract $v^\mu \partial_\mu P^{\kappa}_{.\lambda} dt$, hence these components are

$$P^{\kappa}_{.\lambda} - v^\mu \partial_\mu P^{\kappa}_{.\lambda} dt - P^{\kappa}_{.\rho} \partial_\lambda v^\rho dt + P^{\sigma}_{.\lambda} \partial_\sigma v^\kappa dt. \tag{13.11}$$

The expression $$(v^\mu \partial_\mu P^{\kappa}_{.\lambda} + P^{\kappa}_{.\rho} \partial_\lambda v^\rho - P^{\sigma}_{.\lambda} \partial_\sigma v^\kappa) dt \tag{13.12}$$

is called the *Lie differential of* $P^{\kappa}_{.\lambda}$ *with respect to* $v^\kappa dt$. Hence *if a field is dragged along over* $v^\kappa dt$, *the increase of the field at the fixed point* ξ^κ *is equal to the negative Lie differential in* ξ^κ.

The expression

$$\underset{L}{D} P^{\kappa}_{.\lambda} \overset{\text{def}}{=} v^\mu \partial_\mu P^{\kappa}_{.\lambda} + P^{\kappa}_{.\rho} \partial_\lambda v^\rho - P^{\sigma}_{.\lambda} \partial_\sigma v^\kappa \tag{13.13}$$

is called the *Lie derivative of* $P^{\kappa}_{.\lambda}$ *with respect to* v^κ. From its origin it is clear that this derivative is an affinor with the same valence as $P^{\kappa}_{.\lambda}$. Naturally this can be verified readily by a direct calculation of the law of transformation. Hence *the Lie differential of* $P^{\kappa}_{.\lambda}$ *is a differential comitant of the fields* $P^{\kappa}_{.\lambda}$ *and* v^κ.

For an affinor field of higher valence the Lie derivative can be found in the same way:

$$\underset{L}{D} P^{\kappa_1 \ldots \kappa_p}_{\cdot\;\;\cdot\;\;\lambda_1 \ldots \lambda_q} = v^\mu \partial_\mu P^{\kappa_1 \ldots \kappa_p}_{\cdot\;\;\cdot\;\;\lambda_1 \ldots \lambda_q} + \sum_{i=1}^{i=q} P^{\kappa_1 \ldots \kappa_p}_{\cdot\;\;\cdot\;\;\lambda_1 \ldots \lambda_{i-1}\rho\lambda_{i+1}\ldots\lambda_q} \partial_{\lambda_i} v^\rho - \sum_{j=1}^{j=p} P^{\kappa_1 \ldots \kappa_{j-1}\sigma\kappa_{j+1}\ldots\kappa_p}_{\cdot\;\;\cdot\;\;\lambda_1 \ldots \lambda_q} \partial_\sigma v^{\kappa_j}. \tag{13.14}$$

The Lie derivative of v^κ with respect to v^κ is zero. The Lie derivative of A^κ_λ is zero for every choice of v^κ. For a scalar field we have

$$\underset{L}{D} s = v^\mu \partial_\mu s, \tag{13.15}$$

for a covariant vector field

$$\underset{L}{D} w_\lambda = v^\mu \partial_\mu w_\lambda + w_\mu \partial_\lambda v^\mu, \tag{13.16}$$

and for a covariant q-vector field

$$\underset{L}{D} w_{\lambda_1 \ldots \lambda_q} = v^\mu \partial_\mu w_{\lambda_1 \ldots \lambda_q} + q w_{\rho[\lambda_2 \ldots \lambda_q} \partial_{\lambda_1]} v^\rho. \tag{13.17}$$

To obtain the Lie derivative of a scalar density of weight $+1$ we consider a covariant n-vector $w_{\lambda_1 \ldots \lambda_n}$. According to (13.17) its Lie derivative is

$$\begin{aligned} \underset{L}{D} w_{\lambda_1 \ldots \lambda_n} &= v^\mu \partial_\mu w_{\lambda_1 \ldots \lambda_n} + n w_{\rho[\lambda_2 \ldots \lambda_n} \partial_{\lambda_1]} v^\rho \\ &= v^\mu \partial_\mu w_{\lambda_1 \ldots \lambda_n} + w_{\lambda_1 \ldots \lambda_n} \partial_\mu v^\mu = \partial_\mu v^\mu w_{\lambda_1 \ldots \lambda_n}. \end{aligned} \tag{13.18}$$

Now $w_{1 \ldots n}$ transforms like a scalar density of weight $+1$; hence, if $\mathfrak{p}$ is a scalar density of weight $+1$ we have

$$\underset{L}{D} \mathfrak{p} = \partial_\mu \mathfrak{p} v^\mu = \mathrm{Div}(\mathfrak{p} v). \tag{13.19}$$

For calculations with Lie derivatives the following rules hold:

(1) the Lie derivative of a sum is the sum of the Lie derivatives of the parts;

(2) the Lie derivative of a contraction is the contraction of the Lie derivative;

(3) for the Lie derivative of products and transvections the rule of Leibniz holds.

Using these rules, which are readily verified, several properties of Lie derivatives may be obtained. We will only prove here some formulae for Lie derivatives of densities, which will be used in the following chapters.

Since a scalar density $\mathfrak{p}$ of weight $\mathfrak{k} > 0$ is always the $\mathfrak{k}$-th power of a scalar density of weight $+1$, from (13.19) it follows that

$$\underset{L}{D}\mathfrak{p} = v^{\mu}\partial_{\mu}\mathfrak{p} + \mathfrak{k}\mathfrak{p}\partial_{\mu}v^{\mu} \tag{13.20}$$

and from this we may deduce for an affinor density of weight $\mathfrak{k}$

$$\begin{aligned} \underset{L}{D}\mathfrak{P}^{\kappa_1\ldots\kappa_p}{}_{\lambda_1\ldots\lambda_q} &= v^{\mu}\partial_{\mu}\mathfrak{P}^{\kappa_1\ldots\kappa_p}{}_{\lambda_1\ldots\lambda_q} + \sum_{i=1}^{i=q}\mathfrak{P}^{\kappa_1\ldots\kappa_p}{}_{\lambda_1\ldots\lambda_{i-1}\rho\lambda_{i+1}\ldots\lambda_q}\partial_{\lambda_i}v^{\rho} - \\ &\quad - \sum_{j=1}^{j=p}\mathfrak{P}^{\kappa_1\ldots\kappa_{j-1}\sigma\kappa_{j+1}\ldots\kappa_p}{}_{\lambda_1\ldots\lambda_q}\partial_{\sigma}v^{\kappa_j} + \mathfrak{k}\mathfrak{P}^{\kappa_1\ldots\kappa_p}{}_{\lambda_1\ldots\lambda_q}\partial_{\mu}v^{\mu}. \end{aligned} \tag{13.21}$$

The Lie derivatives of a contravariant vector density of weight $+1$

$$\underset{L}{D}\mathfrak{w}^{\kappa} = v^{\mu}\partial_{\mu}\mathfrak{w}^{\kappa} - \mathfrak{w}^{\mu}\partial_{\mu}v^{\kappa} + \mathfrak{w}^{\kappa}\partial_{\mu}v^{\mu}, \tag{13.22}$$

and of a contravariant p-vector density of weight $+1$

$$\underset{L}{D}\mathfrak{w}^{\kappa_1\ldots\kappa_p} = v^{\mu}\partial_{\mu}\mathfrak{w}^{\kappa_1\ldots\kappa_p} - p\mathfrak{w}^{\sigma[\kappa_2\ldots\kappa_p}\partial_{\sigma}v^{\kappa_1]} + \mathfrak{w}^{\kappa_1\ldots\kappa_p}\partial_{\mu}v^{\mu}, \tag{13.23}$$

are important as special cases of this formula. It may be easily verified that the Lie derivatives of $\mathfrak{E}^{\kappa_1\ldots\kappa_n}$ and $\mathfrak{e}_{\lambda_1\ldots\lambda_n}$ (cf. I, § 8) are zero for every choice of v^{κ}.

14. Differential comitants IV: invariant fields and integral invariants†

If Lie's derivative of any field P with respect to v^{κ} is zero

$$\underset{L}{D}P = 0, \tag{14.1}$$

this field has the following properties:

1. The components of the field at any fixed point do not change if the field is dragged along by any of the transformations of the one-parameter group generated by $v^{\kappa}\,dt$.

† Cf. Goursat 1922. 1, ch. v; Cartan 1922. 2; de Donder 1927. 2; Engel and Faber 1932. 1, ch. ii.

2. The components of the field at any point ξ^κ with respect to (κ) are equal to the components at the point $\xi^\kappa + v^\kappa\, dt$ with respect to the co-ordinate system (κ') which results from (κ) by dragging along over $v^\kappa\, dt$.

If (14.1) holds the field is said to be *absolutely invariant with respect to* v^κ. Hence v^κ is absolutely invariant with respect to v^κ and A^κ_λ, $\mathfrak{E}^{\kappa_1 \dots \kappa_n}$ and $\mathfrak{e}_{\lambda_1 \dots \lambda_n}$ are absolutely invariant with respect to every field v^κ. Sums, products, and transvections of absolutely invariant fields are absolutely invariant. As special cases, we draw attention to the transvection of v^κ by an absolutely invariant field and to the co-(contra-)variant $(n-q)$-vector density corresponding to any absolutely invariant contra-(co-)variant q-vector.

If the q-vector $w_{\lambda_1 \dots \lambda_q}$ is absolutely invariant with respect to v^κ, the integral

$$I_q = \int_{\tau_q} w_{\lambda_1 \dots \lambda_q} \, \underset{q}{dF}^{\lambda_1 \dots \lambda_q} \tag{14.2}$$

over a region τ_q of an X_q in X_n in R is invariant with every point transformation generated by $v^\kappa\, dt$ independently of the choice of τ_q. This follows from the fact that in the process of dragging along, the coordinates of the points of τ_q and the components of $w_{\lambda_1 \dots \lambda_q}$ do not change their values. The expression (14.2) with free choice of τ_q is called an *absolute integral invariant of dimension q of v^κ*. Of course the invariant can also be written with the corresponding contravariant $(n-q)$-vector density instead of $w_{\lambda_1 \dots \lambda_q}$.

The absolute invariance of a field with respect to v^κ is generally lost if v^κ is replaced by σv^κ. If, for instance, $\mathfrak{P}^{\kappa_1 \dots \kappa_p}_{\cdot\;\cdot\;\cdot\;\lambda_1 \dots \lambda_q}$ is absolutely invariant with respect to v^κ its Lie derivative with respect to σv^κ is

$$\sum_{i=1}^{i=q} \mathfrak{P}^{\kappa_1 \dots \kappa_p}_{\cdot\;\cdot\;\cdot\;\lambda_1 \dots \lambda_{i-1} \rho \lambda_{i+1} \dots \lambda_q} v^\rho \partial_{\lambda_i} \sigma - \sum_{j=1}^{j=p} \mathfrak{P}^{\kappa_1 \dots \kappa_{j-1} \sigma \kappa_{j+1} \dots \kappa_p}_{\cdot\;\cdot\;\cdot\;\lambda_1 \dots \lambda_q} v^{\kappa_j} \partial_\sigma \sigma + \\ + \mathfrak{k} \mathfrak{P}^{\kappa_1 \dots \kappa_p}_{\cdot\;\cdot\;\cdot\;\lambda_1 \dots \lambda_q} v^\mu \partial_\mu \sigma \tag{14.3}$$

and this expression is in general not zero for every choice of σ if $\mathfrak{P}$ is not a scalar. Hence the absolute invariance of a field with respect to v^κ does not by any means involve invariance with all transformations which leave the stream-lines of the field v^κ invariant. A field with this more general invariance is called *absolutely invariant with respect to* $\lfloor v^\kappa \rfloor$. Hence the field $\mathfrak{P}$ is absolutely invariant with respect to $\lfloor v^\kappa \rfloor$ if it is absolutely invariant with respect to v^κ, and moreover

$$\sum_{i=1}^{i=q} \mathfrak{P}^{\kappa_1 \dots \kappa_p}_{\cdot\;\cdot\;\cdot\;\lambda_1 \dots \lambda_{i-1} \rho \lambda_{i+1} \dots \lambda_q} v^\rho A^\mu_{\lambda_i} - \sum_{j=1}^{j=p} \mathfrak{P}^{\kappa_1 \dots \kappa_{j-1} \mu \kappa_{j+1} \dots \kappa_p}_{\cdot\;\cdot\;\cdot\;\lambda_1 \dots \lambda_q} v^{\kappa_j} + \\ + \mathfrak{k} \mathfrak{P}^{\kappa_1 \dots \kappa_p}_{\cdot\;\cdot\;\cdot\;\lambda_1 \dots \lambda_q} v^\mu = 0. \tag{14.4}$$

There exist values of p, q, and $\mathfrak{k}$ for which (14.4) can only be satisfied for $\mathfrak{P} = 0$, e.g. $p = 2$, $q = 0$, $\mathfrak{k} \neq 1$ or 2; and $p = 1$, $q = 1$, $\mathfrak{k} > 1$, $n \geqslant 2$ (cf. III, Exx. 2, 3). For covariant q-vectors (14.4) takes the form

$$v^{\mu} w_{\mu\lambda_2\ldots\lambda_q} = 0. \tag{14.5}$$

Hence a scalar, absolutely invariant with respect to v^{κ} is always absolutely invariant with respect to $\lfloor v^{\kappa} \rfloor$ and a covariant n-vector can never be absolutely invariant with respect to $\lfloor v^{\kappa} \rfloor$.

For contravariant p-vector densities of weight $+1$ (14.4) takes the form

$$\mathfrak{w}^{[\kappa_1\ldots\kappa_p} v^{\kappa]} = 0. \tag{14.6}$$

Hence a scalar density of weight $+1$ is never absolutely invariant with respect to $\lfloor v^{\kappa} \rfloor$ and an n-vector density, absolutely invariant with respect to v^{κ} is always absolutely invariant with respect to $\lfloor v^{\kappa} \rfloor$.

From the conditions (14.5) and (14.6) follows the theorem

THEOREM II.14. *If a covariant q-vector, $q \geqslant 1$, is absolutely invariant with respect to v^{κ} its transvection by v^{κ} is absolutely invariant with respect to $\lfloor v^{\kappa} \rfloor$.*

If a contravariant p-vector density of weight $+1$, $p \leqslant n-1$, is absolutely invariant with respect to v^{κ}, its alternating product with v^{κ} is absolutely invariant with respect to $\lfloor v^{\kappa} \rfloor$.

If a scalar density of weight $+1$ is absolutely invariant with respect to v^{κ} its product when multiplied by v^{κ} is absolutely invariant with respect to $\lfloor v^{\kappa} \rfloor$.

From (13.15) and (14.4) we may conclude that a scalar is absolutely invariant with respect to $\lfloor v^{\kappa} \rfloor$ if and only if it is a solution of the linear partial differential equation

$$v^{\mu} \partial_{\mu} f = 0. \tag{14.7}$$

Its gradient is also absolutely invariant with respect to $\lfloor v^{\kappa} \rfloor$, for by differentiating (14.7) we get

$$v^{\nu} \partial_{\nu} \partial_{\mu} f + (\partial_{\nu} f) \partial_{\mu} v^{\nu} = 0. \tag{14.8}$$

But $\overset{1}{f} \partial_{\lambda} \overset{2}{f}$ is also absolutely invariant with respect to $\lfloor v^{\kappa} \rfloor$ if $\overset{1}{f}$ and $\overset{2}{f}$ are both solutions of (14.7) as is seen from

$$v^{\mu} \partial_{\mu} (\overset{1}{f} \partial_{\lambda} \overset{2}{f}) + \overset{1}{f} \partial_{\mu} \overset{2}{f} \partial_{\lambda} v^{\mu} = \overset{1}{f} v^{\mu} \partial_{\mu} \partial_{\lambda} \overset{2}{f} - \overset{1}{f} v^{\mu} \partial_{\lambda} \partial_{\mu} \overset{2}{f} = 0. \tag{14.9}$$

Consequently we have the theorem

THEOREM II.15. *Every quantity, which can be derived from the solutions of (14.7) and their gradients by addition and multiplication only, is absolutely invariant with respect to $\lfloor v^{\kappa} \rfloor$.*

This theorem is a special case of the following more general theorem which can be derived from (14.1) and (14.4):

THEOREM II.16. *Every quantity that can be derived from quantities which are absolutely invariant with respect to $\lfloor v^\kappa \rfloor$, by addition and multiplication only, is absolutely invariant with respect to $\lfloor v^\kappa \rfloor$.*

If $w_{\lambda_1 \dots \lambda_q}$ is absolutely invariant with respect to $\lfloor v^\kappa \rfloor$ the integral, I_q, defined by (14.2) is called an *absolute integral invariant of dimension q of* $\lfloor v^\kappa \rfloor$. The value of an absolute integral invariant of $\lfloor v^\kappa \rfloor$ depends only on the system of *stream-lines*† of v^κ enclosed by the $(q-1)$-dimensional boundary of τ_q. If τ_q is transformed in such a way that no stream-lines are lost or gained, the integral does not change.

By means of integral invariants two other kinds of invariant covariant q-vectors can be formed. If the field $w_{\lambda_1 \dots \lambda_q}$ satisfies the conditions

$$\underset{L}{D} D w = 0 \tag{14.10}$$

it follows from the theorem of Stokes, II.13, that the integral of $\underset{L}{D} w$ over every *closed* X_q vanishes, without it being necessary that the integral of w over this X_q is zero. Consequently the integral of w over every *closed* X_q is invariant if X_q is removed over $v^\kappa dt$. In this case, i.e. if (14.10) holds, w (and the corresponding field $\mathfrak{w}$) is called a *relative invariant* with respect to v^κ and the integral invariant found with w (or $\mathfrak{w}$) a *relative integral invariant of dimension q of* v^κ. The difference between a relative invariant field and an absolute invariant field is, therefore, that the integrals of a relative invariant field over every *closed* τ_q are invariant, but not necessarily those over a τ_q which is not closed.

If the integral of w over every closed τ_q is invariant, from the theorem of Stokes, the integral of Dw over every τ_{q+1} is invariant. Conversely, the relative invariance of w follows from the absolute invariance of Dw. To prove this converse, we show that the operators D and $\underset{L}{D}$ are commutable:

$$\underset{L}{D} D w = D \underset{L}{D} w. \tag{14.11}$$

If w is a scalar the commutability is obvious. Since both operators obey the rules of Leibniz, the relation has only to be proved for a vector w_λ. On one side we have

$$2 \underset{L}{D} D w = 2 v^\kappa \partial_\kappa \partial_{[\mu} w_{\lambda]} + (\partial_\rho w_\lambda) \partial_\mu v^\rho + (\partial_\mu w_\rho) \partial_\lambda v^\rho - \\ - (\partial_\lambda w_\rho) \partial_\mu v^\rho - (\partial_\rho w_\mu) \partial_\lambda v^\rho \tag{14.12}$$

and on the other side

$$\begin{aligned} 2 D \underset{L}{D} w &= 2 (\partial_{[\mu} v^\rho) \partial_{|\rho|} w_{\lambda]} + 2 v^\kappa \partial_\kappa \partial_{[\mu} w_{\lambda]} + 2 (\partial_{[\mu} w_{|\rho|}) \partial_{\lambda]} v^\rho \\ &= 2 v^\kappa \partial_\kappa \partial_{[\mu} w_{\lambda]} + (\partial_\rho w_\lambda) \partial_\mu v^\rho - (\partial_\rho w_\mu) \partial_\lambda v^\rho + \\ &\quad + (\partial_\mu w_\rho) \partial_\lambda v^\rho - (\partial_\lambda w_\rho) \partial_\mu v^\rho. \end{aligned} \tag{14.13}$$

† Cf. III, § 3.

Of course the operators D and $\underset{L}{D}$ are also commutable if they are applied to a contravariant p-vector density of weight $+1$. Accordingly we call $\mathfrak{w}^{\kappa_1 \ldots \kappa_p}$ *relatively invariant with respect to* v^κ if

$$\underset{L}{D}D\mathfrak{w} = D\underset{L}{D}\mathfrak{w} = 0. \tag{14.14}$$

$\mathfrak{w}$ is relatively invariant if and only if the corresponding field w is relatively invariant.

Following the commutability of D and $\underset{L}{D}$ we have the theorem

THEOREM II.17. *If a covariant q-vector is relatively invariant with respect to v^κ, its rotation is absolutely invariant with respect to v^κ and vice versa.*

If a contravariant p-vector density of weight $+1$ is relatively invariant with respect to v^κ, its divergence is absolutely invariant with respect to v^κ and vice versa.

Relative invariance, like absolute invariance, is in general lost if v^κ is multiplied by a scalar σ. If the relative invariance is preserved for every choice of σ the field is called *relatively invariant with respect to* $\lfloor v^\kappa \rfloor$ and the integral belonging to it is called a *relative integral invariant with respect to* $\lfloor v^\kappa \rfloor$. A field $w_{\lambda_1 \ldots \lambda_q}$ is relatively invariant with respect to $\lfloor v^\kappa \rfloor$ if and only if Dw is absolutely invariant with respect to $\lfloor v^\kappa \rfloor$. Hence the necessary and sufficient conditions for the field w to be relatively invariant with respect to $\lfloor v^\kappa \rfloor$ is

$$\begin{aligned} \underset{L}{D}Dw &= 0, \\ TDw &= 0, \end{aligned} \tag{14.15}$$

T symbolizing the operation of transvection with v^κ. In the case of absolute invariance with respect to v^κ combined with relative invariance with respect to $\lfloor v^\kappa \rfloor$ the necessary and sufficient conditions are

$$\begin{aligned} \underset{L}{D}w &= 0, \\ TDw &= 0, \end{aligned} \tag{14.16}$$

and $Dw = 0$ represents a non-trivial case.

Since

$$\begin{aligned} q\partial_{[\lambda_1} v^\mu w_{|\mu|\lambda_2 \ldots \lambda_q]} &= q(\partial_{[\lambda_1} v^\mu) w_{|\mu|\lambda_2 \ldots \lambda_q]} + q v^\mu \partial_{[\lambda_1} w_{|\mu|\lambda_2 \ldots \lambda_q]} \\ &= \underset{L}{D} w_{\lambda_1 \ldots \lambda_q} - v^\mu \partial_\mu w_{\lambda_1 \ldots \lambda_q} + q v^\mu \partial_{[\lambda_1} w_{|\mu|\lambda_2 \ldots \lambda_q]} \\ &= \underset{L}{D} w_{\lambda_1 \ldots \lambda_q} - (q+1) v^\mu \partial_{[\mu} w_{\lambda_1 \ldots \lambda_q]}, \end{aligned} \tag{14.17}$$

we have the identity

$$TDw = -DTw + \underset{L}{D}w. \tag{14.18}$$

Hence the operators T and D are commutable if and only if they are applied to a field which is absolutely invariant with respect to v^κ.

The following table gives a survey of the effect of the operators D, T, DT, and TD when applied to absolutely and relatively invariant quantities.

	I Rel. inv. w.r. to v^κ	*II* Abs. inv. w.r. to v^κ	*III* Abs. inv. w.r. to v^κ Rel. inv. w.r. to $\lfloor v^\kappa \rfloor$	*IV* Rel. inv. w.r. to $\lfloor v^\kappa \rfloor$	*V* Abs. inv. w.r. to $\lfloor v^\kappa \rfloor$
n. and s. conditions	$\underset{L}{D}Dw = 0$	$\underset{L}{D}w = 0$	$\underset{L}{D}w = 0$, $TDw = 0$	$\underset{L}{D}Dw = 0$, $TDw = 0$	$\underset{L}{D}w = 0$, $Tw = 0$
D	II	II	V	V	V
T	—	V	V	—	*0*
DT	—	V	*0*	IV	*0*
TD	V	V	*0*	*0*	*0*

(14.19)

The same holds for contravariant p-vector densities of weight $+1$ if T symbolizes the alternated multiplication with v^κ.

We see from this table that every quantity which is relatively or absolutely invariant with respect to v^κ, is either absolutely invariant with respect to $\lfloor v^\kappa \rfloor$ or it can be used to form a quantity with that invariance.

There is another important theorem concerning absolute and relative invariance which is stated here although the proof has to be postponed until the next chapter:

THEOREM II.18. *If the q-vector $w_{\lambda_1 \ldots \lambda_q}$ is relatively invariant with respect to v^κ and consequently* Rot w *is absolutely invariant, there always exists a q-vector $'w_{\lambda_1 \ldots \lambda_q}$, absolutely invariant with respect to v^κ, such that* Rot $'w$ = Rot w.

If the p-vector density $\mathfrak{w}^{\kappa_1 \ldots \kappa_p}$ of weight $+1$ is relatively invariant with respect to v^κ and consequently Div $\mathfrak{w}$ *is absolutely invariant, there always exists a p-vector density $'\mathfrak{w}^{\kappa_1 \ldots \kappa_p}$ of weight $+1$, absolutely invariant with respect to v^κ, such that* Div $'\mathfrak{w}$ = Div $\mathfrak{w}$.

As will be shown in the next chapter the importance of invariant quantities with respect to v^κ or $\lfloor v^\kappa \rfloor$ is due to the fact that the solution of the differential equations (13.4) and (14.7) can be simplified if such a quantity is known.

To close this section we will deal with some properties of invariant quantities which have to be used in the following chapter.

For $q = n$ it is evident that there exists no n-vector $w_{\lambda_1 \ldots \lambda_n}$ which is absolutely invariant with respect to $\lfloor v^\kappa \rfloor$ because $Tw \neq 0$. The only remaining non-trivial case is that of absolute invariance with respect to v^κ. If $\mathfrak{w}$ is the corresponding scalar density of weight $+1$, the necessary and sufficient condition for this invariance is, as follows from (13.19),

$$\partial_\mu \mathfrak{w} v^\mu = 0. \tag{14.20}$$

A density of weight $+1$ satisfying these conditions is called an *integrating factor* of the differential equations (13.4) and (14.7). In the next chapter it will be shown that such integrating factors always exist, and how they can be used to simplify the process of integration. The vector density $\mathfrak{w} v^\kappa$ of weight $+1$ is absolutely invariant with respect to $\lfloor v^\kappa \rfloor$. In fact $v^{[\kappa} \mathfrak{w} v^{\lambda]} = 0$ and according to (14.20) we have

$$\begin{aligned} \underset{L}{D} \mathfrak{w} v^\kappa &= v^\mu \partial_\mu \mathfrak{w} v^\kappa - \mathfrak{w} v^\mu \partial_\mu v^\kappa + \mathfrak{w} v^\kappa \partial_\mu v^\mu \\ &= v^\mu v^\kappa \partial_\mu \mathfrak{w} - v^\kappa v^\mu \partial_\mu \mathfrak{w} = 0. \end{aligned} \tag{14.21}$$

For $q = n-1$ there are three non-trivial cases, characterized by the following necessary and sufficient conditions for the corresponding contravariant vector density $\mathfrak{w}^\kappa$ of weight $+1$:

relative invariance with respect to v^κ: $\quad D\underset{L}{D}\mathfrak{w} = 0;$ (14.22)

absolute invariance with respect to v^κ: $\quad \underset{L}{D}\mathfrak{w}^\kappa = 0;$ (14.23)

absolute invariance with respect to $\lfloor v^\kappa \rfloor$: $\quad \underset{L}{D}\mathfrak{w}^\kappa = 0; \quad T\mathfrak{w}^\kappa = 0.$ (14.24)

From (14.24) it follows that

$$\begin{aligned} v^\mu \partial_\mu \mathfrak{w}^\kappa &= \mathfrak{w}^\mu \partial_\mu v^\kappa - \mathfrak{w}^\kappa \partial_\mu v^\mu = 2\partial_\mu \mathfrak{w}^{[\mu} v^{\kappa]} - v^\kappa \partial_\mu \mathfrak{w}^\mu + v^\mu \partial_\mu \mathfrak{w}^\kappa \\ &= -v^\kappa \partial_\mu \mathfrak{w}^\mu + v^\mu \partial_\mu \mathfrak{w}^\kappa \end{aligned} \tag{14.25}$$

or

$$D\mathfrak{w} = \partial_\mu \mathfrak{w}^\mu = 0. \tag{14.26}$$

The case of absolute invariance with respect to $\lfloor v^\kappa \rfloor$ has already been mentioned above, $\mathfrak{w}^\kappa / v^\kappa$ being there an integrating factor. In the case of relative invariance with respect to v^κ there exists a scalar density $\mathfrak{p} = \partial_\mu \mathfrak{w}^\mu$, absolutely invariant with respect to v^κ, and this scalar density is an integrating factor of (13.4) and (14.7). Here, according to Theorem II.18, there exists a vector density of weight $+1$, absolutely invariant with respect to v^κ, with divergence $\mathfrak{p}$. In the case of absolute invariance with respect to v^κ the following equations hold

$$\mathfrak{p} \overset{\text{def}}{=} \partial_\mu \mathfrak{w}^\mu, \qquad \partial_\mu \mathfrak{p} v^\mu = 0,$$
$$v^\mu \partial_\mu \mathfrak{w}^\kappa - \mathfrak{w}^\mu \partial_\mu v^\kappa + \mathfrak{w}^\kappa \partial_\mu v^\mu = 0, \tag{14.27}$$

by means of which it may readily be proved that the contravariant bivector density $2v^{[\kappa}\mathfrak{w}^{\lambda]}$ of weight $+1$ is absolutely invariant with respect to $\lfloor v^\kappa \rfloor$. The divergence of this quantity is

$$\partial_\lambda v^\lambda \mathfrak{w}^\kappa - \partial_\lambda v^\kappa \mathfrak{w}^\lambda = (\partial_\lambda v^\lambda)\mathfrak{w}^\kappa + v^\lambda \partial_\lambda \mathfrak{w}^\kappa - (\partial_\lambda v^\kappa)\mathfrak{w}^\lambda - \mathfrak{p} v^\kappa = -\mathfrak{p} v^\kappa. \tag{14.28}$$

For $q = 1$ the conditions for absolute invariance with respect to v^κ are

$$v^\mu \partial_\mu w_\lambda + w_\mu \partial_\lambda v^\mu = 0 \tag{14.29}$$

and from this equation we get by transvection with v^λ

$$v^\lambda v^\mu \partial_\mu w_\lambda + w_\mu v^\lambda \partial_\lambda v^\mu = v^\mu \partial_\mu (w_\lambda v^\lambda) = 0. \tag{14.30}$$

Hence $w_\lambda v^\lambda$ is either a constant or a solution of (14.7). If $w_\lambda v^\lambda = 0$, w_λ is absolutely invariant with respect to $\lfloor v^\kappa \rfloor$.

EXERCISES†

1. If M_1 and M_2 are two manifolds in an $\mathfrak{N}(\underset{0}{\xi^\kappa})$, both of dimension m in $\underset{0}{\xi^\kappa}$, and if M_2 is contained in M_1, there exists an $\mathfrak{N}(\underset{0}{\xi^\kappa})$ where M_1 and M_2 coincide.

2. If the system

$$(a) \qquad F^{\mathfrak{a}}(\xi^\kappa) = 0 \quad (\mathfrak{a} = 1,..., N_1),$$
$$(b) \qquad G^{\mathfrak{b}}(\xi^\kappa) = 0 \quad (\mathfrak{b} = 1,..., N_2) \tag{2 α}$$

is regular in $\underset{0}{\xi^\kappa}$, it is not necessary that the system ($2\alpha a$) should be regular in $\underset{0}{\xi^\kappa}$. Give an example.

3. If the system

$$(a) \qquad F^{\mathfrak{a}_1}(\xi^{\kappa_1}) = 0,$$
$$(b) \qquad G^{\mathfrak{a}_2}(\xi^{\kappa_1}, \xi^{\kappa_2}) = 0, \tag{3 α}$$
$$(c) \qquad H^{\mathfrak{a}_3}(\xi^{\kappa_1}, \xi^{\kappa_2}, \xi^{\kappa_3}) = 0$$

$$(\mathfrak{a}_1 = 1,..., N_1;\ \mathfrak{a}_2 = N_1+1,..., N_1+N_2;\ \mathfrak{a}_3 = N_1+N_2+1,..., N_1+N_2+N_3;$$
$$\kappa_1 = 1,..., n_1;\ \kappa_2 = n_1+1,..., n_1+n_2;\ \kappa_3 = n_1+n_2+1,..., n_1+n_2+n_3),$$

is regular in $\underset{0}{\xi^{\kappa_1}}, \underset{0}{\xi^{\kappa_2}}, \underset{0}{\xi^{\kappa_3}}$ and if it has a minimal regular equivalent subsystem containing equations of ($3\alpha a$) and ($3\alpha b$), the systems ($3\alpha a$) and ($3\alpha a, b$) are regular in $\underset{0}{\xi^{\kappa_1}}$ and $\underset{0}{\xi^{\kappa_1}}, \underset{0}{\xi^{\kappa_2}}$ respectively.

4. A coordinate system (h) is holonomic if and only if‡

$$A_j^\mu A_i^\lambda \partial_{[\mu} A_{\lambda]}^h = 0 \quad (h, i, j = 1,..., n). \tag{4 α}$$

† Cf. the suggestions at the end of the book.
‡ Cf. Schouten and Struik, 1935. 1, p. 68.

5. The pentaspherical coordinates of Darboux in ordinary space are supernumerary coordinates with $\epsilon_1 = 1$; $\epsilon_2 = 1$.†

6. In every point of an X_m in X_n a simple covariant $(n-m)$-vector $f_{\lambda_1\ldots\lambda_{n-m}}$ is given, tangent to the X_m. If $w_{\lambda_1\ldots\lambda_q}$ is a q-vector of X_n $(q \leqslant m)$, its section with E_m is

$$'w_{b_1\ldots b_q} = B^{\lambda_1}_{b_1}\ldots B^{\lambda_q}_{b_q} w_{\lambda_1\ldots\lambda_q}$$
$$= \frac{(q+n-m)!}{q!(n-m)!}\frac{B^{\lambda_1}_{b_1}\ldots B^{\lambda_q}_{b_q} w_{[\lambda_1\ldots\lambda_q} f_{\lambda_{m+1}\ldots\lambda_n]}}{f_{\lambda_{m+1}\ldots\lambda_n}} \quad (b_1,\ldots,b_q = 1,\ldots,m). \tag{6α}$$

In the manifold of all covariant q-vectors of X_m the

$$\xi^\kappa, \qquad {}''w_{\lambda_1\ldots\lambda_q\lambda_{m+1}\ldots\lambda_n} \stackrel{\text{def}}{=} w_{[\lambda_1\ldots\lambda_q} f_{\lambda_{m+1}\ldots\lambda_n]} \tag{6β}$$

form a system of $n+\binom{n}{q+n-m}$ supernumerary coordinates with

$$\epsilon_1 = n-m+\binom{n}{q+n-m}-\binom{m}{q}, \qquad \epsilon_2 = 0.$$

7. Prove the identity‡

$$\int\limits_{\tau_q} (\partial_\mu \mathfrak{u}^{[\kappa_1\ldots\kappa_{p+1}}) \underset{q}{dF}^{|\mu|\lambda_2\ldots\lambda_q]} = \int\limits_{\tau_{q-1}} \mathfrak{u}^{[\kappa_1\ldots\kappa_{p+1}} \underset{q-1}{dF}^{\lambda_2\ldots\lambda_q]} \quad (p = n-q). \tag{7α}$$

8. If $\overset{1}{\underset{L}{D}}$, $\overset{2}{\underset{L}{D}}$, and $\overset{3}{\underset{L}{D}}$ are the symbols of the Lie derivatives belonging to $\underset{1}{v}^\kappa$, $\underset{2}{v}^\kappa$, and $\underset{3}{v}^\kappa \stackrel{\text{def}}{=} 2\underset{[1}{v}^\mu \partial_{|\mu|} \underset{2]}{v}^\kappa$, prove that

$$2\overset{[1}{\underset{L}{D}}\overset{2]}{\underset{L}{D}}u^\kappa = \overset{3}{\underset{L}{D}}u^\kappa. \tag{8α}$$

9. If an X_p and an X_q $(p \leqslant q)$ in X_n contain the point $\underset{0}{\xi}^\kappa$, the intersection of X_p and X_q in a sufficiently small $\mathfrak{N}(\underset{0}{\xi}^\kappa)$ consists of $\underset{0}{\xi}^\kappa$ and a finite number of X_s's; $s = p+q-n,\ldots,p$ for $p+q-n > 0$ and $s = 1,\ldots,p$ for $p+q-n \leqslant 0$. It is possible that $\underset{0}{\xi}^\kappa$ is a point of one or more of the X_s's. If $\underset{0}{\xi}^\kappa$ is not a point of one particular X_s, in every $\mathfrak{N}(\underset{0}{\xi}^\kappa)$ there is at least one point of this X_s.

10. If a system of equations

$$F^\omega(\xi^\kappa) = 0 \quad (\omega = 1,\ldots,N) \tag{10α}$$

with functions F^ω analytic in the null-point $\underset{0}{\xi}^\kappa$ is irregular in $\underset{0}{\xi}^\kappa$, there always exists a finite number of systems, each minimal regular in a point of every given $\mathfrak{N}(\underset{0}{\xi}^\kappa)$, having together the same null points as (10α) in a sufficiently small $\mathfrak{N}(\underset{0}{\xi}^\kappa)$.

† Cf. Klein 93. 1, p. 107; *Enz. d. Math. Wiss.* III. i. 1, p. 663.
‡ Cf. v. Weyssenhoff 1937. 1; Schouten and v. Dantzig, 1940. 1.

III

THE OUTER PROBLEM†

1. Definitions of the outer and inner problems

IN an X_n an E_p-field may be given either by the connecting quantity B_b^κ or by C_λ^x ($b = 1,..., \mathrm{p}$; $x = \mathrm{p}+1,..., \mathrm{n}$) (cf. II, § 10). We suppose that, for some definite choice of the coordinate systems (a) and (x), B_b^κ and C_λ^x are analytic in $\mathfrak{N}(\overset{0}{\xi}{}^\kappa)$, and that they have, in that region, the highest rank (p and $n-p$ respectively). If then we allow only reversible linear transformations of (a) and (x) whose coefficients are analytic in $\mathfrak{N}(\overset{0}{\xi}{}^\kappa)$, $B_{b'}^\kappa$ and $C_\lambda^{x'}$ are analytic for every choice of (b') and (x') in $\mathfrak{N}(\overset{0}{\xi}{}^\kappa)$ and have the highest possible rank in that region.

An X_m ($m \geqslant p$) is said to *envelop the E_p-field* if its tangent E_m contains, at every point, the local E_p of the field. Now the *outer problem* for an E_p-field is the problem of the determination of all *enveloping* X_m's ($m \geqslant p$). The normal systems of enveloping X_m's, called *enveloping normal systems*, are most interesting.

The system of $n-m$ equations

$$F^{\mathfrak{x}}(\xi^\kappa) = \text{const.} \quad (\mathfrak{x} = \mathrm{m}+1,..., \mathrm{n}), \tag{1.1}$$

minimal regular in $\overset{0}{\xi}{}^\kappa$, represents an enveloping normal system of X_m's in an $\mathfrak{N}(\overset{0}{\xi}{}^\kappa)$ if and only if

$$B_b^\mu \partial_\mu F^{\mathfrak{x}} = 0 \quad (b = 1,..., \mathrm{p};\ \mathfrak{x} = \mathrm{m}+1,..., \mathrm{n}); \tag{1.2}$$

in other words, if the $F^{\mathfrak{x}}$ are solutions of the system of p homogeneous linear partial differential equations

$$B_b^\mu \partial_\mu f = 0 \quad (b = 1,..., \mathrm{p}) \tag{1.3}$$

which can also be written in the form

$$C^{\mathrm{p}+1}_{[\lambda_{p+1}} \cdots C^{\mathrm{n}}_{\lambda_n} \partial_{\mu]} f = 0. \tag{1.4}$$

It is important to note that a system given in the form

$$w_{[\lambda_1 \ldots \lambda_q} \partial_{\mu]} f = 0 \quad (p = n-q), \tag{1.5}$$

where $w_{\lambda_1 \ldots \lambda_q}$ is a *simple* q-vector, even though it consists of $\binom{n}{q+1}$

† General references: Lie 1876. 1; 1877. 1; v. Weber 1900. 1; Goursat 1915. 1, 1918. 1, 1921. 1; Engel and Faber 1932. 1; Kähler 1934. 1; Burstin 1935. 3.

equations, always contains just $p = n-q$ linearly independent equations; this follows from the form

$$w_{\lambda_1 \ldots \lambda_q} E^{\lambda_1 \ldots \lambda_q \mu_1 \ldots \mu_p} \partial_{\mu_1} f = 0 \tag{1.6}$$

which is equivalent to (1.5). A suitable form of these independent equations can be obtained in the following way. By interchanging the indices κ it can always be arranged that $w_{1 \ldots q} \neq 0$. Now of the $\binom{n}{q+1}$ equations (1.5) only those which contain the q indices $1, \ldots, q$ and *one* of the other indices are written down. These are just the $n-q$ equations

$$\begin{aligned} w_{[1 \ldots q} \partial_{q+1]} f &= 0, \\ \cdot \quad \cdot \quad \cdot & \quad \cdot \quad \cdot \\ w_{[1 \ldots q} \partial_{n]} f &= 0. \end{aligned} \tag{1.7}$$

Obviously they are linearly independent, each one of them containing a derivative of f which does not occur in the other equations. A suitable choice of the q indices may often lead to simplifications.

Since the gradients of functionally independent scalars are linearly independent (cf. II, § 3) the greatest number $n-\mu$ of functionally independent solutions of (1.3) has to be $\leqslant n-p$. If $\overset{\mathfrak{a}}{f}$ ($\mathfrak{a} = 1, \ldots, \mathrm{n}-\mu$) is such a system of independent solutions, the matrix of $\partial_\lambda \overset{\mathfrak{a}}{f}$ has the rank $n-\mu$ and this implies that the equations

$$\overset{\mathfrak{a}}{f} = \text{const.} \quad (\mathfrak{a} = 1, \ldots, \mathrm{n}-\mu) \tag{1.8}$$

represent a normal system of X_μ's in $\mathfrak{N}(\overset{0}{\xi^\kappa})$ enveloping the E_p-field. There cannot be a normal system of $X_{\mu-1}$'s, because (1.3) would then have more than $n-\mu$ independent solutions. μ is an arithmetic invariant of the E_p-field and of the system (1.3) and the E_p-field is said to be *X_μ-enveloped.*

Now let F be any solution of (1.3). Then F has to be a function of the $\overset{\mathfrak{a}}{f}$, since there are no more than $n-\mu$ functionally independent solutions. Conversely, if F is a function of the $\overset{\mathfrak{a}}{f}$, we have

$$\partial_\mu F = \partial F / \partial \overset{\mathfrak{a}}{f} \, \partial_\mu \overset{\mathfrak{a}}{f} \quad (\mathfrak{a} = 1, \ldots, \mathrm{n}-\mu) \tag{1.9}$$

and consequently F is a solution of (1.3).

The system of $n-p$ linear total differential equations

$$C^x_\mu d\xi^\mu = 0 \quad (x = \mathrm{p}+1, \ldots, \mathrm{n}) \tag{1.10}$$

or, in an equivalent form,

$$B^{[\kappa_1}_{\mathrm{1}} \ldots B^{\kappa_p}_{\mathrm{p}} d\xi^{\kappa]} = 0 \tag{1.11}$$

and the system (1.3), are said to be *adjoint to each other*. If for a function $F(\xi^\kappa)$ the equation

$$d\xi^\lambda \partial_\lambda F = 0 \quad (\mu = 1) \tag{1.12}$$

follows from (1.10), F is called an *integral function* of (1.10) and the equation

$$F = \text{const.} \tag{1.13}$$

an *integral* of (1.10). If F is an integral function of (1.10) it follows from (1.10) and (1.12) that F is a solution of (1.3). Conversely, if F is a solution of (1.3) it follows from (1.10) and (1.12) that F is an integral function of (1.10). Hence the determination of all integral functions of (1.10) and the determination of all solutions of (1.3) constitute the same problem and this is equivalent to the outer problem as far as normal systems of X_m's are concerned.

An X_m $(m \leqslant p)$ is said to be *enveloped by an E_p-field* or to be an *integral-X_m of the E_p-field*, if the tangent E_m is contained at every point in the local E_p of the field. Now the *inner problem* for an E_p-field is the problem of the determination of all enveloped X_m's $(m \leqslant p)$. The normal systems of enveloped X_m's, called *enveloped normal systems*, are most interesting.

Every linear element in an enveloped X_m lies in the local E_p of the field. Hence the system of $n-m$ equations

$$F^{\mathfrak{x}}(\xi^\kappa) = \text{const.} \quad (\mathfrak{x} = \mathrm{m}+1,\ldots,\mathrm{n}), \tag{1.14}$$

minimal regular in $\underset{0}{\xi^\kappa}$, represents an enveloped normal system of X_m's in an $\mathfrak{N}(\underset{0}{\xi^\kappa})$ if and only if (1.10) follows from

$$d\xi^\mu \partial_\mu F^{\mathfrak{x}} = 0 \quad (\mathfrak{x} = \mathrm{m}+1,\ldots,\mathrm{n}). \tag{1.15}$$

If

$$\xi^\kappa = \phi^\kappa(\eta^{\mathfrak{a}}, \overset{\mathfrak{x}}{p}) \quad (\mathfrak{a} = 1,\ldots,\mathrm{m};\ \mathfrak{x} = \mathrm{m}+1,\ldots,\mathrm{n}) \tag{1.16}$$

is a parametric form of the ∞^{n-m} X_m's of the normal system, minimal regular in $\underset{0}{\eta^{\mathfrak{a}}}$ with the $n-m$ parameters $\overset{\mathfrak{x}}{p}$, we have, independently of the choice of the $\overset{\mathfrak{x}}{p}$,

$$d\xi^\kappa = (\partial_{\mathfrak{a}} \phi^\kappa)\, d\eta^{\mathfrak{a}} \quad (\mathfrak{a} = 1,\ldots,\mathrm{m}); \tag{1.17}$$

and from this we may conclude that the X_m's form an enveloped normal system if and only if, for every choice of the parameters $\overset{\mathfrak{x}}{p}$,

$$C^{x}_{\mu}\{\phi^\kappa(\eta^{\mathfrak{a}}, \overset{\mathfrak{x}}{p})\} \partial_{\mathfrak{b}} \phi^\mu = 0 \quad (\mathfrak{a}, \mathfrak{b} = 1,\ldots,\mathrm{m};\ \mathfrak{x} = \mathrm{m}+1,\ldots,\mathrm{n}). \tag{1.18}$$

From this it is seen that in the case of the inner problem we also get a system of partial differential equations of the first order but that this system contains more than one unknown function.

If $\nu \leqslant p$ is the maximum value of m, the E_p-field is called X_ν-*enveloping*. ν is an arithmetic invariant of the field and of the systems (1.3) and (1.10). If $\nu = p$ then $\mu = p$ and the E_p-field is simultaneously X_p-enveloped and X_p-enveloping. Such an E_p-field is called X_p-*forming*. In this case there exists one and only one enveloped and enveloping normal system of X_p's and all enveloped normal systems of X_m's $(m < p)$ are obtained by section of this normal system with an arbitrary normal system of X_{n-p+m}'s. The inner problem is solved if we have the solution of the outer problem only if $\nu = p$. But if $\nu < p$ the connexion between the two problems is more complicated.

The following survey of the necessary and sufficient conditions for enveloping and enveloped normal systems may be useful.

Enveloping normal systems

$$m \geqslant p$$

I. The $F^{\mathfrak{x}}$ are solutions of the linear system

$$B^{\mu}_{b}\partial_{\mu} f = 0 \quad (b = 1,\ldots,\mathrm{p}). \qquad (1.19)$$

II. The system

$$d\xi^{\mu}\partial_{\mu} F^{\mathfrak{x}} = 0 \quad (\mathfrak{x} = \mathrm{m}+1,\ldots,\mathrm{n}) \qquad (1.20)$$

follows from

$$C^{x}_{\mu}\, d\xi^{\mu} = 0 \quad (x = \mathrm{p}+1,\ldots,\mathrm{n}). \qquad (1.21)$$

Enveloped normal systems

$$m \leqslant p$$

I. The system

$$C^{x}_{\mu} d\xi^{\mu} = 0 \quad (x = \mathrm{p}+1,\ldots,\mathrm{n}) \qquad (1.22)$$

follows from

$$d\xi^{\mu}\partial_{\mu} F^{\mathfrak{x}} = 0 \quad (\mathfrak{x} = \mathrm{m}+1,\ldots,\mathrm{n}). \qquad (1.23)$$

II. The ϕ^{κ} are solutions of the system

$$C^{x}_{\mu}\{\phi^{\kappa}(\eta^{\mathfrak{a}}, \overset{\mathfrak{x}}{p})\}\partial_{\mathfrak{b}}\phi^{\mu} = 0 \quad (x = \mathrm{p}+1,\ldots,\mathrm{n}; \; \mathfrak{a},\mathfrak{b} = 1,\ldots,\mathrm{m}; \; \mathfrak{x} = \mathrm{m}+1,\ldots,\mathrm{n}) \qquad (1.24)$$

for all values of the parameters $\overset{\mathfrak{x}}{p}$.

There may exist enveloping and enveloped X_m's not belonging to an enveloping or enveloped normal system and this may occur for every value of m, independent of the values of μ and ν. Naturally these special enveloping or enveloped X_m's cannot be found by the processes described above.

The necessary and sufficient conditions that an X_m with the null form

$$F^{\mathfrak{x}}(\xi^{\kappa}) = 0 \quad (\mathfrak{x} = \mathrm{m}+1,\ldots,\mathrm{n}), \qquad (1.25)$$

minimal regular in $\underset{0}{\xi^{\kappa}}$, and the parametric form

$$\xi^{\kappa} = \phi^{\kappa}(\eta^{\mathfrak{a}}) \quad (\mathfrak{a} = 1,\ldots,\mathrm{m}) \qquad (1.26)$$

minimal regular in $\underset{0}{\eta^{\mathfrak{a}}}$, should be enveloping or enveloped are:

Enveloping X_m

$m \geqslant p$

I. The system

$$B_b^\mu \partial_\mu F^{\mathfrak{x}} = 0 \quad (\mathfrak{x} = \mathrm{m+1,...,n}; \; b = 1,...,\mathrm{p}) \qquad (1.27)$$

follows from

$$F^{\mathfrak{x}}(\xi^\kappa) = 0 \quad (\mathfrak{x} = \mathrm{m+1,...,n}). \qquad (1.28)$$

II. The system

$$d\xi^\mu \partial_\mu F^{\mathfrak{x}} = 0 \quad (\mathfrak{x} = \mathrm{m+1,...,n}) \qquad (1.29)$$

follows from

$$F^{\mathfrak{x}}(\xi^\kappa) = 0 \quad (\mathfrak{x} = \mathrm{m+1,...,n}; \qquad C_\mu^x d\xi^\mu = 0 \quad x = \mathrm{p+1,...,n}). \qquad (1.30)$$

Enveloped X_m

$m \leqslant p$

I. The system

$$C_\mu^x d\xi^\mu = 0 \quad (x = \mathrm{p+1,...,n}) \qquad (1.31)$$

follows from

$$\left.\begin{aligned} F^{\mathfrak{x}}(\xi^\kappa) &= 0 \\ d\xi^\mu \partial_\mu F^{\mathfrak{x}} &= 0 \end{aligned}\right\} (\mathfrak{x} = \mathrm{m+1,...,n}). \qquad (1.32)$$

II. The ϕ^κ are solutions of the system

$$C_\mu^x\{\phi^\kappa(\eta^{\mathfrak{a}})\}\partial_{\mathfrak{b}}\phi^\mu = 0 \quad (x = \mathrm{p+1,...,n}; \; \mathfrak{a},\mathfrak{b} = 1,...,\mathrm{m}). \qquad (1.33)$$

In the following sections of this chapter we consider only the outer problem. The inner problem will be dealt with in Chapter VIII.

2. Construction of a complete system†

By applying the operator $B_b^\mu \partial_\mu$ twice in succession and alternating we get $\binom{p}{2}$ homogeneous linear equations

$$0 = B_{[c}^\nu \partial_{|\nu|} B_{b]}^\mu \partial_\mu f = B_{[c}^\nu(\partial_{|\nu|} B_{b]}^\mu)\partial_\mu f + B_{[c}^\nu B_{b]}^\mu \partial_{[\nu}\partial_{\mu]} f = B_{[c}^\nu(\partial_{|\nu|} B_{b]}^\mu)\partial_\mu f$$
$$(b, c = 1,..., \mathrm{m}). \qquad (2.1)$$

Every solution of (1.3) has to satisfy these $\binom{p}{2}$ equations. Among them there will be a maximum number μ_1, linearly independent of (1.3) and of each other. If $\mu_1 = 0$ the system (1.3) and the adjoint system (1.10) are said to be *complete*. In that case, as we will see later, the E_p-field is X_p-forming. If $\mu_1 \neq 0$ the μ_1 independent equations can be added to the equations of (1.3) so as to get a new system of $p_1 = p + \mu_1 > p$ homogeneous linear equations of the form

$$B_{b_1}^\mu \partial_\mu f = 0 \quad (b_1 = 1,..., \mathrm{p}_1). \qquad (2.2)$$

This system is called the *first derived system* of (1.3) (cf. III, § 11). $B_{b_1}^\kappa$ represents an E_{p_1}-field, each E_{p_1} containing the local E_p of the field represented by B_b^κ. The system (2.2) can be treated in the same way and this leads to the second derived system of (1.3) representing an E_{p_2}-field, $p_2 = p_1 + \mu_2 \geqslant p_1$, etc. This process comes to an end by leading, after ω steps, to a complete system of $p_\omega \leqslant n$ equations. If $p_\omega = n$

† Cf. v. Weber 1900. 1, ch. ii; Goursat 1921. 1, chs. ii, iii; Engel and Faber 1932. 1, ch. i.

the system has no solutions except the trivial one $f = \text{const.}$ and we have $\mu = n$. If $p_\omega < n$ we can here only conclude that $\mu \geqslant p_\omega$. It must be noted, that $\mu_1, \ldots, \mu_\omega$ *are arithmetic invariants of the* E_p*-field and of the systems* (1.3) *and* (1.10) as well as μ.

The expression $B^\nu_{[c}\,\partial_{|\nu|}\,B^\kappa_{b]}$ is not an affinor as is seen from its transformation

$$B^{\nu'}_{[c'}\,\partial_{|\nu'|}\,B^{\kappa'}_{b']} = B^c_{c'}\,B^b_{b'}\,A^{\kappa'}_\kappa B^\nu_{[c}\,\partial_{|\nu|}\,B^\kappa_{b]} + B^\kappa_b\,A^{\kappa'}_\kappa\,B^\nu_c\,B^c_{[c'}\,\partial_{|\nu|}\,B^b_{b']}$$
$$(b, c = 1, \ldots, \mathrm{p};\; b', c' = 1', \ldots, \mathrm{p}'), \qquad (2.3)$$

but the transvection with C^x_κ

$$D_{cb}^{\cdot\cdot x} \overset{\text{def}}{=} -2B^\mu_{[c}(\partial_{|\mu|}\,B^\lambda_{b]})C^x_\lambda = +B^\mu_c\,B^\lambda_b\,C_{\mu\lambda}^{\cdot\cdot x};\;\; C_{\mu\lambda}^{\cdot\cdot x} \overset{\text{def}}{=} 2\partial_{[\mu}\,C^x_{\lambda]}$$
$$(b, c = 1, \ldots, \mathrm{p};\; x = \mathrm{p}+1, \ldots, \mathrm{n}) \qquad (2.4)$$

is an affinor and μ_1 is its x-rank. The E_p-field is X_p-forming if and only if $D_{cb}^{\cdot\cdot x}$ vanishes. The geometrical significance of μ_1 will be seen from the following considerations. At every point the affinor $D_{cb}^{\cdot\cdot x}$ associates with every contravariant bivector of the b-domain a definite contravariant vector of the x-domain. Now a contravariant bivector of the b-domain has been identified with a contravariant bivector of X_n lying in the local E_p; and a contravariant vector of the x-domain represents an E_p in the local E_n possessing the p-direction of the local E_p, but not passing through the contact point. Hence to every infinitesimal parallelogram with a sense in the local E_p through the contact point, $D_{cb}^{\cdot\cdot x}$ adds a parallel E_p in the local E_n. These two E_p's coincide if and only if the transvection of $D_{cb}^{\cdot\cdot x}$ with the bivector of the parallelogram vanishes. In this special case the E_2 of the parallelogram is said to be *holonomic* with respect to the field of p-directions (cf. VIII, § 2). In the general case the two E_p's determine an E_{p+1} through the contact point and, therefore, to every non-holonomic E_2 through the contact point corresponds a definite E_{p+1} containing the local E_p. The totality of all E_{p+1}'s corresponding to all E_2's through the contact point in the local E_p fills up the E_{p_1} of the κ-domain of $B^\kappa_{b_1}$ ($b_1 = 1, \ldots, \mathrm{p}_1$; $p_1 = p + \mu_1$). Now consider any closed curve in X_n through $\overset{}{\underset{0}{\xi}}{}^\kappa$. Through every point of this curve let an arbitrary X_q ($q = n-p$) be laid whose tangent E_q has at all points no direction in common with the local E_p. Then we get a $(q+2)$-dimensional tube with a $(q+1)$-dimensional boundary. The tangent E_{q+1} of this boundary has, at every point, just one direction in common with the local E_p. There is one, and only one, integral curve through $\underset{0}{\xi}{}^\kappa$ on this boundary and this curve is in general not closed. If the closed curve through $\underset{0}{\xi}{}^\kappa$ from which we started is the infinitesimal parallelogram mentioned above, the integral curve through $\overset{}{\underset{0}{\xi}}{}^{\kappa}$ coincides with the parallelogram if and only if the E_2 is *holonomic*. If the E_2 is *not holonomic* the integral curve coincides with the parallelogram only to a first approximation, and already to a second approximation we get an open quadrilateral. The E_{p+1} corresponding to the E_2 of the parallelogram and the tangent E_q of the X_q through $\underset{0}{\xi}{}^{\kappa}$ have just one direction in common and the quadrilateral can be closed by a straight line with that direction.

As we have seen, every given system of homogeneous linear partial differential equations can be extended until there is a complete system having the same solutions as the given system. Hence we may assume the given system to be complete. According to (2.1) and (2.4) the necessary and sufficient conditions for completeness are

$$D_{\dot{c}\dot{b}}{}^{x} \overset{\text{def}}{=} -2B^{\mu}_{[c}(\partial_{|\mu|}\, B^{\lambda}_{b]})C^{x}_{\lambda} = B^{\mu}_{c}\, B^{\lambda}_{b}\, C_{\dot{\mu}\dot{\lambda}}{}^{x} = 0$$
$$(b, c = 1,\ldots, \mathrm{p};\ x = \mathrm{p}+1,\ldots, \mathrm{n}). \quad (2.5)$$

It is our first task to prove that every complete system of p equations has just $n-p$ functionally independent solutions.

3. The solutions of one homogeneous linear partial differential equation of the first order and the integrals and integral functions of the adjoint system of $n-1$ total differential equations†

We consider an equation of the form

$$B^{\mu}\partial_{\mu} f = 0 \quad (3.1)$$

with functions B^{μ} analytic in an $\mathfrak{N}(\underset{0}{\xi}{}^{\kappa})$ and not all zero in $\underset{0}{\xi}{}^{\kappa}$. There exists an $\mathfrak{N}(\underset{0}{\xi}{}^{\kappa})$ where (3.1) represents an E_1-field. The (a)-transformations are here only the multiplications of B^{μ} with a scalar factor, analytic in an $\mathfrak{N}(\underset{0}{\xi}{}^{\kappa})$. (3.1) constitutes a complete system because the process of extension is inapplicable as there is only one equation. The adjoint system is

$$C^{x}_{\mu}\, d\xi^{\mu} = 0 \quad (x = 2,\ldots, \mathrm{n}), \quad (3.2)$$

the C^{x}_{μ} being analytic in an $\mathfrak{N}(\underset{0}{\xi}{}^{\kappa})$ and the rank of C^{x}_{μ} being $n-1$ in that region. (3.2) may also be written

$$B^{[\kappa}\, d\xi^{\lambda]} = 0 \quad (3.3)$$

or

$$d\xi^{\kappa} :: B^{\kappa}, \quad (3.4)$$

† Cf. v. Weber 1900. 1, ch. ii; Goursat 1921. 1, chs. ii, iii; Engel and Faber 1932. 1, ch. i.

or, introducing an auxiliary variable t and fixing the arbitrary scalar factor in B^κ in any way

$$\frac{d\xi^\kappa}{dt} :: B^\kappa. \tag{3.5}$$

The E_1-field $\lfloor B^\kappa \rfloor$ determines a system of ∞^{n-1} curves, the *stream-lines* or *integral curves* of the field and of (3.1) and (3.2). These integral curves are also called the *characteristics* of the field and of (3.1) and (3.2). The linear element $d\xi^\kappa$ of an integral curve satisfies (3.2) and also (3.4). If $F(\xi^\kappa)$ is a solution of (3.1) and, therefore, an integral function of (3.2), the equation

$$d\xi^\mu \partial_\mu F = 0 \tag{3.6}$$

follows from (3.2) and vice versa. This means geometrically that every one of the ∞^1 X_{n-1}'s

$$F(\xi^\kappa) = \text{const.} \tag{3.7}$$

consists of ∞^{n-2} integral curves. Hence the solution of (3.1) is equivalent to the determination of all integral curves, and from this we see that, in fact, the outer problem and the inner problem are the same.

4. Totally integrable systems and the existence theorem of Cauchy-Kowalewski†

If a system of N partial differential equations of order l with n independent variables ξ^κ and M unknown variables $\underset{\mathfrak{b}}{z}$ $(\mathfrak{b} = 1,\dots, M)$

$$\overset{i}{F}(\xi^\kappa, \underset{\mathfrak{b}}{z}, \partial_\lambda \underset{\mathfrak{b}}{z}, \partial_{\lambda_2}\partial_{\lambda_1} \underset{\mathfrak{b}}{z},\dots, \partial_{\lambda_l}\dots\partial_{\lambda_1} \underset{\mathfrak{b}}{z}) = 0 \quad (i = 1,\dots,\mathrm{N};\ \mathfrak{b} = 1,\dots, M) \tag{4.1}$$

is given, every set of functions $\underset{\mathfrak{b}}{z}$ satisfying (4.1) together with their derivatives is called a *solution* of (4.1), and every system of

$$n+\left\{1+n+\binom{n+1}{2}+\binom{n+2}{3}+\dots+\binom{n+l-1}{l}\right\}M \tag{4.2}$$

values
$$\underset{*}{\xi^\kappa},\quad \overset{*}{\underset{\mathfrak{b}}{\eta}},\quad \overset{*}{\underset{\mathfrak{b}}{\eta}}_\lambda,\quad \overset{*}{\underset{\mathfrak{b}}{\eta}}_{\lambda_2\lambda_1} = \overset{*}{\underset{\mathfrak{b}}{\eta}}_{\lambda_1\lambda_2},\quad \dots,\quad \overset{*}{\underset{\mathfrak{b}}{\eta}}_{\lambda_l\dots\lambda_1} = \overset{*}{\underset{\mathfrak{b}}{\eta}}_{(\lambda_l\dots\lambda_1)} \tag{4.3}$$

satisfying the equations

$$\overset{i}{F}(\underset{*}{\xi^\kappa}, \overset{*}{\underset{\mathfrak{b}}{\eta}}, \overset{*}{\underset{\mathfrak{b}}{\eta}}_\lambda, \overset{*}{\underset{\mathfrak{b}}{\eta}}_{\lambda_2\lambda_1},\dots, \overset{*}{\underset{\mathfrak{b}}{\eta}}_{\lambda_l\dots\lambda_1}) = 0 \quad (i = 1,\dots,\mathrm{N}) \tag{4.4}$$

is called a *null point* of the system (4.1) (cf. II, § 3). The system (4.1) is said to be *totally integrable* in an $\mathfrak{N}(\underset{0}{\xi^\kappa}, \overset{0}{\underset{\mathfrak{b}}{\eta}}, \overset{0}{\underset{\mathfrak{b}}{\eta}}_\lambda,\dots, \overset{0}{\underset{\mathfrak{b}}{\eta}}_{\lambda_l\dots\lambda_1})$ if for every null

† Cf. v. Weber 1900. 1, ch. ii; Goursat 1921. 1, chs. i, ii, iii; Engel and Faber 1932. 1, ch. i.

point $\overset{*}{\xi}{}^\kappa$, $\overset{*}{\underset{\mathfrak{b}}{\eta}}$, $\overset{*}{\underset{\mathfrak{b}}{\eta}}{}_\lambda$,..., $\overset{*}{\underset{\mathfrak{b}}{\eta}}{}_{\lambda_1...\lambda_s}$ in this $\mathfrak{N}$ there exists at least one solution satisfying the condition that for $\xi^\kappa = \overset{*}{\xi}{}^\kappa$

$$\underset{\mathfrak{b}}{z} = \overset{*}{\underset{\mathfrak{b}}{\eta}}, \quad \partial_\lambda \underset{\mathfrak{b}}{z} = \overset{*}{\underset{\mathfrak{b}}{\eta}}{}_\lambda, \quad ..., \quad \partial_{\lambda_1...\lambda_s} \underset{\mathfrak{b}}{z} = \overset{*}{\underset{\mathfrak{b}}{\eta}}{}_{\lambda_1...\lambda_s}. \tag{4.5}$$

In general there will be more than one solution satisfying these conditions. Hence we must find

(1) the necessary and sufficient conditions for a system to be totally integrable;

(2) the conditions to be added in order to make the solution of a totally integrable system for a given null point uniquely determined.

Of the results obtained in this matter we only need here the existence theorem of Cauchy-Kowalewski for the case of order one. For this case the theorem may be formulated as follows:

THEOREM III.1. (*Existence theorem of Cauchy-Kowalewski.*)†

1. *Let a system of N partial differential equations of the first order with n independent variables ξ^κ ($\kappa = 1,..., n$), N unknown functions u^k ($k = 1,..., N$), and z parameters $\eta^{\mathfrak{a}}$ ($\mathfrak{a} = 1,..., z$) be given, which can be solved with respect to the $\partial_1 u^k$:*

$$\partial_1 u^k = \Phi^k(\xi^\kappa, u^i, \partial_\beta u^j, \eta^{\mathfrak{a}}) \quad (k, i, j = 1,..., N;\ \mathfrak{a} = 1,..., z;\ \beta = 2,..., n). \tag{4.6}$$

2. *Let the functions Φ^k be analytic in an $\mathfrak{N}(\underset{0}{\xi}{}^\kappa, \underset{0}{c}{}^i, \underset{0}{c}{}^j_\beta, \underset{0}{\eta}{}^{\mathfrak{a}})$.*

3. *Let N functions*

$$\phi^k(\xi^\alpha, \eta^{\mathfrak{a}}) \quad (k = 1,..., N;\ \mathfrak{a} = 1,..., z;\ \alpha = 2,..., n) \tag{4.7}$$

be given, analytic in an $\mathfrak{N}(\underset{0}{\xi}{}^\alpha, \underset{0}{\eta}{}^{\mathfrak{a}})$ and such that

$$\left.\begin{aligned} &\phi^k(\underset{0}{\xi}{}^\alpha, \underset{0}{\eta}{}^{\mathfrak{a}}) = \underset{0}{c}{}^k \\ &\phi^k_\beta(\underset{0}{\xi}{}^\alpha, \underset{0}{\eta}{}^{\mathfrak{a}}) = \underset{0}{c}{}^k_\beta;\ \phi^k_\beta \overset{\text{def}}{=} \partial_\beta \phi^k \end{aligned}\right\} \quad (k = 1,..., N;\ \mathfrak{a} = 1,..., z;\ \alpha, \beta = 2,..., n). \tag{4.8}$$

When these conditions are satisfied there exists one and only one system of solutions $u^k(\xi^\kappa, \eta^{\mathfrak{a}})$, analytic in an $\mathfrak{N}(\underset{0}{\xi}{}^\kappa, \underset{0}{\eta}{}^{\mathfrak{a}})$ such that

$$u^k(\underset{0}{\xi}{}^1, \xi^\alpha, \eta^{\mathfrak{a}}) = \phi^k \quad (k = 1,..., N;\ \mathfrak{a} = 1,..., z;\ \alpha = 2,..., n). \tag{4.9}$$

The proof of this theorem will be found in text-books on analysis.

† 1874. 1.

5. Application of the existence theorem of Cauchy-Kowalewski to the case of one homogeneous linear partial differential equation of the first order†

In order to apply the existence theorem III.1 to the equation (3.1) we interchange the indices κ in such a way that $B^1 \neq 0$ in an $\mathfrak{N}(\overset{}{\underset{0}{\xi^\kappa}})$. This inequality means that each integral curve in this region has just one point in common with each of the hypersurfaces $\xi^1 = \text{const}$. Then there exists an $\mathfrak{N}(\underset{0}{\xi^\kappa})$ where (3.1) is equivalent to an equation of the form

$$\partial_1 f = \lambda^\alpha \partial_\alpha f \quad (\alpha = 2,..., n) \tag{5.1}$$

with coefficients λ^α $(\alpha = 2,..., n)$ analytic in this $\mathfrak{N}(\underset{0}{\xi^\kappa})$. If now $\phi(\xi^\alpha)$ $(\alpha = 2,..., n)$ is an arbitrary function, analytic in an $\mathfrak{N}(\underset{0}{\xi^\alpha})$, it follows from the existence theorem that there exists one and only one function $f(\xi^\kappa)$, analytic in an $\mathfrak{N}(\underset{0}{\xi^\kappa})$, satisfying (5.1) and such that

$$f(\underset{0}{\xi^1}, \xi^\alpha) = \phi(\xi^\alpha) \quad (\alpha = 2,..., n). \tag{5.2}$$

If, for $\phi(\xi^\alpha)$, we take successively $n-1$ functionally independent functions $\phi^\beta(\xi^\alpha)$ $(\alpha, \beta = 2,..., n)$, we get $n-1$ solutions of (5.1). Since each of them is analytic in some $\mathfrak{N}(\underset{0}{\xi^\kappa})$, there exists an $\mathfrak{N}(\underset{0}{\xi^\kappa})$ where they are all analytic. These functions have to be functionally independent because for $\xi^1 = \underset{0}{\xi^1}$ they pass into the functionally independent functions ϕ^β. This proves that (3.1) has $n-1$ independent solutions and that, therefore, $\mu = 1$ for $p = 1$. As a special case we may take for the ϕ^β the $\xi^2,..., \xi^n$. Then we get the *principal solutions* of (3.1) or *principal integral functions* of (3.2) *with respect to* $\xi^1 = \underset{0}{\xi^1}$. Sometimes by a suitable choice of (κ) it may be arranged that these principal solutions are convenient for calculation purposes.

The coordinate system (κ) can always be chosen in such a way that some given X_{n-1} through $\underset{0}{\xi^\kappa}$ is represented by the equation $\xi^1 = \underset{0}{\xi^1}$. Collecting results we have the theorem

THEOREM III.2. (*Existence theorem for one homogeneous equation.*) *If the* B^κ (*or* C^α_μ) *in* (3.1) (*or* (3.2)) *are analytic in an* $\mathfrak{N}(\underset{0}{\xi^\kappa})$ *and if in an arbitrary* X_{n-1} *through* $\underset{0}{\xi^\kappa}$, *having a tangent* E_{n-1} *that nowhere in* $\mathfrak{N}(\underset{0}{\xi^\kappa})$

† Cf. v. Weber 1900. 1, ch. ii; Goursat 1921. 1, chs. ii, iii; Engel and Faber 1932. 1, ch. i.

contains the direction of B^κ, *an arbitrary function of position* ϕ *is given, analytic at all points of the* X_{n-1} *in an* $\mathfrak{N}(\overset{}{\underset{0}{\xi}}{}^\kappa)$, *there exists in some* $\mathfrak{N}(\underset{0}{\xi}{}^\kappa)$ *one and only one solution of* (3.1), *having at all points of* X_{n-1} *in this* $\mathfrak{N}(\underset{0}{\xi}{}^\kappa)$ *the same values as* ϕ. *If a system of* $n-1$ *independent functions* $\overset{1}{\phi},\ldots,\overset{n-1}{\phi}$ *is given, the corresponding solutions* $\overset{1}{f},\ldots,\overset{n-1}{f}$ *are also independent and* $F(\overset{1}{f},\ldots,\overset{n-1}{f})$ *is the general solution of* (3.1).

For later purposes it is important to note that one single solution of the system (3.1) can be uniquely determined by giving one function of $n-1$ variables, for instance, $\phi(\xi^\alpha)$ in (5.2).† Each solution represents a normal system of ∞^1 enveloping X_{n-1}'s and every single X_{n-1} of this system with the equation $f = c$ can, therefore, be determined by giving one function of $n-2$ variables, for instance, the function ψ in the equation

$$\xi^2 = \psi(\xi^3,\ldots,\xi^n) \tag{5.3}$$

which can be obtained by solving ξ^2 from the equation $\phi(\xi^\alpha) = c$. From a geometrical point of view this is evident because the manifold of all integral curves is $(n-1)$-dimensional and in this manifold an X_{n-2} can be determined by one function of $n-2$ variables. The ∞^{n-2} X_1's whose images are the points of this X_{n-2} constitute an enveloping X_{n-1}.

6. Application of the existence theorem of Cauchy-Kowalewski to the adjoint system‡

As in the preceding section we arrange that $B^1 \neq 0$ in an $\mathfrak{N}(\underset{0}{\xi}{}^\kappa)$. Then we write (3.4) in the form

$$\frac{d\xi^\alpha}{d\xi^1} = \frac{B^\alpha}{B^1} \quad (\alpha = 2,\ldots,n). \tag{6.1}$$

If now $\psi^\alpha(\eta^\mathfrak{a})$ $(\alpha = 2,\ldots,n;\ \mathfrak{a} = 2,\ldots,z)$ are arbitrary functions of the $\eta^\mathfrak{a}$, analytic and independent in an $\mathfrak{N}(\underset{0}{\eta}{}^\mathfrak{a})$, it follows from the existence theorem that there exists one and only one system of solutions $\xi^\alpha(\xi^1, \eta^\mathfrak{a})$ of (6.1) analytic in an $\mathfrak{N}(\underset{0}{\xi}{}^1, \underset{0}{\eta}{}^\mathfrak{a})$ and such that

$$\xi^\alpha(\underset{0}{\xi}{}^1, \eta^\mathfrak{a}) = \psi^\alpha(\eta^\mathfrak{a}) \quad (\alpha = 2,\ldots,n;\ \mathfrak{a} = 2,\ldots,z). \tag{6.2}$$

† Nevertheless it is useful to compare the remarks of Goursat 1921. 1, p. 10; 1915. 1, pp. 52, 290, on the doubtfulness of assertions of this kind on the degree of freedom of solutions.

‡ Cf. v. Weber, 1900. 1, ch. ii; Goursat 1921. 1, chs. ii, iii; Engel and Faber 1932. 1, chs. i, iii.

The number of parameters η^a is entirely arbitrary. If we take $z = n$, $\psi^\alpha(\eta^a) = \eta^\alpha$ $(\alpha = 2,\dots,n)$, and $\underset{0}{\eta}^\alpha = \underset{0}{\xi}^\alpha$, it follows that there exists one and only one system of $n-1$ solutions of (6.1), analytic in an $\mathfrak{N}$ of $\xi^1 = \underset{0}{\xi}^1$; $\eta^\alpha = \underset{0}{\xi}^\alpha$, coinciding with η^α for $\xi^1 = \underset{0}{\xi}^1$. Accordingly there exists in this $\mathfrak{N}$ an expansion in a convergent series of the form

$$\xi^\alpha = \eta^\alpha + P_1^\alpha(\xi^1 - \underset{0}{\xi}^1) + P_2^\alpha(\xi^1 - \underset{0}{\xi}^1)^2 + \dots \quad (\alpha = 2,\dots,n), \tag{6.3}$$

with coefficients P analytic in an $\mathfrak{N}$ of $\eta^\alpha = \underset{0}{\xi}^\alpha$. The matrix of the $\partial\xi^\alpha/\partial\eta^\beta$ has for $\xi^1 = \underset{0}{\xi}^1$ the rank $n-1$, and consequently there exists an $\mathfrak{N}$ of $\xi^1 = \underset{0}{\xi}^1$, $\eta^\alpha = \underset{0}{\xi}^\alpha$ where the η^α can be solved from (6.3)

$$\eta^\alpha = F^\alpha(\xi^\kappa) \quad (\alpha = 2,\dots,n), \tag{6.4}$$

with functions F^α, analytic in an $\mathfrak{N}(\underset{0}{\xi}^\kappa)$. Now we will prove that these F^α are functionally independent solutions of the system (3.1) adjoint to (6.1). Their independence follows from the fact that the matrix of $\partial_\beta F^\alpha$, and consequently also the matrix of $\partial_\lambda F^\alpha$, has rank $n-1$ in an $\mathfrak{N}(\underset{0}{\xi}^\kappa)$. The equations (6.3) and (6.4) are valid for every value of the η^α in an $\mathfrak{N}$ of $\eta^\alpha = \underset{0}{\xi}^\alpha$ and constitute a system of the form

$$\begin{aligned} &(a) \qquad \xi^\alpha = \phi^\alpha(\xi^1, \eta^\beta) \\ &(b) \qquad \eta^\alpha = F^\alpha(\xi^\kappa) \end{aligned} \qquad (\alpha, \beta = 2,\dots,n). \tag{6.5}$$

Now (6.5 a) represents a system of solutions of (6.1); hence

$$\frac{d\phi^\alpha}{d\xi^1} = \frac{B^\alpha}{B^1} \quad (\alpha = 2,\dots,n), \tag{6.6}$$

and by differentiation of (6.5 b) with respect to ξ^1, we get

$$0 = \partial_1 F^\alpha + (\partial_\beta F^\alpha)\frac{d\phi^\beta}{d\xi^1} \quad (\alpha, \beta = 2,\dots,n). \tag{6.7}$$

From (6.6) and (6.7) follows

$$B^\mu \partial_\mu F^\alpha = 0 \quad (\alpha = 2,\dots,n) \tag{6.8}$$

valid for arbitrary values of ξ^1 and η^α and consequently also for arbitrary values of the ξ^κ in the region considered. By this it is proved once more that the equation (3.1) has $n-1$ solutions, analytic and independent in an $\mathfrak{N}(\underset{0}{\xi}^\kappa)$.

We are now able to estimate the degree of difficulty of the solution of (3.1). (6.1) is a simultaneous system of $n-1$ ordinary differential equations and it is well known that the determination of *one* solution of this system demands the integration of *one* ordinary differential equation of order $n-1$. According to S. Lie the integration of an ordinary differential equation of order r is called an *operation* r and a quadrature an operation 0. We will denote them in the sequel always by O_r and O_0 respectively. If we have found one integral function of $\overset{1}{F}(\xi^\kappa)$ of (6.1) by means of an operation O_{n-1}, a new coordinate system (κ') can be introduced such that $\xi^{1'} = \overset{1}{F}$. With respect to (κ') we have

$$B^{\mu'}\partial_{\mu'}\xi^{1'} = B^{1'}\partial_{1'}\xi^{1'} = B^{1'} = 0 \quad (\mu' = 1',..., n'), \tag{6.9}$$

and consequently (3.1) takes the form

$$B^{\gamma'}\partial_{\gamma'} f = 0 \quad (\gamma' = 2',..., n') \tag{6.10}$$

with functions $B^{\gamma'}$ analytic in an $\mathfrak{N}(\overset{}{\underset{0}{\xi^{\kappa'}}})$ in which $\xi^{1'}$ only plays the role of an arbitrary parameter. Hence the problem is reduced from n to $n-1$. Continuing in this way, after $n-2$ transformations of coordinates and $n-1$ operations $O_{n-1},..., O_1$, we obtain $n-1$ solutions of (3.1). If from the beginning we already have m independent solutions, obtained in any way, e.g. by a happy guess, we can directly introduce these functions as the first m coordinates of the new coordinate system and we then only need $n-1-m$ operations $O_{n-1-m},..., O_1$. If only one solution is desired, independent of the m solutions already known, only an operation O_{n-1-m} is needed.

7. Solution of a non-homogeneous linear partial differential equation of first order†

A solution of the non-homogeneous equation

$$v^\mu \partial_\mu f = \phi(\xi^\kappa), \tag{7.1}$$

with a function ϕ which is analytic in an $\mathfrak{N}(\underset{0}{\xi^\kappa})$ and functions $v^\mu(\xi^\kappa)$ which are analytic and not all vanishing in this region, can always be written in the form

$$F(f, \xi^\kappa) = 0. \tag{7.2}$$

By differentiation we get

$$\partial_\mu F + \frac{\partial F}{\partial f}\partial_\mu f = 0, \tag{7.3}$$

and from (7.1) and (7.3) we obtain

$$v^\mu \partial_\mu F + \phi \frac{\partial F}{\partial f} = 0. \tag{7.4}$$

† Cf. v. Weber 1900. 1, ch. ii; Goursat 1921. 1, ch. ii; Engel and Faber 1932. 1, ch. i.

This is a homogeneous partial differential equation of first order with $n+1$ independent variables f, ξ^κ. We already know that this equation has just n independent solutions. From each solution containing f, by solving for f, a solution of (7.1) can be obtained. It is certain that at least one of the solutions of (7.4) has to contain f, because, if they were all independent of f, they would constitute a system of n independent solutions of

$$v^\mu \partial_\mu f = 0 \tag{7.5}$$

and, as we have seen, this equation can only have $n-1$ independent solutions. (7.5) is called the *reduced equation* of (7.1). The difference between two solutions of (7.1) is a solution of (7.5). Collecting these results we have the following theorem:

THEOREM III.3. (*Existence theorem for one non-homogeneous equation.*) *If the* v^μ *and* ϕ *in* (7.1) *are analytic in an* $\mathfrak{N}(\overset{}{\underset{0}{\xi}}{}^\kappa)$, *the* v^μ *being not all zero in that region, and if on an arbitrary* X_{n-1} *through* $\underset{0}{\xi}{}^\kappa$, *whose tangent* E_{n-1} *nowhere contains* v^κ, *an arbitrary function of position* $\overset{0}{\phi}$ *is given, analytic at all points of* X_{n-1} *in* $\mathfrak{N}(\underset{0}{\xi}{}^\kappa)$, *there exists in some* $\mathfrak{N}(\underset{0}{\xi}{}^\kappa)$ *one and only one solution* $\overset{0}{f}$ *of* (7.1), *having at all points of* X_{n-1} *in this* $\mathfrak{N}(\underset{0}{\xi}{}^\kappa)$ *the same values as* $\overset{0}{\phi}$. *If* $\overset{1}{f},\dots,\overset{n-1}{f}$ *are* $n-1$ *independent solutions of the reduced equation* (7.5), *the general solution of* (7.1) *has the form*

$$f = \overset{0}{f} + \psi(\overset{1}{f},\dots,\overset{n-1}{f}). \tag{7.6}$$

We remark that one single solution of (7.1) can be determined by giving one function of $n-1$ variables, e.g. $\overset{0}{\phi}$ or the function ψ in (7.6).

When $n-1$ independent solutions of the reduced equation are known, the general solution of (7.1) can be obtained by an operation O_0. For that purpose these $n-1$ solutions are introduced as the last $n-1$ coordinates. Then (7.1) takes the form

$$\sigma \partial_1 f = \phi(\xi^\kappa), \tag{7.7}$$

σ and ϕ being known functions of ξ^κ. Looking upon this equation as an ordinary differential equation in ξ^1 with the parameters $\xi^2,\dots,\xi^n$, the unknown function f is obtained by an operation O_0. From the foregoing results the following theorem may be derived:

THEOREM III.4. *If a vector field* v^κ *is analytic in an* $\mathfrak{N}(\underset{0}{\xi}{}^\kappa)$ *and nowhere zero in that region, there always exists an* $\mathfrak{N}(\underset{0}{\xi}{}^\kappa)$ *where a coordinate system* *(h), $h = 1,\dots,n$, can be found such that $v^\kappa = \underset{1}{e}^\kappa$ and $\xi^2,\dots,\xi^n$ are $n-1$ arbitrarily chosen independent solutions of*

$$v^\mu \partial_\mu f = 0. \tag{7.8}$$

PROOF. Let an arbitrary solution of the non-homogeneous equation

$$v^\mu \partial_\mu f = 1 \tag{7.9}$$

be chosen as coordinate ξ^1 and $n-1$ arbitrary independent solutions of (7.8) as coordinates $\xi^2,\dots,\xi^n$. Then we have

$$v^\mu \overset{h}{e}_\mu = \delta_1^h \quad (h = 1,\dots,n), \tag{7.10}$$

hence

$$v^\kappa = \underset{1}{e}^\kappa. \tag{7.11}$$

As a consequence of this theorem the coordinate system (κ) can always be chosen in such a way that $v^1 = 1$ and $v^2 = 0,\dots, v^n = 0$. Then the homogeneous equation (7.8) takes the form

$$\partial_1 f = 0. \tag{7.12}$$

This form is called the *canonical form* of the homogeneous equation. *It is important to remark that the canonical form is only known if the equation has already been solved.*

8. Conditions for invariant fields in the canonical form†

If the equation $v^\mu \partial_\mu f = 0$ has the canonical form the conditions that any field is invariant with respect to v^κ or to $\lfloor v^\kappa \rfloor$ (cf. II, § 14) take a very simple form. Using the special coordinate system (κ) introduced above, the Lie derivative of the affinor density $\mathfrak{P}^{\kappa_1\dots\kappa_p}{}_{\lambda_1\dots\lambda_q}$ with respect to v^κ has the form

$$\partial_1 \mathfrak{P}^{\kappa_1\dots\kappa_p}{}_{\lambda_1\dots\lambda_q} = 0. \tag{8.1}$$

Hence a quantity is absolutely invariant with respect to v^κ if and only if its components with respect to the special coordinate system (κ) are independent of ξ^1.

The additional condition (II, 14.4) for invariance with respect to $\lfloor v^\kappa \rfloor$ takes the form

$$\sum_{i=1}^{i=q} \mathfrak{P}^{\kappa_1\dots\kappa_p}{}_{\lambda_1\dots\lambda_{i-1}1\lambda_{i+1}\dots\lambda_q} A_{\lambda_i}^\mu - \sum_{j=1}^{j=p} \mathfrak{P}^{\kappa_1\dots\kappa_{j-1}\mu\kappa_{j+1}\dots\kappa_p}{}_{\lambda_1\dots\lambda_q} \underset{1}{e}^{\kappa_j} + \mathfrak{k}\mathfrak{P}^{\kappa_1\dots\kappa_p}{}_{\lambda_1\dots\lambda_q} \underset{1}{e}^\mu = 0; \tag{8.2}$$

and from this general form we get for a covariant q-vector the additional condition

$$w_{1\lambda_2\dots\lambda_q} = 0; \tag{8.3}$$

† Cf. Goursat 1922. 1, ch. v.

and for a contravariant p-vector density of weight $+1$

$$\mathfrak{w}^{[\kappa_1 \ldots \kappa_p} \overset{1}{e}{}^{\kappa]} = 0, \tag{8.4}$$

or
$$\mathfrak{w}^{\alpha_1 \ldots \alpha_p} = 0 \quad (\alpha_1, \ldots, \alpha_p = 2, \ldots, n). \tag{8.5}$$

The condition (8.3) states that $w_{\lambda_1 \ldots \lambda_q}$ is a sum of alternating products of q of the measuring vectors $\overset{2}{e}_\lambda, \ldots, \overset{n}{e}_\lambda$ with arbitrary coefficients. Hence we have the following theorem, completing the theorem II.15:

THEOREM III.5. *A covariant q-vector is absolutely invariant with respect to $\lfloor v^\kappa \rfloor$ if and only if it can be written as a sum of alternating products of gradients of solutions of*

$$v^\mu \partial_\mu f = 0 \tag{8.6}$$

with coefficients that are solutions of (8.6).

Now we are able to prove the theorem II.18 by means of which it is always possible to derive an absolutely invariant q-vector or p-vector density from a relatively invariant one. Let $w_{\lambda_1 \ldots \lambda_q}$ be relatively invariant with respect to v^κ and consequently Dw be absolutely invariant. Then in the canonical form the components of Dw are independent of ξ^1. Hence there exists an equation of the form

$$\partial_{[\mu} w_{\lambda_1 \ldots \lambda_q]} = \overset{1}{W}_{\mu\lambda_1 \ldots \lambda_q} + \overset{1}{e}_{[\mu} \overset{2}{W}_{\lambda_1 \ldots \lambda_q]}, \tag{8.7}$$

$\overset{1}{W}$ and $\overset{2}{W}$ being sums of alternating products of the measuring vectors $\overset{2}{e}_\lambda, \ldots, \overset{n}{e}_\lambda$ with coefficients not depending on ξ^1. Consequently $\overset{1}{W}$ and $\overset{2}{W}$ are absolutely invariant with respect to $\lfloor v^\kappa \rfloor$. If now the rotation of (8.7) is formed we see that the rotations of $\overset{1}{W}$ and $\overset{2}{W}$ have to vanish because $\overset{1}{e}_\lambda$ cannot be a divisor of $D\overset{1}{W}$. Consequently there exist two fields $\overset{1}{w}_{\lambda_1 \ldots \lambda_q}$ and $\overset{2}{w}_{\lambda_2 \ldots \lambda_q}$, both independent of ξ^1, such that

$$\begin{aligned} \overset{1}{W}_{\mu\lambda_1 \ldots \lambda_q} &= \partial_{[\mu} \overset{1}{w}_{\lambda_1 \ldots \lambda_q]}, \\ \overset{2}{W}_{\lambda_1 \ldots \lambda_q} &= \partial_{[\lambda_1} \overset{2}{w}_{\lambda_2 \ldots \lambda_q]}. \end{aligned} \tag{8.8}$$

Substituting (8.8) into (8.7) we get

$$\partial_{[\mu} w_{\lambda_1 \ldots \lambda_q]} = \partial_{[\mu} \overset{1}{w}_{\lambda_1 \ldots \lambda_q]} - \partial_{[\mu} \overset{1}{e}_{\lambda_1} \overset{2}{w}_{\lambda_2 \ldots \lambda_q]}, \tag{8.9}$$

and this equation states that the field

$$'w_{\lambda_1 \ldots \lambda_q} = w_{\lambda_1 \ldots \lambda_q} - \overset{1}{e}_{[\lambda_1} \overset{2}{w}_{\lambda_2 \ldots \lambda_q]}, \tag{8.10}$$

which is obviously absolutely invariant with respect to v^κ, has the same rotation as $w_{\lambda_1\ldots\lambda_q}$. If we had assumed $w_{\lambda_1\ldots\lambda_q}$ to be relatively invariant with respect to $\lfloor v^\kappa \rfloor$, $\overset{2}{W}_{\lambda_1\ldots\lambda_q}$ and $\overset{2}{w}_{\lambda_2\ldots\lambda_q}$ would have vanished and we would have found a field $'w_{\lambda_1\ldots\lambda_q}$ absolutely invariant with respect to $\lfloor v^\kappa \rfloor$.

For the determination of the fields $\overset{1}{W}$ and $\overset{2}{W}$ we need the canonical form of the equation (8.6), i.e. we need one solution of (7.9) and $n-1$ independent solutions of (8.6). The determination of $\overset{1}{W}$ and $\overset{2}{W}$ can then be performed by quadratures only. Consequently we have the more elaborate version of Theorem II.18:

THEOREM III.6. *If the q-vector $w_{\lambda_1\ldots\lambda_q}$ is relatively invariant with respect to v^κ ($\lfloor v^\kappa \rfloor$) and if one solution of the non-homogeneous equation* (7.9) *and $n-1$ independent solutions of the homogeneous equation* (8.6) *are known, it is always possible, by means of quadratures only, to determine a field $'w_{\lambda_1\ldots\lambda_q}$, absolutely invariant with respect to v^κ ($\lfloor v^\kappa \rfloor$) with the same rotation as $w_{\lambda_1\ldots\lambda_q}$.*

If the p-vector density $\mathfrak{w}^{\kappa_1\ldots\kappa_p}$ of weight $+1$ is relatively invariant with respect to v^κ ($\lfloor v^\kappa \rfloor$) and if one solution of the non-homogeneous equation (7.9) *and $n-1$ independent solutions of the homogeneous equation* (8.6) *are known, it is always possible by means of quadratures only, to determine a field $'\mathfrak{w}^{\kappa_1\ldots\kappa_p}$, absolutely invariant with respect to v^κ ($\lfloor v^\kappa \rfloor$) with the same divergence as $\mathfrak{w}^{\kappa_1\ldots\kappa_p}$.*

9. Integrating factors†

It is sometimes possible to simplify the process of integrating the equation (3.1) if the free scalar factor in B^μ can be suitably chosen. As we are dealing only with an E_1-field we write (3.1) and (3.2) conveniently

$$\begin{aligned} &(a) \qquad v^\mu \partial_\mu f = 0, \\ &(b) \qquad w_{\lambda_1\ldots\lambda_{n-1}} d\xi^{\lambda_{n-1}} = 0, \end{aligned} \tag{9.1}$$

v^κ being a contravariant vector and $w_{\lambda_1\ldots\lambda_{n-1}}$ a covariant $(n-1)$-vector, subject to the condition

$$v^{\lambda_1} w_{\lambda_1\ldots\lambda_{n-1}} = 0. \tag{9.2}$$

We prove the theorem

THEOREM III.7. (*First theorem of integrating factors.*) *If v^κ is analytic in $\mathfrak{N}(\overset{0}{\xi^\kappa})$, there exists a scalar density $\mathfrak{p}$ of weight $+1$ such that the divergence of $\mathfrak{p}v^\kappa$ vanishes in that region.*

† Cf. Engel and Faber 1932. 1, ch. ii.

If $w_{\lambda_1 \ldots \lambda_{n-1}}$ is analytic in $\underset{0}{\mathfrak{N}}(\xi^\kappa)$, there exists a scalar p such that $pw_{\lambda_1 \ldots \lambda_{n-1}}$ is a gradient product and consequently the rotation of $pw_{\lambda_1 \ldots \lambda_{n-1}}$ vanishes in that region.

PROOF. The equation (9.1 a) has $n-1$ independent solutions $\overset{x}{s}$ ($x = 2,\ldots, n$), analytic in $\underset{0}{\mathfrak{N}}(\xi^\kappa)$. Their gradients $\overset{x}{s}_\lambda$ are, in that region, analytic, linearly independent and divisors of $w_{\lambda_1 \ldots \lambda_{n-1}}$. Hence $w_{\lambda_1 \ldots \lambda_{n-1}}$ is the alternating product of these gradients to within a scalar factor:

$$pw_{\lambda_1 \ldots \lambda_{n-1}} = \overset{2}{s}_{[\lambda_1} \cdots \overset{n}{s}_{\lambda_{n-1}]}. \tag{9.3}$$

This proves the second part of the theorem. Now if we form the scalar density of weight $+1$ (cf. I (8.3))

$$\mathfrak{p} \overset{\text{def}}{=} \frac{1}{(n-1)!} \overset{2}{s}_{\lambda_1} \cdots \overset{n}{s}_{\lambda_{n-1}} \frac{\mathfrak{E}^{\lambda_1 \ldots \lambda_{n-1} \kappa}}{v^\kappa}, \tag{9.4}$$

it follows that the contravariant vector density

$$\mathfrak{v}^\kappa \overset{\text{def}}{=} \mathfrak{p} v^\kappa \tag{9.5}$$

corresponds to $\overset{2}{s}_{[\lambda_1} \cdots \overset{n}{s}_{\lambda_{n-1}]}$ and that consequently the divergence of $\mathfrak{v}^\kappa$ vanishes. This proves the first part of the theorem.

As we have already mentioned in II, § 14, $\mathfrak{p}$ is called an *integrating factor of* (9.1 a). Similarly we call p an *integrating factor of* (9.1 b). If we had taken, in (9.1 a), a contravariant vector density instead of v^κ, we would have found a scalar as integrating factor. In particular we would have found p if instead of v^κ we had chosen the vector density corresponding to $w_{\lambda_1 \ldots \lambda_{n-1}}$.

If $n-1$ independent solutions of (9.1 a) are known, an integrating factor is easily formed. Since the alternating product of the gradients of these solutions have zero rotation, the corresponding vector density has zero divergence and, therefore, the quotient of this vector density and v^κ is an integrating factor.

If f is a solution of (9.1 a) we have

$$\partial_\mu \mathfrak{p} f v^\mu = \mathfrak{p} v^\mu \partial_\mu f = 0; \tag{9.6}$$

hence $f\mathfrak{p}$ is an integrating factor as well. Conversely, if $\overset{1}{\mathfrak{p}}$ and $\overset{2}{\mathfrak{p}}$ are two integrating factors, we have

$$\begin{aligned} v^\mu \partial_\mu \overset{1}{\mathfrak{p}} \overset{2}{\mathfrak{p}}^{-1} &= -\overset{1}{\mathfrak{p}} \overset{2}{\mathfrak{p}}^{-2} v^\mu \partial_\mu \overset{2}{\mathfrak{p}} + \overset{2}{\mathfrak{p}}^{-1} v^\mu \partial_\mu \overset{1}{\mathfrak{p}} \\ &= \overset{1}{\mathfrak{p}} \overset{2}{\mathfrak{p}}^{-1} \partial_\mu v^\mu - \overset{1}{\mathfrak{p}} \overset{2}{\mathfrak{p}}^{-1} \partial_\mu v^\mu = 0, \end{aligned} \tag{9.7}$$

which proves that $\overset{12}{\mathfrak{p}\mathfrak{p}^{-1}}$ is either a constant or a solution of (9.1 *a*). Of course the same holds for integrating factors of (9.1 *b*). We collect these results in the theorem

THEOREM III.8. (*Second theorem of integrating factors.*) *The product of an integrating factor of a homogeneous linear partial differential equation of the first order and a solution, is an integrating factor. The quotient of two integrating factors is either a constant or a solution.*

If just $n-2$ independent solutions of (9.1 *a*) and one integrating factor $\mathfrak{p}$ of (9.1 *a*) are known, the $n-2$ solutions may be introduced as the first $n-2$ coordinates. With respect to this coordinate system we have

$$\mathfrak{v}^1 = 0, \quad \ldots, \quad \mathfrak{v}^{n-2} = 0; \qquad \mathfrak{v}^\kappa \overset{\text{def}}{=} \mathfrak{p} v^\kappa, \tag{9.8}$$

and the equations (9.1 *b*) are

$$\mathfrak{v}^n \, d\xi^{n-1} - \mathfrak{v}^{n-1} \, d\xi^n = 0, \quad d\xi^1 = 0, \quad \ldots, \quad d\xi^{n-2} = 0. \tag{9.9}$$

$\mathfrak{v}^n$ and $\mathfrak{v}^{n-1}$ cannot vanish, because otherwise ξ^{n-1} or ξ^n would be solutions of (9.1 *a*), and independent of $\xi^1, \ldots, \xi^{n-2}$, constituting a trivial case. Now the divergence of $\mathfrak{v}^\kappa$ vanishes,

$$\partial_{n-1} \mathfrak{v}^{n-1} + \partial_n \mathfrak{v}^n = 0, \tag{9.10}$$

and this equation expresses the necessary and sufficient condition for the left-hand side of (9.9) to be a perfect differential. Hence, integration is possible and

$$F \overset{\text{def}}{=} \int (\mathfrak{v}^n \, d\xi^{n-1} - \mathfrak{v}^{n-1} \, d\xi^n) = \text{const.} \tag{9.11}$$

is an integral of (9.1 *b*) and F an integral function of (9.1 *b*) and a solution of (9.1 *a*). Because $\partial_n F \neq 0$, F is functionally independent of $\xi^1, \ldots, \xi^{n-1}$. This establishes the theorem

THEOREM III.9. (*Third theorem of integrating factors.*) *If $n-2$ independent solutions of a homogeneous linear partial differential equation of first order and one integrating factor are known, the $(n-1)$th solution can be obtained by a quadrature.*

If only $n-2$ independent solutions are known, then to determine the last solution an operation O_1 is needed, viz. the solution of an ordinary differential equation of the first order. If, moreover, an integrating factor is known we need an operation O_0. This is an example of the usefulness of fields invariant with respect to v^κ in so far as they give an opportunity to form integrating factors. Other examples of the use of invariant fields for integrating purposes will be given in V, § 5.

10. Hydrodynamical illustration of integrating factors

The first theorem of integrating factors III.7 can be illustrated by a hydrodynamical model. If a screw-sense in ordinary three-dimensional space is fixed, the density of a fluid, i.e. the mass per parallelepiped of measuring vectors at the point considered, is a scalar density $\mathfrak{m}$ of weight $+1$.† If v^κ is the velocity, $\mathfrak{v}^\kappa = \mathfrak{m}v^\kappa$ is the impulse density of the current.‡ The equation of continuity of the current is

$$\partial_\mu \mathfrak{v}^\mu + \frac{\partial \mathfrak{m}}{\partial t} = 0 \quad (\mu = 1, 2, 3) \tag{10.1}$$

with respect to any affine, not necessarily rectangular, coordinate system. If the current is stationary, $\partial\mathfrak{m}/\partial t$ and the divergence of $\mathfrak{v}^\kappa$ vanish.

To every surface element with a screw-sense *through* it, corresponds, by means of the fixed screw-sense, a contravariant bivector and its corresponding covariant vector density $d\mathfrak{E}_\lambda$ of weight -1.§ $\mathfrak{v}^\mu\, d\mathfrak{E}_\mu$ is the mass of the fluid streaming through the element in the sense accepted per unit of time. Now consider the equation

$$v^\mu \partial_\mu f = 0. \tag{10.2}$$

Space can be divided up into infinitesimal tubes whose surfaces consist of the stream-lines of the field v^κ. The fluid streams in such a way that it does not penetrate the surfaces of these tubes.

First we consider which stationary currents of a *compressible* fluid are possible if the field v^κ is given. To do this a density field $\mathfrak{m}$ has to be determined such that the divergence of $\mathfrak{m}v^\kappa$ vanishes. Hence $\mathfrak{m}$ has to be an integrating factor of (10.2) and to every integrating factor corresponds a possible current. If f is a solution of (10.2), $f\mathfrak{m}$ is also an integrating factor. But from the existence theorem III.2 we have seen that there is one and only one solution of (10.2) taking definitely given values on some definitely given surface, having just one point in common with every stream-line. From this it follows that there exists one and only one field $\mathfrak{m}$ taking definitely given values on this surface. This means that, if the field v^κ in the whole space and the impulse density on this surface are given, the current, viz. the field $\mathfrak{v}^\kappa$, is determined in the whole space. This can be illustrated by an obvious example. Let us suppose that there is a system of pumps, pumping into the mouth of

† The mass per unit of volume in the ordinary sense is not a density but a scalar, because its value does not change with a transformation of coordinates.

‡ Really $\mathfrak{m}$ and $\mathfrak{v}^\kappa$ are Weyl densities, transforming with $|\Delta|$ instead of Δ (cf. I, § 8), but, if a screw sense is fixed, there is no difference between these densities and ordinary densities.

§ Really $d\mathfrak{E}_\lambda$ is a Weyl density, cf. footnote ‡.

every tube on the fixed surface a certain number of particles of the fluid with the velocity v^κ per unit of time. The velocity is given but the number of particles is arbitrary, and the fluid is compressible. If the stationary state is reached, the current in the tubes is determined entirely.

Now we ask which stationary currents are possible if the fluid is *incompressible* and if only the tubes are given, i.e. the field $\lfloor v^\kappa \rfloor$. The density $\mathfrak{m}$ is now known and is the same in all points. If the stream-lines are given by the equation

$$u^\mu \partial_\mu f = 0 \tag{10.3}$$

and if f is any solution and $\mathfrak{p}$ any integrating factor of (10.3), the field

$$v^\kappa = \frac{\mathfrak{p}}{\mathfrak{m}} f u^\kappa \tag{10.4}$$

is a possible velocity field and every velocity field can be obtained by taking all possible integrating factors for $\mathfrak{p}$ and also by taking all possible solutions for f. Hence the current is entirely determined if the magnitude of v^κ is given on the surface mentioned above. To illustrate this we give the system of pumps the order to pump the fluid into every tube with a definite velocity and wait till the stationary state is reached. Since the fluid is incompressible the current in the whole space is then determined.

Of course these hydrodynamic considerations are purely illustrative and they have no demonstrative power in a mathematical sense. But perhaps they are not unwelcome to readers with a more geometrical disposition.

11. The extension of an incomplete system of homogeneous linear partial differential equations of the first order and the corresponding process for the adjoint system†

If the system

$$B_b^\mu \partial_\mu f = 0 \quad (b = 1,\dots, \mathrm{p}) \tag{11.1}$$

is incomplete it can be extended step by step, by successively forming its derived systems, until a complete system with the same solutions is obtained, as was shown in III, § 2. To every derived system obtained in the course of this process a system of total differential equations is adjoined, having the same integrals as the adjoint system of (11.1)

$$C_\mu^x d\xi^\mu = 0 \quad (x = \mathrm{p}+1,\dots, \mathrm{n}). \tag{11.2}$$

† Cf. Goursat 1922. 1, ch. vii; Engel and Faber 1932. 1, ch. ii.

These systems are called the first, second, etc., *derived systems* of (11.2).† In order to find the first derived system of (11.2), adjoint to the first derived system of (11.1)

$$\begin{aligned} B_b^\mu \partial_\mu f &= 0 \\ B_{[c}^\omega \partial_{|\omega|} B_{b]}^\mu \partial_\mu f &= 0 \end{aligned} \quad (b, c = 1,..., \mathrm{p}), \tag{11.3}$$

we note that the quantity taking the place of C_λ^x will have a rank $n-p-\mu_1$, $p+\mu_1$ being the number of linearly independent equations of (11.3) (cf. III, § 2). Hence, if we denote this quantity by $\overset{1}{C}{}_\lambda^{x_1}$ $(x_1 = \mathrm{p}+\mu_1+1,..., \mathrm{n})$, we have (cf. II. (4.8))

$$\begin{aligned} (a) \qquad & B_b^\mu \overset{1}{C}{}_\mu^{x_1} = 0 \\ (b) \qquad & B_{[c}^\omega (\partial_{|\omega|} B_{b]}^\mu) \overset{1}{C}{}_\mu^{x_1} = 0 \end{aligned} \quad (b, c = 1,..., \mathrm{p};\ x_1 = \mathrm{p}+\mu_1+1,..., \mathrm{n}) \tag{11.4}$$

or

$$\begin{aligned} (a) \qquad & B_b^\mu \overset{1}{C}{}_\mu^{x_1} = 0 \\ (b) \qquad & B_{[c}^\mu B_{b]}^\lambda \overset{1}{C}{}_{\mu\lambda}^{\cdot\cdot x_1} = 0 \end{aligned} \quad (b, c = 1,..., \mathrm{p};\ x_1 = \mathrm{p}+\mu_1+1,..., \mathrm{n}). \tag{11.5}$$

The equation (11.5 *b*) expresses that the rotations $\overset{1}{C}{}_{\mu\lambda}^{\cdot\cdot x_1}$ can be written as the sum of simple bivectors each containing one of the C_λ^x as a factor. Hence (11.5 *b*) is equivalent to

$$\overset{1}{C}{}_{\mu\lambda}^{\cdot\cdot x_1} \equiv 0 \ (\mathrm{mod}\ C_\lambda^x). \tag{11.6}$$

From (11.5 *a*) it follows that the $n-p-\mu_1$ covariant vectors $\overset{1}{C}{}_\lambda^{x_1}$ depend linearly on the $n-p$ covariant vectors C_λ^x. Hence there exists an x-transformation $x \to x'$ such that

$$\overset{1}{C}{}_\lambda^{x_1} = \delta_{x'}^{x_1} C_\lambda^{x'} \quad (x' = (\mathrm{p}+1)',..., \mathrm{n}';\ x_1 = \mathrm{p}+\mu_1+1,..., \mathrm{n}). \tag{11.7}$$

Then (11.2) takes the form

$$C_\mu^{x'} d\xi^\mu = 0 \quad (x' = (\mathrm{p}+1)',..., \mathrm{n}') \tag{11.8}$$

and from these equations the *last* $n-p-\mu_1$ form the first derived system of (11.2). Now this process can be continued till we obtain a form of the equations of the system (11.2) in which the *last* $n-p-\mu_1-...-\mu_\omega$ equations (cf. III, § 2) form the last (complete) derived system, the *last* $n-p-\mu_1-...-\mu_{\omega-1}$ equations the $(\omega-1)$th derived system, etc. If $n-p-\mu_1-...-\mu_\omega = 0$, the last derived system vanishes.

† 'Systèmes dérivés', cf. Goursat 1922. 1, ch. vii.

12. Jacobian systems†

If the system (11.1) is complete it can be brought into a normal form. The condition of completeness (2.5) expresses that there exist equations of the form

$$B^{\mu}_{[c}\,\partial_{|\mu|}\,B^{\kappa}_{b]} = \sigma^{a}_{cb}(\xi^{\lambda})B^{\kappa}_{a} \quad (a,b,c = 1,..., \mathrm{p}). \tag{12.1}$$

Now we will prove that there exists an a-transformation $a \to a'$ such that the $\sigma^{a'}_{c'b'}$ all vanish. To this end we use the theorem II.8 and choose p arbitrary gradient vectors $s^{1'}_{\lambda},..., s^{\mathrm{p}'}_{\lambda}$ such that

$$s^{1'}_{[\lambda_1}...s^{\mathrm{p}'}_{\lambda_p}\,C^{\mathrm{p}+1}_{\lambda_{p+1}}...C^{\mathrm{n}}_{\lambda_n]} \neq 0. \tag{12.2}$$

We subject the new components $B^{\kappa}_{b'}$ to the conditions

$$\begin{aligned} &(a) \qquad B^{\mu}_{b'}\,C^{x}_{\mu} = 0 \\ &(b) \qquad B^{\mu}_{b'}\,s^{a'}_{\mu} = \delta^{a'}_{b'} \end{aligned} \quad (a',b' = 1',..., \mathrm{p}';\ x = \mathrm{p}+1,..., \mathrm{n}). \tag{12.3}$$

For every value of $b' = 1',..., \mathrm{p}'$ there are just n equations with a non-vanishing determinant, according to (12.2). Hence the $B^{\kappa}_{b'}$ can be determined uniquely from (12.3). Since the system (11.1) is complete according to our suppositions, (2.5) also holds for the $B^{\kappa}_{b'}$:

$$B^{\mu}_{[c'}(\partial_{|\mu|}\,B^{\lambda}_{b']})C^{x}_{\lambda} = 0 \quad (b',c' = 1',..., \mathrm{p}';\ x = \mathrm{p}+1,..., \mathrm{n}). \tag{12.4}$$

From (12.3 b) we get by differentiation and alternation

$$B^{\mu}_{[c'}(\partial_{|\mu|}\,B^{\lambda}_{b']})s^{a'}_{\lambda} = -B^{\mu}_{[c'}\,B^{\lambda}_{b']}\,\partial_{\mu}\,s^{a'}_{\lambda} = -B^{\mu}_{[c'}\,B^{\lambda}_{b']}\,\partial_{[\mu}\,s^{a'}_{\lambda]} = 0$$

$$(a',b',c' = 1',..., \mathrm{p}'). \tag{12.5}$$

Since the vectors $s^{1'}_{\lambda},..., s^{\mathrm{p}'}_{\lambda}$, $C^{\mathrm{p}+1}_{\lambda},..., C^{\mathrm{n}}_{\lambda}$ are linearly independent according to (12.2), it follows from (12.4) and (12.5) that

$$B^{\mu}_{[c'}\,\partial_{|\mu|}\,B^{\kappa}_{b']} = 0 \quad (b',c' = 1',..., \mathrm{p}'). \tag{12.6}$$

A system satisfying the equations

$$B^{\mu}_{[c}\,\partial_{|\mu|}\,B^{\kappa}_{b]} = 0 \tag{12.7}$$

is called a *Jacobian system* or a *system in Jacobian form.* Every complete system can be brought into Jacobian form by an a-transformation and every Jacobian system is complete. The property of being Jacobian is invariant for transformations of the coordinates ξ^{κ} but not for an a-transformation.

By a suitable interchange of coordinates it can always be made possible to use the first p measuring vectors $\overset{1}{e}_{\lambda},..., \overset{p}{e}_{\lambda}$ for $s^{1'}_{\lambda},..., s^{\mathrm{p}'}_{\lambda}$.

† Cf. v. Weber 1900. 1, ch. ii, § 3; Engel and Faber 1932. 1, ch. i, § 7.

Geometrically this means that by a suitable interchange of coordinates it can always be arranged that the tangent E_{n-p} of the X_{n-p}'s with the equations

$$\xi^1 = \text{const.}, \quad ..., \quad \xi^p = \text{const.} \tag{12.8}$$

has, in the region considered, no direction in common with the local E_p of the field. Using $\overset{1}{e}_\lambda,..., \overset{p}{e}_\lambda$ we get a Jacobian form of the system, particularly adapted to the coordinate system (κ). If we use the indices $\alpha, \beta, \gamma = 1,..., p$ for the resulting a-space, the matrix B^κ_β takes the form

$$\left\| \begin{matrix} 1 & \cdots & \cdots & 0 & B_1^{p+1} & \cdots & \cdots & B_1^n \\ \vdots & \ddots & & \vdots & \vdots & & & \vdots \\ \vdots & & \ddots & \vdots & \vdots & & & \vdots \\ 0 & \cdots & \cdots & 1 & B_p^{p+1} & \cdots & \cdots & B_p^n \end{matrix} \right\| \tag{12.9}$$

and the equations (11.1) take the form

$$\partial_\beta f + B^\zeta_\beta \partial_\zeta f \overset{*}{=} 0 \quad (\beta = 1,..., p;\ \zeta = p+1,..., n). \tag{12.10}$$

Since the system is Jacobian, the coefficients B^ζ_β satisfy the equations

$$B^\eta_{[\gamma} \partial_{|\eta|} B^\zeta_{\beta]} + \partial_{[\gamma} B^\zeta_{\beta]} \overset{*}{=} 0 \quad (\beta, \gamma = 1,..., p;\ \zeta, \eta = p+1,..., n) \tag{12.11}$$

as follows from (12.6). If a system has the form (12.10) it is said to be a *special Jacobian system* or a system in the *special Jacobian form.* It must be noted that, contrarily to the Jacobian form, the special Jacobian form is not invariant for general transformations of the coordinates ξ^κ. Only transformations of the ξ^α $(\alpha = 1,..., p)$ by themselves, combined with arbitrary transformations of the ξ^ζ,

$$\begin{aligned} \xi^{\alpha'} &= f^{\alpha'}(\xi^\alpha) \\ \xi^{\zeta'} &= f^{\zeta'}(\xi^\kappa) \end{aligned} \quad (\alpha = 1,..., p;\ \alpha' = 1',..., p';\ \zeta' = (p+1)',..., n'), \tag{12.12}$$

leave the special Jacobian form invariant. This we prove as follows. For all transformations of coordinates we have

$$\partial_\beta f + B^\zeta_\beta \partial_\zeta f = A^{\beta'}_\beta \partial_{\beta'} f + A^{\zeta'}_\beta \partial_{\zeta'} f + B^\zeta_\beta A^{\beta'}_\zeta \partial_{\beta'} f + B^\zeta_\beta A^{\zeta'}_\zeta \partial_{\zeta'} f$$
$$(\beta = 1,..., p;\ \zeta = p+1,..., n;\ \beta' = 1',..., p';\ \zeta' = (p+1)',..., n'), \tag{12.13}$$

and consequently, the $A^{\beta'}_\zeta$ vanishing for these special transformations

$$\partial_\beta f + B^\zeta_\beta \partial_\zeta f \overset{*}{=} A^{\beta'}_\beta \{\partial_{\beta'} f + (A^\gamma_{\beta'} A^{\zeta'}_\gamma + A^\gamma_{\beta'} B^\zeta_\gamma A^{\zeta'}_\zeta) \partial_{\zeta'} f\} \quad (\beta, \gamma = 1,..., p;$$
$$\zeta = p+1,..., n;\ \beta', \gamma' = 1',..., p';\ \zeta' = (p+1)',..., n'), \tag{12.14}$$

which gives the proof desired and shows that the new coefficients $B^{\zeta'}_{\beta'}$ are

$$B_{\beta'}^{\zeta'} \overset{*}{=} A_{\beta'}^{\beta}(A_{\beta}^{\zeta'}+B_{\beta}^{\zeta}A_{\zeta}^{\zeta'}) \quad (\beta,\gamma = 1,\dots,p;\ \zeta = p+1,\dots,n;$$
$$\beta',\gamma' = 1',\dots,p';\ \zeta' = (p+1)',\dots,n'). \qquad (12.15)$$

It is possible to perform simultaneously an x-transformation, such that the new matrix C_{λ}^{ζ} takes the form (cf. I, § 9)

$$\left\| \begin{matrix} C_1^{p+1} & \dots & C_1^n \\ \vdots & & \vdots \\ C_p^{p+1} & \dots & C_p^n \\ 1 & \dots & 0 \\ \vdots & & \vdots \\ 0 & \dots & 1 \end{matrix} \right\| \qquad (12.16)$$

This new system replacing (x) and belonging to the coordinate system (κ) we denote by (ζ) and give it the indices ζ, η, $\theta = p+1,\dots, n$. Then we have

$$B_{\beta}^{\zeta} \overset{*}{=} -C_{\beta}^{\zeta} \quad (\beta = 1,\dots,p;\ \zeta = p+1,\dots,n). \qquad (12.17)$$

In fact it may be readily verified that

$$B_{\beta}^{\mu} C_{\mu}^{\zeta} \overset{*}{=} 0 \quad (\beta = 1,\dots,p;\ \zeta = p+1,\dots,n). \qquad (12.18)$$

Using the system (ζ), the system adjoint to (12.10) takes the form

$$C_{\beta}^{\zeta} d\xi^{\beta}+d\xi^{\zeta} \overset{*}{=} 0 \quad (\beta = 1,\dots,p;\ \zeta = p+1,\dots,n). \qquad (12.19)$$

The necessary and sufficient conditions for completeness of this system are readily derived from (12.11) and (12.17):

$$C_{[\gamma}^{\eta}\, \partial_{|\eta|}\, C_{\beta]}^{\zeta} - \partial_{[\gamma}\, C_{\beta]}^{\zeta} \overset{*}{=} 0 \quad (\beta,\gamma = 1,\dots,p;\ \zeta,\eta = p+1,\dots,n). \qquad (12.20)$$

Moreover, the special form (12.19) is only invariant for transformations of coordinates of the form (12.12) and not for general transformations. In consequence of (12.15) and (12.17) the transformed coefficients are

$$C_{\beta'}^{\zeta'} \overset{*}{=} A_{\beta'}^{\beta}(C_{\beta}^{\zeta} A_{\zeta}^{\zeta'} - A_{\beta}^{\zeta'}) \quad (\beta = 1,\dots,p;\ \zeta = p+1,\dots,n;\ \beta' = 1',\dots,p';$$
$$\zeta' = (p+1)',\dots,n'). \qquad (12.21)$$

Every complete system and its adjoint system can be brought into the special forms (12.10) *and* (12.19) *respectively for every choice of the coordinate system* (κ) *(after suitable interchange of the* ξ^{κ}*) and for this only algebraic operations are needed.*

13. Solution of a complete system of p homogeneous linear partial differential equations of the first order†

Given a complete system, we have a right to assume that, by algebraic operations only, it has been brought into the special Jacobian form

$$\partial_\beta f + B_\beta^\zeta \partial_\zeta f \overset{*}{=} 0 \quad (\beta = 1,\ldots,p;\ \zeta = p+1,\ldots,n). \tag{13.1}$$

Then it is certain that $\xi^1,\ldots,\ \xi^p$ are not solutions. But $\xi^2,\ldots,\ \xi^p$ are solutions of the first equation

$$\partial_1 f + B_1^\zeta \partial_\zeta f \overset{*}{=} 0 \quad (\zeta = p+1,\ldots,n). \tag{13.2}$$

As was proved, this equation has still $n-p$ other solutions, obtainable by $n-p$ operations $O_{n-p},\ldots,\ O_1$, and there exists one and only one system of $n-p$ solutions passing for $\xi^1 = \underset{0}{\xi^1}$ into $\xi^{p+1},\ldots,\ \xi^n$ (cf. III, § 5). Now $\xi^1,\ldots,\ \xi^p$ and these special $n-p$ solutions may be introduced as new coordinates $\xi^{1'},\ldots,\ \xi^{n'}$. Then

$$A_\beta^{\alpha'} \overset{*}{=} \delta_\beta^{\alpha'},\qquad A_{\beta'}^{\alpha} \overset{*}{=} \delta_{\beta'}^{\alpha};\qquad A_\eta^{\alpha'} \overset{*}{=} 0,\qquad A_{\eta'}^{\alpha} \overset{*}{=} 0 \quad (\alpha,\beta = 1,\ldots,p;$$
$$\alpha',\beta' = 1',\ldots,p';\ \eta = p+1,\ldots,n;\ \eta' = (p+1)',\ldots,n'), \tag{13.3}$$

and consequently (13.1) can be written

$$A_\beta^{\beta'} \partial_{\beta'} f + A_\beta^{\zeta'} \partial_{\zeta'} f + B_\beta^\zeta A_\zeta^{\zeta'} \partial_{\zeta'} f \overset{*}{=} 0 \quad (\beta = 1,\ldots,p;\ \zeta = p+1,\ldots,n;$$
$$\beta' = 1',\ldots,p';\ \zeta' = (p+1)',\ldots,n') \tag{13.4}$$

or

$$\partial_{\beta'} f + \delta_{\beta'}^\beta (A_\beta^{\zeta'} + B_\beta^\zeta A_\zeta^{\zeta'}) \partial_{\zeta'} f \overset{*}{=} 0 \quad (\beta = 1,\ldots,p;\ \zeta = p+1,\ldots,n;$$
$$\beta' = 1',\ldots,p';\ \zeta' = (p+1)',\ldots,n'). \tag{13.5}$$

Hence, if we write

$$B_{\beta'}^{\zeta'} \overset{\text{def}}{=} \delta_{\beta'}^\beta (A_\beta^{\zeta'} + B_\beta^\zeta A_\zeta^{\zeta'}) \quad (\beta = 1,\ldots,p;\ \zeta = p+1,\ldots,n;\ \beta' = 1',\ldots,p';$$
$$\zeta' = (p+1)',\ldots,n') \tag{13.6}$$

the system has once more the special Jacobian form. But now $B_{1'}^{(p+1)'},\ldots,\ B_{1'}^{n'}$ vanish, since $\xi^{2'},\ldots,\ \xi^{n'}$ are solutions of the first equation, and accordingly, dropping the accents for the sake of simplicity, we get the equations in the form

$$\begin{aligned} &(a) \qquad \partial_1 f \overset{*}{=} 0 \\ &(b) \qquad \partial_\gamma f + B_\gamma^\zeta \partial_\zeta f \overset{*}{=} 0 \end{aligned} \quad (\gamma = 2,\ldots,p;\ \zeta = p+1,\ldots,n). \tag{13.7}$$

The conditions (12.11) take the form

$$\begin{aligned} &(a) \qquad \partial_1 B_\gamma^\zeta \overset{*}{=} 0 \\ &(b) \quad B_{[\delta}^\eta \partial_{|\eta|} B_{\gamma]}^\zeta + \partial_{[\delta} B_{\gamma]}^\zeta \overset{*}{=} 0 \end{aligned} \quad (\gamma,\delta = 2,\ldots,p;\ \zeta,\eta = p+1,\ldots,n), \tag{13.8}$$

† Cf. v. Weber 1900. 1, ch. ii; Goursat 1921. 1, ch. ii; Engel and Faber 1932. 1, ch. i.

from which it can be seen that the $p-1$ equations (13.7 b) form a complete system in the $n-1$ variables $\xi^2,..., \xi^n$. This system can be treated similarly. Continuing in this way, after $p-1$ steps one single equation in $n-p$ variables is obtained. This equation has $n-p$ independent solutions, so we have proved that every complete system of p equations has just $n-p$ independent solutions. For every step we need $n-p$ operations $O_{n-p},..., O_1$, and in the aggregate we need therefore p times $n-p$ operations $O_{n-p},..., O_1$ and $p-1$ transformations of coordinates.

After reintroducing the original coordinate system (κ) the $n-p$ solutions obtained pass into $\xi^{p+1},..., \xi^n$ for $\xi^1 = \underset{0}{\xi^1},..., \xi^p = \underset{0}{\xi^p}$. These special solutions are called the *principal solutions* of (13.1) or *principal integral functions* of the adjoint system with respect to

$$\xi^1 = \underset{0}{\xi^1}, \quad ..., \quad \xi^p = \underset{0}{\xi^p}.$$

If $\overset{p+1}{f},..., \overset{n}{f}$ are these principal solutions, any arbitrary function $F(\overset{p+1}{f},..., \overset{n}{f})$ is also a solution, and it is the only solution passing into $F(\xi^{p+1},..., \xi^n)$ for $\xi^1 = \underset{0}{\xi^1},..., \xi^p = \underset{0}{\xi^p}$. The original coordinate system can always be chosen in such a way that any definitely given X_{n-p} through $\underset{0}{\xi^\kappa}$, whose tangent E_{n-p} has no direction in common with the local E_p, has the equations $\xi^1 = \underset{0}{\xi^1},..., \xi^p = \underset{0}{\xi^p}$. Hence, collecting results, we have the theorem (cf. Theorem III.2):

THEOREM III.10. (*Existence theorem for complete homogeneous systems.*) *Let the* B_b^μ *of a complete system* (11.1) *be analytic in an* $\mathfrak{N}(\underset{0}{\xi^\kappa})$ *and the rank of* B_b^μ *be* p *in that region. Then, if we are given* (1) *an arbitrary* X_{n-p} *in* $\mathfrak{N}(\underset{0}{\xi^\kappa})$ *through* $\underset{0}{\xi^\kappa}$ *whose tangent* E_{n-p} *has nowhere a direction in common with the* E_p *of the* μ*-domain of* B_b^μ *and* (2) $n-p$ *arbitrary functions of position in this* X_{n-p}, *analytic and functionally independent in* $\mathfrak{N}(\underset{0}{\xi^\kappa})$, *there exists in some* $\mathfrak{N}(\underset{0}{\xi^\kappa})$ *one and only one system of* $n-p$ *solutions of* (11.1), *having at all points of* X_{n-p} *in this* $\mathfrak{N}(\underset{0}{\xi^\kappa})$ *the same values as those given functions.*

We remark that one single solution f of a complete system of p equations can be determined by one function of $n-p$ variables. Every solution represents a normal system of ∞^1 enveloping X_{n-1}'s with the equation $f =$ const. and every single X_{n-1} of this normal system can, therefore, be determined by one function of $n-p-1$ variables. From a geometrical point of view this is quite evident. The manifold of all integral-X_p's is $(n-p)$-dimensional and in this manifold an X_{n-p-1} can be determined by one function of $n-p-1$ variables. The ∞^{n-p-1} X_p's whose images are the points of this X_{n-p-1} constitute an enveloping X_{n-1}.

It will now be proved that a complete homogeneous linear system of the first order is totally integrable in the sense defined in III, § 4. Let w_λ be a vector in $\underset{0}{\xi}^\kappa$ satisfying the equation

$$B_b^\mu w_\mu = 0 \quad (b = 1,..., \mathrm{p}). \tag{13.9}$$

If $\overset{1}{f},..., \overset{q}{f}$ $(q = n-p)$ are $n-p$ arbitrary independent solutions of a complete system of the form (11.1), w_λ lies in the domain of the vectors $\partial_\lambda \overset{1}{f},..., \partial_\lambda \overset{q}{f}$ in $\underset{0}{\xi}^\kappa$ and consequently there exists a relation of the form

$$w_\lambda = \underset{1}{\alpha}\, \partial_\lambda \overset{1}{f} + ... + \underset{q}{\alpha}\, \partial_\lambda \overset{q}{f} \tag{13.10}$$

with constant coefficients. Hence

$$F = \underset{1}{\alpha} \overset{1}{f} + ... + \underset{q}{\alpha} \overset{q}{f} \tag{13.11}$$

is a solution of (11.1), the gradient of which is equal to w_λ in $\underset{0}{\xi}^\kappa$. This proves that the system is totally integrable. Conversely, if a homogeneous linear system of the first order is totally integrable it has at least $n-p$ independent solutions and, therefore, it has to be complete.

14. Solution of a complete system of p non-homogeneous linear partial differential equations of the first order†

We consider a system of p non-homogeneous equations of the form

$$\underset{b}{v}^\mu \partial_\mu f = \underset{b}{\phi}(\xi^\kappa) \quad (b = 1,..., \mathrm{p}), \tag{14.1}$$

the $\underset{b}{v}^\mu$ and $\underset{b}{\phi}$ being analytic in an $\mathfrak{N}(\underset{0}{\xi}^\kappa)$ and the $\underset{b}{v}^\mu$ linearly independent in that region. A solution can always be written in the form

$$F(f, \xi^\kappa) = 0 \tag{14.2}$$

with $\partial F/\partial f \neq 0$. By differentiation we get

$$\partial_\mu F + \partial F/\partial f\, \partial_\mu f = 0, \tag{14.3}$$

and from (14.1) and (14.3) it follows that

$$\underset{b}{v}^\mu \partial_\mu F + \underset{b}{\phi} \frac{\partial F}{\partial f} = 0 \quad (b = 1,..., \mathrm{p}). \tag{14.4}$$

This is a homogeneous linear system of p equations in the $n+1$ variables

† Cf. v. Weber 1900. 1, ch. ii; Goursat 1921. 1, ch. ii; Engel and Faber 1932. 1, ch. i.

f, ξ^κ. The necessary and sufficient conditions for its completeness here take the form

$$\begin{aligned} &(a) \qquad \underset{[c}{v^\mu}\partial_{|\mu|}\underset{b]}{v^\kappa} = \sigma^a_{cb}(\xi^\lambda)\underset{a}{v^\kappa} \\ &(b) \qquad \underset{[c}{v^\mu}\partial_{|\mu|}\underset{b]}{\phi} = \sigma^a_{cb}(\xi^\lambda)\underset{a}{\phi} \end{aligned} \qquad (a,b,c = 1,\ldots,\mathrm{p}). \tag{14.5}$$

If (14.4) is not complete, this system can be extended until a complete system

$$\underset{\mathfrak{b}}{v^\mu}\partial_\mu F+\underset{\mathfrak{b}}{\phi}\frac{\partial F}{\partial f} = 0 \quad (\mathfrak{b} = 1,\ldots,\mathrm{p}_\omega) \tag{14.6}$$

is obtained. In this latter system the rank of the matrix

$$\left\| \underset{\mathfrak{b}}{v^\mu} \quad \underset{\mathfrak{b}}{\phi} \right\| \quad (\mathfrak{b} = 1,\ldots,\mathrm{p}_\omega) \tag{14.7}$$

is p_ω. To this extended system belongs the non-homogeneous extended system of (14.1):

$$\underset{\mathfrak{b}}{v^\mu}\partial_\mu f = \underset{\mathfrak{b}}{\phi}(\xi^\kappa) \quad (\mathfrak{b} = 1,\ldots,\mathrm{p}_\omega). \tag{14.8}$$

Now there are two possibilities:

1. The $\underset{\mathfrak{b}}{v^\mu}$ are linearly dependent. Then there exists a relation of the form

$$\overset{\mathfrak{b}}{\lambda}\underset{\mathfrak{b}}{v^\kappa} = 0 \quad (\mathfrak{b} = 1,\ldots,\mathrm{p}_\omega) \tag{14.9}$$

with coefficients that are not all zero and it is necessary that

$$\overset{\mathfrak{b}}{\lambda}\underset{\mathfrak{b}}{\phi} \neq 0, \tag{14.10}$$

because otherwise the rank of (14.7) would be $< p_\omega$, which is impossible. From (14.6), (14.9), and (14.10) it follows that $\partial F/\partial f = 0$ contrary to our suppositions. Hence, in this case (14.1) has no solutions.

2. The $\underset{\mathfrak{b}}{v^\mu}$ are linearly independent. In this case we call the *non-homogeneous* system (14.8) *complete. Hence, a non-homogeneous system of the form* (14.1) *is complete if and only if*

(1) *the* $\underset{b}{v^\mu}$ *are linearly independent;*

(2) (14.5 *a*) *is satisfied;*

(3) (14.5 *b*) *is satisfied.*

If (14.1) is complete the homogeneous system (14.4) is complete as well and there exists at least one solution of (14.4) depending on f; for otherwise, (14.4) would have $n+1-p$ independent solutions only dependent on the ξ^κ, and according to (14.4) the $\underset{b}{v^\mu}$ could not be linearly independent. Hence, either (14.1) has no solutions, or it is complete, or it can be extended to a complete non-homogeneous system.

Now suppose (14.1) to be complete. If the $\underset{b}{\phi}$ are replaced by zero, we get the homogeneous system

$$\underset{b}{v}^{\mu}\partial_{\mu}f = 0 \quad (b = 1,..., \mathrm{p}), \tag{14.11}$$

called the *reduced system* of (14.1). Since the $\underset{b}{v}^{\mu}$ are linearly independent, this reduced system is complete according to (14.5a) and it has $n-p$ independent solutions. The difference between two solutions of (14.1) is a solution of (14.11). Collecting these results we have the following theorem (cf. Theorem III.3):

THEOREM III.11. (*Existence theorem for complete non-homogeneous systems.*) *If the* $\underset{b}{v}^{\mu}$ *and* $\underset{b}{\phi}$ *in the complete non-homogeneous system* (14.1) *are analytic in an* $\mathfrak{N}(\underset{0}{\xi}^{\kappa})$ *and the* $\underset{b}{v}^{\mu}$ *are linearly independent in that region, and if on an arbitrary* X_{n-p} *through* $\underset{0}{\xi}^{\kappa}$, *whose tangent* E_{n-p} *nowhere has a direction in common with the* E_p *spanned by the* $\underset{b}{v}^{\kappa}$, *an arbitrary function of position* $\overset{0}{\phi}$ *is given, analytic at all points of* X_{n-p} *in an* $\mathfrak{N}(\underset{0}{\xi}^{\kappa})$, *there exists in some* $\mathfrak{N}(\underset{0}{\xi}^{\kappa})$ *one and only one solution* $\overset{0}{f}$ *of* (14.1), *having on* X_{n-p} *the same values as* $\overset{0}{\phi}$. *If* $\overset{1}{f},..., \overset{n-p}{f}$ *are* $n-p$ *independent solutions of the reduced equation* (14.11), *the general solution of* (14.1) *has the form*

$$f = \overset{0}{f} + \psi(\overset{1}{f},..., \overset{n-p}{f}). \tag{14.12}$$

We note that one single solution of (14.1) can be determined by one function of $n-p$ variables, e.g. $\overset{0}{\phi}$ or the function ψ in (14.12).

It will now be proved that a complete non-homogeneous linear system of the first order is totally integrable in the sense defined in III, § 4. Let w_{λ} be a vector in $\underset{0}{\xi}^{\kappa}$, satisfying the equations

$$\underset{b}{v}^{\mu}w_{\mu} = \underset{b}{\phi}(\underset{0}{\xi}^{\kappa}) \tag{14.13}$$

and $\overset{0}{f}$ an arbitrary solution of the system. Then we have

$$\underset{b}{v}^{\mu}(w_{\mu} - \partial_{\mu}\overset{0}{f}) = 0 \quad (b = 1,..., \mathrm{p}) \tag{14.14}$$

in $\underset{0}{\xi}^{\kappa}$. Now the reduced system is complete and, as we have proved, there exists a solution F of this reduced system such that in $\underset{0}{\xi^\kappa}$

$$\partial_\mu F = w_\mu - \partial_\mu \overset{0}{f}. \tag{14.15}$$

The sum $\overset{0}{f}+F$ is a solution of the non-homogeneous system and according to (14.15) the gradient of this solution is equal to w_λ in $\underset{0}{\xi^\kappa}$.

If $n-p$ independent solutions of the reduced system are known, a solution of the non-homogeneous system can be obtained by a quadrature. To prove this we introduce these $n-p$ solutions as the last $n-p$ coordinates. Then by a suitable linear homogeneous transformation of the left-hand sides of (14.1) it can be arranged that the system takes the form

$$\partial_\beta f = \psi_\beta(\xi^\kappa) \quad (\beta = 1,\ldots,p). \tag{14.16}$$

According to (14.5 a and b) the conditions for completeness of this system are

$$\partial_{[\gamma} \psi_{\beta]} = 0 \quad (\beta, \gamma = 1,\ldots,p), \tag{14.17}$$

and consequently $\psi_\beta \, d\xi^\beta$ is a complete differential in the variables ξ^α ($\alpha = 1,\ldots,p$), if the ξ^ζ ($\zeta = p+1,\ldots,n$) are looked upon as parameters. The integral

$$\int \psi_\beta d\xi^\beta \quad (\beta = 1,\ldots,p) \tag{14.18}$$

is a solution of the non-homogeneous system.

The properties of non-homogeneous systems can be used to prove a generalization of the theorem III.4:

Theorem III.12. *If p vector fields $\underset{b}{v^\kappa}$ $(b = 1,\ldots, \mathrm{p})$ are analytic and linearly independent in an $\mathfrak{N}(\underset{0}{\xi^\kappa})$ and if*

$$\underset{b}{v^\mu} \, \partial_\mu f = 0 \quad (b = 1,\ldots,\mathrm{p}) \tag{14.19}$$

is a Jacobian system, there always exists an $\mathfrak{N}(\underset{0}{\xi^\kappa})$ where a coordinate system (h) $(h = 1,\ldots,\mathrm{n})$ can be found such that $\underset{1}{v^\kappa} = \underset{1}{e^\kappa},\ldots, \underset{\mathrm{p}}{v^\kappa} = \underset{\mathrm{p}}{e^\kappa}$ and that $\xi^{\mathrm{p}+1},\ldots, \xi^{\mathrm{n}}$ are $n-p$ arbitrarily chosen independent solutions of (14.19).

Proof. We consider the p non-homogeneous systems of equations

$$\underset{b}{v^\mu} \, \partial_\mu f = \delta^a_b \quad (b = 1,\ldots,\mathrm{p}) \tag{14.20}$$

for $a = 1,\ldots,$ p. Then, since (14.19) is a Jacobian system and the right-hand sides of (14.20) are constants, each of these p systems is complete according to (14.5). If $\xi^{\mathrm{p}+1},\ldots, \xi^{\mathrm{n}}$ are $n-p$ arbitrary independent solutions of (14.19) it is certain that they are not solutions of any one of the systems (14.20). Also it is evident that no two of the p systems

(14.20) can have a solution in common. Now suppose that ξ^1 is a solution of the first system (14.20) ($a = 1$), ξ^2 a solution of the second system ($a = 2$), etc., until ξ^{p} is a solution of the pth system ($a = \mathrm{p}$). Then it is clear, that the ξ^h ($h = 1,\ldots,\mathrm{n}$) are functionally independent and can be used as coordinates in an $\underset{0}{\mathfrak{N}}(\xi^\kappa)$. As a result of (14.20) we then have

$$\underset{b}{v}^\mu \overset{h}{e}_\mu = \delta_b^h \quad (b = 1,\ldots,\mathrm{p};\ h = 1,\ldots,\mathrm{n}) \tag{14.21}$$

and consequently

$$\underset{b}{v}^\kappa = \underset{b}{e}^\kappa \quad (b = 1,\ldots,\mathrm{p}). \tag{14.22}$$

From this theorem it follows that the coordinate system (κ) can always be chosen in such a way that all components of the $\underset{b}{v}^\kappa$ vanish except

$$\underset{1}{v}^1 = 1, \quad \underset{2}{v}^2 = 1, \quad \ldots, \quad \underset{\mathrm{p}}{v}^p = 1. \tag{14.23}$$

Then the homogeneous system (14.19) takes the form (cf. (7.12))

$$\partial_\beta f = 0 \quad (\beta = 1,\ldots,p). \tag{14.24}$$

This form is called the *canonical form* of the homogeneous system. *It is important to note that the canonical form is only known if the system has already been solved.*

15. Mayer systems†

If in the $n-p$ equations (12.19)

$$d\xi^\zeta \overset{*}{=} -C_\beta^\zeta d\xi^\beta \quad (\beta = 1,\ldots,p;\ \zeta = p+1,\ldots,n) \tag{15.1}$$

the ξ^β ($\beta = 1,\ldots,p$), are looked upon as independent variables and the ξ^ζ ($\zeta = p+1,\ldots,n$) as unknown functions of the ξ^β, from (15.1) we obtain a non-homogeneous system of linear partial differential equations

$$\partial_\beta \xi^\zeta \overset{*}{=} -C_\beta^\zeta(\xi^\kappa) \quad (\beta = 1,\ldots,p;\ \zeta = p+1,\ldots,n) \tag{15.2}$$

with the by-conditions (12.20), viz.

$$\partial_{[\gamma} C_{\beta]}^\zeta \overset{*}{=} C_{[\gamma}^\eta \partial_{|\eta|} C_{\beta]}^\zeta \quad (\beta,\gamma = 1,\ldots,p;\ \zeta,\eta = p+1,\ldots,n). \tag{15.3}$$

A system of the form (15.2) with the by-conditions (15.3) is called a *Mayer system.* To every complete system in the special Jacobian form there belongs, therefore, not only its adjoint system but also one definite Mayer system. Conversely, it is possible to return from (15.2) and (15.3) to (15.1), and consequently to every Mayer system there belongs one definite complete system in the special Jacobian form and its adjoint system. Each of the three systems represents the same normal system of X_p's in X_n.

† Cf. v. Weber 1900. 1, ch. ii, § 5; Engel and Faber 1932. 1, ch. i.

If the functions f^ζ $(\zeta = p+1,..., n)$ are the principal solutions of a Jacobian system with respect to $\xi^\alpha = \underset{0}{\xi}^\alpha$ $(\alpha = 1,..., p)$, i.e. solutions passing into ξ^ζ for $\xi^\alpha = \underset{0}{\xi}^\alpha$, the equations

$$f^\zeta(\xi^\kappa) = C^\zeta \quad (\zeta = p+1,..., n) \tag{15.4}$$

with the constants C^ζ are $n-p$ independent integrals of the adjoint system. The equations

$$f^\zeta(\xi^\kappa) = \underset{0}{\xi}^\zeta \quad (\zeta = p+1,..., n) \tag{15.5}$$

represent the X_p of the normal system through $\underset{0}{\xi}^\kappa$. If from (15.4) the ξ^ζ are solved as functions of the ξ^α $(\alpha = 1,..., p)$ and the C^ζ:

$$\xi^\zeta = \phi^\zeta(\xi^\alpha, C^\eta) \quad (\alpha = 1,..., p;\ \zeta, \eta = p+1,..., n), \tag{15.6}$$

we have the solutions of the Mayer system in a form depending on $n-p$ constants. The equations (15.4), as well as (15.6), represent the normal systems of X_p's in X_n. If in these equations ξ^α is replaced by $\underset{0}{\xi}^\alpha$ we get

$$\xi^\zeta = C^\zeta \tag{15.7}$$

and

$$\xi^\zeta = \phi^\zeta(\underset{0}{\xi}^\alpha, C^\eta) \quad (\alpha = 1,..., p;\ \zeta, \eta = p+1,..., n) \tag{15.8}$$

respectively because the f^ζ become ξ^ζ for $\xi^\alpha = \underset{0}{\xi}^\alpha$. From this it follows that

$$\phi^\zeta(\underset{0}{\xi}^\alpha, C^\eta) = C^\zeta \quad (\alpha = 1,..., p;\ \zeta, \eta = p+1,..., n), \tag{15.9}$$

which proves that a Mayer system has a system of $n-p$ solutions, taking any definitely given arbitrary values C^ζ for $\xi^\alpha = \underset{0}{\xi}^\alpha$. If we choose $C^\zeta = \underset{0}{\xi}^\zeta$, these special solutions will be called the *principal solutions* of the Mayer system with respect to $\xi^\alpha = \underset{0}{\xi}^\alpha$.

We will now prove that the system of solutions of the Mayer system, taking the prescribed values C^ζ for $\xi^\alpha = \underset{0}{\xi}^\alpha$, is the only system satisfying this condition. Naturally we suppose that the C^ζ_β are analytic in an $\mathfrak{N}$ of $\xi^\alpha = \underset{0}{\xi}^\alpha$, $\xi^\zeta = C^\zeta$, and that the solutions considered have the same property. These solutions may then be expanded in power series in $\xi^\alpha - \underset{0}{\xi}^\alpha$ in an $\mathfrak{N}(\underset{0}{\xi}^\alpha)$. According to (15.2) these series have the form

$$\xi^\zeta = C^\zeta - C^\zeta_\beta(\underset{0}{\xi}^\alpha, C^\eta)(\xi^\beta - \underset{0}{\xi}^\beta) + \ldots \quad (\alpha, \beta = 1,..., p;\ \zeta, \eta = p+1,..., n). \tag{15.10}$$

The coefficients of the other terms are obtained by subsequent differentiations of (15.2). In consequence of the conditions (15.3) the values of the derivatives are independent of the order of differentiation. E.g.

$$\partial_\gamma \partial_\beta \xi^\zeta - \partial_\beta \partial_\gamma \xi^\zeta = -2\partial_{[\gamma} C^\zeta_{\beta]} + 2C^\eta_{[\gamma} \partial_{|\eta|} C^\zeta_{\beta]} = 0$$

$$(\beta, \gamma = 1,\ldots,p;\; \zeta, \eta = p+1,\ldots,n). \quad (15.11)$$

Hence the power series are uniquely determined and from this it follows that there is really only one system of solutions with the given initial conditions.

If we consider only the first $t < p$ sets of equations of a Mayer system

$$\partial_{\mathfrak{b}} \xi^\zeta = -C^\zeta_{\mathfrak{b}}(\xi^\kappa) \quad (\mathfrak{b} = 1,\ldots,t;\; \zeta = p+1,\ldots,n), \qquad (15.12)$$

and if the variables $\xi^{t+1},\ldots,\xi^p$ are regarded as parameters, we have a system in t independent variables and $p-t$ parameters. From (15.3) it follows that

$$\partial_{[\mathfrak{c}} C^\zeta_{\mathfrak{b}]} = C^\eta_{[\mathfrak{c}} \partial_{|\eta|} C^\zeta_{\mathfrak{b}]} \quad (\mathfrak{b}, \mathfrak{c} = 1,\ldots,t;\; \eta, \zeta = p+1,\ldots,n); \qquad (15.13)$$

hence *the new system is also a Mayer system.* We call this process the *abbreviation of a Mayer system with respect to* $\xi^1,\ldots,\xi^t$ and (15.12) the *abbreviated system of* (15.2) *with respect to* $\xi^1,\ldots,\xi^t$.

16. Solution of a Mayer system, a special Jacobian system, or its adjoint system according to Mayer†

In order to determine the solutions of the Mayer system

$$\partial_\beta \xi^\zeta = -C^\zeta_\beta(\xi^\kappa) \quad (\beta = 1,\ldots,p;\; \zeta = p+1,\ldots,n) \qquad (16.1)$$

we abbreviate the system with respect to ξ^1. Then we get the Mayer system

$$\partial_1 \xi^\zeta = -C^\zeta_1(\xi^1, \xi^\phi, \xi^\eta) \quad (\phi = 2,\ldots,p;\; \zeta, \eta = p+1,\ldots,n) \qquad (16.2)$$

with the parameters ξ^ϕ ($\phi = 2,\ldots,p$). This system may be regarded as a simultaneous system of $n-p$ ordinary differential equations of the first order with one independent variable ξ^1, $n-p$ unknown functions ξ^ζ, and $p-1$ parameters ξ^ϕ. The system of principal solutions of this system with respect to $\xi^1 = \underset{0}{\xi^1}$ can be obtained by $n-p$ operations $O_{n-p},\ldots, O_1$:

$$\xi^\zeta = F^\zeta(\xi^1, \xi^\phi), \quad F^\zeta(\underset{0}{\xi^1}, \xi^\phi) = \underset{0}{\xi^\zeta} \quad (\phi = 2,\ldots,p;\; \zeta = p+1,\ldots,n). \qquad (16.3)$$

Now we introduce the ξ^α ($\alpha = 1,\ldots,p$) and the $n-p$ functions $\xi^\zeta - F^\zeta(\xi^\alpha)$ as new coordinates:

$$\begin{aligned} \xi^{\alpha'} &= \delta^{\alpha'}_\alpha \xi^\alpha, & &(\alpha = 1,\ldots,p;\; \zeta = p+1,\ldots,n;\; \alpha' = 1',\ldots,p'; \\ \xi^{\zeta'} &= \delta^{\zeta'}_\zeta \{\xi^\zeta - F^\zeta(\xi^\alpha)\} & &\zeta' = (p+1)',\ldots,n'). \quad (16.4) \end{aligned}$$

† Cf. Mayer 1872. 1; v. Weber 1900. 1, ch. ii, § 5; Goursat 1921. 1, p. 81; Engel and Faber 1932. 1, ch. i, § 10.

This is an allowable coordinate transformation because the determinant of $A_\kappa^{\kappa'}$ is equal to *1*. Because this transformation has a form which leaves invariant the special form of the equations (16.1) (cf. (12.12)) the equations (15.1) and (16.1) take the form

$$C_{\beta'}^{\zeta'} d\xi^{\beta'} + d\xi^{\zeta'} = 0 \quad (\beta' = 1',\ldots,p';\ \zeta' = (p+1)',\ldots,n') \tag{16.5}$$

and

$$\partial_{\beta'}\xi^{\zeta'} = -C_{\beta'}^{\zeta'} \quad (\beta' = 1',\ldots,p';\ \zeta' = (p+1)',\ldots,n') \tag{16.6}$$

respectively, the $C_{\beta'}^{\zeta'}$ being defined by (cf. (12.21))

$$C_{\beta'}^{\zeta'} = \delta_{\beta'}^{\beta}(C_\beta^\zeta \delta_\zeta^{\zeta'} - A_\beta^{\zeta'}) \quad (\beta = 1,\ldots,p;\ \beta' = 1',\ldots,p';\ \zeta = p+1,\ldots,n;\ \zeta' = (p+1)',\ldots,n'). \tag{16.7}$$

From (16.7) it follows that

$$C_{1'}^{\zeta'} = \delta_\zeta^{\zeta'}(C_1^\zeta + \partial_1 F^\zeta) = 0 \quad (\zeta = p+1,\ldots,n;\ \zeta' = (p+1)',\ldots,n') \tag{16.8}$$

and, therefore, since (16.5) is complete

$$\partial_{1'} C_{\phi'}^{\zeta'} = \partial_{\phi'} C_{1'}^{\zeta'} = 0 \quad (\phi' = 2',\ldots,p';\ \zeta' = (p+1)',\ldots,n'). \tag{16.9}$$

Hence (16.6) can be written

$$\begin{aligned} &(a)\quad \partial_{1'}\xi^{\zeta'} = 0 \\ &(b)\quad \partial_{\phi'}\xi^{\zeta'} = -C_{\phi'}^{\zeta'}(\xi^{\psi'}, \xi^{\eta'}) \end{aligned} \quad (\phi', \psi' = 2',\ldots,p';\ \zeta', \eta' = (p+1)',\ldots,n'). \tag{16.10}$$

From this we see that (16.10*b*) is a Mayer system with $n-p$ unknown functions and $p-1$ variables. If this system be solved, the solutions of (16.1) can readily be obtained by a coordinate transformation from (κ') to (κ). Treating (16.10*b*) in the same way, and continuing this process step by step, we obtain the solution of (16.1) after applying p times $n-p$ operations $O_{n-p},\ldots, O_1$. The method here described needs just the same number of operations as the method described in III, § 13. But here there is a possibility of reducing the number of operations. The difficulty of the integration of (16.10*b*) depends wholly on the form of the functions $C_{\phi'}^{\zeta'}$ of $\xi^{2'},\ldots,\xi^{n'}$ and this form can be influenced, as we will see. We will prove *that the* $C_{\phi'}^{\zeta'}$ $(\phi' = 2',\ldots,p')$ *vanish if and only if the* C_ϕ^ζ $(\phi = 2,\ldots,p)$ *vanish identically in* $\xi^2,\ldots, \xi^n$ *for* $\xi^1 = \underset{0}{\xi^1}$. From (16.7) it follows that

$$C_{\phi'}^{\zeta'}(\xi^{\psi'}, \xi^{\eta'}) = \delta_{\phi'}^{\beta}\delta_\zeta^{\zeta'} C_\beta^\zeta - \delta_{\phi'}^{\beta} A_\beta^{\zeta'} = \delta_{\phi'}^{\phi}\delta_\zeta^{\zeta'} C_\phi^\zeta + \delta_{\phi'}^{\phi}\delta_\zeta^{\zeta'}\partial_\phi F^\zeta$$
$$(\beta = 1,\ldots,p;\ \phi = 2,\ldots,p;\ \zeta = p+1,\ldots,n;\ \phi', \psi' = 2',\ldots,p';\ \zeta' = (p+1)',\ldots,n'). \tag{16.11}$$

If in these equations we put $\xi^{1'} = \xi^1 = \underset{0}{\xi^1}$, the left-hand side does not change and according to (16.3) we obtain

$$C^{\zeta'}_{\phi'}(\xi^{\psi'},\xi^{\eta'}) = \delta^{\phi}_{\phi'}\delta^{\zeta'}_{\zeta}\, C^{\zeta}_{\phi}(\underset{0}{\xi}^{1},\xi^{\phi},\xi^{\eta})+\delta^{\phi}_{\phi'}\delta^{\zeta'}_{\zeta}(\partial_{\phi}F^{\zeta})_{\xi^{1}=\underset{0}{\xi}^{1}}$$
$$= \delta^{\phi}_{\phi'}\delta^{\zeta'}_{\zeta}\, C^{\zeta}_{\phi}(\underset{0}{\xi}^{1},\xi^{\phi},\xi^{\eta}) = 0 \quad (\phi = 2,\dots,p;\ \zeta,\eta = p+1,\dots,n;$$
$$\phi',\psi' = 2',\dots,p';\ \zeta',\eta' = (p+1)',\dots,n'). \tag{16.12}$$

But if the $C^{\zeta'}_{\phi'}$ are zero we have the solutions of (16.10*b*) without integration:

$$\xi^{\zeta'} = \underset{0}{\xi}^{\zeta'} \quad (\zeta' = (p+1)',\dots,n'); \tag{16.13}$$

and by going back to the coordinate system (κ), we immediately get from (16.13) the principal solutions of (16.1) with respect to $\xi^{\alpha} = \underset{0}{\xi}^{\alpha}$. Thus we have proved the theorem

THEOREM III.13. *If the* C^{ζ}_{ϕ} $(\phi = 2,\dots,p)$ *in the Mayer system*

$$\partial_{\beta}\xi^{\zeta} = -C^{\zeta}_{\beta}(\xi^{\kappa}) \quad (\beta = 1,\dots,p;\ \zeta = p+1,\dots,n) \tag{16.14}$$

vanish identically in $\xi^2,\dots,\xi^n$ *for* $\xi^1 = \underset{0}{\xi}^1$, *the principal solutions with respect to* $\xi^1 = \underset{0}{\xi}^1$ *of the abbreviated system of* (16.14) *with respect to* ξ^1, *i.e.*

$$\partial_1\xi^{\zeta} = -C^{\zeta}_{1}(\xi^{\kappa}) \quad (\zeta = p+1,\dots,n;\ \xi^2,\dots,\xi^p = \text{parameters}), \tag{16.15}$$

are simultaneously the principal solutions of (16.14) *with respect to* $\xi^{\alpha} = \underset{0}{\xi}^{\alpha}$ *if the* $\xi^2,\dots,\xi^p$ *involved in these solutions are considered again as ordinary variables.*

So, for the integration of a Mayer system, satisfying the condition of Theorem III.13, only $n-p$ operations $O_{n-p},\dots, O_1$ are needed.

Now it is always possible to transform the coordinate system (κ) in such a way that the new components of C^{ζ}_{β} satisfy the above condition. In order to avoid the use of too many accents, from now on we call the original system (κ) and this new system (κ'). According to (12.12) the $\xi^{\alpha'}$ have to depend only on the ξ^{α} and we take $\xi^{\zeta'} = \delta^{\zeta'}_{\zeta}\xi^{\zeta}$. Then the transformation of the C^{ζ}_{β} takes the form

$$C^{\zeta'}_{\beta'} = \delta^{\zeta'}_{\zeta}\, C^{\zeta}_{\beta}A^{\beta}_{\beta'} \quad (\beta = 1,\dots,p;\ \zeta = p+1,\dots,n;\ \beta' = 1',\dots,p';$$
$$\zeta' = (p+1)',\dots,n'), \tag{16.16}$$

and from this we see that the $C^{\zeta'}_{\phi'}$ $(\phi' = 2',\dots,p';\ \zeta' = (p+1)',\dots,n')$ vanish identically in $\xi^{2'},\dots,\xi^{n'}$ for $\xi^{1'} = \underset{0}{\xi}^{1'}$ *independently of the values of* C^{ζ}_{β} if and only if all derivatives $A^{\beta}_{\phi'}$ $(\beta = 1,\dots,p;\ \phi' = 2',\dots,p')$ contain

$\xi^{1'}-\underset{0}{\xi}^{1'}$ as a factor. According to Lie the most simple transformation $(\kappa) \to (\kappa')$ with this property is

$$\xi^{1} = \underset{0}{\xi}^{1}+\xi^{1'}, \quad \xi^{\phi} = \underset{0}{\xi}^{\phi}+\xi^{1'}\delta^{\phi}_{\phi'}\xi^{\phi'}, \quad \xi^{\zeta} = \delta^{\zeta}_{\zeta'}\xi^{\zeta'} \quad (\phi = 2,\dots,p;$$
$$\zeta = p+1,\dots,n;\ \phi' = 2',\dots,p';\ \zeta' = (p+1)',\dots,n'). \tag{16.17}$$

From these equations it follows that

$$\underset{0}{\xi}^{1'} = 0;\quad \xi^{1'}-\underset{0}{\xi}^{1'} = \xi^{1'}. \tag{16.18}$$

The form of the equations (16.1) is invariant for the transformation (16.17); hence the system

$$\partial_{\beta'}\xi^{\zeta'} = -C^{\zeta'}_{\beta'} \quad (\beta' = 1',\dots,p';\ \zeta' = (p+1)',\dots,n') \tag{16.19}$$

is a Mayer system. For the $C^{\zeta'}_{\phi'}$ we have according to (16.16) and (16.17)

$$C^{\zeta'}_{\phi'} = \delta^{\zeta'}_{\zeta}\delta^{\phi}_{\phi'}C^{\zeta}_{\phi}\xi^{1'} \quad (\phi = 2,\dots,p;\ \zeta = p+1,\dots,n;\ \phi' = 2',\dots,p';$$
$$\zeta' = (p+1)',\dots,n'), \tag{16.20}$$

which proves that the $C^{\zeta'}_{\phi'}$ really vanish for $\xi^{1'} = 0$. Now we have to be very careful in drawing further conclusions, as (16.17) is not an allowable coordinate transformation in an $\mathfrak{N}(\underset{0}{\xi}^{\kappa})$ in our sense because its determinant vanishes for $\xi^{1} = \underset{0}{\xi}^{1}$. However, the $C^{\zeta'}_{\beta'}$ are analytic in an $\mathfrak{N}(\underset{0}{\xi}^{\kappa})$ and this enables us to handle the equations (16.19) in the ordinary way. Accordingly we determine the principal solutions of

$$\partial_{1'}\xi^{\zeta'} = -C^{\zeta'}_{1'} \quad (\zeta' = (p+1)',\dots,n') \tag{16.21}$$

with respect to $\xi^{1'} = 0$, regarding the $\xi^{\phi'}$ $(\phi' = 2',\dots,p')$ as parameters. These solutions

$$\xi^{\zeta'} = F^{\zeta'}(\xi^{1'},\xi^{\phi'}) \quad (\phi' = 2',\dots,p';\ \zeta' = (p+1)',\dots,n') \tag{16.22}$$

are, as we have seen, also the principal solutions of (16.19) with respect to $\xi^{\alpha'} = \underset{0}{\xi}^{\alpha'}$. From these solutions we would like to obtain the solutions of (16.1). Here the difficulty arises, because the transformation $(\kappa) \to (\kappa')$ is not an allowable coordinate transformation, and accordingly it is doubtful if we can return from the solutions of (16.19) to the solutions of (16.1).† Anyhow, by using (16.17) and (16.22) it is possible to obtain the relations between the ξ^{ζ} and ξ^{α}

$$\xi^{\zeta} = \delta^{\zeta}_{\zeta'}F^{\zeta'}\left(\xi^{1}-\underset{0}{\xi}^{1}, \frac{\xi^{\phi}-\underset{0}{\xi}^{\phi}}{\xi^{1}-\underset{0}{\xi}^{1}}\right) \quad (\phi = 2,\dots,p;\ \zeta = p+1,\dots,n;$$
$$\zeta' = (p+1)',\dots,n'), \tag{16.23}$$

† Obviously this difficulty always arises if the coordinate transformation has the form (12.12) and if, simultaneously, the $A^{\beta}_{\phi'}$ contain $\xi^{1'}-\underset{0}{\xi}^{1'}$ as a factor.

but it is questionable if these expressions for ξ^ζ constitute solutions of (16.1), analytic in an $\mathfrak{N}(\underset{0}{\xi}^\kappa)$. If we could prove that the functions $F^{\zeta'}$ contain the variables $\xi^{\phi'}$ only in the combinations $\xi^{1'}\xi^{\phi'}$ all doubts would vanish, because the transformation from the variables $\xi^1, \ldots, \xi^n$ to the variables $\xi^{1'}$, $\xi^{1'}\xi^{\phi'}$, $\xi^{\zeta'}$ has determinant 1, and is accordingly an allowable coordinate transformation. So this has to be proved.

As was proved in the preceding section, (16.1) has only one system of principal solutions with respect to $\xi^\alpha = \underset{0}{\xi}^\alpha$. Let these principal solutions be

$$\xi^\zeta = \Phi^\zeta(\xi^1, \xi^\phi);\quad \Phi^\zeta(\underset{0}{\xi}^1, \underset{0}{\xi}^\phi) = \underset{0}{\xi}^\zeta \quad (\phi = 2, \ldots, p;\ \zeta = p+1, \ldots, n). \tag{16.24}$$

If these equations are transformed according to (16.17), we get

$$\xi^{\zeta'} = \delta^{\zeta'}_\zeta \Phi^\zeta(\underset{0}{\xi}^1 + \xi^{1'}, \underset{0}{\xi}^\phi + \xi^{1'}\xi^{\phi'}) \quad (\phi = 2, \ldots, p;\ \zeta = p+1, \ldots, n; \\ \phi' = 2', \ldots, p';\ \zeta' = (p+1)', \ldots, n'), \tag{16.25}$$

and it is readily verified that these equations constitute the principal solutions of (16.19) with respect to $\xi^{\alpha'} = \underset{0}{\xi}^{\alpha'}$. Now (16.19) has only one system of principal solutions with respect to $\xi^{\alpha'} = \underset{0}{\xi}^{\alpha'}$, so according to (16.22),

$$F^{\zeta'}(\xi^{1'}, \xi^{\phi'}) = \delta^{\zeta'}_\zeta \Phi^\zeta(\underset{0}{\xi}^1 + \xi^{1'}, \underset{0}{\xi}^\phi + \xi^{1'}\xi^{\phi'}) \quad (\phi = 2, \ldots, p;\ \zeta = p+1, \ldots, n; \\ \phi' = 2', \ldots, p';\ \zeta' = (p+1)', \ldots, n'). \tag{16.26}$$

But this relation shows that the $F^{\zeta'}$ contain the variables $\xi^{\phi'}$ only in the combinations $\xi^{1'}\xi^{\phi'}$ and this means that the desired transformation of solutions is possible.

The determination of the solutions of a complete system of p equations by the Mayer method here described, needs only one coordinate transformation and $n-p$ operations $O_{n-p}, \ldots, O_1$. If only one solution is desired, only one coordinate transformation and one operation O_{n-p} are necessary. If from the beginning we already possess m independent solutions, obtained in any way, we can introduce these functions directly as the first m coordinates, and we then need only one coordinate transformation and $n-p-m$ operations $O_{n-p-m}, \ldots, O_1$.

It is inconvenient that the symmetry of the formulae is disturbed by preferring the coordinate ξ^1. Now it is possible to derive from (16.1) another Mayer system in $n+1$ coordinates without disturbing the symmetry. To do this, according to Mayer, we introduce the coordinates η^0, η^κ by means of the transformation

$$\begin{aligned} \xi^\alpha &= \underset{0}{\xi^\alpha} + \eta^0 \eta^\alpha \\ \xi^\zeta &= \eta^\zeta \end{aligned} \qquad (\alpha = 1,\ldots,p;\ \zeta = p+1,\ldots,n). \tag{16.27}$$

Then we get from (16.1)

$$\text{(a)} \qquad \frac{\partial \eta^\zeta}{\partial \eta^\beta} = -\bar{C}^\zeta_\beta(\eta^{\bar\kappa}), \qquad \bar{C}^\zeta_\beta(\eta^{\bar\kappa}) \overset{\text{def}}{=} \eta^0 C^\zeta_\beta(\underset{0}{\xi^\alpha} + \eta^0\eta^\alpha, \eta^\eta),$$

$$\text{(b)} \qquad \frac{\partial \eta^\zeta}{\partial \eta^0} = -\bar{C}^\zeta_0(\eta^{\bar\kappa}), \qquad \bar{C}^\zeta_0(\eta^{\bar\kappa}) \overset{\text{def}}{=} \eta^\beta C^\zeta_\beta(\underset{0}{\xi^\alpha} + \eta^0\eta^\alpha, \eta^\eta)$$

$$(\alpha, \beta = 1,\ldots,p;\ \zeta, \eta = p+1,\ldots,n;\ \bar\kappa = 0, 1,\ldots,n), \tag{16.28}$$

or

$$\frac{\partial \eta^\zeta}{\partial \eta^{\bar\beta}} = -\bar{C}^\zeta_{\bar\beta}(\eta^{\bar\kappa}) \quad (\zeta = p+1,\ldots,n;\ \bar\beta = 0, 1,\ldots,p;\ \bar\kappa = 0, 1,\ldots,n). \tag{16.29}$$

We call (16.29) the *auxiliary system belonging to* (16.1). From (15.1) we get by means of (16.27) the system

$$\bar{C}^\zeta_{\bar\beta}\, d\eta^{\bar\beta} + d\eta^\zeta = 0 \quad (\zeta = p+1,\ldots,n;\ \bar\beta = 0, 1,\ldots,p), \tag{16.30}$$

called the *auxiliary system belonging to* (15.1). Now (16.30) is derived from the complete system (15.1) by a transformation of coordinates; hence (16.30) is complete as well. Consequently (16.29) is the Mayer system belonging to (16.30), as we can also prove by verifying the conditions

$$\frac{\partial}{\partial \eta^{[\bar\gamma}} \bar{C}^\zeta_{\bar\beta]} = \bar{C}^\eta_{[\bar\gamma} \frac{\partial}{\partial \eta^{|\eta|}} \bar{C}^\zeta_{\bar\beta]} \quad (\bar\beta, \bar\gamma = 0, 1,\ldots,p;\ \zeta, \eta = p+1,\ldots,n). \tag{16.31}$$

The special Jacobian system adjoint to (16.30) is

$$\frac{\partial}{\partial \eta^{\bar\beta}} f - \bar{C}^\zeta_{\bar\beta} \frac{\partial}{\partial \eta^\zeta} f = 0 \quad (\bar\beta = 0, 1,\ldots,p;\ \zeta = p+1,\ldots,n). \tag{16.32}$$

This system may also be derived from (12.10) by means of the transformation (16.27). (16.32) is called the *auxiliary system belonging to* (12.10).

Since the $\bar{C}^\zeta_\beta$ $(\beta = 1,\ldots,p)$, take the value zero for $\eta^0 = 0$ according to (16.28 *a*), the Mayer system (16.30) satisfies the condition of Theorem III.13. η^0 is now assuming the role of ξ^1 and $\underset{0}{\eta^0} = 0$. Applying the process described to this system, we first determine the principal solutions with respect to the *abbreviated auxiliary system of* (16.29) with respect to η^0:

$$\frac{\partial \eta^\zeta}{\partial \eta^0} = -\bar{C}_0^\zeta(\eta^{\bar{\kappa}}) \quad (\zeta = p+1,\ldots,n;\ \bar{\kappa} = 0,1,\ldots,n;\ \eta^1,\ldots,\eta^p = \text{parameters}). \quad (16.33)$$

These solutions

$$\eta^\zeta = F^\zeta(\eta^0,\eta^\alpha), \qquad F^\zeta(\underset{0}{\eta^0},\eta^\alpha) = \underset{0}{\eta^\zeta} \quad (\alpha = 1,\ldots,p;\ \zeta = p+1,\ldots,n) \quad (16.34)$$

are simultaneously the principal solutions of (16.29) with respect to $\eta^{\bar{\alpha}} = \underset{0}{\eta^{\bar{\alpha}}}$ $(\bar{\alpha} = 0,1,\ldots,p)$. We have $\underset{0}{\eta^0} = 0$ whilst the values of the $\underset{0}{\eta^\alpha}$ are arbitrary and of no importance in the sequel.

Now from these solutions the principal solutions of (16.1) with respect to $\xi^\alpha = \underset{0}{\xi^\alpha}$ have to be derived. As in the preceding case the difficulty arises that the transformation (16.27) is not an allowable coordinate transformation but a transformation from n to $n+1$ variables. Consequently, from (16.34) expressions for the ξ^ζ in terms of the ξ^α can be derived if and only if the functions F^ζ contain the η^α only in the combinations $\eta^0\eta^\alpha$. This has to be proved.

As we have shown in III, § 15, the system (16.1) has one and only one system of principal solutions with respect to $\xi^\alpha = \underset{0}{\xi^\alpha}$. Let this be the system

$$\xi^\zeta = \Phi^\zeta(\xi^\alpha), \qquad \Phi^\zeta(\underset{0}{\xi^\alpha}) = \underset{0}{\xi^\zeta} \quad (\alpha = 1,\ldots,p;\ \zeta = p+1,\ldots,n). \quad (16.35)$$

If the transformation (16.27) is applied to (16.35) we get

$$\eta^\zeta = \Phi^\zeta(\underset{0}{\xi^\alpha}+\eta^0\eta^\alpha) \quad (\alpha = 1,\ldots,p;\ \zeta = p+1,\ldots,n) \quad (16.36)$$

and this is a system of principal solutions of (16.29) with respect to $\eta^{\bar{\alpha}} = \underset{0}{\eta^{\bar{\alpha}}}$. Now we know that (16.29) has one, and only one, such system of principal solutions; hence

$$F^\zeta(\eta^0,\eta^\alpha) = \Phi^\zeta(\underset{0}{\xi^\alpha}+\eta^0\eta^\alpha) \quad (\alpha = 1,\ldots,p;\ \zeta = p+1,\ldots,n) \quad (16.37)$$

and this proves that the η^α in F^ζ occur only in the combinations $\eta^0\eta^\alpha$.

We developed Mayer's method here, starting from the Mayer system (16.1). But we could have chosen as well the special Jacobian system (12.10) or its adjoint system (15.1) as a starting-point. For the abbreviated auxiliary system (16.33) is itself a Mayer system and to it belongs the special Jacobian system

$$\frac{\partial}{\partial\eta^0}f-\bar{C}_0^\zeta\frac{\partial}{\partial\eta^\zeta}f=0 \quad (\zeta=p+1,\ldots,n;\ \alpha=1,\ldots,p;\ \eta^\alpha=\text{parameters}) \tag{16.38}$$

and its adjoint complete system

$$\bar{C}_0^\zeta\,d\eta^0+d\eta^\zeta=0 \quad (\zeta=p+1,\ldots,n;\ \alpha=1,\ldots,p;\ \eta^\alpha=\text{parameters}). \tag{16.39}$$

If we call (16.38) the *abbreviated auxiliary system of* (12.10) *with respect to* η^0 and (16.39) the *abbreviated auxiliary system of* (15.1) *with respect to* η^0, we are able to collect results in the following theorem:

THEOREM III.14. *The principal solutions of the Mayer system* (16.1)

$$\partial_\beta\,\xi^\zeta=-C_\beta^\zeta(\xi^\kappa) \quad (\beta=1,\ldots,p;\ \zeta=p+1,\ldots,n), \tag{16.40 a}$$

the principal solutions of the special Jacobian system (12.10)

$$\partial_\beta f-C_\beta^\zeta\,\partial_\zeta f=0 \quad (\beta=1,\ldots,p;\ \zeta=p+1,\ldots,n), \tag{16.40 b}$$

or the principal integral functions of the adjoint complete system (15.1)

$$C_\beta^\zeta\,d\xi^\beta+d\xi^\zeta=0 \tag{16.40 c}$$

with respect to $\xi^\alpha=\underset{0}{\xi^\alpha}$ $(\alpha=1,\ldots,p)$, *are obtainable by the following process*:

1. *By means of the transformation* (16.27)

$$\begin{aligned}\xi^\alpha&=\underset{0}{\xi^\alpha}+\eta^0\eta^\alpha\\ \xi^\zeta&=\eta^\zeta\end{aligned} \qquad (\alpha=1,\ldots,p;\ \zeta=p+1,\ldots,n) \tag{16.41}$$

the auxiliary system of (16.40 *a*), (16.40 *b*), *or* (16.40 *c*) *in* $n+1$ *variables is formed*:

$$\begin{aligned}
&(a)\ (16.29) && \frac{\partial\eta^\zeta}{\partial\eta^{\bar\beta}}=-\bar{C}_{\bar\beta}^\zeta(\eta^{\bar\kappa}),\\
&(b)\ (16.32) && \frac{\partial}{\partial\eta^{\bar\beta}}f-\bar{C}_{\bar\beta}^\zeta\frac{\partial}{\partial\eta^\zeta}f=0,\\
&(c)\ (16.30) && \bar{C}_{\bar\beta}^\zeta\,d\eta^{\bar\beta}+d\eta^\zeta=0\\
& && (\bar\beta=0,1,\ldots,p;\ \zeta=p+1,\ldots,n;\ \bar\kappa=0,1,\ldots,n).
\end{aligned} \tag{16.42}$$

2. *From this auxiliary system the abbreviated auxiliary system with respect to η^0 is formed:*

$$(a)\ (16.33)\qquad \frac{\partial \eta^\zeta}{\partial \eta^0} = -\bar{C}_0^\zeta(\eta^{\bar{\kappa}}),$$

$$(b)\ (16.38)\qquad \frac{\partial}{\partial \eta^0} f - \bar{C}_0^\zeta \frac{\partial}{\partial \eta^\zeta} f = 0, \qquad (16.43)$$

$$(c)\ (16.39)\qquad \bar{C}_0^\zeta\, d\eta^0 + d\eta^\zeta = 0$$

$$(\zeta = p+1,..., n;\ \bar{\kappa} = 0, 1,..., n;\ \eta^\alpha = \text{parameters};\ \alpha = 1,..., p).$$

3. *The principal solutions (principal integral functions) with respect to $\eta^0 = 0$ of this abbreviated auxiliary system are determined and these solutions are simultaneously the principal solutions (principal integral functions) of the auxiliary system with respect to $\eta^{\bar{\alpha}} = \underset{0}{\eta^{\bar{\alpha}}}$ ($\bar{\alpha} = 0, 1,..., p$).*

4. *In these solutions (integral functions), containing the η^α only in the combinations $\eta^0\eta^\alpha$, the $\eta^0\eta^\alpha$ are replaced by $\xi^\alpha - \underset{0}{\xi^\alpha}$ and the η^ζ by ξ^ζ.*

From the above it is clear that, being in possession of a system of principal solutions (principal integral functions) of the abbreviated auxiliary system, we have immediately a system of principal solutions (principal integral functions) of the system to be integrated. But it may happen that we know solutions (integral functions) of the abbreviated auxiliary system, which are *not* principal solutions (principal integral functions). These solutions (integral functions) are in general *not* solutions (integral functions) of the auxiliary system and, therefore, it is not possible to obtain from them solutions (integral functions) of the original system by the simple process of replacing $\eta^0\eta^\alpha$ by $\xi^\alpha - \underset{0}{\xi^\alpha}$ and η^ζ by ξ^ζ. Notwithstanding this, the knowledge of such solutions (integral functions) can be used to facilitate the process of integration, as will be proved for the case of a special Jacobian system (16.40 *b*). The proof implies the proof for the two other cases (16.40 *a*) and (16.40 *c*).

Let $\overset{1}{f}$ be an arbitrary solution of the abbreviated auxiliary system (16.43 *b*) with respect to η^0, which is not a principal solution with respect to $\eta^0 = 0$. Thus $\overset{1}{f}$ is not a solution of the remaining equations

$$\left(\frac{\partial}{\partial \eta^\beta} - \bar{C}_\beta^\zeta \frac{\partial}{\partial \eta^\zeta}\right) f = 0 \quad (\beta = 1,..., p;\ \zeta = p+1,..., n). \qquad (16.44)$$

Now since the auxiliary system (16.42*b*) is Jacobian, we have

$$\left(\frac{\partial}{\partial\eta^0}-\bar{C}_0^\zeta\frac{\partial}{\partial\eta^\zeta}\right)\left(\frac{\partial}{\partial\eta^\beta}-\bar{C}_\beta^\eta\frac{\partial}{\partial\eta^\eta}\right)\overset{1}{f}$$
$$=\left(\frac{\partial}{\partial\eta^\beta}-\bar{C}_\beta^\eta\frac{\partial}{\partial\eta^\eta}\right)\left(\frac{\partial}{\partial\eta^0}-\bar{C}_0^\zeta\frac{\partial}{\partial\eta^\zeta}\right)\overset{1}{f}=0$$
$$(\beta = 1,\ldots,p;\ \zeta,\eta = p+1,\ldots,n), \quad (16.45)$$

and thus all expressions

$$\left(\frac{\partial}{\partial\eta^\beta}-\bar{C}_\beta^\zeta\frac{\partial}{\partial\eta^\zeta}\right)\overset{1}{f} \quad (16.46)$$

are solutions of the abbreviated auxiliary system (16.43*b*). Among them there may be solutions which are independent of each other and of the $\overset{1}{f}$ and the η^α $(\alpha = 1,\ldots,p)$. With these we can proceed in the same way, and so on, till at last a system of s independent solutions $\overset{\mathfrak{a}}{f}$ $(\mathfrak{a} = 1,\ldots,s)$ of the abbreviated auxiliary system is obtained, which cannot be extended in this way any more. Then there have to be relations of the form

$$\left(\frac{\partial}{\partial\eta^\beta}-\bar{C}_\beta^\zeta\frac{\partial}{\partial\eta^\zeta}\right)\overset{\mathfrak{a}}{f}=\overset{\mathfrak{a}}{\Omega}_\beta(\overset{\mathfrak{b}}{f},\eta^\alpha)$$
$$(\alpha,\beta = 1,\ldots,p;\ \zeta = p+1,\ldots,n;\ \mathfrak{a},\mathfrak{b} = 1,\ldots,s). \quad (16.47)$$

When $s = n-p$ we know all the solutions of the abbreviated auxiliary system and consequently also all principal solutions with respect to $\eta^0 = 0$. In that case the integration can be finished in the ordinary way. Suppose now $0 < s < n-p$. The functions $\overset{\mathfrak{a}}{f}$ must be expressible in terms of the principal solutions (yet unknown) $F^\zeta(\eta^0, \eta^\alpha, \eta^\theta)$ with respect to $\eta^0 = 0$ and the η^α $(\alpha = 1,\ldots,p)$:

$$\overset{\mathfrak{a}}{f}(\eta^0,\eta^\alpha,\eta^\zeta)=\overset{\mathfrak{a}}{\phi}(F^\zeta,\eta^\alpha) \quad (\alpha = 1,\ldots,p;\ \zeta = p+1,\ldots,n;\ \mathfrak{a} = 1,\ldots,s). \quad (16.48)$$

If we put $\eta^0 = 0$ in these equations, the F^ζ become the η^ζ and we get the equations

$$\overset{\mathfrak{a}}{f}(0,\eta^\alpha,\eta^\zeta)=\overset{\mathfrak{a}}{\phi}(\eta^\zeta,\eta^\alpha) \quad (\alpha = 1,\ldots,p;\ \zeta = p+1,\ldots,n;\ \mathfrak{a} = 1,\ldots,s), \quad (16.49)$$

by which the functions $\overset{\mathfrak{a}}{\phi}$ are determined, the functions $\overset{\mathfrak{a}}{f}$ being known by hypothesis. Now the rank of the system

$$\overset{\mathfrak{a}}{\phi}(F^\zeta,\eta^\alpha)-\overset{\mathfrak{a}}{f}=0 \quad (\alpha = 1,\ldots,p;\ \zeta = p+1,\ldots,n;\ \mathfrak{a} = 1,\ldots,s) \quad (16.50)$$

in the variables F^ζ, η^α, and $\overset{\mathfrak{a}}{f}$ with respect to the F^ζ must be s because if this rank were $< s$, according to Theorem II.7, there would exist relations between the η^α and $\overset{\mathfrak{a}}{f}$, which is impossible. Hence, just s of the functions F^ζ can be solved from (16.50) in terms of the $\overset{\mathfrak{a}}{f}$, the η^α, and the $n-p-s$ remaining functions F^ζ. By interchanging the indices ζ it can always be arranged that the resulting equations have the form

$$F^{p+\omega} = \psi^{p+\omega}(\overset{\mathfrak{a}}{f}, \eta^\alpha, F^{p+s+1},..., F^n)$$
$$(\alpha = 1,..., p;\ \omega = 1,..., s;\ \mathfrak{a} = 1,..., s). \quad (16.51)$$

The F^ζ being solutions of (16.44) we have

$$\frac{\partial \psi^{p+\omega}}{\partial \overset{\mathfrak{b}}{f}}\left(\frac{\partial}{\partial \eta^\beta} - \bar{C}^\zeta_\beta \frac{\partial}{\partial \eta^\zeta}\right)\overset{\mathfrak{b}}{f} + \frac{\partial \psi^{p+\omega}}{\partial \eta^\beta} = 0$$
$$(\beta = 1,..., p;\ \zeta = p+1,..., n;\ \omega = 1,..., s;\ \mathfrak{b} = 1,..., s) \quad (16.52)$$

or, according to (16.47),

$$\Gamma^{p+\omega}_\beta \overset{\text{def}}{=} \frac{\partial \psi^{p+\omega}}{\partial \overset{\mathfrak{b}}{f}} \overset{\mathfrak{b}}{\Omega}_\beta(\overset{\mathfrak{a}}{f}, \eta^\alpha) + \frac{\partial \psi^{p+\omega}}{\partial \eta^\beta} = 0$$
$$(\alpha, \beta = 1,..., p;\ \omega = 1,..., s;\ \mathfrak{a}, \mathfrak{b} = 1,..., s) \quad (16.53)$$

identically in η^0, η^α, η^ζ. The $\Gamma^{p+\omega}_\beta$ in (16.53) are functions of $\overset{\mathfrak{a}}{f}$, η^α, $F^{p+s+1},..., F^n$:

$$\Gamma^{p+\omega}_\beta = \Gamma^{p+\omega}_\beta(\overset{\mathfrak{a}}{f}, \eta^\alpha, F^{p+s+1},..., F^n)$$
$$(\alpha, \beta = 1,..., p;\ \omega = 1,..., s;\ \mathfrak{a} = 1,..., s) \quad (16.54)$$

and we know that these functions vanish identically in η^0, η^α, η^ζ if $\overset{\mathfrak{a}}{f}$, $F^{p+s+1},..., F^n$ are written as functions of η^0, η^α, η^ζ. Now the n functions η^α, F^ζ $(\zeta = p+1,..., n)$ are functionally independent (because for $\eta^0 = 0$ they become η^α, η^ζ) and these functions can be expressed by means of (16.51) in terms of the n functions $\overset{\mathfrak{a}}{f}$, η^α, $F^{p+s+1},..., F^n$. This proves that the latter n functions are functionally independent as well. From this it follows that the $\Gamma^{p+\omega}_\beta$ vanish identically in $\overset{\mathfrak{a}}{f}$, η^α, $F^{p+s+1},..., F^n$, considered as independent variables. Now consider the s functions

$$'F^{p+\omega} = \psi^{p+\omega}(\overset{\mathfrak{a}}{f}, \eta^\alpha, c^{p+s+1},..., c^n)$$
$$(\alpha = 1,..., p;\ \omega = 1,..., s;\ \mathfrak{a} = 1,..., s), \quad (16.55)$$

where the $c^{p+s+1},\ldots,c^n$ are arbitrary coordinates and where the $\overset{\mathfrak{a}}{f}$ are the given solutions of (16.43 *b*). Then we have, according to (16.47),

$$\left(\frac{\partial}{\partial\eta^\beta}-\bar{C}^\zeta_\beta\frac{\partial}{\partial\eta^\zeta}\right)'F^{p+\omega} = \frac{\partial\psi^{p+\omega}}{\partial\overset{\mathfrak{b}}{f}}\overset{\mathfrak{b}}{\Omega}_\beta+\frac{\partial\psi^{p+\omega}}{\partial\eta^\beta}$$

$$= \Gamma^{p+\omega}_\beta(\overset{\mathfrak{a}}{f},\eta^\alpha,c^{p+s+1},\ldots,c^n) = 0$$

$$(\alpha,\beta = 1,\ldots,p;\ \zeta = p+1,\ldots,n;\ \omega = 1,\ldots,s;\ \mathfrak{b} = 1,\ldots,s), \tag{16.56}$$

hence the $'F^{p+\omega}$ are solutions of (16.44). But since $\overset{\mathfrak{a}}{f}$ and η^α are solutions of (16.43 *b*) this proves that the $'F^{p+\omega}$ are solutions of (16.42 *b*). From these s solutions we can derive solutions of (16.40 *b*) if the $'F^{p+\omega}$ contain the η^α only in the combinations $\eta^0\eta^\alpha$. Now the $F^{p+\omega}$ contain the η^α only in these combinations and, since the same is true for $F^{p+s+1},\ldots, F^n$, this property is not lost if the $F^{p+s+1},\ldots, F^n$ are replaced by constants. Hence it is possible to form s solutions of (16.40 *b*). This proves the theorem†

THEOREM III.15. (*Mayer's theorem of integration.*) *If we know one or more solutions (integral functions) of the abbreviated auxiliary system* (16.43 *a*), (16.43 *b*), *or* (16.43 *c*) *respectively, which are not functions of the* η^α ($\alpha = 1,\ldots,p$) *alone, from these solutions (integral functions) always at least one solution (integral function) of the system* (16.40 *a*), (16.40 *b*), *or* (16.40 *c*) *respectively can be obtained by mere differentiations and eliminations.*

Before closing this section something has to be said concerning the geometrical interpretation of Mayer's method of integration. $n-p$ independent solutions of the special Jacobian system

$$\partial_\beta f-C^\zeta_\beta\partial_\zeta f = 0 \quad (\beta = 1,\ldots,p;\ \zeta = p+1,\ldots,n) \tag{16.57}$$

represent a normal system of ∞^{n-p} integral-X_p's. If we consider the first equation of the system

$$\partial_1 f-C^\zeta_1\partial_\zeta f = 0 \quad (\zeta = p+1,\ldots,n), \tag{16.58}$$

looking upon the $\xi^2,\ldots, \xi^p$ as parameters, $n-p$ independent solutions of this system represent a normal system of ∞^{n-p} integral-X_1's in each of the ∞^{p-1} X_{n-p+1}'s with the equations

$$\xi^2 = c^2,\quad \ldots,\quad \xi^p = c^p. \tag{16.59}$$

These X_1's are the sections of the integral X_p's with the X_{n-p+1}'s. But

† Cf. Mayer 1872. 1; v. Weber 1900. 1, p. 119; Engel and Faber 1932. 1, p. 60.

it is not possible to derive the X_p's from the X_1's because we do not know how to select the ∞^{p-1} X_1's constituting together an integral-X_p. Now if we perform the transformation (16.17) the system (16.57) becomes

$$\partial_{\beta'} f - C^{\zeta'}_{\beta'} \partial_{\zeta'} f = 0 \quad (\beta' = 1', ..., p';\ \zeta' = (p+1)', ..., n') \tag{16.60}$$

and we know that the $C^{\zeta'}_{\phi'}$ $(\phi' = 2', ..., p';\ \zeta' = (p+1)', ..., n')$ vanish for $\xi^{1'} = 0$. $n-p$ independent solutions of the first equation

$$\partial_{1'} f - C^{\zeta'}_{1'} \partial_{\zeta'} f = 0 \quad (\zeta' = (p+1)', ..., n') \tag{16.61}$$

now represent a normal system of ∞^{n-p} X_1's in each of the ∞^{p-1} X_{n-p+1}'s with the equations

$$\xi^{2'} = \frac{\xi^2 - \underset{0}{\xi^2}}{\xi^1 - \underset{0}{\xi^1}} = c^{2'}, \quad ..., \quad \xi^{p'} = \frac{\xi^p - \underset{0}{\xi^p}}{\xi^1 - \underset{0}{\xi^1}} = c^{p'} \tag{16.62}$$

and all these X_{n-p+1}'s contain the X_{n-p} with the equations†

$$\xi^1 = \underset{0}{\xi^1}, \quad ..., \quad \xi^p = \underset{0}{\xi^p} \tag{16.63}$$

with respect to (κ). In all points of this X_{n-p} the system (16.60) reduces to

$$\begin{aligned} \partial_{1'} f - C^{\zeta'}_{1'} \partial_{\zeta'} f &= 0 \quad (\zeta' = (p+1)', ..., n'), \\ \partial_{2'} f &= 0, \\ &\ \ \cdot\ \ \cdot\ \ \cdot \\ \partial_{p'} f &= 0. \end{aligned} \tag{16.64}$$

This means that in every point of this X_{n-p} the tangent E_p of an integral-X_p is spanned by the ∞^{p-1} tangent E_1's of all integral-X_1's for different values of $\xi^{2'}, ..., \xi^{p'}$ through this point. Hence the integral-X_p through any point of the X_{n-p} can be found by taking together all ∞^{p-1} integral-X_1's through this point and this can be done analytically by considering the parameters $\xi^{2'}, ..., \xi^{p'}$ in the solutions of (16.61) as ordinary variables. From this geometrical consideration we see once more that the transformation of coordinates needed can never be an allowable transformation because it is necessary that somewhere a singular X_{n-p} should appear.

With respect to the more symmetrical transformation of Mayer (16.27) similar remarks can be made.

Notwithstanding this geometrical interpretation it cannot be denied that Mayer's method, as described here in the usual way, seems rather

† Of course in the points of this singular X_{n-p} the equations (16.62) do not represent a normal system in the sense of our definition.

artificial. This is the more surprising as we might expect that a method of integration giving such an important reduction in the number of necessary operations would give us at the same time a clear insight into the matter concerned. Now in Chapter VIII, §11 we shall see that Mayer's method is really in no way artificial, but that we need the more general point of view due to Cartan to see it in the right light.

17. X_p-forming systems of p contravariant or $n-p$ covariant vector fields and their integrating factors and comitants†

In order that there should exist a normal system of X_p's whose tangent E_p would contain at every point the directions of p given vectors $\underset{b}{v}^\kappa$ $(b = 1,..., \mathrm{p})$, it is necessary and sufficient that the system

$$\underset{b}{v}^\mu \partial_\mu f = 0 \quad (b = 1,..., \mathrm{p}) \tag{17.1}$$

should be complete. This follows immediately from the theory of complete homogeneous systems. In this case we call the system of p vectors $\underset{b}{v}^\kappa$ X_p-*forming*. Thus the necessary and sufficient condition is that there should exist relations of the form

$$\underset{[c}{v}^\mu \partial_{|\mu|} \underset{b]}{v}^\kappa = \sigma^a_{cb} \underset{a}{v}^\kappa \quad (a, b, c = 1,..., \mathrm{p}). \tag{17.2}$$

Introducing the simple p-vector

$$v^{\kappa_1...\kappa_p} = \underset{1}{v}^{[\kappa_1}...\underset{\mathrm{p}}{v}^{\kappa_p]} \tag{17.3}$$

these conditions can be written in the form

$$v^{[\nu_1...\nu_p}\partial_\mu v^{|\mu|\omega]\kappa_3...\kappa_p} = 0 \tag{17.4}$$

and also in the form

$$v^{\mu[\omega|\kappa_3...\kappa_p|}\partial_\mu v^{\nu_1...\nu_p]} = 0. \tag{17.5}$$

If $w_{\lambda_1...\lambda_q}$ is a simple covariant q-vector field, $q = n-p$, which has at every point the same p-direction as $v^{\kappa_1...\kappa_p}$, we have

$$v^{\mu\kappa_2...\kappa_p}w_{\mu\lambda_2...\lambda_q} = 0 \tag{17.6}$$

and from this equation the following forms of the necessary and sufficient conditions may be readily derived

$$w_{\omega\lambda_2...\lambda_q}\,\partial_\mu\, v^{\mu\omega\kappa_3...\kappa_p} = 0, \tag{17.7}$$

$$v^{\mu\omega\kappa_3...\kappa_p}\partial_\mu\, w_{\omega\lambda_2...\lambda_q} = 0, \tag{17.8}$$

$$w_{[\nu_1...\nu_q}\,\partial_\mu\, w_{\omega]\lambda_2...\lambda_q} = 0, \tag{17.9}$$

$$w_{[\omega|\lambda_2...\lambda_q|}\,\partial_\mu\, w_{\nu_1...\nu_q]} = 0. \tag{17.10}$$

† Cf. v. Weber 1900. 1, ch. ii; Engel and Faber 1932. 1, ch. ii.

As a corollary of (17.10) we may state the theorem

THEOREM III.16. *Every simple covariant q-vector field, $q = n-p$, whose rotation vanishes, is X_p-forming.*

It must be noted that all equations (17.4, 5, 7, 8, 9, 10) remain invariant if v and w get arbitrary scalar factors. Hence these equations really represent conditions for $\lfloor v \rfloor$ and $\lfloor w \rfloor$.

If v and w are X_p-forming and if the equations of these X_p's are

$$\overset{x}{s}(\xi^\kappa) = \text{const.} \quad (x = \mathrm{p}+1,\ldots,\mathrm{n}), \tag{17.11}$$

there exists a scalar p such that

$$w_{\lambda_1\ldots\lambda_q} = p^{-1} \overset{\mathrm{p}+1}{s}_{[\lambda_1}\ldots\overset{\mathrm{n}}{s}_{\lambda_q]} \quad (\overset{x}{s}_\lambda = \partial_\lambda \overset{x}{s}); \tag{17.12}$$

and therefore, w is a gradient product to within a scalar factor. Consequently there exists a scalar density $\mathfrak{p}$ of weight $+1$, such that the p-vector density of weight $+1$, defined by

$$\mathfrak{v}^{\kappa_1\ldots\kappa_p} \stackrel{\text{def}}{=} \mathfrak{p}v^{\kappa_1\ldots\kappa_p} = \frac{1}{(n-p)!} p w_{\lambda_1\ldots\lambda_q} \mathfrak{E}^{\lambda_1\ldots\lambda_q\kappa_1\ldots\kappa_p} \tag{17.13}$$

has divergence zero. This proves the theorem (cf. Theorem III.7)

THEOREM III.17. (*Fourth theorem of integrating factors.*) *If the simple p-vector $v^{\kappa_1\ldots\kappa_p}$ is analytic and X_p-forming in an $\mathfrak{N}(\overset{0}{\xi^\kappa})$, there exists a scalar density $\mathfrak{p}$ of weight $+1$ such that the divergence of $\mathfrak{p}v^{\kappa_1\ldots\kappa_p}$ vanishes in that region.*

If the simple q-vector $w_{\lambda_1\ldots\lambda_q}$ $(q = n-p)$, is analytic and X_p-forming in an $\mathfrak{N}(\overset{0}{\xi^\kappa})$, there exists a scalar p such that the rotation of $pw_{\lambda_1\ldots\lambda_q}$ vanishes in that region.

The factor $\mathfrak{p}$ is called an *integrating factor* or *Lie multiplier* of the complete system (17.1) and p an *integrating factor* of the adjoint complete system

$$w_{\lambda_1\ldots\lambda_q} d\xi^{\lambda_q} = 0. \tag{17.14}$$

An integrating factor $\mathfrak{p}$ is a solution of the system of equations

$$\partial_{\kappa_1} \mathfrak{p}v^{\kappa_1\ldots\kappa_p} = 0 \tag{17.15}$$

which is linear and non-homogeneous in $\log \mathfrak{p}$. We will show that (17.15) is equivalent to the system†

$$\underset{b}{v}^\mu \partial_\mu \mathfrak{p} + \mathfrak{p}\partial_\mu \underset{b}{v}^\mu - 2\mathfrak{p}\sigma^a_{ab} = 0 \quad (a, b = 1,\ldots,\mathrm{p}). \tag{17.16}$$

† Zorawski 1902. 1; de Donder 1908. 1.

We write (17.15) in the form

$$\begin{aligned}0 &= (\partial_{\kappa_1}\mathfrak{p})\underset{[1}{v}^{\kappa_1}\cdots\underset{p]}{v}^{\kappa_p}+\mathfrak{p}(\partial_{\kappa_1}\underset{[1}{v}^{\kappa_1})\underset{2}{v}^{\kappa_2}\cdots\underset{p]}{v}^{\kappa_p}+\mathfrak{p}\underset{[1}{v}^{\kappa_1}(\partial_{|\kappa_1|}\underset{2}{v}^{\kappa_2})\underset{3}{v}^{\kappa_3}\cdots\underset{p]}{v}^{\kappa_p}+\\ &\qquad +\cdots+\mathfrak{p}\underset{[1}{v}^{\kappa_1}\cdots\underset{p-1}{v}^{\kappa_{p-1}}\partial_{|\kappa_1|}\underset{p]}{v}^{\kappa_p}\\ &= (\partial_{\kappa_1}\mathfrak{p})\underset{[1}{v}^{\kappa_1}\cdots\underset{p]}{v}^{\kappa_p}+\mathfrak{p}(\partial_{\kappa_1}\underset{[1}{v}^{\kappa_1})\underset{2}{v}^{\kappa_2}\cdots\underset{p]}{v}^{\kappa_p}+\mathfrak{p}\sigma^{a}_{[1\,2}\underset{|a|}{v}^{\kappa_2}\underset{3}{v}^{\kappa_3}\cdots\underset{p]}{v}^{\kappa_p}+\\ &\qquad +\cdots+(-1)^{p}\mathfrak{p}\sigma^{a}_{[1\,p}\underset{2}{v}^{\kappa_2}\cdots\underset{p-1]}{v}^{\kappa_{p-1}}\underset{a}{v}^{\kappa_p}\\ &\qquad (a = 1,\ldots,p) \qquad (17.17)\end{aligned}$$

and introduce p arbitrary vectors $\overset{1}{u}_\lambda,\ldots,\overset{p}{u}_\lambda$ such that

$$\overset{a}{u}_\lambda \underset{b}{v}^\lambda = \delta^a_b \quad (a, b = 1,\ldots,p). \qquad (17.18)$$

If then (17.17) is transvected with $\overset{2}{u}_{\kappa_2}\cdots\overset{p}{u}_{\kappa_p}$, we get

$$\underset{1}{v}^\mu\partial_\mu\mathfrak{p}+\mathfrak{p}\partial_\mu\underset{1}{v}^\mu+2\mathfrak{p}\sigma^a_{1a} = 0 \quad (a = 1,\ldots,p) \qquad (17.19)$$

and in the same way the other equations (17.16) may be deduced.

The non-homogeneous system

$$\underset{b}{v}^\mu\partial_\mu \log\mathfrak{p} = \underset{b}{\phi} \overset{\text{def}}{=} -\partial_\mu\underset{b}{v}^\mu+2\sigma^a_{ab} \quad (a, b = 1,\ldots,p) \qquad (17.20)$$

is complete (cf. Ex. III, 7). Since the reduced system is evidently complete, we have only to prove that (cf. III, § 14)

$$\underset{[c}{v}^\mu\partial_{|\mu|}\underset{b]}{\phi} = \sigma^a_{cb}\underset{a}{\phi} \quad (a, b, c = 1,\ldots,p). \qquad (17.21)$$

Now on the one hand we have from (17.20)

$$\begin{aligned}\underset{[c}{v}^\mu\partial_{|\mu|}\underset{b]}{\phi} &= -\underset{[c}{v}^\mu\partial_{|\mu}\,\partial_{\omega|}\underset{b]}{v}^\omega+2\underset{[c}{v}^\mu\partial_{|\mu}\,\sigma^a_{a|b]}\\ &= -\underset{[c}{v}^\mu\partial_{|\omega}\,\partial_{\mu|}\underset{b]}{v}^\omega+2\underset{[c}{v}^\mu\partial_{|\mu}\,\sigma^a_{a|b]}\\ &= -\partial_\omega(\sigma^a_{cb}\underset{a}{v}^\omega)+(\partial_\omega\underset{[c}{v}^\mu)\partial_{|\mu|}\underset{b]}{v}^\omega+2\underset{[c}{v}^\mu\partial_{|\mu}\,\sigma^a_{a|b]}\\ &= -3\partial_\mu\,\sigma^a_{[cb}\underset{a]}{v}^\mu-\sigma^a_{cb}\,\partial_\mu\underset{a}{v}^\mu \quad (a, b, c = 1,\ldots,p) \qquad (17.22)\end{aligned}$$

and on the other hand,

$$\sigma^a_{cb}\underset{a}{\phi} = -\sigma^a_{cb}\,\partial_\mu\underset{a}{v}^\mu+2\sigma^a_{cb}\,\sigma^d_{da} \quad (a, b, c, d = 1,\ldots,p), \qquad (17.23)$$

and thus it only remains to prove that

$$-3(\partial_\mu\,\sigma^a_{[cb})\underset{a]}{v}^\mu = 2\sigma^a_{cb}\,\sigma^d_{da} \quad (a, b, c, d = 1,\ldots,p). \qquad (17.24)$$

In order to prove this, we prove the identity

$$\underset{[c}{v}^\mu\partial_{|\mu|}\,\sigma^d_{b\,a]}+2\sigma^e_{[b\,a}\,\sigma^d_{c]e} = 0 \quad (a, b, c, d, e = 1,\ldots,p), \qquad (17.25)$$

from which by contraction over a, d we get the identity

$$3 v^{\mu}_{[c} \partial_{|\mu|} \sigma^{a}_{b\,a]} = -2\sigma^{e}_{b\,a}\sigma^{a}_{c\,e} - 2\sigma^{e}_{a\,c}\sigma^{a}_{b\,e} - 2\sigma^{e}_{c\,b}\sigma^{a}_{a\,e} = -2\sigma^{e}_{c\,b}\sigma^{a}_{a\,e}$$

$$(a,b,c,d,e = 1,\ldots,\mathrm{p}) \qquad (17.26)$$

which is equivalent to (17.24). By transvection of the left-hand side of (17.25) with $\underset{d}{v^{\nu}}$ we get, according to (17.2),

$$\begin{aligned} &\underset{[c}{v^{\mu}}(\partial_{|\mu|}\sigma^{d}_{b\,a]})\underset{d}{v^{\nu}} + 2\sigma^{e}_{[b\,a}\sigma^{d}_{c]e}\underset{d}{v^{\nu}} \\ &\quad = \underset{[c}{v^{\mu}}\partial_{|\mu|}(\sigma^{d}_{b\,a]}\underset{d}{v^{\nu}}) - \sigma^{d}_{[b\,a}\underset{c]}{v^{\mu}}\partial_{\mu}\underset{d}{v^{\nu}} + \sigma^{e}_{[b\,a}\underset{c]}{v^{\mu}}\partial_{\mu}\underset{e}{v^{\nu}} - \sigma^{e}_{[b\,a}\underset{|e|}{v^{\mu}}\partial_{|\mu|}\underset{c]}{v^{\nu}} \\ &\quad = \underset{[c}{v^{\mu}}\partial_{|\mu|}(\underset{b}{v^{\omega}}\partial_{|\omega|}\underset{a]}{v^{\nu}}) - (\underset{[b}{v^{\omega}}\partial_{|\omega|}\underset{a}{v^{\mu}})\partial_{|\mu|}\underset{c]}{v^{\nu}} \\ &\quad = \underset{[b}{v^{\omega}}\underset{a}{v^{\mu}}\partial_{|\omega}\partial_{\mu|}\underset{c]}{v^{\nu}} = 0 \quad (a,b,c,d,e = 1,\ldots,\mathrm{p}) \end{aligned} \qquad (17.27)$$

and this proves (17.25) because the $\underset{b}{v^{\kappa}}$ are linearly independent.

We still note that from (17.16) it follows that *an integrating factor of a Jacobian system* ($\sigma^{a}_{cb} = 0$) *is an integrating factor of each equation of the system.*†

Writing (17.1) in the form

$$v^{\lambda_1 \ldots \lambda_p}\partial_{\lambda_p} f = 0 \qquad (17.28)$$

we see that, according to (17.15),

$$\mathfrak{p} v^{\lambda_1 \ldots \lambda_p}\partial_{\lambda_p} f = \partial_{\lambda_p} f \mathfrak{p} v^{\lambda_1 \ldots \lambda_p} = 0. \qquad (17.29)$$

Hence, $f\mathfrak{p}$ is an integrating factor if f is a solution of (17.1). This proves the theorem (cf. Theorem III.8)

THEOREM III.18. (*Fifth theorem of integrating factors.*) *The product of an integrating factor of a complete homogeneous system of linear partial differential equations of the first order and a solution, is an integrating factor. The quotient of two integrating factors is either a constant or a solution.*

If we had taken, in (17.28), a contravariant p-vector-density $\mathfrak{v}^{\kappa_1 \ldots \kappa_p}$ of weight $+1$ instead of $v^{\kappa_1 \ldots \kappa_p}$, we should have found a scalar as the integrating factor. In particular we should have found p if instead of $v^{\kappa_1 \ldots \kappa_p}$ we had chosen the p-vector density corresponding to $w_{\lambda_1 \ldots \lambda_q}$.

If $n-p$ independent solutions of (17.1) are known, the alternating product of their gradients has rotation zero, and the corresponding p-vector density has thus divergence zero. Its p-direction coincides with the p-direction of $v^{\kappa_1 \ldots \kappa_p}$; hence, by division by $v^{\kappa_1 \ldots \kappa_p}$, we get an integrating factor.

† Lie 1877. 1, p. 505.

Now let us suppose that just $n-p-1$ independent solutions of (17.1) and an integrating factor $\mathfrak{p}$ are known. Then we also know an integrating factor p of (17.14), and $pw_{\lambda_1\ldots\lambda_q}$ has rotation zero. Now if these $n-p-1$ solutions are introduced as the first $n-p-1$ coordinates of a coordinate system (κ), the measuring vectors $\overset{1}{e}_\lambda,\ldots,\overset{q-1}{e}_\lambda$ are all divisors of $w_{\lambda_1\ldots\lambda_q}$. Hence there exists a relation of the form

$$pw_{\lambda_1\ldots\lambda_q} = \overset{1}{e}_{[\lambda_1}\ldots \overset{q-1}{e}_{\lambda_{q-1}} u_{\lambda_q]} \tag{17.30}$$

and from this equation u_λ can be determined uniquely if we impose the supplementary condition that $u_1 = \ldots = u_{q-1} = 0$. Since the rotation of $pw_{\lambda_1\ldots\lambda_q}$ is zero, we have

$$\overset{1}{e}_{[\lambda_1}\ldots \overset{q-1}{e}_{\lambda_{q-1}} \partial_\mu u_{\lambda_q]} = 0. \tag{17.31}$$

Hence, looking upon the u_λ as functions of $\xi^q,\ldots,\xi^n$ and upon the $\xi^1,\ldots, \xi^{q-1}$ as parameters, it follows that

$$\partial_{[\psi} u_{\phi]} = 0 \quad (\phi, \psi = q,\ldots,n) \tag{17.32}$$

and consequently $u_\phi d\xi^\phi$ $(\phi = q,\ldots,n)$ is a complete differential in the variables $\xi^q,\ldots, \xi^n$ with the parameters $\xi^1,\ldots, \xi^{q-1}$. From this it follows that the integral

$$\psi = \int u_\phi d\xi^\phi \quad (\phi = q,\ldots,n) \tag{17.33}$$

can be found if the $\xi^1,\ldots, \xi^{q-1}$ are treated as parameters. The function ψ is a solution of (17.1) functionally independent of the solutions $\xi^1,\ldots, \xi^{q-1}$. Thus we have proved the theorem (cf. Theorem III.9)

THEOREM III.19. (*Sixth theorem of integrating factors.*) *If $n-p-1$ independent solutions of a complete homogeneous system of p partial differential equations of the first order and one integrating factor are known, the $(n-p)$th solution can be obtained by a quadrature.*

18. Invariant fields and integral invariants with respect to X_p-forming p-vector fields

Fields invariant with respect to X_p-forming contravariant p-vector fields can be obtained in a way similar to that described in II, § 14, for contravariant vector fields. We call a field *absolutely invariant* with respect to $\lfloor v^{\kappa_1\ldots\kappa_p}\rfloor$, if it is absolutely invariant with respect to each vector divisor of $v^{\kappa_1\ldots\kappa_p}$. It can be readily proved that it is necessary and sufficient for absolute invariance with respect to $\lfloor v^{\kappa_1\ldots\kappa_p}\rfloor$ for the field to be absolutely invariant with respect to $\lfloor \underset{1}{v}^\kappa\rfloor,\ldots, \lfloor \underset{p}{v}^\kappa\rfloor$, the vectors $\underset{1}{v}^\kappa,\ldots, \underset{p}{v}^\kappa$ being any arbitrarily but definitely chosen linearly independent divisors of $v^{\kappa_1\ldots\kappa_p}$; and that in that case, the field is absolutely invariant with respect to $\lfloor v^{\kappa}\rfloor$, v^{κ} being any divisor of $v^{\kappa_1\ldots\kappa_p}$. Absolute invariance with respect to $v^{\kappa_1\ldots\kappa_p}$ is only defined for $p = 1$ (cf. II, § 14).

For a scalar p the necessary and sufficient condition for absolute invariance takes the form

$$v^{\mu\rho_2\ldots\rho_p}\partial_\mu p = 0; \tag{18.1}$$

for a covariant t-vector $u_{\lambda_1\ldots\lambda_t}$ $(1 \leqslant t \leqslant n-p)$

$$v^{\mu\rho_2\ldots\rho_p}\partial_\mu u_{\lambda_1\ldots\lambda_t} + t u_{\rho_1[\lambda_2\ldots\lambda_t}\partial_{\lambda_1]} v^{\rho_1\ldots\rho_p} = 0, \qquad v^{\mu\rho_2\ldots\rho_p} u_{\mu\lambda_2\ldots\lambda_t} = 0; \tag{18.2}$$

for a contravariant s-vector density $\mathfrak{u}^{\kappa_1\ldots\kappa_s}$ of weight $+1$ $(p \leqslant s \leqslant n-1)$

$$v^{\mu\rho_2\ldots\rho_p}\partial_\mu \mathfrak{u}^{\kappa_1\ldots\kappa_s} - t\mathfrak{u}^{\sigma[\kappa_2\ldots\kappa_s}\partial_\sigma v^{\kappa_1]\rho_2\ldots\rho_p} + \mathfrak{u}^{\kappa_1\ldots\kappa_s}\partial_\mu v^{\mu\rho_2\ldots\rho_p} = 0,$$
$$v^{[\mu|\rho_2\ldots\rho_p|}\mathfrak{u}^{\kappa_1\ldots\kappa_s]} = 0; \tag{18.3}$$

and for a contravariant n-vector density $\mathfrak{u}^{\kappa_1\ldots\kappa_n}$ of weight $+1$

$$v^{\mu\rho_2\ldots\rho_p}\partial_\mu \mathfrak{u}^{\kappa_1\ldots\kappa_n} = 0. \tag{18.4}$$

There can be no absolute invariance for covariant t-vectors with $t > n-p$, for contravariant s-vector densities of weight $+1$ with $s < p$, or for scalar densities.

When the equations (17.1) are written in the canonical form (cf. III, § 14)

$$\partial_\beta f = 0 \quad (\beta = 1,\ldots,p) \tag{18.5}$$

the conditions for absolute invariance with respect to $\lfloor v^{\kappa_1\ldots\kappa_p}\rfloor$ take the following forms (cf. III, § 7):

for a scalar p:

$$\partial_\beta p = 0 \quad (\beta = 1,\ldots,p); \tag{18.6}$$

for a covariant t-vector $u_{\lambda_1\ldots\lambda_t}$ $(1 \leqslant t \leqslant n-p)$:

$$\begin{array}{ll}(a) & \partial_\beta u_{\lambda_1\ldots\lambda_t} = 0 \\ (b) & u_{\beta\lambda_2\ldots\lambda_t} = 0\end{array} \quad (\beta = 1,\ldots,p); \tag{18.7}$$

for a contravariant s-vector density $\mathfrak{u}^{\kappa_1\ldots\kappa_s}$ of weight $+1$ $(p \leqslant s \leqslant n-1)$:

$$\begin{array}{ll}(a) & \partial_\beta \mathfrak{u}^{\kappa_1\ldots\kappa_s} = 0, \\ (b) & \mathfrak{u}^{\kappa_1\ldots\kappa_s} = \underset{1}{e}^{[\kappa_1}\ldots\underset{p}{e}^{\kappa_p}\,{}'\mathfrak{u}^{\kappa_{p+1}\ldots\kappa_s]}\end{array} \quad (\beta = 1,\ldots,p), \tag{18.8}$$

where ${}'\mathfrak{u}^{\kappa_{p+1}\ldots\kappa_s}$ is a suitable contravariant $(s-p)$-vector density of weight $+1$; and for a contravariant n-vector density $\mathfrak{u}^{\kappa_1\ldots\kappa_n}$ of weight $+1$:

$$\partial_\beta \mathfrak{u}^{\kappa_1\ldots\kappa_n} = 0 \quad (\beta = 1,\ldots,p). \tag{18.9}$$

From these forms of the conditions it follows that when an X_p-forming p-vector field is given, there always exist absolutely invariant scalars, covariant t-vectors ($1 \leqslant t \leqslant n-p$), and contravariant s-vector densities of weight $+1$ ($p \leqslant s \leqslant n-1$). In particular, from (18.7) we have the theorem (cf. Theorem III.5)

THEOREM III.20. *A covariant t-vector* $u_{\lambda_1 \ldots \lambda_t}$ ($1 \leqslant t \leqslant n-p$) *is absolutely invariant with respect to* $\lfloor v^{\kappa_1 \ldots \kappa_p} \rfloor$ *if and only if* $u_{\lambda_1 \ldots \lambda_t}$ *can be written as the sum of alternating products of gradients of solutions of the complete system*

$$v^{\mu \kappa_2 \ldots \kappa_p} \partial_\mu f = 0 \tag{18.10}$$

with coefficients which are solutions of (18.10).

From (18.8 b) it follows that for $s = p$

$$\mathfrak{u}^{\kappa_1 \ldots \kappa_p} = {}'\mathfrak{u} \underset{1}{e}^{[\kappa_1} \ldots \underset{p}{e}^{\kappa_p]} = \mathfrak{p} v^{\kappa_1 \ldots \kappa_p}, \tag{18.11}$$

where $'\mathfrak{u}$ and $\mathfrak{p}$ are scalar densities of weight $+1$. But from (18.8 a) we have

$$\partial_\beta \mathfrak{p} v^{\kappa_1 \ldots \kappa_p} = 0 \tag{18.12}$$

and from this it follows that $\mathfrak{p}$ is an integrating factor of the complete system (18.10). Hence, if we know a covariant $(n-p)$-vector or a contravariant p-vector density of weight $+1$, absolutely invariant with respect to $\lfloor v^{\kappa_1 \ldots \kappa_p} \rfloor$, an integrating factor is also known, and the integration can be simplified in the way described in III, § 17. The simplifications which are possible if a covariant t-vector ($1 \leqslant t < n-p$) or a contravariant s-vector density of weight $+1$ ($p < s \leqslant n-1$), absolutely invariant with respect to $\lfloor v^{\kappa_1 \ldots \kappa_p} \rfloor$ is known, will be dealt with in V, § 5.

From the fields which are absolutely invariant with respect to $\lfloor v^{\kappa_1 \ldots \kappa_p} \rfloor$, integral invariants can be deduced as in II, § 14, from fields which are absolutely invariant with respect to $\lfloor v^{\kappa} \rfloor$. For this, if $u_{\lambda_1 \ldots \lambda_t}$ is absolutely invariant with respect to $\lfloor v^{\kappa_1 \ldots \kappa_p} \rfloor$, we form the integral

$$I_t = \int_{\tau_t} u_{\lambda_1 \ldots \lambda_t} \, dF^{\lambda_1 \ldots \lambda_t} \tag{18.13}$$

over a region τ_t in an X_t. This integral, independently of the choice of τ_t, is invariant for all point transformations generated by $v^\kappa dt$, if v^κ is a divisor of $v^{\kappa_1 \ldots \kappa_p}$. From this it follows that I_t is invariant for every point transformation such that each point of τ_t remains on the integral-X_p of (18.10) going through this point. Naturally the integral invariant I_t can also be defined by means of the corresponding $(n-t)$-vector density.

When $u_{\lambda_1 \ldots \lambda_t}$ is not absolutely invariant, but only its rotation has this invariance, according to the theorem of Stokes the integral I_t is invariant if τ_t is closed. In this case $u_{\lambda_1 \ldots \lambda_t}$ is called *relatively invariant* with respect to $\lfloor v^{\kappa_1 \ldots \kappa_p} \rfloor$. Similarly $\mathfrak{u}^{\kappa_1 \ldots \kappa_s}$ is relatively invariant if its divergence is absolutely invariant. The following theorem can be proved in the same way as Theorem III 6.

THEOREM III.21. *If the t-vector $u_{\lambda_1 \ldots \lambda_t}$ is relatively invariant with respect to $\lfloor v^{\kappa_1 \ldots \kappa_p} \rfloor$ and if one solution of each of the p non-homogeneous systems* (14.20) *and n—p independent solutions of the homogeneous system* (14.19) *are known it is always possible by means of quadratures only to determine a field $'u_{\lambda_1 \ldots \lambda_t}$, which is absolutely invariant with respect to $\lfloor v^{\kappa_1 \ldots \kappa_p} \rfloor$ and has the same rotation as $u_{\lambda_1 \ldots \lambda_t}$.*

If the s-vector density $\mathfrak{u}^{\kappa_1 \ldots \kappa_s}$ of weight +1 is relatively invariant with respect to $\lfloor v^{\kappa_1 \ldots \kappa_p} \rfloor$ and if one solution of each of the p non-homogeneous systems (14.20) *and n—p independent solutions of the homogeneous system* (14.19) *are known it is always possible by means of quadratures only to determine a field $'\mathfrak{u}^{\kappa_1 \ldots \kappa_s}$, which is absolutely invariant with respect to $\lfloor v^{\kappa_1 \ldots \kappa_p} \rfloor$ and has the same divergence as $\mathfrak{u}^{\kappa_1 \ldots \kappa_s}$.*

We close this section by proving the theorem stated in II, § 11:

THEOREM III.22. *Every simple covariant q-vector $w_{\lambda_1 \ldots \lambda_q}$, whose rotation vanishes, is a gradient product.*

PROOF. Because the rotation vanishes, from (17.10) it follows that $w_{\lambda_1 \ldots \lambda_q}$ can be written in the form (17.12), that is

$$w_{\lambda_1 \ldots \lambda_q} = \overset{p+1}{s}\, \overset{n}{s}_{[\lambda_1} \ldots s_{\lambda_q]}. \tag{18.14}$$

Forming the rotation of (18.14) we get

$$(\partial_{[\mu} \overset{p+1}{s})\, \overset{n}{s}_{\lambda_1} \ldots s_{\lambda_q]} = 0 \tag{18.15}$$

and from this it follows that the functions $s, \overset{p+1}{s}, \ldots, \overset{n}{s}$ are functionally dependent. Hence there exists an equation of the form

$$s = \phi(\overset{p+1}{s}, \ldots, \overset{n}{s}), \tag{18.16}$$

and this entails that the components of $w_{\lambda_1 \ldots \lambda_q}$ depend only on the variables $\overset{p+1}{s}, \ldots, \overset{n}{s}$ and that consequently $w_{\lambda_1 \ldots \lambda_q}$ represents a q-vector in the X_q of these variables. Now we have proved in II, § 11, that every covariant n-vector in an X_n is a gradient product. Hence $w_{\lambda_1 \ldots \lambda_q}$ is a gradient product.

19. Infinitesimal transformations leaving invariant a given complete homogeneous system†

If $v^{\kappa_1 \ldots \kappa_p}$ is a simple p-vector and

$$v^{\mu\kappa_2 \ldots \kappa_p} \partial_\mu f = 0 \tag{19.1}$$

is a complete system, and if the Lie derivative with respect to some field $\underset{p+1}{v^\kappa}$ satisfies the conditions

$$\underset{L}{D} v^{\kappa_1 \ldots \kappa_p} = \alpha v^{\kappa_1 \ldots \kappa_p}, \tag{19.2}$$

where α is any function of the ξ^κ, the system (19.1) is invariant for the infinitesimal transformation

$$'\xi^\kappa = \xi^\kappa + \underset{p+1}{v^\kappa}\, dt. \tag{19.3}$$

It is also said that (19.1) *admits the infinitesimal transformation* (19.3) and that (19.3) is an *admitted infinitesimal transformation* of (19.1). From a geometrical point of view this means that the integral-X_p's of (19.1) pass into integral-X_p's if they are subjected to the infinitesimal point transformation $\xi^\kappa \to \xi^\kappa + \underset{p+1}{v^\kappa}\, dt$. It must be noted that not every integral-X_p is individually invariant but only the whole system of X_p's. Of course (19.3) always represents an admitted infinitesimal transformation of (19.1) when $\underset{p+1}{v^\kappa}$ is a divisor of $v^{\kappa_1 \ldots \kappa_p}$, because in that case the displacements $\underset{p+1}{v^\kappa}\, dt$ everywhere lie in the integral-X_p and consequently every integral-X_p is individually invariant. If

$$v^{\kappa_1 \ldots \kappa_p} = \underset{1}{v}^{[\kappa_1} \ldots \underset{p}{v}^{\kappa_p]} \tag{19.4}$$

the conditions (19.2) can be also written in the form

$$\underset{[p+1}{v^\mu} \partial_\mu \underset{b]}{v^\kappa} = \underset{p+1,b}{\overset{a}{\sigma}} \underset{a}{v^\kappa} \quad (a, b = 1, \ldots, \mathrm{p}), \tag{19.5}$$

where the σ's are functions of the ξ^κ. From (19.5) it follows that the equation

$$\underset{p+1}{v^\mu} \partial_\mu f = 0 \tag{19.6}$$

constitutes together with (19.1) a complete system of $p+1$ equations. Now we introduce the usual notations of the theory of groups

$$\underset{b}{X} \overset{\text{def}}{=} \underset{b}{v^\mu} \partial_\mu, \qquad \underset{p+1}{X} \overset{\text{def}}{=} \underset{p+1}{v^\mu} \partial_\mu, \qquad (\underset{i}{X}\underset{j}{X}) \overset{\text{def}}{=} \underset{i}{X}\underset{j}{X} - \underset{j}{X}\underset{i}{X} = 2 \underset{[i}{v^\omega} \partial_{|\omega|} \underset{j]}{v^\mu} \partial_\mu$$

$$(b = 1, \ldots, \mathrm{p};\ i, j = 1, \ldots, \mathrm{p}+1). \tag{19.7}$$

† Cf. Lie 1877. 1; v. Weber 1900. 1, ch. ii, § 4; Cartan 1922. 2, ch. ix; Engel and Faber 1932. 1, chs. i, ii.

The operator $(\underset{i}{X}\underset{j}{X})$ is called the *commutator of the operators* $\underset{i}{X}$ *and* $\underset{j}{X}$. With this notation (19.1) takes the form

$$\underset{b}{X}f = 0 \quad (b = 1,\dots,\mathrm{p}). \tag{19.8}$$

In consequence of the completeness of the system (19.1) there exist equations of the form

$$(\underset{c}{X}\underset{b}{X}) = 2\,\overset{a}{\underset{cb}{\sigma}}\,\underset{a}{X} \quad (a, b, c = 1,\dots,\mathrm{p}), \tag{19.9}$$

where the σ's are functions of the ξ^κ, and (19.5) takes the form

$$(\underset{\mathrm{p}+1}{X}\underset{b}{X}) = 2\,\overset{a}{\underset{\mathrm{p}+1,b}{\sigma}}\,\underset{a}{X} \quad (a, b = 1,\dots,\mathrm{p}). \tag{19.10}$$

Now from (19.10) it follows that, if $\overset{1}{f}$ is a solution of (19.1), $\underset{\mathrm{p}+1}{X}\overset{1}{f}$ is either a constant or a solution. But this means that if one or more solutions and an admitted infinitesimal transformation are known and circumstances are favourable, it may be possible to obtain new solutions without any integration.

The abbreviated symbols for infinitesimal transformations satisfy the *identity of Jacobi*,

$$((XY)Z)+((YZ)X)+((ZX)Y) = 0, \tag{19.11}$$

which can be readily proved by writing out the operators. As a consequence of Jacobi's identity the commutator of two admitted infinitesimal transformations is either zero or it represents an admitted infinitesimal transformation.

When (19.1) admits s infinitesimal transformations $\underset{\mathrm{p}+1}{X},\dots,\underset{\mathrm{p}+\mathrm{s}}{X}$ $(s > 1)$, it may be that there exist just z linear relations between the $\underset{1}{X},\dots,\underset{\mathrm{p}+\mathrm{s}}{X}$. Since the $\underset{b}{X}$ $(b = 1,\dots,\mathrm{p})$ are linearly independent, just z of the $\underset{\mathrm{p}+1}{X},\dots,\underset{\mathrm{p}+\mathrm{s}}{X}$ can be solved from these relations. By interchanging indices it can always be arranged that these are $\underset{\mathrm{p}+1}{X},\dots,\underset{\mathrm{p}+\mathrm{z}}{X}$. Then the solutions have the form

$$\underset{\mathfrak{a}}{X} = \overset{b}{\underset{\mathfrak{a}}{\beta}}\underset{b}{X}+\overset{\mathfrak{b}}{\underset{\mathfrak{a}}{\beta}}\underset{\mathfrak{b}}{X} \quad (\mathfrak{a} = \mathrm{p}+1,\dots,\mathrm{p}+\mathrm{z};\ \mathfrak{b} = \mathrm{p}+\mathrm{z}+1,\dots,\mathrm{p}+\mathrm{s};\ b = 1,\dots,\mathrm{p}). \tag{19.12}$$

Now if the commutator with $\underset{c}{X}$ $(c = 1,\dots,\mathrm{p})$ is formed, we get

$$2\,\overset{a}{\underset{c\mathfrak{a}}{\sigma}}\underset{a}{X} = (\underset{c}{X}\overset{b}{\underset{\mathfrak{a}}{\beta}})\underset{b}{X}+2\overset{b}{\underset{\mathfrak{a}}{\beta}}\,\overset{a}{\underset{cb}{\sigma}}\,\underset{a}{X}+(\underset{c}{X}\overset{\mathfrak{b}}{\underset{\mathfrak{a}}{\beta}})\underset{\mathfrak{b}}{X}+2\overset{\mathfrak{b}}{\underset{\mathfrak{a}}{\beta}}\,\overset{a}{\underset{c\mathfrak{b}}{\sigma}}\,\underset{a}{X} \quad (a, b, c = 1,\dots,\mathrm{p};$$
$$\mathfrak{a} = \mathrm{p}+1,\dots,\mathrm{p}+\mathrm{z};\ \mathfrak{b} = \mathrm{p}+\mathrm{z}+1,\dots,\mathrm{p}+\mathrm{s}) \tag{19.13}$$

and from this and the non-existence of linear relations between the $\underset{b}{X}$ and $\underset{\mathfrak{b}}{X}$ it follows that

$$\underset{b}{X}\overset{\mathfrak{b}}{\underset{\mathfrak{a}}{\beta}} = 0 \quad (b = 1,\ldots,\mathrm{p};\ \mathfrak{a} = \mathrm{p}+1,\ldots,\mathrm{p}+\mathrm{z};\ \mathfrak{b} = \mathrm{p}+\mathrm{z}+1,\ldots,\mathrm{p}+\mathrm{s}). \tag{19.14}$$

Hence the $\overset{\mathfrak{b}}{\underset{\mathfrak{a}}{\beta}}$ are either constants or solutions of (19.1).† Conversely it can easily be proved that every operator of the form

$$\overset{b}{\beta}\underset{b}{X}+\overset{\mathfrak{c}}{\beta}\underset{\mathfrak{c}}{X} \quad (b = 1,\ldots,\mathrm{p};\ \mathfrak{c} = \mathrm{p}+1,\ldots,\mathrm{p}+\mathrm{s}) \tag{19.15}$$

represents an admitted infinitesimal transformation if the $\overset{\mathfrak{c}}{\beta}$ are either constants or solutions of (19.1). From this we see that, circumstances being favourable, the s admitted infinitesimal transformations ($s \geqslant 2$) can be used to obtain new solutions without any integration.

When $n-p$ admitted infinitesimal transformations $\underset{y}{X}$ ($y = \mathrm{p}+1,\ldots,\mathrm{n}$) which are linearly independent of each other and of the $\underset{b}{X}$ ($b = 1,\ldots,\mathrm{p}$) are known, the equations

$$\underset{b}{X}f = 0, \qquad \underset{y}{X}f = 0 \quad (b = 1,\ldots,\mathrm{p};\ y = \mathrm{p}+1,\ldots,\mathrm{n}) \tag{19.16}$$

constitute a complete system and there exist relations of the form

$$\begin{aligned} &(a)\quad (\underset{c}{X}\underset{b}{X}) = 2\overset{a}{\underset{cb}{\sigma}}\underset{a}{X} \\ &(b)\quad (\underset{z}{X}\underset{b}{X}) = 2\overset{a}{\underset{zb}{\sigma}}\underset{a}{X} \qquad (a,b,c = 1,\ldots,\mathrm{p};\ x,y,z = \mathrm{p}+1,\ldots,\mathrm{n}). \\ &(c)\quad (\underset{z}{X}\underset{y}{X}) = 2\overset{a}{\underset{zy}{\sigma}}\underset{a}{X}+2\overset{x}{\underset{zy}{\sigma}}\underset{x}{X} \end{aligned} \tag{19.17}$$

Since (19.17 c) has the form (19.12), the $\overset{x}{\underset{zy}{\sigma}}$ *are either constants or solutions of* (19.1). The scalar density

$$\mathfrak{p} = 1 : \underset{[1}{v^1}\ldots\underset{n]}{v^n} \tag{19.18}$$

is obviously an integrating factor of (19.16) and thus satisfies the equations (cf. III, § 17)

$$\underset{j}{v^\mu}\partial_\mu\mathfrak{p}+\mathfrak{p}\partial_\mu\underset{j}{v^\mu}-2\mathfrak{p}\overset{i}{\underset{ij}{\sigma}} = 0 \quad (i,j = 1,\ldots,\mathrm{n}) \tag{19.19}$$

and because all $\overset{z}{\underset{yb}{\sigma}}$ vanish (cf. (19.17)) it also satisfies the equations

$$\underset{b}{v^\mu}\partial_\mu\mathfrak{p}+\mathfrak{p}\partial_\mu\underset{b}{v^\mu}-2\mathfrak{p}\overset{a}{\underset{ab}{\sigma}} = 0 \quad (a,b = 1,\ldots,\mathrm{p}) \tag{19.20}$$

† Lie 1877. 1, p. 498.

showing that $\mathfrak{p}$ is also an integrating factor of the system (19.1). Hence it is always possible to determine an integrating factor if $n-p$ admitted infinitesimal transformations $\underset{y}{X}$, which are linearly independent of each other and of the $\underset{b}{X}$, are known.†

Now suppose that we know one integrating factor $\mathfrak{p}$ and one admitted infinitesimal transformation $\underset{\mathfrak{p}+1}{X}$ of (19.1). If the fields $\underset{b}{v}^\kappa$ are dragged along over $\underset{\mathfrak{p}+1}{v}^\kappa dt$, the new values of the fields $\underset{b}{v}^\kappa$ in ξ^κ are (cf. II, § 13)

$$'\underset{b}{v}^\kappa = \underset{b}{v}^\kappa - \underset{L}{D}\underset{b}{v}^\kappa\, dt = \underset{b}{v}^\kappa - 2 \underset{\mathfrak{p}+1,b}{\overset{a}{\sigma}} \underset{a}{v}^\kappa\, dt \quad (a, b = 1,\ldots, \mathfrak{p}), \tag{19.21}$$

and thus the new value of the field $v^{\kappa_1\ldots\kappa_\mathfrak{p}}$ in ξ^κ is

$$'v^{\kappa_1\ldots\kappa_\mathfrak{p}} = v^{\kappa_1\ldots\kappa_\mathfrak{p}}\,(1-2 \underset{\mathfrak{p}+1,a}{\overset{a}{\sigma}}\, dt) \quad (a = 1,\ldots, \mathfrak{p}). \tag{19.22}$$

The new value of the field $\mathfrak{p}$ in ξ^κ is

$$'\mathfrak{p} = \mathfrak{p} - \underset{L}{D}\mathfrak{p}\, dt = \mathfrak{p} - (\underset{\mathfrak{p}+1}{v}^\mu \partial_\mu \mathfrak{p} + \mathfrak{p}\,\partial_\mu \underset{\mathfrak{p}+1}{v}^\mu)\, dt. \tag{19.23}$$

This new scalar density $'\mathfrak{p}$ is an integrating factor of the new field $'v^{\kappa_1\ldots\kappa_\mathfrak{p}}$, but not of the field $v^{\kappa_1\ldots\kappa_\mathfrak{p}}$, because $'v^{\kappa_1\ldots\kappa_\mathfrak{p}}$ differs from $v^{\kappa_1\ldots\kappa_\mathfrak{p}}$ by the factor $1-2 \underset{\mathfrak{p}+1,a}{\overset{a}{\sigma}}\, dt$. In order to derive from $'\mathfrak{p}$ a new integrating factor of $v^{\kappa_1\ldots\kappa_\mathfrak{p}}$ this factor $1-2 \underset{\mathfrak{p}+1,a}{\overset{a}{\sigma}}\, dt$ has to be considered, and thus

$$''\mathfrak{p} = \mathfrak{p} - (\underset{\mathfrak{p}+1}{v}^\mu \partial_\mu \mathfrak{p} + \mathfrak{p}\,\partial_\mu \underset{\mathfrak{p}+1}{v}^\mu + 2\mathfrak{p} \underset{\mathfrak{p}+1,a}{\overset{a}{\sigma}})\, dt \quad (a = 1,\ldots, \mathfrak{p}) \tag{19.24}$$

is an integrating factor of $v^{\kappa_1\ldots\kappa_\mathfrak{p}}$. When $''\mathfrak{p}-\mathfrak{p}$ happens to be zero, $\mathfrak{p}$ is not only an integrating factor of (19.1) but also of the complete system

$$\underset{b}{X}f = 0; \quad \underset{\mathfrak{p}+1}{X} f = 0 \quad (b = 1,\ldots, \mathfrak{p}). \tag{19.25}$$

When $''\mathfrak{p}-\mathfrak{p} \neq 0$, the quotient

$$\frac{\mathfrak{p}-\mathfrak{p}''}{\mathfrak{p}\, dt} = \underset{\mathfrak{p}+1}{v}^\mu \partial_\mu \log \mathfrak{p} + \partial_\mu \underset{\mathfrak{p}+1}{v}^\mu + 2 \underset{\mathfrak{p}+1,a}{\overset{a}{\sigma}} \quad (a = 1,\ldots, \mathfrak{p}) \tag{19.26}$$

is either a constant or a solution of (19.1). Hence in this case, circumstances being favourable, a new solution can be determined without any integration, if one integrating factor and one admitted infinitesimal transformation are known.‡

† Ibid., p. 507. ‡ Ibid., p. 508.

Now we consider the general case in which some admitted infinitesimal transformations of (19.1), linearly independent of the $\underset{b}{X}$ and some solutions, are known. Then it may be possible:

(1) to determine new admitted infinitesimal transformations by forming commutators;

(2) to determine new solutions by applying the operator of a known infinitesimal transformation to a known solution;

(3) to determine new solutions from linear relations between the known admitted infinitesimal transformations.

These processes can be repeated until no more solutions are obtained. Suppose we then have just u independent solutions $\overset{1}{f},..., \overset{u}{f}$ and among the known admitted infinitesimal transformations just $r-p$, called $\underset{\mathfrak{b}}{X}$ ($\mathfrak{b} = \mathrm{p}+1,..., \mathrm{r}$), which are linearly independent of each other, and of the $\underset{b}{X}$ ($b = 1,..., \mathrm{p}$). Then there exist relations of the form

$$\begin{aligned} &(a)\quad (\underset{c}{X}\underset{b}{X}) = 2\overset{a}{\underset{cb}{\sigma}}\underset{a}{X} \\ &(b)\quad (\underset{\mathfrak{c}}{X}\underset{b}{X}) = 2\overset{a}{\underset{\mathfrak{c}b}{\sigma}}\underset{a}{X} \qquad (a,b,c = 1,..., \mathrm{p};\ \mathfrak{a},\mathfrak{b},\mathfrak{c} = \mathrm{p}+1,..., \mathrm{r}), \\ &(c)\quad (\underset{\mathfrak{c}}{X}\underset{\mathfrak{b}}{X}) = 2\overset{a}{\underset{\mathfrak{c}\mathfrak{b}}{\sigma}}\underset{a}{X}+2\overset{\mathfrak{a}}{\underset{\mathfrak{c}\mathfrak{b}}{\sigma}}\underset{\mathfrak{a}}{X} \end{aligned} \tag{19.27}$$

and all the known admitted infinitesimal transformations have to depend linearly on the $\underset{b}{X}$ and $\underset{\mathfrak{b}}{X}$ with coefficients of the $\underset{\mathfrak{b}}{X}$ only depending on $\overset{1}{f},..., \overset{u}{f}$, because otherwise there would exist more than u known solutions. *In particular the* $\overset{\mathfrak{a}}{\underset{\mathfrak{c}\mathfrak{b}}{\sigma}}$ *in* (19.27 *c*) *have to be* functions of $\overset{1}{f},..., \overset{u}{f}$. Further, by applying any operator $\underset{\mathfrak{b}}{X}$ to $\overset{1}{f},..., \overset{u}{f}$ we always get functions of $\overset{1}{f},..., \overset{u}{f}$:

$$\underset{\mathfrak{b}}{X}\overset{\mathfrak{x}}{f} = \overset{\mathfrak{x}}{\underset{\mathfrak{b}}{\phi}}(\overset{1}{f},..., \overset{u}{f}) \quad (\mathfrak{b} = \mathrm{p}+1,..., \mathrm{r};\ \mathfrak{x} = 1,..., u). \tag{19.28}$$

If an operator of the form

$$X = \overset{b}{\alpha}(\xi^\kappa)\underset{b}{X}+\overset{\mathfrak{b}}{\beta}(\overset{1}{f},..., \overset{u}{f})\underset{\mathfrak{b}}{X} \quad (b = 1,..., \mathrm{p};\ \mathfrak{b} = \mathrm{p}+1,..., \mathrm{r}), \tag{19.29}$$

with arbitrary functions $\overset{b}{\alpha}$ and $\overset{\mathfrak{b}}{\beta}$ of ξ^κ and $\overset{1}{f},..., \overset{u}{f}$ respectively, is applied to one of the known solutions $\overset{1}{f},..., \overset{u}{f}$ there results a function of $\overset{1}{f},..., \overset{u}{f}$. The application of some of these operators may produce zero for each

$\overset{\mathfrak{x}}{f}$ ($\mathfrak{x} = 1,\ldots, u$) individually. The necessary and sufficient conditions for an operator X to have this property are, according to (19.28) and (19.29),

$$\overset{\mathfrak{b}}{\beta}\overset{\mathfrak{b}\,\mathfrak{x}}{\underset{\mathfrak{b}}{\phi}} = 0 \quad (\mathfrak{b} = \mathrm{p}+1,\ldots, \mathrm{r};\ \mathfrak{x} = 1,\ldots, u). \tag{19.30}$$

If the rank of $\overset{\mathfrak{x}}{\underset{\mathfrak{b}}{\phi}}$ is $r-r'$, there are just $r'-p$ linearly independent solutions $\overset{\mathfrak{b}}{\beta}$ and, consequently, $r'-p$ admitted infinitesimal transformations $\underset{\mathfrak{b}'}{\bar{X}}$ ($\mathfrak{b}' = \mathrm{p}+1,\ldots, \mathrm{r}'$) linearly independent of each other and of the $\underset{b}{X}$, and satisfying the conditions

$$\underset{\mathfrak{b}'}{\bar{X}}\overset{\mathfrak{x}}{f} = 0 \quad (\mathfrak{b}' = \mathrm{p}+1,\ldots, \mathrm{r}';\ \mathfrak{x} = 1,\ldots, u). \tag{19.31}$$

Only when $r' = p$ can no operators with this property be formed.

The equations

$$\underset{b}{X}f;\ \underset{\mathfrak{b}'}{\bar{X}}f = 0 \quad (b = 1,\ldots, \mathrm{p};\ \mathfrak{b}' = \mathrm{p}+1,\ldots, \mathrm{r}') \tag{19.32}$$

constitute a complete system of r' independent equations ($p \leqslant r' \leqslant n$), with u known solutions, viz. $\overset{1}{f},\ldots,\overset{u}{f}$. As we have seen in III, § 16, the other $n-r'-u$ solutions can be obtained by means of $n-r'-u$ operations $O_{n-r'-u},\ldots, O_1$. These solutions $\overset{u+1}{f},\ldots, \overset{n-r'}{f}$ are all solutions of (19.1), hence we get in this way $n-r'$ solutions $\overset{1}{f},\ldots, \overset{n-r'}{f}$ of (19.1). Only if $r' = p$ have we gained nothing, because in that case the determination of $n-p-u$ new solutions needs $n-p-u$ operations $O_{n-p-u},\ldots, O_1$ as in the general case. But if $r' > p$, then for the determination of $n-r'-u$ new solutions, only $n-r'-u$ operations $O_{n-r'-u},\ldots, O_1$ are needed, instead of the $n-r'-u$ operations $O_{n-p-u},\ldots, O_{r'-p+1}$, which are needed if only u solutions and no admitted infinitesimal transformations are known. So the advantage depends wholly on the difference $r'-p$.

From (19.27) there exist now relations of the form

$$\begin{aligned}
&(a)\quad (\underset{c}{X}\underset{b}{X}) = 2\overset{a}{\underset{cb}{\sigma}}\underset{a}{X} \\
&(b)\quad (\underset{\mathfrak{c}'}{\bar{X}}\underset{b}{X}) = 2\overset{a}{\underset{\mathfrak{c}'b}{\bar{\sigma}}}\underset{a}{X} \qquad (a,b,c = 1,\ldots, \mathrm{p};\ \mathfrak{a}',\mathfrak{b}',\mathfrak{c}' = \mathrm{p}+1,\ldots, \mathrm{r}'). \\
&(c)\quad (\underset{\mathfrak{c}'}{\bar{X}}\underset{\mathfrak{b}'}{\bar{X}}) = 2\overset{a}{\underset{\mathfrak{c}'\mathfrak{b}'}{\bar{\sigma}}}\underset{a}{X} + 2\overset{\mathfrak{a}'}{\underset{\mathfrak{c}'\mathfrak{b}'}{\bar{\sigma}}}(\overset{1}{f},\ldots, \overset{n-r'}{f})\underset{\mathfrak{a}'}{\bar{X}}
\end{aligned} \tag{19.33}$$

Now let the $\overset{1}{f},\ldots, \overset{n-r'}{f}$ be introduced as the last $n-r'$ coordinates of a coordinate system (κ). Then

$$\underset{b}{v}^{\omega} = 0 \quad (\omega = r'+1,\ldots, n;\ b = 1,\ldots, \mathrm{p}). \tag{19.34}$$

If then we write

$$\left.\begin{array}{ll}(a) & \underset{b}{Y} \overset{\text{def}}{=} \underset{b}{v^{\pi}}\partial_{\pi} \\ (b) & \underset{\mathfrak{b}'}{Y} \overset{\text{def}}{=} \underset{\mathfrak{b}'}{v^{\pi}}\partial_{\pi} \\ (c) & \overset{h}{\underset{ij}{\tau}} \overset{\text{def}}{=} \overset{h}{\underset{ij}{\bar{\sigma}}}\end{array}\right\} \begin{array}{r}\text{for } \xi^{\omega} = c^{\omega} \; (c^{\omega} = \text{constants}; \; b = 1,\ldots,\mathrm{p}; \\ \mathfrak{b}' = \mathrm{p}+1,\ldots,\mathrm{r}'; \; h,i,j = 1,\ldots,\mathrm{r}'; \\ \pi = 1,\ldots,r'; \;\; \omega = r'+1,\ldots,n)\end{array} \quad (19.35)$$

the equations $$\underset{b}{Y}f = 0 \quad (b = 1,\ldots,\mathrm{p}) \quad (19.36)$$

form a system of p independent equations in the r' variables

$$\xi^{\alpha} \quad (\alpha = 1,\ldots,r').$$

From (19.33, 34, 35) we have

$$\begin{array}{ll}(a) & (\underset{c}{Y}\underset{b}{Y}) = 2\overset{a}{\underset{cb}{\tau}}\underset{a}{Y} \\ (b) & (\underset{\mathfrak{c}'}{Y}\underset{b}{Y}) = 2\overset{a}{\underset{\mathfrak{c}'b}{\tau}}\underset{a}{Y} \\ (c) & (\underset{\mathfrak{c}'}{Y}\underset{\mathfrak{b}'}{Y}) = 2\overset{a}{\underset{\mathfrak{c}'\mathfrak{b}'}{\tau}}\underset{a}{Y} + 2\overset{\mathfrak{a}'}{\underset{\mathfrak{c}'\mathfrak{b}'}{\tau}}\underset{\mathfrak{a}'}{Y}\end{array} \qquad \begin{array}{l}(a,b,c = 1,\ldots,\mathrm{p}; \\ \quad \mathfrak{a}',\mathfrak{b}',\mathfrak{c}' = \mathrm{p}+1,\ldots,\mathrm{r}').\end{array} \quad (19.37)$$

From (19.37 a) it follows that the system (19.36) is complete. Every function of the ξ^{ω} $(\omega = r'+1,\ldots,n)$ and of the solutions of (19.36) is a solution of (19.1). Hence the integration of (19.36) supplies all the solutions of (19.1). From (19.37 b) it follows that (19.36) admits all the infinitesimal transformations $\underset{\mathfrak{b}'}{Y}$ $(\mathfrak{b}' = \mathrm{p}+1,\ldots,\mathrm{r}')$. These $\underset{\mathfrak{b}'}{Y}$ are linearly independent of each other and of the $\underset{b}{Y}$ $(b = 1,\ldots,\mathrm{p})$. *In* (19.37 c) *the* $\overset{\mathfrak{a}'}{\underset{\mathfrak{c}'\mathfrak{b}'}{\tau}}$ *must be constant* because the $\overset{\mathfrak{a}'}{\underset{\mathfrak{c}'\mathfrak{b}'}{\bar{\sigma}}}$ in (19.33) depend only on the ξ^{ω} $(\omega = r'+1,\ldots,n)$.

The system (19.36) can be simplified. To do this we bring it first into the special Jacobian form (cf. III, § 12)

$$Y_{\beta}f \overset{\text{def}}{=} \partial_{\beta}f + B^{\zeta}_{\beta}\partial_{\zeta}f \quad (\beta = 1,\ldots,p; \; \zeta = p+1,\ldots,r'), \quad (19.38)$$

which we can do without any integration. Then all commutators $(Y_{\gamma}Y_{\beta})$ vanish. Now if instead of the $r'-p$ infinitesimal transformations $\underset{\mathfrak{b}'}{Y}$ $(\mathfrak{b}' = \mathrm{p}+1,\ldots,\mathrm{r}')$ we introduce the following $r'-p$ infinitesimal transformations,

$$Y_{\eta} = \delta^{\mathfrak{b}'}_{\eta}(\underset{\mathfrak{b}'}{Y} - \underset{\mathfrak{b}'}{v^{\beta}}Y_{\beta}) = \delta^{\mathfrak{b}'}_{\eta}(\underset{\mathfrak{b}'}{v^{\pi}}\partial_{\pi} - \underset{\mathfrak{b}'}{v^{\beta}}\partial_{\beta} - \underset{\mathfrak{b}'}{v^{\beta}}B^{\zeta}_{\beta}\partial_{\zeta}) = \delta^{\mathfrak{b}'}_{\eta}(\underset{\mathfrak{b}'}{v^{\zeta}} - \underset{\mathfrak{b}'}{v^{\beta}}B^{\zeta}_{\beta})\partial_{\zeta}$$

$$(\mathfrak{b}' = \mathrm{p}+1,\ldots,\mathrm{r}'; \; \beta = 1,\ldots,p; \; \zeta, \eta = p+1,\ldots,r'; \; \pi = 1,\ldots,r'), \quad (19.39)$$

these transformations are admitted by the system (19.38) and are linearly independent of each other and of the Y_β ($\beta = 1,\ldots,p$). Since the Y_η do not contain the derivatives with respect to $\xi^1,\ldots,\xi^p$ the following relations hold,

$$\begin{aligned} &(a)\quad (Y_\gamma Y_\beta) = 0 \\ &(b)\quad (Y_\theta Y_\beta) = 0 \qquad\qquad (\beta,\gamma = 1,\ldots,p;\ \zeta,\eta,\theta = p+1,\ldots,r'), \\ &(c)\quad (Y_\theta Y_\eta) = 2\, \overset{\zeta}{\underset{\theta\eta}{\tau}} Y_\zeta \end{aligned} \tag{19.40}$$

with constant coefficients $\overset{\zeta}{\underset{\theta\eta}{\tau}}$. Hence the problem of the integration of a complete system of p equations in n variables with u known solutions and $r > p$ linearly independent admitted infinitesimal transformations is, after applying $n-r'-u$ operations $O_{n-r'-u},\ldots,\ O_1$, reduced to the problem of the integration of a special Jacobian system (19.38) of p equations in r' variables with r' admitted infinitesimal transformations, satisfying the conditions (19.40).†

Using the expressions of the theory of groups we may remark that the constancy of the $\overset{\zeta}{\underset{\theta\eta}{\tau}}$ in (19.40) means that the admitted infinitesimal transformations Y_η ($\eta = p+1,\ldots,r'$) *generate a finite continuous* ($r'-p$)-*parameter group*, i.e. a group whose finite transformations depend on just $r'-p$ parameters. The degree of difficulty of the integration of (19.38) depends wholly on the properties of this group. Here the theory of continuous groups comes in and as we do not suppose the reader to be familiar with the results of that theory necessary for the integration of (19.38) we have to restrict ourselves here to mentioning only three particular cases.‡

1. The group is Abelian, i.e. the $\overset{\zeta}{\underset{\theta\eta}{\tau}}$ vanish. In this case the equations

$$Y_\beta f = 0,\quad Y_{p+1} f = 0,\quad \ldots,\quad Y_{r'-1} f = 0 \quad (\beta = 1,\ldots,p) \tag{19.41}$$

constitute a complete system of $r'-1$ equations in r' variables, admitting the infinitesimal transformation $Y_{r'}$. Therefore, an integrating factor can be determined and the integration of (19.41) can be finished by a quadrature. This furnishes one solution of the system (19.38). In the same way $r'-p-1$ other solutions of (19.38) can be obtained by omitting another one of Y_η ($\eta = p+1,\ldots,r'$). Hence, for the integration of (19.1) in this case $n-r'-u$ operations $O_{n-r'-u},\ldots,\ O_1$ and $r'-p$ quadratures are needed.

† Lie 1877. 1, p. 497. ‡ Ibid., p. 517.

2. The group contains a $(p'-p)$-parameter Abelian sub-group, $p' < r'$. In this case it can be shown that the Y_η may be chosen in such a way that

$$\overset{\zeta'}{\underset{\theta'\eta'}{\tau}} = 0 \quad (\zeta', \eta', \theta' = p+1, ..., p'). \tag{19.42}$$

Then the equations

$$Y_\beta f = 0, \quad Y_{p+1} f = 0, \quad ..., \quad Y_{p'} f = 0 \quad (\beta = 1, ..., p) \tag{19.43}$$

constitute a complete system of p' equations in r' variables whose integration by means of $r'-p'$ operations $O_{r'-p'}, ..., O_1$ furnishes $r'-p'$ new independent solutions of (19.1). Hence, in this case $n-p'-u$ solutions of (19.1) can be determined by means of $n-r'-u$ operations $O_{n-r'-u}, ..., O_1$ and $r'-p'$ operations $O_{r'-p'}, ..., O_1$.

3. The group is *integrable*, i.e. the Y_η can be chosen in such a way that all coefficients $\overset{\zeta}{\underset{\theta\eta}{\tau}}$ vanish when $\zeta \geqslant \eta > \theta$. Then the equations

$$Y_\beta f = 0, \quad Y_{p+1} f = 0, \quad ..., \quad Y_{r'-1} f = 0 \quad (\beta = 1, ..., p) \tag{19.44}$$

form a complete system in r' variables, admitting the infinitesimal transformation $Y_{r'}$. Integration of this system is possible by means of a quadrature and furnishes one solution of the system (19.1). If the coordinate system is changed in such a way that this solution is the new r'th coordinate $\xi^{r'}$, the components $\underset{1}{v}^{r'}, ..., \underset{r'-1}{v}^{r'}$ all vanish and the equations

$$Y_\beta f = 0, \quad Y_{p+1} f = 0, \quad ..., \quad Y_{r'-1} f = 0 \tag{19.45}$$

form a complete system in the variables $\xi^1, ..., \xi^{r'-1}$ admitting the infinitesimal transformation $Y_{r'-1}$. Integration of this system by means of a quadrature furnishes another solution of (9.1). Continuing in this way we get the remaining $r'-p$ solutions of (19.1) by means of $r'-p$ quadratures. Hence, in this case the integration of (19.1) requires $n-r'-u$ operations $O_{n-r'-u}, ..., O_1$ and $r'-p$ quadratures.

EXERCISES†

1. Prove that the x-rank of $D_{\dot{c}\dot{b}}^{\;\;x}$, i.e. the number of linearly independent bivectors $D_{\dot{c}\dot{b}}^{\;\;x}$ ($x = \mathrm{p}+1, ..., \mathrm{n}$) is always $\leqslant \mu - p$.

2. If the affinor density $\mathfrak{P}_\lambda^\kappa$ of weight $\mathfrak{k}$ is absolutely invariant with respect to $\lfloor v^\kappa \rfloor$ and if $n \geqslant 2$, it has either the form

$$\mathfrak{P}_\lambda^\kappa = pA_\lambda^\kappa \quad (\mathfrak{k} = 0), \tag{2α}$$

where p is a scalar, satisfying the condition $\underset{L}{D}p = 0$, or the form

$$\mathfrak{P}_\lambda^\kappa = \mathfrak{v}_\lambda v^\kappa \quad (\mathfrak{k} = 1), \tag{2β}$$

† Cf. the suggestions at the end of the book.

where $\mathfrak{v}_\lambda$ is an arbitrary covariant vector density of weight $+1$, satisfying the conditions

$$\mathfrak{v}_\lambda v^\lambda = 0, \qquad \underset{L}{D}\mathfrak{v}_\lambda = 0. \tag{2γ}$$

3. If the affinor density $\mathfrak{P}^{\kappa\lambda}$ of weight $\mathfrak{k}$ is absolutely invariant with respect to $\lfloor v^\kappa \rfloor$ it has either the form

$$\mathfrak{P}^{\kappa\lambda} = \mathfrak{u}^{[\kappa}v^{\lambda]} \quad (\mathfrak{k} = 1), \tag{3α}$$

where $\mathfrak{u}^\kappa$ is a vector density of weight $+1$, satisfying the condition

$$v^{[\lambda}\underset{L}{D}\mathfrak{u}^{\kappa]} = 0, \tag{3β}$$

or the form

$$\mathfrak{P}^{\kappa\lambda} = \mathfrak{p}v^\kappa v^\lambda \quad (\mathfrak{k} = 2), \tag{3γ}$$

where $\mathfrak{p}$ is a scalar density of weight $+2$ satisfying the condition $\underset{L}{D}\mathfrak{p} = 0$.

4. If the system $w_\lambda d\xi^\lambda = 0$ is complete, and if the w_λ are homogeneous in the ξ^κ, $(w_\lambda \xi^\lambda)^{-1}$ is an integrating factor (Goursat).†

5. Solve the complete system

$$\begin{aligned} \partial_1 f - A_\zeta \xi^\zeta \partial_3 f - B_\zeta \xi^\zeta \partial_4 f &= 0 \\ \partial_2 f - C_\zeta \xi^\zeta \partial_3 f - D_\zeta \xi^\zeta \partial_4 f &= 0 \end{aligned} \qquad (\zeta = 3, 4) \tag{5α}$$

by means of the abbreviated auxiliary system (cf. III, § 16).

6. Solve the complete system

$$\begin{aligned} (vy-ux)\,du &= (u^2+y^2)\,dx+(uv+xy)\,dy, \\ (ux-vy)\,dv &= (uv+xy)\,dx+(v^2+x^2)\,dy \end{aligned} \tag{6α}$$

by means of the abbreviated auxiliary system (cf. III, § 16) (Forsyth).‡

7. Prove, without making use of the completeness of (17.20), that the system (17.15) has at least one solution. From this fact another proof of the completeness of (17.20) can be deduced.

† 1921. 1, p. 133. ‡ Ibid., p. 132.

IV

CLASSIFICATION OF COVARIANT VECTOR FIELDS AND PFAFFIANS†

1. General remarks on classification

LET Ω be a given set of geometric objects (cf. II, § 5) in X_n with the same number of components, N, and the same law of transformation (for instance, the set of all covariant q-vector fields). Let the N components of any object of the set with respect to the coordinate system (κ) be denoted by γ^A. We suppose that the γ^A of all objects of the set are defined in an $\mathfrak{N}(\underset{0}{\xi^\kappa})$. We recall that the coordinate system (κ) in $\mathfrak{N}(\underset{0}{\xi^\kappa})$ is a one-to-one correspondence between the geometric points of $\mathfrak{N}(\underset{0}{\xi^\kappa})$ and the arithmetic points in an $\mathfrak{N}(\overset{\kappa}{\underset{0}{\xi}})$ and that a transformation of (κ) into another coordinate system (κ') in $\mathfrak{N}(\underset{0}{\xi^\kappa})$ means passing to a one-to-one correspondence between the points of $\mathfrak{N}(\underset{0}{\xi^\kappa})$ and the arithmetic points of another region $\mathfrak{N}(\overset{\kappa'}{\underset{0}{\xi}})$, $\overset{\kappa'}{\underset{0}{\xi}}$ being another point of the arithmetic space $\mathfrak{A}_n$ (cf. II, § 2). In $\mathfrak{N}(\underset{0}{\xi^\kappa})$ we will not use all the coordinate transformations of $\mathfrak{P}$ (cf. II, § 2) but only those satisfying the condition that for all allowable coordinate systems the region of $\mathfrak{A}_n$ corresponding to $\mathfrak{N}(\underset{0}{\xi^\kappa})$ is contained in a definitely given region $\underset{*}{\mathfrak{N}} = \mathfrak{N}(\overset{\kappa}{\underset{*}{\xi}})$ of $\mathfrak{A}_n$. $\underset{*}{\mathfrak{N}}$ may be the whole $\mathfrak{A}_n$ but this is not necessary.

Now consider the following system Φ of functions in $\mathfrak{A}_n$,

$$\Phi \begin{cases} \mu_0 \text{ constants: } \phi_1, \ldots, \phi_{\mu_0}; \\ \mu_1 \text{ functions of } 1 \text{ variable: } \phi_{1,1}(\overset{1}{\xi}), \ldots, \phi_{1,\mu_1}(\overset{1}{\xi}); \\ \cdot \quad \cdot \quad \cdot \quad \cdot \quad \cdot \quad \cdot \quad \cdot \quad \cdot \quad \cdot \quad \cdot \quad \cdot \quad \cdot \\ \mu_n \text{ functions of } n \text{ variables: } \phi_{n,1}(\overset{1}{\xi}, \ldots, \overset{n}{\xi}), \ldots, \phi_{n,\mu_n}(\overset{1}{\xi}, \ldots, \overset{n}{\xi}), \end{cases} \tag{1.1}$$

analytic in $\underset{*}{\mathfrak{N}}$. Let the coefficients of the power series in the $\overset{\kappa}{\xi} - \overset{\kappa}{\underset{*}{\xi}}$ of these functions be subject to the condition that they satisfy a certain finite number of inequalities, each containing a finite number of coefficients. When these conditions are satisfied, the choice of the functions

† General references: Cartan 1899. 1; 1945. 1, ch. iii; v. Weber 1900. 1; Goursat 1922. 1.

is free. The functions satisfying these conditions will be called *allowable functions*.

Now let
$$F^A[\overset{1}{\xi},\ldots,\overset{n}{\xi},\Phi] \quad (A = 1,\ldots,N) \tag{1.2}$$
be a *fixed* set of N *functionals* (cf. II, § 5) of $\overset{1}{\xi},\ldots,\overset{n}{\xi}$ and the functions of Φ, satisfying the conditions:

(1) the F^A are analytic in $\overset{*}{\mathfrak{R}}$;

(2) for every allowable coordinate system (κ') and every choice of allowable functions of Φ, the functions $\gamma^{A'}(\xi^{\kappa'})$ defined by
$$\gamma^{A'} = \delta^{A'}_A F^A[\overset{1}{\xi},\ldots,\overset{n}{\xi},\Phi]_{(\overset{\kappa}{\xi}=\delta^{\kappa}_{\kappa'}\xi^{\kappa'})} \quad (A = 1,\ldots,N;\ A' = 1',\ldots,N') \tag{1.3}$$
are components with respect to (κ') of an object of the set Ω in $\underset{0}{\mathfrak{R}}(\xi^{\kappa'})$;

(3) for every choice of an object of Ω it is possible to choose an allowable coordinate system (κ') and allowable functions of Φ, such that the $\gamma^{A'}$ defined by (1.3) are the components of this object with respect to (κ').

If these conditions are satisfied, we call (1.3) a *general representation* of Ω, dependent on μ_0 constants, μ_1 functions of 1 variable, etc., up to μ_n functions of n variables. $\mu_0, \mu_1,\ldots, \mu_n$ are called the *characteristic numbers* of the representation. If another representation is found with characteristic numbers $\nu_0, \nu_1,\ldots, \nu_n$, the first one is said to be *more favourable* than the second if there exists a number $p \leqslant n$ such that $\mu_p < \nu_p$ and $\mu_{p+1} = \nu_{p+1},\ldots, \mu_n = \nu_n$. If for a given representation it can be proved that more favourable representations do not exist, it is called a *normal representation* or *normal form*. A normal representation with $\mu_0 = \mu_1 = \ldots = \mu_n = 0$ is called a *canonical representation* or *canonical form*. In the case of a canonical representation the F^A form a *fixed* set of *functions* of $\overset{1}{\xi},\ldots,\overset{n}{\xi}$ and (1.3) takes the form
$$\gamma^{A'} = \delta^{A'}_A F^A(\xi^{1'},\ldots,\xi^{n'}) \quad (A = 1,\ldots,N;\ A' = 1',\ldots,N'). \tag{1.4}$$

If the set Ω can be subdivided into sub-sets, and if to every sub-set a representation can be found, not valid for any object of another sub-set, we have a classification of the objects of Ω. But it must be noted that, except in the case where only canonical representations occur, a classification is not absolute but may depend on the choice of the representations used.

If a field of quantities $\underset{1}{F}$ in an $\underset{1}{\mathfrak{R}}(\xi^\kappa)$ and a field $\underset{2}{F}$ in an $\underset{2}{\mathfrak{R}}(\xi^\kappa)$ are given, it may be possible to transform the field region of $\underset{1}{F}$ in an $\mathfrak{N}(\underset{1}{\xi^\kappa})$ into the field region of $\underset{2}{F}$ in an $\mathfrak{N}(\underset{2}{\xi^\kappa})$ by a process of dragging along (cf. II, 13), transforming $\underset{1}{F}$ into $\underset{2}{F}$ and $\underset{1}{\xi^\kappa}$ into $\underset{2}{\xi^\kappa}$. In that case the field $\underset{1}{F}$ in $\underset{1}{\xi^\kappa}$ is said to be *isomorphic* with the field $\underset{2}{F}$ in $\underset{2}{\xi^\kappa}$. Sufficient conditions are that the components of $\underset{1}{F}$ with respect to some coordinate system (κ) have the same values as the components of $\underset{2}{F}$ with respect to some other coordinate system (κ') and that $\underset{2}{\xi^{\kappa'}} = \delta^{\kappa'}_\kappa \underset{1}{\xi^\kappa}$. Obviously isomorphic fields have the same representations but, conversely, fields with the same representation are generally not isomorphic.

If a field F is given in an $\mathfrak{N}(\underset{0}{\xi^\kappa})$ and if for every general choice of $\underset{1}{\xi^\kappa}$ and $\underset{2}{\xi^\kappa}$ in an $\mathfrak{N}(\underset{0}{\xi^\kappa})$ the field F in $\underset{1}{\xi^\kappa}$ is isomorphic with the field F in $\underset{2}{\xi^\kappa}$, F is said to be *auto-isomorphic* in this latter $\mathfrak{N}(\underset{0}{\xi^\kappa})$. For instance, every gradient field is auto-isomorphic. But a scalar field is never auto-isomorphic unless it is constant.

2. The systems S, S_1, S_2, S_3, and S_4 of a vector field w_λ (or a Pfaffian $w_\lambda\, d\xi^\lambda$)†

We begin with the classical problem of classification of fields w_λ and write the solution in a form convenient for generalization to the case of fields $w_{\lambda_1 \ldots \lambda_q}$ $(q > 1)$. Let the field w_λ be analytic and not everywhere zero in an $\mathfrak{N}(\underset{0}{\xi^\kappa})$. From w_λ the rotation

$$W_{\mu\lambda} \stackrel{\text{def}}{=} 2\partial_{[\mu} w_{\lambda]} \quad \text{or} \quad W = 2Dw \tag{2.1}$$

may be derived. In general this rotation is neither zero nor simple in $\mathfrak{N}(\underset{0}{\xi^\kappa})$. Now we consider the following five systems of total differential equations

$$(S) \qquad w_\mu\, d\xi^\mu = 0; \tag{2.2}$$

$$(S_1) \qquad W_{\mu\lambda}\, d\xi^\mu = 0; \tag{2.3}$$

$$(S_2) \qquad \begin{cases} w_\mu\, d\xi^\mu = 0, \\ W_{\mu\lambda}\, d\xi^\mu = 0; \end{cases} \tag{2.4}$$

$$(S_3) \qquad W_{\mu[\lambda} w_{\nu]}\, d\xi^\mu = 0; \tag{2.5}$$

$$(S_4) \qquad \begin{cases} w_\mu\, d\xi^\mu = 0, \\ W_{\mu[\lambda} w_{\nu]}\, d\xi^\mu = 0. \end{cases} \tag{2.6}$$

† Cf. Cartan 1899. 1; v. Weber 1900. 1, ch. v; Goursat 1922. 1, ch. i.

$w_\mu \, d\xi^\mu$ is called the *Pfaffian* and (2.2) the *Pfaffian equation* belonging to the field w_λ. The μ-rank of the quantities in the left-hand sides of $S, S_1, \ldots, S_4$ will be denoted in the following way:

$$\begin{array}{ll} & \mu\text{-}rank \\ (S) & c; \\ (S_1) & 2\rho = \textit{rotation class of } w_\lambda; \\ (S_2) & K = \textit{class of } w_\lambda; \textit{ class of } w_\mu \, d\xi^\mu; \\ (S_3) & c_3; \\ (S_4) & k = \textit{similarity class of } w_\lambda; \textit{ class of } \lfloor w_\lambda \rfloor; \\ & \qquad \textit{class of the Pfaffian equation } w_\mu \, d\xi^\mu = 0. \end{array} \tag{2.7}$$

These five integers are arithmetic invariants of the field w_λ. $c = 0$ in points where $w_\lambda = 0$ and $c = 1$ in all other points.

Every linear element $d\xi^\mu$ satisfying S_2, satisfies also S and S_1. Hence $c \leqslant K$; $2\rho \leqslant K$. Every linear element satisfying S_4 satisfies also S and S_3, hence $c \leqslant k$; $c_3 \leqslant k$. The μ-rank of $W_{\mu[\lambda} w_{\nu]}$ cannot be greater than the μ-rank of $W_{\mu\lambda}$, so $c_3 \leqslant 2\rho$. The μ-rank of the system w_μ, $W_{\mu[\lambda} w_{\nu]}$ cannot be greater than the μ-rank of the system w_μ, $W_{\mu\lambda}$, so $k \leqslant K$. Collecting results we have the following inequalities:

$$\begin{array}{ccccc} n \geqslant & K & \geqslant & k & \\ & \mathbin{\rotatebox[origin=c]{90}{$\geqslant$}} & & \mathbin{\rotatebox[origin=c]{90}{$\geqslant$}} & \\ & 2\rho & \geqslant & c_3 & \geqslant 0. \end{array} \tag{2.8}$$

In $\mathfrak{N}(\underset{0}{\xi^\kappa})$ let $\underset{1}{\xi^\kappa}$ be a point where $w_\lambda \neq 0$ and, therefore, $c = 1$. Then there exists an $\mathfrak{N}(\underset{1}{\xi^\kappa})$ where $c = 1$ at all points. In this $\mathfrak{N}(\underset{1}{\xi^\kappa})$ let $\underset{2}{\xi^\kappa}$ be a point where 2ρ has the maximum value occurring in $\mathfrak{N}(\underset{1}{\xi^\kappa})$. Then there exists an $\mathfrak{N}(\underset{2}{\xi^\kappa})$ where $c = 1$ and 2ρ has this maximum value in all points. Proceeding in this way we get at last a point $\underset{5}{\xi^\kappa}$ and an $\mathfrak{N}(\underset{5}{\xi^\kappa})$ in $\mathfrak{N}(\underset{0}{\xi^\kappa})$ where c, 2ρ, K, c_3, and k are all constant. Such a region is called a *region of constant class* of the field w_λ. If a point $\underset{*}{\xi^\kappa}$ has no $\mathfrak{N}(\underset{*}{\xi^\kappa})$ where the invariants are all constant, $\underset{*}{\xi^\kappa}$ is called a *point of diminished class* of the field w_λ. All other points are called *ordinary points* of the field. Hence a region of constant class consists of ordinary points only.

Now let $\underset{0}{\xi^\kappa}$ be an ordinary point and $\mathfrak{N}(\underset{0}{\xi^\kappa})$ a region of constant class of w_λ. Then we form the following comitants from w_λ and $W_{\mu\lambda}$, using the abbreviated notation of I, § 7, and II, § 11:

$$\overset{1}{I} = w, \quad \overset{3}{I} = wW, \quad \overset{5}{I} = wWW;$$
$$\overset{2}{I} = W, \quad \overset{4}{I} = WW, \quad \overset{6}{I} = WWW; \quad \text{etc.} \tag{2.9}$$

2ρ being constant in $\underset{0}{\mathfrak{N}}(\xi^\kappa)$ we have

$$\overset{2\sigma}{I}\begin{cases} \neq 0 & (\sigma \leqslant \rho) \\ = 0 & (\sigma > \rho), \end{cases} \qquad \overset{2\sigma+1}{I} = 0 \quad (\sigma > \rho). \tag{2.10}$$

From (2.9) it follows that

(a) $$\overset{2\sigma+1}{I} = w\overset{2\sigma}{I},$$

(b) $$\overset{2\sigma}{I} = 2D\overset{2\sigma-1}{I}. \tag{2.11}$$

The system S_1' of partial differential equations adjoint to S_1 takes the form (cf. II, §§ 5, 11)

$$(S_1') \quad \overset{2\rho}{I}\bar{f} = 0 \quad (\bar{f} \overset{\text{def}}{=} Df). \tag{2.12}$$

Now there are two cases. In case I w does not lie in the domain of W and consequently $\overset{2\rho+1}{I} \neq 0$. According to the definition $\overset{2\rho+1}{I}$ is a simple covariant $(2\rho+1)$-vector whose domain coincides with the μ-domain of the system w_μ, $W_{\mu\lambda}$. Consequently the system S_2' adjoint to S_2 can be written in the form

$$(S_2') \quad \overset{2\rho+1}{I}\bar{f} = 0. \tag{2.13}$$

Because w does not lie in the domain of W, the μ-domains of $W_{\mu\lambda}$ and $W_{\mu[\lambda}w_{\nu]}$ coincide and we have

$$S_3 = S_1, \qquad S_4 = S_2 \tag{2.14}$$

and $$c_3 = 2\rho, \qquad k = K = 2\rho+1. \tag{2.15}$$

In case II w lies in the domain of W. Consequently we have $\overset{2\rho+1}{I} = 0$, $S_1 = S_2$, $2\rho = K$, and $W_{\mu\lambda}$ can be decomposed in the following way:

$$W_{\mu\lambda} = 2u_{[\mu}w_{\lambda]} + {}^*W_{\mu\lambda} \quad (u_\mu \neq 0), \tag{2.16}$$

${}^*W_{\mu\lambda}$ being a bivector of rank $2\rho-2$ whose domain has nothing in common with the domain of $u_{[\mu}w_{\lambda]}$. Because

$$\overset{2\rho-1}{I} = wW...W = w\,{}^*W...{}^*W \quad (\rho-1 \text{ factors } W \text{ and } {}^*W) \tag{2.17}$$

we have $\overset{2\rho-1}{I} \neq 0$, which also follows from the fact that

$$\overset{2\rho}{I} = 2D\overset{2\rho-1}{I} \tag{2.18}$$

and $\overset{2\rho}{I}$ does not vanish. From (2.17) we see that $\overset{2\rho-1}{I}$ is a simple $(2\rho-1)$-vector. According to (2.16) S_3 can be written

$$-w_\mu u_{[\lambda} w_{\nu]} d\xi^\mu + {}^*W_{\mu[\lambda} w_{\nu]} d\xi^\mu = 0 \tag{2.19}$$

and from this we get by alternated multiplication with u_ω the equation

$${}^*W_{\mu[\lambda} w_\nu u_{\omega]} d\xi^\mu = 0 \tag{2.20}$$

showing that $d\xi^\mu {}^*W_{\mu\lambda}$ either vanishes or lies in the domain of $w_{[\mu} u_{\lambda]}$. Now since the domain of ${}^*W_{\mu\lambda}$ and $w_{[\mu} u_{\lambda]}$ have nothing in common, it follows that $d\xi^\mu {}^*W_{\mu\lambda} = 0$. Replacing $d\xi^\mu {}^*W_{\mu\lambda}$ by zero in (2.19) we get $d\xi^\mu w_\mu = 0$ and this means that the μ-domain of $W_{\mu[\lambda} w_{\nu]}$ coincides with the μ-domain of the system w_μ, ${}^*W_{\mu\lambda}$, that is, with the domain of $\overset{2\rho-1}{I}$. Hence the system S'_3, adjoint to S_3, can be written

$$(S'_3) \quad \overset{2\rho-1}{I}\,\bar{f} = 0. \tag{2.21}$$

Since w_λ lies in the domain of $\overset{2\rho-1}{I}$ we get $S_4 = S_3$ and $k = c_3 = 2\rho-1$. Gathering these results together, we get the following summary of the two cases:

$$\text{(I)} \quad \begin{array}{l} S_3 = S_1, \qquad\qquad S_4 = S_2; \\ S'_3 = S'_1\colon \ (a)\ \overset{2\rho}{I}\bar{f} = 0, \quad S'_4 = S'_2; \quad (b)\ \overset{2\rho+1}{I}\,\bar{f} = 0; \\ \overset{2\rho}{I} \neq 0, \quad \overset{2\rho+1}{I} \neq 0, \quad \overset{2\rho+2}{I} = 0; \\ c_3 = 2\rho, \quad k = K = 2\rho+1. \end{array} \tag{2.22}$$

$$\text{(II)} \quad \begin{array}{l} S_2 = S_1, \qquad\qquad S_4 = S_3; \\ S'_2 = S'_1\colon \ (a)\ \overset{2\rho}{I}\bar{f} = 0, \quad S'_4 = S'_3\colon \quad (b)\ \overset{2\rho-1}{I}\,\bar{f} = 0; \\ \overset{2\rho}{I} \neq 0, \quad \overset{2\rho+1}{I} = 0; \\ K = 2\rho, \quad k = c_3 = 2\rho-1. \end{array} \tag{2.23}$$

Hence the class K is odd in case I and even in case II. The rotation class 2ρ is always the greatest even number $\leqslant K$ and the similarity class k the greatest odd number $\leqslant K$.

3. Completeness of the systems S_1, S_2, S_3, and S_4†

We will prove that the systems S_1, S_2, S_3, and S_4 are always complete.

In case I $\overset{2\rho}{I}$ and $\overset{2\rho+1}{I}$ are simple and their rotations vanish. According to Theorem III.16 this implies that $\overset{2\rho}{I}$ is $X_{n-2\rho}$-forming and that $\overset{2\rho+1}{I}$ is $X_{n-2\rho-1}$-forming and from this the completeness of $S_1 = S_3$ and $S_2 = S_4$ results immediately.

† Cf. Cartan 1899. 1; v. Weber 1900. 1, ch. v; Goursat 1922. 1, ch. i.

In case II $\overset{2\rho}{I}$ is simple and its rotation vanishes. Hence $\overset{2\rho}{I}$ is $X_{n-2\rho}$-forming and $S_1 = S_2$ complete. $\overset{2\rho-1}{I}$ is simple, and from (2.11 *b*) and $\overset{2\rho+1}{I} = 0$ it follows that

$$\overset{2\rho-1}{I}_{\mu_2 \dots [\mu_{2\rho}} \partial_{\lambda_1} \overset{2\rho-1}{I}_{\lambda_2 \dots \lambda_{2\rho}]} = \tfrac{1}{2} \overset{2\rho-1}{I}_{\mu_2 \dots [\mu_{2\rho}} \overset{2\rho}{I}_{\lambda_1 \dots \lambda_{2\rho}]} = 0 \tag{3.1}$$

and according to (3.1) and (III, 17.10) $\overset{2\rho-1}{I}$ is $X_{n-2\rho+1}$-forming. Hence $S_3 = S_4$ is complete.

In case I one single solution of $S'_1 = S'_3$ or $S'_2 = S'_4$ is determined by giving one function of 2ρ or $2\rho+1$ variables respectively. In case II one single solution of $S'_1 = S'_2$ or $S'_3 = S'_4$ is determined by giving one function of 2ρ or $2\rho-1$ variables respectively (cf. III, § 13).

Since S_1 is complete, there exists a normal system of $X_{n-2\rho}$'s, whose tangent $E_{n-2\rho}$ is at every point the support of the domain of $W_{\mu\lambda}$. We call these $X_{n-2\rho}$'s the *supports of rotation* of the field w_λ.

Since S_2 is complete, there exists a normal system of X_{n-K}'s, whose tangent E_{n-K} is at every point the support of the μ-region of the system w_μ, $W_{\mu\lambda}$. We call these X_{n-K}'s the *supports* of the field w_λ.

Since S_4 is complete, there exists a normal system of X_{n-k}'s, whose tangent E_{n-k} is at every point the support of the μ-region of the system w_μ, $W_{\mu[\lambda} w_{\nu]}$. These X_{n-k}'s are called the *characteristics* of the field w_λ.

The relations between them are the following:

$$\begin{aligned} &\text{Case I:} \quad k = K = 2\rho+1, \quad \text{char.} = \text{supp.} \subset \text{supp. of rot.} \\ &\text{Case II:} \quad k+1 = K = 2\rho, \quad \text{char.} \supset \text{supp.} = \text{supp. of rot.} \end{aligned} \tag{3.2}$$

The systems S_1 and S_2 have the remarkable property that their integration is easier than the integration of a general complete system.† Since the rotation of $W_{\mu\lambda}$ is zero, we know that 1 is an integrating factor of S_1. Hence, if $2\rho-1$ independent solutions of S'_1 are known, a 2ρth solution can be obtained by a quadrature (cf. III, § 19). In the same way, since the rotation of $\overset{2\rho+1}{I}$ is zero in case I, in that case the $(2\rho+1)$th solution of $S'_2 = S'_4$ can be obtained by a quadrature if 2ρ independent solutions are already known.‡ If in the case II $2\rho-1$ known solutions of $S'_1 = S'_2$ happen to be independent solutions of $S'_3 = S'_4$ the integration of $S'_1 = S'_2$ is still easier. Because, knowing all the solutions of $S'_3 = S'_4$ we can obtain an integrating factor p of

† Cf. v. Weber 1900. 1, pp. 178, 180; Goursat 1922. 1, pp. 30, 145.

‡ v. Weber 1900. 1, p. 180, and Goursat 1922. 1, p. 31, make the condition that the 2ρ solutions are solutions of $S'_1 = S'_3$. This is not necessary.

$S'_3 = S'_4$ and since Dp is a divisor of $\overset{2\rho}{I}$ in consequence of (2.18), p is a 2ρth solution of $S'_1 = S'_2$.

4. Section of a covariant q-vector field with respect to a set of functions†

We prove first that the rotation of the section of a covariant q-vector field $w_{\lambda_1\ldots\lambda_q}$ with an X_m $(m > q)$ is equal to the section of the rotation of $w_{\lambda_1\ldots\lambda_q}$ with this X_m. Let

$$\xi^\kappa = \xi^\kappa(\eta^a) \quad (a = 1,\ldots, \mathrm{m}) \tag{4.1}$$

be a minimal regular parametric form of the X_m. Then the field of X_m

$$'w_{b_1\ldots b_q} \overset{\text{def}}{=} B_{b_1}^{\lambda_1}\ldots B_{b_q}^{\lambda_q} w_{\lambda_1\ldots\lambda_q}, \qquad B_b^\kappa \overset{\text{def}}{=} \partial_b \xi^\kappa \quad (b = 1,\ldots, \mathrm{m}) \tag{4.2}$$

is the section of $w_{\lambda_1\ldots\lambda_q}$ with the X_m (cf. II, § 7). Now we have

$$\begin{aligned} \partial_{[c}\, 'w_{b_1\ldots b_q]} &= B_{[c}^{\mu}\, \partial_{|\mu|} B_{b_1}^{\lambda_1}\ldots B_{b_q]}^{\lambda_q} w_{\lambda_1\ldots\lambda_q} \\ &= B_{[c}^{\mu}\, B_{b_1}^{\lambda_1}\ldots B_{b_q]}^{\lambda_q}\, \partial_\mu w_{\lambda_1\ldots\lambda_q} \\ &= B_{c}^{\mu}\, B_{b_1}^{\lambda_1}\ldots B_{b_q}^{\lambda_q}\, \partial_{[\mu} w_{\lambda_1\ldots\lambda_q]} \quad (b_1,\ldots, b_q,\, c = 1,\ldots, \mathrm{m}), \end{aligned} \tag{4.3}$$

all terms containing differentiations of the B_b^κ vanishing in consequence of $\partial_{[c}\, \partial_{b]}\, \xi^\kappa = 0$.

Now let $\overset{m+1}{f},\ldots, \overset{n}{f}$ be a set of $n-m$ independent functions of the ξ^κ, analytic in $\mathfrak{N}(\overset{0}{\xi^\kappa})$. Then we form the sections of the field $w_{\lambda_1\ldots\lambda_q}$, analytic in $\mathfrak{N}(\overset{0}{\xi^\kappa})$, with all ∞^{n-m} X_m's, with the equations

$$\overset{m+1}{f} = \overset{m+1}{c}, \quad \ldots, \quad \overset{n}{f} = \overset{n}{c}, \tag{4.4}$$

in which $\overset{m+1}{c},\ldots, \overset{n}{c}$ are arbitrary constants. This process may be called the *section of* $w_{\lambda_1\ldots\lambda_q}$ *with respect to the set of functions* $\overset{m+1}{f},\ldots, \overset{n}{f}$. If we choose the coordinates ξ^κ in such a way that

$$\xi^{m+1} = \overset{m+1}{f}, \quad \ldots, \quad \xi^n = \overset{n}{f} \tag{4.5}$$

and consequently

$$\overset{m+1}{e}_\lambda = \partial_\lambda \overset{m+1}{f}, \quad \ldots, \quad \overset{n}{e}_\lambda = \partial_\lambda \overset{n}{f}, \tag{4.6}$$

then the sections are given by the equation

$$'w_{\beta_1\ldots\beta_q} = w_{\beta_1\ldots\beta_q}(\xi^1,\ldots, \xi^m, \overset{m+1}{c},\ldots, \overset{n}{c}) \quad (\beta_1,\ldots, \beta_q = 1,\ldots, m). \tag{4.7}$$

Hence the process is carried out by first writing $w_{\lambda_1\ldots\lambda_q}$ in terms of the measuring vectors $\overset{1}{e}_\lambda,\ldots, \overset{n}{e}_\lambda$, then dropping all terms containing one or

† Cf. Cartan 1899. 1; v. Weber 1900. 1, ch. ix; Goursat 1922. 1, ch. iv.

more of the vectors $\overset{m+1}{e}_\lambda,\ldots,\overset{n}{e}_\lambda$ and finally replacing $\xi^{m+1},\ldots,\xi^n$ in the remaining terms by $\overset{m+1}{c},\ldots,\overset{n}{c}$.

If the process of section with respect to $\overset{m+1}{f},\ldots,\overset{n}{f}$ is applied to a vector field w_λ of class K and if $'K$ is the class of the section obtained, the difference $\kappa = K - 'K$ is called the *index* of the set of functions $\overset{m+1}{f},\ldots,\overset{n}{f}$ with respect to w_λ. To determine this index it is only necessary to form the comitants $'\overset{1}{I}$, $'\overset{2}{I}$, etc., of the section $'w$. But since $'w$ and $'W$ both come from w and W by section, all comitants $'I$ arise from the corresponding comitants I by section. Hence, to obtain the $'I$'s the coordinate system has to be chosen as above, the I's have to be written in terms of the $\overset{\kappa}{e}_\lambda$, all terms containing one or more of the $\overset{m+1}{e}_\lambda,\ldots,\overset{n}{e}_\lambda$ have to be dropped, and in all other terms $\xi^{m+1},\ldots,\xi^n$ have to be replaced by $\overset{m+1}{c},\ldots,\overset{n}{c}$. This means that one of the $'I$'s, for instance $'\overset{\sigma}{I}$, is zero if and only if

$$\overset{\sigma}{I}_{[\lambda_1\ldots\lambda_\sigma}(\partial_{\lambda_{m+1}}\overset{m+1}{f})\ldots(\partial_{\lambda_n]}\overset{n}{f}) = 0. \tag{4.8}$$

If K is odd (case I) and $m = n-1$, $'\overset{\sigma}{I}$ is zero if and only if $\overset{\sigma}{I}\bar{f} = 0$. There are three sub-cases:

(*a*) f is not a solution of $S_2' = S_4'$ and therefore not a solution of $S_1' = S_3'$. Hence $\overset{2\rho+1}{I}\bar{f} \neq 0$ and $\overset{2\rho}{I}\bar{f} \neq 0$ and consequently

$$'K = K, \quad \kappa = 0; \tag{4.9}$$

(*b*) f is a solution of $S_2' = S_4'$ but not of $S_1' = S_3'$. Hence $\overset{2\rho+1}{I}\bar{f} = 0$ and $\overset{2\rho}{I}\bar{f} \neq 0$ and consequently

$$'K = K-1, \quad \kappa = 1; \tag{4.10}$$

(*c*) f is a solution of $S_1' = S_3'$ and therefore a solution of $S_2' = S_4'$. Hence $\overset{2\rho+1}{I}\bar{f} = 0$ and $\overset{2\rho}{I}\bar{f} = 0$ and consequently $'K \leqslant K-2$.

To deal with this last sub-case we prove that always $'K \geqslant K-2$ if f is a solution of S_2'. If we choose the coordinates in such a way that $\xi^n = f$, $\xi^n = \text{const.}$ has to be an integral of S_2 and, therefore, S_2 is equivalent to

$$\left.\begin{array}{ll} (a) & w_\beta\, d\xi^\beta = 0 \\ (b) & W_{\beta\alpha}\, d\xi^\beta = 0 \\ (c) & W_{\beta n}\, d\xi^\beta = 0 \\ (d) & d\xi^n = 0 \end{array}\right\} \quad (\alpha, \beta = 1,\ldots, n-1). \tag{4.11}$$

Now since S_2 is complete, there must be among these equations just K equations linearly independent of each other. Hence, if we drop the equations (4.11 c, d), the number of linearly independent equations among the remaining ones must be $\geqslant K-2$. But these remaining equations are just the equations of the system S_2 belonging to $'w$. Hence $'K \geqslant K-2$ and from this it follows that

$$'K = K-2, \quad \kappa = 2. \tag{4.12}$$

If K is even (case II) and $m = n-1$ we also have three sub-cases:

(a) f is not a solution of $S'_1 = S'_2$ and therefore not a solution of $S'_3 = S'_4$. Hence $\overset{2\rho}{I}\bar{f} \neq 0$ and $\overset{2\rho-1}{I}\bar{f} \neq 0$ and consequently

$$'K = K, \quad \kappa = 0; \tag{4.13}$$

(b) f is a solution of $S'_1 = S'_2$ but not a solution of $S'_3 = S'_4$. Hence $\overset{2\rho}{I}\bar{f} = 0$ but $\overset{2\rho-1}{I}\bar{f} \neq 0$ and consequently

$$'K = K-1, \quad \kappa = 1; \tag{4.14}$$

(c) f is a solution of $S'_3 = S'_4$ and therefore a solution of $S'_1 = S'_2$. Hence $\overset{2\rho}{I}\bar{f} = 0$ and $\overset{2\rho-1}{I}\bar{f} = 0$ and consequently $'K \leqslant K-2$. As we have already proved that $'K \geqslant K-2$ if f is a solution of S'_2, it follows that

$$'K = K-2, \quad \kappa = 2. \tag{4.15}$$

Collecting results we have the following theorem, valid both for cases I and II:

THEOREM IV.1. *The index of a function f with respect to w_λ is*

0 if f is neither a solution of S'_2 nor of S'_3;
1 if f is a solution of S'_2 but not a solution of S'_3;
2 if f is a solution of S'_2 and of S'_3.

In all cases $c_3 = K-1$ and $K \leqslant n$, hence $c_3 \leqslant n-1$. From this it follows that the system S'_3 has always at least one solution. Consequently there always exist functions with index 2 with respect to w_λ. In addition there are also always functions with index 1 because in case I $\overset{2\rho}{I}$ and $\overset{2\rho+1}{I}$ are simple and $\overset{2\rho}{I}$ lies in the domain of $\overset{2\rho+1}{I}$, and in case II $\overset{2\rho-1}{I}$ and $\overset{2\rho}{I}$ are simple and $\overset{2\rho-1}{I}$ lies in the domain of $\overset{2\rho}{I}$. But functions with index zero do not always exist; they exist if and only if $2\rho+1 < n$ in case I and $2\rho < n$ in case II.

From Theorem IV.1 it follows that for the determination of a function with index 2 or 1 at most an operation O_{K-1} or O_K respectively is necessary, and that such a function can be fixed by giving a function of $K-1$ or K variables respectively (cf. III, §§ 13, 16). There are two exceptions. If $K=1$, a function with index 1 can be found by a quadrature: $f=\int w_\lambda\, d\xi^\lambda$. If $K=2$ it is possible to find a function with index 1 by means of an operation O_1 and such a function can be fixed by giving one function of one variable. To prove this we consider the system S_3', taking for $K=2$ the form

$$w_{[\mu}\,\partial_{\lambda]}f=0. \tag{4.16}$$

If by means of an operation O_1 a solution s of this system has been found, we may without any integration find a function z satisfying the equation

$$w_\lambda = z\partial_\lambda s, \tag{4.17}$$

and this function z has index 1.

The index κ of the set $\overset{m+1}{f},\ldots,\overset{n}{f}$ cannot exceed $2(n-m)$ because every function diminishes the rank at most by 2 and the process of section can be carried out by introducing successively the $n-m$ functions. A necessary and sufficient condition that the set be of index κ with respect to w_λ is that

$$\overset{\sigma}{I}\,\overset{\overline{m+1}}{f}\ldots\overset{\bar{n}}{f}\begin{cases}=0 & (\sigma > K-\kappa)\\ \neq 0 & (\sigma \leqslant K-\kappa)\end{cases} \tag{4.18}$$

as follows from the definition of the index of a set. We will deduce here another frequently used form of this condition. Considering the skew-symmetric matrices†

$$\text{(A)}\ \| W_{\mu\lambda} \|, \qquad \text{(B)}\ \begin{Vmatrix} W_{\mu\lambda} & w_\mu \\ -w_\lambda & 0 \end{Vmatrix},$$

$$\text{(C)}\ \begin{Vmatrix} W_{\mu\lambda} & \overset{m+1}{f_\mu} & \cdots & \overset{n}{f_\mu} \\ -\overset{m+1}{f_\lambda} & 0 & \cdots & 0 \\ \vdots & \vdots & & \vdots \\ -\overset{n}{f_\lambda} & 0 & \cdots & 0 \end{Vmatrix}, \qquad \text{(D)}\ \begin{Vmatrix} W_{\mu\lambda} & w_\mu & \overset{m+1}{f_\mu} & \cdots & \overset{n}{f_\mu} \\ -w_\lambda & 0 & \cdots & \cdots & 0 \\ -\overset{m+1}{f_\lambda} & \vdots & & & \vdots \\ \vdots & \vdots & & & \vdots \\ -\overset{n}{f_\lambda} & 0 & \cdots & \cdots & 0 \end{Vmatrix} \tag{4.19}$$

we use the results of I, § 10. If $K=2\rho+\epsilon$ ($\epsilon = 1$ or 0), the rank of (A) is 2ρ and the rank of (B) is $2\rho+2\epsilon$. If now we call $2R_0$ the rank of (C) and $2R_1$ the rank of (D), we have, according to Theorem I.4:

$$\overset{2(R_0-n+m)}{I}\,\overset{\overline{m+1}}{f}\ldots\overset{\bar{n}}{f}\neq 0, \qquad \overset{2(R_0-n+m+1)}{I}\,\overset{\overline{m+1}}{f}\ldots\overset{\bar{n}}{f}=0 \tag{4.20}$$

† Cf. v. Weber 1900, ch. ix, § 4.

and $$\overset{2(R_1-n+m-1)}{I}\ \overline{\overset{m+1}{w\,f}}\ \ldots\overset{n}{\bar f} \neq 0, \qquad \overset{2(R_1-n+m)}{I}\ \overline{\overset{m+1}{w\,f}}\ \ldots\overset{n}{\bar f} = 0 \tag{4.21}$$

or $$\overset{2(R_1-n+m)-1}{I}\ \overline{\overset{m+1}{f}}\ \ldots\overset{n}{\bar f} \neq 0, \qquad \overset{2(R_1-n+m)+1}{I}\ \overline{\overset{m+1}{f}}\ \ldots\overset{n}{\bar f} = 0. \tag{4.22}$$

In consequence of (4.20) the rank $2\rho'$ of the section of $W_{\mu\lambda}$ is

$$2R_0-2n+2m;$$

hence $$2R_0 = 2\rho'+2(n-m). \tag{4.23}$$

Now either $R_1 = R_0$ or $R_1 = R_0+1$. If $R_1 = R_0$ it follows from (4.20) and (4.22) that the class $K-\kappa$ of the section of w_λ is $2R_0-2n+2m$ and hence

$$2R_0 = 2R_1 = K-\kappa+2n-2m. \tag{4.24}$$

In the same way we get for $R_1 = R_0+1$

$$2R_0 = 2R_1-2 = K-\kappa+2n-2m-1. \tag{4.25}$$

Consequently the equations

$$2\rho' = 2R_0-2(n-m),$$
$$K-\kappa = R_0+R_1-2(n-m) \tag{4.26}$$

are valid in all cases and this implies that the necessary and sufficient conditions (4.18) are equivalent to

$$2R_0 = \begin{cases} K-\kappa+2(n-m) & \text{for } K-\kappa \text{ even,} \\ K-\kappa+2(n-m)-1 & \text{for } K-\kappa \text{ odd;} \end{cases}$$
$$2R_1 = \begin{cases} K-\kappa+2(n-m) & \text{for } K-\kappa \text{ even,} \\ K-\kappa+2(n-m)+1 & \text{for } K-\kappa \text{ odd.} \end{cases} \tag{4.27}$$

When κ has the greatest possible value $2(n-m)$, the set of functions is said to be *conjugate to the field* w_λ. The necessary and sufficient condition is

$$\overset{\sigma}{I}\ \overline{\overset{m+1}{f}}\ \ldots\overset{n}{\bar f} = 0 \quad (\sigma = K-2(n-m)+1), \tag{4.28}$$

or in the other form,

$$2R_0 = \begin{cases} K & \text{for } K \text{ even,} \\ K-1 & \text{for } K \text{ odd;} \end{cases} \qquad 2R_1 = \begin{cases} K & \text{for } K \text{ even,} \\ K+1 & \text{for } K \text{ odd.} \end{cases} \tag{4.29}$$

$z \leqslant n-m$ functions of a conjugate set always form a conjugate sub-set. For, suppose the index of this sub-set were $< 2z$, the other $n-m-z$ functions could never diminish the class by more than $2(n-m-z)$ and accordingly the index of the whole set would be $< 2(n-m)$. This property of conjugate sets makes the determination of these sets much easier. First we determine one function with index 2, which is a solution of S_3':

$$\overset{K-1}{I}\ \bar f = 0. \tag{4.30}$$

If $\overset{m+1}{f}$ is this solution, we determine a solution of the system

$$\overset{K-3}{I}\;\overset{\overline{m+1}}{f}\;\bar{f} = 0. \tag{4.31}$$

This system is complete because it is the system S_3' for the sections of w_λ with the X_{n-1}'s, $\overset{m+1}{f} = \text{const.}$, these sections having the class $K-2$. Then if $\overset{m+2}{f}$ is a solution of (4.31), a solution has to be found of

$$\overset{K-5}{I}\;\overset{\overline{m+1}}{f}\;\overset{\overline{m+2}}{f}\;\bar{f} = 0, \tag{4.32}$$

etc., until $n-m$ functions are obtained. Since at every step only one solution is needed, for the whole process $n-m$ operations O_{K-1}, O_{K-3}, ..., $O_{K+1-2(n-m)}$ are necessary. The $n-m$ solutions can be fixed by giving $n-m$ functions of $K-1$, $K-3$,..., $K+1-2(n-m)$ variables respectively.

When $\kappa = 2(n-m)-1$ the set is called *semi-conjugate to* w_λ. The necessary and sufficient conditions are

$$\overset{\sigma}{I}\;\overset{\overline{m+1}}{f}\cdots\overset{\bar{n}}{f}\begin{cases} = 0 & (\sigma > K-2(n-m)+1) \\ \neq 0 & (\sigma \leqslant K-2(n-m)+1) \end{cases} \tag{4.33}$$

or in the other form

$$2R_0 = \begin{cases} K & \text{for } K \text{ even,} \\ K+1 & \text{for } K \text{ odd;} \end{cases} \qquad 2R_1 = \begin{cases} K+2 & \text{for } K \text{ even,} \\ K+1 & \text{for } K \text{ odd.} \end{cases} \tag{4.34}$$

$z \leqslant n-m$ functions of a semi-conjugate set form either a conjugate or a semi-conjugate sub-set because the other $n-m-z$ functions can never diminish the class by more than $2(n-m-z)$. From this it follows that every function of a semi-conjugate set has an index 1 or 2. To determine a semi-conjugate set we may determine first one function $\overset{m+1}{f}$ with index 1 which is a solution of S_2',

$$\overset{K}{I}\,\bar{f} = 0, \tag{4.35}$$

but not a solution of S_3'. As we have seen above such a function always exists. The sections of w_λ with the X_{n-1}'s, $\overset{m+1}{f} = \text{const.}$, have then the class $K-1$. For these sections we determine a function $\overset{m+2}{f}$ with index 2, that is a solution of the system S_3' of these sections:

$$\overset{K-2}{I}\;\overset{\overline{m+1}}{f}\;\bar{f} = 0, \tag{4.36}$$

etc., until $n-m$ functions are obtained. With every step we have to integrate a system S_3'. Hence we need $n-m$ operations O_K, O_{K-2},..., $O_{K+2-2(n-m)}$. But it is also possible first to reduce the class $n-m-1$ times by 2 and with the last step by 1. Then, if $K > 2(n-m)$, $n-m$ operations O_{K-1}, O_{K-3},..., $O_{K-2(n-m)+3}$, $O_{K-2(n-m)+2}$ are needed. But if

$K = 2(n-m)$ or $2(n-m)-1$ the last step needs only an operation O_1 or O_0 respectively, instead of O_2 or O_1 respectively, as we have seen above. *From this it follows that for* K *even, the determination of a conjugate set and of a semi-conjugate set of* $\frac{1}{2}K$ *functions can always be effected by means of* $\frac{1}{2}K$ *operations* $O_{K-1}, O_{K-3}, \ldots, O_1$.

It is an important question whether it is possible to determine a set of S functions with index κ, given the numbers S and κ and the class of the field w_λ. We prove the theorem

THEOREM IV.2. *A necessary and sufficient condition that a set of* S *functions exists with index* κ *with respect to a field* w_λ *of class* K *is that*

$$\begin{aligned} 0 \leqslant \kappa \leqslant K, \\ 2S \geqslant \kappa, \\ K-\kappa \leqslant n-S. \end{aligned} \tag{4.37}$$

PROOF. The necessity of the conditions is evident. We prove the sufficiency by constructing a set of S functions with the index κ and we will do this moreover in such a way that the set contains as many functions as possible which can be determined without any integrations. To begin with we ask for $u < S$ functions diminishing the class by $K-n+u$ for $n-u \leqslant K$ and leaving the class invariant for $n-u \geqslant K$. These u functions have only to satisfy certain inequalities and can be determined without any integration. If the diminished class is $n-u$ it is always possible to determine $\frac{1}{2}(n-u-K+\kappa+\eta)$ ($\eta = 0$ or 1) functions, reducing the class to $K-\kappa$. Since the total number of functions is S, we have

$$u+\tfrac{1}{2}(n-u-K+\kappa+\eta) = S \tag{4.38}$$

or

$$u = 2S+K-\kappa-n-\eta. \tag{4.39}$$

To get the maximum value of u we have to take $\eta = 0$, and hence

$$u = 2S+K-\kappa-n \tag{4.40}$$

and

$$2K-2n+2S \geqslant \kappa \tag{4.41}$$

because

$$n-u \leqslant K. \tag{4.42}$$

If the class is not diminished, it is always possible to determine $\frac{1}{2}\kappa$ functions for κ even and $\frac{1}{2}(\kappa+1)$ functions for κ odd, reducing the class to $K-\kappa$. Since the total number of functions is S, we have

$$S = \begin{cases} u+\frac{1}{2}\kappa & \text{for } \kappa \text{ even,} \\ u+\frac{1}{2}(\kappa+1) & \text{for } \kappa \text{ odd,} \end{cases} \tag{4.43}$$

or

$$u = \begin{cases} S-\frac{1}{2}\kappa & \text{for } \kappa \text{ even,} \\ S-\frac{1}{2}(\kappa+1) & \text{for } \kappa \text{ odd,} \end{cases} \tag{4.44}$$

and $$2K-2n+2S \leqslant \kappa+1 \tag{4.45}$$
because $$n-u \geqslant K. \tag{4.46}$$

Hence for $2K-2n+2S \geqslant \kappa$ we have first to choose $2S+K-\kappa-n$ functions satisfying certain inequalities and then to determine each of the other $\kappa-K+n-S$ functions successively by the integration of a complete system. These integrations can be effected by $\kappa-K+n-S$ operations $O_{2n-2S+\kappa-K-1}$, $O_{2n-2S+\kappa-K-3}$,..., $O_{K-\kappa+1}$. Taking into account that every solution depends on the choice of the first u functions and of every preceding solution, we see that the $\kappa-K+n-S$ solutions can be fixed by giving $\kappa-K+n-S$ functions of $n-u-1+u = n-1$, $n-2$, ..., $K-\kappa+S$ variables respectively.

For $2K-2n+2S \leqslant \kappa+1$ we have to choose first $S-\frac{1}{2}\kappa$ or $S-\frac{1}{2}(\kappa+1)$ functions satisfying certain inequalities and then to determine each of the other $\frac{1}{2}\kappa$ or $\frac{1}{2}(\kappa+1)$ functions successively by the integration of a complete system. These integrations can be effected by $\frac{1}{2}\kappa$ operations O_{K-1}, O_{K-3},..., $O_{K-\kappa+1}$ for κ even, by $\frac{1}{2}(\kappa+1)$ operations O_{K-1}, O_{K-3},..., $O_{K-\kappa+2}$, $O_{K-\kappa+1}$ for κ odd and $K > \kappa+1$, by $\frac{1}{2}(\kappa+1)$ operations O_{K-1}, O_{K-3},..., O_1 for κ odd and $K = \kappa+1$, and by $\frac{1}{2}(\kappa+1)$ operations O_{K-1}, O_{K-3},..., O_0 for κ odd and $K = \kappa$. As above we may conclude from Theorem III.10 that the $\frac{1}{2}\kappa$ or $\frac{1}{2}(\kappa+1)$ solutions can be fixed by giving $\frac{1}{2}\kappa$ or $\frac{1}{2}(\kappa+1)$ functions of $K-\frac{1}{2}\kappa-1+S$,..., $K-\kappa+S$ or $K-\frac{1}{2}(\kappa+1)+S$, ..., $K-\kappa+S$ variables respectively.

5. Canonical forms of covariant vector fields†

Let $\overset{1}{s}$,..., $\overset{\rho}{s}$ be a set of ρ functions conjugate to w_λ. Then by interchanging the coordinates it can always be arranged that $\overset{1}{s}$,..., $\overset{\rho}{s}$, $\xi^{\rho+1}$,..., ξ^n are functionally independent. Then the Pfaffian $w_\mu\, d\xi^\mu$ can be written in the form

$$w_\mu\, d\xi^\mu = \overset{1}{u}\, d\overset{1}{s}+...+\overset{\rho}{u}\, d\overset{\rho}{s}+\overset{\rho+1}{u}\, d\xi^{\rho+1}+...+\overset{n}{u}\, d\xi^n, \tag{5.1}$$

$\overset{1}{u}$,..., $\overset{n}{u}$ being functions of $\overset{1}{s}$,..., $\overset{\rho}{s}$, $\xi^{\rho+1}$,..., ξ^n. The differential form

$$\overset{\rho+1}{u}\, d\xi^{\rho+1}+...+\overset{n}{u}\, d\xi^n \tag{5.2}$$

is of class 1 if K is odd and of class 0 if K is even because the set $\overset{1}{s}$,..., $\overset{\rho}{s}$ is conjugate. Hence, when K is odd, there exists a function p of $\overset{1}{s}$,..., $\overset{\rho}{s}$, $\xi^{\rho+1}$,..., ξ^n, such that (5.2) is equal to dp if $\overset{1}{s}$,..., $\overset{\rho}{s}$ are looked upon as

† Cf. Cartan 1899. 1; 1945. 1, ch. iii; v. Weber 1900. 1, ch. iv; Goursat 1922. 1, ch. i.

parameters. From this it follows that there exists an equation of the form

$$\overset{\rho+1}{u}\, d\xi^{\rho+1}+\dots+\overset{n}{u}\, d\xi^{n} = dp-(\partial p/\partial \overset{1}{s})\, d\overset{1}{s}-\dots-(\partial p/\partial \overset{\rho}{s})\, d\overset{\rho}{s}, \tag{5.3}$$

and from this equation and (5.1) it follows that $w_\mu\, d\xi^\mu$ can be written in the form

$$w_\mu\, d\xi^\mu = dp+\overset{1}{z}\, d\overset{1}{s}+\dots+\overset{\rho}{z}\, d\overset{\rho}{s}. \tag{5.4}$$

If K is even, (5.2) must vanish if $\overset{1}{s},\dots,\overset{\rho}{s}$ are replaced by any constant values. This is only possible if (5.2) is zero, and thus $w_\mu\, d\xi^\mu$ can be written in the form

$$w_\mu\, d\xi^\mu = \overset{1}{z}\, d\overset{1}{s}+\dots+\overset{\rho}{z}\, d\overset{\rho}{s}. \tag{5.5}$$

In (5.4) and (5.5) the number of variables appearing is just K. Now if a form of $w_\mu\, d\xi^\mu$ containing less than K variables existed the μ-rank of the system w_μ, $W_{\mu\lambda}$ could not be K. That proves the theorem

THEOREM IV.3. *A field w_λ of class K can be expressed in terms of K (and not less) variables and their gradients, and the Pfaffian $w_\mu\, d\xi^\mu$ in terms of K (and not less) variables and their differentials.*

The forms of w_λ corresponding to (5.4) for K odd and to (5.5) for K even,

$$w_\lambda = p_\lambda+\overset{1}{z}\overset{1}{s}_\lambda+\dots+\overset{\rho}{z}\overset{\rho}{s}_\lambda \tag{5.6}$$

and

$$w_\lambda = \overset{1}{z}\overset{1}{s}_\lambda+\dots+\overset{\rho}{z}\overset{\rho}{s}_\lambda \tag{5.7}$$

respectively, are canonical forms of w_λ (cf. IV, § 1). Naturally they can only be obtained in a region of constant class of the field.

If w_λ is written in a canonical form (5.6) or (5.7) respectively, the equations of the supports of rotation, of the supports, and of the characteristics are:

$$K = 2\rho+1\begin{cases} \text{char.} = \text{supp.}\begin{cases} p = \text{const.};\ \overset{1}{s} = \text{const.},\dots,\overset{\rho}{s} = \text{const.} \\ \overset{1}{z} = \text{const.},\dots,\overset{\rho}{z} = \text{const.}\end{cases} \\ \text{supp. of rot.}\begin{cases} \overset{1}{s} = \text{const.},\dots,\overset{\rho}{s} = \text{const.} \\ \overset{1}{z} = \text{const.},\dots,\overset{\rho}{z} = \text{const.}\end{cases}\end{cases} \tag{5.8}$$

$$K = 2\rho\begin{cases} \text{char.}\begin{cases} \overset{1}{s} = \text{const.},\dots,\overset{\rho}{s} = \text{const.} \\ \overset{1}{z} : \overset{2}{z} : \dots : \overset{\rho}{z} = \text{const.}\end{cases} \\ \text{supp.} = \text{supp. of rot.}\begin{cases} \overset{1}{s} = \text{const.},\dots,\overset{\rho}{s} = \text{const.} \\ \overset{1}{z} = \text{const.},\dots,\overset{\rho}{z} = \text{const.}\end{cases}\end{cases} \tag{5.9}$$

To determine a canonical form of w_λ we need for $\epsilon = 0$ at most the ρ operations $O_{K-1}, O_{K-3}, \ldots, O_1$ necessary for the construction of a conjugate system of ρ functions. If $\epsilon = 1$ we need at most the $\rho+1$ operations $O_{K-1}, O_{K-3}, \ldots, O_0$ necessary for the construction of a semi-conjugate system of $\rho+1$ functions.

In the canonical forms (5.6) and (5.7) w_λ appears as a field of class K in the X_K of the variables $\epsilon p, \overset{1}{s}, \ldots, \overset{\rho}{s}, \overset{1}{z}, \ldots, \overset{\rho}{z}$, arising by the reduction of the X_n with respect to the normal system of X_{n-K}'s with the equations

$$\epsilon p = \text{const.}, \quad \overset{\mathfrak{a}}{s} = \text{const.}, \quad \overset{\mathfrak{a}}{z} = \text{const.} \quad (\mathfrak{a} = 1, \ldots, \rho). \tag{5.10}$$

A canonical field of odd class (5.6) has obviously no points of diminished class. But in a canonical field of even class (5.7) the points of diminished class are given by the equations

$$\overset{\mathfrak{a}}{z} = 0 \quad (\mathfrak{a} = 1, \ldots, \rho). \tag{5.11}$$

In these points we have

$$c = 0, \quad K = 2\rho, \quad c_3 = 0, \quad k = 0. \tag{5.12}$$

Given two fields $\overset{0}{w}_\lambda$ in $\mathfrak{N}(\underset{0}{\xi^\kappa})$ and $\overset{1}{w}_\lambda$ in $\mathfrak{N}(\underset{1}{\xi^\kappa})$ of the same class K, we will now prove that the field $\overset{0}{w}_\lambda$ in $\underset{0}{\xi^\kappa}$ is isomorphic with the field $\overset{1}{w}_\lambda$ in $\underset{1}{\xi^\kappa}$, provided that $\underset{0}{\xi^\kappa}$ and $\underset{1}{\xi^\kappa}$ are ordinary points of the fields $\overset{0}{w}_\lambda$ and $\overset{1}{w}_\lambda$ respectively. The necessary and sufficient conditions are that there exist two coordinate systems (κ) and (κ') in an $\mathfrak{N}(\underset{0}{\xi^\kappa})$ and an $\mathfrak{N}(\underset{1}{\xi^\kappa})$ respectively, such that $\underset{1}{\xi^{\kappa'}} = \delta^{\kappa'}_\kappa \underset{0}{\xi^\kappa}$, and that the field $\overset{0}{w}_\lambda$ in an $\mathfrak{N}(\underset{0}{\xi^\kappa})$ has the same form with respect to (κ) as the field $\overset{1}{w}_\lambda$ in an $\mathfrak{N}(\underset{1}{\xi^\kappa})$ with respect to (κ') (cf. IV, § 1). If K is odd we choose the system (κ) in such a way that $\overset{0}{w}_\mu d\xi^\mu$ takes the form

$$d\xi^1 + \xi^2 d\xi^3 + \ldots + \xi^{K-1} d\xi^K. \tag{5.13}$$

In the same way, in $\mathfrak{N}(\underset{1}{\xi^\kappa})$, a coordinate system can be introduced such that in $\mathfrak{N}(\underset{1}{\xi^\kappa})$, the Pfaffian $\overset{1}{w}_\mu d\xi^\mu$ takes the form

$$d\xi^{1'} + \xi^{2'} d\xi^{3'} + \ldots + \xi^{(K-1)'} d\xi^{K'}. \tag{5.14}$$

Finally we introduce in $\mathfrak{N}(\underset{0}{\xi^\kappa})$ a coordinate system (h) $(h = 1, \ldots, n)$, such that

$$d\xi^{\mathrm{1}} + \xi^{\mathrm{2}} d\xi^{\mathrm{3}} + \ldots + \xi^{\mathrm{K-1}} d\xi^{\mathrm{K}} = d\xi^1 + \xi^2 d\xi^3 + \ldots + \xi^{K-1} d\xi^K \tag{5.15}$$

and
$$\underset{1}{\xi}^{\kappa'} = \delta^{\kappa'}_h \underset{0}{\xi}^h \quad (h = 1,\dots, \mathrm{n}). \tag{5.16}$$

For instance, this can be done by the transformation

$$\begin{aligned}
\xi^1 &= \xi^1 + (\underset{1}{\xi}^{1'} - \underset{0}{\xi}^1) - (\underset{1}{\xi}^{2'} - \underset{0}{\xi}^2)(\xi^3 - \underset{0}{\xi}^3) - \dots - (\underset{1}{\xi}^{(K-1)'} - \underset{0}{\xi}^{K-1})(\xi^K - \underset{0}{\xi}^K),\\
\xi^2 &= \xi^2 + (\underset{1}{\xi}^{2'} - \underset{0}{\xi}^2),\\
&\dots\dots\dots\\
\xi^K &= \xi^K + (\underset{1}{\xi}^{K'} - \underset{0}{\xi}^K).
\end{aligned} \tag{5.17}$$

The coordinate systems (h) in $\mathfrak{N}(\underset{0}{\xi}^\kappa)$ and (κ') in $\mathfrak{N}(\underset{1}{\xi}^\kappa)$ satisfy the conditions imposed.

If K is even we choose (κ) in such a way that $\overset{0}{w}_\lambda$ takes the form

$$\overset{0}{w}_\lambda = \xi^1 \overset{2}{e}_\lambda + \dots + \xi^{K-1} \overset{K}{e}_\lambda. \tag{5.18}$$

If $\mathfrak{N}(\underset{0}{\xi}^\kappa)$ is sufficiently small, at least one of the coefficients $\xi^1, \xi^3, \dots, \xi^{K-1}$ does not vanish in $\mathfrak{N}(\underset{0}{\xi}^\kappa)$. By interchanging the indices $1, 3, \dots, K-1$ it can always be arranged that $\xi^1 \neq 0$ in $\mathfrak{N}(\underset{0}{\xi}^\kappa)$. Then we introduce in $\mathfrak{N}(\underset{0}{\xi}^\kappa)$ a new coordinate system by means of the equations

$$\begin{aligned}
\xi^{1'} &= \xi^1/\underset{0}{\xi}^1, & \xi^{2'} &= \xi^2 \underset{0}{\xi}^1,\\
\xi^{3'} &= (\underset{0}{\xi}^1/\xi^1)\xi^3, & \xi^{4'} &= \xi^4,\\
&\dots\dots\dots & &\dots\dots\\
\xi^{(K-1)'} &= (\underset{0}{\xi}^1/\xi^1)\xi^{K-1}, & \xi^{K'} &= \xi^K.
\end{aligned} \tag{5.19}$$

With respect to (κ'), the Pfaffian $\overset{0}{w}_\mu d\xi^\mu$ takes, in $\mathfrak{N}(\underset{0}{\xi}^\kappa)$, the form

$$\xi^{1'}(d\xi^{2'} + \xi^{3'}\, d\xi^{4'} + \dots + \xi^{(K-1)'}\, d\xi^{K'}) \tag{5.20}$$

and we have
$$\underset{0}{\xi}^{1'} = 1. \tag{5.21}$$

In the same way, in $\mathfrak{N}(\underset{1}{\xi}^\kappa)$, a coordinate system (κ'') can be introduced such that, in $\mathfrak{N}(\underset{1}{\xi}^\kappa)$, the Pfaffian $\overset{1}{w}_\mu d\xi^\mu$ takes the form

$$\xi^{1''}(d\xi^{2''} + \xi^{3''}\, d\xi^{4''} + \dots + \xi^{(K-1)''}\, d\xi^{K''}) \tag{5.22}$$

with
$$\underset{1}{\xi}^{1''} = 1. \tag{5.23}$$

Finally we introduce, in $\mathfrak{N}(\underset{0}{\xi}^\kappa)$, a coordinate system (h) $(h = 1,\dots,\mathrm{n})$ such that

$$\xi^1(d\xi^2 + \xi^3\, d\xi^4 + \dots + \xi^{K-1}\, d\xi^K) = \xi^{1'}(d\xi^{2'} + \xi^{3'}\, d\xi^{4'} + \dots + \xi^{(K-1)'}\, d\xi^{K'}) \tag{5.24}$$

and
$$\underset{1}{\xi}^{\kappa''} = \delta^{\kappa''}_h \underset{0}{\xi}^h. \tag{5.25}$$

For instance, this can be done by means of the transformation

$$\begin{aligned}
\xi^1 &= \xi^{1'}\\
\xi^2 &= \xi^{2'}+(\underset{1}{\xi^{2''}}-\underset{0}{\xi^{2'}})-(\underset{1}{\xi^{3''}}-\underset{0}{\xi^{3'}})(\xi^{4'}-\underset{0}{\xi^{4'}})-\ldots-(\underset{1}{\xi^{(K-1)''}}-\underset{0}{\xi^{(K-1)'}})(\xi^{K'}-\underset{0}{\xi^{K'}})\\
\xi^3 &= \xi^{3'}+(\underset{1}{\xi^{3''}}-\underset{0}{\xi^{3'}})\\
&\ldots\ldots\ldots\\
\xi^K &= \xi^{K'}+(\underset{1}{\xi^{K''}}-\underset{0}{\xi^{K'}}).
\end{aligned} \tag{5.26}$$

The coordinate systems (h) in $\mathfrak{N}(\underset{0}{\xi^\kappa})$ and (κ'') in $\mathfrak{N}(\underset{1}{\xi^\kappa})$ satisfy the conditions imposed. Collecting results we get the following theorem:

THEOREM IV.4. (*Theorem of classification of covariant vector fields and Pfaffians.*) *If* $\underset{0}{\xi^\kappa}$ *and* $\underset{1}{\xi^\kappa}$ *are ordinary points of the vector fields* $\overset{0}{w}_\lambda$ *and* $\overset{1}{w}_\lambda$ *respectively, there exists a field region* $\mathfrak{N}(\underset{0}{\xi^\kappa})$ *of* $\overset{0}{w}_\lambda$ *and a field region* $\mathfrak{N}(\underset{1}{\xi^\kappa})$ *of* $\overset{1}{w}_\lambda$ *which are transformable into each other by a process of dragging along transforming* $\overset{0}{w}_\lambda$ *into* $\overset{1}{w}_\lambda$ *and* $\underset{0}{\xi^\kappa}$ *into* $\underset{1}{\xi^\kappa}$, *if and only if* $\overset{0}{w}_\lambda$ *and* $\overset{1}{w}_\lambda$ *have the same class.*

From this theorem follows immediately (cf. IV, § 1):

THEOREM IV.5. (*Theorem of auto-isomorphism of covariant vector fields.*) *Every covariant vector field is auto-isomorphic in every region of constant class.*

6. Properties of the functions p, $\overset{a}{s}$, and $\overset{a}{z}$

It may be asked whether any given function of the ξ^κ can play the role of a p, an s, or a z in (5.4) or (5.5).

Suppose first that K is odd. The field

$$'w_\lambda \overset{\text{def}}{=} w_\lambda - \partial_\lambda p \tag{6.1}$$

has the same rotation as w_λ. Hence p is characterized by the property that $'w_\lambda$ has class 2ρ. From this it follows that it is necessary and sufficient that p is a solution of

$$'\overset{2\rho+1}{I} = \overset{2\rho+1}{I} - \overset{2\rho}{I}\bar{p} = 0. \tag{6.2}$$

This is a non-homogeneous linear partial differential equation of first order. (6.2) implies that

$$\overset{2\rho+1}{I}\,\bar{p} = 0, \qquad \overset{2\rho}{I}\bar{p} \neq 0, \tag{6.3}$$

or in other words, that p is a solution of $S_2' = S_4'$ but not a solution of $S_1' = S_3'$. But these conditions are not sufficient. If w_λ is written in the canonical form

$$w_\lambda = \overset{1}{e}_\lambda + \xi^2 \overset{3}{e}_\lambda + \ldots + \xi^{K-1}\overset{K}{e}_\lambda \tag{6.4}$$

(6.2) takes the form

$$\overset{1}{e}_{[\lambda_1}\cdots\overset{K}{e}_{\lambda_K]}-(\partial_{[\lambda_1}p)\overset{2}{e}_{\lambda_2}\cdots\overset{K}{e}_{\lambda_K]}=0 \quad (K=2\rho+1) \tag{6.5}$$

equivalent to

$$\partial_1 p = 1, \qquad \partial_\omega p = 0 \quad (\omega = K+1,\dots,n) \tag{6.6}$$

and from this we see that (6.5) is a complete non-homogeneous system with the general solution

$$p = \xi^1+\phi(\xi^2,\dots,\xi^K), \tag{6.7}$$

ϕ being an arbitrary function (cf. III, § 7). If p is not a solution of (6.2) the class of $'w_\lambda$ is $2\rho+1$.

In § 5 we have seen that $\overset{1}{s}$ is any function of index 2, that is, any solution of $S'_1 = S'_3$. Now

$$dp+\overset{1}{z}\,d\overset{1}{s} = d(p+\overset{1}{z}\overset{1}{s})-\overset{1}{s}\,d\overset{1}{z} \tag{6.8}$$

and from this it follows that $\overset{1}{s}$ and $\overset{1}{z}$ are interchangeable. Hence, the functions of index 2 and only these functions, can play the role of an s or z.

Now suppose that K is even. As above, we see that the functions of index 2 and only these functions can play the role of an s. But the z and s are no longer on equal footing. If z is any of the functions $\overset{1}{z},\dots,\overset{\rho}{z}$ the field

$$'w_\lambda \overset{\text{def}}{=} z^{-1}w_\lambda \tag{6.9}$$

has class $2\rho-1$. From this it follows that it is necessary and sufficient for z to satisfy the conditions

$$\begin{aligned} &(a) \qquad {}'\overset{2\rho}{I} = z^{-\rho}\overset{2\rho}{I}-2\rho z^{-\rho-1}\bar{z}\overset{2\rho-1}{I} = 0, \\ &(b) \qquad {}'\overset{2\rho-1}{I} = z^{-\rho}\overset{2\rho-1}{I} \neq 0. \end{aligned} \tag{6.10}$$

The inequality is automatically satisfied because $z \neq 0$. Hence the necessary and sufficient condition, in a more simple form, is

$$\overset{2\rho}{I}-2\rho z^{-1}\bar{z}\overset{2\rho-1}{I} = 0. \tag{6.11}$$

This is a non-homogeneous linear partial differential equation of first order in $\log z$. (6.11) implies that

$$\begin{aligned} &\overset{2\rho}{I}\bar{z} = 0, \\ &\overset{2\rho-1}{I}\,\bar{z} \neq 0; \end{aligned} \tag{6.12}$$

hence z has to be a solution of $S'_1 = S'_2$ but cannot be a solution of

$S'_3 = S'_4$, that is, z has to be a function with index 1. But this condition is not sufficient. If w_λ is written in the canonical form

$$w_\lambda = \xi^1 \overset{2}{e}_\lambda + \dots + \xi^{K-1} \overset{K}{e}_\lambda \tag{6.13}$$

(6.11) takes the form

$$\overset{1}{e}_{[\lambda_1} \cdots \overset{K}{e}_{\lambda_K]} - z^{-1}\xi^1(\partial_{[\lambda_1} z)\overset{2}{e}_{\lambda_2} \cdots \overset{K}{e}_{\lambda_K]} - z^{-1}\xi^3(\partial_{[\lambda_1} z)\overset{1}{e}_{\lambda_2}\overset{2}{e}_{\lambda_3}\overset{4}{e}_{\lambda_4} \cdots \overset{K}{e}_{\lambda_K]} - \dots -$$
$$- z^{-1}\xi^{K-1}(\partial_{[\lambda_1} z)\overset{1}{e}_{\lambda_2} \cdots \overset{K-2}{e}_{\lambda_{K-1}}\overset{K}{e}_{\lambda_K]} = 0 \tag{6.14}$$

equivalent to
$$1 - z^{-1}(\xi^1\partial_1 z + \xi^3\partial_3 z + \dots + \xi^{K-1}\partial_{K-1} z) = 0,$$
$$\partial_\omega z = 0 \quad (\omega = K+1, \dots, n), \tag{6.15}$$

from which we see that every function of $\xi^1, \dots, \xi^K$ which is homogeneous of degree one in $\xi^1, \xi^3, \dots, \xi^{K-1}$ is a solution of (6.14).

If z is not a solution of (6.11) the class of $'w_\lambda$ is at least 2ρ because $\overset{2\rho}{'I}$ does not vanish. But because

$$\overset{2\rho+1}{'I} = z^{-\rho-1}\overset{2\rho+1}{I} = 0, \tag{6.16}$$

the class of $'w_\lambda$ has to be 2ρ.

Gathering these results together we get the following summary:

K odd $\begin{cases} p\text{: function with index } 1\text{, satisfying the non-homogeneous linear equation (6.2);} \\ s \text{ and } z\text{: functions with index } 2; \end{cases}$

K even $\begin{cases} s\text{: function with index } 2; \\ z\text{: function with index } 1\text{, satisfying the non-homogeneous linear equation (6.11) in } \log z. \end{cases}$ (6.17)

A canonical form of w_λ being obtained, it is easy to find a system of S functions with index κ, provided that S and κ satisfy the conditions (4.37) of Theorem IV.2. If $K < n$, there exist besides (p), $\overset{a}{s}$, and $\overset{a}{z}$ still $n-K$ other independent functions which can be chosen arbitrarily. These we call *supernumerary functions.*

If κ is even we may choose $\frac{1}{2}\kappa$ from the functions $\overset{a}{s}$ and $S-\frac{1}{2}\kappa$ from the $\overset{a}{z}$ belonging to these $\overset{a}{s}$ and from the supernumerary functions. If κ is odd we may choose $\frac{1}{2}(\kappa-1)$ from the functions $\overset{a}{z}$, then $S-\frac{1}{2}(\kappa+1)$ from the $\overset{a}{s}$ belonging to these $\overset{a}{z}$ and from the supernumerary functions, and finally, the function p for K odd and one function from the $\overset{a}{s}$ not belonging to one of the chosen functions $\overset{a}{z}$ for K even. The conditions (4.37) guarantee that these choices are always possible.

This proves once more that the conditions (4.37) of Theorem IV.2 are not only necessary but also sufficient for the existence of a system of S functions with index κ.

7. Similarity transformations and gradient transformations of a field w_λ†

A transformation of the form

$$'w_\lambda = \sigma w_\lambda, \tag{7.1}$$

where w_λ and σ are analytic and do not vanish in an $\mathfrak{N}(\overset{}{\underset{0}{\xi^\kappa}})$, is called a *similarity transformation*. The transformation of $W_{\mu\lambda}$ is

$$'W_{\mu\lambda} = \sigma W_{\mu\lambda} + 2\sigma_{[\mu} w_{\lambda]}, \qquad \sigma_\mu \overset{\text{def}}{=} \partial_\mu \sigma \tag{7.2}$$

and from this it follows that, for every value of v,

$$'\overset{2v}{I} = \sigma^v \overset{2v}{I} + 2v\sigma^{v-1}\bar{\sigma}\overset{2v-1}{I} \tag{7.3}$$

and

$$'\overset{2v+1}{I} = \sigma^{v+1}\overset{2v+1}{I} \tag{7.4}$$

From this we see *that the similarity class k and the characteristics are invariant for similarity transformations.* But this follows also from the invariance of the system S_4 for these transformations.

In case I we have $K = 2\rho+1$ and from (7.4) we get

$$'\overset{2\rho+3}{I} = 0, \qquad '\overset{2\rho+1}{I} \neq 0. \tag{7.5}$$

If σ is not a solution of $S_2' = S_4'$, that is, if σ has index 0, $\partial_\lambda \sigma$ is not a divisor of $\overset{2\rho+1}{I}$ and from (7.3) it follows that

$$'\overset{2\rho+2}{I} = (2\rho+2)\sigma^\rho\bar{\sigma}\overset{2\rho+1}{I} \neq 0. \tag{7.6}$$

Hence $'K = 2\rho+2 = K+1$. If σ is a solution of $S_2' = S_4'$, that is, if σ has index 1 or 2, $\partial_\lambda \sigma$ is a divisor of $\overset{2\rho+1}{I}$ and we get

$$'\overset{2\rho+2}{I} = 0 \tag{7.7}$$

and $'K = 2\rho+1 = K$. From (7.4) it follows *that the supports are invariant in this sub-case.* For $K = n$ every vector is a divisor of $\overset{2\rho+1}{I}$ and consequently every function is a solution of $S_2' = S_4'$ and this implies *that for $K = n$ it is impossible to get from case* I *to case* II *by a similarity transformation.*

In case II we have $K = 2\rho$ and from (7.4) we get

$$'\overset{2\rho+1}{I} = 0, \qquad '\overset{2\rho-1}{I} \neq 0. \tag{7.8}$$

† Cf. v. Weber 1900. 1, chs. iii, § 2, v, § 4.

If σ is a solution of

$$\overset{2\rho}{I}+2\rho\sigma^{-1}\bar{\sigma}\overset{2\rho-1}{I}=0, \tag{7.9}$$

that is, if σ^{-1} can play the role of a z in the canonical form (5.5), from (7.3) it follows that $'\overset{2\rho}{I}=0$ and $'K=2\rho-1=K-1$. If σ is not a solution of (7.9) we have $'\overset{2\rho}{I}\neq 0$ and $'K=2\rho=K$. The equation (7.9) always has solutions as was proved in IV, § 6.

Collecting results we have the theorem

THEOREM IV.6. *If a field w_λ of class K is subjected to the similarity transformation*

$$'w_\lambda=\sigma w_\lambda \tag{7.10}$$

the class $'K$ of $'w_\lambda$ takes the value

$$\textit{Case I:}\quad K=2\rho+1\begin{cases}'K=K+1 & \textit{if } \sigma \textit{ has index } 0 \quad (\textit{never for } K=n),\\ 'K=K & \textit{if } \sigma \textit{ has index } 1 \textit{ or } 2 \quad (\textit{always for } K=n);\end{cases} \tag{7.11}$$

$$\textit{Case II:}\quad K=2\rho\quad\begin{cases}'K=K & \textit{if } \sigma \textit{ is not a solution of } (7.9),\\ 'K=K-1 & \textit{if } \sigma \textit{ is a solution of } (7.9).\end{cases} \tag{7.12}$$

From this we see that similarity transformations as a rule change an odd class into a higher even class and leave an even class invariant. Only for special choices of σ is an odd class invariant and an even class changed into a (lower) odd class.

If an E_{n-1}-field $\lfloor w_\lambda \rfloor$ is given by an equation $w_\mu\, d\xi^\mu=0$, this equation is equivalent to $'w_\mu\, d\xi^\mu=0$ and, as follows from Theorem IV.6, σ can always be chosen in such a way that $'K$ is odd. Then we have $k='K$ and this means that the equation can always be written in terms of k variables. But since k is a rank, the number of variables cannot be less than k. This proves the theorem (cf. Theorem IV.3):

THEOREM IV.7. *If a covariant vector field w_λ has the similarity class k, there always exists a field σw_λ expressible in terms of k variables and their gradients and never such a field expressible in terms of a smaller number of variables and their gradients. Consequently the Pfaffian equation $w_\mu\, d\xi^\mu=0$ can be expressed in terms of k, and not less, variables and their differentials.*

A transformation of the form

$$'w_\lambda=w_\lambda+\partial_\lambda u, \tag{7.13}$$

where the w_λ and u are analytic and do not vanish in an $\mathfrak{N}(\overset{}{\underset{0}{\xi^\kappa}})$, is called a *gradient transformation.* $W_{\mu\lambda}$ and $\overset{2\nu}{I}$ ($\nu=1,\ldots,\rho$), are invariant for this transformation. Hence, *the rotation class and the supports of rotation are invariant for gradient transformations.* But this follows also from the invariance of the system S_1 for these transformations.

As to $\overset{2\nu+1}{'I}$, we have, for every value of ν,

$$\overset{2\nu+1}{'I} = \overset{2\nu+1}{I} + \bar{u}\overset{2\nu}{I}. \tag{7.14}$$

In case I we have $K = 2\rho+1$ and $\overset{2\rho}{'I} \neq 0$; $\overset{2\rho+2}{'I} = 0$. If u is a solution of

$$\overset{2\rho+1}{I} + \bar{u}\overset{2\rho}{I} = 0, \tag{7.15}$$

that is, if $-u$ can play the role of p in the canonical form (5.4), from (7.14) it follows that $\overset{2\rho+1}{'I} = 0$ and, thus $'K = 2\rho = K-1$. If u is not a solution of (7.15) we have $\overset{2\rho+1}{'I} \neq 0$ and $'K = 2\rho+1 = K$. The equation (7.15) always has solutions, as was proved in IV, § 6.

In case II we have $K = 2\rho$ and $\overset{2\rho}{'I} \neq 0$. If u is a solution of $S_1' = S_2'$, that is, if u has index 1 or 2, $\partial_\lambda u$ is a divisor of $\overset{2\rho}{I}$ and we get

$$\overset{2\rho+1}{'I} = 0 \tag{7.16}$$

and $'K = 2\rho = K$. From the invariance of $W_{\mu\lambda}$ it follows *that the supports are invariant in this sub-case.* For $K = n$ every vector is a divisor of $\overset{2\rho}{I}$ and consequently every function is a solution of $S_1' = S_2'$ and this implies *that for $K = n$ it is impossible to get from case* II *to case* I *by a gradient transformation.* If u is not a solution of $S_1' = S_2'$, that is, if u has index 0, $\partial_\lambda u$ is not a divisor of $\overset{2\rho}{I}$ and from (7.14) it follows that

$$\overset{2\rho+1}{'I} = \bar{u}\overset{2\rho}{I} \neq 0. \tag{7.17}$$

Hence $'K = 2\rho+1 = K+1$. Collecting results we have the theorem

THEOREM IV.8. *If a covariant vector field w_λ is subjected to the gradient transformation*

$$'w_\lambda = w_\lambda + \partial_\lambda u \tag{7.18}$$

the class $'K$ of $'w_\lambda$ takes the value

$$\textit{Case II:}\quad K = 2\rho \quad \begin{cases} 'K = K+1 & \textit{if } u \textit{ has index } 0 \quad (\textit{never for } K = n), \\ 'K = K & \textit{if } u \textit{ has index } 1 \textit{ or } 2 \quad (\textit{always for } K = n); \end{cases} \tag{7.19}$$

$$\textit{Case I:}\quad K = 2\rho+1 \begin{cases} 'K = K & \textit{if } u \textit{ is not a solution of } (7.15), \\ 'K = K-1 & \textit{if } u \textit{ is a solution of } (7.15). \end{cases} \tag{7.20}$$

The following is a summary of all possible cases:

			$'K$	$2'\rho$	$'k$		
simil. transf.	$K = 2\rho+1;$	$\overset{2\rho+1}{I}\,\bar{\sigma} \neq 0$	$K+1$	$2\rho+2$	k		characteristics invariant (7.21)
		$\overset{2\rho+1}{I}\,\bar{\sigma} = 0$	K	2ρ	k	} supp. inv.	
	$K = 2\rho;$	$\overset{2\rho}{I}+2\rho\sigma^{-1}\bar{\sigma}\overset{2\rho-1}{I} = 0$	$K-1$	$2\rho-2$	k		
		$\overset{2\rho}{I}+2\rho\sigma^{-1}\bar{\sigma}\overset{2\rho-1}{I} \neq 0$	K	2ρ	k		
grad. transf.	$K = 2\rho;$	$\overset{2\rho}{I}\bar{u} \neq 0$	$K+1$	2ρ	$k+2$		supp. of rotation invariant (7.22)
		$\overset{2\rho}{I}\bar{u} = 0$	K	2ρ	k	} supp. inv.	
	$K = 2\rho+1;$	$\overset{2\rho+1}{I}+\bar{u}\overset{2\rho}{I} = 0$	$K-1$	2ρ	$k-2$		
		$\overset{2\rho+1}{I}+\bar{u}\overset{2\rho}{I} \neq 0$	K	2ρ	k		

8. Canonical forms with given initial conditions

It is often convenient to have canonical forms satisfying definitely given initial conditions. To get these canonical forms the following theorem is very useful:

THEOREM IV.9. *If $\mathfrak{R}(\overset{}{\underset{0}{\xi^\kappa}})$ is a region of constant class of the field w_λ of class $K = 2\rho+\epsilon$ ($\epsilon = 1$ or 0) and if w_λ and $W_{\mu\lambda}$ in $\underset{0}{\xi^\kappa}$ can be written in the form*

$$\left.\begin{aligned} w_\lambda &= \epsilon \overset{0}{r}_\lambda + \sum_{i=1}^{i=\rho} \overset{i}{t}\overset{i}{r}_\lambda \\ W_{\mu\lambda} &= 2\sum_{i=1}^{i=\rho} \overset{i}{q}_{[\mu}\overset{i}{r}_{\lambda]} \end{aligned}\right\} \quad for \quad \xi^\kappa = \underset{0}{\xi^\kappa}, \tag{8.1}$$

there exists at least one canonical form of w_λ

$$w_\lambda = \epsilon\partial_\lambda \overset{0}{s} + \sum_{i=1}^{i=\rho} \overset{i}{z}\,\partial_\lambda \overset{i}{s} \tag{8.2}$$

analytic in an $\mathfrak{R}(\underset{0}{\xi^\kappa})$ and satisfying in $\underset{0}{\xi^\kappa}$ the conditions

$$\left.\begin{aligned} \partial_\lambda \epsilon \overset{0}{s} &= \epsilon \overset{0}{r}_\lambda, & \overset{i}{z} &= \overset{i}{t} \\ \partial_\lambda \overset{i}{z} &= \overset{i}{q}_\lambda, & \partial_\lambda \overset{i}{s} &= \overset{i}{r}_\lambda \end{aligned}\right\} \quad for \quad \xi^\kappa = \underset{0}{\xi^\kappa}. \tag{8.3}$$

PROOF. If $\epsilon = 1$ we determine a function $\overset{0}{s}$ such that $\partial_\lambda \overset{0}{s} = \overset{0}{r}_\lambda$ in $\underset{0}{\xi^\kappa}$ and that $w_\lambda - \partial_\lambda \overset{0}{s}$ has class 2ρ. The latter condition is satisfied if $\overset{0}{s}$ is a solution of the non-homogeneous equation

$$\overset{2\rho+1}{I} - \bar{s}\overset{0\,2\rho}{I} = 0. \tag{8.4}$$

This equation always has a solution whose gradient in $\underset{0}{\xi^\kappa}$ is equal to $\overset{0}{r}_\lambda$, provided that

$$\overset{2\rho+1}{I} - r\overset{0\,2\rho}{I} = 0 \quad \text{for} \quad \xi^\kappa = \underset{0}{\xi^\kappa}. \tag{8.5}$$

But (8.5) follows from (8.1). Hence the case $\epsilon = 1$ is reduced to the case $\epsilon = 0$.

If $\epsilon = 0$ we determine two functions $\overset{1}{s}$ and $\overset{1}{z}$ such that

$$\overset{1}{z} = \overset{1}{t}, \qquad \partial_\lambda \overset{1}{z} = \overset{1}{q}_\lambda, \qquad \partial_\lambda \overset{1}{s} = \overset{1}{r}_\lambda \quad \text{for} \quad \xi^\kappa = \underset{0}{\xi^\kappa} \tag{8.6}$$

and that $w_\lambda - \overset{1}{z}\,\partial_\lambda \overset{1}{s}$ has class $2\rho-2$. For $\overset{1}{s}$ we have to take a function with index 2, that is, a solution of

$$\overset{2\rho-1\bar{1}}{I}\, s = 0. \tag{8.7}$$

This equation always has a solution whose gradient in $\underset{0}{\xi^\kappa}$ is equal to $\overset{1}{r}_\lambda$, provided that

$$\overset{2\rho-1 1}{I}\, r = 0 \quad \text{for} \quad \xi^\kappa = \underset{0}{\xi^\kappa}. \tag{8.8}$$

But (8.8) follows from (8.1). Now we choose an arbitrary solution $\overset{1}{s}$ with that property and determine $\overset{1}{z}$ in such a way that the other conditions are satisfied. If

$${}'w_\lambda \overset{\text{def}}{=} w_\lambda - \overset{1}{z}\,\partial_\lambda \overset{1}{s} \tag{8.9}$$

we have

$$\overset{2\rho-2}{'I} = \overset{2\rho-2}{I} - 2(\rho-1) zs \overset{\bar{1}1\ 2\rho-4}{I}; \tag{8.10}$$

hence

$$\overset{2\rho-1}{'I} = \overset{2\rho-2}{'I}\,{}'w = \overset{2\rho-1}{I} - 2(\rho-1) zs \overset{\bar{1}1\ 2\rho-3}{I} - zs \overset{1\bar{1}\ 2\rho-2}{I} \tag{8.11}$$

and, according to $\overset{2\rho-1}{'I} = 0$, this yields the equation for $\overset{1}{z}$

$$\overset{2\rho-1}{I} - 2(\rho-1) zs \overset{\bar{1}1\ 2\rho-3}{I} - zs \overset{1\bar{1}\ 2\rho-2}{I} = 0. \tag{8.12}$$

In order to show that this equation has a solution taking in $\underset{0}{\xi^\kappa}$ the value $\overset{1}{t}$, and having in $\underset{0}{\xi^\kappa}$ a gradient equal to $\overset{1}{q}_\lambda$, we introduce in $\mathfrak{N}(\underset{0}{\xi^\kappa})$ a coordinate system (κ) such that $\overset{1}{s} = \xi^{2\rho}$ and that w_λ takes the form

$$w_\lambda = \xi^1 \overset{2}{e}_\lambda + \ldots + \xi^{2\rho-1} \overset{2\rho}{e}_\lambda. \tag{8.13}$$

This is always possible, since $\overset{1}{s}$ has index 2. Then (8.12) takes the form

$$\begin{gathered} \partial_{2\rho-1} \overset{1}{z} = 1, \\ \xi^{2\rho-1} + \xi^1 \partial_1 \overset{1}{z} + \xi^3 \partial_3 \overset{1}{z} + \ldots + \xi^{2\rho-3} \partial_{2\rho-3} \overset{1}{z} - \overset{1}{z} = 0. \end{gathered} \tag{8.14}$$

In order to show that this system is totally integrable, we introduce the auxiliary variable

$$f \overset{\text{def}}{=} \xi^{2\rho-1} - \overset{1}{z}. \tag{8.15}$$

Then the system (8.14) becomes

$$\begin{aligned}&\partial_{2\rho-1} f = 0\\ &\xi^1\partial_1 f+\xi^3\partial_3 f+...+\xi^{2\rho-3}\partial_{2\rho-3} f = f.\end{aligned} \tag{8.16}$$

Since this system is a complete system in log f it follows that (8.12) is totally integrable. Hence there exists a solution of (8.12), taking in $\underset{0}{\xi}^\kappa$ the value $\overset{1}{t}$, and having, in $\underset{0}{\xi}^\kappa$, a gradient equal to $\overset{1}{q}_\lambda$ provided that

$$\overset{2\rho-1}{I} - 2(\rho-1)\overset{11}{qr}\,\overset{2\rho-3}{I} - \overset{11}{tr}\,\overset{2\rho-2}{I} = 0 \quad \text{for} \quad \xi^\kappa = \underset{0}{\xi}^\kappa. \tag{8.17}$$

Now this condition is satisfied as a consequence of (8.1), because in $\underset{0}{\xi}^\kappa$ we have

$$\begin{aligned}\overset{2\rho-1}{I} &- 2(\rho-1)\overset{11}{qr}\,\overset{2\rho-3}{I} - \overset{11}{tr}\,\overset{2\rho-2}{I}\\ &= \overset{2\rho-2}{I}(\overset{11}{tr}+...+\overset{\rho\rho}{tr}) - 2(\rho-1)\overset{2\rho-4}{I}(\overset{22}{tr}+...+\overset{\rho\rho}{tr})\overset{11}{qr} - \overset{2\rho-2}{I}\,\overset{11}{tr}\\ &= (\overset{22}{tr}+...+\overset{\rho\rho}{tr})\{\overset{2\rho-2}{I} - 2(\rho-1)\overset{2\rho-4}{I}(\overset{11}{qr}+...+\overset{\rho\rho}{qr})\} = 0.\end{aligned} \tag{8.18}$$

Starting from the vector $w_\lambda - \overset{1}{z}\partial_\lambda \overset{1}{s}$ of class $2\rho-2$ thus obtained, two functions $\overset{2}{z}$ and $\overset{2}{s}$ can be determined such that

$$\overset{2}{z} = \overset{2}{t}, \quad \partial_\lambda \overset{2}{z} = \overset{2}{q}_\lambda, \quad \partial_\lambda \overset{2}{s} = \overset{2}{r}_\lambda \quad \text{for} \quad \xi^\kappa = \underset{0}{\xi}^\kappa \tag{8.19}$$

and that $w_\lambda - \overset{1}{z}\partial_\lambda \overset{1}{s} - \overset{2}{z}\,\partial_\lambda \overset{2}{s}$ has class $2\rho-4$, etc. This proves the theorem.

EXERCISES†

1. Let a Pfaffian in an $X_{2n+\epsilon}$ be given in the canonical form

$$\epsilon\, d\xi^0 + p_\lambda d\xi^\lambda. \tag{1α}$$

Prove that the equations

$$\overset{2n+\epsilon-2}{I}\ \overset{\bar{1}\,\bar{2}}{ff} = 0 \tag{1β}$$

are equivalent to

$$[\overset{1}{f}, \overset{2}{f}] \overset{\text{def}}{=} \frac{\partial \overset{1}{f}}{\partial p_\lambda}\left(\frac{\partial \overset{2}{f}}{\partial \xi^\lambda} - \epsilon p_\lambda \frac{\partial \overset{2}{f}}{\partial \xi^0}\right) - \frac{\partial \overset{2}{f}}{\partial p_\lambda}\left(\frac{\partial \overset{1}{f}}{\partial \xi^\lambda} - \epsilon p_\lambda \frac{\partial \overset{1}{f}}{\partial \xi^0}\right) = 0.‡ \tag{1γ}$$

2. Prove the identity of Mayer:§

$$[\overset{1}{f}, [\overset{2}{f}, \overset{3}{f}]] + [\overset{2}{f}, [\overset{3}{f}, \overset{1}{f}]] + [\overset{3}{f}, [\overset{1}{f}, \overset{2}{f}]] = -\epsilon \frac{\partial \overset{1}{f}}{\partial \xi^0}[\overset{2}{f}, \overset{3}{f}] - \epsilon \frac{\partial \overset{2}{f}}{\partial \xi^0}[\overset{3}{f}, \overset{1}{f}] - \epsilon \frac{\partial \overset{3}{f}}{\partial \xi^0}[\overset{1}{f}, \overset{2}{f}]. \tag{2α}$$

† Cf. the suggestions at the end of the book. ‡ Cf. Cartan 1899. 1, p. 313.
§ Cf. v. Weber 1900. 1, pp. 369, 581; Goursat 1921. 1, p. 258.

3. Let w_λ be a vector of class $2\rho+\epsilon$ ($\epsilon = 1$ or 0) in X_n. If a vector $u_\lambda \neq 0$ satisfies the equation

$$\overset{2\rho-2+\epsilon}{I} u = 0, \tag{3α}$$

it follows that $\epsilon = 1$ and that $u_\lambda :: w_\lambda$ (Goursat).†

4. Let w_λ be a vector of class $2\rho+\epsilon$ ($\epsilon = 1$ or 0) in X_n. If a vector $u_\lambda \neq 0$ satisfies the equation

$$\overset{2\rho-1+\epsilon}{I} = \overset{2\rho-2+\epsilon}{I} u, \tag{4α}$$

it follows that $\epsilon = 0$ and that $u_\lambda = w_\lambda$ (Goursat).‡

5. If the system $\overset{1}{f},...,\overset{S}{f}$ is conjugate to the field w_λ of class $2\rho+\epsilon$ in X_n, an $(S+1)$th function f, constituting together with $\overset{1}{f},..., \overset{S}{f}$ a conjugate system, is a solution of the system

$$\overset{2\rho+\epsilon-2S-1}{I} \overset{\bar{1}}{f}...\overset{\bar{S}}{f}\bar{f} = 0. \tag{5α}$$

This system is equivalent to the system

$$\overset{2\rho+\epsilon-1}{I} \bar{f} = 0, \quad \overset{2\rho+\epsilon-2}{I} \overset{\bar{1}}{f}\bar{f} = 0, \quad ..., \quad \overset{2\rho+\epsilon-2}{I} \overset{\bar{S}}{f}\bar{f} = 0. \tag{5β}$$

This means that if f has index 2 and if the systems $\overset{1}{f}, f;...; \overset{S}{f}, f$ all have an index $\geqslant 3$, these systems all have index 4 and the system $\overset{1}{f},..., \overset{S}{f}, f$ is conjugate (Cartan).§

6. If the system $\overset{1}{f},..., \overset{S}{f}$ is semi-conjugate to the field w_λ of class $2\rho+\epsilon$ in X_n, an $(S+1)$th function f, constituting together with $\overset{1}{f},..., \overset{S}{f}$ a semi-conjugate system, is a solution of the system

$$\overset{2\rho+\epsilon-2S}{I} \overset{\bar{1}}{f}...\overset{\bar{S}}{f}\bar{f} = 0. \tag{6α}$$

This system is equivalent to the system

$$\overset{2\rho+\epsilon}{I} \bar{f} = 0, \quad \overset{2\rho+\epsilon-2}{I} \overset{\bar{1}}{f}\bar{f} = 0, \quad ..., \quad \overset{\rho+\epsilon-2}{I} \overset{\bar{S}}{f}\bar{f} = 0 \quad \text{(Cartan).}\| \tag{6β}$$

7. If a system of S functions $\overset{1}{f},..., \overset{S}{f}$ ($S < \rho$) is semi-conjugate to a field w_λ of class $2\rho+\epsilon$ in X_n, at least one of these functions has index 1. If $\overset{1}{f},...,\overset{S_1}{f}$ ($S_1 < S$) form a conjugate system, $\overset{S_1+1}{f}$,..., $\overset{S}{f}$ form a semi-conjugate system. Prove by means of an example that the converse is not true.

8. If $\overset{1}{f}$ and $\overset{2}{f}$ are two functions of index 2 with respect to a field w_λ of class $2\rho+1$, the expression (cf. Ex. IV, 1)

$$f = [\overset{1}{f}, \overset{2}{f}] \overset{\text{def}}{=} \frac{\overset{2\rho-1}{I} \overset{\bar{1}}{f}\overset{\bar{2}}{f}}{\overset{2\rho+1}{I}} \tag{8α}$$

is either zero or a function of index 2.

9. If $\overset{1}{f}$ and $\overset{2}{f}$ are two functions of index 1 with respect to a field w_λ of class 2ρ, the expression (cf. Ex. IV, 1)

$$[\overset{1}{f},\overset{2}{f}] \overset{\text{def}}{=} \frac{\overset{2\rho-2}{I} \overset{\bar{1}}{f}\overset{\bar{2}}{f}}{\overset{2\rho}{I}} \tag{9α}$$

is either zero or a function of index 1.

† 1922. 1, p. 172.
‡ Ibid., p. 173.
§ 1899. 1, p. 292; Goursat 1922. 1, p. 174.
‖ 1899. 1, p. 292; Goursat 1922. 1, p. 181.

10. If $\overset{1}{f}$, $\overset{2}{f}$, and $\overset{3}{f}$ are three functions of index $1+\epsilon$ with respect to a field w_λ of class $2\rho+\epsilon$

$$[\overset{[1}{f}, [\overset{2}{f}, \overset{3]}{f}]] = 0 \tag{10 α}$$

(cf. Exx. IV, 1, 8, 9).

11. The section of a field w_λ of class $K = 2\rho+\epsilon$ ($\epsilon = 0$ or 1) with an X_{n-1} has a class

2ρ if $\epsilon = 1$ and if the X_{n-1} consists of $\infty^{2\rho}$ characteristics (= supp.) but not of $\infty^{2\rho-1}$ supports of rotation;

$2\rho-1$ if $\epsilon = 1$ and if the X_{n-1} consists of $\infty^{2\rho-1}$ supports of rotation;

$2\rho-1$ if $\epsilon = 0$ and if the X_{n-1} consists of $\infty^{2\rho-1}$ supports (= supp. of rot.) but not of $\infty^{2\rho-2}$ characteristics;

$2\rho-2$ if $\epsilon = 0$ and if the X_{n-1} consists of $\infty^{2\rho-2}$ characteristics.

V

THE SIMPLEST ARITHMETIC INVARIANTS OF COVARIANT q-VECTOR FIELDS†

1. Introduction

THE method developed in the preceding chapter can only partly be used when $q > 1$. Without further suppositions it only leads to the subdivision into the two cases I and II. If we suppose that the field $w_{\lambda_1...\lambda_q}$ is simple, it is possible by means of a sixth system of total differential equations to subdivide each of these cases into four sub-cases, for three of which normal forms can be established. A further classification is not obtainable by these elementary means and has to be postponed till Chapter VII.

2. The systems S, S_1, S_2, S_3, and S_4 of a q-vector field $w_{\lambda_1...\lambda_q}$‡

Let $w_{\lambda_1...\lambda_q}$ be a q-vector field, not necessary simple, but analytic and not everywhere zero in $\underset{0}{\mathfrak{R}}(\xi^\kappa)$. From $w_{\lambda_1...\lambda_q}$ the rotation

$$W_{\mu\lambda_1...\lambda_q} \stackrel{\text{def}}{=} (q+1)\partial_{[\mu}\, w_{\lambda_1...\lambda_q]} \quad \text{or} \quad W = (q+1)\, Dw \tag{2.1}$$

may be derived. In general this rotation is neither zero nor simple in $\underset{0}{\mathfrak{R}}(\xi^\kappa)$. Now we consider the following five systems of total differential equations:

$$(S) \qquad w_{\mu\lambda_2...\lambda_q}\, d\xi^\mu = 0; \tag{2.2}$$

$$(S_1) \qquad W_{\mu\lambda_1...\lambda_q}\, d\xi^\mu = 0; \tag{2.3}$$

$$(S_2) \qquad \begin{cases} w_{\mu\lambda_2...\lambda_q}\, d\xi^\mu = 0, \\ W_{\mu\lambda_1...\lambda_q}\, d\xi^\mu = 0; \end{cases} \tag{2.4}$$

$$(S_3) \qquad (W_{\mu\lambda_1...\lambda_q} w_{\kappa_1...\kappa_q} - W_{\mu\kappa_1...\kappa_q} w_{\lambda_1...\lambda_q})\, d\xi^\mu = 0$$
$$(\text{or:} \quad W_{\mu\lambda_1...\lambda_q}\, d\xi^\mu :: w_{\lambda_1...\lambda_q}); \tag{2.5}$$

$$(S_4) \qquad \begin{cases} w_{\mu\lambda_2...\lambda_q}\, d\xi^\mu = 0, \\ (W_{\mu\lambda_1...\lambda_q} w_{\kappa_1...\kappa_q} - W_{\mu\kappa_1...\kappa_q} w_{\lambda_1...\lambda_q})\, d\xi^\mu = 0. \end{cases} \tag{2.6}$$

These systems become the corresponding systems (IV, (2.2–6)) if $q = 1$. The μ-rank of the quantities in the left-hand sides of S, S_1,..., S_4 will be denoted in the following way:

$$\begin{array}{ll} & \mu\text{-rank} \\ (S) & c; \\ (S_1) & c_1 = \textit{rotation class of } w_{\lambda_1...\lambda_q}; \\ (S_2) & K = \textit{class of } w_{\lambda_1...\lambda_q}; \\ (S_3) & c_3; \\ (S_4) & k = \textit{similarity class of } w_{\lambda_1...\lambda_q} = \textit{class of } \lfloor w_{\lambda_1...\lambda_q} \rfloor. \end{array} \tag{2.7}$$

These five integers are arithmetic invariants of the field $w_{\lambda_1...\lambda_q}$.

† For general references cf. Goursat 1922. 1, p. 83. ‡ Cf. Goursat 1922. 1, ch. iii.

Every linear element $d\xi^\mu$ satisfying S_2, also satisfies S and S_1. Hence $c \leqslant K$, $c_1 \leqslant K$. Every linear element satisfying S_4 also satisfies S and S_3. Hence $c \leqslant k$, $c_3 \leqslant k$. Comparing S_1 with S_3 and S_2 with S_4 we see that $c_3 \leqslant c_1$ and $k \leqslant K$. Collecting results we have the following inequalities:

$$\begin{array}{ccccc} n & \geqslant & K & \geqslant & k \\ & & \vee\!\!| & & \vee\!\!| \\ & & c_1 & \geqslant & c_3 \geqslant 0. \end{array} \tag{2.8}$$

The notions *region of constant class*, *point of diminished class*, and *ordinary point* of a field $w_{\lambda_1 \ldots \lambda_q}$ are defined just in the same way as for $q = 1$ (cf. IV, § 2). As in IV, § 2, we suppose that $\underset{0}{\xi}{}^\kappa$ is an ordinary point and $\mathfrak{N}(\underset{0}{\xi}{}^\kappa)$ a region of constant class.

S_3 shows that $d\xi^\mu W_{\mu\lambda_1 \ldots \lambda_q}$ is equal to $w_{\lambda_1 \ldots \lambda_q}$ to within a scalar factor and that consequently there exists an equation of the form

$$d\xi^\mu W_{\mu\lambda_1 \ldots \lambda_q} = \alpha w_{\lambda_1 \ldots \lambda_q}, \tag{2.9}$$

where α depends on the choice of $d\xi^\mu$ and is not necessarily $\neq 0$. Now there are two cases. In case I there exist no linear elements $d\xi^\mu$ with $\alpha \neq 0$. In that case every linear element satisfying S_3 also satisfies S_1, and consequently we have

$$S_3 = S_1, \qquad S_4 = S_2 \tag{2.10}$$

and

$$c_3 = c_1, \qquad k = K. \tag{2.11}$$

Conversely, if $S_3 = S_1$, the function α in (2.9) has to be zero; i.e. we have case I.

In case II there exists at least one linear element satisfying (2.9) with $\alpha \neq 0$. From $n - c_3$ independent solutions of S_3, just $n - c_3 - 1$ solutions with $\alpha = 0$ can be derived by linear combination. These $n - c_3 - 1$ solutions are also solutions of S_1, hence $c_1 = c_3 + 1$. Moreover, from the non-vanishing of α, for a suitable choice of $d\xi^\mu$, it follows that w lies in the region of W. This implies that every solution of S_1 is also a solution of S_2, hence $S_1 = S_2$ and $c_1 = K$. As a consequence, all common solutions of S_3 and S_1 are solutions of S_2 and S_4; hence $S_3 = S_4$ and $c_3 = k$. Gathering these results together we have

	c_1	K	c_3	k	
Case I:	$c_1 \leqslant K$	K	$c_3 = c_1 \leqslant K$	$k = K$,	$S_3 = S_1$, $S_4 = S_2$
Case II:	$c_1 = K$	K	$c_3 = K - 1$	$k = K - 1$,	$S_2 = S_1$, $S_4 = S_3$

(2.12)

In case I for $q > 1$ it is possible that all these invariants are equal. For instance, for the field

$$w_{\mu\lambda} = \xi^1 \overset{2}{e}_{[\mu} \overset{3}{e}_{\lambda]} + \xi^4 \overset{5}{e}_{[\mu} \overset{6}{e}_{\lambda]} + \overset{1}{e}_{[\mu} \overset{4}{e}_{\lambda]} \tag{2.13}$$

in an X_n, $n \geqslant 6$, we have $S_1 = S_2 = S_3 = S_4$ and $c_1 = K = c_3 = k = 6$. The four invariants are always equal if $S = S_1$.†

If $w_{\lambda_1 \dots \lambda_q}$ is simple, the systems S and S_4 can be written in another form which is very convenient in many cases. If B^κ_b and C^x_λ are the connecting quantities of the E_{n-q}-field $\lfloor w_{\lambda_1 \dots \lambda_q} \rfloor$, we have

$$\begin{aligned} \lfloor w_{\lambda_1 \dots \lambda_q} \rfloor &= \lfloor C^{\mathrm{p}+1}_{[\lambda_1} \dots C^{\mathrm{n}}_{\lambda_q]} \rfloor \\ \lfloor W_{\mu\lambda_1 \dots \lambda_q} \rfloor &= \lfloor C_{[\mu\lambda_1}^{\cdot\cdot\,[\mathrm{p}+1} C^{\mathrm{p}+2}_{\lambda_2} \dots C^{\mathrm{n}]}_{\lambda_q]} \rfloor \end{aligned} \qquad (p = n-q), \tag{2.14}$$

and from this it follows that S is equivalent to

$$C^x_\mu \, d\xi^\mu = 0 \quad (x = \mathrm{p}+1, \dots, \mathrm{n}), \tag{2.15}$$

and S_4 equivalent to

$$\begin{aligned} &(a) \quad C^x_\mu \, d\xi^\mu = 0 \\ &(b) \quad d\xi^\mu C_{[\mu\lambda_1}^{\cdot\cdot\,[\mathrm{p}+1} C^{\mathrm{p}+2}_{\lambda_2} \dots C^{\mathrm{n}]}_{\lambda_q]} :: C^{\mathrm{p}+1}_{[\lambda_1} \dots C^{\mathrm{n}}_{\lambda_q]} \end{aligned} \qquad (x = \mathrm{p}+1, \dots, \mathrm{n}). \tag{2.16}$$

Now we will prove that these equations are equivalent to

$$\begin{aligned} &(a) \qquad C^x_\mu \, d\xi^\mu = 0 \\ &(b) \qquad C_{\mu\lambda}^{\cdot\cdot\,x} B^\lambda_b \, d\xi^\mu = 0 \end{aligned} \qquad (x = \mathrm{p}+1, \dots, \mathrm{n}). \tag{2.17}$$

This form is very convenient for practical purposes. (2.17 *b*) shows that the $n-p$ covariant vectors $d\xi^\mu C_{\mu\lambda}^{\cdot\cdot\,x}$ can be expressed linearly in the C^x_λ. Hence every linear element, satisfying (2.17), also satisfies S_4. By transvection of (2.16 *b*) with $B^{\lambda_1}_b$ we get

$$d\xi^\mu B^{\lambda_1}_b C_{\mu\lambda_1}^{\cdot\cdot\,[\mathrm{p}+1} C^{\mathrm{p}+2}_{\lambda_2} \dots C^{\mathrm{n}]}_{\lambda_q} = 0, \tag{2.18}$$

and from the linear independence of the C^x_λ it follows that (2.18) is equivalent to (2.17 *b*). Hence every linear element, satisfying S_4, satisfies (2.17).

3. Completeness of the systems S_1, S_2, S_3, and S_4‡

From (2.12), we have only to prove that S_1 and S_4 are complete. For S_1 we have to prove that if

$$\begin{aligned} \underset{1}{v}^\mu W_{\mu\lambda_1 \dots \lambda_q} &= 0, \\ \underset{2}{v}^\mu W_{\mu\lambda_1 \dots \lambda_q} &= 0, \end{aligned} \tag{3.1}$$

it always follows that
$$\underset{[1}{v}^\omega (\partial_\omega \underset{2]}{v}^\mu) W_{\mu\lambda_1 \dots \lambda_q} = 0. \tag{3.2}$$

† E. Goursat 1922. 1, p. 143. In his formula there is a misprint.

‡ Cf. Goursat 1922. 1, ch. iii.

Now from (3.1) we get by differentiation and alternation

$$\underset{[1}{v^{\omega}}(\partial_{|\omega|}\underset{2]}{v^{\mu}})W_{\mu\lambda_1\ldots\lambda_q} = -\underset{[1}{v^{\omega}}\underset{2]}{v^{\mu}}\partial_{\omega} W_{\mu\lambda_1\ldots\lambda_q} = +\tfrac{1}{2}q\underset{[1}{v^{\omega}}\underset{2]}{v^{\mu}}\partial_{[\lambda_1} W_{|\omega\mu|\lambda_2\ldots\lambda_q]}$$

$$= \tfrac{1}{2}q\partial_{[\lambda_1} W_{|\omega\mu|\lambda_2\ldots\lambda_q]}\underset{[1}{v^{\omega}}\underset{2]}{v^{\mu}} - \tfrac{1}{2}qW_{\omega\mu[\lambda_2\ldots\lambda_q}(\partial_{\lambda_1]}\underset{[1}{v^{\omega}})\underset{2]}{v^{\mu}} -$$

$$-\tfrac{1}{2}qW_{\omega\mu[\lambda_2\ldots\lambda_q}(\partial_{\lambda_1]}\underset{[2}{v^{\mu}})\underset{1]}{v^{\omega}} \tag{3.3}$$

because $DW = 0$, and each of the three last terms of (3.3) vanishes in consequence of (3.1).

For S_4 we have to prove that from

$$\begin{aligned} &(a\,\alpha)\quad \underset{1}{v^{\mu}}w_{\mu\lambda_2\ldots\lambda_q} = 0, &&(a\,\beta)\quad \underset{2}{v^{\mu}}w_{\mu\lambda_2\ldots\lambda_q} = 0;\\ &(b\,\alpha)\quad \underset{1}{v^{\mu}}W_{\mu\lambda_1\ldots\lambda_q} = \alpha \underset{1}{w}_{\lambda_1\ldots\lambda_q}, &&(b\,\beta)\quad \underset{2}{v^{\mu}}W_{\mu\lambda_1\ldots\lambda_q} = \alpha \underset{2}{w}_{\lambda_1\ldots\lambda_q} \end{aligned} \tag{3.4}$$

it always follows that

$$\begin{aligned} &(a)\qquad \underset{[1}{v^{\omega}}(\partial_{|\omega|}\underset{2]}{v^{\mu}})w_{\mu\lambda_2\ldots\lambda_q} = 0,\\ &(b)\qquad \underset{[1}{v^{\omega}}(\partial_{|\omega|}\underset{2]}{v^{\mu}})W_{\mu\lambda_1\ldots\lambda_q} :: w_{\lambda_1\ldots\lambda_q}. \end{aligned} \tag{3.5}$$

From ($3.4\,a\,\alpha$, $a\,\beta$) we get by differentiation and alternation

$$\underset{[1}{v^{\omega}}(\partial_{|\omega|}\underset{2]}{v^{\mu}})w_{\mu\lambda_2\ldots\lambda_q} = -\underset{[1}{v^{\omega}}\underset{2]}{v^{\mu}}\partial_{\omega} w_{\mu\lambda_2\ldots\lambda_q}$$

$$= \tfrac{1}{2}(q-1)\underset{[1}{v^{\omega}}\underset{2]}{v^{\mu}}\partial_{[\lambda_2} w_{|\omega\mu|\lambda_3\ldots\lambda_q]} - \tfrac{1}{2}\underset{[1}{v^{\omega}}\underset{2]}{v^{\mu}}W_{\omega\mu\lambda_2\ldots\lambda_q} = 0 \tag{3.6}$$

because the last term vanishes in consequence of (3.4) and the last but one in consequence of ($3.4\,a$). From ($3.4\,b\,\alpha$, $b\,\beta$) we get by differentiation and alternation

$$\underset{[1}{v^{\omega}}(\partial_{|\omega|}\underset{2]}{v^{\mu}})W_{\mu\lambda_1\ldots\lambda_q}$$

$$= -\underset{[1}{v^{\omega}}\underset{2]}{v^{\mu}}\partial_{\omega} W_{\mu\lambda_1\ldots\lambda_q} + \underset{[1}{v^{\omega}}(\partial_{|\omega|}\underset{2]}{\alpha})w_{\lambda_1\ldots\lambda_q} + \alpha \underset{[2\,1]}{v^{\omega}\partial_{\omega} w_{\lambda_1\ldots\lambda_q}}$$

$$= \tfrac{1}{2}q\underset{[1}{v^{\omega}}\underset{2]}{v^{\mu}}\partial_{[\lambda_1} W_{|\omega\mu|\lambda_2\ldots\lambda_q]} + \underset{[1}{v^{\omega}}(\partial_{|\omega|}\underset{2]}{\alpha})w_{\lambda_1\ldots\lambda_q} + q\alpha \underset{[2\,1]}{v^{\omega}\partial_{[\lambda_1} w_{|\omega|\lambda_2\ldots\lambda_q]}} +$$

$$+\alpha \underset{[2\,1]}{v^{\omega} W_{\omega\lambda_1\ldots\lambda_q}}$$

$$= \tfrac{1}{2}q\alpha(\partial_{[\lambda_1}\underset{[2}{v^{\omega}})\underset{1]}{w}_{|\omega|\lambda_2\ldots\lambda_q]} - \tfrac{1}{2}q\alpha(\partial_{[\lambda_1}\underset{[1}{v^{\mu}})\underset{2]}{w}_{|\mu|\lambda_2\ldots\lambda_q]} +$$

$$+\underset{[1}{v^{\omega}}(\partial_{|\omega|}\underset{2]}{\alpha})w_{\lambda_1\ldots\lambda_q} - q\alpha(\partial_{[\lambda_1}\underset{[2}{v^{\omega}})\underset{1]}{w}_{|\omega|\lambda_2\ldots\lambda_q]} + \alpha\underset{[2\,1]}{\alpha w}_{\lambda_1\ldots\lambda_q}$$

$$= \underset{[1}{v^{\omega}}(\partial_{|\omega|}\underset{2]}{\alpha})w_{\lambda_1\ldots\lambda_q}, \tag{3.7}$$

which proves ($3.5\,b$).

Since the systems $S_1, \ldots, S_4$ are complete, there exists in the domain of w, W a gradient product of K factors and in the domain of W a gradient product of c_1 factors which is a divisor of the first gradient product if $c_1 < K$. In case II we have $c_1 = K$ and the gradient product of K factors contains as a divisor a gradient product of $k = K-1$ factors, lying in the μ-domain of $W_{\mu\lambda_1\ldots\lambda_q} w_{\kappa_1\ldots\kappa_q} - W_{\mu\kappa_1\ldots\kappa_q} w_{\lambda_1\ldots\lambda_q}$. These three gradient products are all uniquely determined by the field $w_{\lambda_1\ldots\lambda_q}$ to within a scalar factor.

The coordinate system (κ) can always be chosen in such a way that the gradient product of K factors is equal to $\overset{1}{e}_{[\lambda_1}\ldots\overset{K}{e}_{\lambda_K]}$. Then all components of w and W having an index $> K$ vanish and consequently

$$\partial_\chi w_{\beta_1\ldots\beta_q} = q\partial_{[\beta_1} w_{|\chi|\beta_2\ldots\beta_q]} = 0 \quad (\beta_1,\ldots,\beta_q = 1,\ldots,K;\ \chi = K+1,\ldots,n). \tag{3.8}$$

Hence the components of $w_{\lambda_1\ldots\lambda_q}$ depend only on $\xi^1,\ldots,\xi^K$ and w can be expressed in terms of these K variables and their gradients, whilst the Pfaffians $w_{\mu\lambda_2\ldots\lambda_q} d\xi^\mu$ contain only these K variables and their differentials. Obviously K can never exceed the number of variables used in the expression of $w_{\lambda_1\ldots\lambda_q}$ or $w_{\mu\lambda_2\ldots\lambda_q} d\xi^\mu$ and thus it is impossible to find an expression in less than K variables. This proves the theorem (cf. Theorem IV.3):

THEOREM V.1. *A q-vector field $w_{\lambda_1\ldots\lambda_q}$ of class K can be expressed in terms of K (and not less) variables and their gradients, and the system of Pfaffians $w_{\mu\lambda_2\ldots\lambda_q} d\xi^\mu$ in terms of K (and not less) variables and their differentials.*

As in the case $q = 1$ the systems S_1 and S_2 are easier to integrate than a general complete system.† If we know c_1-1 independent integral functions of S_1, a c_1-th integral function can be determined by a quadrature (cf. IV, § 3, and V, § 4). To prove this we choose the coordinate system (κ) in such a way that $\xi^1,\ldots,\xi^{c_1-1}$ are the c_1-1 known integral functions. If then $F(\xi^\kappa)$ is another independent integral function still unknown, $W_{\mu\lambda_1\ldots\lambda_q}$ can be expressed in terms of $\xi^1,\ldots,\xi^{c_1-1}$, F and $\overset{1}{e}_\lambda,\ldots,\overset{c_1-1}{e}_\lambda$, $\partial_\lambda F$. From this it follows that all components of $W_{\mu\lambda_1\ldots\lambda_q}$ having more than one index $> c_1-1$ must vanish. Now the equations

$$W_{\mu\lambda_1\ldots\lambda_q} d\xi^\mu = 0 \tag{3.9}$$

may be looked upon as equations in ξ^ζ $(\zeta = c_1,\ldots,n)$ with the parameters $\xi^1,\ldots,\xi^{c_1-1}$. Then $d\xi^\alpha = 0$ $(\alpha = 1,\ldots,c_1-1)$, and (3.9) is equivalent to

$$W_{\zeta\beta_1\ldots\beta_q} d\xi^\zeta = 0 \quad (\beta_1,\ldots,\beta_q = 1,\ldots,c_1-1;\ \zeta = c_1,\ldots,n). \tag{3.10}$$

† Cf. Goursat 1922. 1, p. 145.

If now for $\beta_1,\dots,\beta_q$ we choose some *fixed* values such that not all $W_{\zeta\beta_1\dots\beta_q}$ vanish, (3.10) represents one single equation and we will show that the left-hand side is a complete differential. In fact we have, according to the vanishing of DW,

$$\partial_\eta W_{\zeta\beta_1\dots\beta_q} - \partial_\zeta W_{\eta\beta_1\dots\beta_q} = -q\partial_{[\beta_1} W_{|\eta\zeta|\beta_2\dots\beta_q]} = 0$$
$$(\beta_1,\dots,\beta_q = 1,\dots,c_1-1;\ \eta,\zeta = c_1,\dots,n). \quad (3.11)$$

Hence a c_1-th integral function can be obtained by integrating the complete differential in the left-hand side of (3.10), looking upon $\xi^1,\dots,\xi^{c_1-1}$ as parameters.

If in case I we know $K-1$ independent integral functions of $S_2 = S_4$, a Kth independent integral function of $S_2 = S_4$ can be obtained by a quadrature.† To prove this we choose the coordinate system (κ) in such a way that $\xi^1,\dots,\xi^{K-1}$ are the known integral functions of $S_2 = S_4$. If then $F(\xi^\kappa)$ is another independent integral function, $w_{\lambda_1\dots\lambda_q}$ and $W_{\mu\lambda_1\dots\lambda_q}$ can be expressed in terms of $\xi^1,\dots,\xi^{K-1}$, F and $\overset{1}{e}_\lambda,\dots,\overset{K-1}{e}_\lambda$, $\partial_\lambda F$. Hence

$$\begin{aligned} &(a) \qquad w_{\zeta\eta\lambda_3\dots\lambda_q} = 0 \\ &(b) \qquad W_{\zeta\eta\lambda_3\dots\lambda_q} = 0 \end{aligned} \qquad (\zeta,\eta = K,\dots,n). \qquad (3.12)$$

Now the equations of $S_2 = S_4$

$$\begin{aligned} &(a) \qquad w_{\mu\lambda_2\dots\lambda_q}\, d\xi^\mu = 0, \\ &(b) \qquad W_{\mu\lambda_1\dots\lambda_q}\, d\xi^\mu = 0 \end{aligned} \qquad (3.13)$$

are equivalent to a system of K independent equations, of which the $K-1$ equations $d\xi^\alpha = 0$ $(\alpha = 1,\dots,K-1)$ are known and the Kth equation has to be taken either from (3.13 a) or from (3.13 b). Hence, if the values of $\beta_2,\dots,\beta_q$ can be chosen from $1,\dots,K-1$ in such a way that the $w_{\zeta\beta_2\dots\beta_q}$ are not all zero, (3.13) is equivalent to the system

$$\begin{aligned} &(a) \quad w_{\zeta\beta_2\dots\beta_q} d\xi^\zeta = 0 \\ &(b) \qquad\qquad d\xi^\alpha = 0 \end{aligned} \qquad (\beta_2,\dots,\beta_q = 1,\dots,K-1;\ \zeta = K,\dots,n), \qquad (3.14)$$

where $\beta_2,\dots,\beta_q$ have these fixed values. If this choice is impossible, that is, if $\xi^1,\dots,\xi^{K-1}$ are integral functions of (3.13 a), (3.13) is equivalent to the system

$$\begin{aligned} &(a) \quad W_{\zeta\beta_1\dots\beta_q} d\xi^\zeta = 0 \\ &(b) \qquad\qquad d\xi^\alpha = 0, \end{aligned} \qquad (\beta_1,\dots,\beta_q = 1,\dots,K-1;\ \zeta = K,\dots,n), \qquad (3.15)$$

with fixed values of $\beta_1,\dots,\beta_q$, chosen in such a way that not all $W_{\zeta\beta_1\dots\beta_q}$ vanish. In the first case the left-hand side of (3.14 a) is a complete

† Goursat 1922. 1, p. 146, makes the condition that all integral functions of $S_1 = S_3$ occur among the $K-1$ integral functions. This is not necessary (cf. IV, § 3).

differential, if $\xi^1,\dots,\xi^{K-1}$ are looked upon as parameters. In fact, according to (3.12 b)

$$\partial_\eta w_{\zeta\beta_2\dots\beta_q} - \partial_\zeta w_{\eta\beta_2\dots\beta_q} = -(q-1)\partial_{[\beta_2} w_{|\eta\zeta|\beta_3\dots\beta_q]} = 0 \quad (\eta,\zeta = K,\dots,n). \tag{3.16}$$

Hence, a last integral function of $S_2 = S_4$ can be obtained by integrating the complete differential in the left-hand side of (3.14 a). In the second case, looking upon the $\xi^1,\dots,\xi^{K-1}$ as parameters, we get

$$W_{\zeta\beta_1\dots\beta_q} d\xi^\zeta = \partial_\zeta w_{\beta_1\dots\beta_q} d\xi^\zeta = dw_{\beta_1\dots\beta_q} \quad (\zeta = K,\dots,n). \tag{3.17}$$

Hence $w_{\beta_1\dots\beta_q}$ is a last integral function of $S_2 = S_4$.

If in case II the c_1-1 known independent integral functions of $S_1 = S_2$ happen to be also integral functions of $S_3 = S_4$ the integration of $S_1 = S_2$ is still easier as will be shown in the next section (cf. IV, § 3).

4. Similarity transformations of a field $w_{\lambda_1\dots\lambda}$

A transformation of the form

$$'w_{\lambda_1\dots\lambda_q} = \sigma w_{\lambda_1\dots\lambda_q}, \tag{4.1}$$

$w_{\lambda_1\dots\lambda_q}$ and σ being analytic and $\neq 0$ in an $\underset{0}{\mathfrak{N}}(\xi^\kappa)$, is called a *similarity transformation* (cf. IV, § 7). The transformation of $W_{\mu\lambda_1\dots\lambda_q}$ is

$$'W_{\mu\lambda_1\dots\lambda_q} = \sigma W_{\mu\lambda_1\dots\lambda_q} + (q+1)\sigma_{[\mu} w_{\lambda_1\dots\lambda_q]} \quad (\sigma_\mu \overset{\text{def}}{=} \partial_\mu \sigma). \tag{4.2}$$

From this it follows that S, S_4, c, and k are invariant for similarity transformations but that S_1, S_2, S_3, c_1, K, and c_3 are not invariant.

As we have seen in V, § 2, in case I there does not exist a contravariant vector whose transvection with W is equal to w. If σ is not an integral function of $S_2 = S_4$, that is, if $\partial_\lambda \sigma$ is not contained in the domain of the system w, W (only possible if $K < n$), it is always possible to construct a vector v^κ such that the transvections of v^κ with w and W vanish and $v^\lambda \partial_\lambda \sigma = \sigma$. Transvection with $'W$ gives

$$v^\mu\, 'W_{\mu\lambda_1\dots\lambda_q} = \sigma w_{\lambda_1\dots\lambda_q} = 'w_{\lambda_1\dots\lambda_q} \tag{4.3}$$

and this means that $'w_{\lambda_1\dots\lambda_q}$ is in case II with $'K = K+1$, $'k = k = K$. If σ is an integral function of $S_2 = S_4$, $\partial_\lambda \sigma$ lies in the domain of the system w, W and consequently the domain of $'w$, $'W$ is contained in the domain of w, W. Hence $K' \leqslant K$. Now we know that $k' = k$ and this implies that $'w$ cannot be in case II because then, according to (2.12) we would have $'K = 'k+1 = K+1$. Hence $'w$ is in case I with $'K = K$.

If w is in case II it follows from the invariance of S_4 that $'w$ can only be in case I if σ is not an integral function of $S_3 = S_4$, because σ^{-1} has to lead back from case I to case II. But this condition is only necessary and not sufficient. Since w is in case II there exist just $n-c_3$ linearly independent contravariant vector fields, whose transvections with w are all zero and whose transvections with W are either zero or a multiple of w, and among them there is at least one whose transvection with W is not zero. Hence it is always possible to construct $n-c_3 = n-k$ vectors $\underset{1}{v}^\kappa$, $\underset{u}{v}^\kappa$ $(u = 2,..., n-k)$ such that

$$\begin{aligned} &(a) \quad \underset{1}{v}^\mu W_{\mu\lambda_1...\lambda_q} = \alpha w_{\lambda_1...\lambda_q} \quad (\alpha \neq 0),\\ &(b) \quad \underset{u}{v}^\mu W_{\mu\lambda_1...\lambda_q} = 0\\ &(c) \quad \underset{1}{v}^\mu w_{\mu\lambda_2...\lambda_q} = 0 \qquad (u = 2,..., n-k).\\ &(d) \quad \underset{u}{v}^\mu w_{\mu\lambda_2...\lambda_q} = 0 \end{aligned} \tag{4.4}$$

When these fields have been constructed, α is a wholly determined scalar field. Since S_3 is complete there must exist relations of the form

$$\begin{aligned} &(a) \quad \underset{[1}{v}^\mu \partial_{|\mu|} \underset{u]}{v}^\kappa = c^1_{1u} \underset{1}{v}^\kappa + c^v_{1u} \underset{v}{v}^\kappa\\ &(b) \quad \underset{[v}{v}^\mu \partial_{|\mu|} \underset{u]}{v}^\kappa = c^w_{vu} \underset{w}{v}^\kappa \end{aligned} \qquad (u, v, w = 2,..., n-k). \tag{4.5}$$

From (3.7) and $S_3 = S_4$ it follows that

$$2\underset{[1}{v}^\omega(\partial_{|\omega|} \underset{u]}{v}^\mu) W_{\mu\lambda_1...\lambda_q} = -\underset{u}{v}^\omega(\partial_\omega \alpha) w_{\lambda_1...\lambda_q} \tag{4.6}$$

and, from (4.4 a) and (4.5)

$$2c^1_{1u}\alpha = -\underset{u}{v}^\omega \partial_\omega \alpha. \tag{4.7}$$

For $'w$ to be in case I there must exist $n-K'$ linearly independent vectors whose transvections with $'w$ and $'W$ vanish and there must be no vector whose transvection with $'W$ is equal to $'w$. Now $S_3 = S_4 = 'S_4 = 'S_2$ and consequently $'K = k = K-1$ and this implies that these $n-k$ vectors have to depend linearly on the $n-k$ vectors $\underset{1}{v}^\kappa$, $\underset{u}{v}^\kappa$. But this means that the transvections of $\underset{1}{v}^\kappa$, $\underset{u}{v}^\kappa$ with $'W$ must vanish. Hence

$$\begin{aligned} \underset{1}{v}^\mu\, 'W_{\mu\lambda_1...\lambda_q} &= \sigma\alpha w_{\lambda_1...\lambda_q} + \underset{1}{v}^\mu \sigma_\mu w_{\lambda_1...\lambda_q} = 0,\\ \underset{u}{v}^\mu\, 'W_{\mu\lambda_1...\lambda_q} &= \underset{u}{v}^\mu \sigma_\mu w_{\lambda_1...\lambda_q} = 0 \end{aligned} \tag{4.8}$$

or

$$\begin{aligned} \underset{1}{v}^\mu \partial_\mu \log\sigma &= -\alpha,\\ \underset{u}{v}^\mu \partial_\mu \log\sigma &= 0. \end{aligned} \tag{4.9}$$

According to (4.5) and (4.7) the non-homogeneous system (4.9) is complete and always has solutions (cf. III, § 14). Now suppose that there exists a vector u^κ, linearly independent of $\underset{1}{v}^\kappa$, $\underset{u}{v}^\kappa$, whose transvection with $'W$ is equal to $'w$. Then the transvection of u^κ with $'w$ would be zero and in consequence of $'S_2 = 'S_4 = S_4 = S_3$ this would imply that u^κ were linearly dependent on $\underset{1}{v}^\kappa$, $\underset{u}{v}^\kappa$, which contradicts our supposition. Hence, such a vector cannot exist and, therefore, the conditions (4.9) are not only necessary but also sufficient. This does not imply that there are no vectors linearly independent of $\underset{1}{v}^\kappa$, $\underset{u}{v}^\kappa$, whose transvections with $'W$ are zero. E.g. if $'W = 0$ and $W \neq 0$ such vectors are possible.

Collecting results we have the following theorem (cf. Theorem IV.6):

THEOREM V.2. *If a field $w_{\lambda_1 \ldots \lambda_q}$ of class K is subjected to the similarity transformation*

$$'w_{\lambda_1 \ldots \lambda_q} = \sigma w_{\lambda_1 \ldots \lambda_q} \tag{4.10}$$

the class $'K$ of $'w_{\lambda_1 \ldots \lambda_q}$ takes the value

$$\textit{Case I:}\quad K = k \quad \begin{cases} 'K = 'k+1 \text{ if } \sigma \text{ is not an integral function of} \\ \quad S_2 = S_4 \quad (\text{never for } K = n); \\ 'K = 'k = K \text{ if } \sigma \text{ is an integral function of } S_2 = S_4 \\ \quad (\text{always for } K = n). \end{cases} \tag{4.11}$$

$$\textit{Case II:}\quad K = k+1 \quad \begin{cases} 'K = 'k+1 = K \text{ if } \sigma \text{ is not a solution of (4.9)}; \\ 'K = 'k = K-1 \text{ if } \sigma \text{ is a solution of (4.9)}. \end{cases} \tag{4.12}$$

From this we see that similarity transformations as a rule change case I into case II and leave case II invariant. Only for special values of σ case I is left invariant and case II is changed into case I.

The following is a summary of the change of the four arithmetical invariants with similarity transformations changing case I into case II and case II into case I:

$$\begin{array}{lllll} \text{I.} & c_1 \leqslant K & K & c_3 = c_1 \leqslant K & k = K \\ & & \downarrow & & \\ \text{II.} & 'c_1 = K+1 & 'K = K+1 & 'c_3 = K & 'k = K \end{array} \tag{4.13}$$

$$\begin{array}{lllll} \text{II.} & c_1 = K & K & c_3 = K-1 & k = K-1 \\ & & \downarrow & & \\ \text{I.} & 'c_1 \leqslant K-1 & 'K = K-1 & 'c_3 = 'c_1 \leqslant K-1 & 'k = K-1 \end{array} \tag{4.14}$$

If a field $\lfloor w_{\lambda_1 \ldots \lambda_q} \rfloor$ is given by an equation $w_{\mu\lambda_2 \ldots \lambda_q} d\xi^\mu = 0$, this equation is equivalent to $'w_{\mu\lambda_2 \ldots \lambda_q} d\xi^\mu = 0$ and, as follows from Theorem V.2, σ can always be chosen in such a way that $'K = k$ and this means that the equation can always be written in terms of k variables and their differentials. But k being a rank, the number of variables cannot be less than k. This proves the theorem (cf. the theorems IV.3, IV.7, and V.1):

THEOREM V.3. *If a q-vector field $w_{\lambda_1 \ldots \lambda_q}$ has the similarity class k, there always exists a field $\sigma w_{\lambda_1 \ldots \lambda_q}$ expressible in terms of k variables and their gradients and never such a field expressible in terms of a smaller number of variables and their gradients. Consequently the system of Pfaffian equations $w_{\mu\lambda_2 \ldots \lambda_q} d\xi^\mu = 0$ can be expressed in terms of k (and not less) variables and their differentials.*

Now it is easy to prove that if in case II we know $K-1$ independent integral functions of $S_1 = S_2$ and if these functions happen to be also integral functions of $S_3 = S_4$, a Kth independent integral function of $S_1 = S_2$ can be determined without any integration (cf. IV, § 3, and V, § 3). The system $S_3 = S_4$ has only $k = K-1$ independent integral functions; hence, if we choose the coordinate system (κ) in such a way that $\xi^1, \ldots, \xi^k$ are these functions, the equation $w_{\mu\lambda_2 \ldots \lambda_q} d\xi^\mu = 0$ can be expressed in terms of $\xi^1, \ldots, \xi^k$ and their differentials. Consequently the quotient of any two components of $w_{\lambda_1 \ldots \lambda_q}$ with respect to (κ) depends on $\xi^1, \ldots, \xi^k$ and every non-vanishing component of w with respect to (κ) is a Kth integral function of $S_1 = S_2$.

5. On the use of the absolute invariants with respect to $\lfloor v^{\kappa_1 \ldots \kappa_p} \rfloor$ of the X_p-forming p-vector field $v^{\kappa_1 \ldots \kappa_p}$ for integrating purposes†

We will show how the integration of the complete system of p equations

$$v^{\mu\kappa_2 \ldots \kappa_p} \partial_\mu f = 0, \tag{5.1}$$

$v^{\kappa_1 \ldots \kappa_p}$ being a simple X_p-forming p-vector field, can be simplified if a covariant t-vector $u_{\lambda_1 \ldots \lambda_t}$, $1 \leqslant t \leqslant n-p$ or a contravariant s-vector density $\mathfrak{u}^{\kappa_1 \ldots \kappa_s}$ of weight $+1$, $p \leqslant s \leqslant n-1$, absolutely invariant with respect to $\lfloor v^{\kappa_1 \ldots \kappa_p} \rfloor$, is known. The case $t = n-p$ or $s = p$ has already been dealt with in III, § 18. According to Theorem III.20, $u_{\lambda_1 \ldots \lambda_t}$ can be expressed in terms of solutions of (5.1) and their gradients. Now if K is the class of $u_{\lambda_1 \ldots \lambda_t}$ this t-vector can also be expressed in terms of K variables and their gradients and thus these K variables must be solutions of (5.1). Hence $K \leqslant n-p$. In order to determine these K variables the system S_2 has to be integrated and this is always possible by means of at most K operations $O_K, \ldots, O_1$. This proves that the solution of (5.1), needing in general $n-p$ operations $O_{n-p}, \ldots, O_1$, can be effected by means of $n-p$ operations

$$O_K, \quad \ldots, \quad O_1, \quad O_{n-p-K}, \quad \ldots, \quad O_1 \tag{5.2}$$

if a covariant t-vector of class K, absolutely invariant with respect to $\lfloor v^{\kappa_1 \ldots \kappa_p} \rfloor$ (or the corresponding $(n-t)$-vector density), is known.

† Cf. Goursat 1922. 1, ch. v.

If t has the greatest possible value $n-p$, the rotation of $u_{\lambda_1\ldots\lambda_{n-p}}$ must vanish because, as we have seen in III, § 18, an $(n-p+1)$-vector, absolutely invariant with respect to $\lfloor v^{\kappa_1\ldots\kappa_p}\rfloor$, cannot exist. Hence $K = n-p$ and the system to integrate is S_1. As was shown in V, § 3 the last solution of S_1 can be obtained by a quadrature if $n-p-1$ solutions are known and, therefore, the integration of S_1 can be effected by $n-p$ operations $O_{n-p},\ldots, O_2, O_0$. This is in accordance with the fact that from the corresponding p-vector density an integrating factor can be derived without any integration (cf. III, § 18) and that the integration of (5.1), an integrating factor being known, can be effected by means of the operations $O_{n-p},\ldots, O_2, O_0$ (cf. III, § 17).

The method described is most profitable if $K = \frac{1}{2}(n-p)$ for $n-p$ even and $K = \frac{1}{2}(n-p\pm 1)$ for $n-p$ odd, because in these cases the maximum order of the necessary operations is reduced to the lowest possible value of $\frac{1}{2}(n-p)$ and $\frac{1}{2}(n-p+1)$ respectively.

6. Preliminary classification of simple covariant q-vector fields†

If $w_{\lambda_1\ldots\lambda_q}$ is simple and if B_b^κ and C_λ^x are the connecting quantities of the E_p-field of $w_{\lambda_1\ldots\lambda_q}$ $(p = n-q)$, the systems $S, S_1,\ldots, S_4$ can be written in the form

$$(S)\quad w_{\mu\lambda_2\ldots\lambda_q}d\xi^\mu = 0 \quad\text{or}\quad C_\mu^x d\xi^\mu = 0; \tag{6.1}$$

$$(S_1)\quad W_{\mu\lambda_1\ldots\lambda_q}d\xi^\mu = 0; \tag{6.2}$$

$$\begin{aligned}(S_2)\quad & w_{\mu\lambda_2\ldots\lambda_q}d\xi^\mu = 0 \quad\text{or}\quad C_\mu^x d\xi^\mu = 0,\\ & W_{\mu\lambda_1\ldots\lambda_q}d\xi^\mu = 0;\end{aligned} \tag{6.3}$$

$$(S_3)\quad W_{\mu\lambda_1\ldots[\lambda_q}w_{\kappa_1\ldots\kappa_q]}d\xi^\mu = 0 \quad\text{or}\quad W_{\mu\lambda_1\ldots\lambda_q}B_b^{\lambda_q}d\xi^\mu = 0; \tag{6.4}$$

$$\begin{aligned}(S_4)\quad & w_{\mu\lambda_2\ldots\lambda_q}d\xi^\mu = 0 \quad\text{or}\quad C_\mu^x d\xi^\mu = 0;\\ & W_{\mu\lambda_1\ldots[\lambda_q}w_{\kappa_1\ldots\kappa_q]}d\xi^\mu = 0 \quad\text{or}\quad W_{\mu\lambda_1\ldots\lambda_q}B_b^{\lambda_q}d\xi^\mu = 0\end{aligned} \tag{6.5}$$

$$(b = 1,\ldots, \mathrm{p};\ x = \mathrm{p}+1,\ldots, \mathrm{n}).$$

Following E. Grynaeus‡ we may introduce a sixth system

$$(S_5)\quad W_{\mu\lambda_1\ldots[\lambda_{q-1}\lambda_q}w_{\kappa_1\ldots\kappa_q]}d\xi^\mu = 0. \tag{6.6}$$

Evidently S_5 is invariant for similarity transformations and can only be formed for $q > 1$. The μ-rank of the quantity on the left-hand side of (6.6) is denoted by c_5. Since the q-vector is simple, $c = 0$ in points where $w_{\lambda_1\ldots\lambda_q} = 0$ and $c = q$ in all other points. The notions *region of constant class, point of diminished class,* and *ordinary point* are defined as in V, § 2, but now for the six arithmetic invariants c, c_1, K, c_3, k,

† Cf. Grynaeus 1928. 2.

‡ Ibid.

and c_5. As before we suppose that $\underset{0}{\xi}^\kappa$ is an ordinary point and $\mathfrak{N}(\underset{0}{\xi}^\kappa)$ a region of constant class.

If
$$w_{\lambda_1\ldots\lambda_q} = \overset{1}{w}_{[\lambda_1}\ldots\overset{q}{w}_{\lambda_q]} \tag{6.7}$$
we have
$$W_{\mu\lambda_1\ldots\lambda_q} = q(q+1)(\partial_{[\mu}\overset{1}{w}_{\lambda_1})\overset{2}{w}_{\lambda_2}\ldots\overset{q]}{w}_{\lambda_q]} \tag{6.8}$$
and
$$\begin{aligned} W_{\mu\lambda_1\ldots[\lambda_{q-1}\lambda_q}w_{\kappa_1\ldots\kappa_q]} &= q(q+1)(\partial_{[\lambda_{q-1}}\overset{[1}{w}_{\lambda_q})w_{\kappa_1\ldots\kappa_q]}\overset{2}{w}_\mu\overset{3}{w}_{\lambda_1}\ldots\overset{q]}{w}_{\lambda_{q-2}} \\ &= W_{[\lambda_{q-1}\lambda_q\kappa_2\ldots\kappa_q}\overset{[1}{w}_{\kappa_1]}\overset{2}{w}_\mu\overset{3}{w}_{\lambda_1}\ldots\overset{q]}{w}_{\lambda_{q-2}} \\ &= W_{[\lambda_q\kappa_1\ldots\kappa_q}w_{\lambda_{q-1}]\mu\lambda_1\ldots\lambda_{q-2}}. \end{aligned} \tag{6.9}$$

Hence S_5 can be written in the form
$$(S_5)\quad w_{\mu\lambda_1\ldots\lambda_{q-2}[\lambda_{q-1}}W_{\lambda_q\kappa_1\ldots\kappa_q]}d\xi^\mu = 0 \tag{6.10}$$
and from this it follows that every linear element satisfying S satisfies also S_5. Incidentally we see that it is no use forming a system $S_6 = S+S_5$. From (6.8) it follows that
$$W_{\mu\lambda_1\ldots[\lambda_{q-2}\lambda_{q-1}\lambda_q}w_{\kappa_1\ldots\kappa_q]} = 0 \tag{6.11}$$
and this implies that the series $S, S_1, \ldots, S_5$ cannot be continued.

From (6.6) we may derive another form of S_5:
$$(S_5)\quad (\partial_{[\mu}C^{p+1}_{\lambda_1}\ldots C^{n}_{\lambda_q]})B^{\lambda_{q-1}}_b B^{\lambda_q}_c\, d\xi^\mu = 0 \quad (b, c = 1, \ldots, p). \tag{6.12}$$
Now we have
$$\begin{aligned} 2(\partial_{[\mu}C^{p+1}_{\lambda_1}\ldots C^{n}_{\lambda_q]})B^{\lambda_{q-1}}_b B^{\lambda_q}_c &= qC^{\cdot\cdot\,[p+1}_{[\mu\lambda_1}C^{p+2}_{\lambda_2}\ldots C^{n]}_{\lambda_q]}B^{\lambda_{q-1}}_b B^{\lambda_q}_c \\ &= \frac{2}{q+1}B^{\lambda_{q-1}}_b B^{\lambda_q}_c C^{\cdot\cdot\,[p+1}_{\lambda_{q-1}\lambda_q}C^{p+2}_\mu C^{p+3}_{\lambda_1}\ldots C^{n]}_{\lambda_{q-2}} \quad (b, c = 1, \ldots, p), \end{aligned} \tag{6.13}$$
and from this and the linear independence of $C^{p+1}_\lambda, \ldots, C^{n}_\lambda$ we get still another form of S_5
$$(S_5)\quad C^{[x}_\mu C^{\cdot\cdot\,y]}_{\nu\lambda}B^\nu_c B^\lambda_b\, d\xi^\mu = 0 \quad (b, c = 1, \ldots, p;\ x, y = p+1, \ldots, n). \tag{6.14}$$

Hence, c_5 is the μ-rank of $C^{[x}_\mu C^{\cdot\cdot\,y]}_{\nu\lambda}B^\nu_c B^\lambda_b$.

Similarly, it can be shown that S_2 can be written in the form
$$(S_2)\quad W_{\lambda_1\ldots\lambda_q[\mu}w_{\kappa_1\ldots\kappa_q]}\,d\xi^\mu = 0;\ w_{\mu\lambda_2\ldots\lambda_q}\,d\xi^\mu = 0 \tag{6.15}$$
and that there are two other forms of S_4:
$$(S_4)\quad W_{\lambda_1\ldots\lambda_{q-1}[\mu\lambda_q}w_{\kappa_1\ldots\kappa_q]}\,d\xi^\mu = 0;\ w_{\mu\lambda_2\ldots\lambda_q}\,d\xi^\mu = 0 \tag{6.16}$$
and
$$(S_4)\quad w_{\lambda_1\ldots[\lambda_q}W_{\mu\kappa_1\ldots\kappa_q]}\,d\xi^\mu = 0;\ w_{\mu\lambda_2\ldots\lambda_q}\,d\xi^\mu = 0. \tag{6.17}$$

From (6.2), (6.4), and (6.6) it follows that every linear element satisfying S_1 or S_3 also satisfies S_5. Hence $c_5 \leqslant c_1$, $c_5 \leqslant c_3$, $c_5 \leqslant c$. Collecting results we get the following inequalities (cf. (2.8)):

$$\begin{array}{ccccccc} n & \geqslant & K & \geqslant & k & \geqslant & q \\ & & \vee\!\!| & & \vee\!\!| & & \vee\!\!| \\ & & c_1 & \geqslant & c_3 & \geqslant & c_5 \geqslant 0. \end{array} \tag{6.18}$$

So far we have classified into cases I and II. Using S_5 for further classification we get four cases A, B, C, and D. Case A is characterized by $c_5 = 0$. This case only arises if

$$w_{\lambda_1 \ldots [\lambda_q} W_{\mu \kappa_1 \ldots \kappa_q]} = 0, \tag{6.19}$$

that is, if every vector divisor of w is a divisor of W, and this occurs if and only if W can be written in the form

$$W_{\mu \lambda_1 \ldots \lambda_q} = \phi_{[\mu} w_{\lambda_1 \ldots \lambda_q]}. \tag{6.20}$$

Hence $S_4 = S$ in consequence of (6.5) and this implies that S is complete and that w is either a gradient product (case I) or a gradient product to within a scalar factor (case II). In these cases the arithmetic invariants have the following values:

	c_1	K	c_3	k	c_5	
AI:	0	q	0	q	0	(6.21)
AII:	$q+1$	$q+1$	q	q	0	

Case B is characterized by $0 < c_5 < q$ and S_5 being complete. From $c_5 < q$ it follows that there exists at least one linear element satisfying S_5 but not satisfying S and according to (6.10) this implies that there exists a non-vanishing vector v^κ such that

$$v^\mu w_{\mu \lambda_2 \ldots \lambda_q} \neq 0, \qquad v^\mu w_{\mu \lambda_2 \ldots [\lambda_q} W_{\omega \kappa_1 \ldots \kappa_q]} = 0. \tag{6.22}$$

Hence every vector divisor of $v^\mu w_{\mu \lambda_2 \ldots \lambda_q}$ is a divisor of W and this means that just $q-1$ linearly independent vector divisors of w are divisors of W because otherwise we would have had case A. Hence W can be written in the form

$$W_{\mu \lambda_1 \ldots \lambda_q} = v_{[\mu \lambda_1} \overset{2}{w}_{\lambda_2} \ldots \overset{q}{w}_{\lambda_q]}, \tag{6.23}$$

$\overset{2}{w}_\lambda, \ldots, \overset{q}{w}_\lambda$ being linearly independent divisors of $w_{\lambda_1 \ldots \lambda_q}$ and $v_{\mu\lambda}$ a suitable bivector. Consequently, considering (6.6) S_5 can be written in the form

$$\overset{2}{w}_{[\mu} \overset{3}{w}_{\lambda_3} \ldots \overset{q}{w}_{\lambda_q]} v_{[\omega\nu} w_{\kappa_1 \ldots \kappa_q]} \, d\xi^\mu = 0 \tag{6.24}$$

or, more simply,

$$\overset{2}{w}_{[\mu} \overset{3}{w}_{\lambda_3} \ldots \overset{q}{w}_{\lambda_q]} \, d\xi^\mu = 0. \tag{6.25}$$

Now, since S_5 is complete, it follows that the $(q-1)$-vector in (6.25) is a gradient product or a gradient product to within a scalar factor. Hence w can be written in the form

$$w_{\lambda_1\ldots\lambda_q} = \overset{1}{w}_{[\lambda_1}\overset{2}{f}_{\lambda_2}\cdots\overset{q}{f}_{\lambda_q]} \quad (\overset{\mathfrak{a}}{f}_\lambda = \partial_\lambda \overset{\mathfrak{a}}{f};\ \mathfrak{a} = 2,\ldots,q) \tag{6.26}$$

and from this we get for W the form

$$W_{\mu\lambda_1\ldots\lambda_q} = (q+1)(\partial_{[\mu}\overset{1}{w}_{\lambda_1})\overset{2}{f}_{\lambda_2}\cdots\overset{q}{f}_{\lambda_q]}. \tag{6.27}$$

The factor $\overset{1}{w}_\lambda$ in $w_{\lambda_1\ldots\lambda_q}$ is determined mod. $\overset{2}{f}_\lambda,\ldots,\overset{q}{f}_\lambda$. Now according to Theorem V.1 w can be expressed in terms of K variables and their gradients. Hence for $\overset{1}{w}_\lambda$ a vector can be chosen dependent on $K-q+1$ variables and their gradients. This means that we have for $K-q+1$ odd

$$\overset{1}{w}_\lambda = \partial_\lambda p + \overset{1}{z}\,\partial_\lambda \overset{1}{s} + \ldots + \overset{\tau}{z}\,\partial_\lambda \overset{\tau}{s} \quad (K-q+1 = 2\tau+1) \tag{6.28}$$

and for $K-q+1$ even

$$\overset{1}{w}_\lambda = \overset{1}{z}\,\partial_\lambda \overset{1}{s} + \ldots + \overset{\tau+1}{z}\,\partial_\lambda \overset{\tau+1}{s} \quad (K-q+1 = 2\tau+2), \tag{6.29}$$

where $p, \overset{1}{z},\ldots,\overset{\tau}{z}, \overset{1}{s},\ldots,\overset{\tau}{s}$ are functions independent of each other and of $\overset{2}{f},\ldots,\overset{q}{f}$. In both cases $\tau \geqslant 1$ because otherwise we would have had case A. If $K-q+1$ is odd we have $c_1 = K-1 = q+2\tau-1$ and consequently case I with $k = K = q+2\tau$. If $K-q+1$ is even we have

$$c_1 = K = q+2\tau+1$$

and consequently case II with $c_3 = k$. Since k is invariant for similarity transformations, k does not change if (6.29) is divided by $\overset{1}{z}$. But then $\overset{1}{w}_\lambda$ gets the odd class $2\tau+1$ and thus $c_3 = k = q+2\tau$. In these cases the arithmetic invariants have the values

$$\left.\begin{array}{llllll} & c_1 & K & c_3 & k & c_5 \\ \mathrm{B\,I}: & q+2\tau-1 & q+2\tau & q+2\tau-1 & q+2\tau & q-1 \\ \mathrm{B\,II}: & q+2\tau+1 & q+2\tau+1 & q+2\tau & q+2\tau & q-1 \end{array}\right\}\ \tau \geqslant 1. \tag{6.30}$$

Since the number of variables used is $\leqslant n$ we have the following canonical forms:

$$\left.\begin{array}{lll} \mathrm{B\,I}: & (\overset{1}{e}_{[\lambda_1} + \xi^2 \overset{3}{e}_{[\lambda_1} + \ldots + \xi^{2\tau} \overset{2\tau+1}{e}_{[\lambda_1})\ \overset{2\tau+2}{e}_{\lambda_2}\cdots \overset{K}{e}_{\lambda_q]} & (K = q+2\tau) \\ \mathrm{B\,II}: & (\xi^1 \overset{2}{e}_{[\lambda_1} + \ldots + \xi^{2\tau+1} \overset{2\tau+2}{e}_{[\lambda_1})\ \overset{2\tau+3}{e}_{\lambda_2}\cdots \overset{K}{e}_{\lambda_q]}, & (K = q+2\tau+1) \end{array}\right\}\ \tau \geqslant 1. \tag{6.31}$$

The case C is characterized by $0 < c_5 < q$ and by S_5 not being complete. As in case B we may conclude that W has the form (6.23) and that S_5 can be written in the form (6.25) from which it follows that

$c_5 = q-1$. But now S_5 is not complete. That means that for at least one of the vectors in (6.25), e.g. $\overset{2}{w}_{\lambda}$,

$$(\partial_{[\mu} \overset{2}{w}_{\lambda_1})\overset{2}{w}_{\lambda_2}\dots\overset{q}{w}_{\lambda_q]} \neq 0 \tag{6.32}$$

is true.

By differentiation and alternation of the identity

$$\overset{2}{w}_{[\lambda} w_{\lambda_1\dots\lambda_q]} = 0 \tag{6.33}$$

we get
$$(q+1)(\partial_{[\mu}\overset{2}{w}_{\lambda})w_{\lambda_1\dots\lambda_q]} + \overset{2}{w}_{[\lambda} W_{\mu\lambda_1\dots\lambda_q]} = 0, \tag{6.34}$$

or, making use of (6.23),

$$(\partial_{[\mu}\overset{2}{w}_{\lambda})w_{\lambda_1\dots\lambda_q]} = 0. \tag{6.35}$$

If we now write
$$w_{\lambda_1\dots\lambda_q} = \overset{1}{w}_{[\lambda_1}\dots\overset{q}{w}_{\lambda_q]}, \tag{6.36}$$

which is always possible, from (6.35) it follows that $\overset{1}{w}_{\lambda}$ is a divisor of the non-vanishing expression (6.32) and that consequently there exists an equation of the form

$$(\partial_{[\mu}\overset{2}{w}_{\lambda_1})\overset{2}{w}_{\lambda_2}\dots\overset{q}{w}_{\lambda_q]} = u_{[\mu} w_{\lambda_1\dots\lambda_q]} \tag{6.37}$$

with a non-vanishing vector u_{λ}. Differentiation and alternation of (6.35) leads to

$$(\partial_{[\mu}\overset{2}{w}_{\lambda})W_{\omega\lambda_1\dots\lambda_q]} = 0 \tag{6.38}$$

and from this equation and (6.23, 37) it follows that

$$v_{[\mu\lambda} u_{\omega} \overset{1}{w}_{\lambda_1}\dots\overset{q}{w}_{\lambda_q]} = 0. \tag{6.39}$$

This equation expresses the fact that $v_{\mu\lambda}$ can be written as a sum of $q+1$ vector products, each of which contains one of the vectors u_{λ}, $\overset{1}{w}_{\lambda}, \dots$, $\overset{q}{w}_{\lambda_q}$ as a factor:

$$v_{\mu\lambda} = \overset{0}{v}_{[\mu} u_{\lambda]} + \overset{1}{v}_{[\mu}\overset{1}{w}_{\lambda]} + \dots + \overset{q}{v}_{[\mu}\overset{q}{w}_{\lambda]}. \tag{6.40}$$

Substituting this in (6.23) we get

$$W_{\mu\lambda_1\dots\lambda_q} = (\overset{0}{v}_{[\mu} u_{\lambda_1} + \overset{1}{v}_{[\mu}\overset{1}{w}_{\lambda_1})\overset{2}{w}_{\lambda_2}\dots\overset{q}{w}_{\lambda_q]}. \tag{6.41}$$

The $q+2$ vectors $\overset{0}{v}_{\lambda}$, u_{λ}, $\overset{1}{w}_{\lambda}, \dots$, $\overset{q}{w}_{\lambda}$ must be linearly independent because otherwise w would be a factor of W and this would imply $c_5 = 0$. If $\overset{1}{v}_{\lambda}$ depends linearly on $\overset{0}{v}_{\lambda}$, u_{λ}, $\overset{1}{w}_{\lambda}, \dots$, $\overset{q}{w}_{\lambda}$, W is a simple $(q+1)$-vector and we have $c_1 = q+1$ and $K = q+2$, since w is not a factor of W. Hence we have case I with $c_3 = q+1$ and $k = q+2$. If the $q+3$ vectors $\overset{0}{v}_{\lambda}$,

$\overset{1}{v}_\lambda$, $\overset{1}{u}_\lambda$, $w_\lambda, \ldots, \overset{q}{w}_\lambda$ are linearly independent, $c_1 = K = q+3$. Hence we have case II with $c_3 = k = q+2$. In these cases the arithmetic invariants take the values

$$\begin{array}{llllll} & c_1 & K & c_3 & k & c_5 \\ \text{C I:} & q+1 & q+2 & q+1 & q+2 & q-1 \\ \text{C II:} & q+3 & q+3 & q+2 & q+2 & q-1 \end{array} \qquad (6.42)$$

The case D is characterized by $c_5 = q$. Hence $S_5 = S$. Now every linear element satisfying S_1 satisfies also S_5, hence $S_1 = S_2$, $S_3 = S_4$ and $c_3 = k$. From this it follows that in case I we have $S_1 = S_2 = S_3 = S_4$ and $c_1 = K = c_3 = k = q+t$, t being an unknown integer. t cannot be zero, because otherwise $W = 0$ and $c_5 = 0$ in contradiction with $c = q$. If $t = 1$ or 2, W has to be simple and, since $S_1 = S_2$, w has to be a divisor of W. But then we would have the case A with $c_5 = 0$. Hence $t \geqslant 3$. In case II we have $c_1 = K = q+t+1$ and $c_3 = k = q+t$. Since the case II is always transformable into case I we also have in case II $t \geqslant 3$. Hence the arithmetic invariants take the values

$$\begin{array}{llllll} & c_1 & K & c_3 & k & c_5 \\ \text{D I:} & q+t & q+t & q+t & q+t & q \\ \text{D II:} & q+t+1 & q+t+1 & q+t & q+t & q \end{array} \left.\vphantom{\begin{array}{l} a \\ b \end{array}}\right\} t \geqslant 3. \qquad (6.43)$$

The fact that c_5 can only take the values 0, $q-1$ and q can be derived immediately from (6.14). If we write

$$D_{cb}^{\cdot\cdot x} \overset{\text{def}}{=} B_{cb}^{\mu\lambda} C_{\mu\lambda}^{\cdot\cdot x} \quad (b, c = 1, \ldots, \mathrm{p};\ x = \mathrm{p}+1, \ldots, \mathrm{n}), \qquad (6.44)$$

from (6.14) it follows that

$$C_\mu^x \, d\xi^\mu : C_\mu^y \, d\xi^\mu = D_{cb}^{\cdot\cdot x} : D_{cb}^{\cdot\cdot y} \quad (b, c = 1, \ldots, \mathrm{p};\ x, y = \mathrm{p}+1, \ldots, \mathrm{n}) \quad (6.45)$$

valid for all values of $b, c = 1, \ldots, \mathrm{p}$ and $x, y = \mathrm{p}+1, \ldots, \mathrm{n}$. Hence there are three possible cases. Either $D_{cb}^{\cdot\cdot x} = 0$ for all values of $b, c = 1, \ldots, \mathrm{p}$. Then S is complete and $c_5 = 0$. Or the quotient $D_{cb}^{\cdot\cdot x} : D_{cb}^{\cdot\cdot y}$ is independent of the choice of b and c for every choice of x and y. Then there exist $p+1$ linearly independent linear elements satisfying S_5 and among them one not satisfying S. Hence $c_5 = q-1$. Or the quotient $D_{cb}^{\cdot\cdot x} : D_{cb}^{\cdot\cdot y}$ depends on the choice of b and c. In that case there exist only p linearly independent linear elements satisfying S_5 and these lie in the κ-domain of B_b^κ. Hence $c_5 = q$ and $S_5 = S$.

The cases A, B, and C are special cases and all other cases belong to D. Now it is remarkable that in the case D I we have $c_1 = K = c_3 = k$. That implies that if in case I these four invariants are not equal, w belongs to one of the special cases A, B, or C.

With the help of only the elementary means at our disposal in this chapter it is not possible to derive a normal form for the case C. Now in Chapter VII, § 9, we shall prove that every simple covariant q-vector in an X_{q+2} can be written in the form

$$(\overset{1}{s}_{[\lambda_1}+\overset{1}{z}s_{[\lambda_1})(\alpha\overset{1}{z}_{\lambda_2}+\beta s_{\lambda_2})(\overset{3}{s}_{\lambda_3}+\overset{3}{z}s_{\lambda_3})\dots(\overset{q}{s}_{\lambda_q]}+\overset{q}{z}s_{\lambda_q]}) \tag{6.46}$$

containing the $2q+1$ functions $\overset{1}{z}, \overset{3}{z}, \dots, \overset{q}{z}, \overset{1}{s}, \overset{3}{s}, \dots, \overset{q}{s}, s, \alpha, \beta$ and their gradients. If among these functions there are just $q+2$ independent ones we have either the case B I with $\tau = 1$ or the case C I.

If the number of independent functions is $q+3$ we have either the case B II with $\tau = 1$, or the case C II, or the case D I with $t = 3$.

We collect results in the following table.

	c_1	K	c_3	k	c_5	S_5	Possible representations
A I	0	q	0	q	0	—	Grad. prod.
A II	$q+1$	$q+1$	q	q	0	—	Prod. of scalar and q grad.
B I	$q+2\tau-1$	$q+2\tau$	$q+2\tau-1$	$q+2\tau$	$q-1$ } $\tau \geqslant 1$	Compl.	Prod. of vector of class $2\tau+1$ and $q-1$ grad.
B II	$q+2\tau+1$	$q+2\tau+1$	$q+2\tau$	$q+2\tau$	$q-1$		Prod. of vector of class $2\tau+2$ and $q-1$ grad.
C I	$q+1$	$q+2$	$q+1$	$q+2$	$q-1$	Not compl.	Prod. of $q-1$ vectors of class $\leqslant 3$ and one vector of class $\leqslant 4$.
C II	$q+3$	$q+3$	$q+2$	$q+2$	$q-1$		
D I	$q+t$	$q+t$	$q+t$	$q+t$	q } $t \geqslant 3$	$S_5 = S$ Not compl.	General case.
D II	$q+t+1$	$q+t+1$	$q+t$	$q+t$	q		

(6.47)

It is possible to get a subdivision of the cases C and D by determining the maximum number of gradient vectors contained as factors in $w_{\lambda_1\dots\lambda_q}$. To this end we consider the system S'

$$B_b^\mu \partial_\mu f = 0 \quad (b = 1,\dots, \mathrm{p}) \tag{6.48}$$

adjoint to S. Adding the equations (cf. III, §§ 2, 11)

$$B_{[c}^\nu \partial_{|\nu|} B_{b]}^\mu \partial_\mu f = 0 \quad (b, c = 1,\dots, \mathrm{p}) \tag{6.49}$$

we get the first derived system of S', denoted by $S'_{(1)}$, containing $\mathrm{p}+\mu_1$ equations. The adjoint system $S_{(1)}$ is the first derived system of S.

By a suitable linear transformation in x we can always show that $S_{(1)}$ consists of the $q-\mu_1$ equations (cf. III, § 11)

$$C_{\mu}^{\mathrm{p}+\mu_1+1} d\xi^{\mu} = 0, \quad ..., \quad C_{\mu}^{\mathrm{n}} d\xi^{\mu} = 0. \tag{6.50}$$

Then it follows that

$$(a) \quad D_{\dot{c}\dot{b}}^{\cdot\cdot\mathfrak{a}} \neq 0, \qquad (b) \quad D_{\dot{c}\dot{b}}^{\cdot\cdot\mathfrak{x}} = 0 \quad (b, c = 1,..., \mathrm{p};\ \mathfrak{a} = \mathrm{p}+1,..., \mathrm{p}+\mu_1; \ \mathfrak{x} = \mathrm{p}+\mu_1+1,..., \mathrm{n}) \tag{6.51}$$

and (6.51 b) can be written in the form (cf. III, § 11):

$$C_{\dot{\mu}\dot{\lambda}}^{\cdot\cdot\mathfrak{x}} \equiv 0 \ (\mathrm{mod}\ C_{\lambda}^{\mathfrak{x}}) \quad (\mathfrak{x} = \mathrm{p}+\mu_1+1,..., \mathrm{n}). \tag{6.52}$$

If and only if $\mu_1 = 1$ and if $S_{(1)}$ is complete, $w_{\lambda_1...\lambda_q}$ has just $q-1$ gradient factors and we have the case B. Indeed, for $\mu_1 = 1$ the system S_5 reduces to (cf. (6.14))

$$C_{\mu}^{\mathfrak{x}} D_{\dot{c}\dot{b}}^{\cdot\cdot\mathrm{p}+1} d\xi^{\mu} = 0 \quad (\mathfrak{x} = \mathrm{p}+2,..., \mathrm{n}) \tag{6.53}$$

and consequently coincides with $S_{(1)}$. If $\mu_1 > 1$ and if $S_{(1)}$ is complete, $w_{\lambda_1...\lambda_q}$ has just $q-\mu_1$ gradient factors. If $S_{(1)}$ is not complete, we treat $S_{(1)}$ in the same way and get the second derived system $S_{(2)}$ consisting of $q-\mu_1-\mu_2$ equations. If this system is complete the number of gradient factors is $q-\mu_1-\mu_2$. If it is not complete we can proceed in the same way and we get after a number of steps $\leqslant q$ either to the number of gradient factors or to the conclusion that there are no gradient factors at all. In this way, using the derived systems $S_{(1)}$, $S_{(2)}$, etc., we get a subdivision of the cases C and D.

As an example we will derive some normal forms for the simple covariant q-vectors in X_n, $n = q+2$. From the table (6.47) it is clear that only the cases A I, A II, B I, and C I can occur. Since a simple q-vector in E_{q+2} is determined by $2q+1$ numbers, a normal form will contain at most $2q+1$ functions. According to (6.46) we have in abbreviated notation

$$w = (\underset{1}{\bar{s}} + \underset{1}{z}\,\bar{s})(\alpha\,\underset{1}{\bar{z}} + \beta\,\bar{s})(\underset{3}{\bar{s}} + \underset{3}{z}\,\bar{s})...(\underset{q}{\bar{s}} + \underset{q}{z}\,\bar{s}). \tag{6.54}$$

If $\alpha = 0$ or if s, $\underset{1}{s}$, $\underset{1}{z}$, $\underset{3}{s}$, $\underset{4}{s}$,..., $\underset{q}{s}$ are not independent, $\bar{s}$ is a divisor of w and accordingly $\underset{1}{\bar{s}}$, $\underset{3}{\bar{s}}$, $\underset{4}{\bar{s}}$,..., $\underset{q}{\bar{s}}$ and, for $\alpha \neq 0$, $\underset{1}{\bar{z}}$ also are divisors of w. But this is possible if and only if $\lfloor w \rfloor$ is a gradient product. Hence we have the case A I with the canonical form

$$w = \bar{1}\,\bar{2}...\bar{q} \quad (\text{case A I};\ \mu_1, \mu_2,... = 0)\dagger \tag{6.55}$$

or the case A II with the canonical form

$$w = \xi^{q+1}\,\bar{1}\,\bar{2}...\bar{q} \quad (\text{case A II};\ \mu_1, \mu_2,... = 0). \tag{6.56}$$

† In these formulae we have written $\bar{1}$ for the gradient $\bar{\xi}^1$.

If $\alpha \neq 0$ and if $\underset{1}{s}, \underset{1}{s}, \underset{3}{z}, \underset{4}{s}, s, \ldots, \underset{q}{s}$ are independent we may choose $\xi^1 = \underset{1}{s}$, $\xi^2 = \underset{1}{z}$, $\xi^3 = \underset{3}{s}, \ldots, \xi^q = \underset{q}{s}$, $\xi^{n-1} = s$. Then, writing $\psi = \beta/\alpha$, $\underset{3}{z} = \phi^3, \ldots$, $\underset{q}{z} = \phi^q$, (6.54) takes the form

$$w = \alpha(\bar{1}+\xi^2\,\overline{n-1})(\bar{2}+\psi\,\overline{n-1})(\bar{3}+\phi^3\,\overline{n-1})\ldots(\bar{q}+\phi^q\,\overline{n-1}). \quad (6.57)$$

This is a normal form for general simple q-vectors with

$$K > q+1 = n-1,$$

containing $2q+1$ functions $\xi^1, \ldots, \xi^q, \xi^{n-1}, \alpha, \psi, \phi^3, \ldots, \phi^q$.

The system S is

$$\begin{aligned} C^{\mathfrak{p}+1}_\lambda d\xi^\lambda &= d\xi^1+\xi^2\,d\xi^{n-1} = 0,\\ C^{\mathfrak{p}+2}_\lambda d\xi^\lambda &= d\xi^2+\psi\,d\xi^{n-1} = 0,\\ C^{\mathfrak{p}+3}_\lambda d\xi^\lambda &= d\xi^3+\phi^3\,d\xi^{n-1} = 0,\\ &\cdots\cdots\cdots\\ C^{\mathfrak{n}}_\lambda d\xi^\lambda &= d\xi^q+\phi^q\,d\xi^{n-1} = 0, \end{aligned} \quad (6.58)$$

and the system S' has the form

$$\left.\begin{aligned} \partial_n f &= 0,\\ (\partial_{n-1}-\xi^2\partial_1-\psi\partial_2-\phi^{\mathfrak{a}}\partial_{\mathfrak{a}})f &= 0 \end{aligned}\right\} \quad (\mathfrak{a} = 3,\ldots,q). \quad (6.59)$$

To form $S'_{(1)}$ we have to add the equation

$$(\psi_n\,\partial_2+\phi^{\mathfrak{a}}_n\,\partial_{\mathfrak{a}})f = 0 \quad (\psi_n \overset{\text{def}}{=} \partial_n\psi;\ \phi^{\mathfrak{a}}_n \overset{\text{def}}{=} \partial_n\phi^{\mathfrak{a}};\ \mathfrak{a} = 3,\ldots,q). \quad (6.60)$$

Accordingly the system $S_{(1)}$ has the form

$$\left.\begin{aligned} d\xi^1+\xi^2\,d\xi^{n-1} &= 0,\\ \phi^{\mathfrak{a}}_n\,d\xi^2-\psi_n\,d\xi^{\mathfrak{a}}+(\phi^{\mathfrak{a}}_n\psi-\phi^{\mathfrak{a}}\psi_n)\,d\xi^{n-1} &= 0 \end{aligned}\right\} \quad (\mathfrak{a} = 3,\ldots,q) \quad (6.61)$$

and belongs to a simple $(q-1)$-vector (determined to within a scalar factor)

$$\overset{(1)}{w} = C^{\mathfrak{p}+1}(\phi^3_n\,C^{\mathfrak{p}+2}-\psi_n\,C^{\mathfrak{p}+3})\ldots(\phi^q_n\,C^{\mathfrak{n}-1}-\psi_n\,C^{\mathfrak{n}}). \quad (6.62)$$

S is complete if and only if

$$\psi_n = 0, \qquad \phi^{\mathfrak{a}}_n = 0 \quad (\mathfrak{a} = 3,\ldots,q). \quad (6.63)$$

Then we have the case A I or A II already mentioned above. If the conditions (6.63) are not satisfied, we have $\mu_1 = 1$ and either the case B I or the case C I. $S_{(1)}$ coincides with S_5. First we assume that $\psi_n \neq 0$. Then we may choose $\xi^n = \psi$ and $S'_{(1)}$ takes the form

$$\left.\begin{aligned} \partial_n f &= 0\\ (\partial_{n-1}-\xi^2\partial_1-\xi^n\partial_2-\phi^{\mathfrak{a}}\partial_{\mathfrak{a}})f &= 0\\ (\partial_2+\phi^{\mathfrak{a}}_n\,\partial_{\mathfrak{a}})f &= 0 \end{aligned}\right\} \quad (\mathfrak{a} = 3,\ldots,q). \quad (6.64)$$

To form $S'_{(2)}$ we have to add the equations

$$\begin{aligned} \phi^{\mathfrak{a}}_{nn}\,\partial_{\mathfrak{a}} f &= 0 \\ (\phi^{\mathfrak{a}}_{n\,n-1}-\xi^2\phi^{\mathfrak{a}}_{n\,1}-\xi^n\phi^{\mathfrak{a}}_{n\,2}-\phi^{\mathfrak{b}}\phi^{\mathfrak{a}}_{n\mathfrak{b}}+\phi^{\mathfrak{a}}_{2}+\phi^{\mathfrak{b}}_{n}\phi^{\mathfrak{a}}_{\mathfrak{b}})\partial_{\mathfrak{a}} f+\partial_1 f &= 0 \end{aligned} \quad (\mathfrak{a},\mathfrak{b} = 3,\ldots,q). \tag{6.65}$$

The last equation can never vanish, hence $\mu_2 = 1$ or $\mu_2 = 2$. This proves that S_1 cannot be complete and that accordingly we have the case C I. If and only if

$$\phi^{\mathfrak{a}}_{nn} = 0 \quad (\mathfrak{a} = 3,\ldots,q), \tag{6.66}$$

we have $\mu_2 = 1$. Continuing in this way all the invariants $\mu_1,\ldots,\mu_q$ can be determined.

Now we assume that $\psi_n = 0$ and that at least one of the $\phi^{\mathfrak{a}}_n$ is $\neq 0$. By a suitable change of indices we can always arrange that $\phi^3_n \neq 0$. Then we may choose $\xi^n = \phi^3$ and $S'_{(1)}$ takes the form

$$\begin{aligned} \partial_n f &= 0 \\ (\partial_{n-1}-\xi^2\partial_1-\psi\partial_2-\xi^n\partial_3-\phi^{\mathfrak{x}}\partial_{\mathfrak{x}})f &= 0 \quad (\mathfrak{x} = 4,\ldots,q). \\ (\partial_3+\phi^{\mathfrak{x}}_n\,\partial_{\mathfrak{x}})f &= 0 \end{aligned} \tag{6.67}$$

To form $S'_{(2)}$ we have to add the equations

$$\begin{aligned} &\phi^{\mathfrak{x}}_{nn}\,\partial_{\mathfrak{x}} f = 0, \\ &(\phi^{\mathfrak{x}}_{n\,n-1}-\xi^2\phi^{\mathfrak{x}}_{n\,1}-\psi\phi^{\mathfrak{x}}_{n\,2}-\xi^n\phi^{\mathfrak{x}}_{n\,3}-\phi^{\mathfrak{y}}\phi^{\mathfrak{x}}_{n\mathfrak{y}}+\phi^{\mathfrak{x}}_{3}+\phi^{\mathfrak{y}}_{n}\phi^{\mathfrak{x}}_{\mathfrak{y}})\partial_{\mathfrak{x}} f+ \\ &\qquad +(\psi_3+\phi^{\mathfrak{x}}_n\,\partial_{\mathfrak{x}}\psi)\partial_2 f = 0 \quad (\mathfrak{x},\mathfrak{y} = 4,\ldots,q). \end{aligned} \tag{6.68}$$

If

$$\begin{aligned} &\phi^{\mathfrak{x}}_{nn} = 0, \qquad \psi_3+\phi^{\mathfrak{x}}_n\,\partial_{\mathfrak{x}}\psi = 0, \\ &\phi^{\mathfrak{x}}_{n\,n-1}-\xi^2\phi^{\mathfrak{x}}_{n\,1}-\psi\phi^{\mathfrak{x}}_{n\,2}-\xi^n\phi^{\mathfrak{x}}_{n\,3}-\phi^{\mathfrak{y}}\phi^{\mathfrak{x}}_{n\mathfrak{y}}+\phi^{\mathfrak{x}}_{3}+\phi^{\mathfrak{y}}_{n}\phi^{\mathfrak{x}}_{\mathfrak{y}} = 0 \quad (\mathfrak{x} = 4,\ldots,q), \end{aligned} \tag{6.69}$$

all terms in (6.68) vanish and accordingly $S'_{(1)}$ is complete and has $q-1$ independent solutions. Hence we have the case B I with $q-1$ gradient factors. If the coordinate system is chosen in such a way that $\overset{1}{e}_\lambda,\ldots,\overset{q-1}{e}_\lambda$ are these gradient factors, and if the last vector is u_λ, the section of u_λ with the X_3's with the equations $\xi^1 = \text{const.},\ldots,\xi^{q-1} = \text{const.}$ has class 3, because otherwise we would have the case A. Hence w can be written in the form

$$w_{\lambda_1\ldots\lambda_q} = \overset{1}{e}_{[\lambda_1}\cdots\overset{q-1}{e}_{\lambda_{q-1}}(t_{\lambda_q]}+uv_{\lambda_q]}). \tag{6.70}$$

The class of w being $q+2$, the variables $\xi^1,\ldots,\xi^{q-1}$, t, u, v are independent and consequently t, u, and v can be chosen as the last three coordinates. Then we get the canonical form

$$w = \overline{1\ldots q-1}(\bar{q}+\xi^{n-1}\bar{n}) \quad (\text{case B I: } \mu_1 = 1,\ \mu_2 = 0,\ldots,\mu_q = 0). \tag{6.71}$$

If the conditions (6.69) are not satisfied we have either $\mu_2 = 1$ or $\mu_2 = 2$ and the other invariants μ can be obtained by forming the other derived systems of (6.61).

It may happen that the invariants μ are all 1 or 0. In that case there is a number t such that $\mu_1 = \mu_2 = \ldots = \mu_t = 1$ and that all other μ's are zero, since the tth derived system $S_{(t)}$ is complete. A system S with this property is called a *special system*.† It is either in the case A ($\mu_1 = 0$) or in the case B I ($\mu_2 = 0$) or in the *special case* C I. If the quantities belonging to the derived systems $S_{(1)}, \ldots, S_{(t)}$ are

$$\begin{array}{l} \overset{(1)}{w}_{\lambda_1 \ldots \lambda_{q-1}}, \\ \cdot \quad \cdot \quad \cdot \\ \overset{(t)}{w}_{\lambda_1 \ldots \lambda_{q-t}}, \end{array} \tag{6.72}$$

where each of them is defined to within a scalar factor and each is a divisor of the preceding ones, the last one can be chosen as a gradient product. If $t > 1$ the class of $\overset{(1)}{w}$ must be $> q$ because $S_{(1)}$ is not complete. If the class of $\overset{(1)}{w}$ is $q+1$, we have $\mu_2 = 1$ because $\overset{(1)}{w}$ is in the same condition as w.

Now let k_i be the similarity class of $\overset{(i)}{w}$. Then we will prove that $k_i = q+2-i$ $(i = 1, \ldots, t-1)$. The similarity class k of w is equal to q plus the c-rank of $D_{\dot{c}\dot{b}}^{\ x}$. Now for $\mu_1 = 1$ we have

$$D_{\dot{c}\dot{b}}^{\ \mathrm{p}+2} = 0, \quad \ldots, \quad D_{\dot{c}\dot{b}}^{\ \mathrm{n}} = 0 \quad (b, c = 1, \ldots, \mathrm{p}) \tag{6.73}$$

and the c-rank of $D_{\dot{c}\dot{b}}^{\ \mathrm{p}+1}$ is even. This proves that k is equal to q plus an even number. Hence, if $\mu_1 = 1$ and $k \leqslant q+3$ it follows that $k \leqslant q+2$. Now here we have $q+2 = n$ and this implies that $k = q+2$. Since $\overset{(1)}{w}$ is a divisor of w we have $k_1 \leqslant q+2$. Hence $k_1 \leqslant (q-1)+3$ and $\mu_2 = 1$ and from this it follows that $k_1 = q+1$. Now suppose it has already been proved that $k_i = q+2-i$ for some value of $i \leqslant t-2$. Then we know that $k_{i+1} \leqslant q+2-i$. Hence $k_{i+1} \leqslant (q-i-1)+3$ and $\mu_{i+2} = 1$, and from this it follows that $k_{i+1} = q+1-i$. That proves the proposition. $\overset{(t)}{w}$ is a gradient product and its class is $q-t$.

The coordinates can now be chosen in such a way that

$$\overset{(t)}{w} = \bar{1} \ldots \overline{q-t}. \tag{6.74}$$

Then, since $\overset{(t-1)}{w}$ is in case B I the coordinates $\xi^{q-t+1}, \xi^{q-t+2}, \ldots, \xi^n$ can be chosen in such a way that

$$\overset{(t-1)}{w} = \bar{1} \ldots \overline{q-t}(\overline{q-t+1} + \xi^{q-t+2}\bar{n}). \tag{6.75}$$

† Cf. Goursat 1922. 1, p. 326.

The quantity $\overset{(t-2)}{w}$ depends on $q-t+4$ variables. Hence, if ξ^{q-t+3} is chosen in such a way that $\overset{(t-2)}{w}$ depends on $\xi^1,\dots,\xi^{q-t+3}$, ξ^n and if

$$\overset{(t-2)}{w} = \overset{(t-1)}{w}\, u, \tag{6.76}$$

the factor u can be taken in the form

$$u = \kappa\,\overline{q-t+2}+\lambda\,\overline{q-t+3}+\mu\bar{n}. \tag{6.77}$$

Now $S_{(t-1)}$ is the first derived system of $S_{(t-2)}$, hence the rotation of $\overline{q-t+1}+\xi^{q-t+2}\bar{n}$ has to be zero mod $\bar{1},\dots,\overline{q-t}$, $\overline{q-t+1}+\xi^{q-t+2}\bar{n}$, u, or

$$\overline{q-t+2}\,\bar{n} \equiv 0 \pmod{u}, \tag{6.78}$$

and this is only possible if $\lambda = 0$. Neither κ nor μ can vanish because otherwise w would contain more than $q-t$ gradient factors. Taking $\kappa = 1$ and chosing μ/κ as $(q-t+3)$th coordinate instead of ξ^{q-t+3} we get

$$\overset{(t-2)}{w} = \bar{1}\dots\overline{q-t}(\overline{q-t+1}+\xi^{q-t+2}\bar{n})(\overline{q-t+2}+\xi^{q-t+3}\bar{n}). \tag{6.79}$$

Continuing in this way we get at last the normal form

$$w = \alpha\,\bar{1}\dots\overline{q-t}(\overline{q-t+1}+\xi^{q-t+2}\bar{n})(\overline{q-t+2}+\xi^{q-t+3}\bar{n})\dots(\overline{n-2}+\xi^{n-1}\bar{n})$$

(C I, special case; $\mu_1 = \mu_2 = \dots = \mu_t = 1$; $\mu_{t+1} = \mu_{t+2} = \dots = \mu_q = 0$; $t > 1$) (6.80)

for the special case C I for $q+2 = n$.

Using this normal form, S and S' take the form

$$(S)\quad \begin{aligned} &d\xi^1 = 0,\quad \dots,\quad d\xi^{q-t} = 0,\\ &d\xi^{q-t+1}+\xi^{q-t+2}\,d\xi^n = 0,\\ &\cdot\quad\cdot\quad\cdot\quad\cdot\quad\cdot\quad\cdot\quad\cdot\\ &d\xi^{n-2}+\xi^{n-1}\,d\xi^n = 0, \end{aligned} \tag{6.81}$$

$$(S')\quad \begin{aligned} &\partial_{n-1}f = 0,\\ &(\xi^{q-t+2}\partial_{q-t+1}+\dots+\xi^{n-1}\partial_{n-2}-\partial_n)f = 0, \end{aligned} \tag{6.82}$$

$S_1 = S_3$ and $S'_1 = S'_3$ take the form

$$(S_1 = S_3)\quad d\xi^1 = 0,\quad \dots,\quad d\xi^{n-2} = 0;\qquad d\xi^n = 0, \tag{6.83}$$

$$(S'_1 = S'_3)\qquad \partial_{n-1}f = 0, \tag{6.84}$$

and $S_2 = S_4$ takes the form

$$(S_2 = S_4)\qquad d\xi^\kappa = 0. \tag{6.85}$$

If S is not complete, either $\psi_n \neq 0$ or one of the $\phi_n^{\mathfrak{a}}$ is $\neq 0$. In this latter case, by interchanging indices we can always arrange that $\phi_n^3 \neq 0$. If $\psi_n \neq 0$ we may choose $\xi^n = \psi$ and we get the normal form for the case C I:

$$w = (\bar{1}+\xi^2\,\overline{n-1})(\bar{2}+\xi^n\,\overline{n-1})(\bar{3}+\phi^3\,\overline{n-1})\dots(\bar{q}+\phi^q\,\overline{n-1}). \tag{6.86}$$

If $\phi^3_n \neq 0$ we may choose $\xi^n = \phi^3$ and we get the normal form

$$w = (\bar{1}+\xi^2\,\overline{n-1})(\bar{2}+\psi\,\overline{n-1})(\bar{3}+\xi^n\,\overline{n-1})(\bar{4}+\phi^4\,\overline{n-1})...(\bar{q}+\phi^q\,\overline{n-1}) \tag{6.87}$$

for the case C I with the condition that the equations (6.69) are not satisfied.

With the elementary methods developed in this chapter it is not possible to get a complete classification of simple q-vector fields. But they show clearly the way by which a better classification may be obtained. As a first step we will have to look not only for the maximum number of gradient factors but also for the maximum number of vector divisors of class 3, 5, etc. This will be made possible by the methods developed in Chapter VII.

EXERCISES†

1. Prove that every bivector in X_4 can be written in one of the normal forms:

$$\text{Case A I } (\mu_1 = 0, \mu_2 = 0): \quad \bar{1}\,\bar{2};$$

$$\text{Case A II } (\mu_1 = 0, \mu_2 = 0): \quad \xi^3\bar{1}\,\bar{2};$$

$$\text{Case B I } (\mu_1 = 1, \mu_2 = 0): \quad \bar{1}(\bar{2}+\xi^3\bar{4});$$

$$\text{Special Case C I } (\mu_1 = 1, \mu_2 = 1): \quad \alpha(\bar{1}+\xi^2\bar{3})(\bar{2}+\xi^4\bar{3}).$$

2. Prove that every trivector in X_5 can be written in one of the normal forms:

$$\text{Case A I } (\mu_1 = 0, \mu_2 = 0, \mu_3 = 0): \quad \bar{1}\,\bar{2}\,\bar{3};$$

$$\text{Case A II } (\mu_1 = 0, \mu_2 = 0, \mu_3 = 0): \quad \xi^4\,\bar{1}\,\bar{2}\,\bar{3};$$

$$\text{Case B I } (\mu_1 = 1, \mu_2 = 0, \mu_3 = 0): \quad \bar{1}\,\bar{2}(\bar{3}+\xi^4\,\bar{5});$$

$$\text{Special Case C I } (\mu_1 = 1, \mu_2 = 1, \mu_3 = 0): \quad \alpha\,\bar{1}(\bar{2}+\xi^3\,\bar{5})(\bar{3}+\xi^4\,\bar{5});$$

$$(\mu_1 = 1, \mu_2 = 1, \mu_3 = 1): \quad \alpha(\bar{1}+\xi^2\,\bar{5})(\bar{2}+\xi^3\,\bar{5})(\bar{3}+\xi^4\,\bar{5});$$

$$\text{General Case C I } (\mu_1 = 1, \mu_2 = 2): \quad \begin{cases} \alpha(\bar{1}+\xi^2\,\bar{4})(\bar{2}+\xi^5\,\bar{4})(\bar{3}+\phi\,\bar{4}) & (\phi_{55} \neq 0), \\ \alpha(\bar{1}+\xi^2\,\bar{4})(\bar{2}+\psi\,\bar{4})(\bar{3}+\xi^5\,\bar{4}) & (\psi_{55} \neq 0); \end{cases}$$

and that the last two normal forms are equivalent.

3. If in a system S

$$w_{\lambda_1...\lambda_q}\,d\xi^{\lambda_1} = 0 \tag{3 α}$$

$w_{\lambda_1...\lambda_q}$ does not possess $v+1$ independent gradient factors and if in its zth derived system $S_{(z)}$

$$\overset{(z)}{w}_{\lambda_1...\lambda_s}\,d\xi^{\lambda_1} = 0 \quad (z < q) \tag{3 β}$$

$\overset{(z)}{w}_{\lambda_1...\lambda_s}$ has a simple divisor $u_{\lambda_1...\lambda_v}$ $(0 < v < s)$ such that the system

$$u_{\lambda_1...\lambda_v}\,d\xi^{\lambda_1} = 0 \tag{3 γ}$$

† Cf. the suggestions at the end of the book.

is in the special case C I, $w_{\lambda_1...\lambda_q}$ has a simple divisor $U_{\lambda_1...\lambda_{v+2}}$ such that

$$U_{\lambda_1...\lambda_{v+2}}\, d\xi^{\lambda_1} = 0 \tag{3 δ}$$

is in the special case C I (Goursat).†

4. The system S

$$d\xi^1+\phi^1\, d\xi^{n-1} = 0,$$
$$\cdot \quad \cdot \quad \cdot \quad \cdot \quad \cdot \quad \cdot \quad \cdot$$
$$d\xi^{n-2}+\phi^{n-2}\, d\xi^{n-1} = 0 \tag{4 α}$$

is a special system if $\phi^1,..., \phi^{n-2}$ are linear in ξ^κ.

† 1922. 1, p. 334. Goursat makes the condition that w does not possess any gradient factors. This is not necessary.

VI

CONTACT TRANSFORMATIONS†

1. Solution of the inner problem for $q = 1$

FROM the definition of an enveloped X_m of a field of $(n-1)$-directions $\lfloor w_\lambda \rfloor$ it follows that an X_m is enveloped if and only if the section of w_λ with X_m vanishes. Hence, K being the class of w_λ, *the construction of a normal system of enveloped X_m's is equivalent to the construction of a system of $n-m$ functions with index K* (cf. IV, § 4).‡ Now for $\kappa = K$, $S = n-m$ we get from the conditions (IV, 4.37) of Theorem IV.2

$$2(n-m) \geqslant K = 2\rho+\epsilon \quad (\epsilon = 1 \text{ or } 0) \tag{1.1}$$

and from this it follows that the maximum value ν of m is

$$\nu = n-\rho-\epsilon = n-\frac{k+1}{2}. \tag{1.2}$$

In order to determine a normal system of enveloped X_ν's of the field w_λ in the canonical form

$$w_\lambda = \epsilon \partial_\lambda x^0 + p_i \partial_\lambda x^i \quad (i = 1,..., \rho;\ \epsilon = 1 \text{ or } 0) \tag{1.3}$$

the rules of IV, § 6, with

$$\kappa = 2\rho+\epsilon, \qquad S = n-\nu = \rho+\epsilon \tag{1.4}$$

may be applied. Then a system of $\rho+\epsilon$ equations arises,

$$\epsilon x^0 = \text{const.}, \qquad x^k = \text{const.} \quad (k = 1,..., \rho), \tag{1.5}$$

annihilating w_λ and representing a normal system of $\infty^{\rho+\epsilon}$ enveloped X_ν's.

The equations of the supports of rotation, the supports and the characteristics of w_λ are (cf. IV, § 5):

Supports of rotation ($\infty^{2\rho}$ $X_{n-2\rho}$'s) : $x^k = \text{const.}$, $p_i = \text{const.}$; (1.6)

Supports ($\infty^{2\rho+\epsilon}$ $X_{n-2\rho-\epsilon}$'s) : $\epsilon x^0 = \text{const.}$, $x^k = \text{const.}$, $p_i = \text{const.}$; (1.7)

Characteristics ($\infty^{2\rho+2\epsilon-1}$ $X_{n-2\rho-2\epsilon+1}$'s) : $\epsilon x^0 = \text{const.}$, $x^k = \text{const.}$,

$$\epsilon p_1 = \text{const.},\ p_1 : p_2 : \ldots : p_\rho = \text{const.} \quad (k, i = 1,..., \rho), \tag{1.8}$$

and from these equations we see that every enveloped X_ν consists for

† General references: Lie 1890. 1; Cartan 1899. 1; v. Weber 1900. 1; Whittaker 1917. 1; Goursat 1921. 1; Engel and Faber 1932. 1; Eisenhart 1933. 1.

‡ We only consider enveloped X_m's in a region of constant class (cf. IV, § 2). For the construction of singular enveloped X_m's cf. Cartan 1899. 1.

$\epsilon = 0$ of ∞^{ρ} supports (= supp. of rot.) and of $\infty^{\rho-1}$ characteristics, and for $\epsilon = 1$ of ∞^{ρ} supports (= characteristics).

When the X_n is reduced with respect to the normal system of $\infty^{2\rho+\epsilon}$ supports (cf. II, § 4), that is, when w_λ is looked upon as a vector field in the $X_{2\rho+\epsilon}$ of the variables ϵx^0, x^k, p_i, every support is reduced to a point and the $\infty^{\rho+\epsilon}$ X_ν's become the $\infty^{\rho+\epsilon}$ enveloped X_ρ's in this $X_{2\rho+\epsilon}$.

Enveloped normal systems determined in this way for different choices of the canonical form of w_λ are in general different. If we have, for instance, the field in E_3

$$w_\lambda = \overset{1}{e}_\lambda + \xi^2 \overset{3}{e}_\lambda \tag{1.9}$$

in ordinary cartesian coordinates, it is evident that the equations

$$\xi^1 = \text{const.}, \qquad \xi^3 = \text{const.} \tag{1.10}$$

represent a normal system of ∞^2 enveloped straight lines parallel to the 2-axis. If this same field is written in the canonical form

$$w_\lambda = \partial_\lambda(\xi^1 + \xi^2\xi^3) - \xi^3 \overset{2}{e}_\lambda \tag{1.11}$$

we see that there exists a normal system of ∞^2 enveloped straight lines with the equations

$$\xi^1 + \xi^2\xi^3 = \text{const.}, \qquad \xi^2 = \text{const.} \tag{1.12}$$

lying in planes parallel to the 3, 1-plane.†

2. Determination of all enveloped X_m's of a field w_λ without any integration if a canonical representation of w_λ is given

An enveloped normal system of X_ν's

$$\overset{1}{f}(\xi^\kappa) = \text{const.}, \quad \ldots, \quad \overset{\rho+\epsilon}{f}(\xi^\kappa) = \text{const.} \tag{2.1}$$

of a field w_λ being given, w_λ can be expressed linearly in the gradients of $\overset{1}{f}, \ldots, \overset{\rho+\epsilon}{f}$. Then we have for $\epsilon = 0$ a canonical representation of w_λ and for $\epsilon = 1$ at least a canonical representation of $\lfloor w_\lambda \rfloor$. From this it follows that all normal systems of enveloped X_ν's are known if all canonical representations of the field are known.

We will prove now that every single enveloped X_m ($m \leqslant \nu$) can be obtained without any integration, provided that a canonical representation be given and that the X_m lies in a region of constant rank of the field.

Let (1.3) be the given canonical form, and let the normal system

† The general solution of $d\xi^1 + \xi^2\, d\xi^3 = 0$ has either the form (1.10) or the form $\xi^1 = f(\alpha)$, $\xi^2 = -f'(\alpha)$, $\xi^3 = \alpha$, containing one arbitrary function of one parameter (cf. Goursat 1922. 1, p. 331).

with the $\rho+\epsilon$ equations (1.5) be denoted by N. Every enveloped X_m $(1 \leqslant m \leqslant \nu)$ has nothing or at least an $X_{\nu+m-n+1}$ in common with each of the $\infty^{n-\nu}$ X_ν's of N because the tangent E_m of the X_m and the tangent E_ν of X_ν lie at each point in the E_{n-1} of w_λ. In general the section will be an $X_{\nu+m-n+\tau}$ $(1 \leqslant \tau \leqslant n-\nu,\ n-\nu-m \leqslant \tau \leqslant n-m)$. If the X_m lies in a region of constant rank of w_λ, at every point of X_m there exists just one X_ν of N and the ∞^m X_ν's determine an $X_{n-\tau}$ whose tangent $E_{n-\tau}$ contains at every point the tangent E_ν of the X_ν of N through that point. Now we will prove the very remarkable proposition *that in this $X_{n-\tau}$ there exists one and only one enveloped X_ν containing the X_m, and that this X_ν does not belong to N if $n-\tau > \nu$.*

PROOF. We use $\epsilon x^0, x^k, p_i$ $(k, i = 1,\dots,\rho)$ as the first $2\rho+\epsilon$ coordinates of (κ) and denote the other $n-2\rho-\epsilon$ coordinates by $\xi^{2\rho+\epsilon+1},\dots,\xi^n$. Let the enveloped X_m be given by the equations

$$H^{\mathfrak{a}}(\epsilon x^0, x^k, p_i, \xi^{2\rho+\epsilon+1},\dots,\xi^n) = 0 \quad (\mathfrak{a} = \mathrm{m}+1,\dots,\mathrm{n}). \tag{2.2}$$

The rank of the system $H^{\mathfrak{a}}$ in the neighbourhood of a point of the X_m has the highest possible value, viz. $n-m$. If now the rank of the system $H^{\mathfrak{a}}$ with respect to the $n-\rho-\epsilon$ variables p_i, $\xi^{2\rho+\epsilon+1},\dots,\ \xi^n$ were also $n-m$ in that neighbourhood, $n-m$ of these variables could be solved from (2.2) as functions of the other $m-\rho-\epsilon$ variables and the ϵx^0, x^k. These solutions, substituted in (1.3), are to make w_λ vanish. For $\epsilon = 1$ this is impossible because $\partial_\lambda x^0$ could not vanish. For $\epsilon = 0$ this vanishing of w_λ would mean that in the region considered (2.2) would be equivalent to a system consisting of the ρ equations

$$p_i = 0 \quad (i = 1,\dots,\rho) \tag{2.3}$$

and $n-m-\rho$ equations containing only x^k, $\xi^{2\rho+1},\dots,\ \xi^n$. Now (2.3) represents the points of diminished rank (cf. IV, § 2) and this is in contradiction with our supposition. Hence, in both cases, the rank of the system $H^{\mathfrak{a}}$ with respect to p_i, $\xi^{2\rho+\epsilon+1},\dots,\ \xi^n$ is $< n-m$. If this rank is $n-m-\tau'$ $(\tau' \geqslant 1)$, according to the theorem of elimination II.7 there exist just τ' relations between the ϵx^0, x^k and consequently (2.2) is equivalent to a system of $n-m$ equations of the form

$$\begin{aligned} &(a) \quad F^a(\epsilon x^0, x^k) = 0,\\ &(b) \quad F^x(\epsilon x^0, x^k, p_i, \xi^{2\rho+\epsilon+1},\dots,\xi^n) = 0\\ &(a = 1,\dots,\tau';\ x = \tau'+1,\dots,\ n-m;\ i, k = 1,\dots,\rho). \end{aligned} \tag{2.4}$$

The rank of the system F^x with respect to p_i, $\xi^{2\rho+\epsilon+1},\dots,\xi^n$ has to be $n-m-\tau'$ at the null points of (2.4) because otherwise the rank of the system F^a, F^x could not be $n-m$ at these points. The section of X_m with an X_ν of N is obtained if in (2.4) the variables ϵx^0 and x^k are replaced by the constant values belonging to this special X_ν in the equations (1.5). Now the ν variables p_i, $\xi^{2\rho+\epsilon+1},\ldots, \xi^n$ may be used as coordinates in the X_ν and the system of $n-m-\tau'$ equations (2.4 b), whose rank must have the value $n-m-\tau'$ if ϵx^0, x^k are replaced by constants, represents an $X_{\nu+m-n+\tau'}$ in this X_ν. This $X_{\nu+m-n+\tau'}$ is the section of the X_ν with the X_m and consequently $\tau = \tau'$. This means that the number τ, characterized geometrically by the position of the X_m with respect to the X_ν's of N, is, from an algebraical point of view, the highest possible number of equations in ϵx^0, x^k that can be derived algebraically from (2.2).

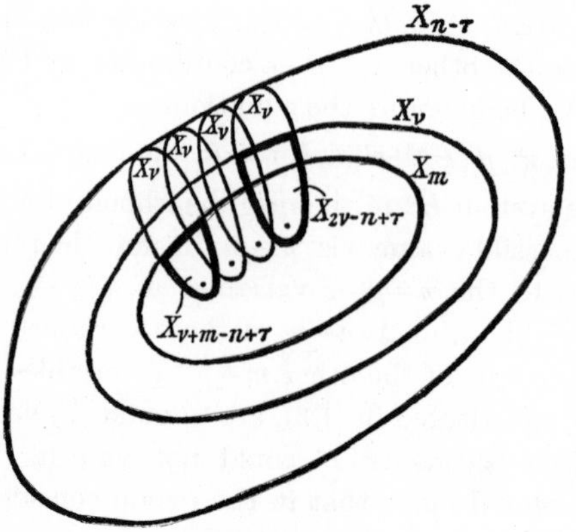

FIG. 2.

Every single X_ν of N is fixed by the $n-\nu = \rho+\epsilon$ values of ϵx^0, x^k. If the X_n is reduced with respect to the normal system of X_ν's, ϵx^0 and x^k can be used as coordinates in the resulting $X_{\rho+\epsilon}$ and in this $X_{\rho+\epsilon}$ every point represents an X_ν of N. The $\tau = \tau'$ equations (2.4 a) determine an $X_{\rho+\epsilon-\tau}$ in this $X_{\rho+\epsilon}$, that is, they single out from the $\infty^{n-\nu}$ X_ν's of N a system of $\infty^{\rho+\epsilon-\tau}$ X_ν's and these X_ν's constitute an $X_{n-\tau}$ in X_n. This is the $X_{n-\tau}$ which was obtained in the foregoing geometrical considerations by taking together all X_ν's through the points of X_m. In this $X_{n-\tau}$ the $n-m-\tau$ equations (2.4 b) determine an X_m and this is the X_m from which we started. Hence, if τ independent equations in ϵx^0, x^k are given, as was done in (2.4 a), this means geometrically that $\infty^{\rho+\epsilon-\tau}$ X_ν's from N are taken together to constitute an $X_{n-\tau}$. Since the equations (2.4 a) belong to the equations of X_m, this means that the resulting $X_{n-\tau}$ contains the X_m. Fig. 2 gives a schematical representation.

Now we have to prove that in the $X_{n-\tau}$ represented by (2.4 a) there exists one and only one enveloped X_ν containing X_m, not belonging to N if $\nu < n-\tau$. For $\tau = n-\nu$ this is trivial because in this case X_m lies in an X_ν of N. If $\tau < n-\nu$ the X_m does not lie in an X_ν of N and consequently the enveloped X_ν containing X_m cannot belong to N. Hence the only thing to be proved is that, for $\tau < n-\nu$, the τ equations (2.4 a) can be completed in one and only one way to a system of $n-\nu$ equations in accordance with (2.4 b) and making $w_\mu \, d\xi^\mu$ vanish.

Since the X_m is enveloped, the equation

$$\epsilon \, dx^0 + p_i \, dx^i = 0 \quad (i = 1,..., \rho) \tag{2.5}$$

is a consequence of

$$dx^\mu \partial_\mu F^a = 0, \qquad dx^\mu \partial_\mu F^x = 0 \quad (a = 1,..., \tau;\ x = \tau+1,..., n-m) \tag{2.6}$$

in consideration of (2.4). Hence there must exist a system of $n-m$ coefficients ϕ_a, ϕ_x, such that the system of n equations

$$(a) \quad \begin{aligned} \epsilon &= \epsilon\phi_a \frac{\partial F^a}{\partial x^0} + \epsilon\phi_x \frac{\partial F^x}{\partial x^0}, \\ p_i &= \phi_a \frac{\partial F^a}{\partial x^i} + \phi_x \frac{\partial F^x}{\partial x^i}, \end{aligned} \qquad (b) \quad \begin{aligned} 0 &= \phi_x \frac{\partial F^x}{\partial p_i}, \\ 0 &= \phi_x \frac{\partial F^x}{\partial \xi^\omega} \end{aligned} \tag{2.7}$$

$$(a = 1,..., \tau;\ x = \tau+1,..., n-m;\ i = 1,..., \rho;\ \omega = 2\rho+\epsilon+1,..., n)$$

is satisfied because of (2.4). If the ϕ_x do not all vanish, (2.7 b) expresses that the rank of the system F^x with respect to p_i, ξ^ω is $< n-m-\tau$ because of (2.4). Now we have seen above that this rank is $n-m-\tau$, hence $\phi_x = 0$ and (2.7) is equivalent to the system of $\rho+\epsilon$ equations

$$\begin{aligned} (a) \quad & \epsilon = \epsilon\phi_a \frac{\partial F^a}{\partial x^0} \\ (b) \quad & p_i = \phi_a \frac{\partial F^a}{\partial x^i} \end{aligned} \qquad (a = 1,..., \tau;\ i = 1,..., \rho) \tag{2.8}$$

that has to be satisfied because of (2.4). From (2.8) it follows that for $\epsilon = 1$ at least one of the functions F^a has to contain x^0. The F^a being independent, the rank of the system F^a has to be τ. Hence it is always possible to choose $\tau-\epsilon$ equations of (2.8 b), constituting together with (2.8 a) a system of τ linear equations in ϕ_a with a non-vanishing determinant. By interchanging indices we can always make these τ equations the first τ equations of (2.8). From these equations the ϕ_a can be solved and by substituting these solutions into the remaining $\rho+\epsilon-\tau$ equations we get a system of $\rho+\epsilon-\tau$ equations in ϵx^0, x^k, and

p_i that has to be satisfied because of (2.4), in other words, that has to depend on (2.2). From the supposition that $\tau < \rho+\epsilon$ it follows that we always get at least one equation. Incidentally we see from the form of (2.8 *b*) that for $\epsilon = 0$ these $\rho-\tau$ equations are linear and homogeneous in the p_i. Now each of the $\rho+\epsilon-\tau$ equations contains just one of the variables $p_{\tau-\epsilon+1},\ldots, p_\rho$ which do not occur in any of the other equations and from this it follows that these equations together with (2.4 *a*) constitute a system of $\rho+\epsilon = n-\nu$ independent equations which are in accordance with (2.4 *b*) and consequently represent an X_ν containing the X_m.

The section of the X_ν constructed in this way with one of the X_ν's of N is obtained by replacing ϵx^0, x^k by the constant values belonging to this latter X_ν. Then the first τ equations (2.4 *a*) of the constructed X_ν are satisfied identically and in the other $\rho+\epsilon-\tau$ equations only the ρ variables p_i remain. In the X_ρ of these p_i these $\rho+\epsilon-\tau$ equations represent an $X_{\tau-\epsilon}$ and from this it follows that the section looked for is really of dimension $\tau-\epsilon+n-2\rho-\epsilon = 2\nu-n+\tau$. In order to prove that there exists only one such X_ν it is sufficient to remark that the equations (2.4 *a*) and (2.8 *a*) only depend on the functions F^a $(a = 1,\ldots, \tau)$, that is, only on the position of the $X_{n-\tau}$ and not on the choice of the X_m. Hence, if we choose instead of the X_m some other arbitrary enveloped $X_{m'}$ $(1 \leqslant m' \leqslant \nu)$ in the $X_{n-\tau}$, having in common with each of the X_ν's of X_n constituting the $X_{n-\tau}$ just an $X_{\nu+m'-n+\tau}$, we arrive at the same X_ν. But then it is also possible to choose the X_ν itself and this proves that there is just one X_ν.

We collect results in the theorem

THEOREM VI.1. *If from a field w_λ of class $2\rho+\epsilon$ in an X_n there is given a normal system N of enveloped X_ν's $(\nu = n-\rho-\epsilon)$ in a region of constant class of w_λ and moreover one single enveloped X_m $(m \leqslant \nu)$, having in common with each of the X_ν's of N through any point of X_m just an $X_{m+\nu-n+\tau}$ $(1 \leqslant \tau \leqslant n-\nu,\ n-\nu-m \leqslant \tau \leqslant n-m)$, then there exists in the $X_{n-\tau}$ constituted by these special X_ν's one and only one enveloped X_ν containing the X_m. This X_ν has just an $X_{2\nu-n+\tau}$ in common with each of the special X_ν's mentioned above and consequently does not belong to N for $\tau < n-\nu$.*

In consequence of this theorem the construction of all enveloped X_m's in a region of constant class of w_λ, starting from a given normal system N of enveloped X_ν's, is reduced to the construction of all enveloped X_ν's in that region, because to every enveloped X_m belongs one and only one enveloped X_ν containing the X_m. So we have found the following rule for the construction of the most general enveloped X_m $(m \leqslant \nu)$:

Rule I *for the construction of the most general enveloped* X_m *of a field* w_λ:

The most general enveloped X_ν $(\nu = n-\rho-\epsilon)$ *of a field* w_λ *of class* $2\rho+\epsilon$ *in a region of constant class of* w_λ *is obtained by*

(1) *determining a canonical form* (1.3) *of* w_λ *and the normal system* N *of* $\infty^{n-\nu}$ *enveloped* X_ν*'s belonging to it*;

(2) *choosing an integer* $\tau \geqslant 1$ *and* $\leqslant n-\nu$;

(3) *choosing* τ *independent equations* (2.4 a) *in the variables* ϵx^0, x^k *with functions* F^a *analytic in the region considered, such that* ϵx^0 *and* $\tau-\epsilon$ *of the variables* x^k *can be solved*;

(4) *forming the* $\rho+\epsilon$ *equations* (2.8), *and*

(5) *eliminating the* τ *parameters* ϕ_a *from* (2.8).

The remaining $\rho+\epsilon-\tau$ *equations* (*for* $\epsilon = 0$ *homogeneous of first degree in the* p_i) *form together with the* τ *equations* (2.4 a) *a system of* $n-\nu$ *independent equations and this system represents an enveloped* X_ν *having in common either nothing or an* $X_{2\nu-n+\tau}$ *with any* X_ν *of* N.

The most general enveloped X_m $(m < \nu)$ *is obtained by completing the system of* $n-\nu$ *equations derived with* $\nu-m$ *arbitrary independent equations.*

According to our supposition the τ equations (2.4 a) can be solved with respect to ϵx^0 and $\tau-\epsilon$ of the x^k. By interchanging the indices k we can always arrange that these $\tau-\epsilon$ variables are $x^1,\dots, x^{\tau-\epsilon}$. Then (2.4 a) takes the form

$$\begin{aligned} &\epsilon x^0-\epsilon\omega^0(x^{\mathfrak{x}}) = 0 \quad &&(\mathfrak{a} = 1,\dots,\tau-\epsilon; \\ &x^{\mathfrak{a}}-\omega^{\mathfrak{a}}(x^{\mathfrak{x}}) = 0 &&\ \mathfrak{x} = \tau-\epsilon+1,\dots,\rho;\ \epsilon = 1 \text{ or } 0). \end{aligned} \tag{2.9}$$

If for the sake of simplicity we write $\underset{a-1}{\phi}$ instead of $\underset{a}{\phi}$ the equations (2.8) now take the form

$$\begin{aligned} &\epsilon = \epsilon\phi_0 \\ &p_{\mathfrak{a}} = \phi_{\mathfrak{a}} \qquad\qquad (\mathfrak{a} = 1,\dots,\tau-\epsilon;\ \mathfrak{x} = \tau-\epsilon+1,\dots,\rho), \\ &p_{\mathfrak{x}} = -\epsilon\frac{\partial\omega^0}{\partial x^{\mathfrak{x}}}-p_{\mathfrak{a}}\frac{\partial\omega^{\mathfrak{a}}}{\partial x^{\mathfrak{x}}} \end{aligned} \tag{2.10}$$

and from this it follows that the equations of the enveloped X_ν are

$$\begin{aligned} &\epsilon x^0 = \epsilon\omega^0(x^{\mathfrak{x}}) \\ &x^{\mathfrak{a}} = \omega^{\mathfrak{a}}(x^{\mathfrak{x}}) \qquad\qquad (\mathfrak{a} = 1,\dots,\tau-\epsilon;\ \mathfrak{x} = \tau-\epsilon+1,\dots,\rho). \\ &p_{\mathfrak{x}} = -\epsilon\frac{\partial\omega^0}{\partial x^{\mathfrak{x}}}-p_{\mathfrak{a}}\frac{\partial\omega^{\mathfrak{a}}}{\partial x^{\mathfrak{x}}} \end{aligned} \tag{2.11}$$

Introducing the function

$$W \stackrel{\text{def}}{=} -\epsilon\omega^0(x^{\mathfrak{x}})-p_{\mathfrak{a}}\,\omega^{\mathfrak{a}}(x^{\mathfrak{x}}) \quad (\mathfrak{a} = 1,\ldots,\tau-\epsilon;\ \mathfrak{x} = \tau-\epsilon+1,\ldots,\rho) \tag{2.12}$$

of the variables $p_{\mathfrak{a}}$ and $x^{\mathfrak{x}}$ the $\rho+\epsilon$ equations (2.11) can be written in the form

$$\begin{aligned} \epsilon x^0 &= -W-p_{\mathfrak{a}}\,x^{\mathfrak{a}} \\ x^{\mathfrak{a}} &= -\frac{\partial W}{\partial p_{\mathfrak{a}}} \qquad (\mathfrak{a} = 1,\ldots,\tau-\epsilon;\ \mathfrak{x} = \tau-\epsilon+1,\ldots,\rho). \\ p_{\mathfrak{x}} &= +\frac{\partial W}{\partial x^{\mathfrak{x}}} \end{aligned} \tag{2.13}$$

Note that the equations (2.13) represent an enveloped X_ν not only if W is chosen according to (2.12) but also if W is any function of $p_{\mathfrak{a}}$, $x^{\mathfrak{x}}$ for $\epsilon = 1$ and any function of $p_{\mathfrak{a}}$, $x^{\mathfrak{x}}$ homogeneous of first degree in the $p_{\mathfrak{a}}$ for $\epsilon = 0$. In fact, according to (2.13) we have for $\epsilon = 1$

$$\begin{aligned} w_\lambda\, d\xi^\lambda &= dx^0+p_{\mathfrak{a}}\,dx^{\mathfrak{a}}+p_{\mathfrak{x}}\,dx^{\mathfrak{x}} = -dW-d(p_{\mathfrak{a}}\,x^{\mathfrak{a}})+p_{\mathfrak{a}}\,dx^{\mathfrak{a}}+\frac{\partial W}{\partial x^{\mathfrak{x}}}\,dx^{\mathfrak{x}} \\ &= -dW+\frac{\partial W}{\partial p_{\mathfrak{a}}}\,dp_{\mathfrak{a}}+\frac{\partial W}{\partial x^{\mathfrak{x}}}\,dx^{\mathfrak{x}} = 0 \\ &\qquad (\mathfrak{a} = 1,\ldots,\tau-\epsilon;\ \mathfrak{x} = \tau-\epsilon+1,\ldots,\rho), \end{aligned} \tag{2.14}$$

and for $\epsilon = 0$

$$\begin{aligned} w_\lambda\, d\xi^\lambda &= p_{\mathfrak{a}}\,dx^{\mathfrak{a}}+p_{\mathfrak{x}}\,dx^{\mathfrak{x}} = -d\left(p_{\mathfrak{a}}\frac{\partial W}{\partial p_{\mathfrak{a}}}\right)+\frac{\partial W}{\partial p_{\mathfrak{a}}}\,dp_{\mathfrak{a}}+\frac{\partial W}{\partial x^{\mathfrak{x}}}\,dx^{\mathfrak{x}} \\ &= -dW+dW = 0. \end{aligned} \tag{2.15}$$

That establishes the rule:†

Rule II *for the construction of the most general enveloped* X_m *of a field* w_λ:

Let (1.3) *be a canonical form of a field* w_λ *of class* $2\rho+\epsilon$ *in a region of constant class of* w_λ, τ *an arbitrary integer* $\geqslant 1$ *and* $\leqslant \rho+\epsilon$, *and* W *a function of* $p_1,\ldots, p_{\tau-\epsilon}$, $x^{\tau-\epsilon+1},\ldots, x^\rho$ *analytic in the region considered and for* $\epsilon = 0$ *homogeneous of first degree in* $p_1,\ldots, p_{\tau-\epsilon}$. *Then the equations* (2.13) *represent an enveloped* X_ν *in the region considered. By a suitable choice of the order of the variables, the integer* τ, *and the function* W, *every enveloped* X_ν *in this region can be obtained and to this end it is even sufficient to consider only functions* W *linear in* $p_1,\ldots, p_{\tau-\epsilon}$. *If* W *is chosen in this special way the enveloped* X_ν *obtained has with any* X_ν *of the normal system of* X_ν*'s belonging to the canonical form* (1.3) *either nothing in common or an* $X_{2\nu-n+\tau}$.

† Cf. Lie 1876, p. 252.

By adjoining $\nu - m$ arbitrary independent equations to (2.13) *the $n-m$ equations of an enveloped X_m are obtained and every enveloped X_m can be found in this way.*

3. Geometrical representation in an $X_{n+\epsilon}$

We will now introduce another geometrical interpretation enabling us to see the problem in quite another light. First it may be remarked that in the determination of all enveloped X_ν's the coordinates $\xi^{2\rho+\epsilon+1}$, ..., ξ^n are not used because the whole process is enacted in the $X_{2\rho+\epsilon}$ of x^0, x^k, and p_i, arising from the X_n by reducing with respect to the normal system of the supports (1.7) of the field w_λ. Hence without loss of generality we can simplify the problem by supposing $n = 2\rho+\epsilon$ and consequently $\nu = \rho$.

When this has been done it is advantageous to change the notation. From now on we write n instead of ρ, and ξ^0, ξ^κ ($\kappa = 1,..., n$) instead of x^0, x^k ($k = 1,..., \rho$), and w_λ ($\lambda = 1,..., n$) instead of p_i ($i = 1,..., \rho$). Then the Pfaffian $\epsilon\, dx^0 + p_i\, dx^i$ takes the form

$$\epsilon\, d\xi^0 + w_\lambda\, d\xi^\lambda \tag{3.1}$$

and we have $\nu = n$. The X_n ($n = 2\rho+\epsilon$) with the coordinates ϵx^0, x^k, p_i is now an $X_{2n+\epsilon}$ with the coordinates $\epsilon\xi^0$, ξ^κ, w_λ. For these $2n+\epsilon$ coordinates we will also sometimes use the notation X^A ($A = 1-\epsilon,..., n, (1),..., (n)$) in such a way that

$$\epsilon X^0 \stackrel{\text{def}}{=} \epsilon\xi^0, \qquad X^\kappa \stackrel{\text{def}}{=} \xi^\kappa, \qquad X^{(\kappa)} \stackrel{\text{def}}{=} w_\kappa \quad ((\kappa) = (1),..., (n)). \tag{3.2}$$

With this notation the Pfaffian (3.1) takes the form

$$W_B\, dX^B \quad (B = 1-\epsilon,..., n, (1),..., (n)), \tag{3.3}$$

W_B being a covariant vector of the $X_{2n+\epsilon}$ with the components

$$\epsilon W_0 \stackrel{\text{def}}{=} \epsilon, \qquad W_\lambda \stackrel{\text{def}}{=} w_\lambda, \qquad W_{(\lambda)} \stackrel{\text{def}}{=} 0 \quad ((\lambda) = (1),..., (n)). \tag{3.4}$$

The normal system N of enveloped X_n's has the $n+\epsilon$ equations

$$\epsilon\xi^0 = \text{const.}, \qquad \xi^\kappa = \text{const.} \tag{3.5}$$

Now for $\epsilon = 0$ we look upon the w_λ as components of a covariant vector of the X_n of the ξ^κ. The combination of a point of this X_n with a covariant vector at that point is called a *vector element of* X_n and the combination of a point of X_n with an E_{n-1} at that point an E_{n-1}-*element of* X_n. Obviously one and only one E_{n-1}-element belongs to each vector element and to every E_{n-1}-element belong ∞^1 vector elements all having the same $(n-1)$-direction. *A point of the X_{2n} with the coordinates ξ^κ, w_λ represents in the X_n a vector element and the special curve of the X_{2n} fixed by ξ^κ, $\lfloor w_\lambda \rfloor$ represents in the X_n an E_{n-1}-element.*

According to S. Lie two neighbouring vector elements ξ^κ, w_λ and $\xi^\kappa+d\xi^\kappa$, $w_\lambda+dw_\lambda$ and their corresponding E_{n-1}-elements are said to be *joined*† if

$$w_\lambda d\xi^\lambda = W_B dX^B = 0 \quad (B = 1,..., n, (1),..., (n)). \tag{3.6}$$

This means geometrically that the point of the first element lies in the E_{n-1} of the second and vice versa, or, more correctly, that there exists an X_{n-1} through the point ξ^κ and $\xi^\kappa+d\xi^\kappa$ tangent to both E_{n-1}'s.

A system of $2n-m$ equations in ξ^κ, w_λ, minimal regular in the region considered, represents an m-dimensional manifold in the X_{2n} of all vector elements of X_n. Such a *vector manifold* is called a *vector*-$\mathfrak{N}_m$ or just an $\mathfrak{N}_m$. If all neighbouring elements of such an $\mathfrak{N}_m$ are joined we call it a *vector*-N_m or just an N_m. According to (3.6) every N_m in X_{2n} represents an enveloped X_m of the field W_B and vice versa and this implies that for an N_m m is always $\leqslant n$. An N_1 is called a *vector-strip*. If the equations of an $\mathfrak{N}_m$ are homogeneous in w_λ, the $\mathfrak{N}_m$ is said to be *homogeneous*. Every homogeneous $\mathfrak{N}_m$ determines uniquely an $(m-1)$-dimensional manifold of E_{n-1}-elements in the X_{2n-1} of all E_{n-1}-elements of X_n. Such an *element manifold* is called an *element*-$\mathfrak{M}_{m-1}$ or just an $\mathfrak{M}_{m-1}$. If all neighbouring elements of such an $\mathfrak{M}_{m-1}$ are joined, we call it an *element*-M_{m-1} or just an M_{m-1}.‡ An M_1 is called a *strip*. It is clear that to every $\mathfrak{M}_{m-1}$ one and only one homogeneous $\mathfrak{N}_m$ belongs and that it is always possible to form a homogeneous $\mathfrak{N}_{m+1}$ from a non-homogeneous $\mathfrak{N}_m$ by adjoining to every vector element of $\mathfrak{N}_m$ all vector elements in the same point with the same $(n-1)$-direction.

If it is possible to derive from the $2n-m$ equations of an $\mathfrak{N}_m$ just $n-t$ equations containing only the variables ξ^κ, these equations represent an X_t in X_n, called the *field region* of the $\mathfrak{N}_m$ and in the homogeneous case also the *field region* of the corresponding $\mathfrak{M}_{m-1}$ (cf. II, § 5). t is called the *field dimension* of $\mathfrak{N}_m$ or $\mathfrak{M}_{m-1}$ respectively. Obviously $0 \leqslant t \leqslant n$. Since there are only ∞^n vector elements at each point of X_n and since an $\mathfrak{N}_m$ contains in the homogeneous case at least ∞^1 vector elements in each of the points of its field region, we have $m-n+1 \leqslant t \leqslant m$ in the non-homogeneous case and $m-n \leqslant t \leqslant m-1$ in the homogeneous case. Hence the field region of an $\mathfrak{N}_1$ or $\mathfrak{M}_1$ is either a curve or a point. A special case is formed by the N_n and M_{n-1} consisting of all the ∞^n vector elements or ∞^{n-1} E_{n-1}-elements tangent to the field region X_t. These special N_n's and M_{n-1}'s are denoted by

† S. Lie uses the term *in vereinigter Lage*, cf. 1876. 1, p. 253.

‡ This is the M_{m-1}, or *Elementverein* of S. Lie, cf. 1876. 1, p. 253; 1890. 1, p. 106.

N^t_n and M^t_{n-1} respectively.† It is evident that N_n and M_{n-1} are wholly determined by their field region.

For $\epsilon = 1$ we look upon $1, w_1,..., w_n$ as components of a covariant vector in the X_{n+1} of ξ^0, ξ^κ and upon $w_1,..., w_n$ as coordinates of an E_n in the local E_{n+1}. As in this way only vector elements with $w_0 = 1$ in the X_{n+1} are considered, there is a one-to-one correspondence between all these vector elements and all these E_n-elements, and consequently also between all $\mathfrak{N}_m$'s and all $\mathfrak{M}_m$'s in X_{n+1}, whilst homogeneous $\mathfrak{N}_m$'s do not occur. The neighbouring elements $\xi^0, \xi^\kappa, w_\lambda$ and $\xi^0+d\xi^0, \xi^\kappa+d\xi^\kappa, w_\lambda+dw_\lambda$ are *joined* if

$$d\xi^0+w_\lambda d\xi^\lambda = 0. \tag{3.7}$$

Hence we have the inequalities $0 \leqslant t \leqslant n+1, m-n \leqslant t \leqslant m$. For the rest, all things are just the same, *mutatis mutandis*, as in the X_n.

Now we are able to represent the results of VI, § 2, geometrically in an $X_{n+\epsilon}$. As was proved in that section, every enveloped X_m can be given by, firstly, $\tau \geqslant 1$ equations in $\epsilon\xi^0, \xi^\kappa$, soluble with respect to $\epsilon\xi^0$, $\xi^1,..., \xi^{\tau-\epsilon}$, secondly, $n+\epsilon-\tau$ equations in $\epsilon\xi^0, \xi^\kappa, w_\lambda$ (for $\epsilon = 0$ homogeneous of first degree in the w_λ) soluble with respect to $w_{\tau-\epsilon+1},..., w_n$, and finally, $\nu-m = n-m$ equations in $\xi^{\tau-\epsilon+1},..., \xi^n, w_1,..., w_{\tau-\epsilon}$.

If $\epsilon = 1$, the first τ equations determine an $X_{n+1-\tau}$ in the X_{n+1} and an $\mathfrak{M}_{2n+1-\tau}$ having this $X_{n+1-\tau}$ as field region and consisting of all E_n-elements whose points lie in the $X_{n+1-\tau}$. The $n+1-\tau$ equations single out from those $\infty^{2n+1-\tau}$ E_n-elements just ∞^n elements tangent to the $X_{n+1-\tau}$ and constituting an $M^{n+1-\tau}_n$ with $X_{n+1-\tau}$ as field region. This $M^{n+1-\tau}_n$ is the image of the enveloped X_n containing the X_m.

If $\epsilon = 0$, the first τ equations determine an $X_{n-\tau}$ in the X_n and an $\mathfrak{N}_{2n-\tau}$ having this $X_{n-\tau}$ as field region and consisting of all vector elements whose points lie in the $X_{n-\tau}$. The $n-\tau$ equations single out from these $\infty^{2n-\tau}$ vector elements just ∞^n elements tangent to the $X_{n-\tau}$ and constituting an $N^{n-\tau}_n$ with $X_{n-\tau}$ as field region. This $N^{n-\tau}_n$ is the image of the enveloped X_n containing the X_m.

Since an $M^{n+1-\tau}_n$ or $N^{n-\tau}_n$ is wholly determined by its field region, it is now immediately clear that the $n+\epsilon-\tau$ equations can be derived from the first τ equations. That these $n+\epsilon-\tau$ equations have to be homogeneous of first degree in the w_λ for $\epsilon = 0$ comes from the fact that a tangent vector remains tangent if it is multiplied by a scalar factor.

The last $n-m$ equations (even for $\epsilon = 0$ not necessarily homogeneous in the w_λ) single out from the $\infty^{\tau-\epsilon}$ elements at every point of the field

† Cf. Lie 1876, p. 255.

region just $\infty^{\tau-n+m-\epsilon}$ elements, and the element-M_m or vector-N_m respectively, constituted by these elements, is the image of the enveloped X_m.

Now it is also immediately clear that in the $X_{2n+\epsilon-\tau}$ determined by the X_m and the X_n's of N there exists one and only one enveloped X_n containing X_m. The image of the X_m is an N_m, having an $X_{n+\epsilon-\tau}$ as field region and the images of all X_n's of the normal system N are the N_n's whose field regions are points. The N_m together with these N_n's determine an $\mathfrak{N}_{2n+\epsilon-\tau}$ consisting of all vector elements whose points lie in the $X_{n+\epsilon-\tau}$ and this $\mathfrak{N}_{2n+\epsilon-\tau}$ is the image of the $X_{2n+\epsilon-\tau}$ determined by the X_m and the normal system N. This $\mathfrak{N}_{2n+\epsilon-\tau}$ is not an $N_{2n+\epsilon-\tau}$, because the $X_{2n+\epsilon-\tau}$ is not enveloped by the field W_B. But in this $\mathfrak{N}_{2n+\epsilon-\tau}$ there exists one and only one N_n containing N_m because N_n must have the $X_{n+\epsilon-\tau}$ as field region and is consequently identical with the $N_n^{n+\epsilon-\tau}$ with this $X_{n+\epsilon-\tau}$ as field region.

4. Contact transformations of the first kind†

In this section we will determine directly all possible canonical representations if one canonical representation is given. When these canonical representations have been found a normal system of enveloped X_n's belongs to every one of them, as we have seen in VI, § 1, and in this way all normal systems of enveloped X_n's can be found.

Since an arbitrary scalar factor in the field W_B is not important, we have to look for all invertible transformations of the variables $_\epsilon\xi^0$, ξ^κ, w_λ of the form

$$\begin{aligned} &(a) \qquad {}_{\epsilon}{}'\xi^0 = {}_{\epsilon}{}'\phi^0({}_\epsilon\xi^0, \xi^\kappa, w_\mu), \\ &(b) \qquad {}'\xi^\kappa = {}'\phi^\kappa({}_\epsilon\xi^0, \xi^\kappa, w_\mu), \\ &(c) \qquad {}'w_\lambda = {}'\psi_\lambda({}_\epsilon\xi^0, \xi^\kappa, w_\mu), \end{aligned} \tag{4.1}$$

leaving the Pfaffian $_\epsilon d\xi^0 + w_\lambda d\xi^\lambda$ invariant to within an arbitrary scalar factor. This means that a relation of the form

$$'\sigma({}_\epsilon d\,'\xi^0 + {}'w_\lambda d\,'\xi^\lambda) = \sigma({}_\epsilon d\xi^0 + w_\lambda d\xi^\lambda), \tag{4.2}$$

has to exist where the σ and $'\sigma$ are two suitable functions of $_\epsilon\xi^0$, ξ^κ, and w_λ or of $_\epsilon{}'\xi^0$, $'\xi^\kappa$, and $'w_\lambda$. From these functions σ' and σ only the quotient

$$(a) \quad \frac{'\sigma}{\sigma} = {}'\Omega({}_\epsilon\xi^0, \xi^\kappa, w_\lambda), \qquad (b) \quad \frac{'\sigma}{\sigma} = \Omega({}_\epsilon{}'\xi^0, {}'\xi^\kappa, {}'w_\lambda) \tag{4.3}$$

† Cf. Lie 1890. 1, chs. v, vi; v. Weber 1900. 1, chs. viii, xi; Whittaker 1917. 1, ch. ix; Goursat 1921. 1, ch. x; Engel and Faber 1932. 1, ch. vi; Eisenhart 1933. 1, ch. vi.

is important. Transformations of this kind are called *contact transformations of the first kind* or briefly *C_1-transformations.* In the $X_{n+\epsilon}$ of $\epsilon\xi^0$, ξ^κ the equations (4.1) can be interpreted in two different ways. First we may look upon $\epsilon\,'\xi^0$, $'\xi^\kappa$, and $'w_\lambda$ as *new components* of the elements $\epsilon\xi^0$, ξ^κ, w_λ. Then (4.1) represents in the $X_{2n+\epsilon}$ of all elements a *coordinate transformation* and (4.2) shows that the form of the condition for joined elements does not change with this transformation. Secondly we may look upon the $\epsilon\,'\xi^0$, $'\xi^\kappa$, and $'w_\lambda$ as the components of a *new element.* Then (4.1) represents in the $X_{2n+\epsilon}$ of all elements an *element transformation* and (4.2) shows that joined elements are transformed into joined elements. But it should be noted, *that two elements belonging to the same point before the transformation, may belong to different points after the transformation.*

We shall always use the second interpretation, that is, *we shall look upon a C_1-transformation as a transformation interchanging the elements and leaving invariant the property of elements of being joined.*

Every transformation of the form (4.1) transforms every $\mathfrak{N}_m$ into an $\mathfrak{N}_m$. Among these the C_1-transformations are characterized by the property that they transform every N_m into an N_m. The field dimension of an $\mathfrak{N}_m$ is not invariant for C_1-transformations.

C_1-transformations possess still another invariance. To show this we consider an arbitrary vector field in $X_{n+\epsilon}$ with the equations

$$\begin{aligned} \epsilon w_0 &= \epsilon, \\ w_\lambda &= f_\lambda(\epsilon\xi^0, \xi^\kappa). \end{aligned} \tag{4.4}$$

If a transformation of the form (4.1) is applied, the $\infty^{n+\epsilon}$ vector elements of the field become another system of $\infty^{n+\epsilon}$ vector elements. This new system constitutes a new vector field in $X_{n+\epsilon}$ if and only if the equations $\epsilon\, d\xi^0 = 0, d\xi^\kappa = 0$ are a consequence of $\epsilon\, d\,'\xi^0 = 0$, $d\,'\xi^\kappa = 0$, and (4.4). Now, according to (4.1) and (4.4), we have

$$\begin{aligned} \epsilon\, d\,'\xi^0 &= \epsilon\left(\partial_0\,'\phi^0 + \frac{\partial\,'\phi^0}{\partial w_\mu}\partial_0 f_\mu\right)d\xi^0 + \epsilon\left(\partial_\lambda\,'\phi^0 + \frac{\partial\,'\phi^0}{\partial w_\mu}\partial_\lambda f_\mu\right)d\xi^\lambda, \\ d\,'\xi^\kappa &= \epsilon\left(\partial_0\,'\phi^\kappa + \frac{\partial\,'\phi^\kappa}{\partial w_\mu}\partial_0 f_\mu\right)d\xi^0 + \left(\partial_\lambda\,'\phi^\kappa + \frac{\partial\,'\phi^\kappa}{\partial w_\mu}\partial_\lambda f_\mu\right)d\xi^\lambda. \end{aligned} \tag{4.5}$$

From this we get the necessary and sufficient condition

$$\overset{\longleftarrow 1 \longrightarrow \quad \longleftarrow n \longrightarrow}{\begin{matrix} \updownarrow 1 \\ \updownarrow n \end{matrix}\left|\begin{matrix} \epsilon\left(\partial_0\,'\phi^0 + \dfrac{\partial\,'\phi^0}{\partial w_\mu}\partial_0 f_\mu\right) & \epsilon\left(\partial_\lambda\,'\phi^0 + \dfrac{\partial\,'\phi^0}{\partial w_\mu}\partial_\lambda f_\mu\right) \\ \epsilon\left(\partial_0\,'\phi^\kappa + \dfrac{\partial\,'\phi^\kappa}{\partial w_\mu}\partial_0 f_\mu\right) & \partial_\lambda\,'\phi^\kappa + \dfrac{\partial\,'\phi^\kappa}{\partial w_\mu}\partial_\lambda f_\mu \end{matrix}\right|} \neq 0. \tag{4.6}$$

A transformation of the form (4.1), satisfying the condition (4.6) is called *field-preserving with respect to the field* ϵw_0, w_λ. From this we see that an element transformation of the form (4.1) 'in general' transforms a covariant vector field into a covariant vector field, but that special transformations exist transforming a given vector field into an $\mathfrak{N}_{n+\epsilon}$ which does not constitute a vector field.

Now let (4.1) be a C_1-transformation, field-preserving with respect to the field ϵw_0, w_λ. Then it follows from (4.2) that the *characteristics and the similarity class k of the field are invariant but that the supports of rotation and the rotation class* 2ρ *are in general not invariant.*

It is easy to reduce the transformation of elements (4.1) for $\epsilon = 1$ to the case $\epsilon = 0$. This can be done by withdrawing the condition $w_0 = 1$ and replacing $w_1,..., w_n$ by $w_1/w_0,..., w_n/w_0$. Then $w_0, w_1,..., w_n$ are at the same time components of a covariant vector and homogeneous components of an E_n in the local E_{n+1}. The equations (4.1) for $\epsilon = 1$ then take the form

$$\begin{aligned} '\xi^0 &= '\phi^0(\xi^0, \xi^\kappa, w_0, w_\lambda), \\ '\xi^\kappa &= '\phi^\kappa(\xi^0, \xi^\kappa, w_0, w_\lambda), \\ 'w_0 &= '\psi_0(\xi^0, \xi^\kappa, w_0, w_\lambda), \\ 'w_\lambda &= '\psi_\lambda(\xi^0, \xi^\kappa, w_0, w_\lambda), \end{aligned} \tag{4.7}$$

with the additional condition that the $'\phi$ are homogeneous of degree zero and the $'\psi$ homogeneous of degree one in the w_0, w_λ. The condition (4.2) takes the form

$$'\sigma('w_0 d'\xi^0 + 'w_\lambda d'\xi^\lambda) = \sigma(w_0 d\xi^0 + w_\lambda d\xi^\lambda). \tag{4.8}$$

Now the equations (4.7) and the conditions (4.8) have the form (4.1) and (4.2) respectively for $\epsilon = 0$ but for a dimension $n+1$ instead of n. Hence it is always possible to consider the case $\epsilon = 1$ as a special sub-case of the case $\epsilon = 0$ and this means that we may first treat the case $\epsilon = 0$ and then transform the results obtained into results for the case $\epsilon = 1$ by specializing for homogeneous functions $'\phi$ and $'\psi$ and returning to non-homogeneous coordinates. This is very often done. But here we will follow another way, treating the equations (4.1, 2) for a general ϵ and specializing later for $\epsilon = 1$ and $\epsilon = 0$.

If we denote σw_λ by q_λ and $'\sigma 'w_\lambda$ by $'q_\lambda$ the condition (4.2) takes the more convenient form

$$\epsilon '\sigma d'\xi^0 + 'q_\lambda d'\xi^\lambda - \epsilon\sigma d\xi^0 - q_\lambda d\xi^\lambda = 0 \tag{4.9}$$

and from this form we see that in the $X_{4n+4\epsilon}$ of the variables $\epsilon\xi^0$, $\epsilon '\xi^0$, ξ^κ, $'\xi^\kappa$, $\epsilon\sigma$, $\epsilon '\sigma$, q_λ, $'q_\lambda$ the equations (4.1) and (4.3*a*) represent an

$X_{2n+3\epsilon-1}$ enveloped by the covariant vector field belonging to the Pfaffian in (4.9). Hence, to get the most general C_1-transformation, we have to determine the most general enveloped $X_{2n+3\epsilon-1}$ such that its $2n+\epsilon+1$ equations can be solved with respect to $\epsilon\xi^0$, ξ^κ, $'\sigma/\sigma$, and w_λ and also with respect to $\epsilon\,'\xi^0$, $'\xi^\kappa$, $'\sigma/\sigma$, and $'w_\lambda$. For $\epsilon = 1$ the maximum dimension of an enveloped manifold is just $2n+3\epsilon-1$. But for $\epsilon = 0$ the maximum dimension is $2n$. Hence in all cases the most general enveloped $X_{2n+2\epsilon}$ has to be constructed first and for $\epsilon = 0$ one equation has to be added (cf. VI, § 2).

To obtain the most general enveloped $X_{2n+2\epsilon}$ we may use the rules given in VI, § 2. Using the first rule we get the $2n+2\epsilon+\tau$ equations

$$F^a(\epsilon\xi^0, \epsilon\,'\xi^0, \xi^\kappa, '\xi^\kappa) = 0 \quad (a = 1,\ldots,\tau); \tag{4.10}$$

$$\begin{aligned} &(a) \qquad \epsilon\sigma = -\epsilon\chi_a \frac{\partial F^a}{\partial \xi^0}, \qquad \epsilon\,'\sigma = \epsilon\chi_a \frac{\partial F^a}{\partial\,'\xi^0};\\ &(b) \qquad q_\lambda = -\chi_a \frac{\partial F^a}{\partial \xi^\lambda}, \qquad 'q_\lambda = \chi_a \frac{\partial F^a}{\partial\,'\xi^\lambda}. \end{aligned} \tag{4.11}$$

By elimination of the τ parameters χ_a we get $2n+2\epsilon$ equations representing an enveloped $X_{2n+2\epsilon}$. Since these equations are homogeneous of the first degree in $\epsilon\sigma$, $\epsilon\,'\sigma$, q_λ, $'q_\lambda$ it is always possible to deduce from them a system of $2n+2\epsilon$ equations only containing the variables $'\sigma/\sigma$, $\epsilon\xi^0$, $\epsilon\,'\xi^0$, ξ^κ, w_λ, $'\xi^\kappa$, $'w_\lambda$. If $\epsilon = 1$ elimination of $'\sigma/\sigma$ leads to $2n+1$ equations in ξ^0, $'\xi^0$, ξ^κ, w_λ, $'\xi^\kappa$, $'w_\lambda$. For $\epsilon = 1$ the order of elimination can also be changed by first eliminating $'\sigma/\sigma$ from (4.11) and then eliminating the parameters χ_a from the resulting $2n$ equations

$$w_\lambda = \frac{\chi_a \dfrac{\partial F^a}{\partial \xi^\lambda}}{\chi_a \dfrac{\partial F^a}{\partial \xi^0}}, \qquad 'w_\lambda = \frac{\chi_a \dfrac{\partial F^a}{\partial\,'\xi^\lambda}}{\chi_a \dfrac{\partial F^a}{\partial\,'\xi^0}} \quad (a = 1,\ldots,\tau). \tag{4.12}$$

The addition of a $(2n+1)$th equation, necessary for $\epsilon = 0$, can be performed by introducing for σ'/σ an arbitrary function, analytic and non-vanishing in the region considered. Then we get $2n$ equations in ξ^κ, w_λ, $'\xi^\kappa$, and $'w_\lambda$.

Now the functions F^a have to be chosen in such a way that the $2n+\epsilon$ equations obtained can be solved with respect to $\epsilon\xi^0$, ξ^κ, w_λ and with respect to $\epsilon\,'\xi^0$, $'\xi^\kappa$, $'w_\lambda$. A necessary and sufficient condition is that the equations (4.10, 11) be soluble with respect to $\epsilon\xi^0$, $\epsilon\sigma$, ξ^κ, q_λ, and χ_a and also with respect to $\epsilon\,'\xi^0$, $\epsilon\,'\sigma$, $'\xi^\kappa$, $'q_\lambda$, and χ_a. If the functional determinant of this system with respect to $\epsilon\xi^0$, $\epsilon\sigma$, ξ^κ, q_λ, and χ_a is written out, it becomes evident that this determinant does not vanish as a consequence of (4.10, 11) if and only if for $\epsilon = 1$ the determinant

$$\begin{vmatrix} \dfrac{\partial F^a}{\partial \xi^0} & \dfrac{\partial F^a}{\partial \xi^\lambda} & 0 \\ \chi_a \dfrac{\partial^2 F^a}{\partial \xi^0 \partial' \xi^\mu} & \chi_a \dfrac{\partial^2 F^a}{\partial \xi^\lambda \partial' \xi^\mu} & \dfrac{\partial F^a}{\partial' \xi^\mu} \\ \chi_a \dfrac{\partial^2 F^a}{\partial \xi^0 \partial' \xi^0} & \chi_a \dfrac{\partial^2 F^a}{\partial \xi^\lambda \partial' \xi^0} & \dfrac{\partial F^a}{\partial' \xi^0} \end{vmatrix} \quad (a = 1,..., \tau) \tag{4.13}$$

(column widths $1, n, \tau$; row heights $\tau, n, 1$)

and for $\epsilon = 0$ the determinant

$$\begin{vmatrix} \dfrac{\partial F^a}{\partial \xi^\lambda} & 0 \\ \chi_a \dfrac{\partial^2 F^a}{\partial \xi^\lambda \partial' \xi^\mu} & \dfrac{\partial F^a}{\partial' \xi^\mu} \end{vmatrix} \quad (a = 1,..., \tau) \tag{4.14}$$

(column widths n, τ; row heights τ, n)

does not vanish identically in χ_a as a result of (4.10, 11). The necessary and sufficient conditions for the solubility with respect to $\epsilon'\xi^0$, $\epsilon'\sigma$, $'\xi^\kappa$, $'q_\lambda$, and χ_a are the same. From the form of the determinants (4.13, 14) it follows that the conditions can only be satisfied if $\tau \leqslant n+\epsilon$.

Solving (4.10, 11) with respect to $\epsilon'\xi^0$, $\epsilon'\sigma$, $'\xi^\kappa$, $'q_\lambda$, and χ_a, and eliminating the χ_a, we get $2n+2\epsilon$ equations of the form

$$\begin{aligned} &(a) \qquad \epsilon'\xi^0 = \epsilon'\Phi^0(\epsilon\xi^0, \epsilon\sigma, \xi^\kappa, q_\lambda), \\ &(b) \qquad '\xi^\kappa = '\Phi^\kappa(\epsilon\xi^0, \epsilon\sigma, \xi^\kappa, q_\lambda), \\ &(c) \qquad 'q_\lambda = '\Psi_\lambda(\epsilon\xi^0, \epsilon\sigma, \xi^\kappa, q_\lambda), \\ &(d) \qquad \epsilon'\sigma = \epsilon'\Psi_0(\epsilon\xi^0, \epsilon\sigma, \xi^\kappa, q_\lambda). \end{aligned} \tag{4.15}$$

From these equations (4.15 a, b) are homogeneous of degree zero and (4.15 c, d) homogeneous of degree one in σ, q_λ. Consequently for $\epsilon = 1$ these equations can be written in the form

$$\begin{aligned} '\xi^0 &= '\Phi^0(\xi^0, 1, \xi^\kappa, w_\mu) = '\phi^0(\xi^0, \xi^\kappa, w_\mu), \\ '\xi^\kappa &= '\Phi^\kappa(\xi^0, 1, \xi^\kappa, w_\mu) = '\phi^\kappa(\xi^0, \xi^\kappa, w_\mu), \\ 'w_\lambda &= \frac{'\Psi_\lambda(\xi^0, 1, \xi^\kappa, w_\mu)}{'\Psi_0(\xi^0, 1, \xi^\kappa, w_\mu)} = '\psi_\lambda(\xi^0, \xi^\kappa, w_\mu), \\ \frac{'\sigma}{\sigma} &= '\Psi_0(\xi^0, 1, \xi^\kappa, w_\mu) = '\Omega_0(\xi^0, \xi^\kappa, w_\mu), \end{aligned} \tag{4.16}$$

and these equations have the form (4.1, 3 a) required. Conversely, if equations of the form (4.1, 3 a) are given it is always possible to deduce equations of the form (4.15) with the necessary homogeneity.

For $\epsilon = 0$ the equations (4.15) can be written in the form

$$\begin{aligned} '\xi^\kappa &= '\Phi^\kappa(\xi^\kappa, \sigma w_\mu) = '\Phi^\kappa(\xi^\kappa, w_\mu), \\ '\sigma\, 'w_\lambda &= '\Psi_\lambda(\xi^\kappa, \sigma w_\mu) = \sigma\, '\Psi_\lambda(\xi^\kappa, w_\mu) \end{aligned} \tag{4.17}$$

and from these equations we get equations of the form (4.1) by replacing $'\sigma/\sigma$ by an arbitrary function. This implies that the $'\phi^\kappa$ in (4.1 *b*) are homogeneous of degree zero in the w_λ for $\epsilon = 0$. Geometrically this means that two covariant vectors at the same point differing only by a scalar factor are transformed by every C_1-transformation into vectors belonging to the same point.

From (4.1 *c*), (4.3 *a*), and (4.17) it follows that

$$'\Psi_\lambda(\xi^\kappa, w_\mu) = '\Omega(\xi^\kappa, w_\mu)'\psi_\lambda(\xi^\kappa, w_\mu) \tag{4.18}$$

and from this it follows that the product of $'\psi_\lambda$ in (4.1) and $'\Omega$ in (4.3 *a*) is homogeneous of degree one in the w_λ. Hence if (4.1) and (4.3 *a*) are given, it is also for $\epsilon = 0$ always possible to deduce equations of the form (4.15) with the necessary homogeneity.

We collect results in the following rule:

Rule I *for the construction of the most general C_1-transformation.*

The most general C_1-transformation in $\epsilon\xi^0$, ξ^κ, w_λ is obtained by

(1) *choosing an arbitrary integer $\tau \geqslant 1$ and $\leqslant n+\epsilon$;*

(2) *choosing τ arbitrary independent equations*

$$F^a(\epsilon\xi^0, \epsilon\,'\xi^0, \xi^\kappa, '\xi^\kappa) = 0 \quad (a = 1,\ldots,\tau) \tag{4.19}$$

with functions F^a, analytic in the region considered and such that the $(n+\tau+\epsilon)$-rowed determinant

$$\overbrace{}^{\epsilon}\;\overbrace{}^{n}\;\overbrace{}^{\tau}$$
$$\begin{array}{l} \tau \\ \\ n \\ \\ \epsilon \end{array}\left|\begin{array}{ccc} \epsilon\dfrac{\partial F^a}{\partial \xi^0} & \dfrac{\partial F^a}{\partial \xi^\lambda} & 0 \\ \epsilon\chi_a\dfrac{\partial^2 F^a}{\partial\xi^0\partial\,'\xi^\mu} & \chi_a\dfrac{\partial^2 F^a}{\partial\xi^\lambda\partial\,'\xi^\mu} & \dfrac{\partial F^a}{\partial\,'\xi^\mu} \\ \epsilon\chi_a\dfrac{\partial^2 F^a}{\partial\xi^0\partial\,'\xi^0} & \epsilon\chi_a\dfrac{\partial^2 F^a}{\partial\xi^\lambda\partial\,'\xi^0} & \epsilon\dfrac{\partial F^a}{\partial\,'\xi^0} \end{array}\right| \quad (a = 1,\ldots,\tau) \tag{4.20}$$

does not vanish identically in the χ_a as a consequence of (4.19);

(3) *writing out the equations*

$$\begin{aligned} \epsilon\sigma &= -\epsilon\chi_a\frac{\partial F^a}{\partial\xi^0}, & \epsilon\,'\sigma &= +\epsilon\chi_a\frac{\partial F^a}{\partial\,'\xi^0} \\ q_\lambda &= -\chi_a\frac{\partial F^a}{\partial\xi^\lambda}, & 'q_\lambda &= +\chi_a\frac{\partial F^a}{\partial\,'\xi^\lambda} \end{aligned} \quad (a = 1,\ldots,\tau); \tag{4.21}$$

(4) *eliminating the* χ_a *from* (4.21) *and writing the remaining* $2n+2\epsilon-\tau$ *equations (homogeneous of degree one in* σ, $'\sigma$, q_λ, *and* $'q_\lambda$) *in the variables* σ'/σ, $\epsilon\xi^0$, $\epsilon\,'\xi^0$, ξ^κ, $w_\lambda = q_\lambda/\sigma$, $'\xi^\kappa$, *and* $'w_\lambda = {}'q_\lambda/{}'\sigma$;

(5) *eliminating* σ'/σ *from these equations for* $\epsilon = 1$ *and replacing* $'\sigma/\sigma$ *by an arbitrary function, analytic and non-vanishing in the region considered, for* $\epsilon = 0$.

By this process $2n+\epsilon-\tau$ *equations in* $\epsilon\xi^0$, ξ^κ, w_λ, $\epsilon\,'\xi^0$, $'\xi^\kappa$, $'w_\lambda$ *are obtained, constituting together with* (4.19) *a system of* $2n+\epsilon$ *equations in these* $4n+2\epsilon$ *variables, soluble with respect to* $\epsilon\xi^0$, ξ^κ, w_λ *and with respect to* $\epsilon\,'\xi^0$, $'\xi^\kappa$, $'w_\lambda$ *and representing the* C_1*-transformation required.*

The number τ plays a very important role. Firstly it indicates the number of equations (4.19) to be chosen arbitrarily at the beginning. But from the form of the additional equations (4.21) it follows that no other equations not containing σ, $'\sigma$, q_λ, and $'q_\lambda$ can be obtained from them and this implies that from the equations (4.1) of the C_1-transformation obtained just τ independent equations in $\epsilon\xi^0$, $\epsilon\,'\xi^0$, ξ^κ, and $'\xi^\kappa$ can be derived. It is clear that to this end only (4.1 *a*) and (4.1 *b*) can be used and, according to the theorem of elimination II.7, consequently the rank of the matrix of $\epsilon\dfrac{\partial\,'\phi^0}{\partial w_\lambda}, \dfrac{\partial\,'\phi^\kappa}{\partial w_\lambda}$ is just $n+\epsilon-\tau$. Since $\tau \geqslant 1$ this rank has always to be $< n+\epsilon$. This can be verified by substituting the $'w_\lambda$ from (4.1 *c*) and the differentials of $'\xi^0$ and $'\xi^\kappa$ from (4.1 *a*, *b*) into (4.2). Then we get the equations

$$\begin{aligned} \epsilon\sigma &= \epsilon\,'\sigma\frac{\partial\,'\phi^0}{\partial\xi^0}+\epsilon\,'\sigma\,'\psi_\mu\frac{\partial\,'\phi^\mu}{\partial\xi^0}, \\ \sigma w_\lambda &= \epsilon\,'\sigma\frac{\partial\,'\phi^0}{\partial\xi^\lambda}+'\sigma\,'\psi_\mu\frac{\partial\,'\phi^\mu}{\partial\xi^\lambda}, \\ 0 &= \epsilon\,'\sigma\frac{\partial\,'\phi^0}{\partial w_\lambda}+'\sigma\,'\psi_\mu\frac{\partial\,'\phi^\mu}{\partial w_\lambda}, \end{aligned} \tag{4.22}$$

and from these it follows in fact that the rank of the matrix of $\epsilon\dfrac{\partial\,'\phi^0}{\partial w_\lambda}$, $\dfrac{\partial\,'\phi^\kappa}{\partial w_\lambda}$ is $< n+\epsilon$.

We call $n+\epsilon-\tau$ the *rank of the* C_1*-transformation.* The geometrical interpretation of the rank can be obtained as follows. Every element at a point $\epsilon\overset{*}{\xi}{}^0$, $\overset{*}{\xi}{}^\kappa$ is transformed by the C_1-transformation into an element whose point lies on the $X_{n+\epsilon-\tau}$ with the equations

$$F^a(\epsilon\overset{*}{\xi}{}^0, \epsilon\,'\xi^0, \overset{*}{\xi}{}^\kappa, '\xi^\kappa) = 0 \quad (a = 1,\ldots, \tau), \tag{4.23}$$

and, according to the invariance of the property of being joined, this element is tangent to the $X_{n+\epsilon-\tau}$. Hence the ∞^n elements belonging to the point $\epsilon\underset{*}{\xi}{}^0, \underset{*}{\xi}{}^\kappa$ are transformed into the $N_n^{n+\epsilon-\tau}$ with this $X_{n+\epsilon-\tau}$ as field region. Similarly by the inverse C_1-transformation the ∞^n elements belonging to a point $\epsilon\,'\underset{*}{\xi}{}^0, '\underset{*}{\xi}{}^\kappa$ are transformed into the $N_n^{n+\epsilon-\tau}$ with the field region

$$F^a(\epsilon\xi^0, \epsilon\,'\underset{*}{\xi}{}^0, \xi^\kappa, '\underset{*}{\xi}{}^\kappa) = 0 \quad (a = 1,..., \tau), \tag{4.24}$$

and the $X_{n+\epsilon-\tau}$ mentioned first is contracted into the point $\epsilon\underset{*}{\xi}{}^0, \underset{*}{\xi}{}^\kappa$. From this it follows that a C_1-transformation and its inverse transformation always have the same rank.

If the rank $n+\epsilon-\tau$ has the minimum value zero, all elements belonging to one and the same point transform into elements belonging to one and the same point as well. Hence in this case the C_1-transformation belongs to one definite point transformation and from this point transformation the C_1-transformation can be derived uniquely for $\epsilon = 1$ and to within a scalar factor for $\epsilon = 0$. C_1-transformations of this special kind are called *extended point transformations*.

Since it is possible to reduce every C_1-transformation with $\epsilon = 1$ to a C_1-transformation with $\epsilon = 0$ by the introduction of homogeneous components, in the geometrical exposition which now follows we consider only the case $\epsilon = 0$. If the equations

$$f^x(\xi^\kappa) = 0 \quad (x = \mathrm{m}+1,..., \mathrm{n}) \tag{4.25}$$

represent an arbitrary X_m in X_n, every vector at a point of the X_m and tangent to the X_m has components of the form

$$w_\lambda = \zeta_x\, \partial_\lambda f^x \quad (x = \mathrm{m}+1,..., \mathrm{n}). \tag{4.26}$$

If now a C_1-transformation of rank $n-\tau$ and with the equations

$$\begin{aligned} &(a) \qquad '\xi^\kappa = '\phi^\kappa(\xi^\kappa, w_\lambda), \\ &(b) \qquad 'w_\lambda = '\psi_\lambda(\xi^\kappa, w_\lambda) \end{aligned} \tag{4.27}$$

is applied, every point of X_m with its ∞^n vector elements is transformed into an $X_{n-\tau}$ with the ∞^n vector elements tangent to it. Since the equations (4.27 a) are homogeneous of degree zero in the w_λ, the equations

$$'\xi^\kappa = '\phi^\kappa(\xi^\kappa, \zeta_x\, \partial_\lambda f^x) \quad (x = \mathrm{m}+1,..., \mathrm{n}) \tag{4.28}$$

are homogeneous of degree zero in the ζ_x. Hence, if the ξ^κ and the $n-m-1$ ratios of the ζ_x are eliminated from (4.25) and (4.28) there remains at least one, and 'in general' one equation, representing an

X_{n-1} containing the points of the transforms of all vector elements tangent to the X_m. If (4.28) is considered as a parametric form of this X_{n-1} with the $2n-m$ parameters ξ^κ, ζ_x, subject to the $n-m$ conditions (4.25), for every linear element $d'\xi^\kappa$ of this X_{n-1} the relation

$$d'\xi^\kappa = \frac{\partial' \phi^\kappa}{\partial \xi^\lambda} d\xi^\lambda + \left\{\frac{\partial' \phi^\kappa}{\partial w_\lambda} d(\zeta_x \, \partial_\lambda f^x)\right\}_{w_\lambda = \zeta_x \partial_\lambda f^x} \qquad (x = \mathrm{m}+1,\ldots,\mathrm{n}) \tag{4.29}$$

holds, where $d\xi^\kappa$ has to satisfy the conditions

$$d\xi^\mu \partial_\mu f^x = 0 \quad (x = \mathrm{m}+1,\ldots,\mathrm{n}). \tag{4.30}$$

Now from (4.22), (4.26), (4.29), and (4.30) we get

$$\begin{aligned} 'w_\lambda d'\xi^\lambda &= {'w_\lambda} \frac{\partial' \phi^\lambda}{\partial \xi^\mu} d\xi^\mu + \left\{'w_\mu \frac{\partial' \phi^\mu}{\partial w_\lambda} d(\zeta_x \, \partial_\lambda f^x)\right\}_{w_\lambda = \zeta_x \partial_\lambda f^x} \\ &= \frac{\sigma}{\sigma'} w_\lambda d\xi^\lambda = \frac{\sigma}{\sigma'} \zeta_x d\xi^\lambda \partial_\lambda f^x = 0 \qquad (x = \mathrm{m}+1,\ldots,\mathrm{n}) \end{aligned} \tag{4.31}$$

and from this it follows that the ∞^n vector elements tangent to the X_m are transformed into the ∞^n vector elements tangent to the X_{n-1}. For $m = n-1$ this implies that a C_1-transformation transforms an X_{n-1} 'in general' into an X_{n-1}. But only 'in general', because to any given C_1-transformation of rank $n-1$ there always exist X_{n-1}'s transforming into a point. If two X_{n-1}'s tangent to each other, are transformed into two X_{n-1}'s it follows from the invariance of the property of being joined that the resulting X_{n-1}'s are tangent to each other as well. The name 'contact transformation' is due to this property.

In order to construct the most general C_1-transformation it is also possible to use the rule II of VI, § 2, instead of the rule I. Writing q_0 and $'q_0$ for $\epsilon\sigma$ and $\epsilon'\sigma$ respectively (4.9) takes the form

$$'q_\lambda d'\xi^\lambda - q_\lambda d\xi^\lambda = 0 \quad (\lambda = 1-\epsilon,\ldots,n). \tag{4.32}$$

If rule II is applied to this Pfaffian we get $2n+2\epsilon$ equations of the form

$$\begin{aligned} &(a) \quad \xi^a - \frac{\partial V}{\partial q_a} = 0, \qquad &(c) \quad q_x + \frac{\partial V}{\partial \xi^x} = 0, \\ &(b) \quad '\xi^b + \frac{\partial V}{\partial' q_b} = 0, \qquad &(d) \quad 'q_y - \frac{\partial V}{\partial' \xi^y} = 0 \end{aligned} \tag{4.33}$$

$$(a = 1-\epsilon,\ldots,\tau_1-\epsilon;\ x = \tau_1-\epsilon+1,\ldots,n;$$
$$b = 1-\epsilon,\ldots,\tau_2-\epsilon;\ y = \tau_2-\epsilon+1,\ldots,n),$$

representing the most general $X_{2n+2\epsilon}$ enveloped by the covariant vector field belonging to (4.32) in the $X_{4n+4\epsilon}$ of ξ^κ, $'\xi^\kappa$, q_λ, $'q_\lambda$ $(\kappa, \lambda = 1-\epsilon,\ldots,n)$. The equations (4.33 a, b) are homogeneous of degree zero and (4.33 c, d)

homogeneous of degree one in the q_λ, $'q_\lambda$ $(\lambda = 1-\epsilon,\ldots,n)$. We obtain from (4.33) by eliminating $'\sigma/\sigma$ for $\epsilon = 1$ and by replacing $'\sigma/\sigma$ by an arbitrary function of ξ^κ and w_λ $(\kappa,\lambda = 1,\ldots,n)$ analytic and non-vanishing in the region considered for $\epsilon = 0$, $2n+\epsilon$ equations in the $4n+2\epsilon$ variables $\epsilon\xi^0$, $\epsilon\,'\xi^0$, ξ^κ, w_λ, $'\xi^\kappa$, $'w_\lambda$ $(\kappa,\lambda = 1,\ldots,n)$. Now the function V has to be chosen in such a way that these $2n+\epsilon$ equations can be solved with respect to $\epsilon\xi^0$, ξ^κ, and w_λ and with respect to $\epsilon\,'\xi^0$, $'\xi^\kappa$, $'w_\lambda$. A necessary and sufficient condition is that the equations (4.33) can be solved with respect to ξ^κ and q_λ and with respect to $'\xi^\kappa$ and $'q_\lambda$ $(\kappa,\lambda = 1-\epsilon,\ldots,n)$. If the functional determinant of (4.33) with respect to ξ^κ and q_λ $(\kappa,\lambda = 1-\epsilon,\ldots,n)$ is written out it becomes evident that this determinant does not vanish if and only if

$$\begin{array}{c} \overset{\longleftarrow \tau_1 \longrightarrow\longleftarrow n+\epsilon-\tau_1 \longrightarrow}{} \\ \begin{array}{l} \updownarrow \tau_2 \\ \updownarrow n+\epsilon-\tau_2 \end{array} \begin{vmatrix} \dfrac{\partial^2 V}{\partial q_a\,\partial\,'q_b} & \dfrac{\partial^2 V}{\partial \xi^x \partial\,'q_b} \\ \dfrac{\partial^2 V}{\partial q_a\,\partial\,'\xi^y} & \dfrac{\partial^2 V}{\partial \xi^x \partial\,'\xi^y} \end{vmatrix} \neq 0 \end{array} \qquad \begin{array}{l} (a = 1-\epsilon,\ldots,\tau_1-\epsilon; \\ x = \tau_1-\epsilon+1,\ldots,n; \\ b = 1-\epsilon,\ldots,\tau_2-\epsilon; \\ y = \tau_2-\epsilon+1,\ldots,n). \end{array} \tag{4.34}$$

The necessary and sufficient conditions for the solubility with respect to $'\xi^\kappa$ and $'q_\lambda$ are the same.

We collect results in the following rule:

Rule II *for the construction of the most general C_1-transformation.*

The most general C_1-transformation in $\epsilon\xi^0$, ξ^κ, w_λ is obtained by

(1) *writing q_0 and $'q_0$ for $\epsilon\sigma$ and $\epsilon\,'\sigma$ respectively;*

(2) *permuting the ξ^κ $(\kappa = 1-\epsilon,\ldots,n)$ in an arbitrary way and the q_λ $(\lambda = 1-\epsilon,\ldots,n)$ in the same way;*

(3) *permuting the $'\xi^\kappa$ $(\kappa = 1-\epsilon,\ldots,n)$ in an arbitrary way and the $'q_\lambda$ $(\lambda = 1-\epsilon,\ldots,n)$ in the same way;*

(4) *choosing two integers τ_1 and τ_2 such that*

$$0 \leqslant \tau_1 \leqslant n+\epsilon, \quad 0 \leqslant \tau_2 \leqslant n+\epsilon, \quad \tau_1+\tau_2 \geqslant 1.$$

(5) *choosing an arbitrary function V of the $2n+2\epsilon$ variables*

$$\begin{array}{ll} q_a, \xi^x & (a = 1-\epsilon,\ldots,\tau_1-\epsilon;\ x = \tau_1-\epsilon+1,\ldots,n), \\ 'q_b, '\xi^y & (b = 1-\epsilon,\ldots,\tau_2-\epsilon;\ y = \tau_2-\epsilon+1,\ldots,n) \end{array} \tag{4.35}$$

analytic in the region considered, homogeneous of degree one in q_a, $'q_b$, and such that the determinant (4.34) *does not vanish in that region;*

(6) *writing out the $2n+2\epsilon$ equations* (4.33) *and deriving from these equations the $2n+\epsilon$ equations in the $4n+2\epsilon$ variables $\epsilon\xi^0$, ξ^κ, w_λ, $\epsilon\,'\xi^0$, $'\xi^\kappa$, $'w_\lambda$ of the most general C_1-transformation:*

(7 *a*) *for* $\epsilon = 0$ *by replacing* $'\sigma/\sigma$ *by an arbitrary function of* ξ^κ *and* w_λ $(\kappa, \lambda = 1,\ldots, n)$, *analytic and non-vanishing in the region considered, and*

(7 *b*) *for* $\epsilon = 1$ *by eliminating* $'\sigma/\sigma$.

If $\epsilon = 1$ there are four possible cases. After the permutations (2) and (3) it may be that

(*a*) σ belongs to the q_a and $'\sigma$ to the $'q_b$;
(*b*) σ belongs to the q_a and $'\sigma$ to the $'q_y$;
(*c*) σ belongs to the q_x and $'\sigma$ to the $'q_b$;
(*d*) σ belongs to the q_x and $'\sigma$ to the $'q_y$.

In case (*a*) the indices a and b may always be permuted afterwards among themselves in such a way that $\sigma = q_0$ and $'\sigma = 'q_0$. If then for the sake of simplicity we write τ_1 instead of $\tau_1 - 1$ and τ_2 instead of $\tau_2 - 1$, (4.33) takes the form

$$\begin{aligned}
&(a) \quad \begin{cases} \xi^0 - \dfrac{\partial V}{\partial \sigma} = 0, \\ \xi^{\mathfrak{a}} - \dfrac{\partial V}{\partial q_{\mathfrak{a}}} = 0 \quad (\mathfrak{a} = 1,\ldots,\tau_1); \end{cases} \\
&(b) \quad \begin{cases} '\xi^0 + \dfrac{\partial V}{\partial\, '\sigma} = 0, \\ '\xi^{\mathfrak{b}} + \dfrac{\partial V}{\partial\, 'q_{\mathfrak{b}}} = 0 \quad (\mathfrak{b} = 1,\ldots,\tau_2); \end{cases} \\
&(c) \quad q_{\mathfrak{x}} + \frac{\partial V}{\partial \xi^{\mathfrak{x}}} = 0 \quad (\mathfrak{x} = \tau_1+1,\ldots,n); \\
&(d) \quad 'q_{\mathfrak{y}} - \frac{\partial V}{\partial\, '\xi^{\mathfrak{y}}} = 0 \quad (\mathfrak{y} = \tau_2+1,\ldots,n) \\
&\qquad (0 \leqslant \tau_1 \leqslant n, \quad 0 \leqslant \tau_2 \leqslant n).
\end{aligned} \tag{4.36}$$

In case (*b*) by suitable permutations and writing τ_1 instead of $\tau_1 - 1$ we obtain

$$\begin{aligned}
&(a) \quad \begin{cases} \xi^0 - \dfrac{\partial V}{\partial \sigma} = 0, \\ \xi^{\mathfrak{a}} - \dfrac{\partial V}{\partial q_{\mathfrak{a}}} = 0 \quad (\mathfrak{a} = 1,\ldots,\tau_1); \end{cases} \qquad (c) \quad q_{\mathfrak{x}} + \frac{\partial V}{\partial \xi^{\mathfrak{x}}} = 0 \quad (\mathfrak{x} = \tau_1+1,\ldots,n); \\
&(b) \quad '\xi^{\mathfrak{b}} + \frac{\partial V}{\partial\, 'q_{\mathfrak{b}}} = 0 \quad (\mathfrak{b} = 1,\ldots,\tau_2); \qquad (d) \quad \begin{cases} '\sigma - \dfrac{\partial V}{\partial\, '\xi^0} = 0, \\ 'q_{\mathfrak{y}} - \dfrac{\partial V}{\partial\, '\xi^{\mathfrak{y}}} = 0 \quad (\mathfrak{y} = \tau_2+1,\ldots,n). \end{cases}
\end{aligned} \tag{4.37}$$

In case (*c*) by suitable permutations and writing τ_2 instead of $\tau_2 - 1$ we obtain

$$(a)\ \xi^{\mathfrak{a}} - \frac{\partial V}{\partial q_{\mathfrak{a}}} = 0\ (\mathfrak{a} = 1,\dots,\tau_1); \qquad (c) \begin{cases} \sigma + \dfrac{\partial V}{\partial \xi^0} = 0, \\ q_{\mathfrak{x}} + \dfrac{\partial V}{\partial \xi^{\mathfrak{x}}} = 0\ (\mathfrak{x} = \tau_1 + 1,\dots, n); \end{cases}$$

$$(b) \begin{cases} '\xi^0 + \dfrac{\partial V}{\partial\, '\sigma} = 0, \\ '\xi^{\mathfrak{b}} + \dfrac{\partial V}{\partial\, 'q_{\mathfrak{b}}} = 0\ (\mathfrak{b} = 1,\dots,\tau_2); \end{cases} \qquad (d)\ 'q_{\mathfrak{y}} - \frac{\partial V}{\partial\, '\xi^{\mathfrak{y}}} = 0\ (\mathfrak{y} = \tau_2 + 1,\dots, n). \tag{4.38}$$

In case (*d*) by suitable permutations we obtain

$$(a)\ \xi^{\mathfrak{a}} - \frac{\partial V}{\partial q_{\mathfrak{a}}} = 0\ (\mathfrak{a} = 1,\dots,\tau_1); \qquad (c) \begin{cases} \sigma + \dfrac{\partial V}{\partial \xi^0} = 0, \\ q_{\mathfrak{x}} + \dfrac{\partial V}{\partial \xi^{\mathfrak{x}}} = 0\ (\mathfrak{x} = \tau_1 + 1,\dots, n); \end{cases}$$

$$(b)\ '\xi^{\mathfrak{b}} + \frac{\partial V}{\partial\, 'q_{\mathfrak{b}}} = 0\ (\mathfrak{b} = 1,\dots,\tau_2); \qquad (d) \begin{cases} '\sigma - \dfrac{\partial V}{\partial\, '\xi^0} = 0, \\ 'q_{\mathfrak{y}} - \dfrac{\partial V}{\partial\, '\xi^{\mathfrak{y}}} = 0\ (\mathfrak{y} = \tau_2 + 1,\dots, n). \end{cases} \tag{4.39}$$

In order to give an example we will write out the conditions for the function V. We choose the case (*b*). In that case (4.34) takes the form

$$\begin{array}{c} \\ \tau_2 \\ 1 \\ n-\tau_2 \end{array} \begin{array}{c} \begin{array}{ccc} \longleftarrow 1 \longrightarrow & \longleftarrow \tau_1 \longrightarrow & \longleftarrow n-\tau_1 \longrightarrow \end{array} \\ \begin{vmatrix} \dfrac{\partial^2 V}{\partial\sigma\partial\, 'q_{\mathfrak{b}}} & \dfrac{\partial^2 V}{\partial q_{\mathfrak{a}}\, \partial\, 'q_{\mathfrak{b}}} & \dfrac{\partial^2 V}{\partial \xi^{\mathfrak{x}} \partial\, 'q_{\mathfrak{b}}} \\ \dfrac{\partial^2 V}{\partial\sigma\partial\, '\xi^0} & \dfrac{\partial^2 V}{\partial q_{\mathfrak{a}}\, \partial\, '\xi^0} & \dfrac{\partial^2 V}{\partial \xi^{\mathfrak{x}} \partial\, '\xi^0} \\ \dfrac{\partial^2 V}{\partial\sigma\partial\, '\xi^{\mathfrak{y}}} & \dfrac{\partial^2 V}{\partial q_{\mathfrak{a}}\, \partial\, '\xi^{\mathfrak{y}}} & \dfrac{\partial^2 V}{\partial \xi^{\mathfrak{x}} \partial\, '\xi^{\mathfrak{y}}} \end{vmatrix} \end{array} \neq 0 \qquad \begin{array}{l} (\mathfrak{a} = 1,\dots,\tau_1; \\ \mathfrak{b} = 1,\dots,\tau_2; \\ \mathfrak{x} = \tau_1 + 1,\dots, n; \\ \mathfrak{y} = \tau_2 + 1,\dots, n). \end{array} \tag{4.40}$$

The function V is called a *generating function* of the C_1-transformation. It is interesting to ask if, given a C_1-transformation, and definite permutations of the variables ξ^κ, q_λ and of $'\xi^\kappa$, $'q_\lambda$ ($\kappa, \lambda = 1-\epsilon,\dots, n$), a generating function exists depending just on the variables q_a, ξ^x, $'q_b$, and $'\xi^y$ ($a = 1-\epsilon,\dots,\tau_1-\epsilon$; $x = \tau_1-\epsilon+1,\dots, n$; $b = 1-\epsilon,\dots,\tau_2-\epsilon$; $y = \tau_2-\epsilon+1,\dots, n$). From (4.33) it follows that V is determined to within an additive constant term if it is possible to express ξ^a, $'\xi^b$, q_x, and $'q_y$ in terms of q_a, $'q_b$, ξ^x, $'\xi^y$ and this is possible if and only if after replacing w_λ and $'w_\lambda$ in (4.1, 3*a*) by q_λ/σ and $'q_\lambda/'\sigma$ ($\lambda = 1,\dots, n$)

respectively, the functional determinant of (4.15) with respect to the variables ξ^a, $'\xi^b$, q_x, and $'q_y$ is $\neq 0$.

For $\epsilon = 0$ (4.15) takes the form

$$\begin{aligned} &'\xi^b - '\Phi^b(\xi^\kappa, q_\lambda) = 0 \\ &'\xi^y - '\Phi^y(\xi^\kappa, q_\lambda) = 0 \quad (b = 1,\dots,\tau_2;\ y = \tau_2+1,\dots,n; \\ &'q_b - '\Psi_b(\xi^\kappa, q_\lambda) = 0 \qquad\qquad \kappa, \lambda = 1,\dots,n) \\ &'q_y - '\Psi_y(\xi^\kappa, q_\lambda) = 0 \end{aligned} \tag{4.41}$$

and the necessary and sufficient conditions that these equations be soluble with respect to ξ^a, $'\xi^b$, q_x, and $'q_y$ is that

$$\begin{array}{c|cc|} & \leftarrow \tau_1 \rightarrow & \leftarrow n-\tau_1 \rightarrow \\ n-\tau_2 & \dfrac{\partial '\Phi^y}{\partial \xi^a} & \dfrac{\partial '\Phi^y}{\partial q_x} \\ \tau_2 & \dfrac{\partial '\Psi_b}{\partial \xi^a} & \dfrac{\partial '\Psi_b}{\partial q_x} \end{array} \neq 0 \quad \begin{array}{l} (a = 1,\dots,\tau_1;\ x = \tau_1+1,\dots,n; \\ \ b = 1,\dots,\tau_2;\ y = \tau_2+1,\dots,n). \end{array} \tag{4.42}$$

Incidentally it follows from (4.41) that the identical transformation can only be obtained for $\tau_1 = n$, $\tau_2 = 0$ or $\tau_1 = 0$, $\tau_2 = n$ because for this transformation we have

$$'\Phi^y = \xi^y, \quad '\Psi_b = q_b. \tag{4.43}$$

For instance, $$V = q_\lambda\, '\xi^\lambda \quad \text{with} \quad '\sigma/\sigma = 1 \tag{4.44}$$

and $$V = -'q_\lambda\, \xi^\lambda \quad \text{with} \quad '\sigma/\sigma = 1 \tag{4.45}$$

are generating functions of the identical transformation for $\epsilon = 0$.

For $\epsilon = 1$ and case (a) (4.15) takes the form

$$\begin{aligned} &'\xi^0 - '\Phi^0(\xi^0, \sigma, \xi^\kappa, q_\lambda) = 0 \\ &'\xi^{\mathfrak{b}} - '\Phi^{\mathfrak{b}}(\xi^0, \sigma, \xi^\kappa, q_\lambda) = 0 \\ &'\xi^{\mathfrak{y}} - '\Phi^{\mathfrak{y}}(\xi^0, \sigma, \xi^\kappa, q_\lambda) = 0 \quad (\mathfrak{b} = 1,\dots,\tau_2;\ \mathfrak{y} = \tau_2+1,\dots,n; \\ &'q_{\mathfrak{b}} - '\Psi_{\mathfrak{b}}(\xi^0, \sigma, \xi^\kappa, q_\lambda) = 0 \qquad\qquad \kappa, \lambda = 1,\dots,n) \\ &'q_{\mathfrak{y}} - '\Psi_{\mathfrak{y}}(\xi^0, \sigma, \xi^\kappa, q_\lambda) = 0 \\ &'\sigma - '\Psi_0(\xi^0, \sigma, \xi^\kappa, q_\lambda) = 0 \end{aligned} \tag{4.46}$$

and as a necessary and sufficient condition that these equations are soluble with respect to ξ^0, $\xi^{\mathfrak{a}}$, $'\xi^0$, $'\xi^{\mathfrak{b}}$, $q_{\mathfrak{x}}$, and $'q_{\mathfrak{y}}$ we get

$$\begin{array}{c|ccc|} & \leftarrow 1 \rightarrow & \leftarrow \tau_1 \rightarrow & \leftarrow n-\tau_1 \rightarrow \\ n-\tau_2 & \dfrac{\partial '\Phi^{\mathfrak{y}}}{\partial \xi^0} & \dfrac{\partial '\Phi^{\mathfrak{y}}}{\partial \xi^{\mathfrak{a}}} & \dfrac{\partial '\Phi^{\mathfrak{y}}}{\partial q_{\mathfrak{x}}} \\ \tau_2 & \dfrac{\partial '\Psi_{\mathfrak{b}}}{\partial \xi^0} & \dfrac{\partial '\Psi_{\mathfrak{b}}}{\partial \xi^{\mathfrak{a}}} & \dfrac{\partial '\Psi_{\mathfrak{b}}}{\partial q_{\mathfrak{x}}} \\ 1 & \dfrac{\partial '\Psi_0}{\partial \xi^0} & \dfrac{\partial '\Psi_0}{\partial \xi^{\mathfrak{a}}} & \dfrac{\partial '\Psi_0}{\partial q_{\mathfrak{x}}} \end{array} \neq 0 \quad \begin{array}{l} (\mathfrak{a} = 1,\dots,\tau_1; \\ \ \mathfrak{x} = \tau_1+1,\dots,n; \\ \ \mathfrak{b} = 1,\dots,\tau_2; \\ \ \mathfrak{y} = \tau_2+1,\dots,n). \end{array} \tag{4.47}$$

In the same way we get in case (b) the necessary and sufficient conditions

$$\begin{array}{cc} & \begin{array}{ccc} \longleftarrow 1 \longrightarrow & \longleftarrow \tau_1 \longrightarrow & \longleftarrow n-\tau_1 \longrightarrow \end{array} \\ \begin{array}{c} \updownarrow 1 \\[2ex] \updownarrow n-\tau_2 \\[2ex] \updownarrow \tau_2 \end{array} & \left|\begin{array}{ccc} \dfrac{\partial\,{}'\Phi^0}{\partial\xi^0} & \dfrac{\partial\,{}'\Phi^0}{\partial\xi^{\mathfrak{a}}} & \dfrac{\partial\,{}'\Phi^0}{\partial q_{\mathfrak{x}}} \\[2ex] \dfrac{\partial\,{}'\Phi^{\mathfrak{y}}}{\partial\xi^0} & \dfrac{\partial\,{}'\Phi^{\mathfrak{y}}}{\partial\xi^{\mathfrak{a}}} & \dfrac{\partial\,{}'\Phi^{\mathfrak{y}}}{\partial q_{\mathfrak{x}}} \\[2ex] \dfrac{\partial\,{}'\Psi_{\mathfrak{b}}}{\partial\xi^0} & \dfrac{\partial\,{}'\Psi_{\mathfrak{b}}}{\partial\xi^{\mathfrak{a}}} & \dfrac{\partial\,{}'\Psi_{\mathfrak{b}}}{\partial q_{\mathfrak{x}}} \end{array}\right| \end{array} \neq 0 \qquad \begin{array}{l} (\mathfrak{a} = 1,\dots,\tau_1; \\ \ \mathfrak{x} = \tau_1+1,\dots,n; \\ \ \mathfrak{b} = 1,\dots,\tau_2; \\ \ \mathfrak{y} = \tau_2+1,\dots,n); \end{array} \tag{4.48}$$

in case (c)

$$\begin{array}{cc} & \begin{array}{ccc} \longleftarrow \tau_1 \longrightarrow & \longleftarrow 1 \longrightarrow & \longleftarrow n-\tau_1 \longrightarrow \end{array} \\ \begin{array}{c} \updownarrow n-\tau_2 \\[2ex] \updownarrow \tau_2 \\[2ex] \updownarrow 1 \end{array} & \left|\begin{array}{ccc} \dfrac{\partial\,{}'\Phi^{\mathfrak{y}}}{\partial\xi^{\mathfrak{a}}} & \dfrac{\partial\,{}'\Phi^{\mathfrak{y}}}{\partial\sigma} & \dfrac{\partial\,{}'\Phi^{\mathfrak{y}}}{\partial q_{\mathfrak{x}}} \\[2ex] \dfrac{\partial\,{}'\Psi_{\mathfrak{b}}}{\partial\xi^{\mathfrak{a}}} & \dfrac{\partial\,{}'\Psi_{\mathfrak{b}}}{\partial\sigma} & \dfrac{\partial\,{}'\Psi_{\mathfrak{b}}}{\partial q_{\mathfrak{x}}} \\[2ex] \dfrac{\partial\,{}'\Psi_0}{\partial\xi^{\mathfrak{a}}} & \dfrac{\partial\,{}'\Psi_0}{\partial\sigma} & \dfrac{\partial\,{}'\Psi_0}{\partial q_{\mathfrak{x}}} \end{array}\right| \end{array} \neq 0 \qquad \begin{array}{l} (\mathfrak{a} = 1,\dots,\tau_1; \\ \ \mathfrak{x} = \tau_1+1,\dots,n; \\ \ \mathfrak{b} = 1,\dots,\tau_2; \\ \ \mathfrak{y} = \tau_2+1,\dots,n); \end{array} \tag{4.49}$$

and in case (d)

$$\begin{array}{cc} & \begin{array}{ccc} \longleftarrow \tau_1 \longrightarrow & \longleftarrow 1 \longrightarrow & \longleftarrow n-\tau_1 \longrightarrow \end{array} \\ \begin{array}{c} \updownarrow 1 \\[2ex] \updownarrow n-\tau_2 \\[2ex] \updownarrow \tau_2 \end{array} & \left|\begin{array}{ccc} \dfrac{\partial\,{}'\Phi^0}{\partial\xi^{\mathfrak{a}}} & \dfrac{\partial\,{}'\Phi^0}{\partial\sigma} & \dfrac{\partial\,{}'\Phi^0}{\partial q_{\mathfrak{x}}} \\[2ex] \dfrac{\partial\,{}'\Phi^{\mathfrak{y}}}{\partial\xi^{\mathfrak{a}}} & \dfrac{\partial\,{}'\Phi^{\mathfrak{y}}}{\partial\sigma} & \dfrac{\partial\,{}'\Phi^{\mathfrak{y}}}{\partial q_{\mathfrak{x}}} \\[2ex] \dfrac{\partial\,{}'\Psi_{\mathfrak{b}}}{\partial\xi^{\mathfrak{a}}} & \dfrac{\partial\,{}'\Psi_{\mathfrak{b}}}{\partial\sigma} & \dfrac{\partial\,{}'\Psi_{\mathfrak{b}}}{\partial q_{\mathfrak{x}}} \end{array}\right| \end{array} \neq 0 \qquad \begin{array}{l} (\mathfrak{a} = 1,\dots,\tau_1; \\ \ \mathfrak{x} = \tau_1+1,\dots,n; \\ \ \mathfrak{b} = 1,\dots,\tau_2; \\ \ \mathfrak{y} = \tau_2+1,\dots,n). \end{array} \tag{4.50}$$

Now for $\epsilon = 1$ we have for the identical transformation

$$'\Phi^0 = \xi^0, \quad '\Phi^{\mathfrak{y}} = \xi^{\mathfrak{y}}, \quad '\Psi_0 = \sigma, \quad '\Psi_{\mathfrak{b}} = q_{\mathfrak{b}}$$

$$(\mathfrak{b} = 1,\dots,\tau_2; \quad \mathfrak{y} = \tau_2+1,\dots,n) \tag{4.51}$$

and from this it follows that the identical transformation cannot be obtained in the cases (a) and (d) because the determinants (4.47) and (4.50) vanish if the values (4.51) are substituted in them. From the form of (4.48) and (4.49) we see that in the cases (b) and (c) the identical transformation can only be obtained if $\tau_1 = n$, $\tau_2 = 0$ or $\tau_1 = 0$, $\tau_2 = n$. Hence generating functions for the identical transformation are in case (b):

$$V = \sigma\,'\xi^0 + q_\lambda\,'\xi^\lambda \quad (\tau_1 = n;\ \tau_2 = 0) \tag{4.52}$$

and

$$V = \sigma\,'\xi^0 - {}'q_\lambda\,\xi^\lambda \quad (\tau_1 = 0;\ \tau_2 = n); \tag{4.53}$$

and in case (c):

$$V = -{}'\sigma\,\xi^0 + q_\lambda\,'\xi^\lambda \quad (\tau_1 = n;\ \tau_2 = 0) \tag{4.54}$$

and

$$V = -{}'\sigma\,\xi^0 - {}'q_\lambda\,\xi^\lambda \quad (\tau_1 = 0;\ \tau_2 = n). \tag{4.55}$$

5. Contact transformations of the third kind†

It may happen that the C_1-transformation leaves the Pfaffian $\epsilon\, d\xi^0 + w_\lambda\, d\xi^\lambda$ invariant and consequently $'\sigma = \sigma$. C_1-transformations of this kind we call *contact transformations of the third kind* or briefly *C_3-transformations.*‡ If a C_3-transformation is field-preserving with respect to the field $\epsilon w_0 = \epsilon$, $w_\lambda = f_\lambda(\epsilon\xi^0, \xi^\kappa)$, it follows from the invariance of $\epsilon\, d\xi^0 + w_\lambda\, d\xi^\lambda$ *that not only the similarity class k and the characteristics are invariant but also the rotation class 2ρ and the supports of rotation and consequently also the class K and the supports.*

C_3-transformations possess still another invariance. If the integral

$$\int_A^B (\epsilon\, d\xi^0 + w_\lambda\, d\xi^\lambda) \tag{5.1}$$

is formed over the field region of an $\mathfrak{N}_1$ with field dimension 1 between the points A and B, it follows from the invariance of the Pfaffian that this integral is invariant with all C_3-transformations. The integral vanishes for every choice of A and B if and only if $\mathfrak{N}_1$ is an N_1. Hence, if the $\mathfrak{N}_1$ is not an N_1 it can never be transformed into an $\mathfrak{N}_1$ with field dimension 0 by a C_3-transformation.

For $\epsilon = 0$ the most general C_3-transformation may be found easily because by application either of the rule I or of the rule II of VI, § 4, we are free to choose $'\sigma/\sigma$ arbitrarily at the end and we may choose $'\sigma/\sigma = 1$.

Applying rule I to the case $\epsilon = 0$ it is convenient to write χ_a instead of χ_a/σ. Then the equations (4.11) take the form

$$w_\lambda = -\chi_a \frac{\partial F^a}{\partial \xi^\lambda}, \qquad 'w_\lambda = \chi_a \frac{\partial F^a}{\partial\, '\xi^\lambda} \quad (a = 1,..., \tau;\ 1 \leqslant \tau \leqslant n) \tag{5.2}$$

and from these $2n$ equations by elimination of the χ_a we get $2n-\tau$ equations which together with (4.10) represent the C_3-transformation.

Applying rule I to the case $\epsilon = 1$ the choice of $'\sigma/\sigma$ is not free and the condition $'\sigma/\sigma = 1$ imposes a restriction on the choice of the functions F^a. From (4.11) it follows that

$$\chi_a \left(\frac{\partial F^a}{\partial \xi^0} + \frac{\partial F^a}{\partial\, '\xi^0}\right) = 0 \quad (a = 1,..., \tau) \tag{5.3}$$

and this equation is satisfied for all values of χ_a if and only if the F^a only depend on ξ^0 and $'\xi^0$ in the combination $'\xi^0 - \xi^0$. Thus, writing

$$Z \stackrel{\text{def}}{=} {'\xi^0} - \xi^0, \tag{5.4}$$

† Cf. Lie 1890. 1, chs. v, vi; v. Weber 1900. 1, chs. viii, xi; Whittaker 1917. 1, ch. ix; Goursat 1921. 1, ch. x; Engel and Faber 1932. 1, ch. vii; Eisenhart 1933. 1, ch. vi.

‡ For $\epsilon = 0$ the C_3-transformations are often called *homogeneous contact transformations.*

the equations (4.10) take the form

$$F^a(Z, \xi^\kappa, {}'\xi^\kappa) = 0 \quad (a = 1,..., \tau), \tag{5.5}$$

and the F^a have to be chosen according to the condition that the determinant

$$\begin{array}{c|ccc|}
 & \longleftarrow 1 \longrightarrow & \longleftarrow n \longrightarrow & \longleftarrow \tau \longrightarrow \\
\tau \updownarrow & \dfrac{\partial F^a}{\partial Z} & \dfrac{\partial F^a}{\partial \xi^\lambda} & 0 \\
n \updownarrow & \chi_a \dfrac{\partial^2 F^a}{\partial Z \partial {}'\xi^\mu} & \chi_a \dfrac{\partial^2 F^a}{\partial \xi^\lambda \partial {}'\xi^\mu} & \dfrac{\partial F^a}{\partial {}'\xi^\mu} \\
1 \updownarrow & \chi_a \dfrac{\partial^2 F^a}{\partial Z^2} & \chi_a \dfrac{\partial^2 F}{\partial \xi^\lambda \partial Z} & \dfrac{\partial F^a}{\partial Z}
\end{array} \quad (a = 1,..., \tau) \tag{5.6}$$

does not vanish as a consequence of (5.5). Writing χ_a for the sake of simplicity instead of χ_a/σ the equations (4.11) take the form

$$\begin{aligned}
1 &= \chi_a \frac{\partial F^a}{\partial Z} \\
w_\lambda &= -\chi_a \frac{\partial F^a}{\partial \xi^\lambda} \quad (a = 1,..., \tau) \\
{}'w_\lambda &= \chi_a \frac{\partial F^a}{\partial {}'\xi^\lambda}
\end{aligned} \tag{5.7}$$

and constitute together with (5.5) a system of $2n+\tau+1$ equations, soluble with respect to Z, ξ^κ, w_λ, and χ_a and with respect to Z, ${}'\xi^\kappa$, ${}'w_\lambda$, and χ_a. The process can be further simplified because at least one of the functions F^a has to depend on Z, the determinant (5.6) not being zero. Hence Z can be solved from one of the equations (5.5) and this solution can be substituted in the other equations. Then the determinant becomes much simpler. We restrict ourselves here only to the statement of this fact.

Using (5.4) we get from (5.7) the equations of the C_3-transformation in the form

$$\begin{aligned}
{}'\xi^0 - \xi^0 &= {}'\chi(\xi^\mu, w_\lambda), & {}'\xi^0 - \xi^0 &= \chi({}'\xi^\mu, {}'w_\lambda), \\
{}'\xi^\kappa &= {}'\phi^\kappa(\xi^\mu, w_\lambda), & \xi^\kappa &= \phi^\kappa({}'\xi^\mu, {}'w_\lambda), \\
{}'w_\lambda &= {}'\psi_\lambda(\xi^\mu, w_\lambda), & w_\lambda &= \psi_\lambda({}'\xi^\mu, {}'w_\lambda).
\end{aligned} \tag{5.8}$$

Collecting results we have the rule

Rule I *for the construction of the most general C_3-transformation:*

The most general C_3-transformation in $\epsilon\xi^0$, ξ^κ, w_λ is obtained by

(1) *choosing an arbitrary integer $\tau \geqslant 1$ and $\leqslant n+\epsilon$;*

(2) *choosing τ arbitrary independent equations*

$$F^a(\epsilon Z, \xi^\kappa, '\xi^\kappa) = 0 \quad (a = 1,..., \tau) \tag{5.9}$$

with functions F^a analytic in the region considered and such that the $(n+\tau+\epsilon)$-rowed determinant

$$\begin{vmatrix} \epsilon \dfrac{\partial F^a}{\partial Z} & \dfrac{\partial F^a}{\partial \xi^\lambda} & 0 \\ \epsilon \chi_a \dfrac{\partial^2 F^a}{\partial Z \partial '\xi^\mu} & \chi_a \dfrac{\partial^2 F^a}{\partial \xi^\lambda \partial '\xi^\mu} & \dfrac{\partial F^a}{\partial '\xi^\mu} \\ \epsilon \chi_a \dfrac{\partial^2 F^a}{\partial Z^2} & \epsilon \chi_a \dfrac{\partial^2 F^a}{\partial \xi^\lambda \partial Z} & \epsilon \dfrac{\partial F^a}{\partial Z} \end{vmatrix} \quad (a = 1,..., \tau) \tag{5.10}$$

(columns: 1, n, τ; rows: τ, n, 1)

does not vanish identically in the χ_a as a consequence of (5.9);

(3) *writing out the $2n+\epsilon$ equations*

$$\begin{gathered} \epsilon = \epsilon \chi_a \frac{\partial F^a}{\partial Z} \quad (a = 1,..., \tau), \\ w_\lambda = -\chi_a \frac{\partial F^a}{\partial \xi^\lambda}, \qquad 'w_\lambda = \chi_a \frac{\partial F^a}{\partial '\xi^\lambda}; \end{gathered} \tag{5.11}$$

(4) *eliminating the χ_a from* (5.11) *and replacing in the remaining $2n+\epsilon-\tau$ equations Z by $'\xi^0-\xi^0$.*

By this process $2n+\epsilon-\tau$ equations in $\epsilon('\xi^0-\xi^0)$, ξ^κ, w_λ, $'\xi^\kappa$, and $'w_\lambda$ are obtained, constituting together with (5.9) *a system of $2n+\epsilon$ equations in these $4n+\epsilon$ variables, soluble with respect to $\epsilon('\xi^0-\xi^0)$, ξ^κ, w_λ and with respect to $\epsilon('\xi^0-\xi^0)$, $'\xi^\kappa$, $'w_\lambda$ and representing the C_3-transformation required.*

Applying rule II in the case $\epsilon = 0$ we have, for $'\sigma = \sigma$,

$$V(q_a, 'q_b, \xi^x, '\xi^y) = \sigma V(w_a, 'w_b, \xi^x, '\xi^y)$$
$$(a = 1,..., \tau_1;\ x = \tau_1+1,..., n;\ b = 1,..., \tau_2;\ y = \tau_2+1,..., n), \tag{5.12}$$

and consequently

$$\begin{aligned} \frac{\partial V(q, 'q, \xi, '\xi)}{\partial q_a} &= \frac{\partial V(w, 'w, \xi, '\xi)}{\partial w_a}, \\ \frac{\partial V(q, 'q, \xi, '\xi)}{\partial 'q_b} &= \frac{\partial V(w, 'w, \xi, '\xi)}{\partial 'w_b}, \\ \frac{\partial V(q, 'q, \xi, '\xi)}{\partial \xi^x} &= \sigma \frac{\partial V(w, 'w, \xi, '\xi)}{\partial \xi^x}, \\ \frac{\partial V(q, 'q, \xi, '\xi)}{\partial '\xi^y} &= \sigma \frac{\partial V(w, 'w, \xi, '\xi)}{\partial '\xi^y}. \end{aligned} \tag{5.13}$$

From this it follows that the equations (4.33) become

$$(a)\quad \xi^a - \frac{\partial V}{\partial w_a} = 0, \qquad (c)\quad w_x + \frac{\partial V}{\partial \xi^x} = 0,$$

$$(b)\quad {}'\xi^b + \frac{\partial V}{\partial\, 'w_b} = 0, \qquad (d)\quad {}'w_y - \frac{\partial V}{\partial\, '\xi^y} = 0$$

$$(a = 1,\ldots,\tau_1;\ x = \tau_1+1,\ldots,n;\ b = 1,\ldots,\tau_2;\ y = \tau_2+1,\ldots,n), \tag{5.14}$$

where V is an arbitrary function of the w_a, $'w_b$, ξ^x, and $'\xi^y$, homogeneous of degree one in w_a, $'w_b$, and satisfies the conditions

$$\overset{\longleftarrow \tau_1 \longrightarrow\ \longleftarrow n-\tau_1 \longrightarrow}{\begin{vmatrix} \dfrac{\partial^2 V}{\partial w_a\, \partial\, 'w_b} & \dfrac{\partial^2 V}{\partial \xi^x \partial\, 'w_b} \\ \dfrac{\partial^2 V}{\partial w_a\, \partial\, '\xi^y} & \dfrac{\partial^2 V}{\partial \xi^x \partial\, '\xi^y} \end{vmatrix}}\begin{matrix} \updownarrow \tau_2 \\ \updownarrow n-\tau_2 \end{matrix} \neq 0. \tag{5.15}$$

The equations (5.14) represent the C_3-transformation. From the homogeneity of the equations (4.15) it follows that in the equations (4.1) not only the $'\phi^\kappa$ are homogeneous of degree zero in the w_λ but, moreover, the $'\psi_\lambda$ are homogeneous of degree one in these variables. But this homogeneity is not characteristic for C_3-transformations because it always occurs if a function homogeneous of degree zero in the w_λ is chosen for $'\sigma/\sigma$.

If we apply rule II in the case $\epsilon = 1$, the choice of σ'/σ is not free and the condition $'\sigma = \sigma$ imposes a restriction on the choice of the generating function V. In order to decide which of the four cases (a), (b), (c), and (d) may occur we return to the equations (4.15) with the variables q_λ, $'q_\lambda$. Comparing (4.15) with (5.8) we get

$$\begin{aligned} '\xi^0 &= {}'\Phi^0(\xi^0, \sigma, \xi^\mu, q_\lambda) = \xi^0 + {}'\chi(\xi^\mu, q_\lambda/\sigma), \\ '\xi^\kappa &= {}'\Phi^\kappa(\xi^0, \sigma, \xi^\mu, q_\lambda) = {}'\phi^\kappa(\xi^\mu, q_\lambda/\sigma) = {}'\phi^\kappa(\xi^\mu, q_\lambda), \\ 'q_\lambda &= {}'\Psi_\lambda(\xi^0, \sigma, \xi^\mu, q_\lambda) = \sigma\, '\psi_\lambda(\xi^\mu, q_\lambda/\sigma) = {}'\psi_\lambda(\xi^\mu, q_\lambda), \\ '\sigma &= {}'\Psi_0(\xi^0, \sigma, \xi^\mu, q_\lambda) = \sigma. \end{aligned} \tag{5.16}$$

From these equations we see that the case (a) cannot occur, because the derivatives of $'\Psi_0$ with respect to ξ^0, ξ^κ, and w_λ vanish. For the three other cases we get the same necessary and sufficient conditions

$$\begin{vmatrix} \dfrac{\partial\, '\Phi^{\mathfrak{y}}}{\partial \xi^{\mathfrak{a}}} & \dfrac{\partial\, '\Phi^{\mathfrak{y}}}{\partial w_{\mathfrak{x}}} \\ \dfrac{\partial\, '\Psi_{\mathfrak{b}}}{\partial \xi^{\mathfrak{a}}} & \dfrac{\partial\, '\Psi_{\mathfrak{b}}}{\partial w_{\mathfrak{x}}} \end{vmatrix} \neq 0 \quad \begin{pmatrix} \mathfrak{a} = 1,\ldots,\tau_1;\ \mathfrak{x} = \tau_1+1,\ldots,n; \\ \mathfrak{b} = 1,\ldots,\tau_2;\ \mathfrak{y} = \tau_2+1,\ldots,n \end{pmatrix}. \tag{5.17}$$

Since the conditions have the same form for the three cases (b), (c), and (d) it follows that for each C_3-transformation there exists at least one generating function for each of these cases. Hence, to construct the most general C_3-transformation it is sufficient to consider one of these cases. We choose the case (b). Then from (4.37 d) it follows that

$$\frac{\partial V}{\partial '\xi^0} = \sigma \tag{5.18}$$

and this implies that V has the form

$$V = \sigma '\xi^0 + U(\sigma, q_{\mathfrak{a}}, 'q_{\mathfrak{b}}, \xi^{\mathfrak{x}}, '\xi^{\mathfrak{y}})$$
$$(\mathfrak{a} = 1,..., \tau_1;\ \mathfrak{x} = \tau_1+1,..., n;\ \mathfrak{b} = 1,..., \tau_2;\ \mathfrak{y} = \tau_2+1,..., n). \tag{5.19}$$

Since V is homogeneous of degree one in σ, $q_{\mathfrak{a}}$, $'q_{\mathfrak{b}}$ we may also write

$$V = \sigma '\xi^0 + \sigma W(w_{\mathfrak{a}}, 'w_{\mathfrak{b}}, \xi^{\mathfrak{x}}, '\xi^{\mathfrak{y}})$$
$$(\mathfrak{a} = 1,..., \tau_1;\ \mathfrak{x} = \tau_1+1,..., n;\ \mathfrak{b} = 1,..., \tau_2;\ \mathfrak{y} = \tau_2+1,..., n). \tag{5.20}$$

Then the equations (4.37) take the form

$$(a)\quad \xi^{\mathfrak{a}} - \frac{\partial W}{\partial w_{\mathfrak{a}}} = 0\ (\mathfrak{a} = 1,..., \tau_1), \qquad (c)\quad w_{\mathfrak{x}} + \frac{\partial W}{\partial \xi^{\mathfrak{x}}} = 0\ (\mathfrak{x} = \tau_1+1,..., n),$$

$$(b)\quad '\xi^{\mathfrak{b}} + \frac{\partial W}{\partial 'w_{\mathfrak{b}}} = 0\ (\mathfrak{b} = 1,..., \tau_2), \qquad (d)\quad 'w_{\mathfrak{y}} - \frac{\partial W}{\partial '\xi^{\mathfrak{y}}} = 0\ (\mathfrak{y} = \tau_2+1,..., n),$$

$$(e)\quad '\xi^0 - \xi^0 = -W + w_{\mathfrak{a}}\frac{\partial W}{\partial w_{\mathfrak{a}}} + 'w_{\mathfrak{b}}\frac{\partial W}{\partial 'w_{\mathfrak{b}}}, \tag{5.21}$$

and we have

$$'w_\lambda d'\xi^\lambda - w_\lambda d\xi^\lambda = -d('\xi^0 - \xi^0) = d\left(W - w_{\mathfrak{a}}\frac{\partial W}{\partial w_{\mathfrak{a}}} - 'w_{\mathfrak{b}}\frac{\partial W}{\partial 'w_{\mathfrak{b}}}\right)$$
$$(\mathfrak{a} = 1,..., \tau_1;\ \mathfrak{b} = 1,..., \tau_2). \tag{5.22}$$

According to (4.40) and (5.20) the conditions for the function W are

$$\overbrace{\quad}^{\tau_1}\ \overbrace{\quad}^{n-\tau_1}$$
$$\begin{matrix} \tau_2 \\ \\ n-\tau_2 \end{matrix}\begin{vmatrix} \dfrac{\partial^2 W}{\partial w_{\mathfrak{a}}\,\partial 'w_{\mathfrak{b}}} & \dfrac{\partial^2 W}{\partial \xi^{\mathfrak{x}}\partial 'w_{\mathfrak{b}}} \\ \dfrac{\partial^2 W}{\partial w_{\mathfrak{a}}\,\partial '\xi^{\mathfrak{y}}} & \dfrac{\partial^2 W}{\partial \xi^{\mathfrak{x}}\partial '\xi^{\mathfrak{y}}} \end{vmatrix} \neq 0 \quad \begin{matrix}(\mathfrak{a} = 1,..., \tau_1;\ \mathfrak{x} = \tau_1+1,..., n; \\ \mathfrak{b} = 1,..., \tau_2;\ \mathfrak{y} = \tau_2+1,..., n).\end{matrix} \tag{5.23}$$

From (5.22) we see that the transformation is a C_3-transformation in ξ^κ, w_λ leaving ξ^0 invariant if and only if W happens to be homogeneous of degree one in $w_{\mathfrak{a}}$, $'w_{\mathfrak{b}}$.

Collecting results we have the rule:

Rule II *for the construction of the most general C_3-transformation:*
The most general C_3-transformation in $\epsilon\xi^0$, ξ^κ, w_λ is obtained by

(1) *permuting the ξ^κ ($\kappa = 1,..., n$) in an arbitrary way and the w_λ ($\lambda = 1,..., n$) in the same way;*

(2) *permuting the* $'\xi^\kappa$ $(\kappa = 1,\ldots,n)$ *in an arbitrary way and the* $'w_\lambda$ $(\lambda = 1,\ldots,n)$ *in the same way;*

(3) *choosing two integers* τ_1 *and* τ_2 *such that* $0 \leqslant \tau_1 \leqslant n$ *and* $0 \leqslant \tau_2 \leqslant n$;

(4) *choosing an arbitrary function* V *of the* $2n$ *variables*

$$\begin{aligned} &w_a,\ \xi^x \quad (a = 1,\ldots,\tau_1;\ x = \tau_1+1,\ldots,n), \\ &'w_b,\ '\xi^y \quad (b = 1,\ldots,\tau_2;\ y = \tau_2+1,\ldots,n), \end{aligned} \tag{5.24}$$

analytic in the region considered, for $\epsilon = 0$ *homogeneous of degree one in* w_a, $'w_b$ *and such that*

$$\begin{vmatrix} \dfrac{\partial^2 V}{\partial w_a \partial' w_b} & \dfrac{\partial^2 V}{\partial \xi^x \partial' w_b} \\ \dfrac{\partial^2 V}{\partial w_a \partial' \xi^y} & \dfrac{\partial^2 V}{\partial \xi^x \partial' \xi^y} \end{vmatrix} \neq 0 \quad \begin{pmatrix} a = 1,\ldots,\tau_1;\ x = \tau_1+1,\ldots,n; \\ b = 1,\ldots,\tau_2;\ y = \tau_2+1,\ldots,n \end{pmatrix} \tag{5.25}$$

(columns: τ_1, $n-\tau_1$; rows: τ_2, $n-\tau_2$)

in that region;

(5) *writing out the* $2n+\epsilon$ *equations*

$$(a)\quad \xi^a = \frac{\partial V}{\partial w_a} \quad (a = 1,\ldots,\tau_1), \qquad (c)\quad w_x = -\frac{\partial V}{\partial \xi^x} \quad (x = \tau_1+1,\ldots,n),$$

$$(b)\quad '\xi^b = -\frac{\partial V}{\partial' w_b} \quad (b = 1,\ldots,\tau_2), \quad (d)\quad 'w_y = \frac{\partial V}{\partial' \xi^y} \quad (y = \tau_2+1,\ldots,n),$$

$$(e)\quad \epsilon\, '\xi^0 - \epsilon \xi^0 = -\epsilon\left(V - w_a \frac{\partial V}{\partial w_a} - 'w_b \frac{\partial V}{\partial' w_b}\right)$$

soluble with respect to $\epsilon('\xi^0 - \xi^0)$, ξ^κ, *and* w_λ *and with respect to* $\epsilon('\xi^0 - \xi^0)$, $'\xi^\kappa$, *and* $'w_\lambda$ *and representing the* C_3*-transformation required.*

6. Contact transformations of the second kind†

If in the equations (4.1) of a C_3-transformation for $\epsilon = 1$ we take

$$\begin{aligned} &(a) \qquad '\xi^0 = \xi^0 + 'f(\xi^\mu, w_\lambda), \\ &(b) \qquad '\xi^\kappa = '\phi^\kappa(\xi^\mu, w_\lambda), \\ &(c) \qquad 'w_\lambda = '\psi_\lambda(\xi^\mu, w_\lambda), \end{aligned} \tag{6.1}$$

the equations (4.2) take the form

$$d'\xi^0 + 'w_\lambda d'\xi^\lambda = d\xi^0 + d'f + 'w_\lambda d'\xi^\lambda = d\xi^0 + w_\lambda d\xi^\lambda. \tag{6.2}$$

From this it follows that the equations (6.1 b, c) of the C_3-transformation in ξ^0, ξ^κ, w_λ represent a transformation in ξ^κ, w_λ leaving the Pfaffian $w_\lambda d\xi^\lambda$ invariant to within an additive complete differential. Though this transformation lacks the typical geometrical properties of a contact

† Cf. Lie 1890. 1, chs. v, vi; v. Weber 1900. 1, chs. viii, xi; Whittaker 1917. 1, ch. ix; Goursat 1921. 1, ch. x; Engel and Faber 1932. 1, ch. vii; Eisenhart 1933. 1, ch. vi.

transformation it is usual to call it by this name. To avoid misunderstandings we will call every invertible transformation of the $\epsilon\xi^0$, ξ^κ, w_λ leaving invariant the Pfaffian $\epsilon\, d\xi^0 + w_\lambda\, d\xi^\lambda$ to within an additive complete differential a *contact transformation of the second kind* or briefly a C_2-transformation. Every C_3-transformation is at the same time a C_1-transformation and a C_2-transformation. A certain duality exists between C_1-transformations and C_2-transformations, closely connected with the duality between the characteristics and the supports of rotation of a vector field.

According to the above definition the invertible transformation

$$
\begin{aligned}
&(a) \qquad & \epsilon\,'\xi^0 &= \epsilon\,'\phi^0(\epsilon\xi^0, \xi^\mu, w_\lambda),\\
&(b) & '\xi^\kappa &= '\phi^\kappa(\epsilon\xi^0, \xi^\mu, w_\lambda),\\
&(c) & 'w_\lambda &= '\psi_\lambda(\epsilon\xi^0, \xi^\mu, w_\lambda)
\end{aligned}
\tag{6.3}
$$

is a C_2-transformation if and only if there exists a relation of the form

$$d\,'s + \epsilon\, d\,'\xi^0 + 'w_\lambda\, d\,'\xi^\lambda = ds + \epsilon\, d\xi^0 + w_\lambda\, d\xi^\lambda, \tag{6.4}$$

s and $'s$ being two suitable functions of $\epsilon\xi^0$, ξ^μ, w_λ or of $\epsilon\,'\xi^0$, $'\xi^\mu$, $'w_\lambda$. Of these functions only the difference

$$'s - s = '\Omega(\epsilon\xi^0, \xi^\kappa, w_\lambda) = \Omega(\epsilon\,'\xi^0, '\xi^\kappa, 'w_\lambda) \tag{6.5}$$

is important. If a C_2-transformation is field-preserving with respect to the field $\epsilon w_0 = \epsilon$, $w_\lambda = f_\lambda(\xi^\kappa)$, it follows from (6.4) *that the rotation class 2ρ and the supports of rotation are invariant but that the similarity class k and the characteristics are in general not invariant.*

C_2-transformations possess still another invariance. If the integral

$$\int (\epsilon\, d\xi^0 + w_\lambda\, d\xi^\lambda) \tag{6.6}$$

is formed over the *closed* field region of an $\mathfrak{N}_1$ with field dimension *1*, it follows from (6.4) that this integral is invariant for C_2-transformations. If the $\mathfrak{N}_1$ is an N_1 the integral is zero, hence the transformed integral is also zero but the transform of the N_1 need not be an N_1. If the integral over a closed field region of an $\mathfrak{N}_1$ with field dimension *1* is not zero, it is impossible to transform the $\mathfrak{N}_1$ into an $\mathfrak{N}_1$ with field dimension zero by a C_2-transformation.

C_2-transformations play an important role in the theory of the transformation of the equations of mechanics.

If we write

$$z \overset{\text{def}}{=} s + \epsilon\xi^0, \qquad 'z \overset{\text{def}}{=} 's + \epsilon\,'\xi^0 \tag{6.7}$$

the equation (6.4) takes the more convenient form

$$d\,'z + 'w_\lambda\, d\,'\xi^\lambda = dz + w_\lambda\, d\xi^\lambda \tag{6.8}$$

and from this form we see that in order to get a C_2-transformation we have to construct a C_3-transformation in the variables z, w_λ, and ξ^κ. If, by applying one of the rules I and II, this has been done, we get, on using (5.8) and (6.7), equations of the form

$$
\begin{aligned}
&(a) \qquad & 's - s + \epsilon '\xi^0 - \epsilon \xi^0 &= '\chi(\xi^\mu, w_\nu), \\
&(b) \qquad & '\xi^\kappa &= '\phi^\kappa(\xi^\mu, w_\nu), \\
&(c) \qquad & 'w_\lambda &= '\psi_\lambda(\xi^\mu, w_\nu).
\end{aligned}
\tag{6.9}
$$

For $\epsilon = 0$ the $2n$ equations (6.9 b, c) represent the C_2-transformation. For $\epsilon = 1$ we have to choose for $'s - s$ an arbitrary function of the ξ^κ, w_λ, analytic in the region considered. Then (6.9 a, b, c) represents the C_2-transformation. If we choose $'s - s = 0$ we get a C_3-transformation. By consideration of the rules for the construction of C_3-transformations, the rules for the construction of the most general C_2-transformation can be formulated as follows:

Rule I *for the construction of the most general C_2-transformation:*

The most general C_2-transformation in $\epsilon\xi^0$, ξ^κ, w_λ is obtained by

(1) *choosing an arbitrary integer $\tau \geqslant 1$ and $\leqslant n+1$;*

(2) *choosing τ arbitrary independent equations*

$$
F^a(z, \xi^\kappa, w_\lambda) = 0 \quad (a = 1,\ldots, \tau),
\tag{6.10}
$$

with functions F^a analytic in the region considered and such that the $(n+\tau+1)$-rowed determinant

$$
\begin{array}{c}
\overbrace{\qquad\quad}^{1}\ \overbrace{\qquad\qquad}^{n}\ \overbrace{\quad\ }^{\tau} \\
\left|\begin{array}{ccc}
\dfrac{\partial F^a}{\partial z} & \dfrac{\partial F^a}{\partial \xi^\lambda} & 0 \\[2ex]
\chi_a \dfrac{\partial^2 F^a}{\partial z \partial '\xi^\mu} & \chi_a \dfrac{\partial^2 F^a}{\partial \xi^\lambda \partial '\xi^\mu} & \dfrac{\partial F^a}{\partial '\xi^\mu} \\[2ex]
\chi_a \dfrac{\partial^2 F^a}{\partial z^2} & \chi_a \dfrac{\partial^2 F^a}{\partial \xi^\lambda \partial z} & \dfrac{\partial F^a}{\partial z}
\end{array}\right|
\begin{array}{l} \}\,\tau \\[3ex] \}\,n \\[3ex] \}\,1 \end{array}
\end{array}
\quad (a = 1,\ldots, \tau)
\tag{6.11}
$$

does not vanish identically in the χ_a as a consequence of (6.10);

(3) *writing out the $2n+1$ equations*

$$
\begin{aligned}
1 &= \chi_a \frac{\partial F^a}{\partial z} \\
w_\lambda &= -\chi_a \frac{\partial F^a}{\partial \xi^\lambda} \qquad (a = 1,\ldots, \tau); \\
'w_\lambda &= \chi_a \frac{\partial F^a}{\partial '\xi^\lambda}
\end{aligned}
\tag{6.12}
$$

(4) *eliminating the χ_a from* (6.12) *and replacing z by $'s - s + \epsilon '\xi^0 - \epsilon \xi^0$ in the remaining $2n+1-\tau$ equations;*

(5) *for $\epsilon = 1$ introducing for $'s - s$ an arbitrary function of ξ^κ, w_λ, analytic in the region considered.*

By these processes we obtain for $\epsilon = 0$ $2n$ *equations in* ξ^κ, w_λ, $'\xi^\kappa$, $'w_\lambda$ *soluble with respect to* ξ^κ, w_λ *and with respect to* $'\xi^\kappa$, $'w_\lambda$ *and representing the* C_2*-transformation and one equation determining the function* $'\Omega$ *in* (6.5). *For* $\epsilon = 1$ *we get* $2n+1$ *equations in* ξ^0, ξ^κ, w_λ, $'\xi^0$, $'\xi^\kappa$, *and* $'w_\lambda$ *soluble with respect to* ξ^0, ξ^κ, w_λ *and with respect to* $'\xi^0$, $'\xi^\kappa$, $'w_\lambda$ *and representing the* C_2*-transformation.*

Rule II *for the construction of the most general* C_2*-transformation:*
The most general C_2*-transformation in* $\epsilon\xi^0$, ξ^κ, w_λ *is obtained by*

(1) *permuting the* ξ^κ *in an arbitrary way and the* w_λ *in the same way;*
(2) *permuting the* $'\xi^\kappa$ *in an arbitrary way and the* $'w_\lambda$ *in the same way;*
(3) *choosing two integers* τ_1 *and* τ_2 *such that* $0 \leqslant \tau_1 \leqslant n$ *and* $0 \leqslant \tau_2 \leqslant n$;
(4) *choosing an arbitrary function* V *of the* $2n$ *variables*

$$\begin{aligned} &w_a,\ \xi^x \quad (a = 1,..., \tau_1;\ x = \tau_1+1,..., n), \\ &'w_b,\ '\xi^y \quad (b = 1,..., \tau_2;\ y = \tau_2+1,..., n) \end{aligned} \tag{6.13}$$

analytic in the region considered and such that

$$\begin{array}{c} \overset{\longleftarrow \tau_1 \longrightarrow \longleftarrow n-\tau_1 \longrightarrow}{} \\ \begin{vmatrix} \dfrac{\partial^2 V}{\partial w_a \partial 'w_b} & \dfrac{\partial^2 V}{\partial \xi^x \partial 'w_b} \\ \dfrac{\partial^2 V}{\partial w_a \partial '\xi^y} & \dfrac{\partial^2 V}{\partial \xi^x \partial '\xi^y} \end{vmatrix} \end{array} \begin{matrix} \updownarrow \tau_2 \\ \updownarrow n-\tau_2 \end{matrix} \neq 0 \qquad \begin{pmatrix} a = 1,..., \tau_1; \\ x = \tau_1+1,..., n; \\ b = 1,..., \tau_2; \\ y = \tau_2+1,..., n \end{pmatrix} \tag{6.14}$$

in that region;

(5) *writing out the* $2n+1$ *equations*

$$\xi^a = \frac{\partial V}{\partial w_a}, \qquad w_x = -\frac{\partial V}{\partial \xi^x} \quad (a = 1,..., \tau_1;\ x = \tau_1+1,..., n),$$

$$'\xi^b = -\frac{\partial V}{\partial 'w_b}, \qquad 'w_y = \frac{\partial V}{\partial '\xi^y} \quad (b = 1,..., \tau_2;\ y = \tau_2+1,..., n),$$

$$'s - s + \epsilon\, '\xi^0 - \epsilon \xi^0 = -\left(V - w_a \frac{\partial V}{\partial w_a} - 'w_b \frac{\partial V}{\partial 'w_b}\right) \tag{6.15}$$

soluble with respect to $\epsilon('\xi^0 - \xi^0)$, ξ^κ, *and* w_λ *and with respect to* $\epsilon('\xi^0 - \xi^0)$, $'\xi^\kappa$, *and* $'w_\lambda$;

(6) *for* $\epsilon = 1$ *introducing for* $'s - s$ *an arbitrary function of* ξ^κ, w_λ, *analytic in the region considered.*

The $2n+\epsilon$ *equations in the variables* $\epsilon\xi^0$, ξ^κ, w_λ, $\epsilon\, '\xi^0$, $'\xi^\kappa$, $'w_\lambda$ *obtained by these processes are soluble with respect to* $\epsilon\xi^0$, ξ^κ, w_λ *and with respect to* $\epsilon\, '\xi^0$, $'\xi^\kappa$, $'w_\lambda$ *and represent the* C_2*-transformation.*

The function V is called a generating function of the C_2-transformation.†

† For doubly homogeneous C-transformations, that is, C-transformations homogeneous in ξ^κ as well as in w_λ, cf. Schouten 1937. 2, 3, 4; 1938. 3.

7. Infinitesimal transformations†

As in III, § 19, we mean by an infinitesimal point transformation in X_n a point transformation of the form

$$'\xi^\kappa = \xi^\kappa + X^\kappa\, dt, \tag{7.1}$$

where X^κ is a contravariant vector field of the X_n and t an independent arbitrary variable. By this transformation a function $f(\xi^\kappa)$ is transformed into

$$f(\xi^\kappa) + Xf\, dt \overset{\text{def}}{=} f(\xi^\kappa) + X^\mu \partial_\mu f(\xi^\kappa)\, dt. \tag{7.2}$$

As in III, § 19, $X = X^\mu \partial_\mu$ is the symbol of the infinitesimal transformation.

If (7.1) is written in the form

$$d\xi^\kappa = X^\kappa\, dt \tag{7.3}$$

we see that the displacements $d\xi^\kappa$ of the points of X_n have the direction of the stream-lines of the field X^κ. For this reason these curves are called the *stream-lines of the infinitesimal transformation* X. The equations of these stream-lines may be obtained by integrating the simultaneous system of ordinary differential equations of the first order

$$\frac{d\xi^\kappa}{dt} = X^\kappa \tag{7.4}$$

and have the form

$$\xi^\kappa = f^\kappa(\underset{0}{\xi^\lambda}, t) \tag{7.5}$$

with the initial conditions $\xi^\kappa = \underset{0}{\xi^\kappa}$ for $t = 0$. If $\underset{0}{\xi^\kappa}$ is taken to be variable the equations (7.5) represent a set of ∞^1 finite point transformations of the X_n, dependent on the parameter t and leaving invariant the stream-lines. This set evidently constitutes a group and is called the *one-parameter group generated by the infinitesimal transformation* X (cf. II, § 13).

Suppose we are given a covariant vector field w_λ. First we wish to find all the infinitesimal transformations leaving this field invariant to within a scalar factor. We therefore have to look for infinitesimal transformations satisfying the equation

$$'w_\lambda\, d\,'\xi^\lambda = (1 + \mu\, dt) w_\lambda\, d\xi^\lambda, \tag{7.6}$$

where μ is a function of the ξ^κ and the $'w_\lambda$ are the functions arising from $w_\lambda(\xi^\kappa)$ if ξ^κ is replaced by $\xi^\kappa + X^\kappa\, dt$:

$$'w_\lambda = w_\lambda + X^\mu \partial_\mu w_\lambda\, dt. \tag{7.7}$$

† Cf. v. Weber 1900. 1, ch. x; Engel and Faber 1932. 1, ch. i.

From (7.7) it follows that (cf. II, § 13)

$$\begin{aligned} {}'w_\lambda \, d\,'\xi^\lambda &= (w_\lambda + X^\mu \partial_\mu w_\lambda \, dt)(d\xi^\lambda + \partial_\omega X^\lambda d\xi^\omega dt) \\ &= (w_\lambda + X^\mu \partial_\mu w_\lambda \, dt + w_\mu \, \partial_\lambda X^\mu \, dt) \, d\xi^\lambda \\ &= (w_\lambda + \underset{L}{D} w_\lambda \, dt) \, d\xi^\lambda. \end{aligned} \tag{7.8}$$

Hence a necessary and sufficient condition is that the Lie derivative of w_λ with respect to X^μ must have the $(n-1)$-direction of w_λ:

$$\begin{aligned} \underset{L}{D} w_\lambda &= X^\mu \partial_\mu w_\lambda + w_\mu \partial_\lambda X^\mu \\ &= X^\mu W_{\mu\lambda} + \partial_\lambda (X^\mu w_\mu) = \mu w_\lambda. \end{aligned} \tag{7.9}$$

First we consider the case when $X^\mu w_\mu = 0$, that is, when the stream-lines of X^κ are integral curves of the field w_λ. If $K = 2\rho + 1$, w_λ does not lie in the domain of $W_{\mu\lambda}$ and consequently it follows from (7.9) that $\mu = 0$. If $K = 2\rho$, (7.9) expresses the fact that $X^\mu W_{\mu\lambda}$ is equal to w_λ to within a scalar factor. Hence (7.9) is equivalent to

$$\begin{aligned} &(a) \quad \left.\begin{aligned} X^\mu W_{\mu\lambda} &= 0 \\ X^\mu w_\mu &= 0 \end{aligned}\right\} \quad \text{for} \quad K = 2\rho + 1, \\ &(b) \quad \left.\begin{aligned} X^\mu W_{\mu[\lambda} w_{\nu]} &= 0 \\ X^\mu w_\mu &= 0 \end{aligned}\right\} \quad \text{for} \quad K = 2\rho. \end{aligned} \tag{7.10}$$

Now we recall that the equations of the system S_4 are (cf. IV, § 2)

$$\begin{aligned} &(S_2 = S_4) \quad \left.\begin{aligned} d\xi^\mu W_{\mu\lambda} &= 0 \\ d\xi^\mu w_\mu &= 0 \end{aligned}\right\} \quad \text{for} \quad K = 2\rho + 1, \\ &(S_3 = S_4) \quad \left.\begin{aligned} d\xi^\mu W_{\mu[\lambda} w_{\nu]} &= 0 \\ d\xi^\mu w_\mu &= 0 \end{aligned}\right\} \quad \text{for} \quad K = 2\rho \end{aligned} \tag{7.11}$$

and that this system determines the characteristics of w_λ, coinciding with the supports for $K = 2\rho + 1$ and constituting a normal system of ∞^k X_{n-k}'s. Comparing (7.10) and (7.11) we get as a necessary and sufficient condition that X leaves w_λ invariant to within a scalar factor in this special case ($X^\mu w_\mu = 0$), *that the stream-lines of X lie in the characteristics of w_λ.*

In the general case we will write F instead of $X^\mu w_\mu$. Then the equations (7.9) take the form

$$\begin{aligned} &(a) \qquad X^\mu W_{\mu\lambda} + \partial_\lambda F = \mu w_\lambda, \\ &(b) \qquad X^\mu w_\mu = F. \end{aligned} \tag{7.12}$$

If $K = 2\rho + 1$ it follows from (7.12) that $\partial_\lambda F$ is either zero or lies in the region of w_λ, $W_{\mu\lambda}$, and consequently F is either a constant or a function with index 1 or 2. If F is constant or if its index is 2, $\partial_\lambda F$

is zero or lies in the region of $W_{\mu\lambda}$ and this implies that $\mu = 0$. For $F = 0$ the equations (7.12) have the same form as (7.10 a). If in this latter case $\underset{1}{X}^{\kappa},\dots, \underset{n-K}{X}^{\kappa}$ is a system of $n-K$ linearly independent solutions of (7.10 a), the most general solution of (7.10 a) has the form

$$\underset{S}{X}^{\kappa} = \overset{1}{\alpha}\underset{1}{X}^{\kappa}+\dots+\overset{n-K}{\alpha}\underset{n-K}{X}^{\kappa}, \tag{7.13}$$

where the α's are arbitrary functions of the ξ^{κ} and the most general infinitesimal transformation whose stream-lines lie in the supports has the form

$$X = \underset{S}{X}. \tag{7.14}$$

If an arbitrary constant or an arbitrary function with index 1 or 2 is chosen for F, μ can be determined uniquely from (7.12 a) because w_{λ} does not lie in the domain of $W_{\mu\lambda}$. Then (7.12) can be solved with respect to the X^{μ} and the difference of two solutions belonging to the same choice of F is always a solution of (7.10 a). Hence, if X^{μ} is an arbitrary solution of (7.12), depending on the choice of F and not satisfying (7.10 a), the most general solution of (7.12) has the form

$$X^{\kappa} = \underset{F}{X}^{\kappa}+\underset{S}{X}^{\kappa}. \tag{7.15}$$

If F is a constant but $\neq 0$, the stream-lines do not lie in the supports but from (7.12) and $\mu = 0$ they lie in the supports of rotation.

We collect results in the theorem:

THEOREM VI.2. *The most general infinitesimal transformation which leaves the field w_{λ} of class $K = 2\rho+1$ invariant to within a scalar factor $1+\mu\, dt$ has the form*

$$X = \underset{F}{X}+\underset{S}{X} \tag{7.16}$$

and there are four possible cases:

(0) $F = 0$; $X = \underset{S}{X}$; $\mu = 0$; *stream-lines in supports = characteristics*;

(1) $F =$ *constant* $\neq 0$; $\mu = 0$; *stream-lines in supports of rotation*;

(2) F *has index 2*; $\mu = 0$;

(3) F *has index 1*; μ *can be derived from* F. (7.17)

If $K = n$ the supports are points and since there is no $\underset{S}{X}$ the case (0) drops out.

In order to get an explicit expression for $\underset{F}{X}$ new coordinates $\xi^{\kappa'}$ may be chosen in such a way that $w_{\lambda}d\xi^{\lambda}$ can be expressed in terms of the $\xi^{\alpha'}$ ($\alpha' = 1',\dots, K'$) and their differentials only. If $K = n$ no change of coordinates is needed. Then $\underset{S}{X}^{\kappa}$ is an arbitrary vector with $\underset{S}{X}^{\alpha'} = 0$

($\alpha' = 1',..., K'$). In the X_K of the $\xi^{\alpha'}$ ($\alpha' = 1',..., K'$), arising from the X_n by reduction with respect to the supports, the equation

$$V^{\alpha'\gamma'}W_{\beta'\gamma'}+v^{\alpha'}w_{\beta'} = A^{\alpha'}_{\beta'} \quad (\alpha',\beta',\gamma' = 1',..., K') \tag{7.18}$$

determines uniquely a contravariant bivector $V^{\alpha'\beta'}$ and a contravariant vector $v^{\alpha'}$ satisfying the conditions

$$v^{\beta'}W_{\beta'\alpha'} = 0, \qquad v^{\beta'}w_{\beta'} = 1 \quad (\alpha',\beta' = 1',..., K') \tag{7.19}$$

as a consequence of (7.18). With respect to these new coordinates the equations (7.12) take the form

$$\begin{aligned} &(a) \qquad \underset{F}{X}^{\gamma'}W_{\gamma'\beta'}+\partial_{\beta'}F = \mu w_{\beta'} \\ &(b) \qquad \underset{F}{X}^{\gamma'}w_{\gamma'} = F \end{aligned} \qquad (\beta',\gamma' = 1',..., K'). \tag{7.20}$$

By transvection with $v^{\beta'}$ we get from (7.20 a)

$$\mu = v^{\beta'}\partial_{\beta'}F \quad (\beta' = 1',..., K') \tag{7.21}$$

and from (7.20 a, b) we get by transvection with $V^{\alpha'\beta'}$ and multiplication by $v^{\alpha'}$ respectively

$$\begin{aligned} &(a) \quad \underset{F}{X}^{\gamma'}W_{\gamma'\beta'}V^{\alpha'\beta'}+V^{\alpha'\beta'}\partial_{\beta'}F = \mu V^{\alpha'\beta'}w_{\beta'} \\ &(b) \qquad \underset{F}{X}^{\gamma'}w_{\gamma'}v^{\alpha'} = Fv^{\alpha'} \end{aligned} \qquad (\alpha',\beta',\gamma' = 1',..., K'). \tag{7.22}$$

From (7.18) and (7.21) addition of (7.22 a) and (7.22 b) gives the explicit expression desired:

$$\begin{aligned} \underset{F}{X}^{\alpha'} &= -V^{\alpha'\beta'}\partial_{\beta'}F+Fv^{\alpha'}+V^{\alpha'\gamma'}w_{\gamma'}v^{\beta'}\partial_{\beta'}F \\ &= -V^{\alpha'\gamma'}W_{\gamma'\delta'}V^{\beta'\delta'}\partial_{\beta'}F+Fv^{\alpha'} \quad (\alpha',\beta',\gamma',\delta' = 1',..., K'). \end{aligned} \tag{7.23}$$

If $K = 2\rho$, w_λ lies in the domain of $W_{\mu\lambda}$ and consequently there exists a contravariant vector p^κ (not uniquely determined) such that

$$p^\mu W_{\mu\lambda} = w_\lambda. \tag{7.24}$$

Since $p^\lambda w_\lambda$ is zero, it follows from (7.12) that

$$p^\lambda \partial_\lambda F = F. \tag{7.25}$$

If F satisfies this condition, (7.12 b) is a consequence of (7.12 a). Since $\partial_\lambda F$ lies in the domain of $W_{\mu\lambda}$ in consequence of (7.12 a), F is a function with index 1 or 2. Now every arbitrary function $f(\xi^\kappa)$ satisfies the condition

$$\begin{aligned} p^\lambda(\partial_\lambda f)W_{[\mu_1\lambda}...W_{\mu_\rho\lambda_\rho]}-2\rho(\partial_{[\mu_1}f)w_{\lambda_1}W_{\mu_2\lambda_2}...W_{\mu_\rho\lambda_\rho]} \\ = (2\rho+1)p^\lambda(\partial_{[\lambda}f)W_{\mu_1\lambda_1}...W_{\mu_\rho\lambda_\rho]} \end{aligned} \tag{7.26}$$

since $K = 2\rho$. Hence, if $\partial_\lambda F$ lies in the domain of $W_{\mu\lambda}$ the right-hand side of (7.26) vanishes for $f = F$ and this implies that F cannot have index 2. Because in this case the second term of the left-hand side of (7.26) would vanish and F would have to be zero in consequence of (7.25). Hence F is either zero or a function with index 1 and from (7.25, 26) it follows that

$$F \overset{2\rho}{I} - 2\rho \overline{F} \overset{-2\rho-1}{I} = 0, \tag{7.27}$$

using the abbreviated notation of IV, § 6. But, as we have seen in IV, § 7, this equation is the necessary and sufficient condition that $(1/F)w_\lambda$ should be of class $K-1$ if $F \neq 0$.

If $F = 0$, (7.12 a) takes the form

$$(a) \quad X^\mu W_{\mu[\lambda} w_{\nu]} = 0 \quad \text{for} \quad \mu \neq 0, \qquad (b) \quad X^\mu W_{\mu\lambda} = 0 \quad \text{for} \quad \mu = 0. \tag{7.28}$$

Now we recall that the equations of the systems S_4 and S_1 are (cf. IV, § 2)

$$(a) \quad (S_3 = S_4) \quad d\xi^\mu W_{\mu[\lambda} w_{\nu]} = 0, \qquad (b) \quad (S_1 = S_2) \quad d\xi^\mu W_{\mu\lambda} = 0. \tag{7.29}$$

(7.29 a) determines the characteristics of w_λ and (7.29 b) the supports, coinciding with the supports of rotation. Comparing (7.28) and (7.29) we find that the necessary and sufficient condition in this special case ($F = 0$), that X leaves w_λ invariant to within a scalar factor, is *that the stream-lines of X lie in the characteristics and for $\mu = 0$ also in the supports of w_λ*. If now $\underset{0}{X^\kappa}, \underset{1}{X^\kappa}, \ldots, \underset{n-K}{X^\kappa}$ is a system of linearly independent solutions of (7.28 a), the last $n-K$ of which are also solutions of (7.28 b), the most general solution of (7.28 b) has the form

$$\underset{S}{X} = \overset{1}{\alpha} \underset{1}{X} + \ldots + \overset{n-K}{\alpha} \underset{n-K}{X} \tag{7.30}$$

and the most general solution of (7.28 a) has the form

$$\underset{C}{X} = \overset{0}{\alpha} \underset{0}{X} + \underset{S}{X}, \tag{7.31}$$

where the α's in (7.30) and (7.31) are arbitrary functions of the ξ^κ. Hence, the most general transformation whose stream-lines lie in the supports or the characteristics has the form

$$X = \underset{S}{X} \quad \text{or} \quad X = \underset{C}{X} \tag{7.32}$$

respectively.

In the general case F is an arbitrary solution of (7.27) and μ an arbitrary function of the ξ^κ. Then (7.12 b) follows from (7.12 a), and (7.12 a) can be solved with respect to the X^μ. The difference between two solutions belonging to the same choice of F and μ is always a solution of (7.28 *b*). Hence, if $\underset{F,\mu}{X^\kappa}$ is an arbitrary solution of (7.12) not satisfying (7.28 *b*), the most general solution of (7.12) has the form

$$X = \underset{F,\mu}{X^\kappa} + \underset{S}{X^\kappa}. \tag{7.33}$$

We collect results in the theorem:

THEOREM VI.3. *The most general infinitesimal transformation, which leaves the field w_λ of class $K = 2\rho$ invariant to within a scalar factor, has the form*

$$X = \underset{F,\mu}{X} + \underset{S}{X} \tag{7.34}$$

and there are four possible cases:

(0) $F = 0$; $\mu = 0$; $X = \underset{S}{X}$; *stream-lines in supports = supports of rotation;*

(1) $F = 0$; $\mu \neq 0$; $X = \underset{C}{X}$; *stream-lines in characteristics;* (7.35)

(2) *F is a solution of* (7.27); $\mu = 0$;

(3) *F is a solution of* (7.27); $\mu \neq 0$ *and arbitrary.*

If $K = n$ the supports are points and since there is no $\underset{S}{X}$, the case (0) drops out.

In order to get an explicit expression for $\underset{F,\mu}{X}$ new coordinates $\xi^{\kappa'}$ may be chosen in such a way that $w_\lambda\, d\xi^\lambda$ can be expressed in terms of the $\xi^{\alpha'}$ $(\alpha' = 1',..., K')$ and their differentials only. Then $\underset{S}{X^\kappa}$ is an arbitrary vector with $\underset{S}{X^{\alpha'}} = 0$ $(\alpha' = 1',..., K')$. In the X_K of the $\xi^{\alpha'}$ $(\alpha' = 1',..., K')$ arising from the X_n by reduction with respect to the supports the equation

$$U^{\alpha'\gamma'} W_{\beta'\gamma'} = A^{\alpha'}_{\beta'} \quad (\alpha', \beta', \gamma' = 1',..., K') \tag{7.36}$$

determines uniquely a contravariant bivector $U^{\alpha'\beta'}$ and (7.24) takes the form

$$p^{\gamma'} W_{\gamma'\beta'} = w_{\beta'} \quad (\beta', \gamma' = 1,..., K'). \tag{7.37}$$

As a result of (7.36) $p^{\gamma'}$ is uniquely determined by (7.37)

$$p^{\alpha'} = U^{\alpha'\beta'} w_{\beta'} \quad (\alpha', \beta' = 1',..., K'). \tag{7.38}$$

The equation (7.12 *a*) takes the form

$$\underset{F,\mu}{X^{\gamma'}} W_{\gamma'\beta'} + \partial_{\beta'} F = \mu w_{\beta'} \quad (\beta', \gamma' = 1',..., K') \tag{7.39}$$

and from this equation we get by transvection with $U^{\alpha'\beta'}$ the explicit expression required:

$$\underset{F,\mu}{X^{\alpha'}} = -U^{\alpha'\beta'} \partial_{\beta'} F + \mu U^{\alpha'\beta'} w_{\beta'} \quad (\alpha', \beta' = 1',..., K'). \tag{7.40}$$

Secondly we wish to find all the infinitesimal transformations which leave a given field w_λ invariant to within an additive gradient. We therefore have to look for infinitesimal transformations satisfying the equation

$$'w_\lambda d'\xi^\lambda = w_\lambda d\xi^\lambda + ds\,dt, \tag{7.41}$$

s being a function of the ξ^κ and the $'w_\lambda$ the functions arising from $w_\lambda(\xi^\kappa)$ if ξ^κ is replaced by $\xi^\kappa + X^\kappa dt$ (cf. 7.7). As a result of (7.8) we get as a necessary and sufficient condition (cf. 7.9)

$$\underset{L}{D} w_\lambda = X^\mu W_{\mu\lambda} + \partial_\lambda(X^\mu w_\mu) = \partial_\lambda s. \tag{7.42}$$

If we write

$$F \overset{\text{def}}{=} X^\mu w_\mu, \qquad G \overset{\text{def}}{=} F - s, \tag{7.43}$$

(7.42) takes the form

$$\begin{aligned} &(a) \qquad X^\mu W_{\mu\lambda} + \partial_\lambda G = 0, \\ &(b) \qquad X^\mu w_\mu = F = G + s. \end{aligned} \tag{7.44}$$

If $K = 2\rho + 1$ it follows from (7.44 a) that $\partial_\lambda G$ lies in the domain of $W_{\mu\lambda}$ and that consequently G is a constant or a function with index 2. If G is a constant (7.44) is equivalent to

$$\begin{aligned} &(a) \quad \left.\begin{aligned} &(\alpha) \quad X^\mu W_{\mu\lambda} = 0 \\ &(\beta) \quad X^\mu w_\mu = F = G + s \end{aligned}\right\} \quad \text{for} \quad F \neq 0, \\ &(b) \quad \left.\begin{aligned} &(\alpha) \quad X^\mu W_{\mu\lambda} = 0 \\ &(\beta) \quad X^\mu w_\mu = 0 \end{aligned}\right\} \quad \text{for} \quad F = 0. \end{aligned} \tag{7.45}$$

Now we recall that the systems S_1 and S_4 are (cf. IV, § 2)

$$(a) \quad (S_1 = S_3) \quad d\xi^\mu W_{\mu\lambda} = 0, \qquad (b) \quad (S_2 = S_4) \quad \begin{cases} d\xi^\mu W_{\mu\lambda} = 0, \\ d\xi^\mu w_\mu = 0. \end{cases} \tag{7.46}$$

(7.46 a) determines the supports of rotation and (7.46 b) the supports, coinciding with the characteristics. Comparing (7.45) and (7.46) we find that a necessary and sufficient condition that X leaves w_λ invariant to within an additive gradient, is *that the stream-lines of X lie in the supports of rotation and for $F = 0$ also in the supports of w_λ*. If now the most general solution of (7.45 b) is written $\underset{S}{X^\kappa}$ as above and if $\underset{*}{X^\kappa}$ is an arbitrary solution of (7.45 $a\,\alpha$) not satisfying (7.45 b), the most general solution of (7.45 $a\,\alpha$) has the form

$$\underset{R}{X^\kappa} = \overset{*}{\alpha}\underset{*}{X^\kappa} + \underset{S}{X^\kappa}, \tag{7.47}$$

$\overset{*}{\alpha}$ being an arbitrary function of the ξ^κ. The most general infinitesimal transformation whose stream-lines lie in the supports of rotation or the supports has the form

$$X = \underset{R}{X} \quad \text{or} \quad X = \underset{S}{X} \tag{7.48}$$

respectively.

If we choose an arbitrary constant or an arbitrary function with index *2* for G and an arbitrary function of the ξ^κ for s, the equations (7.44) can be solved with respect to the X^μ. The difference between two solutions belonging to the same choice of F and s is always a solution of (7.45 *b*). Hence, if $\underset{G,s}{X^\mu}$ is an arbitrary solution of (7.44) not satisfying (7.45 *b* α), the most general solution of (7.44) has the form

$$X^\kappa = \underset{G,s}{X^\kappa} + \underset{S}{X^\kappa}. \tag{7.49}$$

We collect results in the theorem

THEOREM VI.4. *The most general infinitesimal transformation leaving invariant the field* w_λ *of class* $K = 2\rho+1$ *to within an additive gradient has the form*

$$X = \underset{G,s}{X^\kappa} + \underset{S}{X^\kappa} \tag{7.50}$$

and there are four possible cases:

(0) $G =$ *constant*; $F = 0$; $X = \underset{S}{X}$; $\partial_\lambda s = 0$; *stream-lines in supports = characteristics*;

(1) $G =$ *constant*; $F \neq 0$; *stream-lines in supports of rotation*;

(2) G *has index 2*; $s =$ *constant*;

(3) G *has index 2*; s *not constant and arbitrary.* (7.51)

If $K = n$ the supports are points and, since there is no $\underset{S}{X}$, case (0) drops out.

From (7.44) we get after introduction of the special coordinate system (κ') the explicit expression for $\underset{G,s}{X}$

$$\underset{G,s}{X^{\alpha'}} = -V^{\alpha'\beta'}\partial_{\beta'} G + (G+s)v^{\alpha'} \quad (\alpha',\beta' = 1',\ldots,K'), \tag{7.52}$$

$V^{\alpha'\beta'}$ and $v^{\alpha'}$ being defined as before.

If $K = 2\rho$, $\partial_\lambda G$ lies in the domain of $W_{\mu\lambda}$ and consequently G is a constant or a function with index *1* or *2*. From (7.44) it follows that

$$p^\lambda \partial_\lambda G = F = G+s. \tag{7.53}$$

Now we have for G (cf. (7.26))

$$p^\lambda(\partial_\lambda G) W_{[\mu_1\lambda_1}\ldots W_{\mu_\rho\lambda_\rho]} - 2\rho(\partial_{[\mu_1} G) w_{\lambda_1} W_{\mu_2\lambda_2}\ldots W_{\mu_\rho\lambda_\rho]} = 0. \tag{7.54}$$

Accordingly there are four cases. If G is a constant or a function with index *2* we have $F = 0$ and $s = -G$. If G is a solution of

$$G\overset{2\rho}{I} - 2\rho\bar{G}\overset{2\rho-1}{I} = 0 \tag{7.55}$$

we have

$$F = G = p^\lambda \partial_\lambda G, \qquad s = 0. \tag{7.56}$$

If G has index *1* we have

$$s = p^\lambda \partial_\lambda G - G. \tag{7.57}$$

When G has been chosen we get F and s from (7.53). Substituting the value of F in (7.44 b) this equation becomes a consequence of (7.44 a) and (7.44 a) can be solved with respect to X^μ. The difference of two solutions belonging to the same value of G is always a solution of (7.45 b α). Hence, if $\underset{G}{X}{}^\kappa$ is an arbitrary solution of (7.44 a) not satisfying (7.45 b α), the most general solution of (7.44 a) has the form

$$X^\kappa = \underset{G}{X}{}^\kappa + \underset{S}{X}{}^\kappa. \tag{7.58}$$

We collect results in the theorem

THEOREM VI.5. *The most general infinitesimal transformation leaving invariant the field w_λ of class $K = 2\rho$ to within an additive gradient has the form*

$$X = \underset{G}{X} + \underset{S}{X} \tag{7.59}$$

and there are four possible cases:

(0) $G =$ *constant*; $F = 0$; $s = -G$; $X = \underset{S}{X}$; *stream-lines in supports* $=$ *supports of rotation*;
(1) G *has index 2*; $F = 0$; $s = -G$; *stream-lines in characteristics*;
(2) G *is a solution of* (7.55); $F = p^\lambda \partial_\lambda G$; $s = 0$; (7.60)
(3) G *has index 1*; $F = p^\lambda \partial_\lambda G$; $s = p^\lambda \partial_\lambda G - G$.

If $K = n$ the supports are points and, since there is no $\underset{S}{X}$, case (0) drops out.

From (7.44) we get after introduction of the special coordinate system (κ') the explicit expression for $\underset{G}{X}$

$$\underset{G}{X}{}^{\alpha'} = -U^{\alpha'\beta'} \partial_{\beta'} G \quad (\alpha', \beta' = 1', \ldots, K'), \tag{7.61}$$

where $U^{\alpha'\beta'}$ is defined as above.

8. Infinitesimal C_1-transformations and C_2-transformations†

The results of the preceding paragraph will be applied to the case when $K = n$ and $w_\lambda d\xi^\lambda$ is given in the canonical form $\epsilon\, dx^0 + p_i\, dx^i$. As in VI, § 3, we change the notation, writing $\epsilon\, d\xi^0 + w_\lambda d\xi^\lambda$ ($\lambda = 1, \ldots, n$) instead of $\epsilon\, dx^0 + p_i\, dx^i$ ($i = 1, \ldots, \rho$) and

$$\epsilon\, d\xi^0 + w_\lambda d\xi^\lambda = W_B\, dX^B \quad (B = 1-\epsilon, \ldots, n, (1), \ldots, (n)) \tag{8.1}$$

with $\quad \epsilon W_0 = \epsilon, \qquad W_\lambda = w_\lambda, \qquad W_{(\lambda)} = 0 \quad ((\lambda) = (1), \ldots, (n)). \qquad (8.2)$

The infinitesimal C_1-transformations are the infinitesimal transformations in X^A, that is, in $\epsilon\xi^0$, ξ^κ, w_λ, which leave W_B invariant to within a scalar factor and the infinitesimal C_2-transformations are the

† Lie 1890. 1, ch. iii; v. Weber 1900. 1, ch. x; Engel and Faber 1932. 1, §§ 23, 52; Eisenhart 1933. 1, §§ 62–4.

infinitesimal transformations in X^A which leave W_B invariant to within an additive gradient.

The non-vanishing components of the rotation

$$W_{CB} = 2\partial_{[C} W_{B]} \quad (B, C = 1-\epsilon,..., n, (1),..., (n)) \tag{8.3}$$

are in this special case

$$\begin{aligned} W_{(1)1} &= -W_{1(1)} = 1, \\ &\cdots\cdots\cdots \\ W_{(n)n} &= -W_{n(n)} = 1. \end{aligned} \tag{8.4}$$

For $\epsilon = 1$ the quantities V^A and V^{AB}, determined by (cf. (7.18))

$$V^{AC}W_{BC} + V^A W_B = A_B^A \quad (A, B, C = 0, 1,..., n, (1),..., (n)) \tag{8.5}$$

satisfy the equations

$$V^0 = 1, \qquad V^\kappa = 0, \qquad V^{(\kappa)} = 0 \quad ((\kappa) = (1),..., (n)) \tag{8.6}$$

and

$$\begin{aligned} V^{(\lambda)0} &= -V^{0(\lambda)} = -w_\lambda \quad ((\lambda) = (1),..., (n)), \\ V^{(1)1} &= -V^{1(1)} = 1, \\ &\cdots\cdots\cdots \\ V^{(n)n} &= -V^{n(n)} = 1, \end{aligned} \tag{8.7}$$

the components of V^{AB} not written being zero.

For $\epsilon = 0$ the quantities p^A and U^{AB} determined by (cf. (7.36, 37))

$$\begin{aligned} U^{AC}W_{BC} &= A_B^A \\ p^A W_{AB} &= W_B \end{aligned} \quad (A, B, C = 1,..., n, (1),..., (n)) \tag{8.8}$$

satisfy the equations

$$p^\kappa = 0, \qquad p^{(\kappa)} = w_\kappa \quad ((\kappa) = (1),..., (n)) \tag{8.9}$$

and

$$\begin{aligned} U^{(1)1} &= -U^{1(1)} = 1, \\ &\cdots\cdots\cdots \\ U^{(n)n} &= -U^{n(n)} = 1, \end{aligned} \tag{8.10}$$

the components of U^{AB} not written being zero.

For $\epsilon = 1$ the expression (7.23) takes the form

$$\underset{F}{X^A} = -V^{AB}\partial_B F + FV^A + V^{AC}W_C V^B \partial_B F$$
$$(A, B, C = 0, 1,..., n, (1),..., (n)) \tag{8.11}$$

or, written in full,

$$\begin{aligned} \underset{F}{X^0} &= -w_\lambda \frac{\partial F}{\partial w_\lambda} + F, \\ \underset{F}{X^\kappa} &= \frac{\partial F}{\partial w_\kappa}, \\ \underset{F}{X^{(\lambda)}} &= -\frac{\partial F}{\partial \xi^\lambda} + w_\lambda \frac{\partial F}{\partial \xi^0} \quad ((\lambda) = (1),..., (n)), \end{aligned} \tag{8.12}$$

F being an arbitrary function of ξ^0, ξ^κ, and w_λ. F is a constant or the index of F is 2 if and only if F is independent of ξ^0. That proves the theorem (cf. Theorem VI.2)

THEOREM VI.6. *The most general infinitesimal C_1-transformation in ξ^0, ξ^κ, and w_λ has the form*

$$\delta\xi^0 = -w_\lambda \frac{\partial F}{\partial w_\lambda} dt + F\,dt,$$

$$\delta\xi^\kappa = \frac{\partial F}{\partial w_\kappa} dt, \qquad \delta(d\xi^0 + w_\lambda d\xi^\lambda) = \mu\, dt (d\xi^0 + w_\lambda d\xi^\lambda), \tag{8.13}$$

$$\delta w_\lambda = -\frac{\partial F}{\partial \xi^\lambda} dt + w_\lambda \frac{\partial F}{\partial \xi^0} dt, \qquad \mu = \frac{\partial F}{\partial \xi^0},$$

where F is an arbitrary function of ξ^0, ξ^κ and w_λ and there are three possible cases:

(1) $F = constant \neq 0$; *ξ^κ and w_λ invariant*; $\mu = 0$; *trivial C_3-transformation*;

(2) *F independent of ξ^0*; $\mu = 0$; *general C_3-transformation; general C_2-transformation in ξ^κ, w_λ*;

(3) *F arbitrary*; $\mu = \dfrac{\partial F}{\partial \xi^0}$; *general C_1-transformation.* (8.14)

F is called the *characteristic function* of the infinitesimal C_1-transformation. ξ^0 is invariant if F is homogeneous of degree one in w_λ. If, moreover, F is independent of ξ^0, we get a C_3-transformation in ξ^κ, w_λ.

For $\epsilon = 0$ the expression (7.40) takes the form

$$\underset{F,\mu}{X^A} = -U^{AB}\partial_B F + \mu U^{AB} W_B \quad (A, B = 1,..., n, (1),..., (n)), \tag{8.15}$$

or, written in full,

$$\underset{F,\mu}{X^\kappa} = \frac{\partial F}{\partial w_\kappa},$$
$$\underset{F,\mu}{X^{(\lambda)}} = -\frac{\partial F}{\partial \xi^\lambda} + \mu w_\lambda \quad ((\lambda) = (1),..., (n)), \tag{8.16}$$

μ being an arbitrary function of ξ^κ, w_λ and F a solution of (cf. (7.27))

$$W_B \frac{\partial F}{\partial W_B} = w_\lambda \frac{\partial F}{\partial w_\lambda} = F \quad (B = 1,..., n, (1),..., (n)). \tag{8.17}$$

This proves the theorem (cf. Theorem VI.3)

THEOREM VI.7. *The most general infinitesimal C_1-transformation in ξ^κ, w_λ has the form*

$$\delta\xi^\kappa = \frac{\partial F}{\partial w_\kappa} dt,$$
$$\delta(w_\lambda d\xi^\lambda) = \mu\, dt\, w_\lambda d\xi^\lambda, \tag{8.18}$$
$$\delta w_\lambda = -\frac{\partial F}{\partial \xi^\lambda} dt + \mu w_\lambda dt,$$

where μ is an arbitrary function of ξ^κ, w_λ and F is an arbitrary function of ξ^κ, w_λ, homogeneous of degree one in the w_λ, and there are three possible cases:

(1) $F = 0$; *μ arbitrary; similarity transformation in w_λ; special C_1-transformation;*

(2) *F homogeneous of degree 1 in w_λ; $\mu = 0$; general C_3-transformation;*

(3) *F homogeneous of degree 1 in w_λ; μ arbitrary; general C_1-transformation.* (8.19)

F and μ are called the *characteristic functions* of the infinitesimal C_1-transformation.

For $\epsilon = 1$ the expression (7.52) takes the form

$$\underset{G,s}{X^A} = -V^{AB}\partial_B G+(G+s)V^A \quad (A, B = 0, 1,\ldots, n, (1),\ldots, (n)), \tag{8.20}$$

or, written in full,

$$\begin{aligned} \underset{G,s}{X^0} &= -w_\lambda \frac{\partial G}{\partial w_\lambda}+(G+s), \\ \underset{G,s}{X^\kappa} &= \frac{\partial G}{\partial w_\kappa}, \\ \underset{G,s}{X^{(\lambda)}} &= -\frac{\partial G}{\partial \xi^\lambda} \quad ((\lambda) = (1),\ldots, (n)), \end{aligned} \tag{8.21}$$

where G is an arbitrary function of ξ^κ and w_λ and s is an arbitrary function of ξ^0, ξ^κ, w_λ. This proves the theorem (cf. Theorem VI.4)

THEOREM VI.8. *The most general infinitesimal C_2-transformation in ξ^0, ξ^κ, w_λ has the form*

$$\begin{aligned} \delta\xi^0 &= -w_\lambda \frac{\partial G}{\partial w_\lambda} dt+(G+s)\,dt, \\ \delta\xi^\kappa &= \frac{\partial G}{\partial w_\kappa} dt, \qquad \delta(d\xi^0+w_\lambda d\xi^\lambda) = ds dt, \\ \delta w_\lambda &= -\frac{\partial G}{\partial \xi^\lambda} dt, \end{aligned} \tag{8.22}$$

where G is an arbitrary function of ξ^κ, w_λ, and s is an arbitrary function of ξ^0, ξ^κ, w_λ, and there are three possible cases:

(1) $G =$ *constant; s arbitrary; ξ^κ and w_λ invariant; trivial C_2-transformation;*

(2) *G arbitrary; s constant; general C_3-transformation;* (8.23)

(3) *G arbitrary; s arbitrary; general C_2-transformation.*

G and s are called the *characteristic functions* of the infinitesimal C_2-transformation. The transformation in ξ^κ, w_λ is always a C_2-transformation. If, moreover, G is homogeneous of degree one in w_λ we get a C_3-transformation in ξ^κ, w_λ.

For $\epsilon = 0$ the expression (7.61) takes the form

$$\underset{G}{X}^A = -U^{AB}\partial_B G \quad (A, B = 1,..., n, (1),..., (n)), \tag{8.24}$$

or, written in full,

$$\begin{aligned} \underset{G}{X}^\kappa &= \frac{\partial G}{\partial w_\kappa}, \\ \underset{G}{X}^{(\lambda)} &= -\frac{\partial G}{\partial \xi^\lambda} \quad ((\lambda) = (1),..., (n)), \end{aligned} \tag{8.25}$$

where G is an arbitrary function of ξ^κ and w_λ. This proves the theorem (cf. Theorem VI.5)

THEOREM VI.9. *The most general C_2-transformation in ξ^κ, w_λ has the form*

$$\begin{aligned} \delta\xi^\kappa &= \frac{\partial G}{\partial w_\kappa} dt, & \delta(w_\lambda d\xi^\lambda) &= ds dt, \\ \delta w_\lambda &= -\frac{\partial G}{\partial \xi^\lambda} dt, & w_\lambda \frac{\partial G}{\partial w_\lambda} &= G+s = F, \end{aligned} \tag{8.26}$$

where G is an arbitrary function of ξ^κ, w_λ and there are three possible cases:

(1) *G homogeneous of degree 0 in w_λ; $s = -G$; special C_2-transformation; $\delta\xi^\kappa$ lies in the $(n-1)$-direction of w_λ;*

(2) *G homogeneous of degree 1 in w_λ; $s = 0$; general C_3-transformation;*

(3) *G arbitrary; $s = w_\lambda \dfrac{\partial G}{\partial w_\lambda} - G$; general C_2-transformation.*

(8.27)

G is called the *characteristic function* of the infinitesimal C_2-transformation.

From (8.14, 2), (8.19, 2), (8.23, 2), and (8.27, 2) we get the theorem

THEOREM VI.10. *The most general infinitesimal C_3-transformation in $\epsilon\xi^0$, ξ^κ, w_λ has the form*

$$\begin{aligned} \epsilon\,\delta\xi^0 &= -\epsilon w_\lambda \frac{\partial F}{\partial w_\lambda} dt + \epsilon F\, dt, \\ \delta\xi^\kappa &= \frac{\partial F}{\partial w_\kappa} dt, \qquad \delta(\epsilon\, d\xi^0 + w_\lambda d\xi^\lambda) = 0, \\ \delta w_\lambda &= -\frac{\partial F}{\partial \xi^\lambda} dt, \end{aligned} \tag{8.28}$$

where F is an arbitrary function of ξ^κ, w_λ, homogeneous of degree one in the w_λ for $\epsilon = 0$.

F is called the *characteristic function* of the infinitesimal C_3-transformation.

We collect results in the general formulae

$\epsilon = 0$:

$$(a)\quad \delta\xi^\kappa = \frac{\partial F}{\partial w_\kappa}dt,\qquad \delta w_\lambda = -\frac{\partial F}{\partial \xi^\lambda}dt + \mu w_\lambda dt;$$

$\epsilon = 1$:

$$(b)\quad \delta\xi^0 = -w_\lambda \frac{\partial F}{\partial w_\lambda}dt + (F+s)\,dt,\qquad \delta\xi^\kappa = \frac{\partial F}{\partial w_\kappa}dt,\qquad \delta w_\lambda = -\frac{\partial F}{\partial \xi^\lambda}dt + w_\lambda \frac{\partial F}{\partial \xi^0}dt;$$

(8.29)

$\epsilon = 0$:

$$\delta(w_\lambda d\xi^\lambda) = \{(F)-F\}dt + \mu\, dt\, w_\lambda d\xi^\lambda,$$

C_1: $(F) = F$; μ arbitrary,

C_2: $\mu = 0$; F arbitrary,

C_3: $(F) = F$; $\mu = 0$,

$$(F) \overset{\text{def}}{=} w_\lambda \frac{\partial F}{\partial w_\lambda};$$

$\epsilon = 1$:

$$\delta(d\xi^0 + w_\lambda d\xi^\lambda) = \frac{\partial F}{\partial \xi^0}dt(d\xi^0 + w_\lambda d\xi^\lambda) + ds\,dt,$$

C_1: $s = 0$; F arbitrary; $\mu = \dfrac{\partial F}{\partial \xi^0}$,

C_2: $\dfrac{\partial F}{\partial \xi^0} = 0$; s arbitrary,

C_3: $s = 0$; $\mu = \dfrac{\partial F}{\partial \xi^0} = 0$.

(8.30)

9. The bracket expressions of Poisson and Lagrange†

If v_1 and v_2 are arbitrary functions of ξ^κ and w_λ, the expression

$$(v_1, v_2) \overset{\text{def}}{=} \frac{\partial v_1}{\partial w_\lambda}\frac{\partial v_2}{\partial \xi^\lambda} - \frac{\partial v_2}{\partial w_\lambda}\frac{\partial v_1}{\partial \xi^\lambda} \tag{9.1}$$

is called the *bracket expression of Poisson* of v_1 and v_2. If $(v_1, v_2) = 0$, v_1 and v_2 are said to be *in involution with respect to each other*.

Conversely, if ξ^κ and w_λ are arbitrary functions of v_1 and v_2 and eventually also of other variables, the expression

$$\{v_1, v_2\} \overset{\text{def}}{=} \frac{\partial w_\lambda}{\partial v_1}\frac{\partial \xi^\lambda}{\partial v_2} - \frac{\partial w_\lambda}{\partial v_2}\frac{\partial \xi^\lambda}{\partial v_1} \tag{9.2}$$

is called the *bracket expression of Lagrange* of v_1 and v_2. If $v_\mathfrak{b}$ ($\mathfrak{b} = 1,\ldots, 2n$)

† Cf. v. Weber 1900. 1, chs. ix, x; Whittaker 1917. 1, ch. xi; Goursat 1921. 1, ch. vii; Engel and Faber 1932. 1, ch. iii.

are arbitrary independent functions of ξ^κ and w_λ we have

$$\frac{\partial v_{\mathfrak{b}}}{\partial \xi^\lambda}\frac{\partial \xi^\kappa}{\partial v_{\mathfrak{b}}} = \delta^\kappa_\lambda, \qquad \frac{\partial v_{\mathfrak{b}}}{\partial w_\kappa}\frac{\partial w_\lambda}{\partial v_{\mathfrak{b}}} = \delta^\kappa_\lambda$$
$$\frac{\partial v_{\mathfrak{b}}}{\partial \xi^\kappa}\frac{\partial w_\lambda}{\partial v_{\mathfrak{b}}} = 0, \qquad \frac{\partial v_{\mathfrak{b}}}{\partial w_\lambda}\frac{\partial \xi^\kappa}{\partial v_{\mathfrak{b}}} = 0 \qquad (\mathfrak{b} = 1,..., 2n), \tag{9.3}$$

and consequently

$$\sum_{\mathfrak{c}=1}^{\mathfrak{c}=2n} (v_{\mathfrak{a}}, v_{\mathfrak{c}})\{v_{\mathfrak{b}}, v_{\mathfrak{c}}\} = \delta_{\mathfrak{ab}} \quad (\mathfrak{a}, \mathfrak{b}, \mathfrak{c} = 1,..., 2n). \tag{9.4}$$

From these identities it follows that the matrix of $(v_{\mathfrak{a}}, v_{\mathfrak{b}})$ is the inverse of the matrix of $\{v_{\mathfrak{b}}, v_{\mathfrak{a}}\}$ (cf. I, § 3).

For three functions v_1, v_2, and v_3 of ξ^κ and w_λ

$$(v_1,(v_2, v_3))+(v_2,(v_3, v_1))+(v_3,(v_1, v_2)) = 0 \tag{9.5}$$

always holds. This is the *Jacobian identity for Poisson bracket expressions*, which is readily proved by writing out the bracket expressions.

Now we consider the invertible transformation

$$'\xi^\kappa = '\phi^\kappa(\xi^\kappa, w_\lambda), \qquad \xi^\kappa = \phi^\kappa('\xi^\kappa, 'w_\lambda),$$
$$'w_\lambda = '\psi_\lambda(\xi^\kappa, w_\lambda), \qquad w_\lambda = \psi_\lambda('\xi^\kappa, 'w_\lambda). \tag{9.6}$$

A necessary and sufficient condition that (9.6) be a C_2-transformation is that a function $\Omega('\xi^\kappa, 'w_\lambda)$ exists such that

$$w_\lambda d\xi^\lambda = 'w_\lambda d'\xi^\lambda + d\Omega('\xi^\kappa, 'w_\lambda) \tag{9.7}$$

or, in another form, that

$$(a) \quad w_\mu \frac{\partial \xi^\mu}{\partial '\xi^\lambda} = 'w_\lambda + \frac{\partial \Omega}{\partial '\xi^\lambda}, \qquad (b) \quad w_\mu \frac{\partial \xi^\mu}{\partial 'w_\kappa} = \frac{\partial \Omega}{\partial 'w_\kappa}. \tag{9.8}$$

Evidently the equations

$$(a) \quad 'w_\mu \frac{\partial '\xi^\mu}{\partial \xi^\lambda} = w_\lambda + \frac{\partial '\Omega}{\partial \xi^\lambda}, \qquad (b) \quad 'w_\mu \frac{\partial '\xi^\mu}{\partial w_\kappa} = \frac{\partial '\Omega}{\partial w_\kappa} \tag{9.9}$$

represent another system of necessary and sufficient conditions and the functions Ω and $'\Omega$ are connected by the identity

$$'\Omega(\xi^\kappa, w_\lambda) = -\Omega('\xi^\kappa, 'w_\lambda). \tag{9.10}$$

By differentiation of (9.8) we get, according to (9.2),

$$(a) \qquad \{'\xi^\mu, '\xi^\kappa\} \stackrel{\text{def}}{=} 2\frac{\partial w_\lambda}{\partial '\xi^{[\mu}}\frac{\partial \xi^\lambda}{\partial '\xi^{\kappa]}} = 0,$$

$$(b) \qquad \{'w_\lambda, '\xi^\kappa\} \stackrel{\text{def}}{=} \frac{\partial w_\mu}{\partial 'w_\lambda}\frac{\partial \xi^\mu}{\partial '\xi^\kappa} - \frac{\partial w_\mu}{\partial '\xi^\kappa}\frac{\partial \xi^\mu}{\partial 'w_\lambda} = \delta^\lambda_\kappa, \tag{9.11}$$

$$(c) \qquad \{'w_\lambda, 'w_\mu\} \stackrel{\text{def}}{=} 2\frac{\partial w_\kappa}{\partial 'w_{[\lambda}}\frac{\partial \xi^\kappa}{\partial 'w_{\mu]}} = 0.$$

If we now consider the covariant vector in the X_{2n} of $'\xi^\kappa$, $'w_\lambda$ with the $2n$ components

$$w_\mu \frac{\partial \xi^\mu}{\partial {'\xi^\lambda}} - {'w_\lambda}, \qquad w_\mu \frac{\partial \xi^\mu}{\partial {'w_\kappa}} \tag{9.12}$$

the equations (9.11) state that the rotation of this vector vanishes. Hence this vector is the gradient of some function $\Omega('\xi^\kappa, 'w_\lambda)$. But this is just what the conditions (9.8) require and this proves that (9.11) represents still another system of necessary and sufficient conditions that (9.6) be a C_2-transformation.

The matrix of the Lagrange bracket expressions of $'\xi^1, \ldots, '\xi^n, 'w_1, \ldots, 'w_n$ in this order has the form

$$\left\|\begin{array}{cccccccccc}
0 & \cdot & \cdot & \cdot & \cdot & \cdot & \cdot & \cdot & 0 & -1 \\
\cdot & \cdot & \cdot & \cdot & \cdot & \cdot & \cdot & \cdot & -1 & 0 \\
\cdot & \cdot & \cdot & \cdot & \cdot & \cdot & \cdot & \cdot & \cdot & \cdot \\
\cdot & \cdot & \cdot & \cdot & \cdot & 0 & -1 & \cdot & \cdot & \cdot \\
\cdot & \cdot & \cdot & \cdot & 0 & -1 & 0 & \cdot & \cdot & \cdot \\
\cdot & \cdot & \cdot & 0 & +1 & 0 & \cdot & \cdot & \cdot & \cdot \\
\cdot & \cdot & \cdot & +1 & 0 & \cdot & \cdot & \cdot & \cdot & \cdot \\
\cdot & \cdot & \cdot & \cdot & \cdot & \cdot & \cdot & \cdot & \cdot & \cdot \\
0 & +1 & \cdot & \cdot & \cdot & \cdot & \cdot & \cdot & \cdot & \cdot \\
+1 & 0 & \cdot & \cdot & \cdot & \cdot & \cdot & \cdot & \cdot & 0
\end{array}\right\| \tag{9.13}$$

according to (9.11). But since the inverse of this matrix has the same form, the system

$$\begin{aligned}
&(a) \qquad ('\xi^\mu, '\xi^\kappa) \overset{\text{def}}{=} 2 \frac{\partial '\xi^{[\mu}}{\partial w_\lambda} \frac{\partial '\xi^{\kappa]}}{\partial \xi^\lambda} = 0, \\
&(b) \qquad ('w_\lambda, '\xi^\kappa) \overset{\text{def}}{=} \frac{\partial 'w_\lambda}{\partial w_\mu} \frac{\partial '\xi^\kappa}{\partial \xi^\mu} - \frac{\partial '\xi^\kappa}{\partial w_\mu} \frac{\partial 'w_\lambda}{\partial \xi^\mu} = \delta^\kappa_\lambda, \\
&(c) \qquad ('w_\lambda, 'w_\mu) \overset{\text{def}}{=} 2 \frac{\partial 'w_{[\lambda}}{\partial w_\kappa} \frac{\partial 'w_{\mu]}}{\partial \xi^\kappa} = 0
\end{aligned} \tag{9.14}$$

also represents a system of necessary and sufficient conditions that (9.6) be a C_2-transformation.

By writing the expressions $\{v_1, v_2\}$ and (v_1, v_2) in full, using (9.11) and (9.14), it is readily shown *that both bracket expressions* $\{v_1, v_2\}$ *and* (v_1, v_2) *are invariant for C_2-transformations in ξ^κ and w_λ.*

From (9.9 a) it follows that

$$w_\lambda \frac{\partial '\xi^\kappa}{\partial w_\lambda} = {'w_\mu} \frac{\partial '\xi^\mu}{\partial \xi^\lambda} \frac{\partial '\xi^\kappa}{\partial w_\lambda} - \frac{\partial '\Omega}{\partial \xi^\lambda} \frac{\partial '\xi^\kappa}{\partial w_\lambda} \tag{9.15}$$

and accordingly, in consideration of (9.14 *a*) and (9.9 *b*),

$$w_\lambda \frac{\partial '\xi^\kappa}{\partial w_\lambda} = \left('w_\mu \frac{\partial '\xi^\mu}{\partial w_\lambda} - \frac{\partial '\Omega}{\partial w_\lambda}\right)\frac{\partial '\xi^\kappa}{\partial \xi^\lambda} - ('\xi^\kappa, '\Omega) = ('\Omega, '\xi^\kappa). \tag{9.16}$$

From (9.9 *a, b*) and (9.14 *b*) we get

$$\begin{aligned} w_\mu \frac{\partial 'w_\lambda}{\partial w_\mu} &= \left('w_\kappa \frac{\partial '\xi^\kappa}{\partial \xi^\mu} - \frac{\partial '\Omega}{\partial \xi^\mu}\right)\frac{\partial 'w_\lambda}{\partial w_\mu} \\ &= \left('w_\kappa \frac{\partial '\xi^\kappa}{\partial w_\mu} - \frac{\partial '\Omega}{\partial w_\mu}\right)\frac{\partial 'w_\lambda}{\partial \xi^\mu} + 'w_\lambda - ('w_\lambda, '\Omega) \\ &= 'w_\lambda + ('\Omega, 'w_\lambda). \end{aligned} \tag{9.17}$$

Similarly we get the equations

$$'w_\lambda \frac{\partial \xi^\kappa}{\partial 'w_\lambda} = (\Omega, \xi^\kappa), \tag{9.18}$$

$$'w_\mu \frac{\partial w_\lambda}{\partial 'w_\mu} = w_\lambda + (\Omega, w_\lambda). \tag{9.19}$$

From (9.16, 17) we see that $'\xi^\kappa$ and $'w_\lambda$ are homogeneous of degree zero and one respectively in w_λ if and only if (9.6) is a C_3-transformation.

Now we suppose that a system of n independent functions $'\phi^\kappa(\xi^\kappa, w_\lambda)$ be given, whose Poisson brackets all vanish and that we wish to derive a system of n functions $'\psi_\lambda(\xi^\kappa, w_\lambda)$, such that (9.6) is a C_2-transformation. We therefore choose an arbitrary function $'\Omega(\xi^\kappa, w_\lambda)$, satisfying the non-homogeneous system of n linear partial differential equations

$$w_\lambda \frac{\partial '\phi^\kappa}{\partial w_\lambda} = ('\Omega, '\phi^\kappa). \tag{9.20}$$

Since the matrix of the derivatives of the $'\phi^\kappa$ with respect to ξ^κ, w_λ has rank n, the first condition of completeness of this system is satisfied (cf. III, § 14). The second condition is satisfied because

$$('\phi^\kappa, ('\phi^\lambda, '\Omega)) - ('\phi^\lambda, ('\phi^\kappa, '\Omega)) \equiv ('\Omega, ('\phi^\lambda, '\phi^\kappa)) = 0 \tag{9.21}$$

as a consequence of the Jacobian identity. The third condition is satisfied because

$$\begin{aligned} &2\left(\frac{\partial '\phi^{[\kappa}}{\partial w_\mu}\frac{\partial}{\partial \xi^\mu} - \frac{\partial '\phi^{[\kappa}}{\partial \xi^\mu}\frac{\partial}{\partial w_\mu}\right) w_\nu \frac{\partial '\phi^{\lambda]}}{\partial w_\nu} \\ &= 2w_\nu \frac{\partial '\phi^{[\kappa}}{\partial w_\mu}\frac{\partial^2 '\phi^{\lambda]}}{\partial \xi^\mu \partial w_\nu} - 2w_\nu \frac{\partial '\phi^{[\kappa}}{\partial \xi^\mu}\frac{\partial^2 '\phi^{\lambda]}}{\partial w_\mu \partial w_\nu} - 2\frac{\partial '\phi^{[\kappa}}{\partial \xi^\mu}\frac{\partial '\phi^{\lambda]}}{\partial w_\mu} \\ &= 2w_\nu\left('\phi^{[\kappa}, \frac{\partial '\phi^{\lambda]}}{\partial w_\nu}\right) = w_\nu\left('\phi^\kappa, \frac{\partial '\phi^\lambda}{\partial w_\nu}\right) - w_\nu\left('\phi^\lambda, \frac{\partial '\phi^\kappa}{\partial w_\nu}\right) \\ &= w_\nu \frac{\partial}{\partial w_\nu}('\phi^\kappa, '\phi^\lambda) = 0. \end{aligned} \tag{9.22}$$

Since, from the reduced system of (9.20),

$$('\Omega, '\phi^\kappa) = 0, \tag{9.23}$$

the n solutions $'\phi^\kappa$ are known, a solution of (9.20) can be obtained by means of a quadrature (cf. III, § 14). If and only if the $'\phi^\kappa$ are homogeneous of degree zero in w_λ is it possible (but not necessary) to choose a constant for this solution. When the solution $'\Omega$ has been chosen, (9.9) represents $2n$ linear algebraic equations for the $'\psi_\lambda$ and we will show that just n linearly independent linear relations exist between these equations. Transvecting (9.9a) with $\partial '\phi^\kappa/\partial w_\lambda$ and (9.9b) with $\partial '\phi^\kappa/\partial \xi^\lambda$ we get

$$0 = '\psi_\mu \frac{\partial '\phi^\mu}{\partial \xi^\lambda}\frac{\partial '\phi^\kappa}{\partial w_\lambda} - '\psi_\mu \frac{\partial '\phi^\mu}{\partial w_\lambda}\frac{\partial '\phi^\kappa}{\partial \xi^\lambda}$$

$$= w_\lambda \frac{\partial '\phi^\kappa}{\partial w_\lambda} + \frac{\partial '\Omega}{\partial \xi^\lambda}\frac{\partial '\phi^\kappa}{\partial w_\lambda} - \frac{\partial '\Omega}{\partial w_\lambda}\frac{\partial '\phi^\kappa}{\partial \xi^\lambda} = 0, \tag{9.24}$$

and these relations are linearly independent because the matrix of the derivatives of the $'\phi^\nu$ with respect to ξ^κ and w_λ has rank n. Since this rank is n it is not possible for more than n linearly independent linear relations to exist. Hence among the equations (9.9) there are just n independent ones and from these the $'\psi_\lambda$ can be solved uniquely as functions of the ξ^κ and w_λ. Consequently, once the function $'\Omega$ has been chosen, the determination of the $'\psi_\lambda$ requires only the solution of a system of n linear algebraic equations to be found. If the $'\phi^\kappa$ are homogeneous of degree zero in the w_λ and if a constant is chosen for $'\Omega$, the $'\psi_\lambda$ are homogeneous of degree one in the w_λ (according to (9.9)) and the transformation (9.6) is a C_3-transformation.

Similarly it is possible to determine the functions $'\phi^\kappa$ if a system of n functions $'\psi_\lambda$ is given, whose Poisson brackets all vanish. To this end we write the equations (9.9) in the form

$$(a) \quad -'\xi^\mu \frac{\partial 'w_\mu}{\partial \xi^\lambda} = w_\lambda + \frac{\partial '\Omega^*}{\partial \xi^\lambda}, \qquad (b) \quad -'\xi^\mu \frac{\partial 'w_\mu}{\partial w_\kappa} = \frac{\partial '\Omega^*}{\partial w_\kappa}$$

$$('\Omega^* \stackrel{\text{def}}{=} '\Omega - 'w_\mu '\xi^\mu). \tag{9.25}$$

From these equations we get in consideration of (9.14c)

$$w_\mu \frac{\partial 'w_\lambda}{\partial w_\mu} = -'\xi^\nu \frac{\partial 'w_\nu}{\partial \xi^\mu}\frac{\partial 'w_\lambda}{\partial w_\mu} - \frac{\partial '\Omega^*}{\partial \xi^\mu}\frac{\partial 'w_\lambda}{\partial w_\mu}$$

$$= -'\xi^\nu \frac{\partial 'w_\nu}{\partial w_\mu}\frac{\partial 'w_\lambda}{\partial \xi^\mu} - \frac{\partial '\Omega^*}{\partial w_\mu}\frac{\partial 'w_\lambda}{\partial \xi^\mu} + ('\Omega^*, 'w_\lambda) \tag{9.26}$$

$$= ('\Omega^*, 'w_\lambda),$$

and similarly

$$w_\lambda \frac{\partial '\xi^\kappa}{\partial w_\lambda} = -'\xi^\mu \frac{\partial 'w_\mu}{\partial \xi^\lambda}\frac{\partial '\xi^\kappa}{\partial w_\lambda} - \frac{\partial '\Omega^*}{\partial \xi^\lambda}\frac{\partial '\xi^\kappa}{\partial w_\lambda}$$

$$= -'\xi^\kappa - '\xi^\mu \frac{\partial 'w_\mu}{\partial w_\lambda}\frac{\partial' \xi^\kappa}{\partial \xi^\lambda} - \frac{\partial '\Omega^*}{\partial w_\lambda}\frac{\partial '\xi^\kappa}{\partial \xi^\lambda} + ('\Omega^*, '\xi^\kappa)$$

$$= -'\xi^\kappa + ('\Omega^*, '\xi^\kappa). \tag{9.27}$$

Now $'\Omega^*$ has to be chosen in such a way that the non-homogeneous system of n partial differential equations

$$w_\mu \frac{\partial '\psi_\lambda}{\partial w_\mu} = ('\Omega^*, '\psi_\lambda) \tag{9.28}$$

is satisfied. As above it is shown that this system is complete. Since this system is complete and since the n solutions $'\psi_\lambda$ of the reduced system are known, a solution of (9.28) can be obtained by means of a quadrature. As above it can be proved that, this solution being chosen, just n independent linear relations exist between the $2n$ algebraic equations (9.25). Hence the $'\phi^\kappa$ can be solved uniquely from (9.25) as functions of the ξ^κ and w_λ. If the $'\psi_\lambda$ are homogeneous of degree one in the w_λ and if for $'\Omega^*$ a function is chosen, homogeneous of degree one in the w_λ, the $'\phi^\kappa$ are homogeneous of degree zero in the w_λ. From (9.25 *b*) it follows that in this case

$$-'\phi^\mu\, '\psi_\mu = -'\phi^\mu \frac{\partial '\psi_\mu}{\partial w_\lambda} w_\lambda = w_\lambda \frac{\partial '\Omega^*}{\partial w_\lambda} = '\Omega^*. \tag{9.29}$$

Consequently $'\Omega = 0$ and the transformation (9.6) is a C_3-transformation. We collect results in the theorem:†

THEOREM VI.11. *If $'\phi^\kappa(\xi^\mu, w_\lambda)$ [or $'\psi_\lambda(\xi^\kappa, w_\mu)$] are n arbitrary functions, analytic and independent in the region considered and such that all their Poisson brackets vanish, there exists always a system of n functions $'\psi_\lambda(\xi^\kappa, w_\mu)$ [or $'\phi^\kappa(\xi^\mu, w_\lambda)$], such that the equations*

$$'\xi^\kappa = '\phi^\kappa, \qquad 'w_\lambda = '\psi_\lambda \tag{9.30}$$

represent a C_2-transformation in ξ^κ, w_λ. To find these functions, a solution $'\Omega$ [or $'\Omega^*$ respectively] of the complete system of n non-homogeneous equations (9.20) [or (9.28) respectively] has to be obtained. This is always possible by one quadrature. Then to every choice of $'\Omega$ [or $'\Omega^*$] one and only one system of functions $'\psi_\lambda$ [or $'\phi^\kappa$] can be obtained by the solution of n linear algebraic equations.

If and only if the $'\phi^\kappa$ are homogeneous of degree zero in the w_λ a solution

† Lie 1890. 1, ch. v; v. Weber 1900. 1, ch. xi; Goursat 1921. 1, ch. x; Engel and Faber 1932. 1, ch. vi.

$'\Omega = constant$ exists. If and only if the $'\psi_\lambda$ are homogeneous of degree one in the w_λ a solution $'\Omega^*$ homogeneous of degree zero in the w_λ exists. The functions $'\psi_\lambda$ [or $'\phi^\kappa$] belonging to these special solutions are homogeneous of degree one [or zero] in the w_λ and the resulting transformation is a C_3-transformation.

Finally we consider the case when $\tau < n$ functions $'\phi^{\mathfrak{a}}(\xi^\kappa, w_\lambda)$ or $'\psi_{\mathfrak{b}}(\xi^\kappa, w_\lambda)$ $(\mathfrak{a}, \mathfrak{b} = 1,\dots,\tau)$ are given whose Poisson brackets all vanish, and when a C_2-transformation ξ^κ, $w_\lambda \to {}'\xi^\kappa$, $'w_\lambda$ is required such that $'\xi^{\mathfrak{a}} = {}'\phi^{\mathfrak{a}}$ or $'w_{\mathfrak{b}} = {}'\psi_{\mathfrak{b}}$ respectively. We treat here only the case when the functions $'\phi^{\mathfrak{a}}$ are given, the other case being dealt with in the same way. The first thing to do is to complete the set of functions $'\phi^{\mathfrak{a}}$ with $n-\tau$ other functions $'\phi^{\tau+1},\dots, {}'\phi^n$ such that the Poisson brackets of the $'\phi^\kappa$ $(\kappa = 1,\dots, n)$ all vanish. To determine these new functions we choose for $'\phi^{\tau+1}$ a solution of the homogeneous system of τ equations

$$('\phi^{\mathfrak{a}}, f) = 0 \quad (\mathfrak{a} = 1,\dots,\tau). \tag{9.31}$$

According to the identity of Jacobi this system is complete. Since the τ solutions $'\phi^{\mathfrak{a}}$ are known, the determination of $'\phi^{\tau+1}$ requires an operation $O_{2n-2\tau}$. Continuing in this way the functions $'\phi^{\tau+1},\dots, {}'\phi^n$ can be determined by means of $n-\tau$ operations $O_{2n-2\tau}, O_{2n-2\tau-2},\dots, O_2$. Then the function $'\Omega$ can be obtained by means of an operation O_0 and after this the determination of the function $'\psi_\lambda$ requires only algebraical operations. Incidentally we get the result, *that there cannot exist more than n independent functions which are mutually in involution.* Because if $\tau = n$ all solutions of (9.31) are functions of the $'\phi^\kappa$.

In the special case when the $'\phi^{\mathfrak{a}}$ $(\mathfrak{a} = 1,\dots,\tau)$ are all homogeneous of degree zero in the w_λ and when we want a C_3-transformation ξ^κ, $w_\lambda \to {}'\xi^\kappa$, $'w_\lambda$ such that $'\xi^{\mathfrak{a}} = {}'\phi^{\mathfrak{a}}$ $(\mathfrak{a} = 1,\dots,\tau)$, the new functions $'\phi^{\tau+1},\dots,$ $'\phi^n$ have to satisfy the additional condition that they be homogeneous of degree zero in the w_λ. Hence $'\phi^{\tau+1}$ has to be a solution of the system of $\tau+1$ equations

$$\begin{aligned} ('\phi^{\mathfrak{a}}, f) &= 0 \\ w_\lambda \frac{\partial f}{\partial w_\lambda} &= 0 \end{aligned} \quad (\mathfrak{a} = 1,\dots,\tau). \tag{9.32}$$

But, according to the relations

$$\begin{aligned} &\left(\frac{\partial\, '\phi^{\mathfrak{a}}}{\partial w_\lambda}\frac{\partial}{\partial \xi^\lambda} - \frac{\partial\, '\phi^{\mathfrak{a}}}{\partial \xi^\lambda}\frac{\partial}{\partial w_\lambda}\right) w_\mu \frac{\partial f}{\partial w_\mu} - w_\mu \frac{\partial}{\partial w_\mu}\left(\frac{\partial\, '\phi^{\mathfrak{a}}}{\partial w_\lambda}\frac{\partial f}{\partial \xi^\lambda} - \frac{\partial\, '\phi^{\mathfrak{a}}}{\partial \xi^\lambda}\frac{\partial f}{\partial w_\lambda}\right) \\ &\qquad = -\frac{\partial\, '\phi^{\mathfrak{a}}}{\partial \xi^\lambda}\frac{\partial f}{\partial w_\lambda} - w_\mu \frac{\partial^2\, '\phi^{\mathfrak{a}}}{\partial w_\mu\, \partial w_\lambda}\frac{\partial f}{\partial \xi^\lambda} + w_\mu \frac{\partial^2\, '\phi^{\mathfrak{a}}}{\partial w_\mu\, \partial \xi^\lambda}\frac{\partial f}{\partial w_\lambda} \\ &\qquad = ('\phi^{\mathfrak{a}}, f) \quad (\mathfrak{a} = 1,\dots,\tau), \end{aligned} \tag{9.33}$$

this system is complete as well. Consequently by an operation $O_{2n-2\tau-1}$ at least one solution can be obtained independent of the known τ solutions $'\phi^{\mathfrak{a}}$. Continuing in this way the functions $'\phi^{\tau+1},..., '\phi^{n}$ can be obtained by means of $n-\tau$ operations $O_{2n-2\tau-1}, O_{2n-2\tau-3},..., O_1$. Then for the function $'\Omega$ a constant has to be chosen, and after that the functions $'\psi_\lambda$ can be obtained algebraically.

Collecting results we have the theorem:†

THEOREM VI.12. *If* $'\phi^{\mathfrak{a}}(\xi^\kappa, w_\lambda)$ [*or* $'\psi_{\mathfrak{b}}(\xi^\kappa, w_\lambda)$] $(\mathfrak{a}, \mathfrak{b} = 1,..., \tau)$ *are arbitrary functions, analytic and independent in the region considered and such that all their Poisson brackets vanish, there always exists a system of* $n-\tau$ *functions* $'\phi^{\tau+1},..., '\phi^{n}$ [*or* $'\psi_{\tau+1},..., '\psi_n$] *and a system of n functions* $'\psi_\lambda$ [*or* $'\phi^\kappa$ $(\kappa, \lambda = 1,..., n)$] *such that the equations*

$$'\xi^\kappa = '\phi^\kappa, \qquad 'w_\lambda = '\psi_\lambda \tag{9.34}$$

represent a C_2*-transformation. The determination of* $'\phi^{\tau+1},..., '\phi^{n}$ [*or* $'\psi_{\tau+1},..., '\psi_n$] *requires* $n-\tau$ *operations* $O_{2n-2\tau}, O_{2n-2\tau-2},..., O_2$ *and the determination of* $'\Omega$ [*or* $'\Omega^*$] *an operation* O_0. *Then the* $'\psi_\lambda$ [*or* $'\phi^\kappa$] *can be obtained by the solution of a system of n linear algebraic equations.*

If the $'\phi^{\mathfrak{a}}$ [*or* $'\psi_{\mathfrak{b}}$] *are homogeneous of degree zero* [*or one*] *in the* w_λ, *it is possible to determine the functions* $'\phi^{\tau+1},..., '\phi^{n}$ [*or* $'\psi_{\tau+1},..., '\psi_n$] *in such a way that they are homogeneous of degree zero* [*or one*] *in the* w_λ *as well and to this end* $n-\tau$ *operations* $O_{2n-2\tau-1}, O_{2n-2\tau-3},..., O_1$ *are required. Then for* $'\Omega$ [*or* $'\Omega^*$] *a constant* [*or a function homogeneous of degree one in* w_λ] *can be chosen and after that the algebraical determination of the* $'\psi_\lambda$ [*or* $'\phi^\kappa$] *leads to functions homogeneous of degree one* [*or zero*] *in the* w_λ. *In this case the transformation obtained is a* C_3*-transformation.*

In VI, § 11, and VI, § 12, a generalization of this theorem will be obtained.

10. On the transformations of the expressions (F, G) and $w_\lambda \dfrac{dF}{\partial w_\lambda}$‡

As we have seen in VI, § 9, the bracket expression (F, G) of two functions F and G of ξ^κ, w_λ is invariant for C_2-transformations. It may be asked how this expression transforms with C_1-transformations. Now every C_1-transformation can be obtained by first performing a C_3-transformation and subsequently a similarity transformation of w_λ

$$\begin{aligned} 'w_\lambda &= \mu(\xi^\kappa, w_\lambda) w_\lambda, \\ '\xi^\kappa &= \xi^\kappa. \end{aligned} \tag{10.1}$$

† Cf. v. Weber 1900. 1, ch. xi; Goursat 1921. 1, ch. x; Engel and Faber 1932. 1, ch. vi.

‡ Lie 1876. 1, 1877. 1; v. Weber 1900. 1, ch. xi; Goursat 1921. 1, ch. x; Engel and Faber 1932. 1, ch. vi; Eisenhart 1933. 1, ch. vi.

Since (F, G) is invariant for the first transformation, only the transformation (10.1) has to be investigated. Now for any function F of ξ^κ, w_λ we have

$$\begin{aligned}(a)\quad & \frac{\partial F}{\partial' w_\lambda} = \frac{1}{\mu}\frac{\partial F}{\partial w_\lambda} - \frac{1}{\mu}(F)'\frac{\partial \log\mu}{\partial w_\lambda}, \\ (b)\quad & \frac{\partial F}{\partial' \xi^\kappa} = \frac{\partial F}{\partial \xi^\kappa} - (F)'\frac{\partial \log\mu}{\partial \xi^\kappa},\end{aligned} \qquad (F)' \stackrel{\text{def}}{=} {}'w_\lambda \frac{\partial F}{\partial' w_\lambda}, \tag{10.2}$$

and consequently, writing $(F, G)'$ for the transform of (F, G)

$$\begin{aligned}(F,G)' &= \frac{1}{\mu}(F,G) - \frac{1}{\mu}\left\{\frac{\partial F}{\partial w_\lambda}(G)'\frac{\partial \log\mu}{\partial \xi^\lambda} + \frac{\partial G}{\partial \xi^\lambda}(F)'\frac{\partial \log\mu}{\partial w_\lambda}\right\} \\ &= \frac{1}{\mu}(F,G) - \frac{1}{\mu}(G)'(F, \log\mu) + \frac{1}{\mu}(F)'(G, \log\mu) \\ &= \frac{1}{\mu}(F,G) - (F)'\left(G, \frac{1}{\mu}\right) + (G)'\left(F, \frac{1}{\mu}\right).\end{aligned} \tag{10.3}$$

From this equation it follows *that a Poisson bracket, if subjected to a C_1-transformation, gets a factor $1/\mu$ if both functions are homogeneous of degree zero in w_λ*. This condition is sufficient but not necessary.

Writing
$$(F) \stackrel{\text{def}}{=} w_\lambda \frac{\partial F}{\partial w_\lambda}, \tag{10.4}$$

we get from (10.2 a)

$$(F)' = (F) - (F)'(\log\mu) = (F) - (F)(\log\mu)'. \tag{10.5}$$

Hence

$$(F)' = \frac{(F)}{1+(\log\mu)} = (1-(\log\mu)')(F), \tag{10.6}$$

and

$$(1+(\log\mu))(1-(\log\mu)') = 1. \tag{10.7}$$

This proves *that if F is any function of ξ^κ, w_λ, (F) is invariant for all those C_1-transformations for which* $\log\mu$ *is homogeneous of degree zero in the w_λ. This condition is sufficient and necessary.*

For every function F the expressions (F) and $(F)'$ are related in the following way:

$$(F)' = {}'w_\lambda \frac{\partial F}{\partial \xi^\kappa}\frac{\partial \xi^\kappa}{\partial w'_\lambda} + {}'w_\lambda \frac{\partial F}{\partial w_\mu}\frac{\partial w_\mu}{\partial' w_\lambda}. \tag{10.8}$$

Hence, if the transformation $\xi^\kappa, w_\lambda \to {}'\xi^\kappa, {}'w_\lambda$ is a C_2-transformation, from (9.18, 19) it follows that

$$\begin{aligned}(F)' &= (\Omega, \xi^\kappa)\frac{\partial F}{\partial \xi^\kappa} + (F) + (\Omega, w_\lambda)\frac{\partial F}{\partial w_\lambda} \\ &= (F) + (\Omega, F).\end{aligned} \tag{10.9}$$

We collect results in the following table:

	C_1-*transformation*	C_2-*transformation*	C_3-*transformation*
$w_\lambda\, d\xi^\lambda$	$\mu w_\lambda\, d\xi^\lambda$	$w_\lambda\, d\xi^\lambda + d\Omega$	$w_\lambda\, d\xi^\lambda$
(F, G)	$\frac{1}{\mu}(F, G)-(F)'\left(G, \frac{1}{\mu}\right)+(G)'\left(F, \frac{1}{\mu}\right)$	(F, G)	(F, G)
(F)	$\frac{(F)}{1+(\log \mu)} = (F)(1-(\log \mu)')$	$(F)+(\Omega, F)$	(F)

(10.10)

11. Non-homogeneous function groups†

If $F(\xi^\kappa, w_\lambda)$ is a function analytic in $\mathfrak{N}(\underset{0}{\xi^\kappa}, \overset{0}{w_\lambda})$ the equation

$$F(\xi^\kappa, w_\lambda) = \text{constant} \tag{11.1}$$

represents a normal system of ∞^1 $\mathfrak{N}_{2n-1}$'s in $\mathfrak{N}(\underset{0}{\xi^\kappa}, \overset{0}{w_\lambda})$. Conversely the function F is not determined by this normal system. The normal system only determines the set of all analytic functions of ξ^κ, w_λ in $\mathfrak{N}(\underset{0}{\xi^\kappa}, \overset{0}{w_\lambda})$ which can be written as a function of F. Similarly a system of $2n-m$ independent functions $F^x(\xi^\kappa, w_\lambda)$ $(x = \text{m}+1,..., 2\text{n})$, analytic and of rank $2n-m$ in an $\mathfrak{N}(\underset{0}{\xi^\kappa}, \overset{0}{w_\lambda})$ determines a normal system of ∞^{2n-m} $\mathfrak{N}_m$'s with the equations

$$F^x(\xi^\kappa, w_\lambda) = \text{constant} \quad (x = \text{m}+1,..., 2\text{n}). \tag{11.2}$$

Conversely this normal system determines the set of all analytic functions of ξ^κ, w_λ in $\mathfrak{N}(\underset{0}{\xi^\kappa}, \overset{0}{w_\lambda})$ which can be written as functions of the F^x.

If all bracket expressions of the F^x $(x = \text{m}+1,..., 2\text{n})$ can be written as functions of the F^x and if F and G are two arbitrary functions of the F^x, we have

$$(F, G) = \frac{\partial F}{\partial F^x}\frac{\partial G}{\partial F^y}(F^x, F^y) \quad (x, y = \text{m}+1,..., 2\text{n}), \tag{11.3}$$

and this proves that the set of all analytic functions of the F^x has the property that all Poisson brackets of two functions of the set belong to the set. According to S. Lie such a set of functions is called a *function group of dimension* $2n-m$. Any set of $2n-m$ functionally independent functions of the group is called a *basis* or a *coordinate system of the group*. *Evidently the equations* $(F^x, f) = 0$ *form a complete system if and only if the* F^x *form a function group.*

† Lie 1875. 1, 1877. 1; v. Weber 1900. 1, ch. xiv; Goursat 1921. 1, ch. xi; Engel and Faber 1932. 1, §§ 46–9; Eisenhart 1933. 1, § 69.

If we pass from the F^x $(x = \mathrm{m}+1,\ldots, 2\mathrm{n})$ to another coordinate system $F^{x'}(x' = (\mathrm{m}+1)',\ldots, (2\mathrm{n})')$ the transformation of the bracket expressions

$$H^{xy} \stackrel{\text{def}}{=} (F^x, F^y) \quad (x, y = \mathrm{m}+1,\ldots, 2\mathrm{n}) \tag{11.4}$$

is linear and homogeneous:

$$H^{x'y'} \stackrel{\text{def}}{=} (F^{x'}, F^{y'}) = \frac{\partial F^{x'}}{\partial F^x}\frac{\partial F^{y'}}{\partial F^y} H^{xy} \quad (x, y = \mathrm{m}+1,\ldots, 2\mathrm{n}). \tag{11.5}$$

Therefore, we call H^{xy} the *Poisson bivector of the function group.* The rank 2ρ of this bivector is an arithmetic invariant of the function group and is called the *rank of the function group.* Evidently $2\rho \leqslant 2n-m$. If $2\rho = 0$ the function group is said to be *commutative.* All functions of a commutative function group are mutually in involution (cf. VI, § 9).

From the Jacobian identity it follows that

$$(F^{[x}, H^{yz]}) = 0 \quad (x, y, z = \mathrm{m}+1,\ldots, 2\mathrm{n}). \tag{11.6}$$

Now the H^{yz} are functions of the F^x, and consequently this identity takes the form

$$(F^{[x}, F^{|u|})\frac{\partial H^{yz]}}{\partial F^u} = H^{[x|u|}\partial_u H^{yz]} = 0, \qquad \partial_u \stackrel{\text{def}}{=} \frac{\partial}{\partial F^u}$$
$$(x, y, z, u = \mathrm{m}+1,\ldots, 2\mathrm{n}). \tag{11.7}$$

We will prove that this equation expresses the fact that the system of linear homogeneous partial differential equations in the variables F^x

$$H^{[xy}\partial_y f(F^{z]}) = 0 \quad (x, y, z = \mathrm{m}+1,\ldots, 2\mathrm{n}) \tag{11.8}$$

is complete. In fact, according to (11.7) we have

$$2H^{[z|u|}\partial_u H^{x]y} = H^{yu}\partial_u H^{xz} \quad (x, y, z, u = \mathrm{m}+1,\ldots, 2\mathrm{n})\dagger \tag{11.9}$$

and from this it follows that

$$2H^{[z|u|}\partial_u H^{x]y}\partial_y = (\partial_u H^{xz})H^{yu}\partial_y \quad (x, y, z, u = \mathrm{m}+1,\ldots, 2\mathrm{n}). \tag{11.10}$$

Since the rank of H^{xy} is 2ρ the system (11.8) has just $2n-m-2\rho$ independent solutions. These solutions are called the *singular functions of the function group.* The determination of these functions requires $2n-m-2\rho$ operations $O_{2n-m-2\rho},\ldots, O_1$. Because of

$$H^{xy}\partial_y f(F^z) = (F^x, f) \quad (x, y, z = \mathrm{m}+1,\ldots, 2\mathrm{n}) \tag{11.11}$$

the singular functions are those functions *of the group* that are in involution with *all* functions of the group. These functions constitute by themselves a commutative sub-group, called the *null group* of the given group.

† Cf. Lie 1890. 1, p. 234.

The functions of ξ^κ, w_λ (not necessarily belonging to the function group), which are in involution with all functions of the group, are the solutions of the system of $2n-m$ independent linear homogeneous partial differential equations

$$(F^x, F) = 0 \quad (x = \mathrm{m}+1,\ldots, 2\mathrm{n}). \tag{11.12}$$

Since (F^x, F^y) is a function of the group, the identity of Jacobi in the form

$$(F^y,(F^x,F))-(F^x,(F^y,F)) = -((F^x,F^y),F) \quad (x,y = \mathrm{m}+1,\ldots, 2\mathrm{n}) \tag{11.13}$$

expresses the fact that (11.12) is complete. Consequently m independent solutions exist. If $\overset{1}{F}$ and $\overset{2}{F}$ are two solutions of (11.12), according to the identity of Jacobi we have

$$(F^x,(\overset{1}{F},\overset{2}{F})) = ((F^x,\overset{1}{F}),\overset{2}{F})-((F^x,\overset{2}{F}),\overset{1}{F}) = 0 \quad (x = \mathrm{m}+1,\ldots, 2\mathrm{n}) \tag{11.14}$$

and from this it follows that the solutions of (11.12) form an m-dimensional group. This group is called the *polar group* of the given group. The relations between the group and its polar group are reciprocal. Evidently the null group consists of all functions which the group and its polar group have in common. Hence $2n-m-2\rho \leqslant m$ or

$$\rho \geqslant n-m. \tag{11.15}$$

From (11.15) it follows again that there cannot exist a system of more than n independent functions which are mutually in involution (cf. VI, § 9).

It is convenient to choose the basis of the group in such a way that $F^{\mathrm{m}+2\rho+1},\ldots, F^{2\mathrm{n}}$ are singular functions. Then we have

$$H^{x\mathfrak{x}} = 0 \quad (x = \mathrm{m}+1,\ldots, 2\mathrm{n};\ \mathfrak{x} = \mathrm{m}+2\rho+1,\ldots, 2\mathrm{n}) \tag{11.16}$$

and the only components H^{xy} which do not necessarily vanish are

$$H^{\mathfrak{a}\mathfrak{b}} \quad (\mathfrak{a},\mathfrak{b} = \mathrm{m}+1,\ldots,\mathrm{m}+2\rho). \tag{11.17}$$

$H^{\mathfrak{a}\mathfrak{b}}$ $(\mathfrak{a},\mathfrak{b} = \mathrm{m}+1,\ldots,\mathrm{m}+2\rho)$ can be looked upon as a contravariant bivector of rank 2ρ in the $X_{2\rho}$ of the $F^{\mathfrak{a}}$ $(\mathfrak{a} = \mathrm{m}+1,\ldots,\mathrm{m}+2\rho)$, whose components depend on $2n-m-2\rho$ parameters $F^{\mathfrak{x}}$ $(\mathfrak{x} = \mathrm{m}+2\rho+1,\ldots, 2\mathrm{n})$. Then the identity (11.7) takes the form

$$H^{[\mathfrak{a}|\mathfrak{d}|}\partial_{\mathfrak{d}} H^{\mathfrak{b}\mathfrak{c}]} = 0 \quad (\mathfrak{a},\mathfrak{b},\mathfrak{c},\mathfrak{d} = \mathrm{m}+1,\ldots,\mathrm{m}+2\rho). \tag{11.18}$$

In order to bring $H^{\mathfrak{a}\mathfrak{b}}$ into a canonical form we introduce a covariant bivector $L_{\mathfrak{b}\mathfrak{a}}$ of rank 2ρ by means of the equation

$$H^{\mathfrak{a}\mathfrak{c}}L_{\mathfrak{b}\mathfrak{c}} = A^{\mathfrak{a}}_{\mathfrak{b}} \quad (\mathfrak{a},\mathfrak{b} = \mathrm{m}+1,\ldots,\mathrm{m}+2\rho). \tag{11.19}$$

$L_{\mathfrak{ba}}$ is the inverse of $H^{\mathfrak{ab}}$ (cf. I, § 3) and is uniquely determined by (11.19). By differentiation of (11.19) with respect to $F^{\mathfrak{d}}$ we get

$$(\partial_{\mathfrak{d}} H^{\mathfrak{ac}}) L_{\mathfrak{bc}} + H^{\mathfrak{ac}} \partial_{\mathfrak{d}} L_{\mathfrak{bc}} = 0 \quad (\mathfrak{a}, \mathfrak{b}, \mathfrak{c}, \mathfrak{d} = \mathrm{m}+1, \ldots, \mathrm{m}+2\rho). \tag{11.20}$$

Transvection of (11.20) with $H^{\mathfrak{be}}$ gives

$$\partial_{\mathfrak{d}} H^{\mathfrak{ae}} + H^{\mathfrak{ac}} H^{\mathfrak{be}} \partial_{\mathfrak{d}} L_{\mathfrak{bc}} = 0 \quad (\mathfrak{a}, \mathfrak{b}, \mathfrak{c}, \mathfrak{d}, \mathfrak{e} = \mathrm{m}+1, \ldots, \mathrm{m}+2\rho) \tag{11.21}$$

and from this equation we get by transvection with $H^{\mathfrak{fd}}$ and alternation, using (11.18),

$$0 = H^{[\mathfrak{f}|\mathfrak{d}|} \partial_{\mathfrak{d}} H^{\mathfrak{ae}]} = H^{\mathfrak{fd}} H^{\mathfrak{eb}} H^{\mathfrak{ac}} \partial_{[\mathfrak{d}} L_{\mathfrak{bc}]} \quad (\mathfrak{a}, \mathfrak{b}, \mathfrak{c}, \mathfrak{d}, \mathfrak{e}, \mathfrak{f} = \mathrm{m}+1, \ldots, \mathrm{m}+2\rho). \tag{11.22}$$

Since $H^{\mathfrak{ab}}$ has rank 2ρ, (11.22) is equivalent to

$$\partial_{[\mathfrak{c}} L_{\mathfrak{ba}]} = 0 \quad (\mathfrak{a}, \mathfrak{b}, \mathfrak{c} = \mathrm{m}+1, \ldots, \mathrm{m}+2\rho). \tag{11.23}$$

Hence, looking upon the $F^{\mathfrak{x}}$ ($\mathfrak{x} = \mathrm{m}+2\rho+1, \ldots, 2\mathrm{n}$) as parameters, $L_{\mathfrak{ba}}$ is a covariant bivector in the $X_{2\rho}$ of the $F^{\mathfrak{a}}$ ($\mathfrak{a} = \mathrm{m}+1, \ldots, \mathrm{m}+2\rho$) having rotation zero. Consequently $L_{\mathfrak{ba}}$ is the rotation of some vector $L_{\mathfrak{b}}$ of class 2ρ in this $X_{2\rho}$, naturally depending also on the parameters $F^{\mathfrak{x}}$. This implies that there exists a transformation of the F^{x} ($x = \mathrm{m}+1, \ldots, 2\mathrm{n}-\mathrm{m}$) of the form

$$\begin{aligned} F^{\mathfrak{a}'} &= F^{\mathfrak{a}'}(F^{\mathfrak{a}}, F^{\mathfrak{x}}) \\ F^{\mathfrak{x}'} &= \delta^{\mathfrak{x}'}_{\mathfrak{x}} F^{\mathfrak{x}} \end{aligned} \qquad \begin{pmatrix} \mathfrak{a} = \mathrm{m}+1, \ldots, \mathrm{m}+2\rho; \\ \mathfrak{x} = \mathrm{m}+2\rho+1, \ldots, 2\mathrm{n}; \\ \mathfrak{a}' = (\mathrm{m}+1)', \ldots, (\mathrm{m}+2\rho)'; \\ \mathfrak{x}' = (\mathrm{m}+2\rho+1)', \ldots, (2\mathrm{n})' \end{pmatrix} \tag{11.24}$$

which brings $L_{\mathfrak{ba}}$ into a canonical form. The determination of this canonical form requires ρ operations $O_{2\rho-1}, O_{2\rho-3}, \ldots, O_1$ (cf. IV, § 5). The non-vanishing components of $L_{\mathfrak{ba}}$ and $H^{\mathfrak{ab}}$ with respect to this new coordinate system are (for the sake of simplicity we drop the accent):

$$\begin{array}{ll} L_{\mathrm{m}+1,\mathrm{m}+2} = -L_{\mathrm{m}+2,\mathrm{m}+1} = +1, & H^{\mathrm{m}+1,\mathrm{m}+2} = -H^{\mathrm{m}+2,\mathrm{m}+1} = +1, \\ \cdots\cdots\cdots & \cdots\cdots\cdots \\ L_{\mathrm{m}+2\rho-1,\mathrm{m}+2\rho} & H^{\mathrm{m}+2\rho-1,\mathrm{m}+2\rho} \\ \quad = -L_{\mathrm{m}+2\rho,\mathrm{m}+2\rho-1} = +1, & \quad = -H^{\mathrm{m}+2\rho,\mathrm{m}+2\rho-1} = +1. \end{array} \tag{11.25}$$

Note that, because of the special form of the transformation (11.24), the new components $H^{x\mathfrak{x}}$ are also zero. This means that the transformation brings the whole bivector H^{xy} and not only $H^{\mathfrak{ab}}$ into a normal form.

Now we change the notation, writing

$$\begin{aligned} P_1 &= F^{m+1}, & Q^1 &= F^{m+2}, \\ \cdot\ \cdot\ &\cdot\ \cdot\ \cdot & \cdot\ \cdot\ &\cdot\ \cdot \\ P_\rho &= F^{m+2\rho-1}, & Q^\rho &= F^{m+2\rho}, \\ P_{\rho+1} &= F^{m+2\rho+1}, \\ \cdot\ \cdot\ &\cdot\ \cdot\ \cdot \\ P_{2n-m-\rho} &= F^{2n}. \end{aligned} \tag{11.26}$$

Then we get for the bracket expressions of the P's and Q's

$$\begin{aligned} (P_a, P_b) &= 0 \\ (P_a, Q^c) &= \delta_a^c \quad \begin{pmatrix} a, b = 1, \ldots, 2n-m-\rho, \\ c, d = 1, \ldots, \rho \end{pmatrix}. \\ (Q^c, Q^d) &= 0 \end{aligned} \tag{11.27}$$

The null group consists of the functions $P_{\rho+1}, \ldots, P_{2n-m-\rho}$. If and only if $2\rho = 2n-m$ there are just as many functions P as functions Q and a null group does not exist. If $2\rho < 2n-m$ we will try to extend the given group by adding new independent functions of ξ^κ and w_λ in order to get a group without a null group. If we omit the function $P_{\rho+1}$, the remaining $2n-m-1$ functions form a $(2n-m-1)$-dimensional group whose $(m+1)$-dimensional polar group contains $P_{\rho+1}$. But $P_{\rho+1}$ cannot be a singular function of this polar group, because otherwise $P_{\rho+1}$ would have to belong to the $(2n-m-1)$-dimensional group. Now we will prove that there exists in this polar group at least one function $Q^{\rho+1}$ such that

$$(P_{\rho+1}, Q^{\rho+1}) = 1. \tag{11.28}$$

If $R^1, \ldots, R^{m+1}$ are $m+1$ arbitrary independent functions of this polar group, (11.28) is equivalent to

$$(P_{\rho+1}, R^{\mathfrak{a}}) \frac{\partial Q^{\rho+1}}{\partial R^{\mathfrak{a}}} = 1 \quad (\mathfrak{a} = 1, \ldots, m+1). \tag{11.29}$$

This is a non-homogeneous linear partial differential equation in which not all the expressions $(P_{\rho+1}, R^{\mathfrak{a}})$ can vanish simultaneously. Hence there exists at least one solution. If $Q^{\rho+1}$ is such a solution, $Q^{\rho+1}$ is in involution with all the functions $P_1, \ldots, P_\rho, P_{\rho+2}, \ldots, P_{2n-m-\rho}$, and $Q^1, \ldots, Q^\rho$. Hence we have extended the given group to a $(2n-m+1)$-dimensional group with the equations

$$\begin{aligned} (P_a, P_b) &= 0 \\ (P_a, Q^c) &= \delta_a^c \quad \begin{pmatrix} a, b = 1, \ldots, 2n-m-\rho, \\ c, d = 1, \ldots, \rho+1 \end{pmatrix}. \\ (Q^c, Q^d) &= 0 \end{aligned} \tag{11.30}$$

Continuing in this way we get after $2n-m-2\rho$ steps a $(4n-2m-2\rho)$-dimensional group with $2n-m-\rho$ functions P and $2n-m-\rho$ functions Q and with the equations

$$\begin{aligned}(P_a, P_b) &= 0\\ (P_a, Q^b) &= \delta_a^b \quad (a, b = 1, \ldots, 2n-m-\rho).\\ (Q^a, Q^b) &= 0\end{aligned} \tag{11.31}$$

If now $\rho = n-m$, the group (11.31) is $2n$-dimensional and consists of all functions of ξ^κ and w_λ. If $\rho > n-m$ we will try to extend the group (11.31) once more. The polar group of (11.31) is $(2m+2\rho-2n)$-dimensional. If $P_{2n-m-\rho+1}$ is a function of this polar group which is not a constant, this function forms with the $4n-2m-2\rho$ functions of (11.31) a $(4n-2m-2\rho+1)$-dimensional group with a one-dimensional null group and, as above, this group can be extended by adding a suitable function $Q^{2n-m-\rho+1}$ to a $(4n-2m-2\rho+2)$-dimensional group without a null group. Continuing in this way we get after $m+\rho-n$ steps a $2n$-dimensional group with the equations

$$\begin{aligned}(P_\kappa, P_\lambda) &= 0\\ (P_\kappa, Q^\lambda) &= \delta_\kappa^\lambda \quad (\kappa, \lambda = 1, \ldots, n).\\ (Q^\kappa, Q^\lambda) &= 0\end{aligned} \tag{11.32}$$

As was proved in VI, § 9, the equations (11.32) are the necessary and sufficient conditions that the equations

$$'\xi^\kappa = Q^\kappa, \qquad 'w_\lambda = P_\lambda \tag{11.33}$$

and also the equations

$$'\xi^\kappa = P_\kappa, \qquad 'w_\lambda = Q^\lambda \tag{11.34}$$

represent a C_2-transformation. This proves the theorem:

THEOREM VI.13. *If a $(2n-m)$-dimensional function group of rank 2ρ be given, there always exists a C_2-transformation $\xi^\kappa \to {}'\xi^\kappa$, $w_\lambda \to {}'w_\lambda$ such that the group can be written in the canonical form*

$$\begin{aligned}&'\xi^1, \ldots, {}'\xi^\rho,\\ &'w_1, \ldots, {}'w_{2n-m-\rho}\end{aligned} \tag{11.35}$$

and also a C_2-transformation $\xi^\kappa \to {}'\xi^\kappa$, $w_\lambda \to {}'w_\lambda$ such that the group can be written in the canonical form

$$\begin{aligned}&'\xi^1, \ldots, {}'\xi^{2n-m-\rho},\\ &'w_1, \ldots, {}'w_\rho.\end{aligned} \tag{11.36}$$

Here is another form of this theorem, giving a generalization of the first part of Theorem VI.12.

THEOREM VI.14. *If* $'\phi^{\mathfrak{a}}(\xi^{\kappa}, w_{\lambda})$ $(\mathfrak{a} = 1,..., \tau_1)$ *and* $'\psi_{\mathfrak{c}}(\xi^{\kappa}, w_{\lambda})$ $(\mathfrak{c} = 1,..., \tau_2)$ *are arbitrary functions, analytic and independent in the region considered and such that*

$$\begin{aligned} ('\phi^{\mathfrak{a}}, '\phi^{\mathfrak{b}}) &= 0 \\ ('\phi^{\mathfrak{a}}, '\psi_{\mathfrak{c}}) &= \delta^{\mathfrak{a}}_{\mathfrak{c}} \quad (\mathfrak{a}, \mathfrak{b} = 1,..., \tau_1;\ \mathfrak{c}, \mathfrak{d} = 1,..., \tau_2), \\ ('\psi_{\mathfrak{c}}, '\psi_{\mathfrak{d}}) &= 0 \end{aligned} \tag{11.37}$$

$n-\tau_1$ *functions* $'\phi^{\tau_1+1},..., '\phi^{n}$ *and* $n-\tau_2$ *functions* $'\psi_{\tau_2+1},..., '\psi_n$ *always exist, such that the equations* $'\xi^{\kappa} = '\phi^{\kappa}$, $'w_{\lambda} = '\psi_{\lambda}$ $(\kappa, \lambda = 1,..., n)$ *represent a* C_2*-transformation.*

As a consequence of Theorem VI.13 we have the theorem:

THEOREM VI.15. *Two* $(2n-m)$*-dimensional function groups in* ξ^{κ}, w_{λ} *can be transformed into each other by a* C_2*-transformation of the* ξ^{κ}, w_{λ} *if and only if they have the same rank* 2ρ. *Consequently the integers* $2n-m$ *and* 2ρ *are the only arithmetic invariants of a function group with respect to* C_2*-transformations.*

As we have seen, putting a group into a canonical form requires $2n-m-\rho$ operations, viz. the $2n-m-2\rho$ operations $O_{2n-m-2\rho},..., O_1$ for the determination of the singular functions and ρ operations $O_{2\rho-1}$, $O_{2\rho-3},..., O_1$ for putting $L_{\mathfrak{ba}}$ into a canonical form. The group contains a $(2n-m-\rho)$-dimensional commutative sub-group, the group of the functions $P_1,..., P_{2n-m-\rho}$. A τ-dimensional commutative sub-group with $\tau > 2n-m-\rho$ cannot exist, because such a group would form with $P_{2n-m-\rho+1},..., P_n$ a $(\tau+m+\rho-n)$-dimensional commutative group with $\tau+m+\rho-n > n$ which is not possible. Now for application to the theory of systems of partial differential equations often only a $(2n-m-\rho)$-dimensional commutative sub-group is wanted instead of a completely canonical form of the group. Since such a sub-group always contains all singular functions, first $2n-m-2\rho$ independent singular functions have to be determined, requiring $2n-m-2\rho$ operations $O_{2n-m-2\rho},..., O_1$. Then we may choose an arbitrary non-singular function $\overset{1}{F}$ of the group and require a function $\overset{2}{F}$ of the group, in involution with $\overset{1}{F}$. The equation

$$(\overset{1}{F}, \overset{2}{F}) = 0 \tag{11.38}$$

in the $2n-m$ independent variables F^x $(x = \mathrm{m}+1,..., 2\mathrm{n})$ already has $2n-m-2\rho+1$ known independent solutions, viz. $\overset{1}{F}$ and the singular functions. Hence the determination of one solution $\overset{2}{F}$ requires an operation $O_{2\rho-2}$. When $\overset{2}{F}$ has been fixed we determine a function $\overset{3}{F}$ of the group in involution with $\overset{1}{F}$ and $\overset{2}{F}$. This requires an operation $O_{2\rho-4}$. Continuing in this way we get a $(2n-m-\rho)$-dimensional commutative sub-group. We need in all $2n-m-\rho-1$ operations

$$O_{2n-m-2\rho},\ldots, O_1, O_{2\rho-2}, O_{2\rho-4},\ldots, O_2.$$

12. Homogeneous function groups†

A function group F^x $(x = \mathrm{m}+1,\ldots, 2\mathrm{n})$ is called *homogeneous* if all expressions

$$H^x \overset{\text{def}}{=} w_\lambda \frac{\partial F^x}{\partial w_\lambda} \quad (x = \mathrm{m}+1,\ldots, 2\mathrm{n}) \tag{12.1}$$

are functions of the group. If F is an arbitrary function of the group, we have

$$w_\lambda \frac{\partial F}{\partial w_\lambda} = w_\lambda \frac{\partial F}{\partial F^x}\frac{\partial F^x}{\partial w_\lambda} \quad (x = \mathrm{m}+1,\ldots, 2\mathrm{n}) \tag{12.2}$$

and from this it follows that $w_\lambda(\partial F/\partial w_\lambda)$ is a function of the group. Hence the definition of a homogeneous function group is really independent of the choice of the basis F^x.

If f is a function of the polar group, that is, if

$$(F^x, f) = 0 \quad (x = \mathrm{m}+1,\ldots, 2\mathrm{n}), \tag{12.3}$$

applying the operator $w_\lambda(\partial/\partial w_\lambda)$ we get

$$\left(w_\lambda \frac{\partial F^x}{\partial w_\lambda}, f\right) + \left(F^x, w_\lambda \frac{\partial f}{\partial w_\lambda}\right) - (F^x, f) = 0 \quad (x = \mathrm{m}+1,\ldots, 2\mathrm{n}) \tag{12.4}$$

and from this, in consequence of the fact that $w_\lambda(\partial F^x/\partial w_\lambda)$ is a function of the group, it follows that

$$\left(F^x, w_\lambda \frac{\partial f}{\partial w_\lambda}\right) = 0 \quad (x = \mathrm{m}+1,\ldots, 2\mathrm{n}). \tag{12.5}$$

Hence $w_\lambda(\partial f/\partial w_\lambda)$ belongs to the polar group and consequently this polar group is homogeneous as well.

From (12.1) it follows that

$$(H^{[x}, F^{y]}) = \left(w_\lambda \frac{\partial F^{[x}}{\partial w_\lambda}, F^{y]}\right) = w_\lambda \left(\frac{\partial F^{[x}}{\partial w_\lambda}, F^{y]}\right) + \frac{\partial F^{[x}}{\partial w_\lambda}(w_\lambda, F^{y]})$$

$$= \tfrac{1}{2} w_\lambda \frac{\partial}{\partial w_\lambda} H^{xy} + \tfrac{1}{2} H^{xy} = \tfrac{1}{2} H^z \partial_z H^{xy} + \tfrac{1}{2} H^{xy}$$

$$(x, y, z = \mathrm{m}+1,\ldots, 2\mathrm{n}) \tag{12.6}$$

† Lie 1875. 1, 1877. 1; v. Weber 1900. 1, ch. xiv; Goursat 1921. 1, ch. xi; Engel and Faber 1932. 1, §§ 53, 59; Eisenhart 1933. 1, § 70.

and also that

$$(H^{[x}, F^{y]}) = (\partial_z H^{[x})H^{|z|y]} \quad (x, y, z = \mathrm{m}+1,..., 2\mathrm{n}). \tag{12.7}$$

From (12.6) and (12.7) we see that

$$2(\partial_z H^{[x})H^{|z|y]} = H^z \partial_z H^{xy} + H^{xy} \quad (x, y, z = \mathrm{m}+1,..., 2\mathrm{n}) \tag{12.8}$$

and this equation together with (11.7) expresses the fact that the homogeneous linear system of partial differential equations

$$\begin{array}{ll} (a) & H^{xy}\partial_y f(F^z) = 0 \\ (b) & H^{y}\partial_y f(F^z) = 0 \end{array} \quad (x, y, z = \mathrm{m}+1,..., 2\mathrm{n}) \tag{12.9}$$

is complete (cf. (11.8)). In fact we have according to (12.8)

$$\begin{aligned} H^{xy}\partial_y H^z \partial_z - H^y \partial_y H^{xz}\partial_z &= (H^{xy}\partial_y H^z - H^y \partial_y H^{xz})\partial_z \\ &= (H^{xz} - H^{yz}\partial_y H^x)\partial_z \quad (x, y, z = \mathrm{m}+1,..., 2\mathrm{n}). \end{aligned} \tag{12.10}$$

The rank of the system H^{xy}, H^x is $2\rho+\epsilon$, where $\epsilon = 0$ if H^x lies in the domain of H^{xy} and $\epsilon = 1$ in the other case. We call $2\rho+\epsilon$ the *class of the homogeneous function group*. The solutions of (12.9) are those singular functions of the group which are homogeneous of degree zero in the w_λ. If $\epsilon = 0$, all functions of the null group are homogeneous of degree zero in the w_λ but if $\epsilon = 1$ there exists at least one function of the null group without this homogeneity.

For $\epsilon = 1$ we consider next to (12.9) the system of partial differential equations

$$\begin{array}{ll} (a) & H^{xy}\partial_y f = 0 \\ (b) & H^{y}\partial_y f = f \end{array} \quad (x, y, z = \mathrm{m}+1,..., 2\mathrm{n};\ f = f(F^z)), \tag{12.11}$$

being non-homogeneous and linear in $\log f$. Since the reduced system (12.9) is complete and the right-hand side of (12.10) depends linearly only on the $H^{xz}\partial_z$, the three conditions of III, § 14, are satisfied and consequently (12.11) is complete. The general solution (12.11) has the form (cf. III, § 14)

$$f = f^0 \phi(f^1,..., f^\tau) \quad (\tau = 2n-m-2\rho-1), \tag{12.12}$$

f^0 being an arbitrary solution of (12.11) and $f^1,..., f^\tau$ arbitrary independent solutions of the reduced system (12.9).

It is convenient to choose the basis in a special way. For $\epsilon = 0$ we take for $F^{\mathrm{m}+2\rho+1},..., F^{2\mathrm{n}}$ arbitrary independent solutions of (12.9), requiring $2n-m-2\rho$ operations $O_{2n-m-\rho},..., O_1$ and for $F^{\mathrm{m}+1},..., F^{\mathrm{m}+2\rho}$ arbitrary independent solutions of (12.11 *b*) not satisfying (12.11 *a*). For $\epsilon = 1$ we take for $F^{\mathrm{m}+2\rho+1},..., F^{2\mathrm{n}}$ arbitrary independent solutions of (12.11), requiring $2n-m-2\rho$ operations $O_{2n-m-2\rho-1},..., O_0$ and for $F^{\mathrm{m}+1},..., F^{\mathrm{m}+2\rho}$ arbitrary independent solutions of (12.9 *b*) not satisfying (12.9 *a*). The only components of H^{xy} with respect to this basis which do not necessarily vanish are the $H^{\mathfrak{ab}}$ ($\mathfrak{a}, \mathfrak{b} = \mathrm{m}+1,\dots,\mathrm{m}+2\rho$) and for the H^x

$$H^{\mathfrak{a}} = (1-\epsilon)F^{\mathfrak{a}} \quad (\mathfrak{a} = \mathrm{m}+1,\dots,\mathrm{m}+2\rho;$$
$$H^{\mathfrak{x}} = \epsilon F^{\mathfrak{x}} \qquad \mathfrak{x} = \mathrm{m}+2\rho+1,\dots,2\mathrm{n}) \tag{12.13}$$

holds. Then the equations (11.7) and (12.8) take the form

$$H^{\mathfrak{d}[\mathfrak{a}}\partial_{\mathfrak{d}} H^{\mathfrak{bc}]} = 0 \quad (\mathfrak{a},\mathfrak{b},\mathfrak{c},\mathfrak{d} = \mathrm{m}+1,\dots,\mathrm{m}+2\rho) \tag{12.14}$$

and

$$(\partial_{\mathfrak{c}} H^{\mathfrak{a}})H^{\mathfrak{cb}} - (\partial_{\mathfrak{c}} H^{\mathfrak{b}})H^{\mathfrak{ca}} = (1-\epsilon)F^{\mathfrak{c}}\partial_{\mathfrak{c}} H^{\mathfrak{ab}} + \epsilon F^{\mathfrak{x}}\partial_{\mathfrak{x}} H^{\mathfrak{ab}} + H^{\mathfrak{ab}}$$
$$(\mathfrak{a},\mathfrak{b},\mathfrak{c} = \mathrm{m}+1,\dots,\mathrm{m}+2\rho) \tag{12.15}$$

respectively.

In the $X_{2\rho}$ of the $F^{\mathfrak{a}}$ we introduce now a system of $\rho(2\rho-1)$ components $L_{\mathfrak{ba}}$ and a system of 2ρ components $L_{\mathfrak{b}}$ by means of the equations

$$H^{\mathfrak{ac}}L_{\mathfrak{bc}} = A^{\mathfrak{a}}_{\mathfrak{b}},$$
$$H^{\mathfrak{ab}}L_{\mathfrak{b}} = H^{\mathfrak{a}}, \tag{12.16}$$
$$H^{\mathfrak{a}}L_{\mathfrak{ab}} = L_{\mathfrak{b}}.$$

$L_{\mathfrak{ba}}$ and $L_{\mathfrak{b}}$ are uniquely determined by these equations and $L_{\mathfrak{ba}}$ is the inverse of $H^{\mathfrak{ab}}$.

The transformations which are allowable are

$$F^{\mathfrak{a}'} = F^{\mathfrak{a}'}\{F^{\mathfrak{a}}, F^{\mathfrak{x}}\} \quad (\mathfrak{a} = \mathrm{m}+1,\dots,\mathrm{m}+2\rho;\ \mathfrak{x} = \mathrm{m}+2\rho+1,\dots,2\mathrm{n};$$
$$F^{\mathfrak{x}'} = \delta^{\mathfrak{x}'}_{\mathfrak{x}} F^{\mathfrak{x}} \qquad \mathfrak{a}' = (\mathrm{m}+1),\dots,(\mathrm{m}+2\rho)';\ \mathfrak{x}' = (\mathrm{m}+2\rho+1)',\dots,(2\mathrm{n})') \tag{12.17}$$

and with these transformations the $H^{\mathfrak{ab}}$, $L_{\mathfrak{ba}}$, $H^{\mathfrak{a}}$ and $L_{\mathfrak{b}}$ are transformed in the following way

$$H^{\mathfrak{a}'\mathfrak{b}'} = A^{\mathfrak{a}'}_{\mathfrak{a}} A^{\mathfrak{b}'}_{\mathfrak{b}} H^{\mathfrak{ab}}, \qquad H^{\mathfrak{a}'} = A^{\mathfrak{a}'}_{\mathfrak{a}} H^{\mathfrak{a}} + \epsilon A^{\mathfrak{a}'}_{\mathfrak{x}} F^{\mathfrak{x}},$$
$$L_{\mathfrak{b}'\mathfrak{a}'} = A^{\mathfrak{b}}_{\mathfrak{b}'} A^{\mathfrak{a}}_{\mathfrak{a}'} L_{\mathfrak{ba}}, \qquad L_{\mathfrak{b}'} = A^{\mathfrak{b}}_{\mathfrak{b}'} L_{\mathfrak{b}} + \epsilon A^{\mathfrak{a}'}_{\mathfrak{x}} L_{\mathfrak{a}'\mathfrak{b}'} F^{\mathfrak{x}}$$
$$(\mathfrak{a},\mathfrak{b} = \mathrm{m}+1,\dots,\mathrm{m}+2\rho; \qquad \mathfrak{x} = \mathrm{m}+2\rho+1,\dots,2\mathrm{n};$$
$$\mathfrak{a}',\mathfrak{b}' = (\mathrm{m}+1)',\dots,(\mathrm{m}+2\rho)';\ \mathfrak{x}' = (\mathrm{m}+2\rho+1)',\dots,(2\mathrm{n})'). \tag{12.18}$$

Hence, looking upon the $F^{\mathfrak{x}}$ as parameters, both $H^{\mathfrak{ab}}$ and $L_{\mathfrak{ba}}$ transform as bivectors but $H^{\mathfrak{a}}$ and $L_{\mathfrak{b}}$ transform as vectors only if $\epsilon = 0$.

Replacing $H^{\mathfrak{a}}$ by $H^{\mathfrak{ab}}L_{\mathfrak{b}}$ in (12.15) we obtain

$$(\partial_{\mathfrak{c}} H^{\mathfrak{ad}})L_{\mathfrak{d}} H^{\mathfrak{cb}} - (\partial_{\mathfrak{c}} H^{\mathfrak{bd}})L_{\mathfrak{d}} H^{\mathfrak{ca}} + H^{\mathfrak{ad}}H^{\mathfrak{cb}}\partial_{\mathfrak{c}} L_{\mathfrak{d}} - H^{\mathfrak{bd}}H^{\mathfrak{ca}}\partial_{\mathfrak{c}} L_{\mathfrak{d}}$$
$$= H^{\mathfrak{cd}}L_{\mathfrak{d}}\,\partial_{\mathfrak{c}} H^{\mathfrak{ab}} + \epsilon F^{\mathfrak{x}}\partial_{\mathfrak{x}} H^{\mathfrak{ab}} + H^{\mathfrak{ab}}$$
$$(\mathfrak{a},\mathfrak{b},\mathfrak{c},\mathfrak{d} = \mathrm{m}+1,\dots,\mathrm{m}+2\rho;\ \mathfrak{x} = \mathrm{m}+2\rho+1,\dots,2\mathrm{n}) \tag{12.19}$$

and from this equation and (12.14) it follows that

$$2H^{\mathfrak{bc}}H^{\mathfrak{ad}}\partial_{[\mathfrak{c}}L_{\mathfrak{d}]} = -\epsilon F^{\mathfrak{x}}\partial_{\mathfrak{x}}H^{\mathfrak{ab}} - H^{\mathfrak{ab}}$$

$$(\mathfrak{a},\mathfrak{b},\mathfrak{c},\mathfrak{d} = \mathrm{m}+1,\ldots,\mathrm{m}+2\rho;\ \mathfrak{x} = \mathrm{m}+2\rho+1,\ldots,2\mathrm{n}). \quad (12.20)$$

By transvection of (12.20) with $L_{\mathfrak{bc}}$ we get

$$2H^{\mathfrak{ad}}\partial_{[\mathfrak{e}}L_{\mathfrak{d}]} = \epsilon F^{\mathfrak{x}}H^{\mathfrak{ab}}\partial_{\mathfrak{x}}L_{\mathfrak{be}} + A^{\mathfrak{a}}_{\mathfrak{e}}$$

$$(\mathfrak{a},\mathfrak{b},\mathfrak{d},\mathfrak{e} = \mathrm{m}+1,\ldots,\mathrm{m}+2\rho;\ \mathfrak{x} = \mathrm{m}+2\rho+1,\ldots,2\mathrm{n}) \quad (12.21)$$

and from this equation we get by transvection with $L_{\mathfrak{af}}$

$$2\partial_{[\mathfrak{b}}L_{\mathfrak{a}]} = -\epsilon F^{\mathfrak{x}}\partial_{\mathfrak{x}}L_{\mathfrak{ba}} + L_{\mathfrak{ba}}$$

$$(\mathfrak{a},\mathfrak{b} = \mathrm{m}+1,\ldots,\mathrm{m}+2\rho;\ \mathfrak{x} = \mathrm{m}+2\rho+1,\ldots,2\mathrm{n}). \quad (12.22)$$

Now since $F^{\mathfrak{a}}$ is homogeneous of degree $1-\epsilon$ in the w_λ, $H^{\mathfrak{ab}}$ is homogeneous of degree $1-2\epsilon$, and $L_{\mathfrak{ba}}$ homogeneous of degree $2\epsilon-1$. Hence

$$(2\epsilon-1)L_{\mathfrak{ba}} = w_\lambda\frac{\partial}{\partial w_\lambda}L_{\mathfrak{ba}} = (1-\epsilon)F^{\mathfrak{c}}\partial_{\mathfrak{c}}L_{\mathfrak{ba}} + \epsilon F^{\mathfrak{x}}\partial_{\mathfrak{x}}L_{\mathfrak{ba}}$$

$$(\mathfrak{a},\mathfrak{b},\mathfrak{c} = \mathrm{m}+1,\ldots,\mathrm{m}+2\rho;\ \mathfrak{x} = \mathrm{m}+2\rho+1,\ldots,2\mathrm{n}) \quad (12.23)$$

and from this it follows that

$$L_{\mathfrak{ba}} = \begin{cases} -F^{\mathfrak{c}}\partial_{\mathfrak{c}}L_{\mathfrak{ba}} & \text{for } \epsilon = 0 \\ F^{\mathfrak{x}}\partial_{\mathfrak{x}}L_{\mathfrak{ba}} & \text{for } \epsilon = 1 \end{cases} \quad \begin{matrix}(\mathfrak{a},\mathfrak{b},\mathfrak{c} = \mathrm{m}+1,\ldots,\mathrm{m}+2\rho; \\ \mathfrak{x} = \mathrm{m}+2\rho+1,\ldots,2\mathrm{n}).\end{matrix} \quad (12.24)$$

From (12.22) and (12.24) we get

$$2\partial_{[\mathfrak{b}}L_{\mathfrak{a}]} = (1-\epsilon)L_{\mathfrak{ba}} \quad (\mathfrak{a},\mathfrak{b} = \mathrm{m}+1,\ldots,\mathrm{m}+2\rho). \quad (12.25)$$

In the same way as (11.23) was deduced from (11.18) and (11.19), we obtain from (12.14) and (12.16)

$$\partial_{[\mathfrak{c}}L_{\mathfrak{ba}]} = 0 \quad (\mathfrak{a},\mathfrak{b},\mathfrak{c} = \mathrm{m}+1,\ldots,\mathrm{m}+2\rho) \quad (12.26)$$

and this implies that there exists in the $X_{2\rho}$ of the $F^{\mathfrak{a}}$ a vector $L'_{\mathfrak{b}}$ of class 2ρ, depending on the parameters $F^{\mathfrak{x}}$, whose rotation is $L_{\mathfrak{ba}}$. According to (12.25) $L_{\mathfrak{b}}$ is such a vector for $\epsilon = 0$. Hence a transformation of the basis of the form (12.17) exists which brings $L'_{\mathfrak{b}}$ and $L_{\mathfrak{ba}}$ into the canonical form

$$\begin{aligned} L_{(\mathrm{m}+1)'(\mathrm{m}+2)'} &= -L_{(\mathrm{m}+2)'(\mathrm{m}+1)'} = 1, & L'_{(\mathrm{m}+1)'} &= 0, \\ \ldots\ldots\ldots\ldots & & L'_{(\mathrm{m}+2)'} &= F^{(\mathrm{m}+1)'}, \\ L_{(\mathrm{m}+2\rho-1)'(\mathrm{m}+2\rho)'} &= -L_{(\mathrm{m}+2\rho)'(\mathrm{m}+2\rho-1)'} = 1, & \ldots\ldots & \\ & & L'_{(\mathrm{m}+2\rho-1)'} &= 0, \\ & & L'_{(\mathrm{m}+2\rho)'} &= F^{(\mathrm{m}+2\rho-1)'}. \end{aligned} \quad (12.27)$$

Then the new components $H^{\mathfrak{a}'\mathfrak{b}'}$ are

$$\begin{gathered} H^{(m+1)'(m+2)'} = -H^{(m+2)'(m+1)'} = 1 \\ \cdots\cdots\cdots \\ H^{(m+2\rho-1)'(m+2\rho)'} = -H^{(m+2\rho)'(m+2\rho-1)'} = 1. \end{gathered} \tag{12.28}$$

For $\epsilon = 0$ we can take $L'_{\mathfrak{b}} = L_{\mathfrak{b}}$. Then we get for the $H^{\mathfrak{a}'}$

$$\begin{aligned} H^{(m+1)'} &= F^{(m+1)'}, \\ H^{(m+2)'} &= 0, \\ &\cdots\cdots\cdots \\ H^{(m+2\rho-1)'} &= F^{(m+2\rho-1)'}, \\ H^{(m+2\rho)'} &= 0. \end{aligned} \tag{12.29}$$

Now we change the notation, writing

$$\begin{array}{lll} (a) & P_1 = F^{(m+1)'}, & Q^1 = F^{(m+2)'}, \\ & \cdots\cdots & \cdots\cdots \\ & P_\rho = F^{(m+2\rho-1)'}, & Q^\rho = F^{(m+2\rho)'}, \\ & & Q^{\rho+1} = F^{(m+2\rho+1)'}, \\ (b) & & \cdots\cdots \\ & & Q^{2n-m-\rho} = F^{(2n)'}. \end{array} \tag{12.30}$$

Then we get the canonical form of the group:

$$\begin{array}{ll} (P_a, P_b) = 0 & (a, b = 1, \ldots, \rho; \\ (P_a, Q^d) = \delta_a^d & \quad c, d = 1, \ldots, 2n-m-\rho). \\ (Q^c, Q^d) = 0;\ (P_a) = P_a;\ (Q^c) = 0 & \end{array} \tag{12.31}$$

For $\epsilon = 1$, changing the notation according to (12.30a) and writing

$$\begin{gathered} P_{\rho+1} = F^{(m+2\rho+1)'}, \\ \cdots\cdots\cdots \\ P_{2n-m-\rho} = F^{(2n)'}, \end{gathered} \tag{12.32}$$

we have

$$\begin{array}{ll} (P_1) = F^{\mathfrak{x}}\partial_{\mathfrak{x}} P_1, & (Q^1) = F^{\mathfrak{x}}\partial_{\mathfrak{x}} Q^1 \\ \cdots\cdots & \cdots\cdots \\ (P_\rho) = F^{\mathfrak{x}}\partial_{\mathfrak{x}} P_\rho, & (Q^\rho) = F^{\mathfrak{x}}\partial_{\mathfrak{x}} Q^\rho \quad (\mathfrak{x} = m+2\rho+1, \ldots, 2n) \\ (P_{\rho+1}) = P_{\rho+1}, & \\ \cdots\cdots & \\ (P_{2n-m-\rho}) = P_{2n-m-\rho}. & \end{array} \tag{12.33}$$

Now we perform a C_2-transformation in $Q^1, \ldots, Q^\rho, P_1, \ldots, P_\rho$ with a function Ω, depending on the parameters $P_{\rho+1}, \ldots, P_{2n-m-\rho}$ and satisfying the equations (cf. (10.10))

$$\begin{array}{ll} (\Omega, P_1) = P_1 - F^{\mathfrak{x}}\partial_{\mathfrak{x}} P_1, & (\Omega, Q^1) = -F^{\mathfrak{x}}\partial_{\mathfrak{x}} Q^1 \\ \cdots\cdots\cdots & \cdots\cdots \quad (\mathfrak{x} = m+2\rho+1, \ldots, 2n). \\ (\Omega, P_\rho) = P_\rho - F^{\mathfrak{x}}\partial_{\mathfrak{x}} P_\rho, & (\Omega, Q^\rho) = -F^{\mathfrak{x}}\partial_{\mathfrak{x}} Q^\rho \end{array} \tag{12.34}$$

We will prove that this non-homogeneous linear system is complete. Since the reduced system is Jacobian, we have to prove that (cf. III, § 14 (14.5 b))

$$\begin{aligned}(P_a, P_b - F^{\mathfrak{x}}\partial_{\mathfrak{x}} P_b) - (P_b, P_a - F^{\mathfrak{x}}\partial_{\mathfrak{x}} P_a) &= 0 \quad (a,b = 1,\ldots,\rho;\\ (P_a, F^{\mathfrak{x}}\partial_{\mathfrak{x}} Q^b) - (Q^b, P_a - F^{\mathfrak{x}}\partial_{\mathfrak{x}} P_a) &= 0 \quad \mathfrak{x} = \mathrm{m}+2\rho+1,\ldots, 2\mathrm{n})\\ (Q^a, F^{\mathfrak{x}}\partial_{\mathfrak{x}} Q^b) - (Q^b, F^{\mathfrak{x}}\partial_{\mathfrak{x}} Q^a) &= 0 \qquad (12.35)\end{aligned}$$

or

$$\begin{aligned}(P_a, F^{\mathfrak{x}}\partial_{\mathfrak{x}} P_b) - (P_b, F^{\mathfrak{x}}\partial_{\mathfrak{x}} P_a) &= 0 \quad (a,b = 1,\ldots,\rho;\\ (P_a, F^{\mathfrak{x}}\partial_{\mathfrak{x}} Q^b) - (Q^b, F^{\mathfrak{x}}\partial_{\mathfrak{x}} P_a) &= \delta^b_a \quad \mathfrak{x} = \mathrm{m}+2\rho+1,\ldots, 2\mathrm{n}).\\ (Q^a, F^{\mathfrak{x}}\partial_{\mathfrak{x}} Q^b) - (Q^b, F^{\mathfrak{x}}\partial_{\mathfrak{x}} Q^a) &= 0 \qquad (12.36)\end{aligned}$$

Now since $H^{\mathfrak{ab}}$ is homogeneous of degree -1 in w_λ we have

$$-H^{\mathfrak{ab}} = F^{\mathfrak{x}}\partial_{\mathfrak{x}} H^{\mathfrak{ab}} \quad (\mathfrak{a},\mathfrak{b} = \mathrm{m}+1,\ldots,\mathrm{m}+2\rho;\quad \mathfrak{x} = \mathrm{m}+2\rho+1,\ldots, 2\mathrm{n}) \qquad (12.37)$$

and accordingly

$$\begin{aligned} 0 = F^{\mathfrak{x}}\partial_{\mathfrak{x}}(P_a, P_b) &= F^{\mathfrak{x}}\partial_{\mathfrak{x}} \frac{\partial P_a}{\partial F^x}\frac{\partial P_b}{\partial F^y} H^{xy}\\ &= F^{\mathfrak{x}}(\partial_{\mathfrak{x}} P_a, P_b) + F^{\mathfrak{x}}(P_a, \partial_{\mathfrak{x}} P_b) - (P_a, P_b)\\ &= (F^{\mathfrak{x}}\partial_{\mathfrak{x}} P_a, P_b) + (P_a, F^{\mathfrak{x}}\partial_{\mathfrak{x}} P_b),\\ 0 = F^{\mathfrak{x}}\partial_{\mathfrak{x}}(P_a, Q^b) &= (F^{\mathfrak{x}}\partial_{\mathfrak{x}} P_a, Q^b) + (P_a, F^{\mathfrak{x}}\partial_{\mathfrak{x}} Q^b) - \delta^b_a,\\ 0 = F^{\mathfrak{x}}\partial_{\mathfrak{x}}(Q^a, Q^b) &= (F^{\mathfrak{x}}\partial_{\mathfrak{x}} Q^a, Q^b) + (Q^a, F^{\mathfrak{x}}\partial_{\mathfrak{x}} Q^b)\\ &\qquad (a,b = 1,\ldots,\rho;\ \mathfrak{x} = \mathrm{m}+2\rho+1,\ldots, 2\mathrm{n}). \qquad (12.38)\end{aligned}$$

If the solutions $P_{\rho+1},\ldots, P_{2n-m-\rho}$ of the reduced system are known, a solution Ω of (12.34) can be obtained by a quadrature (cf. III, § 14).

Since the bracket expressions are invariant for C_2-transformations, writing P_c, Q^a for the *transformed* functions (cf. 12.31) we have

$$\begin{aligned}(P_c, P_d) &= 0\\ (P_c, Q^b) &= \delta^b_c \quad (a,b = 1,\ldots,\rho;\\ (Q^a, Q^b) &= 0 \qquad c,d = 1,\ldots, 2n-m-\rho).\\ (P_c) = P_c,&\quad (Q^a) = 0\end{aligned} \qquad (12.39)$$

For $\epsilon = 0$ the null group consists of $Q^{\rho+1},\ldots, Q^{2n-m-\rho}$ and for $\epsilon = 1$ of $P_{\rho+1},\ldots, P_{2n-m-\rho}$. If $2\rho < 2n-m$ the group can be extended to a group without null group. In order to prove this we have first to prove that, if a non-singular function F of the group, homogeneous of degree η ($\eta = 0$ or 1) in the w_λ be given, there always exists a function G, homogeneous of degree $1-\eta$ in the w_λ such that

$$(F, G) = H^{xy}\frac{\partial F}{\partial F^x}\frac{\partial G}{\partial F^y} = 1 \quad (x, y = \mathrm{m}+1,\ldots, 2\mathrm{n}). \qquad (12.40)$$

By the condition of homogeneity G has to satisfy the equation

$$H^y \frac{\partial G}{\partial F^y} = (1-\eta)G \quad (y = \mathrm{m}+1,\dots, 2\mathrm{n}). \tag{12.41}$$

If we write a solution of (12.40, 41) in the form

$$\Phi\{G, F^x\} = 0 \quad (x = \mathrm{m}+1,\dots, 2\mathrm{n}), \tag{12.42}$$

we get the homogeneous linear system

$$\left.\begin{aligned} H^{xy}(\partial_x F)\partial_y \Phi + \frac{\partial\Phi}{\partial G} &= 0 \\ H^y \partial_y \Phi + (1-\eta)G\frac{\partial\Phi}{\partial G} &= 0 \end{aligned}\right\} \quad (x, y = \mathrm{m}+1,\dots, 2\mathrm{n}) \tag{12.43}$$

with the independent variables F^x and G. Now, according to (12.8) we have

$$\begin{aligned} &\left(H^{xy}(\partial_x F)\partial_y + \frac{\partial}{\partial G}\right)\left(H^z\partial_z + (1-\eta)G\frac{\partial}{\partial G}\right) - \\ &\qquad - \left(H^y\partial_y + (1-\eta)G\frac{\partial}{\partial G}\right)\left(H^{xz}(\partial_x F)\partial_z + \frac{\partial}{\partial G}\right) \\ &= H^{xy}(\partial_x F)\partial_y H^z\partial_z + (1-\eta)\frac{\partial}{\partial G} - H^y\partial_y(H^{xz}\partial_x F)\partial_z \\ &= (\partial_x F)(H^{xy}\partial_y H^z - H^y\partial_y H^{xz})\partial_z - H^y H^{xz}(\partial_y \partial_x F)\partial_z + (1-\eta)\frac{\partial}{\partial G} \\ &= \{H^{xz}\partial_x F - H^{yz}(\partial_y H^x)\partial_x F - H^y H^{xz}\partial_y \partial_x F\}\partial_z + (1-\eta)\frac{\partial}{\partial G} \\ &= (1-\eta)\left\{H^{xy}(\partial_x F)\partial_y + \frac{\partial}{\partial G}\right\} \quad (x, y, z = \mathrm{m}+1,\dots, 2\mathrm{n}). \end{aligned} \tag{12.44}$$

Hence (12.43) is complete and a solution can be obtained by means of an operation O_{2n-m}.

Now we return to a homogeneous group with $\epsilon = 0$ [or 1] in a canonical form. If the function $Q^{\rho+1}$ [or $P_{\rho+1}$] be omitted, the remaining functions form a $(2n-m-1)$-dimensional homogeneous group whose $(m+1)$-dimensional polar group contains $Q^{\rho+1}$ [or $P_{\rho+1}$] as a non-singular function. As we have proved above there exists in this polar group a function $P_{\rho+1}$ or [$Q^{\rho+1}$] of degree 1 [or 0] in the w_λ, such that

$$(P_{\rho+1}, Q^{\rho+1}) = 1 \tag{12.45}$$

and this function can be obtained by an operation O_{m+1}. If we carry out this process $2n-m-2\rho$ times, the given group is extended by the functions $P_{\rho+1},\dots, P_{2n-m-\rho}$ [or $Q^{\rho+1},\dots, Q^{2n-m-\rho}$] to a $(4n-2m-2\rho)$-dimensional group without null group with the equations

$$\begin{aligned} (P_a, P_b) &= 0 \\ (P_a, Q^b) &= \delta^b_a \\ (Q^a, Q^b) &= 0 \\ (P_b) = P_b, \quad (Q^a) &= 0 \end{aligned} \qquad (a, b = 1, \ldots, 2n-m-\rho). \tag{12.46}$$

If $\rho > n-m$ the group (12.46) contains less than $2n$ functions. According to Theorem VI.12 it is possible to determine $2(m+\rho-n)$ functions $P_{2n-m-\rho+1}, \ldots, P_n, Q^{2n-m-\rho+1}, \ldots, Q^n$, such that

$$\begin{aligned} (P_\lambda, P_\mu) &= 0 \\ (P_\lambda, Q^\kappa) &= \delta^\kappa_\lambda \\ (Q^\kappa, Q^\mu) &= 0 \\ (P_\lambda) = P_\lambda, \quad (Q^\kappa) &= 0 \end{aligned} \qquad (\kappa, \lambda, \mu = 1, \ldots, n) \tag{12.47}$$

and this requires $m+\rho-n$ operations $O_{2(m+\rho-n)-1}, O_{2(m+\rho-n)-3}, \ldots, O_1$.

As was proved in VI, § 9, the equations (12.47) are the necessary and sufficient conditions that the equations

$$\begin{aligned} '\xi^\kappa &= Q^\kappa \\ 'w_\lambda &= P_\lambda \end{aligned} \qquad (\kappa, \lambda = 1, \ldots, n) \tag{12.48}$$

represent a C_3-transformation. This proves the theorem (cf. Theorem VI.13):

Theorem VI.16. *If a $(2n-m)$-dimensional homogeneous function group of class $2\rho+\epsilon$ ($\epsilon = 0$ or 1) be given, a C_3-transformation $\xi^\kappa \to {}'\xi^\kappa$, $w_\lambda \to {}'w_\lambda$ always exists such that for $\epsilon = 0$ the group can be written in the canonical form*

$$\begin{aligned} &'\xi^1, \ldots, {}'\xi^{2n-m-\rho}, \\ &'w_1, \ldots, {}'w_\rho \end{aligned} \tag{12.49}$$

and for $\epsilon = 1$ in the canonical form

$$\begin{aligned} &'\xi^1, \ldots, {}'\xi^\rho, \\ &'w_1, \ldots, {}'w_{2n-m-\rho}. \end{aligned} \tag{12.50}$$

Here is another form of this theorem, giving a generalization of the second part of Theorem VI.12 (cf. Theorem VI.14):

Theorem VI.17. *If $'\phi^\mathfrak{a}(\xi^\kappa, w_\lambda)$ ($\mathfrak{a} = 1, \ldots, \tau_1$) and $'\psi_\mathfrak{c}(\xi^\kappa, w_\lambda)$ ($\mathfrak{c} = 1, \ldots, \tau_2$) are arbitrary functions, analytic and independent in the region considered such that*

$$\begin{aligned} ('\phi^\mathfrak{a}, {}'\phi^\mathfrak{b}) &= 0 \\ ('\phi^\mathfrak{a}, {}'\psi_\mathfrak{d}) &= \delta^\mathfrak{a}_\mathfrak{d} \\ ('\psi_\mathfrak{c}, {}'\psi_\mathfrak{d}) &= 0 \\ ('\phi^\mathfrak{a}) = 0, \quad ('\psi_\mathfrak{c}) &= {}'\psi_\mathfrak{c} \end{aligned} \qquad (\mathfrak{a}, \mathfrak{b} = 1, \ldots, \tau_1;\ \mathfrak{c}, \mathfrak{d} = 1, \ldots, \tau_2), \tag{12.51}$$

there always exist $n-\tau_1$ *functions* $'\phi^{\tau_1+1},\ldots,'\phi^n$, *homogeneous of degree 0 in the* w_λ, *and* $n-\tau_2$ *functions* $'\psi_{\tau_2+1},\ldots,'\psi_n$ *homogeneous of degree 1 in the* w_λ, *such that the equations* $'\xi^\kappa = '\phi^\kappa$, $'w_\lambda = '\psi_\lambda$ *represent a* C_3-*transformation.*

As a consequence of Theorem VI.16 we have the theorem (cf. Theorem VI.15):

THEOREM VI.18. *Two* $(2n-m)$-*dimensional homogeneous function groups in* ξ^κ, w_λ *can be transformed into each other by a* C_3-*transformation of the* ξ^κ, w_λ, *if and only if they have the same class* $2\rho+\epsilon$ ($\epsilon = 1$ *or* 0). *Consequently the integers* $2n-m$ *and* $2\rho+\epsilon$ *are the only arithmetical invariants of a homogeneous function group with respect to* C_3-*transformations.*

A homogeneous group of class 2ρ contains a $(2n-m-\rho)$-dimensional commutative sub-group, the group of the functions $Q^1,\ldots, Q^{2n-m-\rho}$, which only contains functions of degree 0 in the w_λ. A τ-dimensional commutative sub-group with $\tau > 2n-m-\rho$ cannot exist because such a group would form with $Q^{2n-m-\rho+1},\ldots, Q^n$ a $(\tau+m+\rho-n)$-dimensional commutative group with $\tau+m+\rho-n > n$ which is not possible. Now for application to the theory of systems of partial differential equations a $(2n-m-\rho)$-dimensional commutative sub-group, containing only functions of degree 0 in the w_λ, is often all that is wanted instead of a complete canonical form of the group. Since such a sub-group always contains all singular functions, first $2n-m-2\rho$ independent singular functions have to be determined, requiring $2n-m-2\rho$ operations $O_{2n-m-2\rho},\ldots, O_1$. Then we may choose an arbitrary non-singular function $\overset{1}{F}$ of the group, homogeneous of degree 0 in the w_λ, which is a solution of

$$H^y \partial_y f = 0 \quad (y = \mathrm{m}+1,\ldots, 2\mathrm{n}) \tag{12.52}$$

and is not a singular function of the group. The singular functions being solutions of (12.52), a function $\overset{1}{F}$ can be determined by means of an operation $O_{2\rho-1}$. Then we require a function $\overset{2}{F}$ of the group in involution with $\overset{1}{F}$ and homogeneous of degree 0 in the w_λ. The equations

$$\begin{aligned} H^y \partial_y \overset{2}{F} &= 0 \\ (\overset{1}{F}, \overset{2}{F}) = H^{xy}(\partial_x \overset{1}{F})(\partial_y \overset{2}{F}) &= 0 \end{aligned} \qquad (x, y = \mathrm{m}+1,\ldots, 2\mathrm{n}) \tag{12.53}$$

already have $2n-m-2\rho+1$ known independent solutions, viz. $\overset{1}{F}$ and the singular functions. Hence the determination of one solution $\overset{2}{F}$ requires an operation $O_{2\rho-3}$. Continuing in this way we see that the determination of a $(2n-m-\rho)$-dimensional commutative sub-group, containing only functions of degree 0 in the w_λ, requires $2n-m-\rho$ operations $O_{2n-m-2\rho}, \ldots, O_1; O_{2\rho-1}, O_{2\rho-3}, \ldots, O_1$.

EXERCISES†

1. Prove Jacobi's identity for Poisson bracket expressions, using the invariance of these expressions for C_2-transformations.‡

2. The system
$$(F^x, f) = 0 \quad (x = \mathrm{m}+1, \ldots, 2\mathrm{n}) \tag{2 α}$$
is complete if and only if the F^x form the basis of a function group.§

3. The infinitesimal volume in the $X_{2n+\epsilon}$ of the variables $\epsilon\xi^0$, ξ^κ, w_λ is invariant for C_3-transformations and, for $\epsilon = 0$, also for C_2-transformations.‖

4. If X is the symbol of the infinitesimal C_2-transformation in ξ^κ, w_λ (cf. VI, § 8)
$$\begin{aligned} '\xi^\kappa &= \xi^\kappa + \frac{\partial F}{\partial w_\lambda} dt, \\ 'w_\lambda &= w_\lambda - \frac{\partial F}{\partial \xi^\lambda} dt \end{aligned} \tag{4 α}$$
we have
$$Xf = (F, f). \tag{4 β}$$
If F_1 and F_2 are the characteristic functions of the infinitesimal C_2-transformations X_1 and X_2 respectively, prove that (F_1, F_2) is the characteristic function of the C_2-transformation $(X_1 X_2)$.††

5. If
$$\begin{aligned} \delta\xi^\kappa &= \frac{\partial F}{\partial w_\kappa} dt = (F, \xi^\kappa)\, dt \\ \delta w_\lambda &= -\frac{\partial F}{\partial \xi^\lambda} dt = (F, w_\lambda)\, dt \end{aligned} \qquad ((F) = F) \tag{5 α}$$
is a C_3-transformation with the characteristic function F and if the variables ξ^κ, w_λ are transformed into $'\xi^\kappa$, $'w_\lambda$ by a general C_2-transformation, we get a C_3-transformation in $'\xi^\kappa$, $'w_\lambda$ with the same characteristic function F.

If the transformation $\xi^\kappa, w_\lambda \to {}'\xi^\kappa, {}'w_\lambda$ is a general C_1-transformation with $'w_\lambda d'\xi^\lambda = \sigma w_\lambda d\xi^\lambda$, we get a C_1-transformation in $'\xi^\kappa$, $'w_\lambda$ with the characteristic functions σF and $-(\sigma F, 1/\sigma)$:
$$\begin{aligned} \delta\, '\xi^\kappa &= \frac{\partial \sigma F}{\partial\, 'w_\kappa} dt = (\sigma F, '\xi^\kappa)'\, dt, \\ \delta\, 'w_\lambda &= -\frac{\partial \sigma F}{\partial\, '\xi^\lambda} dt - \left(\sigma F, \frac{1}{\sigma}\right)' 'w_\lambda\, dt = (\sigma F, 'w_\lambda)'\, dt - \left(\sigma F, \frac{1}{\sigma}\right)' 'w_\lambda\, dt.‡‡ \end{aligned} \tag{5 β}$$

† Cf. the suggestions at the end of the book.
‡ Cf. Engel and Faber 1932. 1. p. 235.
§ Cf. e.g. ibid., p. 237.
‖ Cf. Eisenhart 1933. 1, p. 281, Ex. 11.
†† Cf. Lie 1890. 1, p. 266.
‡‡ Cf. ibid., p. 267; Engel and Faber 1932. 1, p. 273.

6. If X is the symbol of the infinitesimal C_1-transformation in ξ^0, ξ^κ, w_λ (cf. VI, § 8)

$$'\xi^0 = \xi^0 - w_\lambda \frac{\partial F}{\partial w_\lambda} dt + F\,dt,$$

$$'\xi^\kappa = \xi^\kappa + \frac{\partial F}{\partial w_\kappa} dt, \tag{6α}$$

$$'w_\lambda = w_\lambda - \frac{\partial F}{\partial \xi^\lambda} dt + w_\lambda \frac{\partial F}{\partial \xi^0} dt$$

we have
$$Xf = (F,f) + w_\lambda \frac{\partial F}{\partial \xi^0}\frac{\partial f}{\partial w_\lambda} + (F-(F))\frac{\partial f}{\partial \xi^0} = [F,f] + F\frac{\partial f}{\partial \xi^0}, \tag{6β}$$

where
$$[F,f] \stackrel{\text{def}}{=} (F,f) - (F)\frac{\partial f}{\partial \xi^0} + \frac{\partial F}{\partial \xi^0}(f) \quad \text{(cf. IV, Ex.1)}. \tag{6γ}$$

If F_1 and F_2 are the characteristic functions of the infinitesimal C_1-transformations X_1 and X_2 respectively, prove that

$$F \stackrel{\text{def}}{=} [F_1, F_2] + F_1 \frac{\partial F_2}{\partial \xi^0} - F_2 \frac{\partial F_1}{\partial \xi^0} \tag{6δ}$$

is the characteristic function of the C_1-transformation $(X_1 X_2)$.†

7. Prove that
$$[F, G]' = \sigma^{-1}[F, G] \tag{7α}$$
if
$$d'\xi^0 + 'w_\lambda d'\xi^\lambda = \sigma(d\xi^0 + w_\lambda d\xi^\lambda).‡ \tag{7β}$$

8. Prove that for the transformation (Ex. 7β)

$$[\sigma, '\xi^\kappa] = \sigma \frac{\partial '\xi^\kappa}{\partial \xi^0},$$

$$[\sigma, 'w_\lambda] = \sigma \frac{\partial 'w_\lambda}{\partial \xi^0}, \tag{8α}$$

$$[\sigma, '\xi^0] = \sigma \frac{\partial '\xi^0}{\partial \xi^0} - \sigma^2.§$$

9. If

$$\begin{aligned} \delta\xi^0 &= [F, \xi^0]dt + F\,dt, \\ \delta\xi^\kappa &= [F, \xi^\kappa]dt, \\ \delta w_\lambda &= [F, w_\lambda]dt \end{aligned} \tag{9α}$$

is a C_1-transformation with the characteristic function F and if the variables ξ^0, ξ^κ, w_λ are transformed into $'\xi^0$, $'\xi^\kappa$, $'w_\lambda$ by a general C_1-transformation with $d'\xi^0 + 'w_\lambda d'\xi^\lambda = \sigma(d\xi^0 + w_\lambda d\xi^\lambda)$, we get a C_1-transformation in $'\xi^0$, $'\xi^\kappa$, $'w_\lambda$ with the characteristic function σF.‖

† Cf. Lie 1890. 1, p. 275.

‡ Cf. ibid., p. 123.

§ Cf. ibid., p. 144.

‖ Cf. ibid., p. 276.

VII

THEORY OF VECTOR MANIFOLDS AND ELEMENT MANIFOLDS†

1. The $\mathfrak{N}_m$ and the $\mathfrak{M}_{m-1}$‡

If the system of $2n-m$ equations

$$F^x(\xi^\kappa, w_\lambda) = 0 \quad (x = \mathrm{m}+1,..., 2\mathrm{n}) \tag{1.1}$$

is minimal regular at the null point $\overset{0}{\xi^\kappa}$, $\overset{0}{w_\lambda}$, $\overset{0}{w_\lambda} \neq 0$ (cf. II, § 3) and if the ξ^κ are considered as the coordinates of an X_n and the w_λ as the components of a covariant vector with respect to these coordinates, this system represents a set of ∞^m covariant vectors in the X_n, constituting a *vector manifold* or $\mathfrak{N}_m$ as defined in VI, § 3. This $\mathfrak{N}_m$ is an X_m in the X_{2n} of the ξ^κ and w_λ. If the $\mathfrak{N}_m$ is homogeneous, that is, if the equations (1.1) are homogeneous in the w_λ, the ∞^{m-1} E_{n-1}-elements belonging to these vectors constitute an *element manifold* or $\mathfrak{M}_{m-1}$ as defined in VI, § 3.

If a homogeneous $\mathfrak{N}_m$ be given, it is always possible to construct a non-homogeneous $\mathfrak{N}_{m-1}$ by choosing at every point of the X_n where vectors of the $\mathfrak{N}_m$ exist, one vector from every set of ∞^1 vectors with the same $(n-1)$-direction. This process, executed in a continuous way, is called the *dis-homogenization* of an $\mathfrak{N}_m$. Conversely every non-homogeneous $\mathfrak{N}_{m-1}$ uniquely determines a homogeneous $\mathfrak{N}_m$, obtainable by adding to every vector of the $\mathfrak{N}_{m-1}$ all ∞^1 vectors at the same point with the same $(n-1)$-direction. This process is called the *homogenization* of an $\mathfrak{N}_{m-1}$.

The $\mathfrak{N}_m$ with the minimal regular null form (1.1) can also be given by the parametric form

$$\begin{aligned} &(a) \qquad \xi^\kappa = \xi^\kappa(\eta^a) \\ &(b) \qquad w_\lambda = w_\lambda(\eta^a) \end{aligned} \qquad (a = 1,..., \mathrm{m}) \tag{1.2}$$

minimal regular in an $\mathfrak{N}(\overset{0}{\eta^a})$, the $\overset{0}{\eta^a}$ being the values of η^a leading to $\overset{0}{\xi^\kappa}$ and $\overset{0}{w_\lambda}$, if substituted in (1.2). If the $\mathfrak{N}_m$ is homogeneous, it is always possible to choose the parameters η^a in such a way that the ξ^κ are homogeneous of degree 0 and the w_λ homogeneous of degree 1 in the η^a,

† General references: Lie 1877. 1; v. Weber 1900. 1; Goursat 1921. 1; Engel and Faber 1932. 1; Schouten and v. d. Kulk 1940. 2, 3, 4, 5; 1942. 1; 1943. 1, 2, 3, 4, 5, 6.

‡ Cf. Schouten and v. d. Kulk 1943. 4.

but this special choice of the parameters is not always to be recommended.

Let r be the highest value of the rank of the F^x with respect to the w_λ in the null points of (1.1) lying in an $\mathfrak{N}(\overset{0}{\underset{0}{\xi^\kappa}}, w_\lambda)$. Then evidently $1 \leqslant r \leqslant 2n-m$ and $r \leqslant n$ in the non-homogeneous case and $r \leqslant n-1$ in the homogeneous case. By a suitable change of $\underset{0}{\xi^\kappa}$, $\overset{0}{w_\lambda}$, and $\mathfrak{N}(\underset{0}{\xi^\kappa}, \overset{0}{w_\lambda})$ we can always make this rank equal to r at all points of $\mathfrak{N}(\underset{0}{\xi^\kappa}, \overset{0}{w_\lambda})$. Then we call r the *w_λ-rank of the* $\mathfrak{N}_m$ and also the w_λ-rank of the system (1.1) in this $\mathfrak{N}(\underset{0}{\xi^\kappa}, \overset{0}{w_\lambda})$. According to the theorem of elimination II.7, just $2n-m-r$ equations can be deduced from (1.1) containing only the ξ^κ and constituting together with r equations of (1.1) a system, equivalent to (1.1) and minimal regular in $\mathfrak{N}(\underset{0}{\xi^\kappa}, \overset{0}{w_\lambda})$. Hence (1.1) can be replaced by a system of the form

$$\begin{array}{ll}(a) & F_\beta(\xi^\kappa, w_\lambda) = 0 \\ (b) & G^{\mathfrak{a}}(\xi^\kappa) = 0\end{array} \qquad (\beta = 1,\ldots, r;\ \mathfrak{a} = r+1,\ldots, 2n-m), \tag{1.3}$$

the rank of the F_β with respect to the w_λ being r and the rank of the $G^{\mathfrak{a}}$ with respect to the ξ^κ being $2n-m-r$. This implies that $r \geqslant n-m$ because $2n-m-r \leqslant n$.

The equations (1.3 b) represent the *field region* of the $\mathfrak{N}_m$ (cf. VI, § 3), being an X_t $(t = m-n+r)$ through $\underset{0}{\xi^\kappa}$ in an $\mathfrak{N}(\underset{0}{\xi^\kappa})$ and t is the *field dimension* of the $\mathfrak{N}_m$ (cf. VI, § 3). The equations (1.3 a) fix at every point of this X_t a system of $\infty^{m-t} = \infty^{n-r}$ covariant vectors. Collecting results we have the following relations for the w_λ-rank r and the field dimension t (cf. VI, § 3):

$$t = m-n+r,$$

$1 \leqslant r \leqslant n$; non-homogeneous case,	$m-n+1 \leqslant t \leqslant m$; non-homogeneous case,
$0 \leqslant r \leqslant n-1$; homogeneous case,	$m-n \leqslant t \leqslant m-1$; homogeneous case,
$n-m \leqslant r \leqslant 2n-m$,	$0 \leqslant t \leqslant n$. (1.4)

A system of ∞^{m-t} covariant vectors at a point of X_n is called a $\mathfrak{B}_{m-t}$. Hence *every* $\mathfrak{N}_m$ *is a* $\mathfrak{B}_{m-t}$*-field defined over an* X_t. For $t = m$ a $\mathfrak{B}_{m-t}$ is a covariant vector and the $\mathfrak{N}_m$ a vector field defined over an X_m. In the homogeneous case ∞^{m-t-1} E_{n-1}-elements belong to the ∞^{m-t}

vectors of the $\mathfrak{B}_{m-t}$. This proves once more that in the homogeneous case $t \leqslant m-1$ and $r \leqslant n-1$.

A system of ∞^{m-t-1} E_{n-1}-elements at a point of X_n is called an $\mathfrak{S}^{n-1}_{m-t-1}$. Hence every $\mathfrak{M}_{m-1}$ *is an* $\mathfrak{S}^{n-1}_{m-t-1}$*-field defined over an* X_t. For $t = m-1$ an $\mathfrak{S}^{n-1}_{m-t-1}$ is an E_{n-1}-element and the $\mathfrak{M}_{m-1}$ is a field of E_{n-1}-elements defined over an X_{m-1}.

If the $\mathfrak{N}_m$ is given by its parametric form (1.2), according to the theorem of elimination II.7 *the rank of the* ξ^κ *with respect to the* η^a *is equal to the field dimension* t of the $\mathfrak{N}_m$. In fact, if and only if this rank is t, is it possible to deduce from (1.2*a*) just $n-t$ equations containing the ξ^κ only.

2. Change of the field dimension t of an $\mathfrak{N}_m$ with C_3-transformations†

If the system

$$F^{x'}(\xi^\kappa, w_\lambda) = 0 \quad (x' = (\mathrm{m}+1)', \ldots, (2\mathrm{n})') \tag{2.1}$$

is equivalent to (1.1) in an $\mathfrak{N}(\underset{0}{\xi^\kappa}, \overset{0}{w_\lambda})$, it follows from the second basis theorem II.5 that equations of the form

$$F^{x'} = C^{x'}_x F^x, \quad \det(C^{x'}_x) \neq 0 \quad (x = \mathrm{m}+1, \ldots, 2\mathrm{n};\ x' = (\mathrm{m}+1)', \ldots, (2\mathrm{n})') \tag{2.2}$$

exist with coefficients $C^{x'}_x$ analytic in an $\mathfrak{N}(\underset{0}{\xi^\kappa}, \overset{0}{w_\lambda})$. The transformation (2.2) is called a *basis transformation*. By differentiating (2.2) with respect to the w_λ we get the congruences

$$\frac{\partial F^{x'}}{\partial w_\lambda} \equiv C^{x'}_x \frac{\partial F^x}{\partial w_\lambda} \quad (\mathrm{mod}\ F^x) \quad (x = \mathrm{m}+1, \ldots, 2\mathrm{n};\ x' = (\mathrm{m}+1)', \ldots, (2\mathrm{n})') \tag{2.3}$$

and this implies that the w_λ-rank of (2.1) is the same as the w_λ-rank of (1.1) at every null point of (1.1) in $\mathfrak{N}(\underset{0}{\xi^\kappa}, \overset{0}{w_\lambda})$. Hence r and t are invariants of the $\mathfrak{N}_m$. This also follows geometrically from the fact that the $\mathfrak{N}_m$ is a $\mathfrak{B}_{m-t}$-field over an X_t.

Now r and t are not invariant for C_3-transformations in ξ^κ, w_λ. We will prove the theorem

THEOREM VII.1. *An* $\mathfrak{N}_m$ *whose field dimension* t *has not the highest possible value can always be transformed by means of a* C_3*-transformation into an* $\mathfrak{N}_m$ *with the highest possible field dimension, viz.* n *for* $n \leqslant m$ *or*

† Cf. Schouten and v. d. Kulk 1943. 4, 5.

m for $n \geqslant m$ in the non-homogeneous case and n for $n \leqslant m-1$ or $m-1$ for $n \geqslant m-1$ in the homogeneous case.

Proof. First we prove that for $m \geqslant n$ it is always possible to find a coordinate system (κ') of the X_n such that after the introduction of these coordinates (1.3a) can be solved with respect to $w_{1'},..., w_{r'}$ and (1.3b) with respect to $\xi^{(r+1)'},..., \xi^{(2n-m)'}$. In order that (1.3$b$) can be solved with respect to $\xi^{(r+1)'},..., \xi^{(2n-m)'}$ it is necessary and sufficient that the determinant of the derivatives of the $G^{\mathfrak{a}}$ with respect to the $\xi^{\mathfrak{a}'}$ $(\mathfrak{a}' = (r+1)',..., (2n-m)')$ be $\neq 0$, or, in another form, that

$$G_{[\lambda_1...\lambda_{2n-m-r}} \overset{1'}{e}_{\lambda_{2n-m-r+1}}...\overset{r'}{e}_{\lambda_{2n-m}} \overset{(2n-m+1)'}{e}_{\lambda_{2n-m+1}}...\overset{n'}{e}_{\lambda_n]} \neq 0, \tag{2.4}$$

where

$$G_{\lambda_1...\lambda_{2n-m-r}} \overset{\text{def}}{=} G^{r+1}_{[\lambda_1}...G^{2n-m}_{\lambda_{2n-m-r}]}, \qquad G^{\mathfrak{a}}_{\lambda} \overset{\text{def}}{=} \partial_\lambda G^{\mathfrak{a}} \quad (\mathfrak{a} = r+1,..., 2n-m). \tag{2.5}$$

In order that (1.3a) can be solved with respect to $w_{1'},..., w_{r'}$ it is necessary and sufficient that the determinant of the derivatives of the F_β with respect to the $w_{\beta'}$ $(\beta' = 1',..., r')$ be $\neq 0$, or, in another form,

$$F_{[\lambda_{r+1}...\lambda_n} \overset{1'}{e}_{\lambda_1}...\overset{r'}{e}_{\lambda_r]} \neq 0, \tag{2.6}$$

where

$$F_{\lambda_{r+1}...\lambda_n} \overset{\text{def}}{=} E_{\lambda_1...\lambda_n} F^{\lambda_1}_{1}...F^{\lambda_r}_{r}, \qquad F^{\lambda}_{\beta} \overset{\text{def}}{=} \frac{\partial F_\beta}{\partial w_\lambda} \quad (\beta = 1,..., r). \tag{2.7}$$

Hence we have to determine $m-n+r$ functions $\xi^{1'},..., \xi^{r'}, \xi^{(2n-m+1)'},..., \xi^{n'}$ of the ξ^κ whose gradients $\overset{1'}{e}_\lambda,..., \overset{r'}{e}_\lambda, \overset{(2n-m+1)'}{e}_\lambda, ..., \overset{n'}{e}_\lambda$ satisfy the inequalities (2.4) and (2.6) in an $\mathfrak{N}(\overset{0}{\xi^\kappa})$. Now it is always possible to find in $\overset{0}{\xi^\kappa}$ $m-n+r$ linearly independent covariant vectors $\overset{1'}{u}_\lambda,..., \overset{r'}{u}_\lambda, \overset{(2n-m+1)'}{u}_\lambda, ..., \overset{n'}{u}_\lambda$ satisfying (2.4) and (2.6), if in these equations the measuring vectors are replaced by them and, when these vectors have been fixed, it is always possible to find $m-n+r$ functions whose gradients in $\overset{0}{\xi^\kappa}$ are equal to these vectors. This proves that for $m \geqslant n$ the equations (1.3) can always be brought into the form

$$\begin{aligned} w_{\beta'} &= \Omega_{\beta'}(\xi^{\alpha'}, \xi^{\zeta'}, w_{\mathfrak{b}'}, w_{\eta'}) \\ \xi^{\mathfrak{a}'} &= \Omega^{\mathfrak{a}'}(\xi^{\alpha'}, \xi^{\zeta'}) \end{aligned}$$

$$(\alpha', \beta' = 1',..., r';\ \mathfrak{a}', \mathfrak{b}' = (r+1)',..., (2n-m)';\quad \zeta', \eta' = (2n-m+1)',..., n'). \tag{2.8}$$

Evidently the functions $\xi^{\mathfrak{a}'} - \Omega^{\mathfrak{a}'}$ are independent. Introducing these functions as new coordinates $\xi^{\mathfrak{a}''}$ and dropping the accents for the sake of simplicity, we get equations of the form

$$\begin{aligned} w_\beta &= \chi_\beta(\xi^\alpha, \xi^\zeta, w_\mathfrak{b}, w_\eta) \\ \xi^\mathfrak{a} &= 0 \end{aligned}$$

$$(\alpha, \beta = 1,\dots, r;\ \mathfrak{a}, \mathfrak{b} = r+1,\dots, 2n-m;\ \zeta, \eta = 2n-m+1,\dots, n). \tag{2.9}$$

Now we suppose first that $m > n$. As we have already assumed that $\overset{0}{w}_\lambda \neq 0$, by interchanging of indices we can always make $\overset{0}{w}_n \neq 0$. Then an $\mathfrak{N}(\underset{0}{\xi}^\kappa, \overset{0}{w}_\lambda)$ exists where $w_n \neq 0$ at all points. In this $\mathfrak{N}(\underset{0}{\xi}^\kappa, \overset{0}{w}_\lambda)$ we carry out the C_3-transformation

$$\begin{aligned} 'w_\beta &= w_\beta, & w_\beta &= 'w_\beta \\ 'w_\mathfrak{b} &= -w_n \xi^\mathfrak{b}, & w_\mathfrak{b} &= 'w_n\, '\xi^\mathfrak{b} \\ 'w_\eta &= w_\eta, & w_\eta &= 'w_\eta \\ '\xi^\alpha &= \xi^\alpha, & \xi^\alpha &= '\xi^\alpha \\ '\xi^\mathfrak{a} &= \frac{w_\mathfrak{a}}{w_n}, & \xi^\mathfrak{a} &= -\frac{'w_\mathfrak{a}}{'w_n} \\ '\xi^\zeta &= \xi^\zeta, & \xi^\zeta &= '\xi^\zeta \\ '\xi^n &= \xi^n + \frac{w_\mathfrak{b}}{w_n}\xi^\mathfrak{b}, & \xi^n &= '\xi^n + \frac{'w_\mathfrak{b}}{'w_n}\, '\xi^\mathfrak{b} \end{aligned} \tag{2.10}$$

($\alpha, \beta = 1,\dots, r$; $\mathfrak{a}, \mathfrak{b} = r+1,\dots, 2n-m$; $\zeta = 2n-m+1,\dots, n-1$ for $m > n+1$; ζ does not occur for $m = n+1$; $\eta = 2n-m+1,\dots, n$).

Then (2.9) takes the form

$$\begin{aligned} 'w_\beta &= \bar{\chi}_\beta('\xi^\kappa, 'w_\eta). \quad (\beta = 1,\dots, r;\ \mathfrak{b} = r+1,\dots, 2n-m; \\ 'w_\mathfrak{b} &= 0 \qquad\qquad\qquad\qquad \eta = 2n-m+1,\dots, n) \end{aligned} \tag{2.11}$$

and this system has the $'w_\lambda$-rank $2n-m$ and consequently the field dimension n. This proves the theorem for $m \geqslant n+1$.

Now we suppose that $m \leqslant n$. The first $n-1$ equations (1.1) represent an $\mathfrak{N}_{n+1}$ and we have already proved that they can be brought into the form

$$'F^\mathfrak{x}('\xi^\kappa, 'w_\lambda) = 0 \quad (\mathfrak{x} = \mathrm{m}+1,\dots, \mathrm{m}+\mathrm{n}-1) \tag{2.12}$$

with $'w_\lambda$-rank $n-1$ by a suitable C_3-transformation. If by this C_3-transformation the remaining $n-m+1$ equations take the form

$$'F^\mathfrak{y}('\xi^\kappa, 'w_\lambda) = 0 \quad (\mathfrak{y} = \mathrm{m}+\mathrm{n},\dots, 2\mathrm{n}), \tag{2.13}$$

the $'w_\lambda$-rank of the system (2.12, 13) is $\geqslant n-1$. This proves the theorem for the homogeneous case, because in this case $n-1$ is the maximum value of the $'w_\lambda$-rank. Thus, only the non-homogeneous case with

$m \leqslant n$ remains. For this case we form a homogeneous $\mathfrak{R}_{m+1}$ by homogenization of the $\mathfrak{R}_m$. For a homogeneous $\mathfrak{R}_{m+1}$ it is already proved that by a suitable C_3-transformation its equation could be brought into a form with $'w_\lambda$-rank $n-1$. Now the equations of the $\mathfrak{R}_m$ can always be obtained from the equations of the $\mathfrak{R}_{m+1}$ by adding one suitable equation not homogeneous in the $'w_\lambda$. Then from the first $2n-m-1$ equations $n-1$ of the variables $'w_\lambda$ can be solved and by suitably interchanging the indices we can always arrange that these are $'w_1,..., 'w_{n-1}$. Substituting these values into the last equation, we get an equation in the $'\xi^\kappa$ and $'w_n$ certainly containing $'w_n$ because otherwise the $\mathfrak{R}_m$ would be homogeneous. By the solution of this equation with respect to $'w_n$ we get an equation of the form

$$'w_n - \Omega('\xi^\kappa) = 0. \tag{2.14}$$

Since the derivative of the left-hand side of this equation with respect to $'w_n$ is 1 we see that the $'w_\lambda$-rank of the whole system obtained in this way is just n. This proves the theorem for the last remaining case.

3. Class, rotation class, similarity class, and index of an $\mathfrak{R}_m$†

From the derivatives of the F^x in (1.1) with respect to ξ^κ and w_λ we form at all null points of (1.1) the expressions (cf. VI, §§ 9 and 10)

$$\begin{aligned} K^x &\overset{\text{def}}{=} w_\lambda \frac{\partial F^x}{\partial w_\lambda} = (F^x) \\ K^{xy} &\overset{\text{def}}{=} 2\frac{\partial F^{[x}}{\partial w_\lambda}\frac{\partial F^{y]}}{\partial \xi^\lambda} = (F^x, F^y) \end{aligned} \qquad ((F^x = 0); x, y = \mathrm{m}+1,..., 2\mathrm{n}). \tag{3.1}$$

By a basis transformation $F^x \rightarrow F^{x'}$ (cf. VII, § 2) (F^x) and (F^x, F^y) transform in the following way:

$$\begin{aligned} (F^{x'}) &\equiv C_x^{x'}(F^x) \pmod{F^x} & (x, y &= \mathrm{m}+1,..., 2\mathrm{n}; \\ (F^{x'}, F^{y'}) &\equiv C_x^{x'}C_y^{y'}(F^x, F^y) \pmod{F^x} & x', y' &= (\mathrm{m}+1)',..., (2\mathrm{n})'). \end{aligned} \tag{3.2}$$

Since K^x and K^{xy} are only defined for the elements of $\mathfrak{R}_m$, the formulae of transformation of K^x and K^{xy} are

$$\begin{aligned} K^{x'} &= C_x^{x'}K^x & (x, y &= \mathrm{m}+1,..., 2\mathrm{n}; \\ K^{x'y'} &= C_x^{x'}C_y^{y'}K^{xy} & x', y' &= (\mathrm{m}+1)',..., (2\mathrm{n})'). \end{aligned} \tag{3.3}$$

Hence the K^x transform like the components of a contravariant vector and the K^{xy} like the components of a contravariant bivector. We call K^{xy} the *Poisson bivector of the* $\mathfrak{R}_m$ and also *of the system* (1.1).

† Schouten and v. d. Kulk 1943. 4.

From (3.1) it follows that the $\mathfrak{N}_m$ is homogeneous if K^x vanishes. If $K^{xy} = 0$ the system (1.1) is said to be *in involution*. If a system is in involution all equivalent systems are in involution as well. But it is not necessary that for every basis the functions F^x are in involution (cf. VI, § 9).

$\mathfrak{N}_m$ or the system (1.1) have the following arithmetic invariants with respect to coordinate transformations and basis transformations:

the *rotation class* 2ρ = the rank of K^{xy};

the *class* K = the x-rank of the system K^x, K^{xy};

the *similarity class* k = the greatest odd integer $\leqslant K$;

the *index* l = the rank of K^x, i.e. 0 for $K^x = 0$ and 1 for $K^x \neq 0$.

(3.4)

It is evident that $K \leqslant 2n-m$ and that 2ρ is the greatest even integer $\leqslant K$. If $m = n$ and $t = n$ the $\mathfrak{N}_m$ is a vector field in the X_n of the ξ^κ and K, 2ρ, and k are the invariants defined in IV, § 2. For a non-vanishing vector field $l = 1$.

The transformation of these arithmetic invariants with C_1-, C_2-, and C_3-transformations in ξ^κ, w_λ can be deduced from the transformation of K^{xy} and K^x. From the table of transformations in VI, § 10, we get the table:

	C_1-*transformation* $'w_\lambda\, d'\xi^\lambda = \mu w_\lambda\, d\xi^\lambda$	C_2-*transformation* $'w_\lambda\, d'\xi^\lambda = w_\lambda\, d\xi^\lambda + d\Omega$	C_3-*transformation* $'w_\lambda\, d'\xi^\lambda = w_\lambda\, d\xi^\lambda$
K^{xy}	$\frac{1}{\mu}(K^{xy} + 2\mu v^{[x}K^{y]})$; $v^x \stackrel{\text{def}}{=} \lambda\left(F^x, \frac{1}{\mu}\right)$; $\lambda \stackrel{\text{def}}{=} 1 - {}'w_\lambda \frac{\partial \log \mu}{\partial\, {}'w_\lambda}$	K^{xy}	K^{xy}
K^x	λK^x	$K^x + (\Omega, K^x)$	K^x

(3.5)

l is invariant for C_1-transformations. To prove that k is also invariant for C_1-transformations we consider first the case when K is odd. Then the rank of $K^{xy} + 2\mu v^{[x}K^{y]}$, is either $K-1$ or $K+1$ and consequently the x-rank of $K^{xy} + 2\mu v^{[x}K^{y]}$, λK^x is either K or $K+1$. Now suppose K is even. Then the rank of $K^{xy} + 2\mu v^{[x}K^{y]}$ is either K or $K-2$ and the x-rank of $K^{xy} + 2\mu v^{[x}K^{y]}$, λK^x is either K or $K-1$. In all cases the similarity class of the transformed system is k. 2ρ is invariant for

C_2-transformations. Hence we have the following table of transformations:

	C_1-transformation		*C_2-transformation*		*C_3-transformation*
	K even	*K odd*	*K even*	*K odd*	
K	K or $K-1$	K or $K+1$	K or $K+1$	K or $K-1$	K
2ρ	2ρ or $2\rho-2$	2ρ or $2\rho+2$	2ρ	2ρ	2ρ
k	k	k	k or $k+2$	k or $k-2$	k
$l=1$	1		1 or 0		1
$l=0$	0		0 or 1		0

(3.6)

Though r and t are not invariant for C_3-transformations, there still exists an inequality between K and r. To prove this for the case when $m \geqslant n$ we bring the equations of the $\mathfrak{N}_m$ into the form (2.9) by means of a transformation of coordinates. For this transformation r is invariant. Then we form the matrices

$$(a)\quad \| K^{xy} \|, \qquad (b)\quad \left\| \begin{matrix} K^{xy} & K^{y} \\ -K^{x} & 0 \end{matrix} \right\| \quad (x, y = \mathrm{m}+1, \ldots, 2\mathrm{n}). \tag{3.7}$$

(3.7 a) contains a $(2n-m-r)$-rowed sub-determinant consisting only of zeros and (3.7 b) a $(2n-m-r+1)$-rowed sub-determinant of the same kind. Hence we have for the rank R_0 of (3.7 a) and for the rank R_1 of (3.7 b)

$$R_0 \leqslant 2r, \qquad R_1 \leqslant 2r. \tag{3.8}$$

Now $K = \frac{1}{2}(R+R_0)$ and consequently

$$K \leqslant 2r. \tag{3.9}$$

If we write $K = 2\rho+\epsilon$ ($\epsilon = 1$ or 0) we get the inequalities

$$r \geqslant \rho+\epsilon \tag{3.10}$$

and

$$t \geqslant \rho+m-n+\epsilon, \tag{3.11}$$

fixing the minimal value of the field dimension of $\mathfrak{N}_m$. For general values of m the same inequality holds as we will prove later in this section by using the parametric form of the $\mathfrak{N}_m$. In VII, § 10, we will prove that if an arbitrary $\mathfrak{N}_m$ be given, there always exists a C_3-transformation transforming this $\mathfrak{N}_m$ into an $\mathfrak{N}_m$ whose field dimension has this minimal value.

The arithmetic invariants were defined here starting from the null form (1.1) of the $\mathfrak{N}_m$. But we can also start from the parametric form

(1.2). If U_b is a covariant vector of the X_m of the η^a ($a = 1,\dots,\mathrm{m}$) defined by the equations

$$U_b \overset{\mathrm{def}}{=} w_\lambda\, \partial_b\, \xi^\lambda \quad (b = 1,\dots,\mathrm{m}), \tag{3.12}$$

we have $$w_\lambda\, d\xi^\lambda = w_\lambda(\partial_b\, \xi^\lambda)\, d\eta^b = U_b\, d\eta^b \quad (b = 1,\dots,\mathrm{m}). \tag{3.13}$$

If now we form the rotation of U_b (cf. VI, § 9)

$$U_{cb} \overset{\mathrm{def}}{=} 2\partial_{[c}\, U_{b]} = 2(\partial_{[c}\, w_{|\lambda|})\partial_{b]}\, \xi^\lambda = \{\eta^c, \eta^b\} \quad (b, c = 1,\dots,\mathrm{m}) \tag{3.14}$$

the class $\bar{K}$ of this field U_b is, according to the definition, the b-rank of U_b, U_{cb}. In order to investigate the relations between the class $\bar{K}$ of U_b and the class K of $\mathfrak{N}_m$ we once more use the notation of VI, § 3, writing X^A ($A = 1,\dots,n,(1),\dots,(n)$) for ξ^κ, w_λ with

$$\begin{aligned} X^\kappa &= \xi^\kappa \\ X^{(\kappa)} &= w_\kappa \end{aligned} \quad ((\kappa) = (1),\dots,(n)). \tag{3.15}$$

Then the null form (1.1) takes the form

$$C^x(X^A) = 0 \quad (x = \mathrm{m}+1,\dots,2\mathrm{n};\ A = 1,\dots,n,(1),\dots,(n)) \tag{3.16}$$

and the parametric form (1.2) the form

$$X^A = B^A(\eta^a) \quad (a = 1,\dots,\mathrm{m};\ A = 1,\dots,n,(1),\dots,(n)). \tag{3.17}$$

The covariant connecting quantity (cf. II, § 3) C^x_B of the X_m in the X_{2n} of the X^A represented by (3.16) and also by (3.17) has the components

$$C^x_\lambda = \frac{\partial C^x}{\partial \xi^\lambda}, \qquad C^x_{(\lambda)} = \frac{\partial C^x}{\partial w_\lambda} \quad (x = \mathrm{m}+1,\dots,2\mathrm{n};\ (\lambda) = (1),\dots,(n)) \tag{3.18}$$

and the contravariant connecting quantity B^A_b (cf. II, § 4) has the components

$$B^\kappa_b = \frac{\partial B^\kappa}{\partial \eta^b}, \qquad B^{(\kappa)}_b = \frac{\partial B^{(\kappa)}}{\partial \eta^b} \quad (b = 1,\dots,\mathrm{m};\ (\kappa) = (1),\dots,(n)). \tag{3.19}$$

Now in the X_{2n} of the X^A *we allow only transformations of coordinates which leave $w_\lambda\, d\xi^\lambda$ invariant,* in other words, *C_3-transformations in ξ^κ, w_λ.* Then in this X_{2n} the field w_λ determines uniquely a covariant vector field W_B ($B = 1,\dots,n,(1),\dots,(n)$) with the components

$$\begin{aligned} W_\lambda &= w_\lambda \\ W_{(\lambda)} &= 0 \end{aligned} \quad ((\lambda) = (1),\dots,(n)). \tag{3.20}$$

These equations are invariant for all these allowable coordinate transformations in X_{2n} and we have

$$w_\lambda\, d\xi^\lambda = W_B\, dX^B \quad (B = 1,\dots,n,(1),\dots,(n)). \tag{3.21}$$

The only non-vanishing components of the rotation W_{CB} of W_B are

$$W_{(\lambda)\lambda} = -W_{\lambda(\lambda)} = +1 \quad ((\lambda) = (1),..., (n)). \tag{3.22}$$

Hence W_{CB} has rank $2n$ and from this it follows, firstly, that the characteristics of the field W_B (cf. IV, § 3) are curves and, secondly, that a contravariant bivector V^{AB} exists which is the inverse of $-W_{CB}$ (cf. I, § 3) and is uniquely determined by the equations

$$V^{AB} W_{CB} = A^A_C \quad (A, B, C = 1,..., n, (1),..., (n)). \tag{3.23}$$

The non-vanishing components of this bivector are

$$V^{(\kappa)\kappa} = -V^{\kappa(\kappa)} = +1 \quad ((\kappa) = (1),..., (n)). \tag{3.24}$$

From W_B and V^{AB} we form the vector

$$V^A = V^{AB} W_B \quad (A, B = 1,..., n, (1),..., (n)) \tag{3.25}$$

with the components

$$V^\kappa = 0, \qquad V^{(\kappa)} = w_\kappa \quad ((\kappa) = (1),..., (n)). \tag{3.26}$$

Then from (3.25) it follows that

$$V^A W_A = 0 \qquad (A = 1,..., n, (1),..., (n)) \tag{3.27}$$

and

$$V^A W_{AB} = W_B \quad (A, B = 1,..., n, (1),..., (n)). \tag{3.28}$$

The equations (3.27) and (3.28) express the fact that *the characteristics of the field W_B are the stream-lines of the field V^A*. From

$$V^B C^x_B = V^B \partial_B C^x = V^{(\lambda)} \frac{\partial C^x}{\partial X^{(\lambda)}} = w_\lambda \frac{\partial C^x}{\partial w_\lambda}$$
$$(x = \mathrm{m}+1,..., 2\mathrm{n};\ B = 1,..., n, (1),...,(n);\ (\lambda) = (1),..., (n)) \tag{3.29}$$

it follows *that the $\mathfrak{N}_m$ is homogeneous if and only if the X_m in X_{2n} consists of ∞^{m-1} characteristics of the field W_B*.

The equations (3.1) can be written in the form

$$(a)\quad K^x = C^x_{(\lambda)} V^{(\lambda)} = C^x_A V^A \qquad (b)\quad K^{xy} = C^x_A C^y_B V^{AB}$$
$$(x, y = \mathrm{m}+1,...,2\mathrm{n};\ A, B = 1,..., n, (1),..., (n);\ (\lambda) = (1),..., (n)) \tag{3.30}$$

and these equations express the fact *that K^x and K^{xy} arise from the reduction of V^A and V^{AB} respectively with respect to the X_m* (cf. II, § 7). Therefore it is now evident geometrically that K^x vanishes if and only if V^A lies in the tangent E_m of the X_m.

From (3.12) and (3.14) we get

$$(a)\quad U_b = B^B_b W_B \qquad (b)\quad U_{cb} = B^C_c B^B_b W_{CB}$$
$$(b, c = 1,..., \mathrm{m};\ B, C = 1,..., n, (1),..., (n)) \tag{3.31}$$

and these equations express the fact *that U_b and U_{cb} arise from the section of*

W_B and W_{CB} with the X_m (cf. II, § 7). Therefore it is now evident geometrically that U_b vanishes if and only if the tangent E_m of the X_m is contained in the $(2n-1)$-direction of W_B. U_{cb} being the rotation of U_b, in that case also U_{cb} vanishes. The vanishing of U_b means that the equations

$$w_\lambda d\xi^\lambda = U_b d\eta^b = 0 \tag{3.32}$$

hold on the X_m and that consequently the $\mathfrak{N}_m$ is an N_m. We collect results in the following theorem:

THEOREM VII.2. *If in the X_{2n} of the variables ξ^κ, w_λ only C_3-transformations are allowed as coordinate transformations, the invariant fields W_B, W_{CB} and V^A, V^{AB} are* a priori *fixed. If now in this X_{2n} an X_m is given, this X_m represents an $\mathfrak{N}_m$ in the X_n of the ξ^κ and the tangent E_m of the X_m forms at every point of the X_m from W_B and W_{CB} by section U_b and U_{cb} and from V^A and V^{AB} by reduction K^x and K^{xy}. The vanishing of K^x, U_b, K^{xy}, or U_{cb} has the following meaning:*

$K^x = 0$ *in one point of* X_m:	V^A *lies in the tangent* E_m *of* X_m.
$K^x = 0$ *over* X_m:	*the* $\mathfrak{N}_m$ *is homogeneous* (*n.a.s.*).
$U_b = 0$ *in one point of* X_m:	W_B *contains the tangent* E_m *of* X_m.
$U_b = 0$ *over* X_m:	*the* $\mathfrak{N}_m$ *is an* N_m (*n.a.s.*); $U_{cb} = 0$.
$K^{xy} = 0$:	$(F^x, F^y) = 0$ *in consideration of* (1.1).
$U_{cb} = 0$:	$\{\eta^c, \eta^b\} = 0$ *in consideration of* (1.2).

(3.33)

At a point of the X_m we introduce a local coordinate system in the local E_{2n} with the measuring vectors $\underset{i}{e^h}$; $\overset{h}{e_i}$ $(h, i = 1, \ldots, 2n)$, in such a way that the E_m is spanned by the m vectors $\underset{1}{e^h}, \ldots, \underset{m}{e^h}$. Then we have at that point

$$\begin{aligned} K^{xy} &\overset{*}{=} V^{xy} \\ U_{cb} &\overset{*}{=} W_{cb} \end{aligned} \qquad (b, c = 1, \ldots, m;\ x, y = m+1, \ldots, 2n). \tag{3.34}$$

If then $2\bar{p}$ is the rank of U_{cb} at that point, there exists at least one non-vanishing $2\bar{p}$-rowed sub-determinant in the matrix of the W_{cb}. By interchanging the indices $1, \ldots, m$ it can always be arranged that this is the determinant

$$\begin{vmatrix} W_{11} & \cdots & W_{1,2\bar{p}} \\ \vdots & & \vdots \\ W_{2\bar{p},1} & \cdots & W_{2\bar{p},2\bar{p}} \end{vmatrix} \tag{3.35}$$

Now this determinant is to within a non-vanishing scalar factor, equal to the $(2n-2\bar{\rho})$-rowed sub-determinant

$$\begin{vmatrix} V^{2\bar{\rho}+1,2\bar{\rho}+1} & \ldots & V^{2\bar{\rho}+1,\mathrm{m}} & V^{2\bar{\rho}+1,\mathrm{m}+1} & \ldots & V^{2\bar{\rho}+1,2\mathrm{n}} \\ \vdots & & \vdots & \vdots & & \vdots \\ V^{\mathrm{m},2\bar{\rho}+1} & \ldots & V^{\mathrm{m},\mathrm{m}} & V^{\mathrm{m},\mathrm{m}+1} & \ldots & V^{\mathrm{m},2\mathrm{n}} \\ V^{\mathrm{m}+1,2\bar{\rho}+1} & \ldots & V^{\mathrm{m}+1,\mathrm{m}} & K^{\mathrm{m}+1,\mathrm{m}+1} & \ldots & K^{\mathrm{m}+1,2\mathrm{n}} \\ \vdots & & \vdots & \vdots & & \vdots \\ V^{2\mathrm{n},2\bar{\rho}+1} & \ldots & V^{2\mathrm{n},\mathrm{m}} & K^{2\mathrm{n},\mathrm{m}+1} & \ldots & K^{2\mathrm{n},2\mathrm{n}} \end{vmatrix} \tag{3.36}$$

from the matrix of the V^{hi}. As we see (3.36) contains in the lower right-hand corner the matrix of the K^{xy}. Now by a suitable homogeneous linear transformation of the measuring vectors $\overset{\mathrm{m}+1}{e_i},\ldots,\overset{2\mathrm{n}}{e_i}$ it can always be arranged that K^{xy} has the canonical form and then the matrix of the K^{xy} contains a $(2n-m-\rho)$-rowed sub-determinant consisting only of zeros. As a result of this the rank of the matrix (3.36) $\leqslant 2(2n-2\bar{\rho}-2n+m+\rho) = -4\bar{\rho}+2m+2\rho$ and, since this rank is $2n-2\bar{\rho}$, we have

$$2\bar{\rho}-2\rho \leqslant 2(m-n). \tag{3.37}$$

We started from the covariant bivector U_{cb}. But it is equally possible to start from the contravariant bivector K^{xy}. Then m and $2n-m$ change their roles and by a similar reasoning we get the inequality

$$2\rho-2\bar{\rho} \leqslant 2(n-m). \tag{3.38}$$

Hence from (3.37) and (3.38) we have

$$2\bar{\rho} = 2\rho+2(m-n). \tag{3.39}$$

Now suppose K to be even. Then an equation of the form

$$K^x = \alpha_y K^{xy} \quad (x,y = \mathrm{m}+1,\ldots,2\mathrm{n}) \tag{3.40}$$

exists, or, using the special local coordinate system,

$$V^x = \alpha_y V^{xy} \quad (x,y = \mathrm{m}+1,\ldots,2\mathrm{n}), \tag{3.41}$$

and consequently an equation of the form

$$V^h = \alpha_y V^{hy}+\beta^b A_b^h \quad (b = 1,\ldots,\mathrm{m};\ y = \mathrm{m}+1,\ldots,2\mathrm{n};\ h = 1,\ldots,2\mathrm{n}) \tag{3.42}$$

exists. Transvection with W_{ih} ($i, h = 1,\ldots, 2n$) gives

$$W_i = -W_{ih}V^h = \alpha_y A_i^y - \beta^b W_{ih} A_b^h$$
$$(b = 1,\ldots, m;\ y = m+1,\ldots, 2n;\ h, i = 1,\ldots, 2n) \quad (3.43)$$

and consequently we have

$$U_b = \beta^a U_{ab} \quad (a, b = 1,\ldots, m) \quad (3.44)$$

expressing the fact that the class of U_b is even. In a similar way it can be proved that K is even if the class of U_b is even. Hence, the relations between the arithmetic invariants K, 2ρ, and k of the $\mathfrak{N}_m$ and the arithmetic invariants $\bar{K}$, $2\bar{\rho}$, and $\bar{k}$ of the field U_b are

$$\begin{aligned} \bar{K} &= K+2(m-n), \\ 2\bar{\rho} &= 2\rho+2(m-n), \\ \bar{k} &= k+2(m-n). \end{aligned} \quad (3.45)$$

It should be noted that these equations are valid both for $m \geqslant n$ and for $m < n$. For $m < n$ it follows from (3.45) that $K \geqslant 2(n-m)$. Hence, if the system (1.1) is in involution (viz. $K = 1$ or 0), we always have $m \geqslant n$ (cf. VI, § 9). For $m > n$ it follows from (3.45) that $\bar{K} \geqslant 2(m-n)$. Hence, if the $\mathfrak{N}_m$ is an N_m (viz. $\bar{K} = 0$), we always have $m \leqslant n$ (cf. VI, § 3).

We are now able to prove the inequality (3.11) for all values of m. This inequality can now be written

$$2t \geqslant \bar{K}. \quad (3.46)$$

In order that we can derive from (1.2a) just $n-t$ relations between the ξ^κ it is necessary and sufficient that the rank of the ξ^κ with respect to the η^a is t, or, in other words, that there exist just t linear independent vectors among the n gradient vectors $\partial_b \xi^\kappa$ ($\kappa = 1,\ldots, n$) in the X_m of the η^a. Now (3.12) expresses the vector U_b linearly in these gradient vectors and consequently the class $\bar{K}$ of U_b can never be $> 2t$.

Now it can be proved *that for a system in involution there always exists a basis transformation* $F^x \to F^{x'}$ *such that the expressions* $(F^{x'}, F^{y'})$ *vanish not only for elements of the* $\mathfrak{N}_m$ *but identically*. If $K^{xy} = 0$ we have always $m \geqslant n$. In VII, § 2, it was proved that for $m \geqslant n$ the equations of the $\mathfrak{N}_m$ can always be written in the form

$$H_{\beta'} \stackrel{\text{def}}{=} w_{\beta'} - \Omega_{\beta'}(\xi^{\alpha'}, \xi^{\zeta'}, w_{\mathfrak{b}'}, w_{\eta'}) = 0$$
$$H^{\mathfrak{a}'} \stackrel{\text{def}}{=} \xi^{\mathfrak{a}'} - \Omega^{\mathfrak{a}'}(\xi^{\alpha'}, \xi^{\zeta'}) = 0$$
$$(\alpha', \beta' = 1',\ldots, r';\ \mathfrak{a}', \mathfrak{b}' = (r+1)',\ldots, (2n-m)';$$
$$\zeta', \eta' = (2n-m+1)',\ldots, n') \quad (3.47)$$

by a suitable transformation of the coordinates ξ^κ. Forming the bracket expressions with respect to $\xi^{\kappa'}$, $w_{\lambda'}$ we get

$$(H_{\beta'}, H_{\gamma'}) = 2\frac{\partial H_{[\beta'}}{\partial w_{\delta'}}\frac{\partial H_{\gamma']}}{\partial \xi^{\delta'}} + 2\frac{\partial \Omega_{[\beta'}}{\partial w_{\eta'}}\frac{\partial \Omega_{\gamma']}}{\partial \xi^{\eta'}} = -\frac{\partial \Omega_{\gamma'}}{\partial \xi^{\beta'}} + \frac{\partial \Omega_{\beta'}}{\partial \xi^{\gamma'}} + \frac{\partial \Omega_{[\beta'}}{\partial w_{\eta'}}\frac{\partial \Omega_{\gamma']}}{\partial \xi^{\eta'}},$$

$$(H_{\beta'}, H^{\mathfrak{a}'}) = \frac{\partial H_{\beta'}}{\partial w_{\delta'}}\frac{\partial H^{\mathfrak{a}'}}{\partial \xi^{\delta'}} + \frac{\partial H_{\beta'}}{\partial w_{\eta'}}\frac{\partial H^{\mathfrak{a}'}}{\partial \xi^{\eta'}} = -\frac{\partial \Omega^{\mathfrak{a}'}}{\partial \xi^{\beta'}} + \frac{\partial \Omega_{\beta'}}{\partial w_{\eta'}}\frac{\partial \Omega^{\mathfrak{a}'}}{\partial \xi^{\eta'}},$$

$$(H^{\mathfrak{a}'}, H^{\mathfrak{b}'}) = 0 \quad (\beta', \gamma', \delta' = 1', ..., r';\ \mathfrak{a}', \mathfrak{b}' = (r+1)', ..., (2n-m)';$$
$$\eta' = (2n-m+1)', ..., n'). \quad (3.48)$$

These expressions have to vanish in consideration of (3.47) and they contain neither the $w_{\beta'}$ nor the $\xi^{\mathfrak{a}'}$. Consequently they vanish identically. Now bracket expressions are invariant for coordinate transformations. Hence, if we return to the coordinates ξ^{κ} in the expressions $H_{\beta'}$ and $H^{\mathfrak{a}}$ these expressions represent a basis whose bracket expressions all vanish identically.

To close this section we will establish the relations between the class of a non-homogeneous $\mathfrak{N}_m$ and the $\mathfrak{N}_{m+1}$ derived from it by the process of homogenization. If the $\mathfrak{N}_m$ is given by its parametric form (1.2), the parametric form of the $\mathfrak{N}_{m+1}$ is

$$\begin{aligned} {}^*\xi^{\kappa} &= \xi^{\kappa}(\eta^a) \\ {}^*w_{\lambda} &= \eta^0 w_{\lambda}(\eta^a) \end{aligned} \quad (a = 1, ..., m) \quad (3.49)$$

with the parameters η^0, η^a ($a = 1, ..., m$). Consequently we have for the vector and the bivector of this $\mathfrak{N}_{m+1}$

$$\begin{aligned} {}^*U_b &= \eta^0 U_b, & {}^*U_{cb} &= \eta^0 U_{cb} \\ {}^*U_0 &= 0 & {}^*U_{0b} &= U_b \end{aligned} \quad (b, c = 1, ..., m) \quad (3.50)$$

and from this it follows, writing $K = 2\rho+\epsilon$, $\bar{K} = 2\bar{\rho}+\epsilon$ ($\epsilon = 1$ or 0) that

$$\begin{aligned} {}^*\bar{K} &= \bar{K}+\epsilon, \\ {}^*K &= K+\epsilon-2. \end{aligned} \quad (3.51)$$

This proves the theorem:

THEOREM VII.3. *By homogenization of a non-homogeneous $\mathfrak{N}_m$ of class $K = 2\rho$ or $K = 2\rho+1$ we get a homogeneous $\mathfrak{N}_{m+1}$ of class $K-2$ or $K-1$ respectively. Conversely we get by dis-homogenization of a homogeneous $\mathfrak{N}_m$ of class $K = 2\rho$ a non-homogeneous $\mathfrak{N}_{m-1}$ whose class is either $K+1$ or $K+2$.*

4. The principal theorem of the $\mathfrak{N}_m$†

An $\mathfrak{N}_{m'}$ ($m' < m$) whose vector elements all belong to a given $\mathfrak{N}_m$ is called an *integral-$\mathfrak{N}_{m'}$ of this $\mathfrak{N}_m$*.

† Cf. Schouten and v. d. Kulk 1943. 4, 5.

An $\mathfrak{N}_m$ is said to be totally integrable with respect to integral-$\mathfrak{N}_{m'}$'s of class K' and field dimension t' if at least one $\mathfrak{N}_{m'}$ of class K' and field dimension t' containing $\underset{*}{\xi}^\kappa$, $\overset{*}{w}_\lambda$ and consisting only of vector elements belonging to $\mathfrak{N}_m$ exists for every choice of the element $\underset{*}{\xi}^\kappa$, $\overset{*}{w}_\lambda$ of the $\mathfrak{N}_m$ in the region considered.

The notion of total integrability with respect to integral-$\mathfrak{N}_{m'}$'s of class K' and an *arbitrary* field dimension is invariant for C_3-transformation, but this invariance is disturbed if the field dimension is also prescribed.

An integral-$\mathfrak{N}_{m'}$, with $m' = n$, $t' = n$, $K' = 1$, is a gradient field $\partial_\lambda p$, satisfying the system of $2n-m < n$ equations (cf. (1.1))

$$F^x(\xi^\kappa, \partial_\lambda p) = 0 \quad (x = \mathrm{m}+1, \dots, 2\mathrm{n}). \tag{4.1}$$

Thus the problem of finding an ordinary solution of a system of $2n-m < n$ partial differential equations of the first order with one unknown function is equivalent to the problem of finding an integral-$\mathfrak{N}_n$ with class 1 and field dimension n of a given $\mathfrak{N}_m$ $(m > n)$. In the same way the generalized notion of a solution of a system of partial differential equations of the first order with one unknown function, due to S. Lie, is connected with the integral-$\mathfrak{N}_m$'s with class 1 and a field dimension $< n$.

If $m' = n$, $K' > 1$, and $t' = n$, an integral-$\mathfrak{N}_{m'}$ of class $K' = 2\rho'+\epsilon'$ represents a solution of the system of $2n-m$ multilinear partial differential equations of the first order

$$F^x(\xi^\kappa, \epsilon'\partial_\lambda \overset{0}{p} + \overset{1}{q}\partial_\lambda \overset{1}{p} + \dots + \overset{\rho'}{q}\partial_\lambda \overset{\rho'}{p}) = 0 \quad (x = \mathrm{m}+1, \dots, 2\mathrm{n}). \tag{4.2}$$

For $t' < n$ we get a generalization of the ordinary notion of solution, corresponding to Lie's generalization for the case $K' = 1$.

Given an $\mathfrak{N}_m$ of class K and field dimension t we now have to face the following questions:

1. For which values of m', K', and t' is the $\mathfrak{N}_m$ totally integrable?
2. How can the integral-$\mathfrak{N}_{m'}$'s be determined in the case of total integrability?
3. Do integral-$\mathfrak{N}_{m'}$'s of class K' and field dimension t' exist in the case where there is no total integrability for m', K', and t'?
4. How can the $\mathfrak{N}_{m'}$'s be determined in this latter case?

To answer the first question we look first for all integral-$\mathfrak{N}_{m'}$'s of class K' with an arbitrary field dimension t'. If such an $\mathfrak{N}_{m'}$ exists, it must be possible, by adding $m-m'$ equations to the equations of the $\mathfrak{N}_m$, to get a system of $2n-m'$ equations representing the $\mathfrak{N}_{m'}$. In the X_{2n} these $2n-m'$ equations represent an $X_{m'}$ imbedded in the X_m of $\mathfrak{N}_m$. Hence the section of W_B with this $X_{m'}$ is identical with the section of U_b with this $X_{m'}$ and this section must have the class $\bar{K}' = K'+2(m'-n)$. Hence the determination of an integral-$\mathfrak{N}_{m'}$ of class K' is equivalent to the determination of an $X_{m'}$ in the X_m of the η^a whose section with U_b has class $\bar{K}'$. If the $\mathfrak{N}_m$ is totally integrable with respect to integral-$\mathfrak{N}_{m'}$'s of class K', this means that there exists through every point of the X_m of the η^a in the region considered at least one $X_{m'}$ whose section with U_b has class $\bar{K}'$. So the problem is to construct a normal system of $\infty^{m-m'}$ $X_{m'}$'s of this kind in this X_m, or, in other words, to determine a system of $m-m'$ independent functions of the η^a with index $\bar{K}-\bar{K}' = K-K'+2(m-m')$ with respect to U_b.

Now according to Theorem IV.2, a covariant vector field of class K in an X_n being given, a system of S independent functions with index κ with respect to this field exists if and only if the relations

$$\begin{aligned} 0 \leqslant \kappa \leqslant K&, \\ 2S \geqslant \kappa&, \\ K-\kappa \leqslant n-S& \end{aligned} \tag{4.3}$$

are satisfied. Replacing n, K, κ, and S by m, $\bar{K} = K+2(m-n)$, $\bar{K}-\bar{K}' = K-K'+2(m-m')$, and $m-m'$ respectively, we get the inequalities

$$\begin{aligned} 0 \leqslant \bar{K}-\bar{K}' = K-K'+2(m-m') \leqslant \bar{K} = K+2(m-n)&, \\ 2(m-m') \geqslant \bar{K}-\bar{K}' = K-K'+2(m-m')&, \\ \bar{K}' = K'+2(m'-n) \leqslant m'&, \end{aligned} \tag{4.4}$$

and this proves the theorem

THEOREM VII.4. (*Principal theorem of the* $\mathfrak{N}_m$.) *An* $\mathfrak{N}_m$ *of class* K *is totally integrable with respect to integral-*$\mathfrak{N}_{m'}$*'s of class* K' *if and only if*

$$\begin{aligned} K \leqslant K' \leqslant K+2(m-m')&, \\ 2n-2m' \leqslant K' \leqslant 2n-m'&. \end{aligned} \tag{4.5}$$

We may note that (non-singular) integral-$\mathfrak{N}_{m'}$'s with a class

$$K' > K+2(m-m')$$

cannot exist because a section of U_b can never have a class higher than the class of U_b.

Until now we have left the field dimension t' of the integral-$\mathfrak{N}_{m'}$ entirely free. Now consider an integral-$\mathfrak{N}_{m'}$ with field dimension t'. In the X_n of the ξ^κ the $\mathfrak{N}_m$ is a $\mathfrak{B}_{m-t}$-field over an X_t and the $\mathfrak{N}_{m'}$ a

$\mathfrak{B}_{m'-t'}$-field over an $X_{t'}$. Since $\mathfrak{N}_{m'}$ is contained in $\mathfrak{N}_m$ it is necessary that

$$0 \leqslant t' \leqslant t \tag{4.6}$$

and

$$m' \geqslant t' \geqslant t-(m-m'). \tag{4.7}$$

In the X_{2n} of ξ^κ, w_λ the equations

$$\xi^\kappa = \text{const.} \tag{4.8}$$

represent a normal system of ∞^n X_n's, invariant for all transformations of the ξ^κ into themselves but not invariant for C_3-transformations. If now the equations of the $\mathfrak{N}_m$ are written in the form (1.3), the equations (1.3 b) single out from these ∞^n X_n's just ∞^t X_n's and the X_m of $\mathfrak{N}_m$ in the X_{2n} intersects each of these ∞^t X_n's just in an X_{m-t}. In the same way the $\mathfrak{N}_{m'}$ singles out just $\infty^{t'}$ X_n's and the $X_{m'}$ of $\mathfrak{N}_{m'}$ intersects each of these $\infty^{t'}$ X_n's in an $X_{m'-t'}$. That gives another proof of the inequalities (4.6) and (4.7).

In the X_m of the η^a the equations (4.8) fix a system of ∞^t X_{m-t}'s. One of the ∞^t $\mathfrak{B}_{m-t}$'s constituting the $\mathfrak{N}_m$ contains ∞^{m-t} vector elements whose images are the points of one of these ∞^t X_{m-t}'s. Hence the X_{m-t} is the image of the point of the field region X_t of the $\mathfrak{N}_m$ where this special $\mathfrak{B}_{m-t}$ has its place. The image of the $\mathfrak{N}_{m'}$ in the X_m of the η^a is an $X_{m'}$ and the fact that this $\mathfrak{N}_{m'}$ is a $\mathfrak{B}_{m'-t'}$-field over an $X_{t'}$ in X_n corresponds to the fact that the $X_{m'}$ intersects just $\infty^{t'}$ of the ∞^t X_{m-t}'s fixed by (4.8) and each of them in an $X_{m'-t'}$. This has as a consequence that to construct an integral $\mathfrak{N}_{m'}$ of class K' and field dimension t' it is sufficient to construct an $X_{m'}$ in the X_m of the η^a reducing the class of U_b from $\bar{K}$ to $\bar{K}'$ and intersecting $\infty^{t'}$ of the ∞^t X_{m-t}'s represented by the equations

$$\xi^\kappa(\eta^a) = \text{const.} \tag{4.9}$$

just in an $X_{m'-t'}$.

Now suppose the $X_{m'}$ has the equations

$$f^{m'+1}(\eta^a) = 0, \quad \ldots, \quad f^m(\eta^a) = 0 \quad (a = 1,\ldots, \mathrm{m}). \tag{4.10}$$

Then the necessary and sufficient conditions that the $X_{m'}$ and one of the X_{m-t}'s represented by (4.9), which have at least one point in common with the $X_{m'}$, intersect just in an $X_{m'-t'}$ are

$$\begin{aligned} &(a) \qquad (\partial_{[b_1} \xi^{\kappa_1})\ldots(\partial_{b_{t'}} \xi^{\kappa_{t'}})(\partial_{b_{m'+1}} f^{m'+1})\ldots(\partial_{b_m]} f^m) \neq 0,\\ &(b) \qquad (\partial_{[b_1} \xi^{\kappa_1})\ldots(\partial_{b_{t'+1}} \xi^{\kappa_{t'+1}})(\partial_{b_{m'+1}} f^{m'+1})\ldots(\partial_{b_m]} f^m) = 0. \end{aligned} \tag{4.11}$$

The condition (4.11 b) is always satisfied if $t' = m'$. We consider the following cases:

1. *The case $m > n$; $t' = t$; $m' = m-1$.*

If $m' = m-1$ there is only one function f. The index of this function with respect to U_b being 2, 1, or 0 there are three sub-cases:

$$\begin{aligned} &(a) \qquad \bar{K}' = \bar{K}-2, \qquad K' = K, \\ &(b) \qquad \bar{K}' = \bar{K}-1, \qquad K' = K+1, \\ &(c) \qquad \bar{K}' = \bar{K}, \qquad K' = K+2, \end{aligned} \tag{4.12}$$

and according to (4.6, 7) in each sub-case we have $t' = t$ or $t' = t-1$. But because of (4.7) $t' = t$ can only occur if $t \leqslant m'$.

In the sub-case (4.12 *a*) f is a solution of the system S'_3 of the field U_b, hence

$$\begin{aligned} &(a) \qquad U_{[c_1 b_1} \ldots U_{c_{\bar{\rho}} b_{\bar{\rho}}} \partial_{b]} f = 0 \qquad \text{for} \quad \bar{K} = 2\bar{\rho}+1 \\ &(b) \qquad U_{[c_1 b_1} \ldots U_{c_{\bar{\rho}-1} b_{\bar{\rho}-1}} U_c \partial_{b]} f = 0 \quad \text{for} \quad \bar{K} = 2\bar{\rho} \end{aligned} \tag{4.13}$$

$$(b, b_1, \ldots, b_{\bar{\rho}}, c, c_1, \ldots, c_{\bar{\rho}} = 1, \ldots, \mathrm{m}).$$

In the sub-case (4.12 *b*) f is a solution of S'_2 but not a solution of S'_3, hence

$$\begin{aligned} &\left.\begin{aligned} &(a) \qquad U_{[c_1 b_1} \ldots U_{c_{\bar{\rho}} b_{\bar{\rho}}} U_c \partial_{b]} f = 0 \\ &(b) \qquad U_{[c_1 b_1} \ldots U_{c_{\bar{\rho}} b_{\bar{\rho}}} \partial_{b]} f \neq 0 \end{aligned}\right\} \quad \text{for} \quad \bar{K} = 2\bar{\rho}+1 \\ &\left.\begin{aligned} &(c) \qquad U_{[c_1 b_1} \ldots U_{c_{\bar{\rho}} b_{\bar{\rho}}} \partial_{b]} f = 0 \\ &(d) \qquad U_{[c_1 b_1} \ldots U_{c_{\bar{\rho}-1} b_{\bar{\rho}-1}} U_c \partial_{b]} f \neq 0 \end{aligned}\right\} \quad \text{for} \quad \bar{K} = 2\bar{\rho} \end{aligned} \tag{4.14}$$

$$(b, b_1, \ldots, b_{\bar{\rho}}, c, c_1, \ldots, c_{\bar{\rho}} = 1, \ldots, \mathrm{m}).$$

In the sub-case (4.12 *c*) f is not a solution of S'_2, hence

$$\begin{aligned} &U_{[c_1 b_1} \ldots U_{c_{\bar{\rho}} b_{\bar{\rho}}} U_c \partial_{b]} f \neq 0 \quad \text{for} \quad \bar{K} = 2\bar{\rho}+1 \\ &U_{[c_1 b_1} \ldots U_{c_{\bar{\rho}} b_{\bar{\rho}}} \partial_{b]} f \neq 0 \qquad \text{for} \quad \bar{K} = 2\bar{\rho} \end{aligned} \tag{4.15}$$

$$(b, b_1, \ldots, b_{\bar{\rho}}, c, c_1, \ldots, c_{\bar{\rho}} = 1, \ldots, \mathrm{m}).$$

In all three sub-cases according to (4.11) we have the additional conditions

$$\begin{aligned} &(\partial_{[b_1} \xi^{\kappa_1}) \ldots (\partial_{b_t} \xi^{\kappa_t}) \partial_{b]} f \neq 0 \qquad \text{for} \quad t' = t \\ &\left.\begin{aligned} &(\partial_{[b_1} \xi^{\kappa_1}) \ldots (\partial_{b_{t-1}} \xi^{\kappa_{t-1}}) \partial_{b]} f \neq 0 \\ &(\partial_{[b_1} \xi^{\kappa_1}) \ldots (\partial_{b_t} \xi^{\kappa_t}) \partial_{b]} f = 0 \end{aligned}\right\} \quad \text{for} \quad t' = t-1 \end{aligned} \tag{4.16}$$

$$(b, b_1, \ldots, b_t = 1, \ldots, \mathrm{m}).$$

That there is only an inequality for $t' = t$ arises from the fact that (4.11 *b*) is automatically satisfied for $t' = t$, $m' = m-1$, the rank of $\partial_b \xi^\kappa$ being t.

Now we know that the systems S'_2 and S'_3 are complete. Further it is known that U_b lies in the b-domain of $\partial_b \xi^\kappa$. From this follow the necessary and sufficient conditions that an $\mathfrak{N}_m$ be totally integrable with respect to integral-$\mathfrak{N}_{m-1}$'s with $t' = t$, $t < m$:

for $K' = K = 2\rho+1$:

U_{cb} *does not lie in the b-domain of* $\partial_b \xi^\kappa$;

for $K' = K = 2\rho$:

$U_{[c_1 b_1} \dots U_{c_{\bar{\rho}-1} b_{\bar{\rho}-1}} U_{c]}$ *does not lie in the b-domain of* $\partial_b \xi^\kappa$;

(we notice that this condition is always satisfied if the domain of U_{cb} and the b-domain of $\partial_b \xi^\kappa$ have no domain in common with a dimension $> 2\bar{\rho}-2$);

for $K' = K+1$:

U_{cb} *does not lie in the b-domain of* $\partial_b \xi^\kappa$;

for $K' = K+2$:

No conditions.

We must now investigate when these conditions are satisfied. For $m \geqslant n$ the equations of the $\mathfrak{N}_m$ can be written in the form (2.9). If in these equations the m variables ξ^α, ξ^ζ, $w_{\mathfrak{b}}$, and w_η ($\alpha = 1,\dots,r$; $\zeta, \eta = 2n-m+1,\dots,n$; $\mathfrak{b} = r+1,\dots,2n-m$) are looked upon as parameters, the derivatives of the $\xi^{\mathfrak{a}}$ with respect to the parameters are all zero and the ξ^α, ξ^ζ are parameters. Hence for $m \geqslant n$ it is always possible to choose the parameters in (1.2) in such a way that $\partial_b \xi^1,\dots, \partial_b \xi^t$ are linearly independent gradient vectors and that the derivatives $\partial_b \xi^{t+1},\dots, \partial_b \xi^n$ all vanish. When the parameters have been chosen in this way we have

$$U_b = w_1 \partial_b \xi^1 + \dots + w_t \partial_b \xi^t \quad (b = 1,\dots,\mathrm{m}) \tag{4.17}$$

and $$U_{cb} = 2(\partial_{[c} w_{|1|}) \partial_{b]} \xi^1 + \dots + 2(\partial_{[c} w_{|t|}) \partial_{b]} \xi^t \quad (b, c = 1,\dots,\mathrm{m}). \tag{4.18}$$

If now U_{cb} were contained in the b-domain of $\partial_b \xi^\kappa$ the t covariant vectors $\partial_b w_1,\dots, \partial_b w_t$ would have to be contained in that domain and consequently the rank of the functional matrix of the parametric form would have to be $t+n-t = n$. But since this rank is m this case cannot occur for $m > n$. Hence U_{cb} cannot lie in the b-domain of $\partial_b \xi^\kappa$ if $m > n$. *This proves for* $m > n$, $t < m$, *and* $K = 2\rho+1$ *the total integrability of an* $\mathfrak{N}_m$ *with respect to integral-*$\mathfrak{N}_{m-1}$*'s of class* K, $K+1$, *and* $K+2$ *and field dimension* t *and for* $m > n$, $t < m$, *and* $K = 2\rho$ *the total integrability with respect to integral-*$\mathfrak{N}_{m-1}$*'s of class* $K+1$ *and* $K+2$ *and field dimension* t.

Now suppose the domain of U_{cb} and the b-domain of $\partial_b \xi^\kappa$ have just a $(2\bar{\rho}-1)$-dimensional domain in common. Then U_{cb} must lie in a $(t+1)$-dimensional domain spanned by $\partial_b \xi^1,\dots, \partial_b \xi^t$ and a $(t+1)$th covariant vector, and the vectors $\partial_b w_1,\dots, \partial_b w_t$ would have to lie in that domain.

Hence the rank of the functional matrix of the parametric form could be at most $t+1+n-t = n+1$. Since this rank is m this case cannot occur for $m > n+1$ and consequently $U_{[c_1 b_1} \cdots U_{c_{\bar{p}-1} b_{\bar{p}-1}} U_{c]}$ cannot lie in the b-domain of $\partial_b \xi^\kappa$ for $m > n+1$. *This proves for* $m > n+1$, $t < m$, *and* $K = 2\rho$ *the total integrability of an* $\mathfrak{N}_m$ *with respect to integral-*$\mathfrak{N}_{m-1}$*'s of class* K, $K+1$, *and* $K+2$ *and field dimension* t.

If the $\mathfrak{N}_m$ is homogeneous and the $\mathfrak{N}_{m-1}$ of class K, the $\mathfrak{N}_{m-1}$ has to be homogeneous as well. Because otherwise by the process of homogenization of the $\mathfrak{N}_{m-1}$ an $\mathfrak{N}_m$ of class $K-2$ could be obtained and this $\mathfrak{N}_m$ would have to be identical with the given $\mathfrak{N}_m$ of class K, which is impossible.

Finally, we will prove *that a non-homogeneous* $\mathfrak{N}_m$ *with an even class* $K = 2\rho$ *is also totally integrable with respect to integral-*$\mathfrak{N}_{m-1}$*'s of class* 2ρ *and field dimension* t *if* $m > n$, $t < m$. According to (4.5) it is certain that an $\mathfrak{N}_m$ is not totally integrable with respect to integral-$\mathfrak{N}_{m-1}$'s of a class $< K$. Hence there exists an element $\underset{*}{\xi^\kappa}, \overset{*}{w}_\lambda$ of the $\mathfrak{N}_m$ which does not belong to an integral-$\mathfrak{N}_{m-1}$ of a class $< 2\rho$. $\mathfrak{N}(\underset{*}{\xi^\kappa}, \overset{*}{w}_\lambda)$ may be chosen so small that the same holds for every element in $\mathfrak{N}(\underset{*}{\xi^\kappa}, \overset{*}{w}_\lambda)$. Then by homogenization of the $\mathfrak{N}_m$ we form a homogeneous $\mathfrak{N}_{m+1}$. This $\mathfrak{N}_{m+1}$ has the same field region as the $\mathfrak{N}_m$, contains the element $\underset{*}{\xi^\kappa}, \overset{*}{w}_\lambda$, and has the class $K-2$ as was proved in VII, § 3. Since $m+1 > n+1$ the $\mathfrak{N}_{m+1}$ is totally integrable with respect to integral-$\mathfrak{N}_m$'s with the same field region and the class $K-2$. We choose an arbitrary integral-$\mathfrak{N}_m$ containing $\underset{*}{\xi^\kappa}, \overset{*}{w}_\lambda$. This integral-$\mathfrak{N}_m$ has to be homogeneous, because otherwise we could get back to the $\mathfrak{N}_{m+1}$ by the process of homogenization and this would imply that $\mathfrak{N}_{m+1}$ was of class $K-4$. Hence the integral-$\mathfrak{N}_m$ can be dis-homogenized and this can be done in such a way that the resulting $\mathfrak{N}_{m-1}$ contains $\underset{*}{\xi^\kappa}, \overset{*}{w}_\lambda$. This $\mathfrak{N}_{m-1}$ has the same field region and its class is either $K-1$ or K. If now we apply a similarity transformation $w_\lambda \rightarrow \sigma w_\lambda$ to this $\mathfrak{N}_{m-1}$ we can make the transformed $\mathfrak{N}_{m-1}$ contain $\underset{*}{\xi^\kappa}, \overset{*}{w}_\lambda$ and be contained in the original $\mathfrak{N}_m$. Its class is either $K-2$ or $K-1$ or K. But the values $K-2$ and $K-1$ are impossible because of the choice of $\underset{*}{\xi^\kappa}, \overset{*}{w}_\lambda$ and this proves that there exists for every vector element in $\mathfrak{N}(\xi^\kappa, \overset{*}{w}_\lambda)$ a non-homogeneous integral-$\mathfrak{N}_m$ of class K, containing just this vector element and having the same field region as the $\mathfrak{N}_m$.

Collecting results we have the theorem

THEOREM VII.5. *Every $\mathfrak{N}_m$ $(m > n)$ of class $K = 2\rho+1$ and field dimension $t < m$ is totally integrable with respect to integral-$\mathfrak{N}_{m-1}$'s of class K, $K+1$, and $K+2$ and with the same field region as $\mathfrak{N}_m$.*

Every non-homogeneous $\mathfrak{N}_m$ $(m > n)$ of class $K = 2\rho$ and field dimension $t < m$ is totally integrable with respect to non-homogeneous integral-$\mathfrak{N}_{m-1}$'s of class K and integral-$\mathfrak{N}_{m-1}$'s of class $K+1$ and $K+2$ which have the same field region as $\mathfrak{N}_m$.

Every homogeneous $\mathfrak{N}_m$ of class $K = 2\rho$ and field dimension $t < m$ is for $m > n$ totally integrable with respect to integral-$\mathfrak{N}_{m-1}$'s of class $K+1$ and $K+2$ which have the same field region as $\mathfrak{N}_m$, and for $m > n+1$ also with respect to homogeneous integral-$\mathfrak{N}_{m-1}$'s of class K and with the same field region as $\mathfrak{N}_m$.

If the $\mathfrak{N}_m$ is homogeneous every integral-$\mathfrak{N}_{m-1}$ of class $K+1$ is non-homogeneous and can be obtained from the $\mathfrak{N}_m$ by dis-homogenization. Hence it follows from Theorem VII.5, *that the process of dis-homogenization of an $\mathfrak{N}_m$ can always be carried out in such a way that the resulting $\mathfrak{N}_{m-1}$ is of class $K+1$ and contains any arbitrarily chosen vector element of the $\mathfrak{N}_m$.*

2. *The case $m > n$; $t' = t$; m' arbitrary; $K' = K$.*

If $K = 2\rho+1$ and consequently the $\mathfrak{N}_m$ non-homogeneous, and if we choose an arbitrary vector element ξ^κ, $\overset{*}{w}_\lambda$ of $\mathfrak{N}_m$, according to Theorem VII.5 a series $\mathfrak{N}_m, \mathfrak{N}_{m-1}, \dots, \mathfrak{N}_n$ can be constructed, all containing ξ^κ, $\overset{*}{w}_\lambda$ and having the same field region and the same class K and such that every vector manifold of the series is contained in all the preceding manifolds.

If $K = 2\rho$ and if the $\mathfrak{N}_m$ is non-homogeneous the same holds and $\mathfrak{N}_{m-1}, \dots, \mathfrak{N}_n$ are all non-homogeneous.

If $K = 2\rho$ and if the $\mathfrak{N}_m$ is homogeneous and $m > n+1$, in the same way a series $\mathfrak{N}_m, \mathfrak{N}_{m-1}, \dots, \mathfrak{N}_{n+1}$ of homogeneous manifolds can be constructed, but this series ends with $\mathfrak{N}_{n+1}$. It is always possible to construct a non-homogeneous $\mathfrak{N}_n$ contained in $\mathfrak{N}_{n+1}$, containing ξ^κ, $\overset{*}{w}_\lambda$ and having the same field region, but this $\mathfrak{N}_n$ is of class $K+1$. In fact a homogeneous $\mathfrak{N}_{n+1}$ can never be totally integrable for non-homogeneous integral-$\mathfrak{N}_n$'s with the same field region and the same class K, because, if this were possible, the $\mathfrak{N}_{n+1}$ could be regained from the $\mathfrak{N}_n$ by the process of homogenization and accordingly the $\mathfrak{N}_n$ would have to be of class $K-2$.

Collecting results we have the theorem

THEOREM VII.6. *Every non-homogeneous $\mathfrak{N}_m$ $(m > n)$ of class K is totally integrable with respect to non-homogeneous $\mathfrak{N}_{m'}$'s $(m' = m-1,..., n)$ of class K which have the same field region as $\mathfrak{N}_m$.*

Every homogeneous $\mathfrak{N}_m$ $(m > n+1)$ of class K is totally integrable with respect to homogeneous $\mathfrak{N}_{m'}$'s $(m' = m-1,..., n+1)$ of class K with the same field region as $\mathfrak{N}_m$ and with respect to non-homogeneous $\mathfrak{N}_n$'s of class $K+1$ with the same field region as $\mathfrak{N}_m$.

3. *The case $m > n$; $t' = t$; m' and K' arbitrary; $n \leqslant m' < m$.*

To avoid unnecessary repetitions we assume that from now on in this section all vector manifolds which occur contain some arbitrarily chosen vector element $\overset{*}{\xi^\kappa}$, $\overset{*}{w_\lambda}$ of $\mathfrak{N}_m$ and that they all have the same field region as $\mathfrak{N}_m$. In addition to the conditions (4.5) we evidently have the condition

$$m' \geqslant t \tag{4.19}$$

and the condition following from (3.46):

$$K' \leqslant 2t-2(m'-n). \tag{4.20}$$

There are three sub-cases:

(*a*) *$\mathfrak{N}_m$ is non-homogeneous and $K'-K$ even.* In this sub-case a series $\mathfrak{N}_m$, $\mathfrak{N}_{m-1}$,..., $\mathfrak{N}_{m-p}$ $(p \overset{\text{def}}{=} \frac{1}{2}(K'-K))$ of classes K, $K+2$,..., K' exists. All these vector manifolds are non-homogeneous. Now $m-p \geqslant m'$. If $m-p = m'$ the $\mathfrak{N}_{m'}$ is of class K'. If $m-p > m'$ a series $\mathfrak{N}_{m-p}$, $\mathfrak{N}_{m-p-1}$,..., $\mathfrak{N}_{m'}$ of class K' can be constructed. All these vector manifolds are non-homogeneous. In either case we get an $\mathfrak{N}_{m'}$ of class K'.

(*b*) *$\mathfrak{N}_m$ is non-homogeneous and $K'-K$ odd.* In this sub-case a non-homogeneous $\mathfrak{N}_{m'+1}$ can be constructed as in sub-case (*a*). Then, since $m'+1 > n$, a non-homogeneous $\mathfrak{N}_{n'}$ of class K' can be constructed. Hence in this case also we always get a non-homogeneous $\mathfrak{N}_{m'}$ of class K'.

(*c*) *$\mathfrak{N}$ is homogeneous and $K'-K$ even.* If we omit the case $m' = n$, $p \overset{\text{def}}{=} \frac{1}{2}(K'-K) = 0$ we have the following possibilities:

(c_1) $m = n+1$. Then $m' = n$ and an $\mathfrak{N}_n$ of class K' can be constructed.

(c_2) $m > n+1$; $m-p-1 \geqslant n$; $m-p = m'$. Dis-homogenization of $\mathfrak{N}_m$ leads to an $\mathfrak{N}_{m-1}$ of class $K+1$. Since this $\mathfrak{N}_{m-1}$ is non-homogeneous a non-homogeneous series $\mathfrak{R}_{m-1}, \ldots, \mathfrak{R}_{m-p-1}$ of classes $K+1$, $K+3, \ldots,$ $K'+1$ can be constructed and by homogenization of this series a homogeneous series $\mathfrak{R}_m, \ldots, \mathfrak{R}_{m-p} = \mathfrak{R}_{m'}$ of classes K, $K+2, \ldots, K'$.

(c_3) $m > n+1$; $m-p-1 \geqslant n$; $m-p > m'$; $m' > n$. The homogeneous series $\mathfrak{R}_m, \ldots, \mathfrak{R}_{m-p}$ of classes K, $K+2, \ldots, K'$ can be constructed as under (c_2). Starting from $\mathfrak{R}_{m-p}$ a homogeneous series $\mathfrak{R}_{m-p}, \ldots, \mathfrak{R}_{m'}$ of class K' can be constructed.

(c_4) $m > n+1$; $m-p-1 \geqslant n$; $m-p > m'$; $m' = n$. The homogeneous series $\mathfrak{R}_m, \ldots, \mathfrak{R}_{m-p}$ of classes K, $K+2, \ldots, K'$ can be constructed as under (c_2). Starting from $\mathfrak{R}_{m-p}$ a homogeneous series $\mathfrak{R}_{m-p}, \ldots, \mathfrak{R}_{m'+1}$ of class K' can be constructed. But starting from the $\mathfrak{R}_{m-p+1}$ of class $K'-2$ of the first series a homogeneous series $\mathfrak{R}_{m-p+1}, \ldots, \mathfrak{R}_{m'+1} = \mathfrak{R}_{n+1}$ of class $K'-2$ can be constructed and from the $\mathfrak{R}_{n+1}$ we get an $\mathfrak{R}_n$ of class K'.

(c_5) $m > n+1$; $m-p-1 < n$. Since $m-p \geqslant m' \geqslant n$ we have in this sub-case $m-p = n$, $m' = n$. A non-homogeneous series $\mathfrak{R}_{m-1}, \ldots,$ $\mathfrak{R}_{m-p}$ of classes $K+1$, $K+3, \ldots, K'-1$ can be constructed and, by homogenization, a series $\mathfrak{R}_m, \ldots, \mathfrak{R}_{m-p+1} = \mathfrak{R}_{m'+1}$ of classes K, $K+2, \ldots,$ $K'-2$. From the $\mathfrak{R}_{m'+1}$ an $\mathfrak{R}_{m'}$ of class K' can be constructed.

$\mathfrak{R}_m$ *is homogeneous and* $K'-K$ *odd.* $m'+1$ being $> n$ as in case (c), a homogeneous $\mathfrak{R}_{m'+1}$ of class $K'-1$ can always be found. From this $\mathfrak{R}_{m'+1}$ a non-homogeneous $\mathfrak{R}_{m'}$ of class K' can be constructed.

Collecting results we have the theorem

THEOREM VII.7. *Every non-homogeneous* $\mathfrak{R}_m$ $(m > n)$ *of class* K *is totally integrable with respect to integral-*$\mathfrak{R}_{m'}$*'s of class* K' *and with the same field region as* $\mathfrak{R}_m$, *if the conditions*

$$K \leqslant K' \leqslant K+2(m-m'), \quad K' \leqslant 2n-m', \quad n \leqslant m' < m \tag{4.21}$$

are satisfied. The integral-$\mathfrak{R}_{m'}$ *may be subjected to the condition of being non-homogeneous.*

Every homogeneous $\mathfrak{R}_m$ $(m > n)$ *of class* K *is totally integrable with respect to integral-*$\mathfrak{R}_{m'}$*'s of class* K' *and with the same field region* $\mathfrak{R}_m$, *if the conditions* (4.21) *are satisfied and if* $K' = K$ *and* $m' = n$ *are not simultaneously true. The integral-*$\mathfrak{R}_{m'}$ *may be subjected to the condition of being homogeneous.*

Comparing this result with the theorem VII.4 we get the theorem

THEOREM VII.8. *Every* $\mathfrak{R}_m$ *of class* K *is totally integrable with respect to integral-*$\mathfrak{R}_{m'}$*'s of class* K' *which have the same field region as* $\mathfrak{R}_m$, *if* K' *and* m' *satisfy the conditions of integrability* (4.5) *of an* $\mathfrak{R}_m$ *with respect* *to integral-$\mathfrak{N}_{m'}$'s of class K' and if, moreover, $n \leqslant m' < m$ and for a homogeneous $\mathfrak{N}_m$ $K' = K$ and $m' = n$ do not hold simultaneously.*

An $\mathfrak{N}_m$ $(m > n)$ of field dimension n is a $\mathfrak{V}_{m-n}$-field. Hence from Theorem VII.7 we get for $t = n$†

THEOREM VII.9. *Every non-homogeneous $\mathfrak{V}_{m-n}$-field of class K is totally integrable with respect to integral-$\mathfrak{V}_{m'-n}$-fields of class K' if the conditions* (4.21) *are satisfied. The integral-$\mathfrak{V}_{m'-n}$-field may be subjected to the condition of being non-homogeneous.*

Every homogeneous $\mathfrak{V}_{m-n}$-field of class K is totally integrable with respect to integral-$\mathfrak{V}_{m'-n}$-fields of class K' if the conditions (4.21) *are satisfied and if $K' = K$ and $m' = n$ do not hold simultaneously. The integral-$\mathfrak{V}_{m'-n}$-field may be subjected to the condition of being homogeneous.*

A $\mathfrak{V}_0$-field is a vector field and is always non-homogeneous. Hence from Theorem VII.9 we get, for $t = n$ and $m' = n$,

THEOREM VII.10. *Every non-homogeneous $\mathfrak{V}_{m-n}$-field of class K is totally integrable with respect to integral vector fields of class K' if and only if*

$$K \leqslant K' \leqslant K+2(m-n) \quad (K' \leqslant n). \tag{4.22}$$

Every homogeneous $\mathfrak{V}_{m-n}$-field of class K is totally integrable with respect to integral vector fields of class K' if and only if

$$K+1 \leqslant K' \leqslant K+2(m-n) \quad (K' \leqslant n). \tag{4.23}$$

A homogeneous $\mathfrak{V}_{m-n}$-field determines at every point of the X_n a system of ∞^{m-n-1} $(n-1)$-directions, that is, an $\mathfrak{S}_d^{n-1}$ with $d = m-n-1$ (cf. VII, § 1) and conversely, the $\mathfrak{V}_{m-n}$-field is completely determined by the $\mathfrak{S}_d^{n-1}$-field. If a vector field, whose $(n-1)$-direction at every point belongs to an $\mathfrak{S}_d^{n-1}$-field, is called an *integral vector field of the $\mathfrak{S}_d^{n-1}$-field*, from Theorem VII.10 we get, for $t = n$ and $m' = n$,

THEOREM VII.11.‡ *Every $\mathfrak{S}_d^{n-1}$-field of class K is totally integrable with respect to integral vector fields of class K' if and only if*

$$K+1 \leqslant K' \leqslant K+2(d+1) \quad (K' \leqslant n). \tag{4.24}$$

5. Determination of the integral-$\mathfrak{N}_{m'}$'s of class K', $K \leqslant K' \leqslant K+2(m-m')$ by extending the system of equations of the $\mathfrak{N}_m$§

The construction of an integral-$\mathfrak{N}_{m'}$ $(m' < m)$ of class K' requires the determination of a system of $m-m'$ functions of the η^a $(a = 1,\dots, \text{m})$ with index $\bar{K}-\bar{K}' = 2(m-m')-(K'-K)$ with respect to the field U_b.

† Cf. Schouten and v. d. Kulk 1943. 2.
‡ Cf. ibid. 1942. 1; 1943. 1.
§ Cf. ibid. 1943. 2.

If $K'-K$ is *even*, according to the results of IV, § 4, we have first to determine a conjugate system of $\frac{1}{2}(\bar{K}-\bar{K}') = m-m'-\frac{1}{2}(K'-K)$ functions by means of $m-m'-\frac{1}{2}(K'-K)$ operations

$$O_{K+2(m-n)-1}, \quad O_{K+2(m-n)-3}, \quad \ldots, \quad O_{K'+2(m'-n)+1}$$

and then without integration $\frac{1}{2}(K'-K)$ functions with index 0.

If $K'-K$ is *odd*, we have first to determine a semi-conjugate system of $\frac{1}{2}(\bar{K}-\bar{K}'+1) = m-m'-\frac{1}{2}(K'-K-1)$ functions by means of $m-m'-\frac{1}{2}(K'-K+1)$ operations

$$O_{K+2(m-n)-1}, \quad O_{K+2(m-n)-3}, \quad \ldots, \quad O_{K'+2(m'-n)+2}$$

and one operation

$$O_{K'+2(m'-n)+1}, \quad \text{or} \quad O_1, \quad \text{or} \quad O_0$$

for $K'+2(m'-n) > 1$, or $= 1$, or $= 0$ respectively and then without integration $\frac{1}{2}(K'-K-1)$ functions with index zero.

The determination of the conjugate or semi-conjugate system requires as a first step the determination of a function $f(\eta^a)$ with index 1 if $K'-K$ is odd and $2(m-m') = K'-K+1$ and with index 2 in all other cases. In the X_m of the η^a the equation

$$f(\eta^a) = c \quad (a = 1,\ldots,\mathrm{m}) \tag{5.1}$$

represents an X_{m-1} in this X_m and by a suitable choice of the constant c we can always ensure that this X_{m-1} lies in a region of constant class of the field U_b. Then the section of U_b with this X_{m-1} has class $\bar{K}-1$ or $\bar{K}-2$ respectively.

If the η^a are solved from the equations (1.2), and if these solutions are substituted into (5.1), we get an equation

$$F^0(\xi^\kappa, w_\lambda) = 0 \tag{5.2}$$

constituting, together with (1.1), a system of $2n-m+1$ equations representing an $\mathfrak{N}_{m-1}$ of class $K+1$ or K respectively.

First we consider the case when the $\mathfrak{N}_{m-1}$ has to be of class K. As in VI, § 10, we use the notation

$$(F^0) \overset{\text{def}}{=} w_\lambda \frac{\partial F^0}{\partial w_\lambda}, \qquad (F^x) \overset{\text{def}}{=} w_\lambda \frac{\partial F^x}{\partial w_\lambda} \quad (x = \mathrm{m}+1,\ldots,2\mathrm{n}). \tag{5.3}$$

For K *odd* we know already that (cf. 3.1)

$$\begin{aligned} &(a) \qquad (F^{[x_1}, F^{x_2})\ldots(F^{x_{K-2}}, F^{x_{K-1}})(F^{x_K]}) \not\equiv 0 \pmod{F^x}, \\ &(b) \qquad (F^{[x_1}, F^{x_2})\ldots(F^{x_K}, F^{x_{K+1}]}) \equiv 0 \pmod{F^x} \\ &\qquad\qquad (x, x_1,\ldots, x_{K+1} = \mathrm{m}+1,\ldots, 2\mathrm{n}) \end{aligned} \tag{5.4}$$

and consequently F^0 is a solution of the system of congruences

$$(F^{[x_1}, F^{x_2})\ldots(F^{x_K}, F^{0]}) \equiv 0 \pmod{F^x, F^0} \tag{5.5}$$
$$(x, x_1,\ldots, x_K = \mathrm{m}+1,\ldots, 2\mathrm{n})$$

or, in another form,

$$(F^{[x_1}, F^{x_2})...(F^{x_K]}, F^0) \equiv 0 \pmod{F^x, F^0}$$
$$(x, x_1, ..., x_K = \mathrm{m}+1, ..., 2\mathrm{n}), \qquad (5.6)$$

independent of the F^x.

For K *even* we know already that

$$\begin{aligned}
&(F^{[x_1}, F^{x_2})...(F^{x_{K-1}}, F^{x_K]}) \not\equiv 0 \pmod{F^x}\\
&(F^{[x_1}, F^{x_2})...(F^{x_{K-1}}, F^{x_K})(F^{x_{K+1}]}) \equiv 0 \pmod{F^x}\\
&(F^{[x_1}, F^{x_2})...(F^{x_{K+1}}, F^{x_{K+2}]}) \equiv 0 \pmod{F^x}\\
&\qquad (x, x_1, ..., x_{K+2} = \mathrm{m}+1, ..., 2\mathrm{n})
\end{aligned} \qquad (5.7)$$

and consequently F^0 is a solution of the system of congruences

$$\begin{aligned}
&(F^{[x_1}, F^{x_2})...(F^{x_{K-1}}, F^{x_K})(F^{0]}) \equiv 0 \pmod{F^x, F^0},\\
&(F^{[x_1}, F^{x_2})...(F^{x_{K+1}]}, F^0) \equiv 0 \pmod{F^x, F^0}\\
&\qquad (x, x_1, ..., x_{K+1} = \mathrm{m}+1, ..., 2\mathrm{n}).
\end{aligned} \qquad (5.8)$$

It is inconvenient that the relations (5.5), (5.6), and (5.8) are congruences. In order to get equations instead of congruences we write the equations of the $\mathfrak{N}_m$ in the form (1.3) and introduce the $G^{\mathfrak{a}}$ as $2n-m-r$ new coordinates $\xi^{1'}, ..., \xi^{(2n-m-r)'}$ in the X_n, taking $\xi^{\kappa'} = \xi^{\kappa}$ for $\kappa > 2n-m-r$. After the introduction of the $\xi^{\kappa'}$ into (1.3a) these equations contain only the variables $\xi^{(2n-m-r+1)'}, ..., \xi^{n'}$ and the $w_{\lambda'}$. If then the matrix of the derivatives of the left-hand sides of these equations with respect to $w_{1'}, ..., w_{(2n-m-r)'}$ has rank $r-r'$, we have $r' = 0$ and $r' \geqslant m+2r-2n$. From the theorem of elimination II.7 it follows that there exist just r' equations only containing the variables $\xi^{(2n-m-r+1)'}, ..., \xi^{n'}, w_{(2n-m-r+1)'}, ..., w_{n'}$. Hence, since the $w_{\lambda'}$-rank of (1.3a) is r, just r' of the variables $w_{(2n-m-r+1)'}, ..., w_{n'}$ can be solved from them and just $r-r'$ of the remaining variables $w_{\lambda'}$ from the remaining $r-r'$ equations. Consequently, by interchanging the indices and dropping the accents we can always ensure that the equations (1.3) take the form

$$\begin{aligned}
&(a)\ w_\beta - \psi_\beta(\xi^{\mathfrak{a}}, \xi^{\mathfrak{x}}, w_b, w_{\mathfrak{y}}) = 0 && (\alpha, \beta = 1, ..., r-r';\\
&(b)\ w_{\mathfrak{b}} - \psi_{\mathfrak{b}}(\xi^{\mathfrak{a}}, \xi^{\mathfrak{x}}, w_{\mathfrak{y}}) = 0 && a, b = r-r'+1, ..., 2n-m-r;\\
&(c)\ \xi^{\alpha} = 0 && \mathfrak{a}, \mathfrak{b} = 2n-m-r+1, ..., 2n-m-r+r';\\
&(d)\ \xi^{a} = 0 && \mathfrak{x}, \mathfrak{y} = 2n-m-r+r'+1, ..., n).
\end{aligned} \qquad (5.9)$$

This form we call a *reduced form* of the equations of the $\mathfrak{N}_m$. The $2n-m-r$ equations (5.9c, d) represent the field region of the $\mathfrak{N}_m$. In this $X_t = X_{m-n+r}$ the $\xi^{\mathfrak{a}}$ and $\xi^{\mathfrak{x}}$ can be used as coordinates. Then the $w_{\mathfrak{b}}$ and $w_{\mathfrak{y}}$ are the components of the sections of the vector elements of $\mathfrak{N}_m$ with X_t. At every point of X_t the equations (5.9 b) establish r' independent relations between these sections. Hence the section of the $\mathfrak{N}_m$ with X_t is an $\mathfrak{N}_{2t-r'}$ consisting of ∞^t $\mathfrak{V}_{t-r'}$'s, one in each point of X_t. By the $r-r'$ equations (5.9 a) each of the vector elements of the $\mathfrak{N}_{2t-r'}$ in the X_t is connected with $\infty^{2n-m-2r+r'}$ vector elements in X_n constituting all together the $\infty^{2n-m-2r+2t} = \infty^m$ vector elements of the $\mathfrak{N}_m$. From this we see that r' is an arithmetic invariant of the $\mathfrak{N}_m$ with respect to coordinate transformations. This can be verified by a direct calculation. A special case arises if $r' = 0$. Then the $\mathfrak{N}_{2t-r'}$ is an $\mathfrak{N}_{2t}$ consisting of all vector elements of the X_t.

Notice that the reduced form of the equations of an $\mathfrak{N}_m$ can always be obtained *by algebraical operations only*. The Poisson bracket expressions of the left-hand sides of (5.9) are independent of w_β, $w_{\mathfrak{b}}$, ξ^α, and ξ^a. From this it follows that every function of these bracket expressions, vanishing in consequence of (5.9), vanishes identically. But the same does not hold for the expressions formed from these left-hand sides by means of the operator $w_\lambda(\partial/\partial w_\lambda)$ because these expressions depend also on w_β and $w_{\mathfrak{b}}$.

If the equations of the $\mathfrak{N}_m$ have the reduced form, (5.4) (K *odd*) takes the form

$$\begin{array}{ll}(a) & (F^{[x_1}, F^{x_2})\dots(F^{x_{K-2}}, F^{x_{K-1}})(F^{x_K]}) \not\equiv 0 \pmod{F^x} \\ (b) & (F^{[x_1}, F^{x_2})\dots(F^{x_K}, F^{x_{K+1}]}) = 0 \end{array} \qquad (5.10)$$

$$(x, x_1, \dots, x_{K+1} = \mathrm{m}+1, \dots, 2\mathrm{n})$$

and (5.7) (K *even*) takes the form

$$\begin{array}{ll}(a) & (F^{[x_1}, F^{x_2})\dots(F^{x_{K-1}}, F^{x_K]}) \not\equiv 0 \\ (b) & (F^{[x_1}, F^{x_2})\dots(F^{x_{K-1}}, F^{x_K})(F^{x_{K+1}]}) \equiv 0 \pmod{F^x} \\ (c) & (F^{[x_1}, F^{x_2})\dots(F^{x_{K+1}}, F^{x_{K+2}]}) = 0 \end{array} \qquad (5.11)$$

$$(x, x_1, \dots, x_{K+2} = \mathrm{m}+1, \dots, 2\mathrm{n}).$$

The matrix of the bracket expressions (F^x, F^y) takes the form (cf. 5.9)

$$\begin{array}{c|cccc|}
 & \overleftrightarrow{r-r'} & \overleftrightarrow{r'} & \overleftrightarrow{2n-m-2r+r'} & \overleftrightarrow{r-r'} \\
r-r' & (\psi_\gamma, \psi_\beta) & \partial_{\mathfrak{b}}\psi_\gamma + (\psi_\gamma, \psi_{\mathfrak{b}}) & -\dfrac{\partial\psi_\gamma}{\partial w_a} & \delta^\alpha_\gamma \\
r' & -\partial_{\mathfrak{c}}\psi_\beta - (\psi_\beta, \psi_{\mathfrak{c}}) & 2\partial_{[\mathfrak{c}}\psi_{\mathfrak{b}]} + (\psi_{\mathfrak{c}}, \psi_{\mathfrak{b}}) & 0 & 0 \\
2n-m-2r+r' & \dfrac{\partial\psi_\beta}{\partial w_b} & 0 & 0 & 0 \\
r-r' & -\delta^\delta_\beta & 0 & 0 & 0
\end{array}$$

$$(\alpha, \beta, \gamma, \delta = 1, \dots, r-r';\ a, b = r-r'+1, \dots, 2n-m-r;$$
$$\mathfrak{b}, \mathfrak{c} = 2n-m-r+1, \dots, 2n-m-r+r') \qquad (5.12)$$

which we write conveniently

$$\begin{array}{c|cccc|}
 & \overleftrightarrow{r-r'} & \overleftrightarrow{r'} & \overleftrightarrow{2n-m-2r+r'} & \overleftrightarrow{r-r'} \\
r-r' & H_{\gamma\beta} & H_{\gamma\mathfrak{b}} & -H^a_\gamma & \delta^\alpha_\gamma \\
r' & -H_{\beta\mathfrak{c}} & H_{\mathfrak{cb}} & 0 & 0 \\
2n-m-2r+r' & H^b_\beta & 0 & 0 & 0 \\
r-r' & -\delta^\delta_\beta & 0 & 0 & 0
\end{array}$$

$(\alpha,\beta,\gamma,\delta = 1,...,r-r';\ \mathfrak{b},\mathfrak{c} = 2n-m-r+1,...,2n-m-r+r';$
$a,b = r-r'+1,..., 2n-m-r).$ (5.13)

According to (5.10) and (5.11 a,c) the rank of this matrix is 2ρ. Hence, if $2r_0$ is the rank of

$H_{\mathfrak{cb}} = 2\partial_{[\mathfrak{c}}\psi_{\mathfrak{b}]}+(\psi_{[\mathfrak{c}},\psi_{\mathfrak{b}]})$ $(\mathfrak{b},\mathfrak{c} = 2n-m-r+1,...,2n-m-r+r'),$ (5.14)

we have $2r_0 \leqslant r'$, and from the form of (5.13) we see that

$$2\rho = 2(r-r')+2r_0. \tag{5.15}$$

If $r' = 0$ we have $r_0 = 0$ and $\rho = r$.

According to (5.10 a) and (5.11 b) the matrix

$$\begin{array}{|ccccc|}
\overleftrightarrow{r-r'} & \overleftrightarrow{r'} & \overleftrightarrow{2n-m-2r+r'} & \overleftrightarrow{r-r'} & \overleftrightarrow{1} \\
H_{\gamma\beta} & H_{\gamma\mathfrak{b}} & -H^a_\gamma & \delta^\alpha_\gamma & w_\gamma-(\psi_\gamma) \\
-H_{\beta\mathfrak{c}} & H_{\mathfrak{cb}} & 0 & 0 & w_\mathfrak{c}-(\psi_\mathfrak{c}) \\
H^b_\beta & 0 & 0 & 0 & 0 \\
-\delta^\delta_\beta & 0 & 0 & 0 & 0 \\
-w_\beta+(\psi_\beta) & -w_\mathfrak{b}+(\psi_\mathfrak{b}) & 0 & 0 & 0
\end{array}$$

$(\alpha,\beta,\gamma,\delta = 1,...,r-r';\ a,b = r-r'+1,...,2n-m-r;$
$\mathfrak{b},\mathfrak{c} = 2n-m-r+1,...,2n-m-r+r')$ (5.16)

has mod $F^\mathfrak{x}$ the rank $2\rho+2\epsilon$. Hence the matrix

$$\begin{array}{|cc|}
\overleftrightarrow{r'} & \overleftrightarrow{1} \\
H_{\mathfrak{cb}} & w_\mathfrak{c}-(\psi_\mathfrak{c}) \\
-w_\mathfrak{b}+(\psi_\mathfrak{b}) & 0
\end{array} \quad (\mathfrak{b},\mathfrak{c} = 2n-m-r+1,...,2n-m-r+r') \tag{5.17}$$

has mod $F^\mathfrak{x}$ the rank $2r_0+2\epsilon$. For $r' = 0$ this matrix reduces to zero. Hence r' can only be zero if K is even.

Now we have to investigate how far it is possible, if we assume the reduced form of the equations of the $\mathfrak{N}_m$, to choose the additional equation of the $\mathfrak{N}_{m-1}$ in such a way that we get for F^0 equations instead of the congruences (5.5), (5.6), and (5.8). To that end we consider the $2n-m$ equations (5.9) completed by the m equations

$$\xi^\mathfrak{a} = \xi^\mathfrak{a}, \qquad \xi^\mathfrak{x} = \xi^\mathfrak{x}, \qquad w_b = w_b, \qquad w_\mathfrak{y} = w_\mathfrak{y}$$

$(b = r-r'+1,...,2n-m-r;\ \mathfrak{a} = 2n-m-r+1,...,2n-m-r+r';$
$\mathfrak{x},\mathfrak{y} = 2n-m-r+r'+1,...,n)$ (5.18)

as a parametric form of the $\mathfrak{N}_m$ with the m parameters $\xi^{\mathfrak{a}}$, $\xi^{\mathfrak{x}}$, $w_{\mathfrak{b}}$, $w_{\mathfrak{y}}$. The vector $U_{\mathfrak{b}}$ in (3.12) passes into the vector in the X_m of these parameters with the components

$$\psi_{\mathfrak{b}}, \quad w_{\mathfrak{y}}, \quad 0, \quad 0. \tag{5.19}$$

If now $'F^0(\xi^{\mathfrak{a}}, \xi^{\mathfrak{x}}, w_{\mathfrak{b}}, w_{\mathfrak{y}})$ is a function with index 2 with respect to this vector field, the equation

$$'F^0(\xi^{\mathfrak{a}}, \xi^{\mathfrak{x}}, w_{\mathfrak{b}}, w_{\mathfrak{y}}) = \text{const.} \tag{5.20}$$

represents a normal system of ∞^1 X_{m-1}'s in the X_m, reducing the class of (5.19) by 2, independently of the choice of the constant. Consequently, the equation

$$F^0(\xi^\kappa, w_\lambda) \overset{\text{def}}{=} {'F^0}(\xi^{\mathfrak{a}}, \xi^{\mathfrak{x}}, w_{\mathfrak{b}}, w_{\mathfrak{y}}) = \text{const.} \tag{5.21}$$

added to the equations (5.9) represents, independently of the choice of the constant, an $\mathfrak{N}_{m-1}$ of class K. Consequently, the relations (5.5), (5.6), and (5.8) now hold not only mod F^x, F^0 but also mod F^x. Now in consequence of the reduced form of the equations of the $\mathfrak{N}_m$ the bracket expressions (F^0, F^x) are independent of the variables w_β, w_b, ξ^α, and ξ^a. Hence instead of (5.6) and (5.8) we get for K odd

$$(F^{[x_1}, F^{x_2})\ldots(F^{x_K]}, F^0) = 0 \quad (x_1, \ldots, x_K = \mathrm{m}+1, \ldots, 2\mathrm{n}) \tag{5.22}$$

and for K even

$$\begin{aligned} &(a) \qquad (F^{[x_1}, F^{x_2})\ldots(F^{x_{K-1}}, F^{x_K})(F^{0]}) \equiv 0 \ (\text{mod } F^x) \\ &(b) \qquad (F^{[x_1}, F^{x_2})\ldots(F^{x_{K+1}}, F^{0]}) = 0 \\ &\qquad\qquad (x, x_1, \ldots, x_{K+1} = \mathrm{m}+1, \ldots, 2\mathrm{n}). \end{aligned} \tag{5.23}$$

Now we will prove that the restriction mod F^x in (5.23 a) can be dropped. Since the function F^0 does not depend on ξ^α, ξ^a, w_β, and $w_{\mathfrak{b}}$, the equations (5.22) and (5.23 b) express the fact that the matrix

$$\overset{\longleftarrow r-r' \longrightarrow \longleftarrow r' \longrightarrow \longleftarrow 2n-m-2r+r' \longrightarrow \longleftarrow r-r' \longrightarrow \longleftarrow 1 \longrightarrow}{\left\| \begin{array}{ccccc} H_{\gamma\beta} & H_{\gamma\mathfrak{b}} & -H^a_\gamma & \delta^\alpha_\gamma & -(\psi_\gamma, F^0) \\ -H_{\beta\mathfrak{c}} & H_{\mathfrak{c}\mathfrak{b}} & 0 & 0 & \partial_{\mathfrak{c}} F^0 - (\psi_{\mathfrak{c}}, F^0) \\ H^b_\beta & 0 & 0 & 0 & -\dfrac{\partial F^0}{\partial w_b} \\ -\delta^\delta_\beta & 0 & 0 & 0 & 0 \\ -(F^0, \psi_\beta) & -\partial_{\mathfrak{b}} F^0 - (F^0, \psi_{\mathfrak{b}}) & \dfrac{\partial F^0}{\partial w_a} & 0 & 0 \end{array} \right\|}$$

$$(\alpha, \beta, \gamma, \delta = 1, \ldots, r-r';\ a, b = r-r'+1, \ldots, 2n-m-r;$$
$$\mathfrak{b}, \mathfrak{c} = 2n-m-r+1, \ldots, 2n-m-r+r') \tag{5.24}$$

has rank 2ρ and this is the case if and only if the matrix

$$\overbrace{\qquad r' \qquad}\ \overbrace{2n-m-2r+r'}\ \overbrace{\qquad 1 \qquad}$$
$$\left\| \begin{array}{ccc} H_{\mathfrak{cb}} & 0 & \partial_{\mathfrak{c}} F^0 - (\psi_{\mathfrak{c}}, F^0) \\ 0 & 0 & -\dfrac{\partial F^0}{\partial w_b} \\ -\partial_{\mathfrak{b}} F^0 - (F^0, \psi_{\mathfrak{b}}) & \dfrac{\partial F^0}{\partial w_a} & 0 \end{array} \right\|$$
$$(a, b = r-r'+1, \ldots, 2n-m-r;$$
$$\mathfrak{b}, \mathfrak{c} = 2n-m-r+1, \ldots, 2n-m-r+r') \qquad (5.25)$$

has rank $2r_0$ (cf. (5.15)). Necessary and sufficient conditions are that $\partial F^0/\partial w_b$ vanishes and that the matrix

$$\| A \| \equiv \left\| \begin{array}{cc} H_{\mathfrak{cb}} & \partial_{\mathfrak{c}} F^0 - (\psi_{\mathfrak{c}}, F^0) \\ -\partial_{\mathfrak{b}} F^0 - (F^0, \psi_{\mathfrak{b}}) & 0 \end{array} \right\|$$
$$(\mathfrak{b}, \mathfrak{c} = 2n-m-r+1, \ldots, 2n-m-r+r') \qquad (5.26)$$

has rank $2r_0$. For K odd these are all the conditions for F^0. For K even we have the additional condition (5.23 a), expressing the fact that the matrix

$$\overbrace{r-r'}\ \overbrace{\qquad r' \qquad}\ \overbrace{2n-m-2r+r'}\ \overbrace{r-r'}\ \overbrace{\quad 1 \quad}\ \overbrace{\quad 1 \quad}$$
$$\left\| \begin{array}{cccccc} H_{\gamma\beta} & H_{\gamma\mathfrak{b}} & -H^a_\gamma & \delta^\alpha_\gamma & -(\psi_\gamma, F^0) & w_\gamma - (\psi_\gamma) \\ -H_{\beta\mathfrak{c}} & H_{\mathfrak{cb}} & 0 & 0 & \partial_{\mathfrak{c}} F^0 - (\psi_{\mathfrak{c}}, F^0) & w_{\mathfrak{c}} - (\psi_{\mathfrak{c}}) \\ H^b_\beta & 0 & 0 & 0 & -\dfrac{\partial F^0}{\partial w_b} & 0 \\ -\delta^\delta_\beta & 0 & 0 & 0 & 0 & 0 \\ -(F^0, \psi_\beta) & -\partial_{\mathfrak{b}} F^0 - (F^0, \psi_{\mathfrak{b}}) & \dfrac{\partial F^0}{\partial w_a} & 0 & 0 & (F^0) \\ -w_\beta + (\psi_\beta) & -w_{\mathfrak{b}} + (\psi_{\mathfrak{b}}) & 0 & 0 & -(F^0) & 0 \end{array} \right\|$$
$$(\alpha, \beta, \gamma, \delta = 1, \ldots, r-r'; \ a, b = r-r'+1, \ldots, 2n-m-r;$$
$$\mathfrak{b}, \mathfrak{c} = 2n-m-r+1, \ldots, 2n-m-r+r') \qquad (5.27)$$

has mod F^x the rank 2ρ. Now we have $\partial F^0/\partial w_b = 0$ according to (5.23 b) and thus the necessary and sufficient conditions are that the matrix

$$\| B \| \equiv \left\| \begin{array}{ccc} H_{\mathfrak{cb}} & \partial_{\mathfrak{c}} F^0 - (\psi_{\mathfrak{c}}, F^0) & \psi_{\mathfrak{c}} - (\psi_{\mathfrak{c}}) \\ -\partial_{\mathfrak{b}} F^0 + (\psi_{\mathfrak{b}}, F^0) & 0 & (F^0) \\ -\psi_{\mathfrak{b}} + (\psi_{\mathfrak{b}}) & -(F^0) & 0 \end{array} \right\|$$
$$(\mathfrak{b}, \mathfrak{c} = 2n-m-r+1, \ldots, 2n-m-r+r') \qquad (5.28)$$

has mod F^x the rank $2r_0$. But this restriction mod F^x can be dropped because the functions occurring in (5.28) do not depend on w_β, w_b, ξ^α, and ξ^a.

Collecting results we have for $K' = K$ the following necessary and sufficient conditions

	$\frac{\partial F^0}{\partial w_b}$	$\| A \|$	$\| B \|$	
$K = 2\rho+1$ . . .	0	rank $2r_0$	—	
$K = 2\rho$ . . .	0	rank $2r_0$	rank $2r_0$	(5.29)

and these conditions can be expressed by means of equations only without making any use of congruences.

We mention a few special cases:

$$K = 0: \quad \begin{matrix} (F^0) = 0 \\ (F^x, F^0) = 0 \end{matrix} \quad (x = \mathrm{m}+1,..., 2\mathrm{n}). \tag{5.30}$$

$$K = 1: \quad (F^x, F^0) = 0 \quad (x = \mathrm{m}+1,..., 2\mathrm{n}). \tag{5.31}$$

$$K = 2: \quad \begin{matrix} (F^x, F^y)(F^0)+(F^y, F^0)(F^x)+(F^0, F^x)(F^y) = 0 \\ (F^x, F^y)(F^z, F^0)+(F^y, F^z)(F^x, F^0)+(F^z, F^x)(F^y, F^0) = 0 \end{matrix}$$
$$(x, y, z = \mathrm{m}+1,..., 2\mathrm{n}). \tag{5.32}$$

$$K = 3: \quad (F^x, F^y)(F^z, F^0)+(F^y, F^z)(F^x, F^0)+(F^z, F^x)(F^y, F^0) = 0$$
$$(x, y, z = \mathrm{m}+1,..., 2\mathrm{n}). \tag{5.33}$$

We know that the determination of $f(\eta^a)$ requires an operation $O_{\overline{K}-1} = O_{K+2(m-n)-1}$. Further, the $2n-m$ solutions F^x of (5.22) and (5.23) are known. From this it follows that (5.22) and (5.23) are each equivalent to a complete system of $2n-K-m+1$ equations in ξ^κ, w_λ of which $2n-m$ solutions are known. Incidentally, we see that the systems (5.30) and (5.31) are complete as was already proved in VI, § 12, and VI, § 11, respectively.

If the $\mathfrak{N}_{m-1}$ has to be of class $K+1$ and if the equations of the $\mathfrak{N}_m$ have the reduced form, we already have the relations (5.10) for K odd and (5.11) for K even. The relations for F^0 are for K *odd*:

(*a*) $(F^{[x_1}, F^{x_2})...(F^{x_K]}, F^0) \neq 0$

(*b*) $(F^{[x_1}, F^{x_2})...(F^{x_K}, F^{x_{K+1}})(F^{0]}) \equiv 0 \pmod{F^x}$ (5.34)

$$(x, x_1,..., x_{K+1} = \mathrm{m}+1,..., 2\mathrm{n}),$$

and for K *even*:

(*a*) $(F^{[x_1}, F^{x_2})...(F^{x_{K-1}}, F^{x_K})(F^{0]}) \not\equiv 0 \pmod{F^x}$

(*b*) $(F^{[x_1}, F^{x_2})...(F^{x_{K-1}}, F^{x_K})(F^{x_{K+1}]}, F^0) = 0$ (5.35)

$$(x, x_1,..., x_{K+1} = \mathrm{m}+1,..., 2\mathrm{n}).$$

We must not be surprised that in these cases an inequality always occurs, because a function $f(\eta^a)$ with index 1 has to satisfy the condition of being a solution of S'_2 but not a solution of S'_3 (cf. IV, § 4). Now we will prove that the restriction mod F^x can be dropped in (5.34 *b*) and (5.35 *a*). If K is *odd* the inequality (5.34 *a*) expresses the fact that the matrix (5.24) has rank $\geqslant 2\rho+2$ and the congruence (5.34 *b*) expresses the fact that the matrix (5.27) has mod F^x the rank $2\rho+2$. But this is only possible if the matrix (5.25) has rank $\geqslant 2r_0+2$ and the matrix

$$\overset{\longleftarrow r' \longrightarrow \longleftarrow 2n-m-2r+r' \longrightarrow \longleftarrow 1 \longrightarrow \longleftarrow 1 \longrightarrow}{\left\| \begin{matrix} H_{\mathfrak{cb}} & 0 & \partial_{\mathfrak{c}} F^0-(\psi_{\mathfrak{c}}, F^0) & w_{\mathfrak{c}}-(\psi_{\mathfrak{c}}) \\ 0 & 0 & -\dfrac{\partial F^0}{\partial w_b} & 0 \\ -\partial_{\mathfrak{b}} F^0-(F^0, \psi_{\mathfrak{b}}) & \dfrac{\partial F^0}{\partial w_a} & 0 & (F^0) \\ -w_{\mathfrak{b}}+(\psi_{\mathfrak{b}}) & 0 & -(F^0) & 0 \end{matrix} \right\|}$$

$$(a, b = r-r'+1,..., 2n-m-r;$$
$$\mathfrak{b}, \mathfrak{c} = 2n-m-r+1,..., 2n-m-r+r') \quad (5.36)$$

has mod F^x rank $2r_0+2$. The first condition is satisfied if and only if either $\partial F^0/\partial w_b \neq 0$ or $\partial F^0/\partial w_b = 0$ and the rank of $\| A \|$ (5.26) is equal to $2r_0+2$. But if $\partial F^0/\partial w_b \neq 0$ the second condition can only be satisfied if the rank of the matrix (5.17) is $2r_0$. Since this is impossible we have as necessary and sufficient conditions that

$$\frac{\partial F^0}{\partial w_b} = 0 \quad (5.37)$$

and that the matrix $\| A \|$ (5.26) has rank $2r_0+2$ and the matrix $\| B \|$ (5.28) has rank $2r_0+2$. As before, the restriction mod F^x can be dropped, since the functions occurring in $\| B \|$ are independent of w_β, w_b, ξ^α, and ξ^a.

If K is *even* the equation (5.35 *b*) expresses the fact that the matrix (5.24) has rank 2ρ and the inequality (5.35 *a*) shows that the matrix (5.27) has mod F^x a rank $\geqslant 2\rho+2$. But this is the case if and only if the matrix (5.25) has rank $2r_0$ and the matrix (5.36) has mod F^x a rank $\geqslant 2r_0+2$. The first condition is satisfied if and only if $\partial F^0/\partial w_b = 0$ and the matrix $\|A\|$ (5.26) has rank $2r_0$. Then the second condition becomes the condition that the matrix $\|B\|$ (5.28) has rank $2r_0+2$ (cf. (5.26)) and the restriction mod F^x can be dropped as above. Collecting results we have for $K' = K+1$ the following necessary and sufficient conditions

	$\dfrac{\partial F^0}{\partial w_b}$	$\| A \|$	$\| B \|$
$K = 2\rho+1$ . . .	0	rank $2r_0+2$	rank $2r_0+2$
$K = 2\rho$ . . .	0	rank $2r_0$	rank $2r_0+2$

(5.38)

and these conditions can be expressed by means of equations only without making any use of congruences.

We mention a few special cases:

$$K = 0: \quad \begin{matrix} (F^0) \neq 0 \\ (F^x, F^0) = 0 \end{matrix} \quad (x = \mathrm{m}+1,\ldots, 2\mathrm{n}). \tag{5.39}$$

$$K = 1: \quad \begin{matrix} (F^x, F^0) \neq 0 \\ (F^y, F^0)(F^x)+(F^0, F^x)(F^y) = 0 \end{matrix} \quad (x, y, z = \mathrm{m}+1,\ldots, 2\mathrm{n}). \tag{5.40}$$

$$K = 2: \quad \begin{matrix} (F^x, F^y)(F^0)+(F^y, F^0)(F^x)+(F^0, F^x)(F^y) \neq 0 \\ (F^x, F^y)(F^z, F^0)+(F^y, F^z)(F^x, F^0)+(F^z, F^x)(F^y, F^0) = 0 \end{matrix}$$

$$(x, y, z = \mathrm{m}+1,\ldots, 2\mathrm{n}). \tag{5.41}$$

$$K = 3: \quad \begin{matrix} (F^x, F^y)(F^z, F^0)+(F^y, F^z)(F^x, F^0)+(F^z, F^x)(F^y, F^0) \neq 0 \\ (F^0, F^{[x})(F^y, F^z)(F^{u]}) = 0 \end{matrix}$$

$$(x, y, z, u = \mathrm{m}+1,\ldots, 2\mathrm{n}). \tag{5.42}$$

In the special case $r' = 0$ we have $K = 2r$ and the conditions for F^0 take the simple form

$$K' = K: \qquad \frac{\partial F^0}{\partial w_b} = 0, \quad (F^0) = 0. \tag{5.43}$$

$$K' = K+1: \qquad \frac{\partial F^0}{\partial w_b} = 0, \quad (F^0) \neq 0. \tag{5.44}$$

We know that the determination of a function $f(\eta^a)$ with index 1 requires for $K+2(m-n) > 2$ an operation $O_{K+2(m-n)}$ and for $K+2(m-n) = 2$ (that is, only for $K = 0$, $m = n+1$) an operation O_1 (cf. IV, § 4). Further, the $2n-m$ solutions F^x of (5.34 b) and (5.35 b) are known. From this it follows that the system (5.34 b), and for $K+2(m-n) > 2$ also the system (5.35 b), is equivalent to a complete system of $2n-m-K$ equations in ξ^κ, w_λ of which $2n-m$ solutions are known. In the case when $K = 0$, $m = n+1$ we have the system (5.39) with $m = n+1$, and in this case the F^x are all homogeneous of degree zero in the w_λ. Now it is really possible to find a solution of the system

$$\begin{matrix} (F^x, F^0) = 0, \qquad (F^x) = 0 \\ (F^0) \neq 0 \end{matrix} \quad (x = \mathrm{n}+2,\ldots, 2\mathrm{n}) \tag{5.45}$$

by means of an operation O_1. We consider the auxiliary system

$$\begin{matrix} (F^x, F^0) = 0, \qquad (F^x) = 0 \\ (F^0) = 0 \end{matrix} \quad (x = \mathrm{n}+2,\ldots, 2\mathrm{n}). \tag{5.46}$$

This system is complete and the $n-1$ solutions F^x are known. Hence a solution $F^{\mathrm{n}+1}$ can be determined by an operation O_1. Then the functions $F^{\mathrm{n}+1},\ldots, F^{2\mathrm{n}}$ are in involution and homogeneous of degree zero in the w_λ. Hence, as was proved in VI, § 9, it is possible by algebraic operations only to determine n functions $G_{n+1},\ldots, G_{2n}$, homogeneous of degree 1 in the w_λ such that

$$(F^A, G_B) = \delta^A_B \quad (A, B = n+1,\ldots, 2n). \tag{5.47}$$

Each of these functions G_B is a solution of (5.45).

If the function F^0 is determined we have obtained a system of $2n-m+1$ equations representing an $\mathfrak{N}_{m-1}$ of class K or $K+1$ respectively. This system can be dealt with in the same way. Continuing in this way we get at last an $\mathfrak{N}_{m'}$ of class K'. Of course the numbers and the order of the operations required are the same as those of the operations required for the determination of the $m-m'$ functions of the η^a dealt with earlier in this section.

6. Solution of a system of partial differential equations of the first order in involution according to Jacobi and Lie†

If a system of $2n-m$ partial differential equations of first order in involution

$$F^x(\xi^\kappa, \partial_\lambda p) = 0 \quad (m \geqslant n;\ x = m+1,\ldots, 2n) \tag{6.1}$$

is given, a solution in the ordinary sense is any function $p(\xi^\kappa)$ satisfying (6.1). The vector field $\partial_\lambda p$ is an integral-N_n of class 1 and with a field dimension n of the system of class $K = 1$ (non-homogeneous case) or $K = 0$ (homogeneous case)

$$F^x(\xi^\kappa, w_\lambda) = 0, \qquad (F^z, F^y) = 0 \quad (x, y = m+1,\ldots, 2n). \tag{6.2}$$

The determination of an integral-N_n of class 1 is a special case of the problem dealt with in the preceding section. Using the method described in that section, by adding to the $2n-m$ functions F^x just $m-n$ functions $F^{n+1},\ldots, F^m$ of ξ^κ and w_λ, such that the class of the system of n equations

$$F^x = 0; \qquad F^{n+1} = c^{n+1}, \quad \ldots, \quad F^m = c^m \tag{6.3}$$

is one, we get an integral-$\mathfrak{N}_n$ of the system (6.2). Since the class is one the resulting $\mathfrak{N}_n$ is an N_n. As we have seen in the preceding section the operations required are in the non-homogeneous case ($K = 1$).

$$O_{2(m-n)}, \quad O_{2(m-n-1)}, \quad \ldots, \quad O_2 \tag{6.4}$$

and in the homogeneous case ($K = 0$)

$$O_{2(m-n)-1}, \quad O_{2(m-n-1)-1}, \quad \ldots, \quad O_1. \tag{6.5}$$

The method is known as *Jacobi's second method*.‡

† Cf. Lie 1876. 1; 1877. 1; v. Weber 1900. 1, ch. xiv; Goursat 1921. 1, ch. xi; Engel and Faber 1932. 1, chs. iv, v, § 60.

‡ Cf., e.g., 1900. 1, p. 499 ff.

If the additional functions are chosen in such a way that the w_λ-rank of (6.3) is just n, the field dimension of the N_n is n and consequently the N_n is a vector field of class *1*, that is, a gradient field. From this gradient field $\partial_\lambda p$ a solution p in the ordinary sense mentioned above can be obtained by means of an operation O_0. Since an $(m-n+1)$th constant is introduced with this quadrature, the solution obtained depends on $m-n+1$ arbitrary constants. Such a solution is called a *complete solution* in the ordinary sense of (6.1). The N_n depends on $m-n$ arbitrary constants and this means that the ∞^m vector elements of the $\mathfrak{N}_m$ expressed by (6.2) are decomposed into ∞^{m-n} sets of ∞^n vector elements, each set constituting an N_n. Now following S. Lie we call a system of ∞^{m-n} N_n's with *arbitrary* field dimensions, constituting together the $\mathfrak{N}_m$ a *complete solution* in a generalized sense of the system (6.1). The great importance of this generalized notion of a complete solution is due to the fact that it is *invariant for C_3-transformations,* whereas the ordinary notion of a complete solution obviously has not this invariance. In the sequel we will always use the term solution in this generalized sense.

By means of the theory of function groups it is sometimes possible to obtain a complete solution without needing all the operations (6.4) or (6.5) respectively. This is always the case if from one of the complete systems necessary for the construction of the $m-n$ additional functions more than one solution is known. The method is developed by S. Lie.†

The following theorem, due to S. Lie,‡ will often be used

THEOREM VII.12. *If $f^1,\dots, f^z$ are z independent known functions of ξ^κ and w_λ, satisfying an equation of the form*

$$w_\lambda d\xi^\lambda = g_1 df^1+\dots+g_z df^z+dU(\xi^\kappa, w_\mu) \tag{6.6}$$

the function U can be determined to within an additional function of $f^1,\dots,$ f^z by a quadrature and, once U has been fixed, the functions $g_1,\dots, g_z$ can be determined without any integration.

PROOF. Let $h^{z+1},\dots, h^{2n}$ be arbitrary functions of ξ^κ and w_λ independent of each other and of $f^1,\dots, f^z$. Then from (6.6) it follows that

$$\begin{aligned} &(a) \qquad w_\lambda \frac{\partial \xi^\lambda}{\partial f^{\mathfrak{b}}} = g_{\mathfrak{b}} + \frac{\partial U}{\partial f^{\mathfrak{b}}} \\ &(b) \qquad w_\lambda \frac{\partial \xi^\lambda}{\partial h^{\mathfrak{y}}} = \frac{\partial U}{\partial h^{\mathfrak{y}}} \end{aligned} \qquad (\mathfrak{b} = 1,\dots, \mathrm{z};\ \mathfrak{y} = \mathrm{z}+1,\dots, 2\mathrm{n}). \tag{6.7}$$

† 1877. 1.

‡ 1877. 1, p. 465.

From (6.7 b) U can be found by a quadrature to within an additional function of the $f^{\mathfrak{b}}$. If U is fixed by choosing this function arbitrarily the $g_{\mathfrak{b}}$ are uniquely determined by (6.7 a).

If $K = 1$ and if more than one solution of the system

$$(F^x, F) = 0 \quad (x = \mathrm{m}+1, \ldots, 2\mathrm{n}) \tag{6.8}$$

is known, according to Jacobi's identity every Poisson bracket of two solutions is a solution. Hence we may assume that we know $m - m_1 > 1$ solutions $F^{\mathrm{m}_1+1}, \ldots, F^{\mathrm{m}}$, such that all Poisson brackets of the $F^{\mathfrak{x}}$ ($\mathfrak{x} = \mathrm{m}_1+1, \ldots, 2\mathrm{n}$) are functions of the $F^{\mathfrak{x}}$. Then the $F^{\mathfrak{x}}$ form a $(2n - m_1)$ dimensional function group G_1. If $2\rho_1$ is the rank of G_1 (cf. VI, § 11), the null group of G_1, containing all the F^x ($x = \mathrm{m}+1, \ldots, 2\mathrm{n}$), is $(2n - m_1 - 2\rho_1)$-dimensional and the greatest commutative sub-groups of G_1 are $(2n - m_1 - \rho_1)$-dimensional and contain the null group (cf. VI, § 11). Hence $2n - m_1 - \rho_1 \leqslant n$ or

$$\rho_1 \geqslant n - m_1. \tag{6.9}$$

The equations

$$F^{\mathrm{m}_1+1} = \text{const.}, \quad \ldots, \quad F^{\mathrm{m}} = \text{const.}, \quad F^x = 0 \quad (x = \mathrm{m}+1, \ldots, 2\mathrm{n}) \tag{6.10}$$

represent in the X_n a system of ∞^{m-m_1} integral-$\mathfrak{N}_{m_1}$'s of class $2\rho_1+1$ and in the X_m of the η^a a system of X_{m_1}'s whose sections with U_b are all of class $2\rho_1 + 2(m_1 - n) + 1$. We require all integral-$\mathfrak{N}_n$'s of class 1, or in other words, all X_n's in the X_m whose sections with U_b are of class 1.

If $\rho_1 = n - m_1$ we have $m_1 < n$ and the sections of U_b with the ∞^{m-m_1} X_{m_1}'s are of class 1. This case always occurs if the number of known solutions of (6.8) has the maximum value m, that is, if $m_1 = 2n - m$, because on the one side we have $\rho_1 \geqslant n - m_1$ according to (6.9) and on the other side in the matrix of the Poisson brackets of the $F^{\mathfrak{x}}$ ($\mathfrak{x} = \mathrm{m}_1+1, \ldots, 2\mathrm{n}$), all brackets containing one of the functions F^x ($x = \mathrm{m}+1, \ldots, 2\mathrm{n}$) vanish, hence $2\rho_1 \leqslant m - m_1 = 2(n - m_1)$. Conversely we will prove that if $\rho_1 = n - m_1$ the maximum number m of independent solutions of (6.8) can be obtained by means of a quadrature. The group G_1 contains an n-dimensional commutative sub-group. Hence according to VI, § 11, the group can be written in the canonical form

$$\begin{matrix} P_1, & \ldots, & P_{n-m_1}, \\ Q^1, & \ldots, & Q^n \end{matrix} \tag{6.11}$$

and m_1 functions $P_{n-m+1}, \ldots, P_n$ exist such that there is a relation of the form

$$w_\lambda \, d\xi^\lambda = P_\lambda \, dQ^\lambda + dU. \tag{6.12}$$

If in this relation the Q^λ are expressed in terms of the $F^{\mathfrak{x}}$ ($\mathfrak{x} = \mathrm{m}_1+1, \ldots, 2\mathrm{n}$) we get a relation of the form

$$w_\lambda \, d\xi^\lambda = G_{\mathfrak{x}} \, dF^{\mathfrak{x}} + dU \quad (\mathfrak{x} = \mathrm{m}_1+1, \ldots, 2\mathrm{n}). \tag{6.13}$$

According to Theorem VII.12 the function U can be determined by a quadrature and after that the $G_{\mathfrak{x}}$ by algebraic operations only. We must remember that it is not necessary to know the canonical form of the group G_1.

From (6.13) it follows that

$$G_{\mathfrak{x}}\,\partial_\lambda F^{\mathfrak{x}} = w_\lambda - \partial_\lambda U$$
$$G_{\mathfrak{x}}\frac{\partial F^{\mathfrak{x}}}{\partial w_\mu} = -\frac{\partial U}{\partial w_\mu} \qquad (\mathfrak{x} = \mathrm{m}_1+1,\dots,2\mathrm{n}) \tag{6.14}$$

and

$$(\partial_{[\mu}\,G_{|\mathfrak{x}|})\partial_{\lambda]}\,F^{\mathfrak{x}} = 0$$
$$\frac{\partial G_{\mathfrak{x}}}{\partial w_\kappa}\partial_\lambda F^{\mathfrak{x}} - (\partial_\lambda G_{\mathfrak{x}})\frac{\partial F^{\mathfrak{x}}}{\partial w_\kappa} = \delta^\kappa_\lambda \quad (\mathfrak{x} = \mathrm{m}_1+1,\dots,2\mathrm{n}). \tag{6.15}$$
$$\frac{\partial G_{\mathfrak{x}}}{\partial w_{[\mu}}\frac{\partial F^{\mathfrak{x}}}{\partial w_{\lambda]}} = 0$$

Consequently, if F is an arbitrary function of ξ^κ and w_λ, we have

$$(F, F^{\mathfrak{x}})\,dG_{\mathfrak{x}} - (F, G_{\mathfrak{x}})\,dF^{\mathfrak{x}}$$
$$= \left(\frac{\partial F}{\partial w_\lambda}\partial_\lambda F^{\mathfrak{x}} - \frac{\partial F^{\mathfrak{x}}}{\partial w_\lambda}\partial_\lambda F\right)\left((\partial_\kappa G_{\mathfrak{x}})\,d\xi^\kappa + \frac{\partial G_{\mathfrak{x}}}{\partial w_\mu}dw_\mu\right) -$$
$$-\left(\frac{\partial F}{\partial w_\lambda}\partial_\lambda G_{\mathfrak{x}} - \frac{\partial G_{\mathfrak{x}}}{\partial w_\lambda}\partial_\lambda F\right)\left((\partial_\kappa F^{\mathfrak{x}})\,d\xi^\kappa + \frac{\partial F^{\mathfrak{x}}}{\partial w_\mu}dw_\mu\right)$$
$$= \frac{\partial F}{\partial w_\lambda}dw_\lambda + (\partial_\lambda F)\,d\xi^\lambda = dF \quad (\mathfrak{x} = \mathrm{m}_1+1,\dots,2\mathrm{n}). \tag{6.16}$$

Hence, replacing F by F^x,

$$dF^x = (F^x, F^{\mathfrak{x}})\,dG_{\mathfrak{x}} - (F^x, G_{\mathfrak{x}})\,dF^{\mathfrak{x}} = -(F^x, G_{\mathfrak{x}})\,dF^{\mathfrak{x}}$$
$$(x = \mathrm{m}+1,\dots,2\mathrm{n};\ \mathfrak{x} = \mathrm{m}_1+1,\dots,2\mathrm{n}) \tag{6.17}$$

and, since the $F^{\mathfrak{x}}$ are independent,

$$(F^x, G_{\mathfrak{x}}) = -\delta^x_{\mathfrak{x}} \quad (x = \mathrm{m}+1,\dots,2\mathrm{n};\ \mathfrak{x} = \mathrm{m}_1+1,\dots,2\mathrm{n}). \tag{6.18}$$

This proves that $G_{\mathrm{m}_1+1},\dots, G_{\mathrm{m}}$ are solutions of (6.8). Now among the $2n+m-2m_1$ solutions $F^{\mathfrak{x}}$, $G_{\mathrm{m}_1+1},\dots, G_{\mathrm{m}}$ there have to be m independent ones. Because otherwise there could not be $2n$ independent functions among the $F^{\mathfrak{x}}$, $G_{\mathfrak{x}}$ ($\mathfrak{x} = \mathrm{m}_1+1,\dots,2\mathrm{n}$) and, as a consequence of (6.13), $w_\lambda\,d\xi^\lambda$ could not be of class $2n$. Hence if $\rho_1 = n-m_1$, the maximum number of solutions of (6.8) can always be obtained by means of a quadrature. When this has been done we have $m_1 = 2n-m$ and $\rho_1 = m-n = n-m_1$.

Now we will prove that in this special case ($m_1 = 2n-m$, $\rho_1 = m-n$) the complete solution of (6.1) can be obtained without any integrations.

If the n-dimensional commutative sub-group $Q^1,\ldots, Q^n$ were known, this group containing the F^x ($x = \mathrm{m}+1,\ldots, 2\mathrm{n}$), it would be possible to find without any integrations $m-n$ functions $F^{(\mathrm{n}+1)'},\ldots, F^{\mathrm{m}'}$ of this group independent of each other and of the F^x ($x = \mathrm{m}+1,\ldots, 2\mathrm{n}$). Then the equations

$$F^{(\mathrm{n}+1)'} = \text{const.}, \quad \ldots, \quad F^{\mathrm{m}'} = \text{const.}, \quad F^x = 0 \quad (x = \mathrm{m}+1,\ldots, 2\mathrm{n}) \tag{6.19}$$

would represent in the X_n the ∞^{m-n} integral-N_n's of class 1 forming a complete solution and in the X_m of the η^a a system of ∞^{m-n} X_n's whose sections with U_b have class 1. But, since the commutative sub-group is not obtainable without integrations, we have to look for another process to construct these integral-N_n's. Each of these integral-N_n's consists of ∞^{m-n} of the $\infty^{2(m-n)}$ integral-$\mathfrak{N}_{2n-m}$'s with the equations (6.10), that is,

$$F^{2\mathrm{n}-\mathrm{m}+1} = \text{const.}, \quad \ldots, \quad F^{\mathrm{m}} = \text{const.}, \quad F^x = 0 \quad (x = \mathrm{m}+1,\ldots, 2\mathrm{n}). \tag{6.20}$$

These $\infty^{2(m-n)}$ $\mathfrak{N}_{2n-m}$'s are called the *characteristics* of the $\mathfrak{N}_m$ and they are always known if *all* solutions of (6.8) are known. In the X_m of the η^a these same equations (6.20) represent a system of $\infty^{2(m-n)}$ X_{2n-m}'s whose sections with U_b have class 1 because they are contained in the ∞^{m-n} X_n's mentioned above. The sections with the rotation of U_b vanish and consequently, the class of U_b being $2(m-n)+1$, *the* $\infty^{2(m-n)}$ X_{2n-m}*'s are the supports of rotation of the field* U_b (cf. IV, § 3). Hence we have to find a method for taking together ∞^{m-n} of these X_{2n-m}'s in such a way that the section of the resulting X_n with U_b has class one.

We will prove first that in an X_n in X_m with this property there always exists an X_{m-n} having just one point in common with each of the supports of rotation and such that its section with U_b vanishes. To this end we choose a coordinate system $\zeta^{\mathfrak{a}}$ ($\mathfrak{a} = 1,\ldots, n$) in this X_n such that the section with U_b is just $\overset{1}{e}_{\mathfrak{b}}$ ($\mathfrak{b} = 1,\ldots, n$) and that the ∞^{m-n} X_{2n-m}'s are represented by the equations

$$\zeta^2 = \text{const.}, \quad \ldots, \quad \zeta^{m-n+1} = \text{const.} \tag{6.21}$$

The tangent E_{2n-m} is the intersection of the $m-n$ E_{n-1}'s of the vectors $\overset{2}{e}_{\mathfrak{b}},\ldots, \overset{m-n+1}{e_{\mathfrak{b}}}$ and, since this E_{2n-m} is not contained in the E_{n-1} of $\overset{1}{e}_{\mathfrak{b}}$, the section of U_b with the X_{2n-m} really does not vanish. Now the ∞^{2n-m} X_{m-n}'s with the equations

$$\zeta^1 = \text{const.}, \quad \zeta^{m-n+2} = \text{const.}, \quad \ldots, \quad \zeta^n = \text{const.} \tag{6.22}$$

have just one point in common with each of the X_{2n-m}'s represented by (6.21) and their section with U_b vanishes.

Secondly, it has to be proved that if any X_{m-n} in the X_m of the η^a be given, such that it has at most one point in common with each of the supports of rotation and such that its section with U_b vanishes, the ∞^{m-n} supports of rotation which have just one point in common with this X_{m-n} constitute an X_n whose section with U_b has class 1. Now, since the class of U_b is odd the supports of rotation each consist of ∞^1 of the $(2n-m-1)$-dimensional characteristics of U_b (cf. IV, § 3). Consequently the X_n to be constructed consists of ∞^{m-n+1} characteristics. If now the X_m is reduced with respect to these characteristics we get an $X_{2(m-n)+1}$ with a vector field of class $2(m-n)+1$ and a system of $\infty^{2(m-n)}$ curves, arising from the $\infty^{2(m-n)}$ supports of rotation, whose sections with the reduced field do not vanish, in other words, whose directions do not lie in the $2(m-n)$-direction of the reduced field. The reduction of the given X_{m-n} is an X_{m-n} having at most one point in common with each of these curves and the reduction of the X_n to be constructed is the X_{m-n+1} formed by this reduced X_{m-n} and the ∞^{m-n} curves intersecting it. The section of the reduced field with this X_{m-n+1} cannot vanish because otherwise the sections with all the ∞^{m-n} curves would vanish. Since the X_{m-n} is enveloped by the reduced field, the coordinates θ^A $(A = 0, 1, \ldots, 2(m-n))$ in the $X_{2(m-n)+1}$ can always be chosen in such a way that the reduced field is

$$\overset{0}{e}_B + \theta^1 \overset{2}{e}_B + \ldots + \theta^{2(m-n)-1} \overset{2(m-n)}{e_B} \quad (B = 0, \ldots, 2(m-n)), \tag{6.23}$$

and so that the equations of the reduced X_{m-n} are

$$\theta^0 = 0, \quad \theta^2 = 0, \quad \theta^4 = 0, \quad \ldots, \quad \theta^{2(m-n)} = 0. \tag{6.24}$$

Then since the $\infty^{2(m-n)}$ curves are the supports of rotation of the reduced field, they have the equations

$$\theta^1 = \text{const.}, \quad \theta^2 = \text{const.}, \quad \ldots, \quad \theta^{2(m-n)} = \text{const.} \tag{6.25}$$

and from this it follows that the equations of the X_{m-n+1} are

$$\theta^2 = 0, \quad \theta^4 = 0, \quad \ldots, \quad \theta^{2(m-n)} = 0. \tag{6.26}$$

Consequently the section of the rotation of the reduced field with the X_{m-n+1} vanishes, and from this it follows that the class of this section is 1. But since the X_{m-n+1} is the reduction of the X_n, this implies that the section of U_b with the X_n has class 1. This proves the proposition.

The construction of an enveloped X_{m-n} of U_b is not immediately possible because the field U_b is not given in a canonical form. But in the X_{2n} a field in canonical form is given, viz. the field of the Pfaffian $w_\lambda d\xi^\lambda$. Hence an enveloped X_n of this field can be constructed without any integration, using one of the two rules given in VI, § 2. The section of this X_n with the X_m is the X_{m-n} required, provided that the X_n be chosen in such a way that this X_{m-n} has not more than one point in common with each of the supports of rotation of U_b. Since this condition is expressible by means of inequalities no serious difficulties can arise. The X_n in the X_{2n} represents an N_n, and the N_{m-n} represented by the X_{m-n} in X_m can be obtained by adding the n equations of this X_n to the $2n-m$ equations of the $\mathfrak{N}_m$. The integral-$\mathfrak{N}_n$ of class *1* required is obtained by taking together all the ∞^{m-n} $\mathfrak{N}_{2n-m}$'s having just one vector element in common with the N_{m-n}. If an integral-$\mathfrak{N}_n$ is desired containing a particular vector element of the $\mathfrak{N}_m$, the auxiliary N_n has to be chosen in such a way that it contains this element.

Collecting results we get the rule:

Rule for the construction of the integral-$\mathfrak{N}_n$'s of class 1 of an $\mathfrak{N}_m$ of class $K = 1$ if $\rho_1 = n-m_1$.

If, of the non-homogeneous system in involution

$$F^x(\xi^\kappa, \partial_\lambda p) = 0 \quad (x = \mathrm{m+1,..., 2n}), \tag{6.27}$$

$2n-m_1$ independent solutions of the auxiliary system

$$(F^x, F) = 0, \quad F^x = F^x(\xi^\kappa, w_\lambda) \quad (x = \mathrm{m+1,..., 2n}) \tag{6.28}$$

are known, constituting a $(2n-m_1)$-dimensional function group of rank $2\rho_1$, and if $\rho_1 = n-m_1$, the other solutions of (6.28) *can be obtained by means of a quadrature.*

If in this way m independent solutions

$$F^{\mathrm{2n-m+1}}, \ldots, F^{\mathrm{m}}, \quad F^{\mathrm{m+1}}, \ldots, F^{\mathrm{2n}} \tag{6.29}$$

of (6.28) *are obtained, the equations*

$$F^{\mathrm{2n-m+1}} = \text{const.}, \quad \ldots, \quad F^{\mathrm{m}} = \text{const.}, \quad F^x = 0 \quad (x = \mathrm{m+1,..., 2n}) \tag{6.30}$$

represent a system of $\infty^{2(m-n)}$ $\mathfrak{N}_{2n-m}$'s called the characteristics of the $\mathfrak{N}_m$ with the equations

$$F^x(\xi^\kappa, w_\lambda) = 0. \tag{6.31}$$

To construct an integral-$\mathfrak{N}_n$ of class 1 of the $\mathfrak{N}_m$ an arbitrary N_n has to be chosen in such a way that the n equations of the N_n added to the $2n-m$ equations of the $\mathfrak{N}_m$ form a system of $3n-m$ independent equations, which represent an N_{m-n} having not more than one vector element in common with each of the characteristics. Then all the ∞^{m-n} characteristics which have just one vector element in common with this N_{m-n} taken together constitute an integral-$\mathfrak{N}_n$ of class 1 of the $\mathfrak{N}_m$.

The method described requires no integrations if all solutions of (6.28) are known and one quadrature if only $2n-m_1$ solutions are known but $\rho_1 = n-m_1$. But if no solutions at all of (6.28), except the F^x, are known, the $2(m-n)$ other solutions have first to be determined and this requires (cf. III, § 16) in the most unfavourable case $2(m-n)$ operations

$$O_{2(m-n)},\quad O_{2(m-n)-1},\quad \ldots,\quad O_1. \tag{6.32}$$

This latter method is due to Cauchy for $m = 2n-1$ and generalized by Lie for $m < 2n-1$. It is known as the *generalized method of Cauchy*. Using this method the theory of function groups enables us to stop the ordinary process of determining solutions of (6.28) as soon as we have got enough solutions for a function group with $\rho_1 = n-m_1$ to arise. We can then obtain the other solutions by means of a quadrature.

S. Lie has also given a method of integration for the case when $\rho_1 > n-m_1$.† Then the group G_1 contains at most $(2n-m_1-\rho_1)$-dimensional commutative sub-groups, $2n-m_1-\rho_1 < n$. We wish to find a group G_2 satisfying the following conditions:

1. G_2 contains G_1 and its dimension $2n-m_2$ is $> 2n-m_1$.
2. All functions of G_2 are solutions of (6.28).
3. The rank $2\rho_2$ of G_2 is so small that G_2 contains commutative sub-groups with a dimension $> 2n-m_1-\rho_1$:

$$\rho_2 < \rho_1+m_1-m_2.$$

The determination of one new solution F^{m_1} of (6.28) requires an operation O_{m+m_1-2n}. From this solution possibly more new solutions can be obtained without integration by forming the Poisson brackets with $F^{\mathrm{m}_1+1},\ldots, F^{\mathrm{m}}$ and this process can be continued till all the solutions obtained in this way and the $F^{\mathfrak{x}}$ ($\mathfrak{x} = \mathrm{m}_1+1,\ldots, 2\mathrm{n}$) form a group. But if this group is $(2n-m_2)$-dimensional and of rank $2\rho_2$ there is no guarantee that $\rho_2 < \rho_1+m_1-m_2$. This difficulty can be avoided *by taking for* F^{m_1} *a function of the polar group of the null group of* G_1. We will prove that a necessary and sufficient condition is that F^{m_1} is a solution of the system

$$(F^{[\mathfrak{x}_1}, F^{\mathfrak{x}_2})\ldots(F^{\mathfrak{x}_{2\rho_1-1}}, F^{\mathfrak{x}_{2\rho_1}})(F^{\mathfrak{x}_{2\rho_1+1}]}, F^{\mathrm{m}_1}) = 0 \quad (\mathfrak{x} = \mathrm{m}_1+1,\ldots, 2\mathrm{n}). \tag{6.33}$$

If the functions $F^{\mathrm{m}_1+1},\ldots, F^{\mathrm{m}}$ were chosen in such a way that $F^{\mathrm{m}_1+2\rho_1+1},\ldots, F^{\mathrm{m}}$ and the F^x ($x = \mathrm{m}+1,\ldots, 2\mathrm{n}$) form the $(2n-m_1-2\rho_1)$-dimensional null group of G_1 and that $F^{\mathrm{m}_1+1},\ldots, F^{\mathrm{m}_1+2\rho_1}$ do not belong to this null group, the bracket expressions of any function of the null group with all functions of G_1 would be zero and, therefore, the only equations

† 1877. 1.

of (6.33) whose left-hand sides do not vanish identically would be those containing only the indices $m_1+1,\dots, m_1+2\rho_1$ in the first ρ_1 brackets and one of the indices $m_1+2\rho_1+1,\dots, 2n$ in the last bracket. Hence for this special choice of $F^{m_1+1},\dots, F^m$ the remaining equations of (6.33) are

$$(F^{[m_1+1}, F^{m_1+2})\dots(F^{m_1+2\rho_1-1}, F^{m_1+2\rho_1]})(F^{x_1}, F^{m_1}) = 0$$
$$(x_1 = m+2\rho_1+1,\dots, 2n). \qquad (6.34)$$

Since G_1 is of rank $2\rho_1$ the factor standing before (F^{x_1}, F^{m_1}) cannot vanish, and consequently (6.33) takes the form

$$(F^{x_1}, F^{m_1}) = 0 \quad (x_1 = m_1+2\rho_1+1,\dots, 2n), \qquad (6.35)$$

expressing the fact that F^{m_1} is in involution with all the functions of the null group of G_1. Now this special choice of $F^{m_1+2\rho_1+1},\dots, F^m$ cannot be attained without integration and consequently the equations (6.35) cannot be used. But the equivalent system (6.33), requiring only the knowledge of $2n-m_1$ arbitrary independent functions of G_1 is obtainable without any integration. Since F^{m_1} is obtained as a solution of (6.33), it is a solution of (6.28) as well. Hence, if by forming the bracket expressions of F^{m_1} we get new solutions of (6.33) and if this process is continued till no further solutions of (6.33) can be obtained, all solutions obtained in this way form a $(2n-m_2)$-dimensional group G_2, satisfying the first and the second condition. Since the null group of G_2 contains the null group of G_1 we have

$$2n-m_2-2\rho_2 \geqslant 2n-m_1-2\rho_1 \qquad (6.36)$$

and consequently

$$\rho_2 \leqslant \rho_1+\tfrac{1}{2}(m_1-m_2) \qquad (6.37)$$

which proves that the third condition is also satisfied. Since $2n-m_1$ solutions of (6.33) are known, viz. $F^{\mathfrak{x}}$ ($\mathfrak{x} = m_1+1,\dots, 2n$), the determination of F^{m_1} requires an operation $O_{2(m_1-n+\rho_1)}$.

If $\rho_2 = n-m_2$ the group G_2 contains n-dimensional commutative sub-groups and all solutions of (6.28) can be obtained by means of a quadrature. If $\rho_2 > n-m_2$ the group G_2 can be dealt with in the same way and we get a $(2n-m_3)$-dimensional group G_3 of rank $2\rho_3$ containing $(2n-m_3-\rho_3)$-dimensional commutative sub-groups. This requires an operation $O_{2(m_2-n+\rho_2)}$. Because

$$\begin{aligned} m_3 &< m_2, \\ \rho_3 &\leqslant \rho_2+\tfrac{1}{2}(m_2-m_3), \qquad (6.38) \\ m_3-n+\rho_3 &< m_2-n+\rho_2 \end{aligned}$$

we get, after $s-1 \leqslant m_1-n+\rho_1$ steps, a group G_s with $\rho_s = n-m_s$, containing n-dimensional commutative sub-groups. In the most unfavourable case, that is, if no new solution can ever be found by forming bracket expressions, the method requires $m_1-n+\rho_1$ operations

$$O_{2(m_1-n+\rho_1)}, \quad O_{2(m_1-n+\rho_1-1)}, \quad \ldots, \quad O_2 \tag{6.39}$$

and a quadrature. Collecting results we get the rule:

Rule for the construction of the integral-$\mathfrak{R}_n$'s of class 1 of an $\mathfrak{R}_m$ of class $K = 1$ if $\rho_1 > n-m_1$.†

If, of the non-homogeneous system in involution (6.27), *$2n-m_1$ independent solutions of the auxiliary system* (6.28) *are known, constituting a $(2n-m_1)$-dimensional function group of rank $2\rho_1$, and if $\rho_1 > n-m_1$, the other solutions of* (6.28) *can be obtained by means of $m_1-n+\rho_1$ operations $O_{2(m_1-n+\rho_1)}, O_{2(m_1-n+\rho_1-1)}, \ldots, O_2$ and a quadrature, but, if circumstances are favourable, less than $m_1-n+\rho_1$ operations or operations of lower even orders may be sufficient. If m independent solutions of* (6.28) *are obtained in this way, all integral-$\mathfrak{R}_n$'s of class 1 can be obtained by the process described in the rule on p.* 312 *without any integrations.*

If $K = 0$ and if more than one solution of the system

$$(F^x, F) = 0 \quad (x = \mathrm{m}+1, \ldots, 2\mathrm{n}) \tag{6.40}$$

is known, according to VI (12.4) not only the Poisson brackets of two solutions but also the functions obtained from solutions by applying the operator $w_\lambda(\partial/\partial w_\lambda)$ are solutions. Hence we may assume that we know $m-m_1 > 1$ solutions $F^{\mathrm{m}_1+1}, \ldots, F^{\mathrm{m}}$ such that all the Poisson brackets and all the functions $(F^{\mathrm{m}_1+1}), \ldots, (F^{\mathrm{m}})$ (cf. VI, § 10) are functions of the $F^{\mathfrak{x}}$ ($\mathfrak{x} = \mathrm{m}_1+1, \ldots, 2\mathrm{n}$). Then the $F^{\mathfrak{x}}$ form a homogeneous $(2n-m_1)$-dimensional function group G_1. If $K_1 = 2\rho_1+\epsilon_1$ is the class of G_1, the null group of G_1, containing all the F^x ($x = \mathrm{m}+1, \ldots, 2\mathrm{n}$), is $(2n-m_1-2\rho_1)$-dimensional and the greatest commutative sub-groups of G_1 are $(2n-m_1-\rho_1)$-dimensional and contain the null group (cf. VI, § 12). Hence $2n-m_1-\rho_1 \leqslant n$ or

$$\rho_1 \geqslant n-m_1. \tag{6.41}$$

In VI, § 12, we have seen that, if K_1 is even, the null group contains only homogeneous functions of degree zero in the w_λ and $(2n-m_1-\rho_1)$-dimensional commutative sub-groups exist which contain only functions with this homogeneity.

If K_1 is odd, we have to proceed in the same way as in the non-homogeneous case. Hence the determination of all integral-$\mathfrak{R}_n$'s of class 1 then requires in the most unfavourable case $m_1-n+\rho_1$ operations

† Cf. Lie 1877. 1, p. 476; v. Weber 1900. 1, p. 565; Goursat 1921. 1, p. 441; Engel and Faber 1932. 1, p. 323.

$$O_{2(m_1-n+\rho_1)},\quad O_{2(m_1-n+\rho_1-1)},\quad \ldots,\quad O_2 \tag{6.42}$$

and a quadrature.

If K_1 is even and $\rho_1 = n-m_1$, the determination of all integral-$\mathfrak{N}_n$'s of class 1 requires no integrations because $U = 0$ in (6.12). Hence the only remaining case is $K_1 = 2\rho_1$ ($\rho_1 > n-m_1$). In this case we try to form a homogeneous function group G_2 satisfying the three conditions on p. 313. To that end we determine a solution F^{m_1} of the system

$$\begin{aligned}
&(a)\quad (F^{[\mathfrak{x}_1}, F^{\mathfrak{x}_2})\ldots(F^{\mathfrak{x}_{2\rho_1-1}}, F^{\mathfrak{x}_{2\rho_1}})(F^{\mathfrak{x}_{2\rho_1+1}]}, F^{\mathrm{m}_1}) = 0,\\
&(b)\quad (F^{[\mathfrak{x}_1}, F^{\mathfrak{x}_2})\ldots(F^{\mathfrak{x}_{2\rho_1-1}}, F^{\mathfrak{x}_{2\rho_1}]})(F^{\mathrm{m}_1})+\\
&\qquad +2\rho(F^{\mathrm{m}_1}, F^{[\mathfrak{x}_1})(F^{\mathfrak{x}_2}, F^{\mathfrak{x}_3})\ldots(F^{\mathfrak{x}_{2\rho_1-2}}, F^{\mathfrak{x}_{2\rho_1-1}})(F^{\mathfrak{x}_{2\rho_1}]}) = 0\\
&\qquad\qquad (\mathfrak{x}_1,\ldots,\mathfrak{x}_{2\rho_1+1} = \mathrm{m}_1+1,\ldots,2\mathrm{n}).
\end{aligned}\tag{6.43}$$

If $F^{\mathrm{m}_1+1},\ldots, F^{\mathrm{m}}$ were chosen in such a way that $F^{\mathrm{m}_1+2\rho_1+1},\ldots, F^{\mathrm{m}}$ together with F^{x} ($x = \mathrm{m}+1,\ldots, 2\mathrm{n}$) form the null group of G_1 and that $F^{\mathrm{m}_1+1},\ldots,$ $F^{\mathrm{m}_1+2\rho_1}$ do not belong to this null group, the system (6.43 a) would be equivalent to the system

$$(F^{x_1}, F^{\mathrm{m}_1}) = 0 \quad (x_1 = \mathrm{m}_1+2\rho_1+1,\ldots, 2\mathrm{n}) \tag{6.44}$$

and (6.43 b) equivalent to the equation

$$\begin{aligned}
&(F^{[\mathrm{m}_1+1}, F^{\mathrm{m}_1+2})\ldots(F^{\mathrm{m}_1+2\rho_1-1}, F^{\mathrm{m}_1+2\rho_1]})(F^{\mathrm{m}_1})+\\
&+2\rho(F^{\mathrm{m}_1}, F^{[\mathrm{m}_1+1})(F^{\mathrm{m}_1+2}, F^{\mathrm{m}_1+3})\ldots(F^{\mathrm{m}_1+2\rho_1-2}, F^{\mathrm{m}_1+2\rho_1-1})(F^{\mathrm{m}_1+2\rho_1]}) = 0.
\end{aligned}\tag{6.45}$$

Now (6.44) expresses the fact that F^{m_1} belongs to the polar group of the null group of G_1 and (6.45) that (F^{m_1}) can be expressed in terms of the $F^{\mathfrak{x}}$ ($\mathfrak{x} = \mathrm{m}_1+1,\ldots, 2\mathrm{n}$) and F^{m_1}. The special choice of the functions $F^{\mathrm{m}_1+2\rho_1+1},\ldots, F^{\mathrm{m}}$ cannot be attained without integration, but in order to write down the equations (6.43) only $2n-m_1$ arbitrary independent functions of G_1 are required.

The functions $F^{\mathrm{m}_1+1},\ldots, F^{\mathrm{m}_1+2\rho_1}$ in (6.45) are arbitrary functions of G_1 not belonging to the null group of G_1. If G_1 is written in the canonical form VI, § 12 (12.31)

$$\begin{aligned}
&(P_a, P_b) = 0\\
&(P_a, Q^d) = \delta_a^d \qquad (a, b = 1,\ldots, \rho_1;\\
&(Q^c, Q^d) = 0 \qquad\quad c, d = 1,\ldots, 2n-m_1-\rho_1)\\
&(P_a) = P_a,\quad (Q^c) = 0
\end{aligned}\tag{6.46}$$

the null group consists of $Q^{\rho_1+1},\ldots, Q^{2n-m_1-\rho_1}$ and for $F^{\mathrm{m}_1+1},\ldots, F^{\mathrm{m}_1+2\rho_1}$ the functions $P_1, Q^1,\ldots, P_{\rho_1}, Q^{\rho_1}$ can be chosen. Then the equation (6.45) takes the form

$$(F^{\mathrm{m}_1}) = -(Q^1, F^{\mathrm{m}_1})P_1 - \ldots - (Q^{\rho_1}, F^{\mathrm{m}_1})P_{\rho_1}. \tag{6.47}$$

As was proved in VI, § 12, the group G_1 can be extended by m_1 functions $P_{\rho_1+1},\dots, P_n$ and $Q^{2n-m_1-\rho_1+1},\dots, Q^n$, homogeneous of degree 1 or 0 respectively in the w_λ, such that $'\xi^\kappa = Q^\kappa$; $'w_\lambda = P_\lambda$ $(\kappa, \lambda = 1,\dots, n)$ represents a C_3-transformation in ξ^κ, w_λ. Then (6.47) can be written in the form

$$(F^{m_1}) = {}'w_1 \frac{\partial F^{m_1}}{\partial\, 'w_1} + \dots + {}'w_{\rho_1} \frac{\partial F^{m_1}}{\partial\, 'w_{\rho_1}}. \tag{6.48}$$

On the other side, since (F^{m_1}) is invariant for C_3-transformations (cf. VI (10.10)), we have

$$(F^{m_1}) = {}'w_\lambda \frac{\partial F^{m_1}}{\partial\, 'w_\lambda}. \tag{6.49}$$

Comparing (6.48) and (6.49) we see that F^{m_1} is homogeneous of degree 0 in the variables $'w_{\rho_1+1},\dots, {}'w_n$, that is, in the variables $P_{\rho_1+1},\dots, P_n$. Now F^{m_1} belongs to the polar group of the null group of G_1. From this it follows that $P_{\rho_1+1},\dots, P_{2n-m_1-\rho_1}$ drop out and that the general solution of (6.43) has the form

$$F^{m_1} = \Phi\left(P_1,\dots, P_{\rho_1}, \frac{P_{2n-m_1-\rho_1+1}}{P_n},\dots, \frac{P_{n-1}}{P_n}, Q^\kappa\right). \tag{6.50}$$

Hence the system (6.43) expresses the fact that F^{m_1} is a function of the functions of G_1 and of those functions of the polar group of G_1 which are homogeneous of degree 0 in the w_λ. Of course (6.50) cannot be used for the determination of F^{m_1}, since the canonical form of G_1 is not obtainable without integrations. But this equation is very useful for attaining some properties of the solutions of (6.43). The system (6.43) is complete as can readily be verified, using the form (6.44, 45). Since $2n-m_1$ solutions are known, viz. the $F^{\mathfrak{x}}$ $(\mathfrak{x} = m_1+1,\dots, 2n)$, the determination of F^{m_1} requires an operation $O_{2(m_1-n+\rho_1)-1}$. The order of this operation is lower by 1 than in the non-homogeneous case.

From the form (6.50) of the general solution of (6.43) it follows that all Poisson brackets of a solution with the $F^{\mathfrak{x}}$ $(\mathfrak{x} = m_1+1,\dots, 2n)$ and all functions arising from solutions by applying the operator $w_\lambda(\partial/\partial w_\lambda)$ have the form (6.50) and consequently are solutions of (6.43). But if the Poisson bracket of two solutions is formed, this expression satisfies (6.43 *a*) but not necessarily (6.43 *b*). If F^{m_1} and the $F^{\mathfrak{x}}$ happen to form a $(2n-m_1+1)$-dimensional homogeneous group G_2, all functions of G_2 are solutions of (6.43) and consequently all functions of the null group of G_2 are homogeneous of degree 0 in the w_λ. In fact, the coefficient of (F^{m_1}) in (6.45) cannot vanish and this implies that $(F^{m_1}) = 0$ if all the expressions $(F^{m_1}, F^{\mathfrak{x}})$ $(\mathfrak{x} = m_1+1,\dots, 2n)$ vanish. Accordingly the class of G_2 is even. If F^{m_1} and the $F^{\mathfrak{x}}$ $(\mathfrak{x} = m_1+1,\dots, 2n)$ do not form a group, but if, by applying the operator $w_\lambda(\partial/\partial w_\lambda)$ to F^{m_1} or forming the Poisson bracket of F^{m_1} and one of the $F^{\varkappa}$, a function F^{m_1-1} can be formed, such that it is independent of the F^{m_1} and the $F^{\varkappa}$ and such that F^{m_1-1}, F^{m_1} and the $F^{\varkappa}$ form a $(2n-m_1+2)$-dimensional homogeneous group G_2, the bracket expression (F^{m_1}, F^{m_1-1}) belongs to G_2 and consequently all functions of G_2 satisfy the equations (6.43). Hence the functions of the null group of G_2 are homogeneous of degree 0 in the w_λ and this implies that the class of G_2 is even. But if F^{m_1}, F^{m_1-1} and the $F^{\varkappa}$ do not form a group, in order to form a group it is necessary to add the function (F^{m_1-1}, F^{m_1}) and this function satisfies (6.43 a) but not necessarily (6.43 b).† We give an example. Let

$$\begin{aligned} F^8 &\overset{\text{def}}{=} Q^2 = 0 \\ F^7 &\overset{\text{def}}{=} Q^3 = 0 \end{aligned} \tag{6.51}$$

be the equations of an $\mathfrak{N}_{14}$ in X_8 and let

$$\begin{aligned} F^6 &\overset{\text{def}}{=} P_1 \\ F^5 &\overset{\text{def}}{=} Q^1 \end{aligned} \tag{6.52}$$

be two known solutions of (6.40). Then the group G_1 consists of P_1, Q^1, Q^2, and Q^3 and we have $m_1 = 12$, $\rho_1 = 1$. From the solutions of (6.43) we choose

$$F^4 \overset{\text{def}}{=} Q^1\frac{P_4}{P_8}+Q^4. \tag{6.53}$$

From F^4, F^5, F^6, F^7, and F^8 only the solution

$$F^3 \overset{\text{def}}{=} (F^6, F^4) = \frac{P_4}{P_8} \tag{6.54}$$

can be formed and from $F^3,\ldots, F^8$ only the solution

$$F^2 \overset{\text{def}}{=} (F^3, F^4) = \frac{1}{P_8}. \tag{6.55}$$

Now F^2 does not have the form (6.50) and consequently is not a solution of (6.43). The functions $F^2,\ldots, F^8$ or P_1, Q^1, Q^2, Q^3, P_4, Q^4, P_8 form a seven-dimensional group G_2 of class 5. Its null group is three-dimensional and consists of Q^2, Q^3, and the function P_8, not homogeneous of degree 0 in the w_λ.

When G_2 has been obtained by an operation $O_{2(m_1-n+\rho_1)-1}$, by forming of bracket expressions and by applying the operator $w_\lambda(\partial/\partial w_\lambda)$, there are two possible cases. If $m_2 \geqslant m_1-2$ we have seen that the class of G_2 is even. Then by means of an operation $O_{2(m_2-n+\rho_2)-1}$, by forming bracket expressions and by applying the operator $w_\lambda(\partial/\partial w_\lambda)$, a group G_3 can be formed. Because $m_2+\rho_2 < m_1+\rho_1$ the order of this operation is at least lower by 2 than the order of the preceding operation. If

† The opposite assertion in v. Weber 1900. 1, p. 579, is erroneous and the proof, given there, that the class of G_2 is always even, is not valid. Engel and Faber 1932. 1, § 60, give the correct treatment.

$m_2 < m_1-2$ the forming of G_3 requires an operation $O_{2(m_2-n+\rho_2)-1}$ if the class of G_2 is even and an operation $O_{2(m_2-n+\rho_2)}$ if this class is odd. Now we have (cf. (6.36))

$$2(m_2-n+\rho_2) \leqslant 2(m_1-n+\rho_1)-(m_1-m_2), \tag{6.56}$$

and because $m_2 \leqslant m_1-3$ this implies that

$$2(m_2-n+\rho_2) \leqslant 2(m_1-n+\rho_1)-4. \tag{6.57}$$

From this we see that the order of the operation is lower by at least *3* or *4* than the order of the preceding operation. Hence in all cases the order of the operation required for the determination of G_3 is lower by at least *2* than the order of the operation required for the determination of G_2 and this implies that the construction of all integral-$\mathfrak{R}_n$'s of class one requires $m_1-n+\rho_1$ operations

$$O_{2(m_1-n+\rho_1)-1},\quad O_{2(m_1-n+\rho_1)-3},\quad \ldots,\quad O_1 \tag{6.58}$$

and a quadrature for K even in the most unfavourable case, but that it is possible that the process can be effected by fewer operations or operations of lower odd or even order. Collecting results we get the rule:

Rule for the construction of the integral-$\mathfrak{R}_n$'s of class 1 of an $\mathfrak{R}_m$ of class $K = 0$.†

If, of the homogeneous system in involution (6.27), $2n-m_1$ *independent solutions of the auxiliary system* (6.40) *are known, constituting a* $(2n-m_1)$*-dimensional homogeneous function group of class* $K_1 = 2\rho_1+1$, *the other solutions of* (6.40) *can be obtained by means of* $m_1-n+\rho_1$ *operations*

$$O_{2(m_1-n+\rho_1)},\quad O_{2(m_1-n+\rho_1-1)},\quad \ldots,\quad O_2 \tag{6.59}$$

and a quadrature.

If $K_1 = 2\rho_1$ *and if the function groups from* G_σ *onwards are of odd class, the other solutions of* (6.40) *can be obtained by means of* $m_1-n+\rho_1$ $(+1$ *for* $\sigma = 1)$ *operations*

$$\sigma > 1: \begin{cases} O_{2(m_1-n+\rho_1)-1}, & O_{2(m_1-n+\rho_1-1)-1}, & \ldots, & O_{2(m_1-n+\rho_1-\sigma)+3}, \\ O_{2(m_1-n+\rho_1-\sigma)}, & O_{2(m_1-n+\rho_1-\sigma-1)}, & \ldots, & O_2,\quad O_0, \end{cases} \tag{6.60}$$

$$\sigma = 1:\quad O_{2(m_1-n+\rho_1)},\quad O_{2(m_1-n+\rho_1-1)},\quad \ldots,\quad O_2,\quad O_0.$$

In both cases, if circumstances are favourable, less than $m_1-n+\rho_1(+1)$ *operations or operations of lower even order for* $K_1 = 2\rho_1+1$ *and lower even or odd order for* $K_1 = 2\rho_1$ *may be sufficient.*

If m independent solutions of (6.40) *are obtained in this way, all integral-$\mathfrak{R}_n$'s of class 1 can be obtained without any integrations by the process described in the rule on p.* 312.

† Cf. Lie 77.1, p. 487; v. Weber 1900. 1, p. 581; Goursat 1921. 1, p. 452; Engel and Faber 1932. 1, p. 333.

7. Construction of all integral-$\mathfrak{N}_{m'}$'s ($m' < m$) of a class $K' < K$†

No integral-$\mathfrak{N}_{m'}$'s exist with a class $> K+2(m-m')$. The only integral-$\mathfrak{N}_{m'}$'s still to be constructed are those with a class $K' < K$. To this end we add to the $2n-m$ equations of the $\mathfrak{N}_m$ for K' odd the equations

$$K^{[x_1 x_2} \ldots K^{x_{K'} x_{K'+1}]} = 0 \quad (x_1,\ldots, x_{K'+1} = \mathrm{m}+1,\ldots, 2\mathrm{n}) \tag{7.1}$$

and for K' even the equations

$$\left.\begin{aligned} K^{[x_1 x_2} \ldots K^{x_{K'-1} x_{K'}} K^{x_{K'+1}]} &= 0 \\ K^{[x_1 x_2} \ldots K^{x_{K'+1} x_{K'+2}]} &= 0 \end{aligned}\right. \quad (x_1,\ldots, x_{K'+2} = \mathrm{m}+1,\ldots, 2\mathrm{n}). \tag{7.2}$$

We call $2n-m^*$ ($m^* < m$) the number of mutually independent equations in ξ^κ, w_λ in the system thus obtained. Either this system is incompatible or it represents an $\mathfrak{N}_{m^*}$ of a class K^*, such that every integral-$\mathfrak{N}_{m'}$ of class K' of the $\mathfrak{N}_m$ is also an integral-$\mathfrak{N}_{m'}$ of the $\mathfrak{N}_{m^*}$. In the case of incompatibility the $\mathfrak{N}_m$ does not have any integral-$\mathfrak{N}_{m'}$'s of class K'. Conversely every integral-$\mathfrak{N}_{m'}$ of the $\mathfrak{N}_{m^*}$ is also an integral-$\mathfrak{N}_{m'}$ of the $\mathfrak{N}_m$, because the $\mathfrak{N}_{m^*}$ is contained in the $\mathfrak{N}_m$. If now

$$\left.\begin{aligned} K^* \leqslant K' &\leqslant K^*+2(m^*-m') \\ 2n-2m' \leqslant K' &\leqslant 2n-m' \end{aligned}\right. \quad (m' \leqslant m^*), \tag{7.3}$$

the $\mathfrak{N}_{m^*}$ is totally integrable with respect to integral-$\mathfrak{N}_{m'}$'s of class K'. Then these integral-$\mathfrak{N}_{m'}$'s can be constructed in the ordinary way and the problem is solved. If $K' > K^*+2(m^*-m')$ or if $m' > m^*$ neither the $\mathfrak{N}_{m^*}$ nor the $\mathfrak{N}_m$ have any integral $\mathfrak{N}_{m'}$'s of class K'. If

$$K' \leqslant K^*+2(m^*-m') \quad (m' \leqslant m^*)$$

but $K^* > K'$, the system of equations of the $\mathfrak{N}_{m^*}$ has to be extended in the same way, and so on. In all cases we get, after a finite number of steps either an incompatible system, or a vector manifold admitting no integral-$\mathfrak{N}_{m'}$'s of class K' or a vector manifold totally integrable with respect to integral-$\mathfrak{N}_{m'}$'s of class K'. Only in the last case does the $\mathfrak{N}_m$ possess integral-$\mathfrak{N}_{m'}$'s of class K' and these are identical with the integral-$\mathfrak{N}_{m'}$'s of class K' of the last vector manifold obtained. These integral-$\mathfrak{N}_{m'}$'s can be obtained as described in VII, §§ 4, 5, eventually taking into account special conditions with respect to their field dimension. Collecting results we get the theorem

THEOREM VII.13. *If an $\mathfrak{N}_m$ of class K possesses integral-$\mathfrak{N}_{m'}$'s of class $K' < K$, by a process requiring no integrations an $\mathfrak{N}_{m^*}$ ($m^* < m$) can be constructed, which has the same integral-$\mathfrak{N}_{m'}$'s of class K' as the $\mathfrak{N}_m$ and which is totally integrable with respect to these integral-$\mathfrak{N}_{m'}$'s.*

† Cf. Schouten and v. d. Kulk 1942. 1.

For $K > 1$ and $K' = 1$ ($m' = n$) the method described reduces to the well-known method of extending a system of $2n-m$ partial differential equations of the first order

$$F^x(\xi^\kappa, w_\lambda) = 0, \qquad w_\lambda = \partial_\lambda p \quad (x = \mathrm{m}+1,..., 2\mathrm{n}) \tag{7.4}$$

by adding the equations

$$(F^x, F^y) = 0 \quad (x, y = \mathrm{m}+1,..., 2\mathrm{n}), \tag{7.5}$$

handling the resulting system in the same way, and so on. If (7.4) has solutions we get at last a system in involution which has the same solutions as (7.4).

8. Complete classification of simple covariant q-vector fields†

The results obtained enable us to perfect the classification of simple covariant q-vector fields (or systems of Pfaffians) already prepared in Chapter V.

A simple covariant q-vector field ($q > 1$) determines a homogeneous $\mathfrak{N}_{n+q}$ with field dimension n by means of the equation

$$w_{[\lambda_1 \ldots \lambda_q} w_{\lambda]} = 0. \tag{8.1}$$

In fact there exist among the equations (8.1) just $n-q$ linear independent ones, e.g. if $w_{1 \ldots q} \neq 0$,

$$\begin{aligned} F^{\mathrm{n+q+1}}(\xi^\kappa, w_\lambda) &\overset{\mathrm{def}}{=} w_{[1 \ldots q} w_{q+1]} = 0, \\ &\cdots\cdots\cdots \\ F^{2\mathrm{n}}(\xi^\kappa, w_\lambda) &\overset{\mathrm{def}}{=} w_{[1 \ldots q} w_{n]} = 0. \end{aligned} \tag{8.2}$$

The class of this $\mathfrak{N}_{n+q}$ is always even and $\leqslant n-q$. The integral-$\mathfrak{N}_n$'s with field dimension n are the vector fields which are divisors of $w_{\lambda_1 \ldots \lambda_q}$. If q linearly independent vector divisors are obtained, their alternated product is equal to $w_{\lambda_1 \ldots \lambda_q}$ to within a scalar factor which can be determined later. Hence a scalar factor in one of the divisors is not important and we may content ourselves with looking only for integral-$\mathfrak{N}_n$'s of an odd class K'. In consequence of Theorem VII.8 the $\mathfrak{N}_{n+q}$ is totally integrable with respect to integral-$\mathfrak{N}_n$'s of an odd class K' and with a field dimension n if and only if

$$K+1 \leqslant K' \leqslant K+2q-1 \quad (K' \leqslant n). \tag{8.3}$$

No integral-$\mathfrak{N}_n$'s of a class $> K+2q$ exist. Hence we have the theorem

THEOREM VII.14. *If* $\overset{0}{w}_\lambda$ *is a divisor of the simple q-vector field* $w_{\lambda_1 \ldots \lambda_q}$ ($q > 1$) *in* $\xi^\kappa = \underset{0}{\xi^\kappa}$, *if the class of the homogeneous* $\mathfrak{N}_{n+q}$ *with the equations*

$$w_{[\lambda_1 \ldots \lambda_q} w_{\lambda]} = 0 \tag{8.4}$$

† Cf. Schouten and v. d. Kulk 1940. 1, 2, 3, 4; 1942. 1.

is K in an $\mathfrak{N}(\xi^\kappa, \overset{0}{w}_\lambda)$, *and if* K' *is an odd integer* $\geqslant K+1$, $\leqslant K+2q-1$, *and* $\leqslant n$, *the q-vector* $\underset{0}{w}_{\lambda_1\ldots\lambda_q}$ *possesses at least one divisor* w_λ *of class* K' *taking the values* $\overset{0}{w}_\lambda$ *for* $\xi^\kappa = \underset{0}{\xi^\kappa}$.

If, for $\overset{0}{w}_\lambda$, we take successively q linearly independent divisors of $w_{\lambda_1\ldots\lambda_q}$ in $\xi^\kappa = \underset{0}{\xi^\kappa}$ we get the theorem

THEOREM VII.15. *Every simple q-vector field can be written as the product of a scalar and q vectors of classes* $K_1,\ldots, K_q$, *the* $K_1,\ldots, K_q$ *being arbitrarily chosen odd integers* $\geqslant K+1$, $\leqslant K+2q-1$, *and* $\leqslant n$. *Vector divisors of a class* $> K+2q$ *do not exist.*

$w_{\lambda_1\ldots\lambda_q}$ may have vector divisors of a class $\leqslant K$. In order to obtain these we first determine the divisors of class 1 by adding the equations

$$(F^x, F^y) = 0 \quad (x, y = \mathrm{n+q+1,\ldots, 2n}), \tag{8.5}$$

dealing with the resulting system in the same way, and so on, until we get an incompatible system or a system totally integrable with respect to integral vector fields of class 1. If the maximum number of linearly independent integral vector fields of class 1 thus obtained is $\beta_1 = \gamma_1$, the q-vector $w_{\lambda_1\ldots\lambda_q}$ has just $\beta_1 = \gamma_1$ vector divisors of class 1. Subsequently the divisors of a class $\leqslant 3$ are determined by adding the equations

$$(F^{[x}, F^y)(F^z, F^{u]}) = 0 \quad (x, y, z, u = \mathrm{n+q+1,\ldots, 2n}) \tag{8.6}$$

instead of (8.5) and dealing with the resulting system in the same way, and so on. If the maximum number of linearly independent integral vector fields thus obtained is β_3 and if the maximum number of these vector fields which are linearly independent of each other and of the γ_1 fields of class 1 is γ_3, the q-vector $w_{\lambda_1\ldots\lambda_q}$ has as a divisor a product of at most γ_1 vectors of class 1 and γ_3 vectors of class 3. This process can be continued until q linearly independent vector divisors of lowest class are obtained. We use the following notations, K' being odd:

$\alpha_{K'}$ = maximum number of linearly independent vector divisors of class K';

$\beta_{K'}$ = maximum number of linearly independent vector divisors of classes $\leqslant K'$;

$\gamma_{K'}$ = maximum number of vector divisors of class K' which are linearly independent of each other and of all vector divisors of odd classes $\leqslant K'-2$.

The numbers $\alpha_{K'}$, $\beta_{K'}$, and $\gamma_{K'}$ are arithmetic invariants of the field $w_{\lambda_1\ldots\lambda_q}$. They can be obtained by algebraic processes and differentiations only. The geometrical signification of $\beta_{K'}$ can be obtained as follows. For the determination of all vector divisors of classes $\leqslant K'$ the equations

$$(F^{[x_1}, F^{x_2})\ldots(F^{x_{K'}}, F^{x_{K'+1}]}) = 0 \quad (x_1,\ldots, x_{K'+1} = \mathrm{n+q+1,\ldots, 2n}) \tag{8.7}$$

have to be added and this process has to be repeated as often as necessary. If vector divisors of classes $\leqslant K'$ exist, the system finally obtained represents a homogeneous $\mathfrak{N}_{n+q'}$ ($q' \leqslant q$) with field dimension n. This $\mathfrak{N}_{n+q'}$ fixes a $\mathfrak{B}_{q'}$ (that is, a system of $\infty^{q'}$ covariant vectors) at every point of X_n. All vector divisors of classes $\leqslant K'$ are vector fields contained in this $\mathfrak{B}_{q'}$-field. Hence, if at any point of the X_n in the region considered, we construct in the domain of all covariant vectors at that point the smallest linear manifold containing the local $\mathfrak{B}_{q'}$, the dimension of this linear manifold is $\beta_{K'}$. From this it follows that

$$0 \leqslant \beta_{K'-2} \leqslant \beta_{K'} \quad (K' \geqslant 3). \tag{8.8}$$

From the definition of $\gamma_{K'}$ it follows that

$$0 \leqslant \gamma_{K'} = \beta_{K'} - \beta_{K'-2} \quad (K' \geqslant 3) \tag{8.9}$$

and, from the definition of $\alpha_{K'}$,

$$0 \leqslant \alpha_{K'} \leqslant \beta_{K'}. \tag{8.10}$$

Vector divisors of classes $> K+2q-1$ do not exist, and for

$$K+1 \leqslant K' \leqslant K+2q-1$$

we have total integrability. Hence

$$\begin{aligned} \alpha_{K'} &= q \quad \text{for} \quad K+1 \leqslant K' \leqslant K+2q-1, \\ \alpha_{K'} &= 0 \quad \text{for} \quad K' > K+2q-1, \\ \beta_{K'} &= q \quad \text{for} \quad K+1 \leqslant K', \\ \gamma_{K'} &= 0 \quad \text{for} \quad K+3 \leqslant K'. \end{aligned} \tag{8.11}$$

Finally we get from (8.9)

$$\sum_{K'=1}^{K'=K+1} \gamma_{K'} = \beta_{K+1} = q, \tag{8.12}$$

and from this it follows that it is always possible to determine γ_1 vector divisors of class 1, γ_3 vector divisors of class 3, and so on up to γ_{K+1} vector divisors of class $K+1$, which together form a system of q linearly independent vector divisors of $w_{\lambda_1\ldots\lambda_q}$. We collect results in the theorem

THEOREM VII.16. *A simple covariant q-vector field $w_{\lambda_1\ldots\lambda_q}$ is the product of a scalar and γ_1 vectors of class 1, γ_3 vectors of class 3, and so on up to*

γ_{K+1} *vectors of class* $K+1$. *No factorization containing more than* $\gamma_1+\gamma_3+...+\gamma_{2l+1}$ *factors of classes* $\leqslant 2l+1$ $(2l+1 = 1,..., K+1)$ *exists. The arithmetic invariants* $\gamma_1,..., \gamma_{K+1}$ *can be determined by algebraic processes and differentiations only.*

As a first example we consider the field

$$w_{\lambda_1...\lambda_q} = \overset{n-q+1}{e}_{[\lambda_1} \; ... \; \overset{n-1}{e}_{\lambda_{q-1}}(\overset{n}{e}_{\lambda_q]}+\xi^1\overset{2}{e}_{\lambda_q]}+...+\xi^{n-q-1}\overset{n-q}{e}_{\lambda_q]}) \quad (n-q = \text{even}). \tag{8.13}$$

Because of $w_{n-q+1...n} = (q!)^{-1}$ the equations of the $\mathfrak{N}_{n+q}$ are

$$\begin{aligned} w_{[n-q+1...n}\, w_{1]} &= 0, \\ \cdot \quad \cdot \quad \cdot &\quad \cdot \quad \cdot \quad \cdot \\ w_{[n-q+1...n}\, w_{n-q]} &= 0 \end{aligned} \tag{8.14}$$

or, written in full,

$$\begin{aligned} F^{n+q+1}(\xi^\kappa, w_\lambda) &\overset{\text{def}}{=} w_1 = 0, \\ F^{n+q+2}(\xi^\kappa, w_\lambda) &\overset{\text{def}}{=} w_2 - w_n \xi^1 = 0, \\ \cdot \quad \cdot \quad \cdot \quad \cdot \quad &\cdot \quad \cdot \quad \cdot \quad \cdot \quad \cdot \\ F^{2n-1}(\xi^\kappa, w_\lambda) &\overset{\text{def}}{=} w_{n-q-1} = 0, \\ F^{2n}(\xi^\kappa, w_\lambda) &\overset{\text{def}}{=} w_{n-q} - w_n \xi^{n-q-1} = 0. \end{aligned} \tag{8.15}$$

All components of K^{xy} vanish except

$$\begin{aligned} K^{n+q+1,n+q+2} &= -K^{n+q+2,n+q+1} = -w_n, \\ \cdot \quad \cdot \quad \cdot \quad \cdot \quad &\cdot \quad \cdot \quad \cdot \quad \cdot \quad \cdot \\ K^{2n-1,2n} &= -K^{2n,2n-1} = -w_n \end{aligned} \tag{8.16}$$

and thus $K = n-q$. To find the integral vector fields of classes $< n-q$ we have to add the equations

$$K^{[n+q+1,n+q+2}...K^{2n-1,2n]} = 0, \tag{8.17}$$

reducing here to one equation

$$w_n = 0. \tag{8.18}$$

The extended system consists of $n-q+1$ equations, and since it is of class zero it is totally integrable with respect to integral vector fields of the classes $1, 3,..., 2q-3$ and has no integral vector field of class $> 2q-2$. In fact we see immediately from the equations (8.15) and (8.18) that all the components of w_λ except $w_{n-q+1},..., w_{n-1}$ vanish and, accordingly, the integral vector fields are all the fields which depend linearly on $\overset{n-q+1}{e}_\lambda,..., \overset{n-1}{e}_\lambda$. Evidently there can be no field among them which has a class $> 2q-2$. If $2q-2 < n-q$ the q-vector $w_{\lambda_1...\lambda_q}$ has vector divisors of the classes $1, 3,..., 2q-3$ and of all odd classes $> n-q$

and $\leqslant n$. But if $2q-2 \geqslant n-q$, vector divisors of all odd classes $\leqslant n$ exist. Hence

$$\begin{array}{lll}
\alpha_1 = q-1, & \beta_1 = q-1, & \gamma_1 = q-1, \\
\alpha_3 = q-1 & \beta_3 = q-1 & \gamma_3 = 0, \\
\cdots & \cdots & \cdots \\
\alpha_{2q-3} = q-1, & & \\
\cdots & \beta_{n-q-1} = q-1 & \gamma_{n-q-1} = 0, \\
\alpha_{n-q+1} = q, & \beta_{n-q+1} = q & \gamma_{n-q+1} = 1, \\
 & & \gamma_{n-q+2} = 0, \\
\cdots & \cdots & \cdots \\
\alpha_n = q \text{ or } \alpha_{n-1} = q; & \beta_n = q \text{ or } \beta_{n-1} = q; & \gamma_n = 0 \text{ or } \gamma_{n-1} = 0.
\end{array} \tag{8.19}$$

As another example we take the trivector field

$$w_{\lambda_1 \lambda_2 \lambda_3} = \overset{1}{e}_{[\lambda_1}(\overset{2}{e}_{\lambda_2}+\xi^3\overset{4}{e}_{\lambda_2})(\overset{5}{e}_{\lambda_3]}+\xi^6\overset{7}{e}_{\lambda_3]}+\xi^8\overset{9}{e}_{\lambda_3]}) \quad (n = 9). \tag{8.20}$$

Because $w_{125} = 1/6$ the equations of the $\mathfrak{N}_{12}$ are

$$\begin{aligned}
w_{[125}w_{3]} &= 0, \\
w_{[125}w_{4]} &= 0, \\
w_{[125}w_{6]} &= 0, \\
&\cdots \\
w_{[125}w_{9]} &= 0
\end{aligned} \tag{8.21}$$

or

$$\begin{aligned}
F^{13} &\overset{\text{def}}{=} w_3 = 0, \\
F^{14} &\overset{\text{def}}{=} w_4-\xi^3 w_2 = 0, \\
F^{15} &\overset{\text{def}}{=} w_6 = 0, \\
F^{16} &\overset{\text{def}}{=} w_7-\xi^6 w_5 = 0, \\
F^{17} &\overset{\text{def}}{=} w_8 = 0, \\
F^{18} &\overset{\text{def}}{=} w_9-\xi^8 w_5 = 0.
\end{aligned} \tag{8.22}$$

All components of K^{xy} vanish except

$$\begin{aligned}
K^{13,14} &= -K^{14,13} = -w_2, \\
K^{15,16} &= -K^{16,15} = -w_5, \\
K^{17,18} &= -K^{18,17} = -w_5.
\end{aligned} \tag{8.23}$$

Accordingly $K = 6$. The $\mathfrak{N}_{12}$ is totally integrable with respect to integral vector fields of classes 7 and 9.

In order to find the integral vector fields of class 1 we have to add the equations

$$w_2 = 0, \qquad w_5 = 0. \tag{8.24}$$

The extended system has class zero and every vector divisor of class 1

is a product of a scalar with $\overset{1}{e}_\lambda$. Hence $\beta_1 = \gamma_1 = 1$. To determine the integral vector fields of classes $\leqslant 3$ instead of (8.24) we have to add the equations

$$w_2 w_5 = 0, \qquad w_5 w_5 = 0, \tag{8.25}$$

which reduce to one equation $w_5 = 0$. The extended system has class 2. All components of w_λ have to vanish, except w_1, w_2, and w_4 and these components have to satisfy the relations

$$w_4 - \xi^3 w_2 = 0. \tag{8.26}$$

Accordingly the vector divisors of classes $\leqslant 3$ are all the vector fields of the classes 1 and 3 which are linearly dependent on $\overset{1}{e}_\lambda$ and $\overset{2}{e}_\lambda + \xi^3 \overset{4}{e}_\lambda$. Hence $\beta_3 = 2$, $\gamma_3 = 1$. To find the integral vector fields of classes $\leqslant 5$ instead of (8.24) the equation

$$w_2 w_5 w_5 = 0 \tag{8.27}$$

has to be added. There are three possible cases.

(*a*) $w_2 = 0$; $w_5 \neq 0$. All components of w_λ vanish except w_1, w_5, w_7, and w_9 and these components have to satisfy the conditions

$$\begin{aligned} w_7 - \xi^6 w_5 &= 0, \\ w_9 - \xi^8 w_5 &= 0. \end{aligned} \tag{8.28}$$

The vector divisors belonging to this case are all the vector fields of classes $\leqslant 5$ which are linearly dependent on $\overset{1}{e}_\lambda$ and $\overset{5}{e}_\lambda + \xi^6 \overset{7}{e}_\lambda + \xi^8 \overset{9}{e}_\lambda$.

(*b*) $w_2 \neq 0$, $w_5 = 0$. All components of w_λ vanish except w_1, w_2, and w_4 and these components have to satisfy the equations

$$w_4 - \xi^3 w_2 = 0. \tag{8.29}$$

The vector divisors belonging to this case are all the vector fields of classes $\leqslant 5$ which are linearly dependent on $\overset{1}{e}_\lambda$ and $\overset{2}{e}_\lambda + \xi^3 \overset{4}{e}_\lambda$.

(*c*) $w_2 = 0$, $w_5 = 0$. All components of w_λ vanish except w_1. The vector divisors belonging to this case are products of $\overset{1}{e}_\lambda$ with a scalar. Taking these cases together we get $\beta_5 = 3$, $\gamma_5 = 1$. Hence

$$\begin{aligned} \alpha_1 &= 1, & \beta_1 &= 1, & \gamma_1 &= 1; \\ \alpha_3 &= 2, & \beta_3 &= 2, & \gamma_3 &= 1; \\ \alpha_5 &= 3, & \beta_5 &= 3, & \gamma_5 &= 1; \\ \alpha_7 &= 3, & \beta_7 &= 3, & \gamma_7 &= 0; \\ \alpha_9 &= 3, & \beta_9 &= 3, & \gamma_9 &= 0. \end{aligned} \tag{8.30}$$

Consequently we have for the divisors of $w_{\lambda_1 \lambda_2 \lambda_3}$:

Classes 7 and 9. Every vector at a point $\underset{0}{\xi}^\kappa$ being a divisor of

$w_{\lambda_1 \lambda_2 \lambda_3}$ in $\underset{0}{\xi}^{\kappa}$ belongs to at least one divisor field of each of the classes *7* and *9*.

Class 5. Every vector at a point $\underset{0}{\xi}^{\kappa}$, being either linearly dependent on $\overset{1}{e}_\lambda$ and $\overset{5}{e}_\lambda+\xi^6\overset{7}{e}_\lambda+\xi^8\overset{9}{e}_\lambda$ or linearly dependent on $\overset{1}{e}_\lambda$ and $\overset{2}{e}_\lambda+\xi^3\overset{4}{e}_\lambda$, belongs to at least one divisor field of class *5*.

Class 3. Every vector at a point $\underset{0}{\xi}^{\kappa}$ being linearly dependent on $\overset{1}{e}_\lambda$ and $\overset{2}{e}_\lambda+\xi^3\overset{4}{e}_\lambda$ belongs to at least one divisor field of class *3*.

Class 1. The only divisors of $w_{\lambda_1 \lambda_2 \lambda_3}$ of class *1* are the gradient fields differing from $\overset{1}{e}_\lambda$ only by a scalar factor.

9. Normal forms of simple covariant q-vector fields and systems of Pfaffian equations†

According to Theorem VII.16 every simple covariant q-vector can be written as the product of a scalar and q vectors of classes $\leqslant K+1$. If $n-q$ is odd, we have $K \leqslant n-q-1$ and the classes of all vector divisors are $\leqslant n-q$. Hence in this case a representation of the q-vector field depending on at most $q(n-q)+1$ functions is obtained. Since an $(n-q)$-direction in E_n is determined by $q(n-q)$ numbers (cf. I, § 2), the representation thus obtained is a *normal form* (cf. IV, § 1).

Every system of q linearly independent Pfaffian equations can be written in the form

$$w_{\lambda_1 \ldots \lambda_q}\, d\xi^{\lambda_q} = 0, \tag{9.1}$$

$w_{\lambda_1 \ldots \lambda_q}$ being a simple q-vector, and consequently the following theorem, concerning systems of q Pfaffian equations for $n-q$ odd, follows from Theorem VII.16:

THEOREM VII.17. *For $n-q$ odd, every system of $q<n$ linearly independent Pfaffian equations in n variables is equivalent to a system of q Pfaffian equations of classes $\leqslant n-q$ and consequently can be written in the normal form*

$$\left.\begin{array}{l} d\overset{1,0}{s}+\overset{1,1}{z}\,d\overset{1,1}{s}+\ldots+\overset{1,l}{z}\,d\overset{1,l}{s}=0 \\ \cdot\quad\cdot\quad\cdot\quad\cdot\quad\cdot\quad\cdot\quad\cdot\quad\cdot\quad\cdot\quad\cdot \\ d\overset{q,0}{s}+\overset{q,1}{z}\,d\overset{q,1}{s}+\ldots+\overset{q,l}{z}\,d\overset{q,l}{s}=0 \end{array}\right. \quad \left(l=\frac{n-q-1}{2}\right). \tag{9.2}$$

If $n-q$ is even we have $K \leqslant n-q$ and according to Theorem VII.16 there exist q linearly independent vector divisors of classes $\leqslant n-q+1$. Hence we get a representation of the q-vector field depending on at

† Cf. Schouten and v. d. Kulk 1943. 3.

most $q(n-q+1)+1$ functions, that is, q functions more than a normal form can contain. In order to get a normal form in this case we choose an arbitrary function $p(\xi^\kappa)$ whose gradient p_λ is not a divisor of $w_{\lambda_1\ldots\lambda_q}$ and form the simple $(q+1)$-vector

$$w_{[\lambda_1\ldots\lambda_q}p_{\lambda]}. \tag{9.3}$$

The class $\overset{q+1}{K}$ of the $\mathfrak{N}_{n+q+1}$ belonging to this $(q+1)$-vector is $\leqslant n-q-2$ and $\leqslant K$. Hence $\overset{q+1}{K} \leqslant K-2$ for $K = n-q$ and $\overset{q+1}{K} \leqslant K$ for $K < n-q$, and according to Theorem VII.16 there exist $q+1$ linearly independent vector divisors of (9.3) of classes $\leqslant K-1$ for $K = n-q$ and of classes $\leqslant K+1$ for $K < n-q$. Among these there always exist q vectors $\overset{1}{u}_\lambda,\ldots, \overset{q}{u}_\lambda$, which constitute together with p_λ a system of linearly independent divisors of (9.3) and every vector divisor of $w_{\lambda_1\ldots\lambda_q}$ can be expressed linearly in the u_λ and p_λ. A consequence of this is that there exist q linearly independent vector divisors of $w_{\lambda_1\ldots\lambda_q}$ of the form

$$\overset{\mathfrak{a}}{w}_\lambda = \overset{\mathfrak{a}}{u}_\lambda + \overset{\mathfrak{a}}{\lambda} p_\lambda \quad (\mathfrak{a} = 1,\ldots, q). \tag{9.4}$$

Since these divisors have classes $\leqslant K+1$ for $K = n-q$ and $\leqslant K+3$ for $K < n-q$ they can be written

$$\overset{\mathfrak{a}}{w}_\lambda = \partial_\lambda \overset{\mathfrak{a},0}{s} + \overset{\mathfrak{a},1}{z}\, \partial_\lambda \overset{\mathfrak{a},1}{s} + \ldots + \overset{\mathfrak{a},h-1}{z}\, \partial_\lambda \overset{\mathfrak{a},h-1}{s} + \overset{\mathfrak{a},h}{z}\, \partial_\lambda p$$

$$\left(\mathfrak{a} = 1,\ldots, q;\ h = \begin{cases} \tfrac{1}{2}K & \text{for} \quad K = n-q \\ \tfrac{1}{2}K+1 & \text{for} \quad K < n-q \end{cases}\right). \tag{9.5}$$

We call this factorization of $w_{\lambda_1\ldots\lambda_q}$ the *factorization with respect to* p_λ.

Since the maximum number of independent functions occurring in the $\overset{\mathfrak{a}}{w}_\lambda$ is $q(n-q)+1$ for $K = n-q$ and $q(K+2)+1$ for $K < n-q$, we get for $w_{\lambda_1\ldots\lambda_q}$ a form containing $q(n-q)+2$ or $q(K+2)+2$ independent functions for $K = n-q$ or $K < n-q$ respectively. Hence the factorization of $w_{\lambda_1\ldots\lambda_q}$ with respect to p_λ only gives a normal form if

$$K < n-q-2.$$

To derive a normal form for $n-q$ even, which is valid in all cases, we consider the null form of the $\mathfrak{N}_{n+q}$ belonging to $w_{\lambda_1\ldots\lambda_q}$

$$B_b^\lambda(\xi^\kappa) w_\lambda = 0 \quad (b = 1,\ldots, \mathrm{n-q}) \tag{9.6}$$

and the parametric form of this $\mathfrak{N}_{n+q}$

$$\begin{aligned} w_\lambda &= \eta_x\, C_\lambda^x(\xi^\kappa) \\ \xi^\kappa &= \xi^\kappa \end{aligned} \quad (x = \mathrm{n-q+1,\ldots, n}) \tag{9.7}$$

with the parameters η_x and ξ^κ. The C_λ^x $(x = \mathrm{n-q+1,\ldots,n})$ are q arbitrary vector divisors of $w_{\lambda_1\ldots\lambda_q}$. With this notation, slightly modified in order to adapt it to this special problem, the Poisson brackets take the form

$$K_{cb} \overset{\text{def}}{=} 2B^{\mu}_{[c}(\partial_{|\mu|}\, B^{\lambda}_{b]})w_{\lambda} \quad (b, c = 1,..., \mathrm{n-q}) \tag{9.8}$$

and the class of the $\mathfrak{N}_{n+q}$ is the rank of this bivector. The class $\overline{K} = K+2q$ is the rank of the bivector with the components

$$U^{\kappa\lambda} \overset{\text{def}}{=} \frac{\partial w_\mu}{\partial \xi^\kappa}\frac{\partial \xi^\mu}{\partial \xi^\lambda} - \frac{\partial w_\mu}{\partial \xi^\lambda}\frac{\partial \xi^\mu}{\partial \xi^\kappa} = 2\eta_x\, \partial_{[\kappa}\, C^x_{\lambda]}$$

$$U^{x\lambda} \overset{\text{def}}{=} \frac{\partial w_\mu}{\partial \eta_x}\frac{\partial \xi^\mu}{\partial \xi^\lambda} = C^x_\lambda \qquad (x, y = \mathrm{n-q+1,..., n}), \tag{9.9}$$

$$U^{xy} \overset{\text{def}}{=} 0$$

and with the matrix

$$\begin{array}{c} \\ n\updownarrow \\ q\updownarrow \end{array}\left\| \begin{array}{cc} \overleftrightarrow{\quad n \quad} & \overleftrightarrow{\quad q \quad} \\ 2\eta_x\, \partial_{[\kappa}\, C^x_{\lambda]} & -C^y_\kappa \\ C^x_\lambda & 0 \end{array} \right\| \qquad (x, y, z = \mathrm{n-q+1,..., n}). \tag{9.10}$$

If all C^x_λ $(x = \mathrm{n-q+1,..., n})$ are gradient vectors we have $\overline{K} = 2q$ and $K = 0$. But, if $w_{\lambda_1...\lambda_q}$ does not have q linearly independent gradient divisors, K may have the highest value, as we see from the example (8.13) where $q-1$ gradient divisors exist.

Next to (9.6) we consider the equation

$$B^{\mu_1}_{[1}(\partial_{|\mu_1|}\, B^{\lambda_1}_{2})...B^{\mu_l}_{2l-1}(\partial_{|\mu_l|}\, B^{\lambda_l}_{2l]})\, w_{\lambda_1}...w_{\lambda_l} = 0 \quad (l = \tfrac{1}{2}(n-q)) \tag{9.11}$$

in the w_λ. If $K < n-q$ this equation is satisfied as a consequence of (9.6). But if $K = n-q$ the system (9.6, 11) represents a homogeneous $\mathfrak{N}_{n+q-1}$ with field dimension n and with an even class $K^* \geqslant K$. Then, because $K^* \leqslant n-q+1$, we have $K^* = K$. Hence the $\mathfrak{N}_{n+q-1}$ is totally integrable with respect to integral vector fields of class $n-q+1$. If $K < n-q$ the $\mathfrak{N}_{n+q}$ is totally integrable with respect to integral vector fields of an odd class K', provided that

$$K+1 \leqslant K' \leqslant K+2q-1 \quad (K' \leqslant n). \tag{9.12}$$

Collecting results we may state that (9.6, 11) represent:

for $K < n-q$	for $K = n-q$
an $\mathfrak{N}_{n+q}$ with field dimension n and class $< n-q$, totally integrable with respect to integral vector fields of class $K+3$.	an $\mathfrak{N}_{n+q-1}$ with field dimension n and class $n-q$, totally integrable with respect to integral vector fields of class $K+1$.

Now let

$$\overset{1}{v}_\lambda = \overset{0}{s}_\lambda + z\overset{11}{s}_\lambda + ... + z\overset{hh}{s}_\lambda \quad (2h = K-2\eta+2) \tag{9.13}$$

be a canonical form of an integral vector field of this $\mathfrak{N}_{n+q-\eta}$ ($\eta = 0$ or 1) of class $K-2\eta+3$. We suppose that this normal form is chosen in such a way that $\overset{0}{s}_\lambda$ is not a divisor of $w_{\lambda_1\ldots\lambda_q}$ (cf. IV, § 6). $\overset{1}{v}_\lambda$ is a vector divisor of $w_{\lambda_1\ldots\lambda_q}$. From (9.6) we get

$$B_b^\lambda \overset{1}{v}_\lambda = B_b^\lambda \overset{0}{s}_\lambda + \overset{1}{z} B_b^\lambda \overset{1}{s}_\lambda + \ldots + \overset{h}{z} B_b^\lambda \overset{h}{s}_\lambda = 0$$
$$(b = 1,\ldots,\mathrm{n-q};\ 2h = K-2\eta+2), \quad (9.14)$$

and from this it follows that

$$B_{[c}^\mu(\partial_{|\mu|} B_{b]}^\lambda)\overset{1}{v}_\lambda = -B_{[c}^\mu B_{b]}^\lambda(\overset{1}{z}_{[\mu} \overset{1}{s}_{\lambda]} + \ldots + \overset{h}{z}_{[\mu} \overset{h}{s}_{\lambda]})$$
$$(b, c = 1,\ldots,\mathrm{n-q};\ 2h = K-2\eta+2). \quad (9.15)$$

Now both for $\eta = 0$ and for $\eta = 1$ we have

$$B_{[b_1}^{\mu_1}(\partial_{|\mu_1|} B_{b_2}^{\lambda_1})\ldots B_{b_{2h-1}}^{\mu_h} \partial_{|\mu_h|} B_{b_{2h}]}^{\lambda_h} w_{\lambda_1}\ldots w_{\lambda_h} = 0$$
$$(b_1,\ldots, b_{2h} = 1,\ldots,\mathrm{n-q};\ 2h = K-2\eta+2) \quad (9.16)$$

and, by replacing w_λ in this equation by $\overset{1}{v}_\lambda$, we get

$$B_{[b_1}^{\mu_1} B_{b_2}^{\lambda_1}\ldots B_{b_{2h-1}}^{\mu_h} B_{b_{2h}]}^{\lambda_h} (\overset{1}{z}_{\mu_1} \overset{1}{s}_{\lambda_1} + \ldots + \overset{h}{z}_{\mu_1} \overset{h}{s}_{\lambda_1})\ldots(\overset{1}{z}_{\mu_h} \overset{1}{s}_{\lambda_h} + \ldots + \overset{h}{z}_{\mu_h} \overset{h}{s}_{\lambda_h}) = 0$$
$$(b_1,\ldots, b_{2h} = 1,\ldots,\mathrm{n-q};\ 2h = K-2\eta+2), \quad (9.17)$$

or

$$h!\, B_{[b_1}^{\mu_1} B_{b_2}^{\lambda_1}\ldots B_{b_{2h-1}}^{\mu_h} B_{b_{2h}]}^{\lambda_h} \overset{1}{z}_{\mu_1} \overset{1}{s}_{\lambda_1} \overset{2}{z}_{\mu_2} \overset{2}{s}_{\lambda_2}\ldots \overset{h}{z}_{\mu_h} \overset{h}{s}_{\lambda_h} = 0$$
$$(b_1,\ldots, b_{2h} = 1,\ldots,\mathrm{n-q};\ 2h = K-2\eta+2). \quad (9.18)$$

This equation expresses the fact that the $2h$ covariant vectors

$$B_b^\mu \overset{1}{z}_\mu,\ldots, B_b^\mu \overset{h}{z}_\mu, B_b^\mu \overset{1}{s}_\mu,\ldots, B_b^\mu \overset{h}{s}_\mu$$
$$(b = 1,\ldots,\mathrm{n-q};\ 2h = K-2\eta+2) \quad (9.19)$$

are linearly dependent. Hence at least one relation of the form

$$B_b^\lambda(\overset{11}{\alpha z}_\lambda + \overset{11}{\beta s}_\lambda + \ldots + \overset{hh}{\alpha z}_\lambda + \overset{hh}{\beta s}_\lambda) = 0 \quad (2h = K-2\eta+2) \quad (9.20)$$

exists in which the coefficients α and β cannot all vanish simultaneously. If all coefficients β vanish and, for instance, $\overset{1}{\alpha} \neq 0$, (9.13) can be written in the form

$$\overset{1}{v}_\lambda = \partial_\lambda(\overset{0}{s} + \overset{11}{zs}) - \overset{11}{sz}_\lambda + \overset{22}{zs}_\lambda + \ldots + \overset{hh}{zs}_\lambda \quad (9.21)$$

and with respect to this canonical form of $\overset{1}{v}_\lambda$ the coefficient $\overset{1}{\alpha}$ plays the same role as $\overset{1}{\beta}$ with respect to (9.13). Hence we may assume that at least one of the coefficients β does not vanish and by interchanging indices we can always make $\overset{h}{\beta} \neq 0$. Then, by dividing the vector between the brackets in (9.20) by $\overset{h}{\beta}$ we get a vector $\overset{2}{v}_\lambda$ of the form

$$\overset{2}{v}_\lambda = \overset{1}{\alpha}\overset{1}{z}_\lambda+\overset{1}{\beta}\overset{1}{s}_\lambda+\dots+\overset{h-1}{\alpha}\,\overset{h-1}{z}_\lambda+\overset{h-1}{\beta}\,\overset{h-1}{s}_\lambda+\overset{h}{\alpha}\overset{h}{z}_\lambda+\overset{h}{s}_\lambda \tag{9.22}$$

in which α and β are written for the α's and β's from (9.20) divided by $\overset{h}{\beta}$. In $\overset{2}{v}_\lambda$ some of the coefficients α and β or all these coefficients may vanish and consequently the class of $\overset{2}{v}_\lambda$ is $\leqslant 4h-1$. $\overset{1}{v}_\lambda$ and $\overset{2}{v}_\lambda$ are both vector divisors of $w_{\lambda_1\dots\lambda_q}$ and since $\overset{1}{v}_\lambda$ contains $\overset{0}{s}_\lambda$, these vectors are linearly independent.

If $\overset{h}{s}_\lambda$ is not a divisor of $w_{\lambda_1\dots\lambda_q}$, this q-vector can be factorized with respect to $\overset{h}{s}_\lambda$. Among the resulting q vectors there always exist $q-2$ vectors linearly independent of each other and of $\overset{1}{v}_\lambda$ and $\overset{2}{v}_\lambda$. These $q-2$ vectors all have the form $u_\lambda+\lambda\overset{h}{s}_\lambda$, u_λ being a vector of a class $\leqslant K-1$ for $K=n-q$ and $\leqslant K+1$ for $K<n-q$ and consequently $\leqslant 2h-1$ in all cases. Hence we have found a factorization of $w_{\lambda_1\dots\lambda}$ of the form

$$\begin{aligned}
\overset{1}{v}_\lambda &= \overset{1,0}{s}_\lambda+\overset{1,1}{z}\,\overset{1,1}{s}_\lambda+\dots+\overset{1,h}{z}\,\overset{1,h}{s}_\lambda,\\
\overset{2}{v}_\lambda &= \overset{1}{\alpha}\overset{1,1}{z}_\lambda+\overset{1}{\beta}\overset{1,1}{s}_\lambda+\dots+\overset{h-1}{\alpha}\,\overset{1,h-1}{z}_\lambda+\overset{h-1}{\beta}\,\overset{1,h-1}{s}_\lambda+\overset{h}{\alpha}\overset{1,h}{z}_\lambda+\overset{1,h}{s}_\lambda,\\
\overset{3}{v}_\lambda &= \overset{3,0}{s}_\lambda+\overset{3,1}{z}\,\overset{3,1}{s}_\lambda+\dots+\overset{3,h-1}{z}\,\overset{3,h-1}{s}_\lambda+\overset{3,h}{z}\,\overset{1,h}{s}_\lambda,\\
&\dots\dots\dots\dots\dots\dots\\
\overset{q}{v}_\lambda &= \overset{q,0}{s}_\lambda+\overset{q,1}{z}\,\overset{q,1}{s}_\lambda+\dots+\overset{q,h-1}{z}\,\overset{q,h-1}{s}_\lambda+\overset{q,h}{z}\,\overset{1,h}{s}_\lambda\\
&\qquad\qquad (h=\tfrac{1}{2}K-\eta+1),
\end{aligned} \tag{9.23}$$

in which we have written $\overset{1,0}{s},\dots,\overset{1,h}{s},\overset{1,1}{z},\dots,\overset{1,h}{z}$ instead of $\overset{0}{s},\dots,\overset{h}{s},\overset{1}{z},\dots,\overset{h}{z}$.

If $\overset{1,h}{s}_\lambda$ is a divisor of $w_{\lambda_1\dots\lambda_q}$ at least one of the vectors $\overset{1,1}{s}_\lambda,\dots,\overset{1,h-1}{s}_\lambda$ is not a divisor, because otherwise $\overset{1,0}{s}_\lambda$ would be a divisor in contradiction with our suppositions. If now, for instance, $\overset{1,1}{s}_\lambda$ is not a divisor the vector $\overset{1,h}{s}_\lambda+\overset{1,1}{s}_\lambda$ is also not a divisor. Then $\overset{1}{v}_\lambda$ and $\overset{2}{v}_\lambda$ can be written in the form

$$\begin{aligned}
\overset{1}{v}_\lambda &= \overset{1,0}{s}_\lambda+(\overset{1,1}{z}-\overset{1,h}{z})\overset{1}{s}_\lambda+\overset{1,2}{z}\,\overset{1,2}{s}_\lambda+\dots+\overset{1,h-1}{z}\,\overset{1,h-1}{s}_\lambda+\overset{1,h}{z}(\overset{1,h}{s}_\lambda+\overset{1,1}{s}_\lambda),\\
\overset{2}{v}_\lambda &= \overset{1}{\alpha}(\overset{1,1}{z}_\lambda-\overset{1,h}{z}_\lambda)+(\overset{1}{\beta}-1)\overset{1,1}{s}_\lambda+\overset{2}{\alpha}\overset{1,2}{z}_\lambda+\overset{2}{\beta}\overset{1,2}{s}_\lambda+\dots+\overset{h-1}{\alpha}\,\overset{1,h-1}{z}_\lambda+\\
&\qquad+\overset{h-1}{\beta}\,\overset{1,h-1}{s}_\lambda+(\overset{h}{\alpha}+\overset{1}{\alpha})\overset{1,h}{z}_\lambda+(\overset{1,h}{s}_\lambda+\overset{1,1}{s}_\lambda)
\end{aligned} \tag{9.24}$$

and in this form $\overset{1,1}{z} - \overset{1,h}{z}$, $\overset{1}{\beta} - 1$, and $\overset{1,h}{s} + \overset{1,1}{s}$ play the same role as $\overset{1,1}{z}$, $\overset{1}{\beta}$, and $\overset{1,h}{s}$ in (9.23) and the vector $\overset{1,h}{s}_\lambda + \overset{1,1}{s}_\lambda$ occurring in $\overset{1}{v}_\lambda$ and $\overset{2}{v}_\lambda$ is not a divisor of $w_{\lambda_1\ldots\lambda_q}$. Hence, by factorizing $w_{\lambda_1\ldots\lambda_q}$ with respect to $\overset{1,h}{s}_\lambda + \overset{1,1}{s}_\lambda$ a factorization of the form (9.23) can be obtained. Since (9.23) contains just $2hq$ independent functions, that is, $q(n-q)$ for $K = n-q$ and

$$q(K+2) \leqslant q(n-q)$$

for $K < n-q$ the form obtained is a normal form.

If $K < n-q$ the $\mathfrak{N}_{n+q}$ is totally integrable with respect to integral vector fields of class $K+1$ and consequently it is possible to find q linearly independent vector divisors of class $K+1$. If $n-q$ is even and thus $q(K+1) < q(n-q)$, a normal form can be constructed, containing q functions less than (9.23). But this normal form is not contained in (9.23) as a special case.

From the results obtained we get the following theorem concerning systems of q Pfaffian equations for $n-q$ even (cf. Theorem VII.17):

Theorem VII.18. *For $n-q$ even, every system of $q < n$ linearly independent Pfaffian equations in n variables is equivalent to a system of $q-1$ Pfaffian equations of classes $\leqslant n-q+1$ and one Pfaffian equation of a class $\leqslant 2(n-q)-1$ and consequently can be written in the normal form*

$$\begin{gathered}
d\overset{1,0}{s} + \overset{1,1}{z}\, d\overset{1,1}{s} + \ldots + \overset{1,l}{z}\, d\overset{1,l}{s} = 0, \\
\overset{1}{\alpha}\, d\overset{1,1}{z} + \overset{1}{\beta}\, d\overset{1,1}{s} + \ldots + \overset{l-1}{\alpha}\, d\overset{1,l-1}{z} + \overset{l-1}{\beta}\, d\overset{1,l-1}{s} + \overset{l}{\alpha}\, d\overset{1,l}{z} + d\overset{1,l}{s} = 0, \\
d\overset{3,0}{s} + \overset{3,1}{z}\, d\overset{3,1}{s} + \ldots + \overset{3,l}{z}\, d\overset{1,l}{s} = 0, \\
\cdots\cdots\cdots \\
d\overset{q,0}{s} + \overset{q,1}{z}\, d\overset{q,1}{s} + \ldots + \overset{q,l}{z}\, d\overset{1,l}{s} = 0 \\
(l = \tfrac{1}{2}(n-q)). \qquad (9.25)
\end{gathered}$$

10. Canonical forms of the equations of an $\mathfrak{N}_m$†

In this section we establish the theorem

Theorem VII.19. *If the class K and the index l of an $\mathfrak{N}_m$ are constant in an $\mathfrak{N}(\underset{0}{\xi}{}^\kappa, \overset{0}{w}_\lambda)$, there exists a C_3-transformation ξ^κ, $w_\lambda \to {}'\xi^\kappa$, ${}'w_\lambda$ such that the equations of the $\mathfrak{N}_m$ in this $\mathfrak{N}(\underset{0}{\xi}{}^\kappa, \overset{0}{w}_\lambda)$ can be written in the form*

† Cf. Schouten and v. d. Kulk 1943. 4, 6.

$$\begin{array}{ll} '\xi^1 = 0, & 'w_1 = 0, \\ \cdot\ \cdot\ \cdot\ \cdot & \cdot\ \cdot\ \cdot\ \cdot \\ & 'w_\rho = 0, \\ '\xi^{2n-m-\rho-1} = 0, & \\ & 'w_{2n-m-\rho} = 1 \end{array} \tag{10.1}$$

for $K = 2\rho+1,\ l = 1$;

$$\begin{array}{ll} '\xi^1 = 0, & 'w_1 = 0, \\ \cdot\ \cdot\ \cdot\ \cdot & \cdot\ \cdot\ \cdot\ \cdot \\ & 'w_{\rho-1} = 0, \\ '\xi^{2n-m-\rho} = 0, & \\ & 'w_\rho = 1 \end{array} \tag{10.2}$$

for $K = 2\rho,\ l = 1$;

$$\begin{array}{ll} '\xi^1 = 0, & 'w_1 = 0, \\ \cdot\ \cdot\ \cdot\ \cdot & \cdot\ \cdot\ \cdot\ \cdot \\ '\xi^{2n-m-\rho} = 0, & 'w_\rho = 0 \end{array} \tag{10.3}$$

for $K = 2\rho,\ l = 0$.

We consider an $\mathfrak{N}_m$ of class K and index l in the X_n of the ξ^κ with the parametric form

$$\begin{aligned} w_\lambda &= w_\lambda(\eta^a) \\ \xi^\kappa &= \xi^\kappa(\eta^a) \end{aligned} \qquad (a = 1,\ldots, \mathrm{m}) \tag{10.4}$$

and another $\mathfrak{N}_m$ (denoted by $'\mathfrak{N}_m$) of the same class and index in the X_n of the $'\xi^\kappa$ (denoted by $'X_n$) with the parametric form

$$\begin{aligned} 'w_\lambda &= 'w_\lambda('\eta^a) \\ '\xi^\kappa &= '\xi^\kappa('\eta^a) \end{aligned} \qquad (a = 1,\ldots, \mathrm{m}). \tag{10.5}$$

In the X_m of the η^a we have the Pfaffian

$$C_b\, d\eta^b = w_\lambda\, d\xi^\lambda, \qquad C_b \overset{\text{def}}{=} w_\lambda \frac{\partial \xi^\lambda}{\partial \eta^b} \quad (b = 1,\ldots, \mathrm{m}) \tag{10.6}$$

and in the X_m of the $'\eta^a$ (denoted by $'X_m$) the Pfaffian

$$'C_b\, d'\eta^b = 'w_\lambda\, d'\xi^\lambda, \qquad 'C_b \overset{\text{def}}{=} 'w_\lambda \frac{\partial\, '\xi^\lambda}{\partial\, '\eta^b} \quad (b = 1,\ldots, \mathrm{m}). \tag{10.7}$$

Both Pfaffians have the class $K+2(m-n)$. Hence they can be brought into the same canonical form by means of two coordinate transformations $\eta^a \rightarrow \eta^{a'}$ and $'\eta^a \rightarrow '\eta^{a'}$. Dropping these new accents for the sake of simplicity the equations

$$'\eta^a = \eta^a \quad (a = 1,\ldots, \mathrm{m}) \tag{10.8}$$

represent a one-to-one correspondence between the points of the X_m and the points of the $'X_m$, that is, a one-to-one correspondence between the vector elements of $\mathfrak{N}_m$ and the vector elements of $'\mathfrak{N}_m$. From (10.6) and (10.7) it follows that for this correspondence the equation

$$'w_\lambda d\,'\xi^\lambda - w_\lambda d\xi^\lambda = 0 \tag{10.9}$$

holds and this means that the correspondence is a C_3-transformation of a special kind, since it is only defined for vector elements of the $\mathfrak{N}_m$ and of the $'\mathfrak{N}_m$ and not for any other vector elements of the X_n or $'X_n$. Now this C_3-transformation has to be extended to a C_3-transformation defined for all vector elements.

To this end we consider the $4n$-dimensional space with the coordinates ξ^κ, w_λ, $'\xi^\kappa$, $'w_\lambda$ and in this space we introduce another notation for the coordinates (cf. VI, § 3, VII, § 3), writing for these $4n$ coordinates X^P $(P = 1,\dots, n, (1),\dots, (n), 1',\dots, n', (1'),\dots, (n'))$ with the formulae of definition

$$X^\kappa \stackrel{\text{def}}{=} \xi^\kappa, \qquad X^{(\kappa)} \stackrel{\text{def}}{=} w_\kappa, \qquad X^{\kappa'} \stackrel{\text{def}}{=} {}'\xi^\kappa, \qquad X^{(\kappa')} \stackrel{\text{def}}{=} {}'w_\kappa$$
$$((\kappa) = (1),\dots, (n);\ (\kappa') = (1'),\dots, (n')). \tag{10.10}$$

In the X_{2n} of the ξ^κ and w_λ we have

$$w_\lambda d\xi^\lambda = W_B dX^B \quad (B = 1,\dots, n, (1),\dots, (n)), \tag{10.11}$$

W_B being defined by

$$W_\lambda \stackrel{\text{def}}{=} w_\lambda, \qquad W_{(\lambda)} \stackrel{\text{def}}{=} 0 \quad ((\lambda) = (1),\dots, (n)) \tag{10.12}$$

and in the X_{2n} of the $'\xi^\kappa$ and $'w_\lambda$ we have

$$'w_\lambda d\,'\xi^\lambda = W_{B'} dX^{B'} \quad (B' = 1',\dots, n', (1'),\dots, (n')), \tag{10.13}$$

$W_{B'}$ being defined by

$$W_{\lambda'} \stackrel{\text{def}}{=} {}'w_\lambda, \qquad W_{(\lambda')} = 0 \quad ((\lambda') = (1'),\dots, (n')). \tag{10.14}$$

In the X_{4n} of the X^P we have the Pfaffian

$$W_{B'} dX^{B'} - W_B dX^B = {}'w_\lambda d\,'\xi^\lambda - w_\lambda d\xi^\lambda$$
$$(B = 1,\dots, n, (1),\dots, (n);\ B' = 1',\dots, n', (1'),\dots, (n')) \tag{10.15}$$

and the equations

$$\begin{aligned} \xi^\kappa &= \xi^\kappa(\eta^a), & '\xi^\kappa &= {}'\xi^\kappa(\eta^a) \\ w_\lambda &= w_\lambda(\eta^a), & 'w_\lambda &= {}'w_\lambda(\eta^a) \end{aligned} \quad (a = 1,\dots, \mathrm{m}) \tag{10.16}$$

or, taken together,

$$X^P = \Phi^P(\eta^a) \quad (P = 1,\dots, n, (1),\dots, (n), 1',\dots, n', (1'),\dots, (n');$$
$$a = 1,\dots, \mathrm{m}), \tag{10.17}$$

arising from (10.4) and (10.5) in consequence of (10.8). (10.17) represents an X_m in the X_{4n} at each point of which

$$W_{B'} dX^{B'} - W_B dX^B = 0. \tag{10.18}$$

Hence this X_m is on one hand an integral-X_m of the Pfaffian (10.15) and represents on the other hand a transformation of the vector elements of $\mathfrak{N}_m$ into the vector elements of $'\mathfrak{N}_m$. But not every integral-X_m of (10.15) represents such a transformation. The necessary and sufficient conditions that it does are that the two systems of $2n$ equations

$$\begin{array}{ll} X^A = \Phi^A(\eta^a) & (a = 1,\ldots, \mathrm{m}; \\ & A = 1,\ldots, n, (1),\ldots, (n); \\ X^{A'} = \Phi^{A'}(\eta^a) & A' = 1',\ldots, n', (1'),\ldots, (n')) \end{array} \tag{10.19}$$

contained in (10.17) represent an $\mathfrak{N}_m$ in X_n and an $'\mathfrak{N}_m$ in $'X_n$ respectively, and this is the case if and only if $\partial_b \Phi^A$ and $\partial_b \Phi^{A'}$ both have the highest possible rank m.

In order to obtain the geometrical significance of this condition we consider two normal systems of ∞^{2n} X_{2n}'s in the X_{4n}, one defined by

$$X^{A'} = \text{const.} \quad (A' = 1',\ldots, n', (1'),\ldots, (n')) \tag{10.20}$$

and the other by

$$X^{A} = \text{const.} \quad (A = 1,\ldots, n, (1),\ldots, (n)). \tag{10.21}$$

We denote the X_{2n}'s of the first system by $\overset{1}{X}_{2n}$ and the X_{2n}'s of the second by $\overset{2}{X}_{2n}$. Through every point of the X_{4n} there is just one $\overset{1}{X}_{2n}$ and one $\overset{2}{X}_{2n}$. The contravariant measuring vectors in the X_{4n} being $\underset{Q}{e}^P$ (P, $Q = 1,\ldots, n, (1),\ldots, (n), 1',\ldots, n', (1'),\ldots, (n')$), the tangent E_{2n} of the $\overset{1}{X}_{2n}$'s is spanned at every point by the $\underset{B}{e}^P$ ($B = 1,\ldots, n, (1),\ldots, (n)$) and the tangent E_{2n} of the $\overset{2}{X}_{2n}$'s by the $\underset{B'}{e}^P$ ($B' = 1',\ldots, n', (1'),\ldots, (n')$). We denote them by $\overset{1}{E}_{2n}$ and $\overset{2}{E}_{2n}$ respectively. Now the tangent E_m of the X_m represented by (10.17) is spanned by the m vectors $\partial_b \Phi^P$ ($b = 1,\ldots, \mathrm{m}$). If this tangent E_m at some point had a direction in common with the local $\overset{1}{E}_{2n}$, there would exist a linear equation of the form

$$\mu^b \partial_b \Phi^P = \overset{B}{\sigma} \underset{B}{e}^P \quad (b = 1,\ldots, \mathrm{m};\ B = 1,\ldots, n, (1),\ldots, (n);$$
$$P = 1,\ldots, n, (1),\ldots, (n), 1',\ldots, n', (1'),\ldots, (n')) \tag{10.22}$$

with coefficients μ^b not vanishing simultaneously. But from this it would follow that

$$\mu^b \partial_b \Phi^{A'} = 0 \quad (b = 1,\ldots, \mathrm{m};\ A' = 1',\ldots, n', (1'),\ldots, (n')) \tag{10.23}$$

and that consequently $\partial_b \Phi^{A'}$ would have a rank $< m$. Conversely, if

$\partial_b \Phi^{A'}$ has a rank $< m$, a relation of the form (10.23) has to exist and consequently a relation of the form (10.22) with coefficients μ^b not vanishing simultaneously. Since the roles of $\overset{1}{X}_{2n}$ and $\overset{2}{X}_{2n}$ are interchangeable this proves that the analytical condition formulated above is equivalent to the geometrical condition that the tangent E_m of the X_m has neither a direction in common with the local $\overset{1}{E}_{2n}$ nor with the local $\overset{2}{E}_{2n}$ at all points of the X_m in the region considered.

$\mathfrak{N}_m$ and $'\mathfrak{N}_m$ are either both homogeneous or both non-homogeneous because a C_3-transformation can never transform a homogeneous $\mathfrak{N}_m$ into a non-homogeneous one. Now we recall that the $\mathfrak{N}_m$ in the X_n of the ξ^κ is homogeneous if and only if in the X_{2n} of the X^A ($A = 1,\ldots, n, (1),\ldots, (n)$) the vector V^A, lying in the direction of the characteristics of the Pfaffian $W_B\, dX^B$, is tangent to the X_m which is the image of the $\mathfrak{N}_m$ in this X_{2n} (cf. VII, § 3). The same holds *mutatis mutandis* for the $'\mathfrak{N}_m$ in the $'X_n$ of the $'\xi^\kappa$ and the vector $V^{A'}$ in the X_{2n} of the $X^{A'}$ ($A' = 1',\ldots, n', (1'),\ldots, (n')$), lying in the direction of the characteristics of $W_{B'}\, dX^{B'}$. If now from V^A and $V^{A'}$ we form the vector $\overline{V}^P$ of the X_{4n}

$$\overline{V}^A \overset{\text{def}}{=} -V^A, \qquad \overline{V}^{A'} \overset{\text{def}}{=} V^{A'} \quad (A = 1,\ldots, n, (1),\ldots, (n); \quad A' = 1',\ldots, n', (1'),\ldots, (n')), \tag{10.24}$$

this vector $\overline{V}^P$ lies in the direction of the characteristics of the Pfaffian (10.15). If $\overline{V}^P$ lies in the tangent E_m of the X_m in X_{4n}, a linear relation of the form

$$\overline{V}^P = \lambda^b\, \partial_b \Phi^P \quad (b = 1,\ldots, \mathrm{m};\ P = 1,\ldots, n, (1),\ldots, (n), 1',\ldots, n', (1'),\ldots, (n')) \tag{10.25}$$

exists with coefficients λ^b not all vanishing simultaneously, and by writing out this equation we get the equations

$$\begin{aligned} &(a)\quad V^A = -\lambda^b \partial_b \Phi^A \quad (b = 1,\ldots, \mathrm{m};\ A = 1,\ldots, n, (1),\ldots, (n);\\ &(b)\quad V^{A'} = \lambda^b \partial_b \Phi^{A'} \qquad\qquad A' = 1',\ldots, n', (1'),\ldots, (n')), \end{aligned} \tag{10.26}$$

expressing the fact that $\mathfrak{N}_m$ and $'\mathfrak{N}_m$ are homogeneous. If $\overline{V}^P$ does not lie in the tangent E_m of the X_m in the X_{4n}, the relations (10.26 *a*) and (10.26 *b*) could possibly exist, but not with the same coefficients. Hence from this non-coincidence alone it does not follow that $\mathfrak{N}_m$ and $'\mathfrak{N}_m$ are non-homogeneous. Now in this case the direction of $\overline{V}^P$ and the tangent-E_m of the X_m form an E_{m+1}. If this E_{m+1} has a direction in common with $\overset{1}{E}_{2n}$, a vector of the form

$$\nu^b \partial_b X^P + \nu \overline{V}^P \quad (b = 1,\ldots, \mathrm{m};\ P = 1,\ldots, n, (1),\ldots, (n), 1',\ldots, n', (1'),\ldots, (n')) \tag{10.27}$$

exists with a non-vanishing coefficient ν and coefficients ν^b not all vanishing simultaneously, lying in $\overset{1}{E}_{2n}$. But this implies that

$$\nu^b \partial_b X^{A'} + \nu \overline{V}^{A'} = 0 \quad (b = 1,\dots,\mathrm{m};\ A' = 1',\dots,n', (1'),\dots,(n')) \quad (10.28)$$

and this is only possible if $'\mathfrak{N}_m$ is homogeneous. The same holds *mutatis mutandis* with respect to $\overset{2}{E}_{2n}$. Hence the additional condition for the non-homogeneity of $\mathfrak{N}_m$ and $'\mathfrak{N}_m$ is that this E_{m+1} has neither a direction in common with $\overset{1}{E}_{2n}$ nor with $\overset{2}{E}_{2n}$. We collect results in the theorem

THEOREM VII.20. *An integral-X_m of the Pfaffian $'w_\lambda d\,'\xi^\lambda - w_\lambda d\xi^\lambda$ in the X_{4n} of the variables ξ^κ, w_λ, $'\xi^\kappa$, $'w_\lambda$ represents a one-to-one C_3-transformation of the vector elements of an $\mathfrak{N}_m$ in the X_n into the vector elements of an $'\mathfrak{N}_m$ in the $'X_n$ of the $'\xi^\kappa$ if and only if the tangent E_m of the X_m in the X_{4n} at every point of the region considered has a direction in common neither with the local tangent $\overset{1}{E}_{2n}$ of the normal system of ∞^{2n} $\overset{1}{X}_{2n}$'s with the equations $'\xi^\kappa = $ const., $'w_\lambda = $ const. nor with the local tangent $\overset{2}{E}_{2n}$ of the normal system of ∞^{2n} $\overset{2}{X}_{2n}$'s with the equations $\xi^\kappa = $ const., $w_\lambda = $ const.*

The $\mathfrak{N}_m$ and the $'\mathfrak{N}_m$ are both non-homogeneous if the direction of the characteristics of the Pfaffian and the tangent E_m determine at every point of the region considered an E_{m+1} which has a direction in common neither with the local $\overset{1}{E}_{2n}$ nor with the local $\overset{2}{E}_{2n}$, and they are both homogeneous in the other case.

If $m = 2n$ we get the theorem

THEOREM VII.21. *An integral-X_{2n} of the Pfaffian $'w_\lambda d\,'\xi^\lambda - w_\lambda d\xi^\lambda$ in the X_{4n} of the variables ξ^κ, w_λ, $'\xi^\kappa$, $'w_\lambda$ represents a C_3-transformation $\xi^\kappa, w_\lambda \rightarrow {}'\xi^\kappa, {}'w_\lambda$ if and only if the tangent E_{2n} of the X_{2n} in the X_{4n} at every point of the region considered has a direction in common neither with the local tangent $\overset{1}{E}_{2n}$ of the normal system of ∞^{2n} $\overset{1}{X}_{2n}$'s with the equations $'\xi^\kappa = $ const., $'w_\lambda = $ const. nor with the local tangent $\overset{2}{E}_{2n}$ of the normal system of ∞^{2n} $\overset{2}{X}_{2n}$'s with the equations $\xi^\kappa = $ const., $w_\lambda = $ const.*

Suppose that the $\mathfrak{N}_m$ and the $'\mathfrak{N}_m$ are both non-homogeneous and that the integral-X_m in X_{4n}, representing a C_3-transformation of the vector elements of $\mathfrak{N}_m$ into the vector elements of $'\mathfrak{N}_m$ is found. Then if it is possible to construct an integral-X_{2n}, containing this integral-X_m such that its tangent E_{2n} at every point of the region considered has a direction in common neither with the local $\overset{1}{E}_{2n}$ nor with the local $\overset{2}{E}_{2n}$, this integral-X_{2n} represents the extended C_3-transformation required.

If $m = 2n-1$ the construction of this integral-X_{2n} is very simple. The tangent E_{2n-1} has a direction in common neither with the local $\overset{1}{E}_{2n}$ nor with the local $\overset{2}{E}_{2n}$ and since the $\mathfrak{N}_m$ and $'\mathfrak{N}_m$ are both non-homogeneous this E_{2n-1} together with the direction of the characteristic of the Pfaffian $'w_\lambda\, d\, '\xi^\lambda - w_\lambda d\xi^\lambda$ determines an E_{2n} which has no direction in common with $\overset{1}{E}_{2n}$ or $\overset{2}{E}_{2n}$. Hence if a characteristic is laid through each point of the X_{2n-1} these characteristics taken together form an X_{2n} representing the extended C_3-transformation.

If $m < 2n-1$ in the non-homogeneous case, we need an auxiliary theorem. If a covariant vector field w_λ in an X_n is given and if at a point of the region considered the sections of w_λ and $W_{\mu\lambda} = 2\partial_{[\mu} w_{\lambda]}$ with an E_p both vanish, this E_p is said to be an *integral-E_p of the field w_λ*. Hence every tangent E_p of an integral-X_p of the field w_λ is an integral-E_p. We can now formulate the auxiliary theorem (cf. VI (1.2))

THEOREM VII.22. *If an integral-X_m of a field w_λ of class $K = 2\rho$ through the point $\overset{}{\underset{0}{\xi}}{}^\kappa$ is given and also an integral-E_ν $(\nu = n-\rho)$ of this field at $\underset{0}{\xi}{}^\kappa$, containing the tangent E_m of the X_m at that point, there always exists an integral-X_ν of the field, containing the integral-X_m and having a tangent E_ν at $\underset{0}{\xi}{}^\kappa$ coinciding with the given integral-E_ν.*

PROOF. The system S_4 of w_λ (cf. IV, § 2)

$$\begin{aligned} w_\mu\, d\xi^\mu &= 0, \\ W_{\mu[\lambda} w_{\nu]}\, d\xi^\mu &= 0 \end{aligned} \qquad (10.29)$$

is complete and has $2\rho-1$ independent integral functions. These functions, equated to constants, give the equations of the normal system of the $\infty^{2\rho-1}$ $(n-2\rho+1)$-dimensional characteristics of the field. If the characteristic is laid through every point of the integral-X_m, an $X_{m'}$ $(m \leqslant m' \leqslant m+n-2\rho+1)$ is obtained. This $X_{m'}$ is an integral-$X_{m'}$ because its sections with w_λ and $W_{\mu\lambda}$ vanish. Now we choose the coordinate system in such a way that

$$\xi^1 = \text{const.}, \quad ..., \quad \xi^{2\rho-1} = \text{const.} \qquad (10.30)$$

are the equations of the characteristics. Then, since the $X_{m'}$ consists of characteristics, its equations can be written in the form

$$F^{\mathfrak{a}}(\xi^a) = 0 \quad (a = 1,..., 2\rho-1;\ \mathfrak{a} = \mathrm{m}'+1,..., \mathrm{n}). \qquad (10.31)$$

Now the integral-E_ν at $\underset{0}{\xi}{}^\kappa$ contains not only the tangent E_m of the X_m but according to (10.29) the tangent $E_{n-2\rho+1}$ of the characteristic through $\overset{0}{\xi}{}^{\kappa}$ also. Consequently this integral-E_ν contains the tangent $E_{m'}$ of $X_{m'}$. Hence, if $\overset{0}{r}_\lambda$ is a covariant vector in $\overset{0}{\xi}{}^{\kappa}$ whose $(n-1)$-direction contains the integral-X_ν, at that point there exists at least one relation of the form

$$\overset{0}{r}_\lambda = \overset{0}{\sigma}_{\mathfrak{a}} (\partial_\lambda F^{\mathfrak{a}})_{\xi^\kappa = \overset{0}{\xi}{}^\kappa} \quad (\mathfrak{a} = \mathrm{m}'+1, \ldots, \mathrm{n}) \tag{10.32}$$

with *constant* coefficients, not all vanishing simultaneously. Consequently the equation

$$\overset{0}{\sigma}_{\mathfrak{a}} F^{\mathfrak{a}}(\xi^a) = 0 \quad (\mathfrak{a} = \mathrm{m}'+1, \ldots, \mathrm{n};\ a = 1, \ldots, 2\rho-1) \tag{10.33}$$

represents an X_{n-1} consisting wholly of characteristics, containing the $X_{m'}$, and having at $\overset{0}{\xi}{}^{\kappa}$ a tangent E_{n-1} containing the given integral-E_ν. Since the ξ^a are integral functions of S_4, $\overset{0}{\sigma}_{\mathfrak{a}} F^{\mathfrak{a}}$ is also an integral function of S_4 and consequently a function with index 2 (cf. IV, § 4). Hence the section of w_λ with the X_{n-1} with the equation (10.33) has the class $K-2$. Collecting results we have obtained an X_{n-1} with a field of class $K-2$ and in this X_{n-1} an integral-X_m through $\overset{0}{\xi}{}^{\kappa}$ with a tangent E_m at $\overset{0}{\xi}{}^{\kappa}$ being contained in a given integral-E_ν. This means that the dimension of the problem is lowered by 1 and the class by 2. Repeating this process $\rho-1$ times we get at last an $X_{n-\rho} = X_\nu$ through $\overset{0}{\xi}{}^{\kappa}$ containing the integral-X_m and tangent to the integral-E_ν at $\overset{0}{\xi}{}^{\kappa}$, whose section with w_λ vanishes. This proves the theorem.

According to this auxiliary theorem VII.22 we only have to prove now that at every point of the X_{m+1} of the X_{4n}, determined by the integral-X_m and the characteristics, it is always possible to construct an integral-E_{2n}, containing the tangent E_{m+1} of the X_{m+1} and having no direction in common with the local $\overset{1}{E}_{2n}$ or with the local $\overset{2}{E}_{2n}$. The vector $\overline{W}_Q$ with the components (cf. (10.12))

$$\overline{W}_B \overset{\text{def}}{=} -W_B, \qquad \overline{W}_{B'} \overset{\text{def}}{=} W_{B'} \quad (B = 1, \ldots, n, (1), \ldots, (n); \\ B' = 1', \ldots, n', (1'), \ldots, (n')) \tag{10.34}$$

has class $4n$ and consequently its rotation defines a null system in the local E_{4n}. Two directions are said to be *in involution* if the transvection of two contravariant vectors in these directions with this rotation vanishes. The set of all directions in involution with all directions of an E_p form an E_{4n-p}, called the *null-E_{4n-p}* of E_p and denoted by $N(E_p)$. It is well known from the theory of null systems and readily proved that $N(N(E_p)) = E_p$ and that E_q lies in $N(E_p)$ if and only if E_p lies in $N(E_q)$. Obviously $N(E_p)$ contains E_p if and only if all directions of E_p are mutually in involution. From the definition of $\overset{1}{E}_{2n}$ and $\overset{2}{E}_{2n}$ it follows that

$$\overset{2}{E}_{2n} = N(\overset{1}{E}_{2n}), \qquad \overset{1}{E}_{2n} = N(\overset{2}{E}_{2n}), \tag{10.35}$$

and from the definition of $\overline{W}_Q$ and $\overline{V}^P$ (cf. (10.24)) it follows that the E_1 of $\overline{V}^P$ is the null-E_1 of the E_{4n-1} of $\overline{W}_Q$, in other words, that $\overline{V}^P$ is in involution with all integral-E_1's.

Now we try to construct through the integral-E_{m+1} an integral-E_{m+2} having no directions in common with $\overset{1}{E}_{2n}$ or $\overset{2}{E}_{2n}$. To this end we have to add to the E_{m+1} an E_1 lying in $N(E_{m+1})$. This $N(E_{m+1})$ is an E_{4n-m-1} and intersects each of $\overset{1}{E}_{2n}$ and $\overset{2}{E}_{2n}$ in at least an E_{2n-m-1}. We will show that this section is just an E_{2n-m-1}. If the dimension of the section with $\overset{1}{E}_{2n}$ (or $\overset{2}{E}_{2n}$) was $> 2n-m-1$, there would exist an E_{4n-1} containing $N(E_{m+1})$ and $\overset{1}{E}_{2n}$ (or $\overset{2}{E}_{2n}$). But since this E_{4n-1} contains $N(E_{m+1})$ the $N(E_{4n-1})$ would have to be contained in E_{m+1}. Now $N(E_{4n-1})$ is an E_1, and its direction is in involution with all directions of E_{4n-1} and thus with all directions of $\overset{1}{E}_{2n}$ (or $\overset{2}{E}_{2n}$), and this would imply that the direction of $N(E_{4n-1})$ was contained in $\overset{2}{E}_{2n}$ (or $\overset{1}{E}_{2n}$). Since the E_{m+1} has no direction in common with $\overset{1}{E}_{2n}$ or $\overset{2}{E}_{2n}$, this is impossible.

In the $(4n-m-1)$-dimensional $N(E_{m+1})$ we have now:

(1) the E_{m+1};

(2) the $(2n-m-1)$-dimensional section with $\overset{1}{E}_{2n}$;

(3) the $(2n-m-1)$-dimensional section with $\overset{2}{E}_{2n}$;

and these three linear manifolds have no direction in common. Moreover, we have

$$4n-m-1 > m+1+2n-m-1 \tag{10.36}$$

and this implies that it is always possible to construct in the E_{4n-m-1} an E_{m+2}, containing the E_{m+1} and having a direction in common neither with $\overset{1}{E}_{2n}$ nor with $\overset{2}{E}_{2n}$. When this integral-E_{m+2} has been obtained, in this E_{m+2} an integral-E_{m+1} can be constructed, so that the direction of $\overline{V}^P$ is not contained in it. This last integral-E_{m+1} can be handled in the same way as the integral-E_m and the result is an integral-E_{m+2}, determining together with $\overline{V}^P$ an integral-E_{m+3} having no direction in common either with $\overset{1}{E}_{2n}$ or with $\overset{2}{E}_{2n}$. Continuing in this way we obtain at last an integral-E_{2n-1} determining together with $\overline{V}^P$ an integral-E_{2n} containing the integral-E_{m+1} and having no direction in common either with $\overset{1}{E}_{2n}$ or with $\overset{2}{E}_{2n}$. This proves the possibility of the construction of the extended C_3-transformation for the case when $\mathfrak{N}_m$ and $'\mathfrak{N}_m$ are both non-homogeneous.

If $\mathfrak{N}_m$ and $'\mathfrak{N}_m$ are both homogeneous it is always possible to derive from them two non-homogeneous vector manifolds $\mathfrak{N}_{m-1}$ and $'\mathfrak{N}_{m-1}$ by the process of dis-homogenization. As was proved in VII, § 4, this can always be done in such a way that the class is raised by *1*. Then $\mathfrak{N}_{m-1}$ and $'\mathfrak{N}_{m-1}$ have the same class and consequently there exists a C_3-transformation ξ^κ, $w_\lambda \rightarrow {}'\xi^\kappa$, $'w_\lambda$ fixing a one-to-one correspondence between the vector elements of $\mathfrak{N}_{m-1}$ and the vector elements of $'\mathfrak{N}_{m-1}$. Now every C_3-transformation transforms parallel vectors at the same point into parallel vectors belonging to one point, and this implies that the C_3-transformation obtained also fixes a one-to-one correspondence between the vector elements of $\mathfrak{N}_m$ and the vector elements of $'\mathfrak{N}_m$. This proves the theorem

THEOREM VII.23. *If an $\mathfrak{N}_m$ in ξ^κ, w_λ and an $'\mathfrak{N}_m$ in $'\xi^\kappa$, $'w_\lambda$ be given, there exists a C_3-transformation ξ^κ, $w_\lambda \rightarrow {}'\xi^\kappa$, $'w_\lambda$, fixing a one-to-one correspondence between the vector elements of $\mathfrak{N}_m$ and the vector elements of $'\mathfrak{N}_m$ if and only if $\mathfrak{N}_m$ and $'\mathfrak{N}_m$ have the same class and the same index.*

From this theorem the principal theorem VII.19 of this section is a direct consequence. The canonical forms mentioned in Theorem VII.19 are the simplest possible. They have the property that the field dimension t has the minimal value $\rho+\epsilon+m-n$. But they can be replaced by other canonical forms with an arbitrary value of t, provided that $\rho+\epsilon+m-n \leqslant t \leqslant m+l-1$ and $t \leqslant n$. If we choose the following canonical forms:

$$\begin{array}{ll}
\xi^1 = 0, & w_1 = 0, \\
\cdot\quad\cdot\quad\cdot & \cdot\quad\cdot\quad\cdot \\
\xi^\rho = 0, & \begin{array}{l} w_{\rho-1} = 0, \\ w_\rho = l-\epsilon, \end{array} \\
\xi^{\rho+1} = 0, & w_{\rho+u+1} = 0, \\
\cdot\quad\cdot\quad\cdot & \cdot\quad\cdot\quad\cdot\quad\cdot \\
\xi^{\rho+u} = 0, & \begin{array}{l} w_{\rho+u+v-1} = 0, \\ w_{\rho+u+v} = \epsilon \end{array}
\end{array} \tag{10.37}$$

with the conditions

$$\begin{gathered} \rho+u \leqslant n, \qquad u \geqslant 0, \qquad \rho \geqslant l-\epsilon, \\ \rho+v \leqslant n+l-1, \qquad v \geqslant \epsilon, \\ 2\rho+u+v = 2n-m, \end{gathered} \tag{10.38}$$

the field dimension is

$$t = n-\rho-u. \tag{10.39}$$

From (10.38) we get the inequalities

$$\begin{array}{ll} u \leqslant n-\rho, & u \geqslant 0, \\ u \leqslant 2n-m-2\rho-\epsilon, & u \geqslant n-m-\rho-l+1 \end{array} \tag{10.40}$$

for u, and consequently

$$\begin{array}{ll} (a)\ \ t \geqslant 0, & (b)\ \ t \leqslant n-\rho, \\ (c)\ \ t \geqslant m-n+\rho+\epsilon, & (d)\ \ t \leqslant m-1+l \end{array} \tag{10.41}$$

for t. The conditions (10.41 a), (10.41 c), and (10.41 d) are in accordance with the conditions (1.4) and (3.11), and because of $2\rho+\epsilon \leqslant 2n-m$ there can never be a contradiction between (10.41 b) and (10.41 c). If $\rho \leqslant n-m+1-l$, (10.41 b) is a consequence of (10.41 d). But if $\rho > n-m+1-l$, the canonical form (10.37) cannot be used for $n-\rho < t \leqslant m-1+l$. In this special case we can use the canonical form

$$(A) \qquad \xi^1 = 0, \quad \ldots, \quad \xi^{n-t} = 0;$$

$$(B) \qquad \left.\begin{array}{r} \xi^{n-t+1}+\alpha w_{2n-\rho-t+1} = 0 \\ \cdot\quad\cdot\quad\cdot\quad\cdot\quad\cdot\quad\cdot\quad\cdot\quad\cdot \\ \xi^{\rho}+\alpha w_n = 0 \end{array}\right\} \alpha = \frac{1}{\xi^{2n-m-\rho+1}w_{2n-m-\rho+1}+\ldots+\xi^n w_n};$$

$$(C) \qquad w_1 = l-\epsilon, \qquad w_2 = 0, \quad \ldots, \quad w_{2n-m-\rho-1} = 0, \qquad w_{2n-m-\rho} = \epsilon \tag{10.42}$$

with the conditions

$$\begin{array}{llll} (a)\ 0 \leqslant n-t, & (b)\ n-t \leqslant \rho, & (c)\ 0 \leqslant 2n-\rho-t, & (d)\ 2n-\rho-t \leqslant n, \\ (e)\ 0 \leqslant \rho, & (f)\ \rho \leqslant n, & (g)\ 2n-m-\rho+1 \leqslant 2n-\rho-t+1, & \\ (h)\ l \leqslant 2n-m-\rho, & & (i)\ 2n-m-\rho \leqslant n, & \\ (j)\ 2n-m-\rho+1 \leqslant n, & & (k)\ 2n-m-\rho+1 > n-t. & \end{array} \tag{10.43}$$

The conditions (a), (e), and (g) are trivial and the conditions (b) and (j) are consequences of the conditions of this special case. (c) is a consequence of (a) and (f), (d) is identical with (b), and (f) is a consequence of $2\rho+\epsilon \leqslant 2n-m$. ($h$) is a consequence of this same inequality because

$l = 0$ for $\rho = 0$, $\epsilon = 0$. (i) is a consequence of (j), and (k) is a consequence of (3.11). The only non-vanishing bracket expressions of the left-hand sides of (10.42) are

$$(w_1, \xi^1) = 1, \quad \dots, \quad (w_{n-t}, \xi^{n-t}) = 1,$$
$$(w_{n-t+1}, \xi^{n-t+1} + \alpha w_{2n-\rho-t+1}) = 1, \quad \dots, \quad (w_\rho, \xi^\rho + \alpha w_n) = 1. \tag{10.44}$$

From the canonical forms obtained we see that to every system of values n, m, ϵ, l, ρ, and t, satisfying the conditions (cf. (1.4) and (3.11))

$$\begin{aligned} m-n \leqslant t \leqslant m+l-1 \quad (l = 0 \text{ or } 1), \\ 0 \leqslant t \leqslant n, \\ 2\rho+\epsilon \leqslant 2n-m \quad (\epsilon = 0 \text{ or } 1;\ \epsilon \geqslant l), \\ \rho+m-n+\epsilon \leqslant t \end{aligned} \tag{10.45}$$

there always exists an $\mathfrak{N}_m$ in X_n of class $2\rho+\epsilon$, index l, and field dimension t. All these canonical forms have the property that the functions in the left-hand sides form a homogeneous function group. If the constants in the right-hand sides are brought to the left, the left-hand sides form a not always homogeneous function group and the bracket expressions are all constant. Then the equations form a reduced form of the $\mathfrak{N}_m$ (cf. VII, § 5). This proves the theorem

THEOREM VII.24. *The equations of an $\mathfrak{N}_m$ in X_n can always be brought into a reduced form such that all right-hand sides are zero, all left-hand sides form a function group, and all bracket expressions are constant.*

This theorem can also be proved without using the Theorems VII.19 and VII.23. We suppose first that 2ρ of the $2n-m$ equations can be chosen in such a way that all right-hand sides are zero and that the bracket expressions are constants. Afterwards it will be proved that this is always possible. Then by means of a linear transformation with *constant* coefficients we can always make the matrix of the bracket expressions take the normal form, only consisting of elements $+1$, -1, and 0. Writing

$$\begin{aligned} '\xi^1 = 0, \quad \dots, \quad '\xi^\rho = 0, \\ 'w_1 = 0, \quad \dots, \quad 'w_\rho = 0 \end{aligned} \tag{10.46}$$

for these 2ρ equations, we have

$$('w_1, '\xi^1) = 1, \quad \dots, \quad ('w_\rho, '\xi^\rho) = 1, \tag{10.47}$$

whilst all other bracket expressions belonging to these 2ρ equations vanish. As was proved in VI, § 9, by means of $n-\rho$ operations $O_{2(n-\rho)}, O_{2(n-\rho-1)}, \dots, O_2$ and a quadrature it is always possible to construct $2(n-\rho)$ functions $'\xi^{\rho+1}, \dots, '\xi^n, 'w_{\rho+1}, \dots, 'w_n$, such that $('w_\lambda, '\xi^\kappa) = \delta^\kappa_\lambda$

($\kappa, \lambda = 1, \ldots, n$). Now the remaining $2n-m-2\rho$ equations of the $\mathfrak{N}_m$ can be written in the form

$$\begin{aligned} F^{2n-2\rho}('\xi^{\rho+1}, \ldots, '\xi^n, 'w_{\rho+1}, \ldots, 'w_n) &= 0, \\ \cdots\cdots\cdots & \\ F^{m+1}('\xi^{\rho+1}, \ldots, '\xi^n, 'w_{\rho+1}, \ldots, 'w_n) &= 0. \end{aligned} \tag{10.48}$$

Since the rank of this system is $2n-m-2\rho$, just $2n-m-2\rho$ of the variables in the brackets can be solved. If this solution is effected and the right-hand sides of the equations obtained are brought to the left, all bracket expressions of the left-hand sides with the functions $'\xi^1, \ldots, '\xi^\rho, 'w_1, \ldots, 'w_\rho$ vanish. But the bracket expressions of these left-hand sides with each other also vanish, because, since the rotation class of $\mathfrak{N}_m$ is 2ρ, they have to vanish in consequence of (10.46) and (10.48) and this is only possible if they vanish identically. Hence a reduced form of the equations of the $\mathfrak{N}_m$, satisfying the conditions of Theorem VII.24 is obtained.

Now we have to prove that 2ρ of the $2n-m$ equations of the $\mathfrak{N}_m$ can be chosen in the special way mentioned above. This can be done by induction. Suppose the proof be given for the $\mathfrak{N}_m$'s in X_m with rotation class $2(\rho-1)$. In the matrix of the bracket expressions of the left-hand sides of the equations of an $\mathfrak{N}_m$ with rotation class 2ρ there always exists a 2ρ-rowed main sub-determinant† not vanishing for vector elements of the $\mathfrak{N}_m$. By interchanging indices we can always make this the matrix of the bracket expressions of $F^{2n}, \ldots, F^{2n-2\rho+1}$ and by a linear transformation of these functions with coefficients, that are not in general constant, we can always make this latter matrix take the normal form

$$\begin{array}{c} \longleftarrow\qquad 2\rho \qquad\longrightarrow \\ \begin{array}{c|ccccccc|} & F^{2n} & F^{2n-1} & & & & F^{2n-2\rho+2} & F^{2n-2\rho+1} \\ F^{2n} & 0 & +1 & \cdot & \cdot & \cdot & 0 & 0 \\ F^{2n-1} & -1 & 0 & \cdot & \cdot & \cdot & 0 & 0 \\ & \cdot & \cdot & \cdot & & & \cdot & \cdot \\ & \cdot & \cdot & & \cdot & & \cdot & \cdot \\ & \cdot & \cdot & & & \cdot & \cdot & \cdot \\ F^{2n-2\rho+2} & 0 & 0 & \cdot & \cdot & \cdot & 0 & +1 \\ F^{2n-2\rho+1} & 0 & 0 & \cdot & \cdot & \cdot & -1 & 0 \end{array} \end{array} \tag{10.49}$$

† A main sub-determinant is a determinant lying symmetrically with respect to the main diagonal.

for *all vector elements of the* $\mathfrak{N}_m$. Hence the $2(\rho-1)$ equations

$$F^{2n} = 0, \quad \ldots, \quad F^{2n-2\rho+3} = 0 \tag{10.50}$$

represent for $\rho > 1$ an $\mathfrak{N}_{2n-2\rho+2}$ with rotation class $2(\rho-1)$ and, as we have assumed, these equations can be replaced by $2(\rho-1)$ other equations such that the bracket expressions on the left-hand sides are all constant. Even by a suitable linear transformation with *constant* coefficients we can make the matrix of the bracket expressions of the $2(\rho-1)$ new functions $F^{2n},\ldots, F^{2n-2\rho+3}$ have the values (10.49) but now not only for vector elements of the $\mathfrak{N}_m$ but *for all vector elements.* Moreover, by a suitable linear transformation of $F^{2n-2\rho+2}$ and $F^{2n-2\rho+1}$ with, in general, not constant coefficients we can make the bracket expressions containing these functions keep the values (10.49) *for vector elements of the* $\mathfrak{N}_m$. Hence, if $\rho > 1$, after this transformation the $2\rho-1$ equations

$$F^{2n} = 0, \quad \ldots, \quad F^{2n-2\rho+2} = 0 \tag{10.51}$$

represent an $\mathfrak{N}_{2n-2\rho+1}$ with the rotation class $2(\rho-1)$. The first $2\rho-2$ equations are already chosen in such a way that the bracket expressions of their left-hand sides are constant. Hence Theorem VII.24 (already proved for that case) can be applied to this system, and this implies that the last equation can be replaced by another one, such that all the bracket expressions of the left-hand sides of all $2\rho-1$ equations are constant. Moreover, by a suitable linear transformation of $F^{2n-2\rho+1}$ with, in general, not constant coefficients we can make the bracket expressions containing $F^{2n-2\rho+1}$ keep the values (10.49) *for vector elements of the* $\mathfrak{N}_m$. If $\rho = 1$ the matrix (10.49) takes the form

$$\begin{array}{c|cc} & F^{2n} & F^{2n-1} \\ \hline F^{2n} & 0 & 1 \\ F^{2n-1} & -1 & 0 \end{array} \tag{10.52}$$

Now we try to replace $F^{2n-2\rho+1}$ by another function G, satisfying the conditions

(1) $(F^{2n}, G) = 0, \quad \ldots, \quad (F^{2n-2\rho+3}, G) = 0, \qquad (F^{2n-2\rho+2}, G) = 1;$ (10.53)

(2) $G = 0$ for all vector elements of the $\mathfrak{N}_m$; (10.54)

(3) the functional matrix of

$$F^{2n}, \quad \ldots, \quad F^{2n-\rho+2}, \qquad G, \qquad F^{2n-2\rho}, \quad \ldots, \quad F^{m+1} \tag{10.55}$$

has the rank $2n-m$ for all vector elements of the $\mathfrak{N}_m$.

We choose the coordinates X^A $(A = 1, \ldots, 2n)$ in the X_{2n} of ξ^κ and w_λ such that

$$X^{2n} = F^{2n}, \quad \ldots, \quad X^{2n-2\rho+1} = F^{2n-2\rho+1}. \tag{10.56}$$

Then the first condition takes for $\rho > 1$ the form (cf. VII, § 3)

$$V^{2n,B}\partial_B G = 0, \quad \ldots, \quad V^{2n-2\rho+3,B}\partial_B G = 0, \qquad V^{2n-2\rho+2,B}\partial_B G = 1$$
$$(B = 1, \ldots, 2n), \tag{10.57}$$

and for $\rho = 1$

$$V^{2n,B}\partial_B G = 1 \quad (B = 1, \ldots, 2n). \tag{10.58}$$

Now from Jacobi's identity we get for every set of three arbitrary functions P, Q, and R of ξ^κ and w_λ

$$\begin{aligned} &V^{CD}(\partial_{[C} R)\partial_{|D|} V^{BA}(\partial_B Q)(\partial_{A]} P) \\ &\quad = (V^{[C|D|}\partial_D V^{BA]})(\partial_C R)(\partial_B Q)(\partial_A P) + \\ &\qquad + V^{[C|D|}(\partial_C R)V^{BA]}\{(\partial_D \partial_B Q)\partial_A P + (\partial_B Q)(\partial_D \partial_A P)\} = 0 \end{aligned}$$
$$(A, B, C, D = 1, \ldots, 2n). \tag{10.59}$$

Since the last term vanishes identically we have the identity

$$V^{[C|D|}\partial_D V^{BA]} = 0 \quad (A, B, C, D = 1, \ldots, 2n) \tag{10.60}$$

and from this identity and from the constancy of the right-hand sides of (10.57) it follows that the non-homogeneous system (10.57) is complete (cf. III, § 14). In III, § 14, it was proved that there exists one and only one solution of (10.57) or (10.58) respectively, coinciding with an arbitrarily chosen function of position on an $X_{2n-2\rho+1}$ whose tangent $E_{2n-2\rho+1}$ has no direction in common with the $(2\rho-1)$-vector

$$V^{2n[A_1} \ldots V^{|2n-2\rho+2|A_{2\rho-1}]} \quad (A_1, \ldots, A_{2\rho-1} = 1, \ldots, 2n). \tag{10.61}$$

Now we have, according to the values (10.49) of the bracket expressions,

$$\begin{aligned} &(2\rho-1)!\, V^{2n[A_1} \ldots V^{|2n-2\rho+2|A_{2\rho-1}]}(\partial_{A_1} X^{2n}) \ldots (\partial_{A_{2\rho-2}} X^{2n-2\rho+3})(\partial_{A_{2\rho-1}} X^{2n-2\rho+1}) \\ &\quad = (-1)^{\rho-1} V^{2n,\,2n-1} V^{2n-1,\,2n} V^{2n-2,\,2n-3} V^{2n-3,\,2n-2} \ldots \\ &\qquad \ldots V^{2n-2\rho+4,\,2n-2\rho+3} V^{2n-2\rho+3,\,2n-2\rho+4} V^{2n-2\rho+2,\,2n-2\rho+1} = +1 \end{aligned}$$
$$(A_1, \ldots, A_{2\rho-1} = 1, \ldots, 2n) \tag{10.62}$$

holding for all vector elements of the $\mathfrak{N}_m$. From this it follows that the left-hand side of (10.62) is $\neq 0$ in a neighbourhood of the $\mathfrak{N}_m$ and this implies that we can use the $X_{2n-2\rho+1}$ with the equations

$$\begin{aligned} X^{2n} = 0, \quad \ldots, \quad X^{2n-2\rho+3} = 0, \qquad &X^{2n-2\rho+1} = 0, \quad \text{for} \quad \rho > 1, \\ &X^{2n-1} = 0, \quad \text{for} \quad \rho = 1. \end{aligned}$$
$$\tag{10.63}$$

For the function of position in this $X_{2n-2\rho+1}$ we choose now a function having the value 0 at all points. Then, since the $\mathfrak{N}_m$ is contained in the $X_{2n-2\rho+1}$ the second condition is satisfied. All derivatives of G with respect to $X^1, \ldots, X^{2n-2\rho}$ and $X^{2n-2\rho+2}$ vanish on the $X_{2n-2\rho+1}$. Hence, in consideration of (10.49), the equations (10.57) take for all vector elements of the $\mathfrak{N}_m$ the form

$$\partial_{2n} G = 0, \quad \ldots, \quad \partial_{2n-2\rho+3} G = 0, \qquad \partial_{2n-2\rho+1} G = 1 \tag{10.64}$$

for $\rho > 1$ and

$$\partial_{2n-1} G = 1 \tag{10.65}$$

for $\rho = 1$, from which we see that the third condition is also satisfied. The determination of G requires an operation $O_{2n-2\rho+2}$ (cf. III, § 14). If we take G as a new function $F^{2n-2\rho+1}$, the bracket expressions of $F^{2n}, \ldots, F^{2n-2\rho+1}$ have the values (10.49) not only for the vector elements of $\mathfrak{N}_m$ but for all vector elements. This proves the theorem. Moreover we have proved that the reduced form of Theorem VII.24 can always be obtained by means of n operations

$$O_{2n}, \quad O_{2n-2}, \quad \ldots, \quad O_2 \tag{10.66}$$

and a quadrature.

Since the equations of the $\mathfrak{N}_m$ are brought into a reduced form with constant bracket expressions, by means of a linear transformation with constant coefficients we can always make the matrix of the bracket expressions take the normal form

$$\begin{array}{r} \updownarrow 2\rho \\ \\ \updownarrow 2n-m-2\rho \end{array} \left\| \begin{array}{cccccccc} \multicolumn{6}{c}{\longleftarrow 2\rho \longrightarrow} & \multicolumn{2}{c}{\longleftarrow 2n-m-2\rho \longrightarrow} \\ 0 & +1 & \cdot & \cdot & 0 & 0 & \cdot\ \cdot & 0 \\ -1 & 0 & & & \cdot & \cdot & & \cdot \\ \cdot & & \cdot & & \cdot & \cdot & & \cdot \\ \cdot & & & 0 & +1 & \cdot & & \cdot \\ 0 & \cdot & \cdot & -1 & 0 & 0 & \cdot\ \cdot & 0 \\ 0 & \cdot & \cdot & \cdot & 0 & 0 & \cdot\ \cdot & 0 \\ \cdot & & & & \cdot & \cdot & & \cdot \\ \cdot & & & & \cdot & \cdot & & \cdot \\ 0 & \cdot & \cdot & \cdot & 0 & 0 & \cdot\ \cdot & 0 \end{array} \right\|. \tag{10.67}$$

This proves the theorem (cf. Theorem VII.23 and VI, § 9)

Theorem VII.25. *If an $\mathfrak{N}_m$ in ξ^κ, w_λ and an $'\mathfrak{N}_m$ in $'\xi^\kappa$, $'w_\lambda$ be given, there exists a C_2-transformation ξ^κ, $w_\lambda \rightarrow {}'\xi^\kappa$, $'w_\lambda$, fixing a one-to-one correspondence between the vector elements of $\mathfrak{N}_m$ and the vector elements of $'\mathfrak{N}_m$ if and only if $\mathfrak{N}_m$ and $'\mathfrak{N}_m$ have the same rotation class.*

EXERCISES†

1. The system

$$\begin{aligned}\xi^1\xi^2-(\partial_4 f)\partial_5 f &= 0,\\ \xi^3\xi^4-(\partial_6 f)\partial_1 f &= 0,\\ \xi^5\xi^6-(\partial_2 f)\partial_3 f &= 0\end{aligned} \tag{1α}$$

is not in involution. Prove that $K = 3$ and $\overline{K} = 9$. By equating the bracket expressions to zero we get a system of six equations in involution. Solve these equations. In parametric space the three new equations diminish $\overline{K}$ by 8 though in general a system of three functions cannot have an index > 6. How is this possible?

2. If an $\mathfrak{N}_m$ in X_n of class $K > 0$ is given and if, by adding $m-m'$ equations we get an $\mathfrak{N}_{m'}$ of a class $K' < K$, the $X_{m'}$ in the parametric X_m always consists of points of diminished class of the field U_b.

† Cf. the suggestions at the end of the book.

VIII

THE INNER PROBLEM

1. The simplest form of the inner problem

As in Chapter III we consider an E_r-field in an X_n, given by its connecting quantities B^κ_b, C^x_λ ($b = 1,\ldots, r$; $x = r+1,\ldots, n$), analytic in an $\mathfrak{N}(\overset{0}{\xi}{}^\kappa)$. The B^κ_b ($b = 1,\ldots, r$) are r arbitrary linearly independent contravariant vectors *in* the E_r and the C^x_λ ($x = r+1,\ldots, n$) $n-r$ arbitrary linearly independent covariant vectors *through* the E_r. Now the inner problem, already defined in III, § 1, will be formulated with respect to the minimal regular parametric form

$$\xi^\kappa = f^\kappa(z^{\mathfrak{a}}) \quad (\mathfrak{a} = \dot{1},\ldots, \dot{m}) \tag{1.1}$$

of the integral-X_m of the E_r-field. The tangent E_m at an arbitrary point $z^{\mathfrak{a}}$ of the X_m is spanned by the m-vectors

$$\partial_{\mathfrak{b}} f^\kappa, \quad \partial_{\mathfrak{b}} \overset{\text{def}}{=} \frac{\partial}{\partial z^{\mathfrak{b}}} \quad (\mathfrak{b} = \dot{1},\ldots, \dot{m}). \tag{1.2}$$

This E_m is contained in the local E_r if and only if

$$C^x_\lambda \partial_{\mathfrak{b}} f^\lambda = 0 \quad (\mathfrak{b} = \dot{1},\ldots, \dot{m};\ x = r+1,\ldots, n). \tag{1.3}$$

In this equation the C^x_λ at the point $\xi^\kappa = f^\kappa(z^{\mathfrak{a}})$ have to be expressed as functions of the $z^{\mathfrak{a}}$ by means of (1.1). Hence the inner problem is in this formulation the problem of the solution of the equations (1.3) in $z^{\mathfrak{a}}$ with the unknown functions $f^\kappa(z^{\mathfrak{a}})$, which enter in (1.3) not only by their derivatives $\partial_{\mathfrak{b}} f^\lambda$ but also occur themselves in the C^x_λ.

For $m = 1$ the problem is very simple. The stream-lines of any vector field v^κ satisfying the condition $C^x_\lambda v^\lambda = 0$, expressing that v^κ lies in all points in the local E_r, are integral-X_1's of the E_r-field. The equations of these integral-X_1's are the ordinary differential equations

$$C^x_\lambda \frac{df^\lambda}{dt} = 0 \quad (x = r+1,\ldots, n), \tag{1.4}$$

t being a parameter on the X_1.

The difficulties begin with $m > 1$. E. Cartan has developed a method for the determination of the integral-X_m's of an E_r-field and E. Kähler, J. M. Thomas, and C. Burstin have applied this method to the more general form of the inner problem first formulated by Goursat. The method of Cartan will first be explained for the simple form of the problem shown in this section.

2. The integral-E_m's of an E_r-field

If the equations (1.3) are differentiated, after alternation over $\mathfrak{cb}$ we get the equations

$$C_{\mu\lambda}^{\cdot\cdot x}(\partial_{\mathfrak{c}} f^\mu)\partial_{\mathfrak{b}} f^\lambda = 0 \quad (\mathfrak{b}, \mathfrak{c} = \dot{1},..., \dot{m};\ x = r+1,..., n) \tag{2.1}$$

containing the rotations of the $n-r$ vectors C_λ^x $(x = r+1,..., n)$

$$C_{\mu\lambda}^{\cdot\cdot x} \stackrel{\text{def}}{=} 2\partial_{[\mu} C_{\lambda]}^x \quad (x = r+1,..., n). \tag{2.2}$$

(2.1) expresses the fact that the sections of these bivectors with the integral-X_m's vanish. Following Cartan we call an E_m an *m-dimensional integral element* or an *integral-E_m of the E_r-field* if in the region considered it is contained in E_r and all its sections with the rotations (2.2) vanish.† For $m = 0$ or $m = 1$ the sections with the rotations always vanish and, therefore, every E_1 in the local E_r is an integral-E_1. Evidently an $E_{m'}$ contained in an integral-E_m is an integral-$E_{m'}$. From the definition of an integral-E_m we get the following theorem:

THEOREM VIII.1. *An X_m is an integral-X_m of an E_r-field if and only if its tangent E_m's are all integral-E_m's.*

If an E_m in ξ^κ is spanned by the m contravariant vectors $U_{\mathfrak{b}}^\kappa$ $(\mathfrak{b} = \dot{1},..., \dot{m})$, $U_{\mathfrak{b}}^\kappa$ is the contravariant connecting quantity of the E_m, and the ξ^κ, $U_{\mathfrak{b}}^\kappa$ can be looked upon as a system of $n(1+m)$ supernumerary coordinates in the manifold of all E_m's in X_n. The necessary and sufficient conditions that an E_m is contained in the local E_r are

$$C_\lambda^x U_{\mathfrak{b}}^\lambda = 0 \quad (\mathfrak{b} = \dot{1},..., \dot{m};\ x = r+1,..., n) \tag{2.3}$$

and the necessary and sufficient conditions that an E_m is an integral-E_m are that

$$\begin{aligned} C_\lambda^x U_{\mathfrak{b}}^\lambda &= 0 \\ C_{\mu\lambda}^{\cdot\cdot x} U_{\mathfrak{c}}^\mu U_{\mathfrak{b}}^\lambda &= 0 \end{aligned} \quad (\mathfrak{b}, \mathfrak{c} = \dot{1},..., \dot{m};\ x = r+1,..., n). \tag{2.4}$$

Two integral-E_1's in the same point, given by the vectors U^κ and V^κ are said to be *in involution with respect to the E_r-field* if

$$C_{\mu\lambda}^{\cdot\cdot x} U^\mu V^\lambda = 0 \quad (x = r+1,..., n). \tag{2.5}$$

All the integral-E_1's that are in involution with all E_1's contained in an integral-E_m form a linear manifold called the *null-space* of the integral-E_m and denoted by $H(E_m)$ following Cartan.‡ Obviously $H(E_m)$ can be obtained by the intersection of the $(n-1)$-directions of the $(m+1)(n-r)$ covariant vectors

$$C_\lambda^x, \quad C_{\mu\lambda}^{\cdot\cdot x} U_{\mathfrak{c}}^\mu \quad (\mathfrak{c} = \dot{1},..., \dot{m};\ x = r+1,..., n). \tag{2.6}$$

$H(E_0)$ is the local E_r itself. From (2.4) it follows that E_m is contained

† An integral-E_2 is the same as the holonomic E_2 in III, § 2.

‡ Cartan calls $H(E_m)$ the polar space of E_m.

in $H(E_m)$. Hence, if we write $m+1+r_{m+1}$ for the dimension of $H(E_m)$, we have $r \geqslant m+1+r_{m+1} \geqslant m$ or

$$r-m-1 \geqslant r_{m+1} \geqslant -1. \tag{2.7}$$

If an E_{m+1} in the local E_r contains an integral-E_m, this E_{m+1} is spanned by the m vectors $U^\kappa_{\mathfrak{b}}$ ($\mathfrak{b} = \dot{1},..., \dot{m}$) and some other vector U^κ of the E_r. This E_{m+1} is an integral-E_{m+1} if and only if next to (2.4) the relations

$$\begin{aligned} C^x_\lambda U^\lambda &= 0 \\ C_{\mu\lambda}^{\cdot\cdot x} U^\mu_{\mathfrak{c}} U^\lambda &= 0 \end{aligned} \qquad (\mathfrak{c} = \dot{1},..., \dot{m};\ x = \mathrm{r}+1,..., \mathrm{n}) \tag{2.8}$$

hold. These relations express the fact that U^κ is contained in $H(E_m)$. This proves the theorem

THEOREM VIII.2. *An E_{m+1} contained in E_r and containing an integral-E_m is an integral-E_{m+1} if and only if it is contained in $H(E_m)$.*

From this theorem we see that integral-E_{m+1}'s containing a given integral-E_m exist if and only if $r_{m+1} \geqslant 0$ and that in this case there are $\infty^{r_{m+1}}$ of these integral-E_{m+1}'s ($\infty^0 = 1$).

3. Regular chains. Cartan's theory of integrability

We consider an integral-E_m of an E_r-field with the coordinates $\underset{0}{\xi}{}^\kappa$, $\underset{0}{U}{}^\kappa_{\mathfrak{b}}$. If then ξ^κ, $U^\kappa_{\mathfrak{b}}$ are the coordinates of another integral-E_m it may happen that r_{m+1} has the same value for both integral-E_m's if ξ^κ, $U^\kappa_{\mathfrak{b}}$ lies in a sufficiently small $\mathfrak{N}(\underset{0}{\xi}{}^\kappa, \underset{0}{U}{}^\kappa_{\mathfrak{b}})$. Then r_{m+1} is constant in this $\mathfrak{N}(\underset{0}{\xi}{}^\kappa, \underset{0}{U}{}^\kappa_{\mathfrak{b}})$. In this case the element $\underset{0}{\xi}{}^\kappa$, $\underset{0}{U}{}^\kappa_{\mathfrak{b}}$ is said to be a *regular integral element.* Evidently every integral-E_m in $\mathfrak{N}(\underset{0}{\xi}{}^\kappa, \underset{0}{U}{}^\kappa_{\mathfrak{b}})$ is regular as well. If the element $\underset{0}{\xi}{}^\kappa$, $\underset{0}{U}{}^\kappa_{\mathfrak{b}}$ is not regular, there exists in *every* $\mathfrak{N}(\underset{0}{\xi}{}^\kappa, \underset{0}{U}{}^\kappa_{\mathfrak{b}})$ at least one integral-E_m with a lower value of r_{m+1}.

A set of integral elements in $\underset{0}{\xi}{}^\kappa$,

$$\underset{0}{\xi}{}^\kappa = E_0 \subset E_1 \subset E_2 ... \subset E_m, \tag{3.1}$$

each containing all preceding elements (this is meant by the sign $\subset$ in (3.1)), is called a *regular chain* if $E_1,..., E_{m-1}$ are all regular. E_m may be regular or irregular. If an E_m with the coordinates $\underset{0}{\xi}{}^\kappa$, $\underset{0}{U}{}^\kappa_{\mathfrak{b}}$ is the last element of a regular chain it follows from the definition of regularity that every integral-E_m in a sufficiently small $\mathfrak{N}(\underset{0}{\xi}{}^\kappa, \underset{0}{U}{}^\kappa_{\mathfrak{b}})$ is the last element of a regular chain.

The following theorem is due to E. Cartan:

THEOREM VIII.3. (*Cartan's theorem of integrability.*) *If the integral-E_m with the coordinates $\underset{0}{\xi}^\kappa$, $\underset{0}{U}{}^\kappa_{\mathfrak{b}}$ is the last element of a regular chain, there always exists an integral-X_m through $\underset{0}{\xi}^\kappa$ and tangent to the integral-E_m at that point.*

The proof of this theorem will be given in the following sections. An integral-X_m having at least one tangent E_m which is the last element of a regular chain will be called a *regular integral-X_m*.

If the element $\underset{0}{\xi}^\kappa$, $\underset{0}{U}{}^\kappa_{\mathfrak{b}}$ is the last element of a regular chain, every integral-E_m in a sufficiently small $\mathfrak{N}(\underset{0}{\xi}^\kappa, \underset{0}{U}{}^\kappa_{\mathfrak{b}})$ has the same property and as a consequence of Theorem VIII.3 to every one of these integral elements an integral-X_m can be constructed. Hence the theorem of integrability gives the solution of the inner problem for all values of m for which regular chains exist. According to Cartan the maximum value of m is called the *genus* g of the E_r-field. g is an arithmetic invariant of the field. Integral-X_m's with $m > g$ may exist but they cannot be regular. Also irregular integral-X_m's may exist with $m \leqslant g$. Theorem VIII.3 deals only with regular integral-X_m's.

First a preliminary orientation will be given, elucidating the way to be followed for the construction of a real proof.

4. A preliminary orientation

Through $\underset{0}{\xi}^\kappa$ an integral-X_m may be given and ξ^κ, $U^\kappa_{\mathfrak{b}}$ may be the coordinates of its tangent E_m at ξ^κ. The $U^\kappa_{\mathfrak{b}}$ are only defined on the X_m and they satisfy the equations (2.4). If $\underset{0}{\xi}^\kappa$, $\underset{0}{U}{}^\kappa_{\mathfrak{b}}$ are the coordinates of the tangent E_m in $\underset{0}{\xi}^\kappa$, we suppose that this integral-E_m is regular, that is, that there exists an $\mathfrak{N}(\underset{0}{\xi}^\kappa, \underset{0}{U}{}^\kappa_{\mathfrak{b}})$ where r_{m+1} is constant. Now we have to investigate whether it is possible to construct an integral-X_{m+1} through the X_m.

The equations (2.8),

$$\begin{aligned} &(a) \qquad C^x_\lambda U^\lambda = 0 \\ &(b) \qquad C_{\mu\lambda}^{\cdot\cdot x} U^\mu_{\mathfrak{c}} U^\lambda = 0 \end{aligned} \qquad (\mathfrak{c} = \dot{1},..., \dot{m};\ x = \mathrm{r}+1,..., \mathrm{n}), \qquad (4.1)$$

for the unknown vector U^κ have just $r_{m+1}+m+1$ linearly independent solutions for every element ξ^κ, $U^\kappa_{\mathfrak{b}}$ in $\mathfrak{N}(\underset{0}{\xi}^\kappa, \underset{0}{U}{}^\kappa_{\mathfrak{b}})$. Every solution is a vector defined over X_m in an $\mathfrak{N}(\underset{0}{\xi}^\kappa)$. If $r_{m+1} \geqslant 0$ we choose one definite solution u^κ nowhere lying in the tangent E_m and by means of this vector we construct a new X_m, called $'X_m$, by moving every point ξ^κ of X_m from ξ^κ to

$$'\xi^\kappa = \xi^\kappa + u^\kappa\, dt. \tag{4.2}$$

The fields $U^\kappa_{\mathfrak{b}}$ ($\mathfrak{b} = \dot{1},..., \dot{m}$) we drag along over $u^\kappa dt$ (cf. II, § 13). Then the fields dragged along are tangent to $'X_m$ and their components on $'X_m$ are

$$'U^\kappa_{\mathfrak{b}} = U^\kappa_{\mathfrak{b}} + U^\sigma_{\mathfrak{b}}\, \partial_\sigma u^\kappa dt \quad (\mathfrak{b} = \dot{1},..., \dot{m};\ \sigma = 1,..., n). \tag{4.3}$$

In this formula u^κ is a field in $\mathfrak{N}(\overset{}{\underset{0}{\xi^\kappa}})$, arising from the values u^κ on X_m by an arbitrary but analytic extension over $\mathfrak{N}(\underset{0}{\xi^\kappa})$. As in (4.3) the derivatives $\partial_\sigma u^\kappa$ occur only in transvections with the vectors $U^\sigma_{\mathfrak{b}}$ all lying in the tangent E_m, the choice of this extension does not influence the values of $'U^\kappa_{\mathfrak{b}}$.

The values of the fields C^x_λ and $C_{\mu\lambda}^{\cdot\cdot x}$ in $'\xi^\kappa$ are

$$\begin{matrix} C^x_\lambda + u^\nu \partial_\nu C^x_\lambda dt \\ C_{\mu\lambda}^{\cdot\cdot x} + u^\nu \partial_\nu C_{\mu\lambda}^{\cdot\cdot x} dt \end{matrix} \quad (x = \mathrm{r}+1,..., \mathrm{n}). \tag{4.4}$$

Now, according to (4.1 a), we have

$$\begin{aligned} (C^x_\mu + u^\nu \partial_\nu C^x_\mu dt)(U^\mu_{\mathfrak{b}} + U^\sigma_{\mathfrak{b}}\, \partial_\sigma u^\mu dt) \\ = u^\nu(\partial_\nu C^x_\mu) U^\mu_{\mathfrak{b}}\, dt + C^x_\mu U^\sigma_{\mathfrak{b}}\, \partial_\sigma u^\mu\, dt \\ = u^\nu(\partial_\nu C^x_\mu) U^\mu_{\mathfrak{b}}\, dt - u^\mu(\partial_\sigma C^x_\mu) U^\sigma_{\mathfrak{b}}\, dt \\ (\mathfrak{b} = \dot{1},..., \dot{m};\ x = \mathrm{r}+1,..., \mathrm{n};\ \sigma = 1,..., n) \end{aligned} \tag{4.5}$$

and this expression vanishes in consequence of (4.1 b). Hence $'U^\kappa_{\mathfrak{b}}$ satisfies the first condition for integral elements. From (4.1 b) it follows that

$$\begin{aligned} (C_{\mu\lambda}^{\cdot\cdot x} + u^\nu \partial_\nu C_{\mu\lambda}^{\cdot\cdot x} dt)(U^\mu_{\mathfrak{c}} + U^\sigma_{\mathfrak{c}} \partial_\sigma u^\mu dt)(U^\lambda_{\mathfrak{b}} + U^\tau_{\mathfrak{b}}\, \partial_\tau u^\lambda dt) \\ = 3u^\nu U^\mu_{\mathfrak{c}} U^\lambda_{\mathfrak{b}}\, \partial_{[\nu} C_{\mu\lambda]}^{\cdot\cdot x} dt - 2u^\mu C_{\mu\lambda}^{\cdot\cdot x} U^\sigma_{[\mathfrak{c}}\, \partial_{|\sigma|}\, U^\lambda_{\mathfrak{b}]} dt \\ (\mathfrak{b}, \mathfrak{c} = \dot{1},..., \dot{m};\ x = \mathrm{r}+1,..., \mathrm{n};\ \sigma, \tau = 1,..., n). \end{aligned} \tag{4.6}$$

$\partial_{[\nu} C_{\mu\lambda]}^{\cdot\cdot x}$ vanishes according to (2.2). Since the m vectors $U^\kappa_{\mathfrak{b}}$ are X_m-forming there exist on X_m relations of the form (cf. III, § 17)

$$U^\sigma_{[\mathfrak{c}}\, \partial_{|\sigma|}\, U^\lambda_{\mathfrak{b}]} = \overset{\mathfrak{a}}{\underset{\mathfrak{cb}}{\sigma}}\, U^\lambda_{\mathfrak{a}} \quad (\mathfrak{a}, \mathfrak{b}, \mathfrak{c} = \dot{1},..., \dot{m};\ \sigma = 1,..., n), \tag{4.7}$$

and this implies that the last term in (4.6) also vanishes. Hence $'U^\kappa_{\mathfrak{b}}$ also satisfies the second condition for integral elements. This can be seen more easily by noticing that the vectors $'U^\kappa_{\mathfrak{b}}$ are all tangent to the $'X_m$ and that consequently the validity of the second condition follows from the validity of the first.

Since the $'X_m$ is defined in an $\mathfrak{N}(\overset{}{\underset{0}{\xi^\kappa}})$ and r_{m+1} is constant in an $\mathfrak{N}(\underset{0}{\xi^\kappa}, \underset{0}{U^\kappa_\mathfrak{b}})$ we can proceed with the $'X_m$ in the same way as with the X_m, that is, we can construct a field $'u^\kappa$ and a new manifold $''X_m$, etc. All the X_m's obtained in this way after an infinite number of steps taken together form the integral-X_{m+1} required.

Naturally these considerations, making use of 'neighbouring X_m's' and an 'infinite number' of steps, though interesting from a geometrical point of view do not really prove anything. But as they indicate how a real proof should be built up, they have some heuristic value. With every step the choice of u^κ is free. Hence, if we wish to get a definite process allowing the building of a differential equation it will be necessary to fix these solutions. If a general $X_{n-r_{m+1}}$ is laid through the integral-X_m its tangent $E_{n-r_{m+1}}$ intersects the $E_{m+1+r_{m+1}} = H(E_m)$ in an E_{m+1} and this implies that in this $X_{n-r_{m+1}}$ a 'neighbouring' X_m can be constructed. This new X_m can be dealt with in the same way, and so on, the $X_{n-r_{m+1}}$ always being the same during the whole process. Proceeding in this way we may cherish hopes that just one integral-X_{m+1} can be constructed, containing the X_m and lying in the $X_{n-r_{m+1}}$. The analytic considerations following here have to establish the necessary and sufficient conditions that these hopes be realized. To avoid unnecessary repetitions we consider immediately the generalized form of the inner problem.

5. The generalized form of the inner problem

Let a system of scalars and not necessarily simple covariant alternating quantities

$$\overset{\chi}{w}_{\lambda_1 \ldots \lambda_{q_\chi}} \quad (\chi = 1, \ldots, N;\ q_\chi = 0, 1, \ldots, n-1)\dagger \tag{5.1}$$

be given, which are analytic in the region considered. Let the *minimum valence* of these quantities be denoted by $v_{\min}$. An E_m at a point of X_n is called an *m-dimensional integral element* or an *integral-E_m* of (5.1) if the E_m-components of all quantities $\overset{\chi}{w}$ and of all natural derivatives $D\overset{\chi}{w}$ vanish. The E_m-component of a scalar is defined as the value of the scalar at the point of the E_m. From these definitions it follows that every $E_{m'}$ $(m' < m)$ contained in an integral-E_m is an integral-$E_{m'}$ and that the integral-E_0's or *integral points* are the points of the manifold $\mathfrak{M}_0$ whose equations are obtained by equating to zero all scalars among the $\overset{\chi}{w}$. We suppose that these equations are always regular of some dimension

† Note that $q_\chi = 0$ gives the scalars.

r_0 in a null point $\underset{0}{\xi}^\kappa$ and that consequently $\mathfrak{M}_0$ is an X_{r_0} in $\mathfrak{N}(\underset{0}{\xi}^\kappa)$. In points not belonging to $\mathfrak{M}_0$ no integral elements exist. If there are no scalars among the $\overset{\chi}{w}$, $\mathfrak{M}_0$ is identical with $\mathfrak{N}(\underset{0}{\xi}^\kappa)$ and $r_0 = n$. An X_m is called an *integral*-X_m of (5.1) if all its tangent-E_m's are integral-E_m's.

If for $\overset{\chi}{w}$ we take the $n-r$ vectors C_λ^{x} ($\mathrm{x} = \mathrm{r}+1,\ldots,\mathrm{n}$) of VIII, § 1, the integral-E_m's and integral-X_m's are the same as in VIII, § 2. But if instead of the C_λ^{x} the $(n-r)$-vector $C_{[\lambda_1}^{\mathrm{r}+1}\ldots C_{\lambda_{n-r}]}^{\mathrm{n}}$ is taken, the integral-E_m's have quite another meaning because then it is only necessary that the E_m-component of this $(n-r)$-vector vanishes and not the E_m-components of all the vectors C_λ^{x} ($\mathrm{x} = \mathrm{r}+1,\ldots,\mathrm{n}$).

The inner problem in the generalized form formulated first by E. Goursat† and dealt with by E. Kähler,‡ J. M. Thomas,§ and C. Burstin‖ is the problem of the determination of all integral-X_m's of the system (5.1) for all possible values of m. In order to distinguish both cases, we call a system consisting only of scalars, $n-r$ vectors, and some of the natural derivatives of these quantities or all of them, a *Cartan system*, and a general system of the form (5.1) a *Goursat system.* If the natural derivatives of the quantities of a Goursat system vanish or are sums of quantities each containing a quantity of the system as a divisor, the system is called *closed.*†† Every system can be made closed by adding the natural derivatives of all its quantities. If the system contains no scalars it is said to be *scalar free*. The most important integral-X_m's are those belonging to a normal system of integral-X_m's. If the maximum value of the dimension of these normal systems is ν the system (5.1) is said to be X_ν-*forming* (cf. III, § 1).

In order to get an analytical formulation of the inner problem we use ξ^κ, $v^{\kappa_1\ldots\kappa_m}$ as supernumerary coordinates with $\epsilon_1 = \binom{n}{m} - m(n-m) - 1$, $\epsilon_2 = 1$ in the $\{n+m(n-m)\}$-dimensional manifold of all E_m's in X_n (cf. II, § 9). The necessary and sufficient conditions that the E_m with the coordinates ξ^κ, $v^{\kappa_1\ldots\kappa_m}$ be an integral-E_m is that

$$\begin{aligned} &(a) && \overset{\chi}{w}_{\lambda_1\ldots\lambda_{q_\chi}} v^{\lambda_1\ldots\lambda_m} = 0 \quad (0 \leqslant q_\chi \leqslant m), \\ &(b) && \partial_{[\lambda}\overset{\chi}{w}_{\lambda_1\ldots\lambda_{q_\chi}]} v^{\lambda\lambda_1\ldots\lambda_{m-1}} = 0 \quad (0 \leqslant q_\chi \leqslant m-1), \\ &(c) && v^{[\kappa_1\ldots\kappa_m} v^{\lambda_1]\ldots\lambda_m} = 0 \quad (\chi = 1,\ldots,N). \end{aligned} \tag{5.2}$$

† 1922. 1, pp. 111 ff. ‡ 1934. 1.
§ 1934. 4. ‖ 1935. 3.
†† Cartan 1945. 1, p. 51, uses the term *système fermé*.

In (5.2 *a*) only the quantities $\overset{\chi}{w}$ with a valence $\leqslant m$ occur and in (5.2 *b*) those with a valence $\leqslant m-1$. Since the section of a covariant q-vector with an E_m vanishes identically for $m < q$, the quantities $\overset{\chi}{w}$ with a valence $> m$ do not occur at all. Hence every E_m with $m < v_{\text{min}}$ is an integral-E_m.

The system (5.1) can be brought into a more convenient form. To that end we form a closed system by adding all natural derivatives and we write this closed system in the form

$$\begin{array}{ll} \overset{\chi_0}{u} & (\chi_0 = 1,\dots, N_0), \\ \overset{\chi_1}{u}_\lambda & (\chi_1 = 1,\dots, N_1), \\ \cdot\;\cdot\;\cdot\;\cdot & \cdot\;\cdot\;\cdot\;\cdot \\ \overset{\chi_\sigma}{u}_{\lambda_1\dots\lambda_\sigma} & (\chi_\sigma = 1,\dots, N_\sigma). \end{array} \tag{5.3}$$

Notice that the $D\overset{\chi_\rho}{u}_{\lambda_1\dots\lambda_\rho}$ are zero mod $\overset{\chi_\tau}{u}$; $\rho, \tau = 0,\dots, \sigma$. It may happen that some of the quantities in (5.3) can be written as a sum of quantities each containing a quantity of the system with a lower valence as a divisor. Evidently these quantities can be dropped. If this is done we denote the maximum valence of the remaining quantities by v_{max}. For a Cartan system we have $v_{\text{min}} = 0$ if the system is not scalar-free and $v_{\text{min}} = 1$ otherwise; further, $v_{\text{max}} = 1$ if the system

$$B_b^\lambda \, \partial_\lambda f = 0 \tag{5.4}$$

is complete and $v_{\text{max}} = 2$ otherwise.

If m is definitely chosen, the system (5.3) can be simplified by dropping all quantities with a valence $> m$ and by multiplying each of the remaining ones with a valence $\rho < m$ with all possible combinations of $m-\rho$ covariant measuring vectors. Then all these quantities together with the $\overset{\chi_m}{u}_{\lambda_1\dots\lambda_m}$ constitute a closed system (with respect to integral-X_m's) consisting only of quantities of valence m,

$$\overset{\omega_m}{U}_{\lambda_1\dots\lambda_m} \quad (\omega_m = 1,\dots, \overset{m}{N}), \tag{5.5}$$

and the equations (5.2) can be written in the form

$$\left.\begin{array}{l} \overset{\omega_m}{U}_{\lambda_1\dots\lambda_m} v^{\lambda_1\dots\lambda_m} = 0 \\ v^{[\kappa_1\dots\kappa_m} v^{\lambda_1]\dots\lambda_m} = 0 \end{array}\right\} \quad (\omega_m = 1,\dots, \overset{m}{N}). \tag{5.6}$$

Each of the quantities $\overset{\chi}{w}$ and $D\overset{\chi}{w}$ with a valence $\leqslant m$ is now a divisor of at least one of the quantities $\overset{\omega_m}{U}$. But notice that the system (5.6) is only equivalent to the system (5.2) as far as m-dimensional integral elements are concerned.

If we require all integral elements with a dimension $m' \geqslant m$, the closed system

$$\begin{aligned} &\overset{\omega_m}{U}_{\lambda_1\ldots\lambda_m} \quad (\omega_m = 1,\ldots,\overset{m}{N}),\\ &\overset{\chi_{m+1}}{u}_{\lambda_1\ldots\lambda_{m+1}} \quad (\chi_{m+1} = 1,\ldots,N_{m+1}),\\ &\cdot \quad \cdot \quad \cdot \quad \cdot \quad \cdot \quad \cdot \quad \cdot \quad \cdot \\ &\overset{\chi_\sigma}{u}_{\lambda_1\ldots\lambda_\sigma} \quad (\chi_\sigma = 1,\ldots,N_\sigma) \end{aligned} \tag{5.7}$$

is equivalent to the system (5.3). The closed system (5.7) is frequently used.

Now we start from a given integral-E_m with the coordinates ξ^κ, $v^{\kappa_1\ldots\kappa_m}$. Then (5.6) is satisfied. Let u^κ be a vector in ξ^κ determining with E_m an E_{m+1} in ξ^κ. The necessary and sufficient conditions that this E_{m+1} is an integral-E_{m+1} are

$$\begin{aligned} &\overset{\omega_m}{U}_{\lambda_1\ldots\lambda_m} v^{[\lambda_1\ldots\lambda_m} u^{\lambda_{m+1}]} = 0 \quad (\omega_m = 1,\ldots,\overset{m}{N};\\ &\overset{\chi_{m+1}}{u}_{\lambda_1\ldots\lambda_{m+1}} v^{\lambda_1\ldots\lambda_m} u^{\lambda_{m+1}} = 0 \qquad \chi_{m+1} = 1,\ldots,N_{m+1}). \end{aligned} \tag{5.8}$$

All vectors u^κ satisfying these equations determine a linear manifold in ξ^κ called the *null-space* of E_m and denoted by $H(E_m)$. Evidently E_m is contained in $H(E_m)$. As in VIII, § 2, we denote the dimension of $H(E_m)$ by $m+1+r_{m+1}$. Integral-E_{m+1}'s containing E_m exist if and only if $r_{m+1} \geqslant 0$ and in this case there are $\infty^{r_{m+1}}$ of these integral-E_{m+1}'s.

The equations of $\mathfrak{M}_0$ are

$$\overset{\omega_0}{U}_{\lambda_1\ldots\lambda_m} = 0 \quad (\omega_0 = 1,\ldots,\overset{0}{N}) \tag{5.9}$$

or

$$\overset{\chi_0}{u} = 0 \quad (\chi_0 = 1,\ldots,N_0). \tag{5.10}$$

For a scalar-free Cartan system we have $r_0 = n$ and $r_1 = r-1$.

A Cartan system or a Goursat system containing scalars can always be reduced to a scalar-free system. $\mathfrak{M}_0$ is an X_{r_0} and since the $\partial_\lambda \overset{\chi_0}{u}$ occur among the $\overset{\chi_1}{u}_\lambda$ every integral-E_m is contained in the tangent E_{r_0} of X_{r_0}. By interchanging the variables ξ^κ we can always ensure that $\xi^{r_0+1},\ldots, \xi^n$ can be solved from (5.10) as functions of $\xi^1,\ldots, \xi^{r_0}$. The variables $\xi^1,\ldots, \xi^{r_0}$ can be looked upon as coordinates in $\mathfrak{M}_0$. If then for all values of σ $'\overset{\chi_\sigma}{u}_{\alpha_1\ldots\alpha_\sigma}$ $(\alpha_1,\ldots, \alpha_\sigma = 1,\ldots, r_0)$ is the section of $\overset{\chi_\sigma}{u}_{\lambda_1\ldots\lambda_\sigma}$ with X_{r_0} at any point of X_{r_0}, the determination of all integral elements in X_n of the system

(5.3) is equivalent to the determination of all integral elements in X_r of the system

$$\begin{matrix} \overset{\chi_1}{'u_\alpha} \quad (\chi_1 = 1,\dots,N_1), \\ \cdot \quad \cdot \quad \cdot \quad \cdot \quad \cdot \quad \cdot \quad \cdot \\ \overset{\chi_{\rho'}}{'u_{\alpha_1\dots\alpha_{\rho'}}} \quad (\chi_{\rho'} = 1,\dots,N_{\rho'}) \end{matrix} \qquad (\alpha, \alpha_1,\dots,\alpha_{\rho'} = 1,\dots,r_0;\ \rho' \leqslant \rho;\ \rho' \leqslant r_0). \tag{5.11}$$

6. Regular chains of integral elements

We consider an integral-E_m with the coordinates $\underset{0}{\xi^\kappa}$, $\underset{0}{v^{\kappa_1\dots\kappa_m}}$. If r_{m+1} has the same value for $\underset{0}{\xi^\kappa}$, $\underset{0}{v^{\kappa_1\dots\kappa_m}}$ as for every other integral element ξ^κ, $v^{\kappa_1\dots\kappa_m}$ in an $\mathfrak{N}(\underset{0}{\xi^\kappa}, \underset{0}{v^{\kappa_1\dots\kappa_m}})$ the integral element $\underset{0}{\xi^\kappa}$, $\underset{0}{v^{\kappa_1\dots\kappa_m}}$ is said to be *regular*. If $\underset{0}{\xi^\kappa}$, $\underset{0}{v^{\kappa_1\dots\kappa_m}}$ is regular, every integral element in a sufficiently small $\mathfrak{N}(\underset{0}{\xi^\kappa}, \underset{0}{v^{\kappa_1\dots\kappa_m}})$ is regular as well.†

A set of integral elements

$$\underset{0}{\xi^\kappa} = \underset{0}{E} \subset E_1 \subset E_2 \subset \dots \subset E_m, \tag{6.1}$$

each containing all preceding elements (this is meant by the sign $\subset$) is called a *regular chain* if $E_1,\dots, E_{m-1}$ are all regular. The last element of the chain E_m may be regular or irregular. If $\underset{0}{\xi^\kappa}$, $\underset{0}{v^{\kappa_1\dots\kappa_m}}$ is the last element of a regular chain it follows from this definition *that every chain, whose elements are sufficiently close to the corresponding elements of this regular chain, is regular as well and that consequently every integral-E_m in a sufficiently small $\mathfrak{N}(\underset{0}{\xi^\kappa}, \underset{0}{v^{\kappa_1\dots\kappa_m}})$ is the last element of a regular chain.*

For regular chains the following theorem holds (cf. Theorem VIII.3):

THEOREM VIII.4. (*Theorem of integrability of Cartan–Kähler.*) *If the integral-E_m with the coordinates $\underset{0}{\xi^\kappa}$, $\underset{0}{v^{\kappa_1\dots\kappa_m}}$ is the last element of a regular chain, there always exists an integral-X_m through $\underset{0}{\xi^\kappa}$ and tangent to the integral-E_m at that point.*

An integral-X_m having at least one tangent E_m which is the last element of a regular chain will be called a *regular integral-X_m*. Since every

† This is the original condition of regularity of E. Cartan. E. Kähler uses another definition making the extra condition that the equation (5.6) be regular in $\underset{0}{\xi^\kappa}$, $\underset{0}{v^{\kappa_1\dots\kappa_m}}$ (1934. 1, p. 23). From this it would appear that a regular chain of a Goursat system has to satisfy more conditions than a regular chain of a Cartan system. But this is not true. As will be proved later the elements of a regular chain, according to the definition of Cartan, automatically satisfy the extra condition of Kähler.

integral-E_m sufficiently near to the last element of a regular chain is itself the last element of a regular chain, Theorem VIII.4 solves the inner problem for all values of m for which regular chains exist. The maximum value of m is called the *genus* g of the Goursat system. Obviously g is an arithmetic invariant of the system. Integral X_m's with $m > g$ may exist but they cannot be regular. Also irregular integral-X_m's may exist with $m \leqslant g$. Theorem VIII.4 deals only with regular integral-X_m's. Hence for $m > g$ the inner problem cannot be solved by means of the theorem of integrability VIII.4 alone.

For the proof of the theorem of integrability VIII.4 we need an auxiliary theorem proved in the next section.

7. First theorem of uniqueness

We will prove the theorem

THEOREM VIII.5. (*First theorem of uniqueness.*) *If in* X_n *an integral-*E_m *of the system* (5.1) *with the coordinates* $\underset{0}{\xi}^{\kappa}$, $\underset{0}{v}^{\kappa_1\ldots\kappa_m}$, *an integral-*$X_m$ *of this system, and an* $X_{n-r_{m+1}}$ *are given, satisfying the following conditions*:

(1) *the integral-*E_m *is regular*;

(2) *the system*

$$\begin{array}{ll}(a) & \overset{\omega_m}{U}_{\lambda_1\ldots\lambda_m} v^{\lambda_1\ldots\lambda_m} = 0 \\ (b) & v^{[\kappa_1\ldots\kappa_m} v^{\lambda_1]\ldots\lambda_m} = 0\end{array} \quad (\omega_m = 1,\ldots,\overset{m}{N}) \qquad (7.1)$$

is regular in $\underset{0}{\xi}^{\kappa}$, $\underset{0}{v}^{\kappa_1\ldots\kappa_m}$;†

(3) *the* X_m *contains* $\underset{0}{\xi}^{\kappa}$ *and is in* $\underset{0}{\xi}^{\kappa}$ *tangent to the integral-*E_m;

(4) *the* $X_{n-r_{m+1}}$ *contains the* X_m *and its tangent* $E_{n-r_{m+1}}$ *in* $\underset{0}{\xi}^{\kappa}$ *has just an* E_{m+1} *in common with* $H(E_m)$,

there exists one and only one integral-X_{m+1}, *containing the integral-*X_m *and contained in the* $X_{n-r_{m+1}}$. *The tangent* E_{m+1} *in* $\underset{0}{\xi}^{\kappa}$ *of this integral-*X_{m+1} *coincides with the section of the* $E_{n-r_{m+1}}$ *with* $H(E_m)$.

PROOF. The proof will be divided into four parts:

(*a*) *Suitable choice of the coordinate system*

Let the coordinates ξ^{κ} ($\kappa = 1,\ldots,n$) be chosen in such a way that $\underset{0}{\xi}^{\kappa} = 0$ and that the equations of the given $X_{n-r_{m+1}}$ take the form

$$\xi^{n-\rho+1} = 0, \quad \ldots, \quad \xi^n = 0 \quad (\rho \overset{\text{def}}{=} r_{m+1}) \qquad (7.2)$$

† Kähler's conditions of regularity contain (1) and (2). (2) is the extra condition mentioned in the footnote on p. 358.

and the equations of the given integral-X_m the form

$$\xi^{m+1} = 0, \quad \ldots, \quad \xi^n = 0. \tag{7.3}$$

Then the $X_{n-\rho}$ consists of coordinate curves of the variables $\xi^1, \ldots, \xi^{n-\rho}$ and the X_m of coordinate curves of the variables $\xi^1, \ldots, \xi^m$. For the coordinates of the integral-E_m in $\underset{0}{\xi^\kappa}$ we choose

$$\underset{0}{\xi^\kappa}, \quad \underset{0}{v^{\kappa_1 \ldots \kappa_m}} = m!\, \underset{1}{e}^{[\kappa_1} \ldots \underset{m}{e}^{\kappa_m]}. \tag{7.4}$$

Then $\underset{0}{v^{1 \ldots m}} = 1$. Moreover, the coordinates will be chosen in such a way that the E_{m+1} in $\underset{0}{\xi^\kappa}$, being the section of the tangent $E_{n-\rho}$ with $H(E_m)$, is spanned by the vectors $\underset{1}{e^\kappa}, \ldots, \underset{m+1}{e^\kappa}$.

(b) Construction of an auxiliary vector

The vector $\underset{m+1}{e^\kappa}$ in $\underset{0}{\xi^\kappa}$ is contained in $H(E_m)$ and in the tangent $E_{n-\rho}$. With respect to the special coordinate system introduced *this vector is the only vector in the E_{m+1} whose first m components are zero whilst the $(m+1)$th component has the value 1.* Now we will show that for every E_m (not necessarily an integral-E_m) with the coordinates ξ^κ, $v^{\kappa_1 \ldots \kappa_m}$ in an $\mathfrak{N}(\underset{0}{\xi^\kappa}, \underset{0}{v^{\kappa_1 \ldots \kappa_m}})$ there exists at least one vector v^κ satisfying the congruences and equations

$$\begin{array}{ll} (a) & \left.\begin{array}{l} \overset{\omega_m}{U}_{\lambda_1 \ldots \lambda_m} v^{[\lambda_1 \ldots \lambda_m} v^{\lambda_{m+1}]} \equiv 0 \\ \overset{\chi_{m+1}}{u}_{\lambda_1 \ldots \lambda_{m+1}} v^{\lambda_1 \ldots \lambda_m} v^{\lambda_{m+1}} \equiv 0 \end{array}\right\} \left(\operatorname{mod} \overset{\omega_m}{U}_{\lambda_1 \ldots \lambda_m} v^{\lambda_1 \ldots \lambda_m}\right), \\ (b) & v^{n-\rho+1} = 0, \quad \ldots, \quad v^n = 0, \\ (c) & v^1 = 0, \quad \ldots, \quad v^m = 0, \qquad (\omega_m = 1, \ldots, \overset{m}{N}; \\ (d) & v^{m+1} = 1. \qquad\qquad \chi_{m+1} = 1, \ldots, N_{m+1}). \end{array} \tag{7.5}$$

First we consider the case in which ξ^κ, $v^{\kappa_1 \ldots \kappa_m}$ is an integral-E_m. Then the modulus restriction in (7.5a) drops out and the equations (7.5a) express the fact that v^κ lies in $H(E_m)$. Since $H(E_m)$ has dimension $m+1+\rho$, (7.5 a) contains just $n-m-1-\rho$ linearly independent equations. Hence (7.5) is equivalent to a system of $n-m-1-\rho+\rho+m+1=n$ equations. We will show that these equations are linearly independent. (7.5 b) expresses the fact that v^κ lies in the $E_{n-\rho}$ spanned by the vectors $\underset{1}{e^\kappa}, \ldots, \underset{n-\rho}{e^\kappa}$. In all points of the given $X_{n-\rho}$ this $E_{n-\rho}$ coincides with the tangent $E_{n-\rho}$. Hence, if ξ^κ, $v^{\kappa_1 \ldots \kappa_m}$ are replaced by $\underset{0}{\xi^\kappa}$, $\underset{0}{v^{\kappa_1 \ldots \kappa_m}}$ the section of $H(E_m)$ with this $E_{n-\rho}$ is spanned by the vectors $\underset{1}{e^\kappa}, \ldots, \underset{m+1}{e^\kappa}$ and from

(7.5) it follows that for these special values of ξ^κ and $v^{\kappa_1\ldots\kappa_m}$ only one solution exists, viz. $v^\kappa = \underset{m+1}{e^\kappa}$. The matrix of the left-hand sides of the n equations under consideration depends only on ξ^κ and $v^{\kappa_1\ldots\kappa_m}$ and consequently has the rank n in $\xi^\kappa = \underset{0}{\xi^\kappa}$, $v^{\kappa_1\ldots\kappa_m} = \underset{0}{v^{\kappa_1\ldots\kappa_m}}$. Hence, there exists an $\mathfrak{N}(\underset{0}{\xi^\kappa}, \underset{0}{v^{\kappa_1\ldots\kappa_m}})$ where this rank is n and where only one solution v^κ exists. From (7.5) it follows that this solution has the form

$$v^\kappa = \underset{m+1}{e^\kappa} + F^\zeta(\xi^\kappa, v^{\kappa_1\ldots\kappa_m})\underset{\zeta}{e^\kappa} \quad (\zeta = m+2,\ldots, n-\rho), \tag{7.6}$$

the F^ζ being functions computable from (7.5). Since the relations (7.5 a) are equations if and only if the E_m is an integral-E_m and are congruences in the other case, the functions F^ζ are only defined at the null points of (7.1).

If the E_m is not an integral-E_m, from the solution (7.6) solutions of (7.5) can be derived for the case when (7.5 a) are congruences. The system (7.1) is regular and consequently represents in the $\left\{n+\binom{n}{m}-1\right\}$-dimensional manifold of all elements ξ^κ, $v^{\kappa_1\ldots\kappa_m}$ in an $\mathfrak{N}(\underset{0}{\xi^\kappa}, \underset{0}{v^{\kappa_1\ldots\kappa_m}})$ a manifold with a definite dimension, consisting of all integral-E_m's in this neighbourhood. If d is the dimension of this manifold, just d can be chosen among the ξ^κ and the quotients $v^{\kappa_1\ldots\kappa_m}/v^{1\ldots m}$ such that the other ξ^κ and quotients can be expressed in terms of them. Then the functions F^ζ in (7.6) depend only on these d variables and, therefore, denoting these variables by ξ^ϵ, $'v^{\epsilon_1\ldots\epsilon_m}$, relations of the form

$$G^\zeta(\xi^\epsilon, {}'v^{\epsilon_1\ldots\epsilon_m}) = F^\zeta(\xi^\kappa, v^{\kappa_1\ldots\kappa_m}) \quad (\zeta = m+2,\ldots, n-\rho) \tag{7.7}$$

must be valid in the null points of (7.1). But in this way we have found functions G^ζ defined for all values of ξ^ϵ, $'v^{\epsilon_1\ldots\epsilon_m}$ in some $\mathfrak{N}(\underset{0}{\xi^\epsilon}, \underset{0}{'v^{\epsilon_1\ldots\epsilon_m}})$. Hence, since the ξ^ϵ, $'v^{\epsilon_1\ldots\epsilon_m}$ occur among the ξ^κ, $v^{\kappa_1\ldots\kappa_m}/v^{1\ldots m}$, the equations

$$H^\zeta(\xi^\kappa, v^{\kappa_1\ldots\kappa_m}) \overset{\text{def}}{=} G^\zeta(\xi^\epsilon, {}'v^{\epsilon_1\ldots\epsilon_m}) \quad (\zeta = m+2,\ldots, n-\rho), \tag{7.8}$$

valid not only in the null points of (7.1) but in all points of $\mathfrak{N}(\underset{0}{\xi^\kappa}, \underset{0}{v^{\kappa_1\ldots\kappa_m}})$, define a system of functions H^ζ in all points of this neighbourhood coinciding with the F^ζ in all null points of (7.1). From this it follows that the vector

$$'v^\kappa = \underset{m+1}{e^\kappa} + H^\zeta(\xi^\kappa, v^{\kappa_1\ldots\kappa_m})\underset{\zeta}{e^\kappa} \quad (\zeta = m+2,\ldots, n-\rho) \tag{7.9}$$

coincides with v^κ in all null points of (7.1) and consequently satisfies the relations (7.5) in these null points. Now since the system (7.1) is regular in $\mathfrak{N}(\underset{0}{\xi^\kappa}, \underset{0}{v^{\kappa_1\ldots\kappa_m}})$ the first basis theorem II.4 can be applied and from this theorem it follows immediately that $'v^{\kappa}$ satisfies the congruences (7.5 a) in $\mathfrak{N}(\underset{0}{\xi}^{\kappa}, \underset{0}{v}^{\kappa_1 \ldots \kappa_m})$. This proves the existence of at least one solution $'v^{\kappa}$ in all cases. But notice that, in the case when E_m is not an integral-E_m, $'v^{\kappa}$ depends on the choice of the ξ^{ϵ}, $'v^{\epsilon_1 \ldots \epsilon_m}$ and is not uniquely determined.

(c) *Construction of the system of differential equations of the* X_{m+1}

The integral-X_{m+1} has to be contained in the $X_{n-\rho}$ and consequently its tangent E_{m+1} in $\underset{0}{\xi}^{\kappa}$ has to be contained in $H(E_m)$ and in the tangent $E_{n-\rho}$ of the $X_{n-\rho}$. This proves the second part of Theorem VIII.5, provided that an integral-X_{m+1} exists which satisfies the conditions of the first part of that theorem. Hence, the tangent E_{m+1} in $\underset{0}{\xi}^{\kappa}$ is spanned by the vectors $\underset{1}{e}^{\kappa},\ldots, \underset{m+1}{e}^{\kappa}$ and consequently the variables $\xi^1,\ldots, \xi^{m+1}$ can be used as coordinates in the X_{m+1} in an $\mathfrak{N}(\underset{0}{\xi}^{\kappa})$. This implies that a parametric form

$$\xi^{\kappa} = f^{\kappa}(\xi^1,\ldots, \xi^{m+1}) \tag{7.10}$$

of the X_{m+1} exists. Since the X_{m+1} is contained in the given $X_{n-\rho}$ we have

$$f^1 = \xi^1, \quad \ldots, \quad f^{m+1} = \xi^{m+1}; \qquad f^{\zeta} = \phi^{\zeta}(\xi^1,\ldots, \xi^{m+1});$$
$$f^{n-\rho+1} = 0, \quad \ldots, \quad f^n = 0 \quad (\zeta = m+2,\ldots, n-\rho), \tag{7.11}$$

the ϕ^{ζ} being now the functions which are still unknown. The problem is to find differential equations for these ϕ^{ζ}.

The tangent E_{m+1} of the X_{m+1} at any point of the X_{m+1} in $\mathfrak{N}(\underset{0}{\xi}^{\kappa})$ is spanned by the $m+1$ vectors

$$\partial_1 f^{\kappa}, \quad \ldots, \quad \partial_{m+1} f^{\kappa}. \tag{7.12}$$

This E_{m+1} has to be an integral-E_{m+1}. Necessary and sufficient conditions are that the E_m spanned by the m vectors

$$\partial_1 f^{\kappa}, \quad \ldots, \quad \partial_m f^{\kappa} \tag{7.13}$$

is an integral-E_m and that, as a consequence of (7.11), the vector $\partial_{m+1} f^{\kappa}$ lies in $H(E_m)$. Now the coordinates of this E_m are

$$\xi^{\kappa} = f^{\kappa}, \qquad v^{\kappa_1 \ldots \kappa_m} = (\partial_1 f^{[\kappa_1}) \ldots (\partial_m f^{\kappa_m]}) \tag{7.14}$$

and according to (7.11) the vector $\partial_{m+1} f^{\kappa}$ satisfies the equation

$$\partial_{m+1} f^{\kappa} = \underset{m+1}{e}^{\kappa} + (\partial_{m+1} \phi^{\zeta}) \underset{\zeta}{e}^{\kappa} \quad (\zeta = m+2,\ldots, n-\rho). \tag{7.15}$$

From this it follows that $\partial_{m+1} f^{\kappa}$ has to satisfy (7.5). Now, since (7.5) has only one solution in the case when the E_m is an integral-E_m, it follows that

$$\partial_{m+1} \phi^{\zeta} = H^{\zeta}(\xi^{\kappa}, v^{\kappa_1 \ldots \kappa_m}) \quad (\zeta = m+2,\ldots, n-\rho). \tag{7.16}$$

In these equations the values of ξ^κ and $v^{\kappa_1\ldots\kappa_m}$ resulting from (7.14) have to be substituted and according to (7.11) these values all depend on $\xi^1,\ldots, \xi^{m+1}, \phi^\zeta, \partial_1\phi^\zeta,\ldots, \partial_m\phi^\zeta$. Hence we get a system of partial differential equations of the form

$$\partial_{m+1}\phi^\zeta = \Phi^\zeta(\xi^1,\ldots,\xi^{m+1},\phi^\eta,\partial_1\phi^\eta,\ldots,\partial_m\phi^\eta) \quad (\zeta,\eta = m+2,\ldots,n-\rho). \tag{7.17}$$

The initial conditions are

$$\phi^\zeta(\xi^1,\ldots,\xi^m, 0) = 0 \tag{7.18}$$

because the X_m has to be contained in the X_{m+1}. Now according to the existence theorem of Cauchy-Kowalewski III.1 there exists one and only one system of solutions of (7.17) satisfying (7.18). Hence there exists at most one integral-X_{m+1} contained in the $X_{n-\rho}$ and containing the X_m.

(*d*) *Proof of the existence of the* X_{m+1}

We now have to prove that (7.10) together with (7.11) always represent an integral-X_{m+1} if the equations (7.17) and the initial conditions (7.18) are satisfied. Naturally we are not allowed now to suppose that the E_m spanned by the vectors (7.13) is an integral-E_m. But because the functions H^ζ in (7.16) are defined in all points of $\mathfrak{N}(\underset{0}{\xi}^\kappa, \underset{0}{v}^{\kappa_1\ldots\kappa_m})$ the equations (7.16) exist as well. As a consequence of the existence theorem III.1 the equations (7.17) and the initial conditions (7.18) determine one single X_{m+1}. From (7.18) it follows already that this X_{m+1} contains X_m. Hence, the only thing to be proved is that the X_{m+1} is really an integral-X_{m+1}. Necessary and sufficient conditions for this are that the equations

$$\begin{aligned} &\overset{\omega_m}{U}_{\lambda_1\ldots\lambda_m} t^{[\lambda_1\ldots\lambda_m}\partial_{m+1} f^{\lambda_{m+1}]} = 0 \quad &(\omega_m = 1,\ldots,\overset{m}{N};\\ &\overset{\chi_{m+1}}{u}_{\lambda_1\ldots\lambda_{m+1}} t^{\lambda_1\ldots\lambda_m}\partial_{m+1} f^{\lambda_{m+1}} = 0 \quad &\chi_{m+1} = 1,\ldots,N_{m+1}) \end{aligned} \tag{7.19}$$

with

$$t^{\kappa_1\ldots\kappa_m} \overset{\text{def}}{=} (\partial_1 f^{[\kappa_1}) \ldots (\partial_m f^{\kappa_m]}) \tag{7.20}$$

are satisfied. Since the system (7.1) is regular there exist among these equations (7.1) just $n+\binom{n}{m}-1-d$ independent ones, representing the d-dimensional manifold of all integral-E_m's in $\mathfrak{N}(\underset{0}{\xi}^\kappa, \underset{0}{v}^{\kappa_1\ldots\kappa_m})$. Among these $n+\binom{n}{m}-1-d$ equations there may be some belonging to (7.1*b*). Since $t^{\kappa_1\ldots\kappa_m}$ is a simple m-vector according to the definition (7.20) these equations can be omitted. The remaining $t \leqslant n+\binom{n}{m}-1-d$ equations all belong to (7.1 a). These equations are all linear and homogeneous in the $v^{\kappa_1\ldots\kappa_m}$ and can be written in the form

$$\overset{\tau}{\theta}(\xi^\kappa, v^{\kappa_1\ldots\kappa_m}) \overset{\text{def}}{=} \overset{\tau}{z}_{\lambda_1\ldots\lambda_m} v^{\lambda_1\ldots\lambda_m} = 0 \quad (\tau = 1,\ldots, t). \tag{7.21}$$

Now the equations

$$\left.\begin{aligned} &\overset{\omega_m}{U}_{\lambda_1\ldots\lambda_m} v^{[\lambda_1\ldots\lambda_m} v^{\lambda_{m+1}]} = 0 \\ &\overset{\chi_{m+1}}{u}_{\lambda_1\ldots\lambda_{m+1}} v^{\lambda_1\ldots\lambda_m} v^{\lambda_{m+1}} = 0 \end{aligned}\right. \quad (\omega_m = 1,\ldots, \overset{m}{N};\ \chi_{m+1} = 1,\ldots, N_{m+1}) \tag{7.22}$$

have to be satisfied if for ξ^κ, $v^{\kappa_1\ldots\kappa_m}$ we take the coordinates of an integral-E_m and for v^κ the values

$$v^\kappa = \underset{m+1}{e^\kappa} + H^\zeta(\xi^\kappa, v^{\kappa_1\ldots\kappa_m}) \underset{\zeta}{e^\kappa} \quad (\zeta = m+2,\ldots, n-\rho) \tag{7.23}$$

because the functions H^ζ have been constructed in such a way that the validity of (7.22) is a consequence of the validity of (7.1). Hence, according to the first basis theorem II.4 we have the congruences

$$\left.\begin{aligned} &\overset{\omega_m}{U}_{\lambda_1\ldots\lambda_m} v^{[\lambda_1\ldots\lambda_m} v^{\lambda_{m+1}]} \equiv 0 \\ &\overset{\chi_{m+1}}{u}_{\lambda_1\ldots\lambda_{m+1}} v^{\lambda_1\ldots\lambda_m} v^{\lambda_{m+1}} \equiv 0 \end{aligned}\right\} (\operatorname{mod} \overset{\tau}{\theta}(\xi^\kappa, v^{\kappa_1\ldots\kappa_m}))$$

$$(\omega_m = 1,\ldots, \overset{m}{N};\ \chi_{m+1} = 1,\ldots, N_{m+1};\ \tau = 1,\ldots, t) \tag{7.24}$$

valid for all values of ξ^κ and $v^{\kappa_1\ldots\kappa_m}$ in $\mathfrak{N}(\overset{0}{\xi^\kappa}, \overset{0}{v^{\kappa_1\ldots\kappa_m}})$ satisfying (7.1 b), if v^κ is replaced by the values (7.23). From this and (7.5), (7.6), (7.20), and (7.21) it follows that

$$\begin{aligned} &(a) \quad \overset{\omega_m}{U}_{\lambda_1\ldots\lambda_m} t^{[\lambda_1\ldots\lambda_m} \partial_{m+1} f^{\lambda_{m+1}]} \equiv 0 \\ &(b) \quad \overset{\chi_{m+1}}{u}_{\lambda_1\ldots\lambda_{m+1}} t^{\lambda_1\ldots\lambda_m} \partial_{m+1} f^{\lambda_{m+1}} \equiv 0 \end{aligned} \Bigg\} (\operatorname{mod} \overset{\tau}{z}_{\lambda_1\ldots\lambda_m} t^{\lambda_1\ldots\lambda_m})$$

$$(\omega_m = 1,\ldots, \overset{m}{N};\ \chi_{m+1} = 1,\ldots, N_{m+1};\ \tau = 1,\ldots, t) \tag{7.25}$$

if in these congruences we put

$$\begin{aligned} f^1 = \xi^1, \quad \ldots, \quad f^{m+1} = \xi^{m+1}, \\ f^\zeta = \xi^\zeta \quad (\zeta = m+2,\ldots, n-\rho), \\ f^{n-\rho+1} = 0, \quad \ldots, \quad f^n = 0, \end{aligned} \tag{7.26}$$

and if the ξ^ζ are looked upon as functions of $\xi^1,\ldots, \xi^{m+1}$,

$$\xi^\zeta = \phi^\zeta(\xi^1,\ldots, \xi^{m+1}) \quad (\zeta = m+2,\ldots, n-\rho). \tag{7.27}$$

In consequence of the construction of the $\overset{\tau}{z}_{\lambda_1\ldots\lambda_m}$, among the congruences (7.25 a) the congruences

$$\overset{\tau}{z}_{\lambda_1\ldots\lambda_m} t^{[\lambda_1\ldots\lambda_m} \partial_{m+1} f^{\lambda_{m+1}]} \equiv 0 \ (\operatorname{mod} \overset{\sigma}{\theta}) \quad (\sigma, \tau = 1,\ldots, t) \tag{7.28}$$

occur and among the congruences (7.25 b) there are the congruences

$$\partial_{[\lambda_1} \overset{\tau}{z}_{\lambda_2\ldots\lambda_{m+1}]}\, t^{\lambda_1\ldots\lambda_m}\, \partial_{m+1} f^{\lambda_{m+1}} \equiv 0 \pmod{\overset{\sigma}{\theta}} \quad (\sigma,\tau = 1,\ldots,t). \quad (7.29)$$

Now we use the identity

$$(m+1)(\partial_{[\lambda_1}\overset{\tau}{z}_{\lambda_2\ldots\lambda_{m+1}]})(\partial_1\xi^{\lambda_1})\ldots(\partial_{m+1}\xi^{\lambda_{m+1}})$$
$$= m\,\partial_{[1}\{\overset{\tau}{z}_{|\lambda_1\ldots\lambda_m|}(\partial_2\xi^{\lambda_1})\ldots(\partial_{m]}\xi^{\lambda_{m-1}})\partial_{m+1}\xi^{\lambda_m}\} + (-1)^m\partial_{m+1}\overset{\tau}{\theta}$$
$$(\tau = 1,\ldots,t) \quad (7.30)$$

and a set of m auxiliary vectors $\overset{i}{w}_\lambda$ $(i = 1,\ldots,m)$ defined by the equations

$$\begin{aligned} &\overset{i}{w}_\lambda\, \partial_1 f^\lambda = 0 \\ &\cdot \quad \cdot \quad \cdot \quad \cdot \quad \cdot \quad \cdot \\ &\overset{i}{w}_\lambda\, \partial_{i-1} f^\lambda = 0 \\ &\overset{i}{w}_\lambda\, \partial_i f^\lambda = 1 \quad \text{(not to be summed over } i\text{);} \\ &\overset{i}{w}_\lambda\, \partial_{i+1} f^\lambda = 0 \\ &\cdot \quad \cdot \quad \cdot \quad \cdot \quad \cdot \quad \cdot \\ &\overset{i}{w}_\lambda\, \partial_n f^\lambda = 0 \end{aligned} \quad (7.31)$$

in which the f^λ have the values from (7.26). The equations (7.31) always have analytic solutions in an $\mathfrak{N}(\underset{0}{\xi^1},\ldots,\underset{0}{\xi^{m+1}})$ and these solutions are functions of $\xi^1,\ldots,\xi^{m+1}$. By transvection of (7.28) with $\overset{i}{w}_{\lambda_{m+1}}$ we get

$$\overset{\tau}{z}_{\lambda_1\ldots\lambda_m}(\partial_1\xi^{\lambda_1})\ldots(\partial_{i-1}\xi^{\lambda_{i-1}})(\partial_{i+1}\xi^{\lambda_i})\ldots(\partial_{m+1}\xi^{\lambda_m}) \equiv 0 \pmod{\overset{\sigma}{\theta}}$$
$$(\sigma,\tau = 1,\ldots,t) \quad (7.32)$$

and if these values are substituted into (7.30) we get the differential equations in $\overset{\tau}{\theta}$

$$\partial_{m+1}\overset{\tau}{\theta} \equiv 0 \pmod{\overset{\sigma}{\theta}, \partial_1\overset{\sigma}{\theta},\ldots,\partial_m\overset{\sigma}{\theta}} \quad (\sigma,\tau = 1,\ldots,t) \quad (7.33)$$

with coefficients which are analytic in $\mathfrak{N}(\underset{0}{\xi^1},\ldots,\underset{0}{\xi^{m+1}})$. Now we know that for $\xi^{m+1} = 0$

$$(\partial_{[1}f^{\kappa_1})\ldots(\partial_{m]}f^{\kappa_m}) = \underset{1}{e}^{[\kappa_1}\ldots\underset{m}{e}^{\kappa_m]} \quad (7.34)$$

and that consequently this m-vector satisfies (7.1) at all points of the X_m. Hence

$$\overset{\tau}{\theta}(\xi^1,\ldots,\xi^m,0) = 0 \quad (\tau = 1,\ldots,t). \quad (7.35)$$

According to the existence theorem III.1 there exists one and only one system of solutions of (7.33) which vanish for $\xi^{m+1} = 0$. Now evidently $\overset{\tau}{\theta} = 0$ are such solutions and consequently the only solutions. This implies that the quantities $\overset{\tau}{z}_{\lambda_1\ldots\lambda_m} t^{\lambda_1\ldots\lambda_m}$ in (7.25) all vanish and therefore the equations (7.19) are satisfied.

8. Proof of the theorem of integrability of Cartan-Kähler. Second theorem of uniqueness

The theorem of integrability of Cartan-Kähler can now be proved by repeated application of the first theorem of uniqueness proved in the preceding section. But here a difficulty arises. Though the elements $E_0, \ldots, E_{m-1}$ of a regular chain are all regular it is not yet certain that they also satisfy the second condition of Theorem VIII.5, viz. that their equations are regular.

Therefore we have first to prove the following auxiliary theorem

THEOREM VIII.6. *Every element E_p $(1 \leqslant p \leqslant m)$ of a regular chain $E_0, \ldots, E_m$ with the coordinates $\underset{0}{\xi}^\kappa$, $\underset{0}{v}^{\kappa_1\ldots\kappa_p}$ satisfies the condition that the equations*

$$
\begin{array}{lll}
(a) & \overset{\omega_p}{U}_{\lambda_1\ldots\lambda_p} v^{\lambda_1\ldots\lambda_p} = 0 & \\
(b) & v^{[\kappa_1\ldots\kappa_p} v^{\lambda_1]\ldots\lambda_p} = 0 & (\omega_p = 1, \ldots, \overset{p}{N})
\end{array} \tag{8.1}
$$

are regular of the dimension

$$M_p + 1 \overset{\text{de}}{=} \sum_{i=0}^{i=p} r_i - \tfrac{1}{2}p(p-1) + 1 \tag{8.2}$$

in $\underset{0}{\xi}^\kappa$, $\underset{0}{v}^{\kappa_1\ldots\kappa_p}$.

Notice that the theorem holds for $p = m$ though the E_m is not necessarily regular.

PROOF. Let the coordinate system be chosen in such a way that the E_p in $\underset{0}{\xi}^\kappa$ is spanned by the measuring vectors $\underset{1}{e}^\kappa, \ldots, \underset{p}{e}^\kappa$ for every value of $p > 0$. The ξ^κ, $v^{\kappa_1\ldots\kappa_p}$ represent a system of supernumerary coordinates with $\epsilon_1 = \binom{n}{p} - p(n-p) - 1$, $\epsilon_2 = 1$ (cf. II, § 9) in the manifold of all E_p's in $\mathfrak{R}(\underset{0}{\xi}^\kappa, \underset{0}{v}^{\kappa_1\ldots\kappa_p})$. If we write $v^{1\ldots p} = 1$ the ξ^κ, $v^{\kappa_1\ldots\kappa_p}$ except $v^{1\ldots p}$ constitute a system of supernumerary coordinates with $\epsilon_1 = \binom{n}{p} - p(n-p) - 1$, $\epsilon_2 = 0$ in the same manifold (cf. II, § 9). Consequently, according to Theorem II.10, the system arising from (8.1) by equating $v^{1\ldots p}$ to 1 is regular of dimension M_p in $\underset{0}{\xi}^\kappa$, $\underset{0}{v}^{\kappa_1\ldots\kappa_m}$ if

(8.1) is regular of dimension M_p+1 in $\underset{0}{\xi}^\kappa$, $\underset{0}{v}^{\kappa_1\ldots\kappa_m}$, and vice versa. In the sequel, if $v^{1\ldots p}$ is not considered as a variable, we always take

$$v^{1\ldots p} = 1 \; (p = 1,\ldots,m).$$

By means of (8.1 b) just $\binom{n}{p}-p(n-p)-1$ of the variables $v^{\kappa_1\ldots\kappa_p}$ can be expressed in terms of the remaining $p(n-p)$ variables. In order to obtain a convenient form of the equations we write (cf. I, § 7, and II, § 9) for one definite choice of p

$$U^\kappa_\beta \overset{\text{def}}{=} v^{1\ldots(\beta-1)\,\kappa\,(\beta+1)\ldots p} \quad (\beta = 1,\ldots,p). \tag{8.3}$$

Then, according to $v^{1\ldots p} = 1$ and (8.1 b) we have

$$U^\alpha_\beta = \delta^\alpha_\beta \quad (\alpha,\beta = 1,\ldots,p) \tag{8.4}$$

and

$$v^{\kappa_1\ldots\kappa_p} = p!\, U^{[\kappa_1}_1\ldots U^{\kappa_p]}_p. \tag{8.5}$$

In consideration of (8.4) the equation (8.5) expresses $v^{\kappa_1\ldots\kappa_p}$ in terms of the $p(n-p)$ variables

$$U^\zeta_\beta = v^{1\ldots(\beta-1)\,\zeta\,(\beta+1)\ldots p} \quad (\beta = 1,\ldots,p;\; \zeta = p+1,\ldots,n). \tag{8.6}$$

We remark that for $v^{\kappa_1\ldots\kappa_p} = \underset{0}{v}^{\kappa_1\ldots\kappa_p}$ the U^κ_β have the values

$$\underset{0}{U}^\alpha_\beta = \delta^\alpha_\beta, \qquad \underset{0}{U}^\zeta_\beta = 0 \quad (\alpha,\beta = 1,\ldots,p;\; \zeta = p+1,\ldots,n). \tag{8.7}$$

As was proved in II, § 9, the system (8.1 b) is regular of dimension $p(n-p)+1$ in all its null points. Consequently, according to Theorem II.10, the system

$$\overset{\omega_p}{U}_{\lambda_1\ldots\lambda_p} U^{\lambda_1}_1\ldots U^{\lambda_p}_p = 0 \quad (\omega_p = 1,\ldots,\overset{p}{N}) \tag{8.8}$$

is regular of dimension M_p in $\underset{0}{\xi}^\kappa$, $\underset{0}{U}^\zeta_\beta$ if (8.1) is regular of dimension M_p+1 in $\underset{0}{\xi}^\kappa$, $\underset{0}{v}^{\kappa_1\ldots\kappa_m}$ for $U^\alpha_\beta = \delta^\alpha_\beta$, and vice versa.

The ξ^κ, U^ζ_β are non-supernumerary coordinates in the manifold of all E_p's in $\mathfrak{N}(\underset{0}{\xi}^\kappa, \underset{0}{U}^\zeta_\beta)$ and the ξ^κ, U^κ_β supernumerary coordinates with $\epsilon_1 = p^2$, $\epsilon_2 = 0$ if the U^α_β are looked upon as free variables. Hence, since (8.4) is regular it follows from Theorem II.10 that the system (8.8) is regular of dimension M_p+p^2 in $\underset{0}{\xi}^\kappa$, $\underset{0}{U}^\kappa_\beta$ if the system (8.1) is regular of dimension M_p+1 in $\underset{0}{\xi}^\kappa$, $\underset{0}{v}^{\kappa_1\ldots\kappa_m}$, and vice versa, and if the condition $U^\alpha_\beta = \delta^\alpha_\beta$ is dropped.

U^κ_β is a special form of the contravariant connecting quantity of E_p. If $U^\kappa_{\mathfrak{b}}$ ($\mathfrak{b} = 1,\ldots,\mathfrak{p}$) is a general form of this quantity the ξ^κ and $U^\kappa_{\mathfrak{b}}$ can be used as supernumerary coordinates with $\epsilon_1 = 0$, $\epsilon_2 = p^2$ in the manifold of all E_p's in $\mathfrak{N}(\underset{0}{\xi}^\kappa, \underset{0}{U}^\kappa_{\mathfrak{b}})$. Since the regularity of a system is invariant for transformations of coordinates, it follows that the system

$$\overset{\omega_p}{U}_{\lambda_1\ldots\lambda_p} U_1^{\lambda_1}\ldots U_{\mathrm{p}}^{\lambda_p} \quad (\omega_p = 1,\ldots,\overset{p}{N}) \tag{8.9}$$

is regular of dimension M_p+p^2 in $\underset{0}{\xi}^\kappa$, $\underset{0}{U}{}^\kappa_{\mathfrak{b}}$ if (8.1) is regular of dimension M_p+1 in $\underset{0}{\xi}^\kappa$, $\underset{0}{v}{}^{\kappa_1\ldots\kappa_m}$, and vice versa.

The system (8.8) can be put in a more convenient form. If the $\overset{\omega_p}{U}$ are written out in terms of the $\overset{\chi_\rho}{u}$ (cf. VIII, § 5), (8.8) takes the form

$$\overset{\chi_\rho}{u}_{\lambda_1\ldots\lambda_\rho} \delta^{\kappa_{\rho+1}}_{\lambda_{\rho+1}}\ldots\delta^{\kappa_p}_{\lambda_p} U^{\lambda_1}_{[1}\ldots U^{\lambda_p}_{p]} = 0 \quad (\chi_\rho = 1,\ldots,N_\rho;\ 0 \leqslant \rho \leqslant p). \tag{8.10}$$

Now (8.10) is equivalent to

$$\overset{\chi_\rho}{u}_{\lambda_1\ldots\lambda_\rho} U^{\lambda_1}_{\beta_1}\ldots U^{\lambda_\rho}_{\beta_\rho} = 0 \quad (\chi_\rho = 1,\ldots,N_\rho;\ 0 \leqslant \rho \leqslant p;\ \beta_1,\ldots,\beta_\rho = 1,\ldots,p). \tag{8.11}$$

Hence, if we write

$$\overset{\chi_\rho}{F}{}^{\kappa_{\rho+1}\ldots\kappa_p} \quad (\chi_\rho = 1,\ldots,N_\rho) \tag{8.12}$$

for the left-hand side of (8.10) and

$$'\overset{\chi_\rho}{F}_{\beta_1\ldots\beta_\rho} \quad (\chi_\rho = 1,\ldots,N_\rho;\ \beta_1,\ldots,\beta_\rho = 1,\ldots,p) \tag{8.13}$$

for the left-hand side of (8.11), we have

$$\overset{\chi_\rho}{F}{}^{\kappa_{\rho+1}\ldots\kappa_p} = {}'\overset{\chi_\rho}{F}_{[1\ldots\rho} U^{\lambda_{\rho+1}}_{\rho+1}\ldots U^{\lambda_p}_{p]} \delta^{\kappa_{\rho+1}}_{\lambda_{\rho+1}}\ldots\delta^{\kappa_p}_{\lambda_p} \quad (\chi_\rho = 1,\ldots,N_\rho). \tag{8.14}$$

Differentiating this equation, according to (8.11) we get in $\underset{0}{\xi}^\kappa$, $\underset{0}{U}{}^\kappa_\beta$

$$\begin{aligned} d\overset{\chi_\rho}{F}{}^{\kappa_{\rho+1}\ldots\kappa_p} &= (d\,'\overset{\chi_\rho}{F}_{[1\ldots\rho})\delta^{\lambda_{\rho+1}}_{\rho+1}\ldots\delta^{\lambda_p}_{p]}\delta^{\kappa_{\rho+1}}_{\lambda_{\rho+1}}\ldots\delta^{\kappa_p}_{\lambda_p} \\ &= (d\,'\overset{\chi_\rho}{F}_{[1\ldots\rho})\delta^{\kappa_{\rho+1}}_{\rho+1}\ldots\delta^{\kappa_p}_{p]} \end{aligned}$$
$$(\chi_\rho = 1,\ldots,N_\rho) \tag{8.15}$$

and consequently

$$d\,\overset{\chi_\rho}{F}{}^{\alpha_{\rho+1}\ldots\alpha_p} = d\,'\overset{\chi_\rho}{F}_{\beta_1\ldots\beta_\rho} \quad (\chi_\rho = 1,\ldots,N_\rho;\ \beta_1,\ldots,\beta_\rho,\alpha_{\rho+1},\ldots,\alpha_p = \text{even permutation of } 1,\ldots,p;\ 0 \leqslant \rho \leqslant p), \tag{8.16}$$

the differentials of $\overset{\chi_\rho}{F}{}^{\kappa_{\rho+1}\ldots\kappa_p}$ with at least one index $p+1,\ldots,n$ being zero. That proves that among the differentials of the left-hand side of (8.10) there are as many linearly independent ones as among the differentials of the left-hand side of (8.11) and that consequently (8.11) is regular of dimension M_p+p^2 in $\overset{}{\underset{0}{\xi}}{}^\kappa$, $\underset{0}{U}{}^\kappa_\beta$ if (8.8) is, and vice versa (the condition $U^\alpha_\beta = \delta^\alpha_\beta$ being dropped).

Since the transformation from the U^κ_β to the $U^\kappa_{\mathfrak{b}}$ disturbs neither the regularity nor the dimensionality we may state finally *that the system* (8.1) *is regular of dimension M_p+1 in $\underset{0}{\xi}{}^\kappa$, $\underset{0}{v}{}^{\kappa_1\ldots\kappa_p}$ if and only if the system*

$$\overset{\chi_\rho}{u}_{\lambda_1\ldots\lambda_\rho} U^{\lambda_1}_{\mathfrak{b}_1}\ldots U^{\lambda_\rho}_{\mathfrak{b}_\rho} = 0 \quad (\chi_\rho = 1,\ldots,N_\rho;\ 0 \leqslant \rho \leqslant p;\ \mathfrak{b}_1,\ldots,\mathfrak{b}_\rho = 1,\ldots,\mathrm{p}) \tag{8.17}$$

is regular of dimension M_p+p^2 in $\underset{0}{\xi}{}^\kappa$, $\underset{0}{U}{}^\kappa_{\mathfrak{b}}$.

The proof of Theorem VIII.6 will be executed by induction. The equations $\overset{\chi_0}{u} = 0$ form a system which is regular of dimension r_0 in $\underset{0}{\xi}{}^\kappa$ (cf. VIII, § 5). Moreover we assume now that the system (8.17) is regular of dimension M_p+p^2 in $\underset{0}{\xi}{}^\kappa$, $\underset{0}{U}{}^\kappa_{\mathfrak{b}}$. Then among the equations (8.17) there are just $n+np-M_p-p^2$, forming a system which is minimal regular in $\underset{0}{\xi}{}^\kappa$, $\underset{0}{U}{}^\kappa_{\mathfrak{b}}$ and equivalent to (8.17). This system may be written in the form

$$\overset{\omega}{\Phi}(\xi^\kappa, U^\kappa_{\mathfrak{b}}) = 0 \quad (\omega = 1,\ldots,n+np-M_p-p^2;\ \mathfrak{b} = 1,\ldots,\mathrm{p}). \tag{8.18}$$

The differentials $d\overset{\omega}{\Phi}$ are linearly independent in $\underset{0}{\xi}{}^\kappa$, $\underset{0}{U}{}^\kappa_{\mathfrak{b}}$. Now let $\underset{0}{U}{}^\kappa_{\mathrm{p}+1}$ be a vector in $\underset{0}{\xi}{}^\kappa$ determining with the E_p of the chain the E_{p+1} of the chain. Then $\underset{0}{U}{}^\kappa_{\mathfrak{b}'}$ ($\mathfrak{b}' = 1,\ldots,\mathrm{p}+1$; $\kappa = 1,\ldots,n$) is the contravariant connecting quantity of this E_{p+1}. Hence the system whose regularity has to be proved is

$$\overset{\chi_\rho}{u}_{\lambda_1\ldots\lambda_\rho} U^{\lambda_1}_{\mathfrak{b}'_1}\ldots U^{\lambda_\rho}_{\mathfrak{b}'_\rho} = 0 \quad (\chi_\rho = 1,\ldots,N_\rho;\ \rho \leqslant p+1;\ \mathfrak{b}'_1,\ldots,\mathfrak{b}'_\rho = 1,\ldots,\mathrm{p}+1). \tag{8.19}$$

This system consists of (1) the equations (8.17), (2) the equations

$$\left\{\overset{\chi_\rho}{u}_{\lambda_1\ldots\lambda_\rho} U^{\lambda_1}_{\mathfrak{b}_1}\ldots U^{\lambda_{\rho-1}}_{\mathfrak{b}_{\rho-1}}\right\} U^{\lambda_\rho}_{\mathrm{p}+1} = 0 \quad (\chi_\rho = 1,\ldots,N_\rho;\ \rho \leqslant p+1;\ \mathfrak{b}_1,\ldots,\mathfrak{b}_{\rho-1} = 1,\ldots,\mathrm{p}). \tag{8.20}$$

If the $\mathfrak{b}_1,\ldots, \mathfrak{b}_{\rho-1}$ are replaced in (8.20) by all the values 1,..., p there appears in the brackets on the left-hand side of (8.20) a certain number of covariant vectors. Since the E_p is regular in $\underset{0}{\xi}{}^\kappa$, $\underset{0}{U}{}^\kappa_{\mathfrak{b}}$, among these covariant vectors there exist at every point of an $\mathfrak{N}(\underset{0}{\xi}{}^\kappa, \underset{0}{U}{}^\kappa_{\mathfrak{b}})$ just $n-p-1-r_{p+1}$ linearly independent ones. If for these vectors we write

$$\overset{\theta}{X}_\lambda(\xi^\nu, U^\kappa_{\mathfrak{b}}) \quad (\theta = 1,\ldots,n-p-1-r_{p+1};\ \mathfrak{b} = 1,\ldots,\mathrm{p}) \tag{8.21}$$

the system (8.19) is equivalent to its sub-system

$$\begin{aligned} \overset{\omega}{\Phi}(\xi^\nu, U^\kappa_{\mathfrak{b}}) &= 0 \quad (\omega = 1,\ldots, n+np-M_p-p^2), \\ \overset{\theta}{X}_\lambda(\xi^\nu, U^\kappa_{\mathfrak{b}}) U^\lambda_{\mathfrak{p}+1} &= 0 \quad (\theta = 1,\ldots, n-p-1-r_{p+1};\ \mathfrak{b} = 1,\ldots, \mathfrak{p}). \end{aligned} \tag{8.22}$$

The differentials $d\overset{\omega}{\Phi}$ are linearly independent. Now we have

$$d(\overset{\theta}{X}_\lambda U^\lambda_{\mathfrak{p}+1}) = (d\overset{\theta}{X}_\lambda) U^\lambda_{\mathfrak{p}+1} + \overset{\theta}{X}_\lambda dU^\lambda_{\mathfrak{p}+1} \quad (\theta = 1,\ldots, n-p-1-r_{p+1}) \tag{8.23}$$

and from this and the linear independence of the $\overset{\theta}{X}_\lambda$ it follows that the differentials of the left-hand side of (8.22) are all linearly independent. Hence the system (8.19) is equivalent to a minimal regular sub-system and is consequently regular in $\underset{0}{\xi}^\kappa$, $\underset{0}{U}^\kappa_{\mathfrak{b}}$. The minimal regular system (8.22) consists of $n+np-M_p-p^2+n-p-1-r_{p+1}$ equations, and from this it follows that

$$n(p+2)-M_{p+1}-(p+1)^2 = n(p+1)-M_p-p^2+n-p-1-r_{p+1} \tag{8.24}$$

or

$$M_{p+1} = M_p+r_{p+1}-p. \tag{8.25}$$

Now the system $\overset{\omega_0}{U} = 0$ is regular of dimension r_0 in $\underset{0}{\xi}^\kappa$, hence

$$M_p = r_0+r_1+\ldots+r_p-\binom{p}{2}. \tag{8.26}$$

This proves Theorem VIII.6.

In order to prove the theorem of integrability of Cartan-Kähler VIII.4 we start from a regular chain $E_0,\ldots, E_m$ in $\underset{0}{\xi}^\kappa$ and choose an arbitrary X_{n-r_1} through $\underset{0}{\xi}^\kappa$ whose tangent E_{n-r_1} in $\underset{0}{\xi}^\kappa$ has just the E_1 of the chain in common with $H(E_0)$. Then the tangent E_{n-r_1} of the X_{n-r_1} has at every point of an $\mathfrak{N}(\underset{0}{\xi}^\kappa)$ just an E_1 in common with the manifold of all integral-E_1's at that point. The stream-lines of this E_1-field are integral-X_1's and the stream-line through $\underset{0}{\xi}^\kappa$ is the integral-X_1 tangent to the E_1 of the chain in $\underset{0}{\xi}^\kappa$. Now through this integral-X_1 we choose an arbitrary X_{n-r_2} whose tangent E_{n-r_2} in $\underset{0}{\xi}^\kappa$ has just the E_2 of the chain in common with $H(E_1)$. This is always possible because this E_2 is contained in $H(E_1)$ and $n-r_2 \geqslant 2$, the dimension of $H(E_1)$ being $2+r_2$. E_2 satisfies the condition of the first theorem of uniqueness VIII.5 and from this theorem it follows that there exists one and only one integral-X_2 in X_{n-r} containing the integral-X_1 constructed and tangent to the E_2 of the chain in $\underset{0}{\xi}^\kappa$. Since every element $E_1,\ldots, E_{m-1}$ of the chain satisfies the conditions of Theorem VIII.5 it is possible to continue in this way and to construct after a finite number of steps an integral-X_m through $\underset{0}{\xi}^\kappa$ tangent to the E_m of the chain in $\underset{0}{\xi}^\kappa$. This proves the theorem of integrability of Cartan-Kähler VIII.4.

In the preceding discussion we have first chosen an X_{n-r_1}, then, after the construction of the integral-X_1 an X_{n-r_2} containing this X_1, etc. But it is also possible to choose the $X_{n-r_1},\ldots, X_{n-r_m}$ at once if this is done in a suitable way. Then we get a uniquely determined set of integral manifolds $X_1, X_2,\ldots, X_m$. The following theorem indicates how the $X_{n-r_1},\ldots, X_{n-r_m}$ have to be chosen:

THEOREM VIII.7. (*Second theorem of uniqueness.*) *If a regular chain* $E_0,\ldots, E_m$ *is given and if a set of manifolds*

$$X_{n-r_1} \subset X_{n-r_2} \subset \ldots \subset X_{n-r_m} \tag{8.27}$$

through $\underset{0}{\xi}^\kappa$ *is given, subject to the condition that the tangent* E_{n-r_q} *of* X_{n-r_q} $(q = 1,\ldots, m)$ *in* $\underset{0}{\xi}^\kappa$ *has just the* E_q *of the chain in common with* $H(E_{q-1})$, *there exists one and only one set of integral manifolds*

$$X_1 \subset X_2 \subset \ldots \subset X_m \tag{8.28}$$

through $\underset{0}{\xi}^\kappa$ *such that* X_q $(q = 1,\ldots, m)$ *is contained in* X_{n-r_q} *and is in* $\underset{0}{\xi}^\kappa$ *tangent to the* E_q *of the chain.*

PROOF. Starting from the X_{n-r_1} an E_1-field is constructed as above and the integral-X_1 through $\underset{0}{\xi}^\kappa$ belonging to it. The X_{n-r_1} being contained in the X_{n-r_2}, this X_1 is contained in the X_{n-r_2}. Hence an integral-X_2 can be constructed containing the X_1 and contained in the X_{n-r_2} and consequently in the X_{n-r_3}, etc.

In order to prove that it is always possible to give a set of manifolds of the form (8.27) we have to prove that $n-r_q < n-r_{q+1}$ or $r_{q+1} < r_q$ $(q = 1,\ldots, m-1)$. Now the integers r_q $(q \leqslant m)$ cannot be < -1 according to their definition. If an integral element E_{q-1} is contained in an integral element E_q and if $r_{q+1} \geqslant 0$, $H(E_{q-1})$ consists of all integral-E_q's containing E_{q-1} and $H(E_q)$ of all integral-E_{q+1}'s containing E_q and consequently $H(E_q)$ is contained in $H(E_{q-1})$. Hence $q+1+r_{q+1} \leqslant q+r_q$ or $r_{q+1} < r_q$. If $r_{q+1} = -1$ $(r_q \geqslant 0)$, $H(E_q)$ coincides with E_q, and consequently $H(E_q)$ is contained in $H(E_{q-1})$ and $r_{q+1} < r_q$. The case $r_{q+1} = -1$, $r_q = -1$ cannot occur because at least one integral-E_q exists which contains E_{q-1}. Hence in all cases $r_q < r_{q-1}$ $(q = 2,\ldots, m)$.

$H(E_0)$ has to be contained in the tangent E_{r_0} of $\mathfrak{M}_0$ and consequently $r_1+1 \leqslant r_0$ or $r_1 < r_0$. If r_χ is the last positive term of the set and consequently $r_{\chi+1} = -1$, it follows that an integral-E_χ contained in an integral-$E_{\chi+1}$ cannot exist and that consequently there cannot exist an integral element of a dimension higher than χ and the last element of a regular chain. That proves that χ is equal to g, the genus of the system as defined in VIII, § 6. Collecting results we get the following relations for the r_i $(i = 0,..., n-1)$

$$r_{i+1} < r_i, \qquad r_i \geqslant 0, \qquad 0 \leqslant i \leqslant g, \qquad r_{g+1} = -1. \tag{8.29}$$

9. The general integral-X_m of a Goursat system

The theorem of integrability of Cartan-Kähler VIII.4 expresses the fact that to every regular chain $E_0,..., E_m$ there exists at least one integral-X_m tangent to the last element of the chain. Further we have seen that every integral-E_m in a sufficiently small neighbourhood of this E_m is itself the last element of a regular chain. The second theorem of uniqueness VIII.7 gives the rule for the construction of an integral-X_m tangent to the last element of a regular chain.

Now it may be asked whether it is possible to obtain *every* integral-X_m tangent to this last element by a suitable choice of the manifolds (8.27).

We prove the theorem

THEOREM VIII.8. (*Third theorem of uniqueness.*) *If*

$$\underset{0}{\xi}^\kappa = \underset{0}{E}_0 \subset \underset{0}{E}_1 \subset ... \subset \underset{0}{E}_m \quad (\underset{0}{\xi}^\kappa, \underset{0}{v}^{\kappa_1...\kappa_m} = \text{coord. of } \underset{0}{E}_m) \tag{9.1}$$

is a given regular chain, and if the coordinate system is chosen in such a way that $\underset{0}{\xi}^\kappa = 0$ *and that* $\underset{0}{E}_q$ $(q = 1,..., m)$ *is spanned by the measuring vectors*

$$\underset{1}{e}^\kappa,..., \underset{q}{e}^\kappa \tag{9.2}$$

and $H(\underset{0}{E}_{q-1})$ *by the measuring vectors*

$$\underset{1}{e}^\kappa,..., \underset{q+r_q}{e}^\kappa, \tag{9.3}$$

whilst the equations of $\mathfrak{M}_0$ *are*

$$\xi^{r_0+1} = 0, \quad ..., \quad \xi^n = 0, \tag{9.4}$$

there always exists one and only one integral-X_m with equations of the form

$$\begin{aligned} \xi^{m+1} &= f^{m+1}(\xi^1,..., \xi^m), \\ &\cdots\cdots \\ \xi^{r_0} &= f^{r_0}(\xi^1,..., \xi^m), \\ \xi^{r_0+1} &= 0, \quad ..., \quad \xi^n = 0 \end{aligned} \tag{9.5}$$

satisfying the conditions

$$
\left.\begin{array}{l}
f^{m+1}(\xi^1,\ldots,\xi^m) = \phi^{m+1}(\xi^1,\ldots,\xi^m) \\
\cdot\ \cdot\ \cdot\ \cdot\ \cdot\ \cdot\ \cdot\ \cdot\ \cdot\ \cdot\ \cdot\ \cdot \\
f^{m+r_m}(\xi^1,\ldots,\xi^m) = \phi^{m+r_m}(\xi^1,\ldots,\xi^m)
\end{array}\right\} \quad (r_m \text{ equations}),
$$

$$
\left.\begin{array}{l}
f^{m+r_m+1}(\xi^1,\ldots,\xi^{m-1},\underset{0}{\xi}^m) = \phi^{m+r_m+1}(\xi^1,\ldots,\xi^{m-1}) \\
\cdot\ \cdot\ \cdot\ \cdot\ \cdot\ \cdot\ \cdot\ \cdot\ \cdot\ \cdot\ \cdot\ \cdot\ \cdot\ \cdot \\
f^{m-1+r_{m-1}}(\xi^1,\ldots,\xi^{m-1},\underset{0}{\xi}^m) = \phi^{m-1+r_{m-1}}(\xi^1,\ldots,\xi^{m-1})
\end{array}\right\} \quad \begin{array}{c}(r_{m-1}-r_m-1 \\ \text{equations}),\end{array}
$$

$$
\cdot\ \cdot\ \cdot\ \cdot\ \cdot\ \cdot\ \cdot\ \cdot\ \cdot\ \cdot\ \cdot\ \cdot\ \cdot\ \cdot
$$

$$
\left.\begin{array}{l}
f^{3+r_2}(\xi^1,\underset{0}{\xi}^2,\ldots,\underset{0}{\xi}^m) = \phi^{3+r_2}(\xi^1) \\
\cdot\ \cdot\ \cdot\ \cdot\ \cdot\ \cdot\ \cdot\ \cdot\ \cdot\ \cdot \\
f^{1+r_1}(\xi^1,\underset{0}{\xi}^2,\ldots,\underset{0}{\xi}^m) = \phi^{1+r_1}(\xi^1)
\end{array}\right\} \quad (r_1-r_2-1 \text{ equations}),
$$

$$
\left.\begin{array}{l}
f^{2+r_1}(\underset{0}{\xi}^1,\ldots,\underset{0}{\xi}^m) = \phi^{2+r_1} \\
\cdot\ \cdot\ \cdot\ \cdot\ \cdot\ \cdot\ \cdot\ \cdot \\
f^{r_0}(\underset{0}{\xi}^1,\ldots,\underset{0}{\xi}^m) = \phi^{r_0}
\end{array}\right\} \quad (r_0-r_1-1 \text{ equations}),
\tag{9.6}
$$

in which the $\phi^{m+1},\ldots,\phi^{1+r_1}$ *are arbitrarily given functions, analytic in an* $\mathfrak{N}(\underset{0}{\xi}^\kappa)$ *and* $\phi^{2+r_1},\ldots,\phi^{r_0}$ *arbitrarily given constants, satisfying the conditions that the values of* $\phi^{m+1},\ldots,\phi^{r_0}$ *and the values of all first derivatives of*

$$\phi^{m+1},\ldots,\phi^{1+r_1}$$

with respect to the ξ^κ *are sufficiently small in* $\mathfrak{N}(\underset{0}{\xi}^\kappa)$.

Every integral-X_m *through a point* $\underset{*}{\xi}^\kappa$ *in* $\mathfrak{N}(\underset{0}{\xi}^\kappa)$ *having in* $\underset{*}{\xi}^\kappa$ *a tangent* E_m *with the coordinates* $\underset{*}{\xi}^\kappa$, $\underset{*}{v}^{\kappa_1\ldots\kappa_m}$ *contained in a sufficiently small* $\mathfrak{N}(\underset{0}{\xi}^\kappa, \underset{0}{v}^{\kappa_1\ldots\kappa_m})$ *has equations of the form* (9.5) *and satisfies initial conditions of the form* (9.6).

Proof. $H(\underset{0}{E}_q)$ is contained in $H(\underset{0}{E}_{q-1})$. $H(\underset{0}{E}_0)$ is contained in the tangent E_{r_0} of $\mathfrak{M}_0$ and $H(\underset{0}{E}_{m-1})$ contains all the elements of the chain. Hence it is always possible to choose the coordinate system in the special way required. We will make use of the second theorem of uniqueness VIII.7, and to that end we choose the X_{n-r_q} $(q = 1,\ldots,m)$ in such a way that the r_q equations of X_{n-r_q} for every choice of q are

$$\begin{aligned}
&\xi^{q+1} = \underset{0}{\xi}^{q+1}, \quad \dots, \quad \xi^m = \underset{0}{\xi}^m \quad ((m-q) \text{ equations});\\
&\left.\begin{aligned}
\xi^{m+1} &= \phi^{m+1}(\xi^1,\dots,\xi^q,\underset{0}{\xi}^{q+1},\dots,\underset{0}{\xi}^m)\\
&\cdot\ \cdot\ \cdot\ \cdot\ \cdot\ \cdot\ \cdot\ \cdot\ \cdot\ \cdot\\
\xi^{m+r_m} &= \phi^{m+r_m}(\xi^1,\dots,\xi^q,\underset{0}{\xi}^{q+1},\dots,\underset{0}{\xi}^m)
\end{aligned}\right\} (r_m \text{ equations});\\
&\left.\begin{aligned}
\xi^{m+r_m+1} &= \phi^{m+r_m+1}(\xi^1,\dots,\xi^q,\underset{0}{\xi}^{q+1},\dots,\underset{0}{\xi}^{m-1})\\
&\cdot\ \cdot\ \cdot\ \cdot\ \cdot\ \cdot\ \cdot\ \cdot\ \cdot\ \cdot\\
\xi^{m-1+r_{m-1}} &= \phi^{m-1+r_{m-1}}(\xi^1,\dots,\xi^q,\underset{0}{\xi}^{q+1},\dots,\underset{0}{\xi}^{m-1})
\end{aligned}\right\} \begin{matrix}(r_{m-1}-r_m-1\\ \text{equations}),\end{matrix}\\
&\cdot\ \cdot\ \cdot\ \cdot\ \cdot\ \cdot\ \cdot\ \cdot\ \cdot\ \cdot\ \cdot\ \cdot\\
&\left.\begin{aligned}
\xi^{q+2+r_{q+1}} &= \phi^{q+2+r_{q+1}}(\xi^1,\dots,\xi^q)\\
&\cdot\ \cdot\ \cdot\ \cdot\ \cdot\ \cdot\ \cdot\ \cdot\\
\xi^{q+r_q} &= \phi^{q+r_q}(\xi^1,\dots,\xi^q)
\end{aligned}\right\} (r_q-r_{q+1}-1 \text{ equations}).
\end{aligned} \tag{9.7}$$

Together with $$\xi^{q+r_q+1} = \underset{0}{\xi}^{q+r_q+1}, \quad \dots, \quad \xi^n = \underset{0}{\xi}^n \tag{9.8}$$
this system represents a parametric form of the X_{n-r_q} with the parameters $\xi^1,\dots,\ \xi^q,\ \xi^{q+r_q+1},\dots,\ \xi^n$ which is minimal regular at $\underset{0}{\xi}^1,\dots,\ \underset{0}{\xi}^q$, $\underset{0}{\xi}^{q+r_q+1},\dots,\ \underset{0}{\xi}^n$. Since the equations (9.7, 8) of the $X_{n-r_{q+1}}$ are obtained from the equations (9.7, 8) of the X_{n-r_q} by dropping r_q-r_{q+1} equations and replacing $\underset{0}{\xi}^{q+1}$ by ξ^{q+1} in the others, the X_{n-r_q} is contained in the $X_{n-r_{q+1}}$.

Now we choose for the point of the regular chain the point $\underset{*}{\xi}^\kappa$ defined by

$$\begin{aligned}
\underset{*}{\xi}^1 &= \underset{0}{\xi}^1, \quad \dots, \quad \underset{*}{\xi}^m = \underset{0}{\xi}^m,\\
\underset{*}{\xi}^{m+1} &= \phi^{m+1}(\underset{0}{\xi}^1,\dots,\underset{0}{\xi}^m),\\
&\cdot\ \cdot\ \cdot\ \cdot\ \cdot\ \cdot\ \cdot\ \cdot\\
\underset{*}{\xi}^{m+r_m} &= \phi^{m+r_m}(\underset{0}{\xi}^1,\dots,\underset{0}{\xi}^m),\\
\underset{*}{\xi}^{m+r_m+1} &= \phi^{m+r_m+1}(\underset{0}{\xi}^1,\dots,\underset{0}{\xi}^{m-1}),\\
&\cdot\ \cdot\ \cdot\ \cdot\ \cdot\ \cdot\ \cdot\ \cdot\ \cdot\ \cdot\\
\underset{*}{\xi}^{m-1+r_{m-1}} &= \phi^{m-1+r_{m-1}}(\underset{0}{\xi}^1,\dots,\underset{0}{\xi}^{m-1}),\\
&\cdot\ \cdot\ \cdot\ \cdot\ \cdot\ \cdot\ \cdot\ \cdot\ \cdot\ \cdot\ \cdot\\
\underset{*}{\xi}^{3+r_2} &= \phi^{3+r_2}(\underset{0}{\xi}^1),\\
&\cdot\ \cdot\ \cdot\ \cdot\ \cdot\ \cdot\\
\underset{*}{\xi}^{1+r_1} &= \phi^{1+r_1}(\underset{0}{\xi}^1),\\
\underset{*}{\xi}^{2+r_1} &= \phi^{2+r_1},\\
&\cdot\ \cdot\ \cdot\ \cdot\ \cdot\\
\underset{*}{\xi}^{r_0} &= \phi^{r_0},\\
\underset{*}{\xi}^{r_0+1} &= \underset{0}{\xi}^{r_0+1}, \quad \dots, \quad \underset{*}{\xi}^n = \underset{0}{\xi}^n
\end{aligned} \tag{9.9}$$

contained in all manifolds (9.7, 8). If $\underset{0}{\xi}^{\kappa}$, $\underset{0}{v}^{\kappa_1 \ldots \kappa_{r_1+1}}$ are the coordinates of $H(\underset{0}{E_0})$, the values of the functions ϕ in $\underset{0}{\xi}^1, \ldots, \underset{0}{\xi}^m$ can be chosen so small that $\underset{*}{\xi}^{\kappa}$ lies in some given $\mathfrak{N}(\underset{0}{\xi}^{\kappa})$ and that moreover $H(\underset{*}{E_0})$, consisting of all integral elements in $\underset{*}{\xi}^{\kappa}$, lies in some given $\mathfrak{N}(\underset{0}{\xi}^{\kappa}, \underset{0}{v}^{\kappa_1 \ldots \kappa_{r_1+1}})$. Now $H(\underset{0}{E_0})$ is spanned by the vectors $\underset{1}{e}^{\kappa}, \ldots, \underset{r_1+1}{e}^{\kappa}$. Hence, if $\underset{*}{v}^{\kappa_1 \ldots \kappa_{r_1+1}}$ is an (r_1+1)-vector in $H(\underset{*}{E_0})$, the values of the functions $\phi^{m+1}, \ldots, \phi^{r_0}$ at $\underset{0}{\xi}^1, \ldots, \underset{0}{\xi}^m$ can be chosen in such a way that $\underset{*}{v}^{1 \ldots r_1+1} \neq 0$ and that $\underset{*}{v}^{\kappa_1 \ldots \kappa_{r_1+1}}$ lies in a sufficiently small neighbourhood of the (r_1+1)-vector $\underset{1}{e}^{[\kappa_1} \ldots \underset{r_1+1}{e}^{\kappa_{r_1+1}]}$ at $\underset{*}{\xi}^{\kappa}$. Since the parameters in the parametric form of X_{n-r_1} are $\xi^1, \xi^{r_1+2}, \ldots, \xi^n$, the component $v^{1, r_1+2 \ldots n}$ of the tangent $(n-r_1)$-vector of X_{n-r_1} cannot vanish at $\underset{*}{\xi}^{\kappa}$. Consequently (cf. I, Ex. 2) the tangent E_{n-r_1} of X_{n-r_1} at $\underset{*}{\xi}^{\kappa}$ and the E_{r_1+1} spanned by the $\underset{1}{e}^{\kappa}, \ldots, \underset{r_1+1}{e}^{\kappa}$ at that point have just an E_1 in common. But from this it follows that since $H(\underset{*}{E_0})$ with the coordinates $\underset{*}{\xi}^{\kappa}$, $\underset{*}{v}^{\kappa_1 \ldots \kappa_{r_1+1}}$ is sufficiently close to $\underset{0}{\xi}^{\kappa}$, $\underset{0}{v}^{\kappa_1 \ldots \kappa_{r_1+1}}$ it has just an E_1 in common with the tangent E_{n-r_1} of the X_{n-r_1} in $\underset{*}{\xi}^{\kappa}$. We choose this E_1 as second element $\underset{*}{E_1}$ of the set to be constructed. The functions ϕ and their derivatives can be chosen so small that $\underset{*}{E_1}$ is contained in a given neighbourhood of $\underset{0}{E_1}$. Now the component $v^{1, 2, 3+r_2 \ldots n}$ of the tangent $(n-r_2)$-vector of the X_{n-r_2} in $\underset{*}{\xi}^{\kappa}$ is $\neq 0$. Hence, the tangent E_{n-r_2} of the X_{n-r_2} in $\underset{*}{\xi}^{\kappa}$ has just an E_2 in common with the E_{2+r_2} spanned in $\underset{*}{\xi}^{\kappa}$ by the measuring vectors $\underset{1}{e}^{\kappa}, \ldots, \underset{2+r_2}{e}^{\kappa}$. Since $H(\underset{0}{E_1})$ is spanned by the measuring vectors $\underset{1}{e}^{\kappa}, \ldots, \underset{2+r_2}{e}^{\kappa}$ in $\underset{0}{\xi}^{\kappa}$, $H(\underset{*}{E_1})$ is close to the E_{2+r_2} spanned by the measuring vectors $\underset{1}{e}^{\kappa}, \ldots, \underset{2+r_2}{e}^{\kappa}$ in $\underset{*}{\xi}^{\kappa}$. From this it follows that the tangent E_{n-r_2} of the X_{n-r_2} in $\underset{*}{\xi}^{\kappa}$ has just an E_2 in common with this E_{2+r_2} and consequently with $H(\underset{*}{E_1})$. We choose this E_2 as third element $\underset{*}{E_2}$ of the chain. Continuing in this way a chain of integral elements

$$\underset{*}{E_0}, \quad \underset{*}{E_1}, \quad \ldots, \quad \underset{*}{E_m} \tag{9.10}$$

can be constructed. If the functions ϕ and their derivatives are sufficiently small in $\xi^1 = \underset{0}{\xi}^1, \ldots, \xi^m = \underset{0}{\xi}^m$ we can always make the $\underset{*}{E_q}$ $(q = 1, \ldots, m)$ lie in given neighbourhoods of the $\underset{0}{E_q}$ and consequently the constructed chain is regular. This chain, together with the manifolds (9.7, 8), satisfies all conditions of the second theorem of uniqueness VIII.7. According to this theorem there exists a set of integral manifolds (8.28). Since $\underset{*}{E}_m$ is sufficiently close to $\underset{0}{E}_m$, for the vector $\underset{*}{v}^{\kappa_1 \dots \kappa_m}$ in $\underset{*}{E}_m$ we always have $\underset{*}{v}^{1 \dots m} \neq 0$. This implies that the variables $\xi^1, \dots, \xi^m$ can be used as coordinates in the X_m in an $\mathfrak{N}(\underset{0}{\xi}^\kappa)$ and that consequently the equations of the X_m can be written in the parametric form (9.5). According to the second theorem of uniqueness VIII.7 the X_m is contained in the X_{n-r_m} of (9.7, 8) with the equations

$$\begin{aligned} \xi^{m+1} &= \phi^{m+1}(\xi^1, \dots, \xi^m), \\ &\cdots\cdots\cdots \\ \xi^{m+r_m} &= \phi^{m+r_m}(\xi^1, \dots, \xi^m) \end{aligned} \tag{9.11}$$

and as a result of (9.5) this leads to the first set of initial conditions (9.6). The $X_{n-r_{m-1}}$ of (9.7, 8) with the equations

$$\begin{aligned} \xi^m &= \underset{0}{\xi}^m, \\ \xi^{m+1} &= \phi^{m+1}(\xi^1, \dots, \xi^{m-1}, \underset{0}{\xi}^m), \\ &\cdots\cdots\cdots\cdots \\ \xi^{m+r_m} &= \phi^{m+r_m}(\xi^1, \dots, \xi^{m-1}, \underset{0}{\xi}^m), \\ \xi^{m+r_m+1} &= \phi^{m+r_m+1}(\xi^1, \dots, \xi^{m-1}), \\ &\cdots\cdots\cdots\cdots \\ \xi^{m-1+r_{m-1}} &= \phi^{m-1+r_{m-1}}(\xi^1, \dots, \xi^{m-1}) \end{aligned} \tag{9.12}$$

has to intersect the X_m in an X_{m-1}. In view of (9.5) this leads to the second set of initial conditions (9.6). Continuing in this way all the initial conditions (9.6) can be obtained except for the last set. But according to (9.9) this last set is a consequence of the fact that $\underset{*}{\xi}^\kappa$ is a point of the X_m. This proves the first part of the theorem.

If an integral-X_m through a point $\underset{*}{\xi}^\kappa$ in an $\mathfrak{N}(\underset{*}{\xi}^\kappa)$ is known and has in $\underset{*}{\xi}^\kappa$ a tangent E_m with the coordinates $\underset{*}{\xi}^\kappa$, $\underset{*}{v}^{\kappa_1 \dots \kappa_m}$ contained in a sufficiently small $\mathfrak{N}(\underset{0}{\xi}^\kappa, \underset{0}{v}^{\kappa_1 \dots \kappa_m})$, obviously $\underset{*}{v}^{1 \dots m} \neq 0$ and this implies that $\xi^1, \dots, \xi^m$ can be used as coordinates in the X_m in an $\mathfrak{N}(\underset{0}{\xi}^\kappa)$. But from this it follows that the X_m has equations of the form (9.5). From this parametric form the functions ϕ in (9.6) can be computed, and this proves that the equations (9.5) with the initial conditions (9.6) can really represent every integral-X_m of this kind. This proves the second part of the theorem. The equations (9.5) and the conditions (9.6) establish a one-to-one correspondence between the integral-X_m's in an $\mathfrak{N}(\overset{}{\underset{0}{\xi^\kappa}})$ whose tangent E_m's are sufficiently close to $\underset{0}{E_m}$ and the sets of

$$\begin{array}{l} r_m \text{ arbitrary functions of } m \text{ variables,} \\ s_{m-1} \overset{\text{def}}{=} r_{m-1}-r_m-1 \text{ arbitrary functions of } m-1 \text{ variables,} \\ s_{m-2} \overset{\text{def}}{=} r_{m-2}-r_{m-1}-1 \text{ arbitrary functions of } m-2 \text{ variables,} \\ \cdots\cdots\cdots\cdots\cdots\cdots \\ s_1 \overset{\text{def}}{=} r_1-r_2-1 \text{ arbitrary functions of } 1 \text{ variable,} \\ s_0 \overset{\text{def}}{=} r_0-r_1-1 \text{ constants,}\dagger \end{array} \tag{9.13}$$

satisfying the condition that their values and the values of their derivatives with respect to the ξ^κ are sufficiently small in $\underset{0}{\xi^\kappa}$. This one-to-one correspondence will be called a *general integral-X_m of the Goursat system.* With the construction of this general integral-X_m the inner problem is solved for all *regular* integral-X_m's.

According to Cartan the integers s in (9.13) are called the *characters* of the system. If the word character is used without mentioning the number, s_1 is always meant. All characters are $\geqslant 0$ because $r_q < r_{q-1}$.

Now one could hope that these characters would in some way characterize the most profitable way of representation of a general integral-X_m, in other words, that it would never be possible to represent a general integral-X_m by means of equations and conditions containing less free functions and free constants. But this is not the case. In order to get a counter-example we consider the Pfaffian equation of class $2\rho+1$ in an $X_{2\rho+1}$

$$C_\lambda d\xi^\lambda = d\xi^1 + \sum_{i=1}^{i=\rho} \xi^{2i} d\xi^{2i+1} = 0 \quad (\lambda = 1,\ldots, 2\rho+1). \tag{9.14}$$

This equation represents an $E_{2\rho}$-field in $X_{2\rho+1}$. Now the X_ρ with the equations

$$\xi^1 = \Phi(\xi^3, \xi^5,\ldots, \xi^{2\rho+1}), \quad \xi^{2i} = -\partial\Phi/\partial\xi^{2i+1} \quad (i = 1,\ldots, \rho), \tag{9.15}$$

Φ being an arbitrary function of ξ^3, ξ^5,..., $\xi^{2\rho+1}$, is obviously a general integral-X_ρ of the field. This integral-X_ρ is general, because every integral-X_ρ in which ξ^3, ξ^5,..., $\xi^{2\rho+1}$ can be used as coordinates can be represented by equations of the form (9.15) and it depends only on one function of ρ variables. Now we will determine r_1,..., r_ρ for this case. Every vector $\underset{1}{v^\kappa}$ satisfying the equation

$$C_\lambda \underset{1}{v^\lambda} = 0 \tag{9.16}$$

† In 1945. 1 Cartan defines s_0 in a slightly different way. He takes $s_0 = n-r_1-1$ as a consequence of the fact that his system is scalar-free, i.e. $r_0 = n$.

lies in an integral-E_1. Hence $r_1 = 2\rho-1$. If $\underset{1}{v}^\kappa$ is chosen, every vector $\underset{2}{v}^\kappa$ satisfying the equations

$$\begin{aligned} C_\lambda \underset{2}{v}^\lambda &= 0, \\ C_{\mu\lambda} \underset{1}{v}^\mu \underset{2}{v}^\lambda &= 0 \end{aligned} \tag{9.17}$$

with $\underset{1}{v}^\kappa$ spans an integral-E_2. Consequently $H(E_1)$ is the section of the $E_{2\rho}$'s of C_λ and $C_{\mu\lambda}\underset{1}{v}^\mu$. Hence $r_2 = 2\rho-3$. Continuing in this way we get

$$r_i = 2\rho-2(i-1)-1, \quad s_i = 1, \quad g = \rho \quad (i = 1,..., \rho), \tag{9.18}$$

and this implies that the general integral-X_ρ given by (9.5) and (9.6) depends on ρ functions of ρ, $\rho-1$,..., 1 variables respectively and one constant. But as we have seen that there exists a representation depending only on one function of ρ variables, (9.5) and (9.6) do not give the most profitable representation.

It is not yet known in which cases such more profitable representations of the general integral-X_m can be found. But it is highly probable that the number of functions of m variables on which a general integral-X_m depends is always r_m.†

10. Relations between the arithmetic invariants r_i, s_i, g, and g'

In some special cases more relations between the arithmetic invariants r_i, s_i, and g can be established.

We first consider a Goursat system whose quantities $\overset{\chi}{w}_{\lambda_1...\lambda_{q_\chi}}$, after multiplication with suitable scalar factors, can be expressed in terms of at most n' scalars and their gradients. We call n' the *similarity class* of the Goursat system. If these n' scalars are chosen as the first n' coordinates ξ^1,..., $\xi^{n'}$ the equations (5.2) can be written in these n' coordinates. The quantities $'\overset{\chi}{w}_{\alpha_1...\alpha_{q_\chi}}$ $(\alpha_1,..., \alpha_{q_\chi} = 1,..., n')$ occurring in this form of the equations arise from the quantities $\overset{\chi}{w}_{\lambda_1...\lambda_{q_\chi}}$ $(\lambda_1,..., \lambda_{q_\chi} = 1,..., n)$ by the reduction with respect to the normal system of $\infty^{n'}$ $X_{n-n'}$'s with the equations

$$\xi^1 = \text{const.}, \quad ..., \quad \xi^{n'} = \text{const.} \tag{10.1}$$

(the *characteristics* of the Goursat system), reducing the X_n to an $X_{n'}$. The invariants of the resultant Goursat system in the $X_{n'}$ will be denoted by r'_i, s'_i, and g'. All objects in $X_{n'}$ will be denoted by letters with an accent. The tangent $E_{n-n'}$'s of the characteristics (10.1) are integral-

† Cf. Janet 1929. 1, p. 86; Cartan 1945. 1, p. 76.

$E_{n-n'}$'s of the original system. Every integral-E'_m of the reduced system together with the local $E_{n-n'}$ determines an integral-$E_{m+n-n'}$ of the original system.

If $\bar{E}_m$ is an integral-E_m in X_n having just an $E_{\bar{t}_m}$ in common with the local $E_{n-n'}$, from $\bar{E}_m$ there arises by the process of reduction an integral-$E'_{m-\bar{t}_m}$ in $X_{n'}$, denoted by $\bar{E}'_{m-\bar{t}_m}$. If for $\bar{E}'_{m-\bar{t}_m}$ the invariant $\bar{r}'_{m-\bar{t}_m+1}$ is $\geqslant 0$ there exists an integral-$E'_{m-\bar{t}_m+1}$ through $\bar{E}'_{m-\bar{t}_m}$. This $E'_{m-\bar{t}_m+1}$ and $E_{n-n'}$ determine an integral-$E_{m-\bar{t}_m+1+n-n'}$ in X_n containing $\bar{E}_m$ and $\infty^{n-n'-\bar{t}_m}$ integral-E_{m+1}'s in X_n through $\bar{E}_m$ each reducing to $E'_{m-\bar{t}_m+1}$ by the process of reduction. Hence to the $\infty^{\bar{r}'_{m-\bar{t}_m+1}}$ integral-$E'_{m-\bar{t}_m+1}$'s through $\bar{E}'_{m-\bar{t}_m}$ belong $\infty^{\bar{r}'_{m-\bar{t}_m+1}+n-n'-\bar{t}_m}$ integral-E'_{m+1}'s through $\bar{E}_m$. Every other integral-E_{m+1} through $\bar{E}_m$ has a section with $E_{n-n'}$ of a dimension $> \bar{t}_m$ and consequently its reduction is $\bar{E}'_{m-\bar{t}_m}$. Accordingly there exist only $\infty^{n-n'-\bar{t}_m-1}$ integral-E_{m+1}'s of this latter kind. Hence

$$\bar{r}_{m+1} = \bar{r}'_{m-\bar{t}_m+1}+n-n'-\bar{t}_m. \tag{10.2}$$

If $\bar{E}_m$ is regular we have $\bar{r}_{m+1} = r_{m+1}$ and in the other case, $\bar{r}_{m+1} > r_{m+1}$. The same holds for $\bar{r}'_{m-\bar{t}_m+1}$ and $r'_{m-\bar{t}_m+1}$. If $\bar{r}'_{m-\bar{t}_m+1} = -1$ there are no integral-$E'_{m-\bar{t}_m+1}$'s through $\bar{E}'_{m-\bar{t}_m}$ and consequently every integral-E_{m+1} through $\bar{E}_m$ reduces to $\bar{E}'_{m-\bar{t}_m}$ by the process of reduction. Hence there are $\infty^{n-n'-\bar{t}_m-1}$ integral-E_{m+1}'s through $\bar{E}_m$ and this implies that (10.2) holds in that case also.

In $\bar{E}_m$ there can always be found an integral-$E_{m-\bar{t}_m}$, denoted by $\bar{E}_{m-\bar{t}_m}$, having no direction in common with $E_{n-n'}$ and reducing to $\bar{E}'_{m-\bar{t}_m}$ by the process of reduction. Since $\bar{E}_{m-\bar{t}_m}$ is contained in $\bar{E}_m$ we always have

$$H(\bar{E}_{m-\bar{t}_m}) \supset H(\bar{E}_m). \tag{10.3}$$

Now every integral-$E_{m-\bar{t}_m+1}$ through $\bar{E}_{m-\bar{t}_m}$ lies in $H(\bar{E}_{m-\bar{t}_m})$. Together with $E_{n-n'}$ this $E_{m-\bar{t}_m+1}$ determines a flat space which we will denote by E_μ. This E_μ contains $\bar{E}_{m-\bar{t}_m}$ and $E_{n-n'}$ and consequently also $\bar{E}_m$. Every E_1 in E_μ not lying in $\bar{E}_m$ spans together with $\bar{E}_m$ an integral-E_{m+1} and consequently lies in $H(\bar{E}_m)$. Hence E_μ is contained in $H(\bar{E}_m)$ and accordingly

$$H(\bar{E}_{m-\bar{t}_m}) \subset H(\bar{E}_m). \tag{10.4}$$

This proves that

$$H(\bar{E}_{m-\bar{t}_m}) = H(\bar{E}_m) \tag{10.5}$$

and

$$\bar{r}_{m+1} = \bar{r}_{m-\bar{t}_m+1}-\bar{t}_m. \tag{10.6}$$

Now consider a regular chain

$$\underset{0}{E'_0} \subset \underset{0}{E'_1} \subset \ldots \subset \underset{0}{E'_{g'}} \tag{10.7}$$

in $X_{n'}$. In X_n a chain of integral elements

$$\underset{0}{E_0} \subset \underset{0}{E_1} \subset \ldots \subset \underset{0}{E_{g'}} \tag{10.8}$$

always exists, such that $\underset{0}{E_q}$ $(q = 0,\ldots, g')$ becomes $\underset{0}{E'_q}$ by the process of reduction. Then for this chain we have

$$\underset{0}{t_0} = \underset{0}{t_1} = \ldots = \underset{0}{t_{g'}} = 0, \tag{10.9}$$

and accordingly

$$\underset{0}{r_q} = r'_q + n - n' \quad (q = 1,\ldots, g'+1). \tag{10.10}$$

If $\bar{E}_q$ is sufficiently close to $\underset{0}{E_q}$ its reduction $\bar{E}'_q$ is close to $\underset{0}{E'_q}$. Hence these neighbourhoods can be taken so small that $\bar{r}'_{q+1}$ has the same value as $\underset{0}{r'_{q+1}}$ and so that $\bar{t}_q$ is zero. From this it follows that $\bar{r}_{q+1} = \underset{0}{r_{q+1}}$. Since this reasoning holds for every value of q, the chain (10.8) is regular and $\underset{0}{r_{q+1}} = r_{q+1}$.

Now we will prove that an integral-E_m $(m > g')$ passing by the process of reduction into a regular integral-$E'_{g'}$ is regular itself. Denoting this E_m by $\underset{0}{E_m}$ we have

$$\underset{0}{t_m} = m - g' \tag{10.11}$$

and, according to (10.2) and (10.11),

$$\underset{0}{r_{m+1}} = r'_{g'+1} + n - n' - m + g' = -1 + n - n' - m + g'. \tag{10.12}$$

Now let $\bar{E}_m$ be an integral-E_m in the neighbourhood of $\underset{0}{E_m}$. If the reduction of $\bar{E}_m$ is $\bar{E}'_\sigma$, we have

$$\bar{t}_m = m - \sigma \tag{10.13}$$

and, according to (10.2) and (10.13),

$$\bar{r}_{m+1} = \bar{r}'_{\sigma+1} + n - n' - m + \sigma. \tag{10.14}$$

Now suppose first that $\sigma \leqslant g'$. The dimension of $H(\bar{E}'_\sigma)$ is $\bar{r}'_{\sigma+1} + \sigma + 1$ and the dimension $H(E'_{g'})$ is $r'_{g'+1} + g' + 1 = g'$. Hence, if $\bar{E}'_\sigma$ were regular we would have

$$\bar{r}'_{\sigma+1} + \sigma + 1 = r'_{\sigma+1} + \sigma + 1 \geqslant g'. \tag{10.15}$$

But if $\bar{E}'_\sigma$ is not regular the dimension of $H(\bar{E}'_\sigma)$ is greater than in the regular case, and this proves that in both cases

$$\bar{r}'_{\sigma+1} + \sigma + 1 \geqslant g'. \tag{10.16}$$

If $\sigma > g'$ we have

$$\bar{r}'_{\sigma+1} + \sigma + 1 > \sigma > g' \tag{10.17}$$

and this proves that (10.16) is valid in all cases. But from (10.12), (10.14), and (10.16) it follows that $\bar{r}_{m+1} \geqslant \underset{0}{r_{m+1}}$ and this proves that $\underset{0}{E_m}$ is regular.

The property just proved enables us to extend the regular chain $\underset{0}{E}_0, \ldots, \underset{0}{E}_{g'}$. It is always possible to find a set of integral elements

$$\underset{0}{E}_{g'+1} \subset \ldots \subset \underset{0}{E}_{g'+n-n'} \tag{10.18}$$

such that the reduction of every one of these elements is $\underset{0}{E}'_{g}$. Then all these elements are regular. An integral-$E_{g'+n-n'+1}$ containing $\underset{0}{E}_{g'+n-n}$ cannot exist because its reduction would be an integral-$E_{g'+1}$ containing $E_{g'}$ and this is impossible. Hence

$$g = g'+n-n'. \tag{10.19}$$

This can also be seen from (10.12) because for $m = g$ we get

$$\underset{0}{r}_{g+1} = -1+n-n'-g+g' = -1. \tag{10.20}$$

Collecting results, we have for the invariants in X_n and $X_{n'}$:

$$\begin{aligned} &(a) && r_q = r'_q+n-n' \quad (q = 0,\ldots,g'+1),\\ &(b) && s_1 = s'_1, \quad \ldots, \quad s_{g'} = s'_{g'},\\ &(c) && r_{g'+u+1} = n-n'-u-1 \quad (u = 1,\ldots,n-n'),\\ &(d) && s_{g'+1} = 0, \quad \ldots, \quad s_g = 0,\\ &(e) && g = g'+n-n'. \end{aligned} \tag{10.21}$$

The genus g' will be called the *reduced genus* of the system.

The $\underset{0}{E}_m$'s $(m > g')$ of the regular chain constructed all have a g'-dimensional reduction. It is interesting to ask whether a regular integral-E_m can exist with a reduction of a dimension lower or higher than g'. Let $\bar{E}_m$ be an integral-E_m and $'\bar{E}_{m-\bar{t}_m}$ its reduction. Then

$$\bar{r}_{m+1} = \bar{r}'_{m-\bar{t}_m+1}+n-n'-\bar{t}_m \tag{10.22}$$

according to (10.2). Now for a regular E_m we have, according to (10.21 *c*),

$$r_{m+1} = -1+n-n'-m+g'. \tag{10.23}$$

Hence, if $\bar{E}_m$ is regular, $\bar{r}_{m+1} = r_{m+1}$ and accordingly

$$\bar{r}'_{m-\bar{t}_m+1} = \bar{t}_m-m+g'-1. \tag{10.24}$$

Now if $\bar{t}_m > m-g'$ we have $m-\bar{t}_m-1 \leqslant g'$ and accordingly $\bar{r}'_{m-\bar{t}_m-1} \geqslant r'_{m-\bar{t}_m-1}$ and from this

$$r'_{m-\bar{t}_m+1}-r'_{g'+1} \leqslant g'-m+\bar{t}_m \tag{10.25}$$

follows as a necessary condition. This condition is satisfied if and only if

$$s'_{m-\bar{t}_m+1} = 0, \quad \ldots, \quad s'_{g'} = 0. \tag{10.26}$$

From (10.24) it follows that the dimension of $H(\bar{E}'_{m-\bar{t}_m})$ is equal to g'.

But $H(\bar{E}'_{m-\bar{t}_m})$ contains $\bar{E}'_{m-\bar{t}_m}$ and this implies that $m-\bar{t}_m \leqslant g'$. Hence the case $\bar{t}_m < m-g'$ cannot occur.

We will prove that the condition (10.26) is also sufficient for the existence of regular integral-$\bar{E}_m$'s with $m > g'$ and $\bar{t}_m > m-g'$. In order to construct such an integral-$\bar{E}_m$ we consider a regular integral-$E'_{m-\bar{t}_m}$ and form the integral-$E_{m-\bar{t}_m+n-n'}$ whose reduction is $E'_{m-\bar{t}_m}$. In this $E_{m-\bar{t}_m+n-n'}$ an integral-E_m, denoted by $\bar{E}_m$ can always be chosen such that $E'_{m-\bar{t}_m}$ is the reduction of $\bar{E}_m$. Then we have, according to (10.2),

$$\bar{r}_{m+1} = r'_{m-\bar{t}_m+1}+n-n'-\bar{t}_m. \tag{10.27}$$

Now we have, according to (10.25) and (10.26),

$$r'_{m-\bar{t}_m+1} = g'-m+\bar{t}_m-1. \tag{10.28}$$

From (10.27) and (10.28) it follows that

$$\bar{r}_{m+1} = n-n'+g'-m-1 \tag{10.29}$$

and according to (10.21 c) this proves that $\bar{E}_m$ is regular.

Collecting results, we say *that regular integral-E_m's ($g'+1 \leqslant m \leqslant g$) with $\bar{t}_m < m-g'$ cannot exist, that those with $\bar{t}_m = m-g'$ always exist, and that those with $\bar{t}_m > m-g'$ exist if and only if $s'_{m-\bar{t}_m+1}, \ldots, s'_{g'}$ vanish.*

If a Goursat system in X_n of similarity class n' and with genus g is reduced, the problem of the determination of all regular integral-X_g's is brought back to the simpler problem of the determination of all regular integral-$X_{g'}$'s of a Goursat system in $X_{n'}$ of class n' and with genus g'. But in order to execute this reduction the n' scalars have to be determined, and this is not possible without integration. If the system is a Cartan system it is necessary to determine the integral functions of the system S_4 (cf. V, § 2).

If a Goursat system is closed and if all quantities with a valence $> g$ have been dropped, it is clear that the remaining quantities with a valence $> g'$ have no influence on the result and can be dropped as well. Hence

$$v_{\max} \leqslant g'. \tag{10.30}$$

We now derive some further relations between r_i, s_i, and g valid for scalar-free Cartan systems. In order to derive a relation between the s_i we consider three elements E_{q-1}, E_q, E_{q+1} ($q-1 \geqslant 1$) of a regular chain. If $'E_q$ is an integral element containing E_{q-1}, contained in E_{q+1} and sufficiently close to E_q, the dimensions of $H(E_q)$ and $H('E_q)$ are both $q+1+r_{q+1}$. If E_q is spanned by E_{q-1} and a vector v^κ and $'E_q$ by E_{q-1} and a vector $'v^\kappa$, E_{q+1} is spanned by E_{q-1}, v^κ, and $'v^\kappa$. Hence $H(E_{q+1})$ consists of all E_1's which are in involution with E_{q-1}, v^κ, and $'v^\kappa$ and this implies that $H(E_{q+1})$ is the section of $H(E_q)$ and $H('E_q)$. Now

$H(E_q)$ and $H('E_q)$ are both contained in $H(E_{q-1})$ and from this the inequality

$$2(q+1)+2r_{q+1}-q-r_q \leqslant q+2+r_{q+2} \tag{10.31}$$

or

$$s_q = r_q-r_{q+1}-1 \geqslant r_{q+1}-r_{q+2}-1 = s_{q+1} \tag{10.32}$$

follows. Consequently, because $r_{g+1} = -1$ we have

$$s_1 \geqslant s_2 \geqslant \dots \geqslant s_g \geqslant 0. \tag{10.33}$$

Notice that these inequalities do not necessarily hold for a Goursat system.

If a scalar-free Cartan system is given in the form C_λ^x ($x = \mathrm{r}+1,\dots,\mathrm{n}$) we consider m vectors $\underset{1}{v}^\kappa,\dots, \underset{m}{v}^\kappa$ spanning an integral-E_m. Necessary and sufficient conditions are

$$\begin{aligned} C_\lambda^x \underset{\mathfrak{a}}{v}^\lambda &= 0 \\ C_{\mu\lambda}^{\cdot\cdot x} \underset{\mathfrak{c}}{v}^\mu \underset{\mathfrak{b}}{v}^\lambda &= 0 \end{aligned} \quad (\mathfrak{a}, \mathfrak{b}, \mathfrak{c} = 1,\dots, m;\ x = \mathrm{r}+1,\dots,\mathrm{n}). \tag{10.34}$$

The E_1 of a vector $\underset{m+1}{v}^\kappa$ is an integral-E_1 and is in involution with all E_1's in E_m if and only if

$$\begin{aligned} C_\lambda^x \underset{m+1}{v}^\lambda &= 0 \\ C_{\mu\lambda}^{\cdot\cdot x} \underset{\mathfrak{b}}{v}^\mu \underset{m+1}{v}^\lambda &= 0 \end{aligned} \quad (\mathfrak{b} = 1,\dots, m;\ x = \mathrm{r}+1,\dots,\mathrm{n}). \tag{10.35}$$

If R_{m+1} is the λ-rank of the set of quantities

$$C_\lambda^x,\quad \underset{\mathfrak{b}}{v}^\mu C_{\mu\lambda}^{\cdot\cdot x} \quad (\mathfrak{b} = 1,\dots, m;\ x = \mathrm{r}+1,\dots,\mathrm{n}), \tag{10.36}$$

the dimension of $H(E_m)$ is

$$m+1+r_{m+1} = n-R_{m+1}. \tag{10.37}$$

Now we know that $R_1 = n-r$ and $r_0 = n$. Hence

$$r_1 = r-1, \qquad s_0 = n-r. \tag{10.38}$$

Since the λ-rank of the set of $2(n-r)$ covariant vectors

$$C_\lambda^x,\qquad \underset{1}{v}^\mu C_{\mu\lambda}^{\cdot\cdot x} \quad (x = \mathrm{r}+1,\dots,\mathrm{n}) \tag{10.39}$$

is $n-r_2-2$, among these vectors there exist just $n-r_2-2$ linearly independent ones. Hence

$$n-r_2-2 \leqslant 2(n-r) = 2n-2r_1-2 \tag{10.40}$$

or

$$s_0 = r_0-r_1-1 \geqslant r_1-r_2-1 = s_1. \tag{10.41}$$

Combining this with (10.33) we get

$$s_0 \geqslant s_1 \geqslant s_2 \geqslant \dots \geqslant s_g \geqslant 0. \tag{10.42}$$

Now we have

$$\sum_{i=0}^{i=g} s_i = r_0 - r_{g+1} - g - 1 = r_0 - g = n - g \tag{10.43}$$

and from (10.38), (10.42), and (10.43) it follows that

$$(g+1)(n-r) \geqslant n-g \tag{10.44}$$

or

$$g \geqslant \frac{r}{n-r+1}. \tag{10.45}$$

This inequality for g can be improved. If k is the class of the system of $n-r$ Pfaffian equations

$$C_\lambda^x d\xi^\lambda = 0 \quad (x = \mathrm{r+1,...,n}) \tag{10.46}$$

this system can be written in k variables. Hence in this case $n' = k$. In the X_k of these variables the system represents an E_{k-n+r}-field and for the genus g' of this field we have, according to (10.45),

$$g' \geqslant \frac{k-n+r}{n-r+1} \tag{10.47}$$

and consequently

$$g = g'+n-k \geqslant \frac{r}{n-r+1} + (n-k)\left(1-\frac{1}{n-r+1}\right). \tag{10.48}$$

For two special cases the invariant g of a scalar-free Cartan system will be determined here. If (10.46) is complete we have

$$B_c^\mu B_b^\lambda C_{\mu\lambda}^{\cdot\cdot x} = 0 \quad (b, c = \mathrm{1,...,r};\ x = \mathrm{r+1,...,n}), \tag{10.49}$$

and from this it follows that $H(E_1)$ coincides with the local E_r for every choice of the integral-E_1, and that consequently $2+r_2 = r$ and $s_1 = 0$. Hence all numbers s_i $(i > 0)$ are zero and $g = r$. Conversely, if $g = r$ it follows that $s_1 = 0$ and that consequently (10.46) is complete. Since the class is $n-r$ we have $n-k = 2g-r$.

Now we consider an E_r-field chosen as general as possible. If $\underset{1}{v}^\kappa, \ldots, \underset{m}{v}^\kappa$ span an integral-E_m $(m = 1, \ldots, g)$ the λ-rank of the system

$$C_\lambda^x, \quad \underset{1}{v}^\mu C_{\mu\lambda}^{\cdot\cdot x}, \quad \ldots, \quad \underset{m}{v}^\mu C_{\mu\lambda}^{\cdot\cdot x} \quad (x = \mathrm{r+1,...,n}) \tag{10.50}$$

is $m+1+r_{m+1}$. Now the maximum λ-rank is $(n-r)(m+1)$ for $m \leqslant g-1$. Hence, since the E_r-field is chosen as general as possible we have

$$r_{m+1} = n-(n-r)(m+1)-m-1 = (r-n-1)m+r-1 \qquad (m = 0, \ldots, g-1) \tag{10.51}$$

and accordingly, because $r_{g+1} = -1$,

$$s_1 = n-r, \ s_2 = n-r, \ \ldots, \ s_{g-1} = n-r, \ s_g = n-g(n-r+1). \tag{10.52}$$

Now from (10.45) it follows that

$$(g+1)(n-r+1) > n \tag{10.53}$$

and this implies that s_g is equal to the remainder R when n is divided by $n-r+1$ and that

$$g = \frac{n-R}{n-r+1}. \tag{10.54}$$

This formula imposes a strong restriction on the possible regular integral-X_m's of a general E_r-field in an X_n. For instance, in an X_8 a general E_4-field can have at most regular integral-X_1's, a general E_5-field or E_6-field at most regular integral-X_2's, and a general E_7-field at most regular integral-X_4's.

For the general E_r-field $k = n$ always except when $r = 1$ or when n is even and $r = n-1$. In this latter case we have an E_{n-1}-field of class $n-1$. From (10.54) we can easily show that in this case

$$g \leqslant \tfrac{1}{2}(n-k+r). \tag{10.55}$$

The same inequality holds in the first special case. It is highly probable that this inequality, giving an *upper* limit of g, is always valid but as yet a proof has not been given.

11. The s-number ζ and the simplifications of the integration for $\zeta < g+1$

If for a Goursat system

$$s_{\zeta-1} \neq 0, \qquad s_i = 0 \quad (i \geqslant \zeta) \tag{11.1}$$

ζ is called the s-number of the system. Obviously $\zeta \leqslant g+1$. ζ is invariant for changes of the number of variables in which the system is expressed. By (10.42) a scalar-free Cartan system has the s-number ζ if

$$s_{\zeta-1} \neq 0, \qquad s_\zeta = 0. \tag{11.2}$$

In consequence of (10.21)

$$\zeta \leqslant g'+1. \tag{11.3}$$

Cartan† has given a method to simplify the determination of an integral-X_g of a scalar-free Cartan system if $\zeta < g$. We will show that this method can also be applied to Goursat systems. From (11.1) and $r_{g+1} = -1$ it follows that

$$r_\zeta = g-\zeta, \quad r_{\zeta+1} = g-\zeta-1, \quad \ldots, \quad r_g = 0. \tag{11.4}$$

If $E_{\zeta-1}$ is a regular integral-$E_{\zeta-1}$ in $\underset{0}{\xi}{}^\kappa$ and the last element of a regular chain, according to (11.4) $H(E_{\zeta-1})$ is an E_g. Any E_1 in E_g not lying in $E_{\zeta-1}$ spans together with $E_{\zeta-1}$ an integral-E_ζ. Now $H(E_\zeta)$ is contained in $H(E_{\zeta-1})$, and consequently, since the dimension of $H(E_\zeta)$ is always

† 1901. 1, pp. 288 ff.

$\geqslant \zeta+1+r_{\zeta+1} = g$, this dimension must be equal to g. Hence E_ζ is regular and the last element of a regular chain. Continuing in this way it can be proved that E_g is the last element of a regular chain.

Since $E_{\zeta-1}$ is the last element of a regular chain there exists an integral-$X_{\zeta-1}$ tangent to $E_{\zeta-1}$. We will prove that there exists one and only one integral-X_g containing $X_{\zeta-1}$. To that end we choose an arbitrary X_{n-r_ζ} containing $X_{\zeta-1}$ whose tangent E_{n-r_ζ} in $\underset{0}{\xi}{}^\kappa$ has just an E_ζ in common with $H(E_{\zeta-1})$. This is always possible because $g \leqslant n$ and consequently $n-r_\zeta \geqslant \zeta$. Since $E_{\zeta-1}$ is regular and the last element of a regular chain, this common E_ζ is also regular and the last element of a regular chain. Hence, according to the first theorem of uniqueness VIII.5 there exists one and only one integral-X_ζ contained in X_{n-r_ζ} and containing $X_{\zeta-1}$, whose tangent E_ζ in $\underset{0}{\xi}{}^\kappa$ coincides with the common integral-E_ζ mentioned above. If now X_g is an integral-X_g containing $X_{\zeta-1}$ the section of X_g and X_{n-r_ζ} is an integral-$X_{\zeta'}$ $(\zeta' \geqslant \zeta)$. Since the tangent E_{n-r_ζ} in $\underset{0}{\xi}{}^\kappa$ contains no integral elements of more than ζ dimensions it is necessary that $\zeta' = \zeta$, and this implies that the section of X_g with X_{n-r_ζ} coincides with the integral-X_ζ constructed. This holds for every choice of X_{n-r_ζ} and consequently there exists one and only one integral-X_g containing $X_{\zeta-1}$.

Obviously this integral-X_g can be obtained by constructing all integral-X_ζ's belonging to all possible X_{n-r_ζ}'s. To execute this in a practical way we start from a sufficiently general arbitrary $X_{n-r_\zeta-1}$ containing $X_{\zeta-1}$ and an arbitrary system of ∞^{r_ζ} X_{n-r_ζ}'s containing this $X_{n-r_\zeta-1}$, depending on $r_\zeta = g-\zeta$ parameters and filling up the whole $\mathfrak{N}(\underset{0}{\xi}{}^\kappa)$. Then in a general X_{n-r_ζ} of the system we have the following problem. In the X_{n-r_ζ} there is a Goursat system, arising from the original one by section with this X_{n-r_ζ}. Further, in this X_{n-r_ζ} an integral-$X_{\zeta-1}$ is given and the problem is to construct an integral-X_ζ containing this $X_{\zeta-1}$. We denote the arithmetic invariants in X_{n-r_ζ} by r'_i and s'_i. A sufficiently general integral-E_m $(m \leqslant \zeta)$ in X_{n-r_ζ}, denoted by E'_m, is also a regular integral-E_m in X_n, denoted by E_m. The dimension of $H(E_m)$ is $m+1+r_{m+1}$ and $H(E'_m)$ is the section of $H(E_m)$ with the tangent-E_{n-r_ζ} of X_{n-r_ζ}. Accordingly the dimension of $H(E'_m)$ is

$$m+1+r'_{m+1} = m+1+r_{m+1}-r_\zeta = m+1+r_{m+1}-g+\zeta \quad (11.5)$$

and consequently

$$r'_{m+1} = r_{m+1}-g+\zeta \quad (m \leqslant \zeta). \quad (11.6)$$

Collecting results we get the following equations

$$r_\zeta = g-\zeta,\ r_{\zeta+1} = g-\zeta-1,\ \ldots,\ r_g = 0,\ r_{g+1} = -1$$
$$r'_0 = r_0-g+\zeta, \ldots, r'_{\zeta-1} = r_{\zeta-1}-g+\zeta,\ r'_\zeta = 0, \quad r'_{\zeta+1} = -1,$$
$$s'_0 = s_0, \quad \ldots, \quad s'_{\zeta-1} = s_{\zeta-1}, \qquad s'_\zeta = 0. \tag{11.7}$$

Hence the problem of the determination of all integral-X_g's of a Goursat system in X_n is reduced to the problem of the determination of all integral-X_ζ's of a Goursat system of genus ζ in an $X_{n-g+\zeta}$. The $X_{n-g+\zeta}$ and the Goursat system depend on $g-\zeta$ parameters.†

If $n' < n$ there are two possible methods. Either the system can be written with n' variables and the problem can be reduced to the problem of the determination of all integral-$X_{g-n+n'}$'s of a Goursat system of genus $g' = g-n+n'$ in an $X_{n'}$. Or, using the identities $s_i = 0$ $(i > g')$ the problem can be reduced to the problem of the determination of all integral-X_ζ's of a Goursat system of genus ζ in an $X_{n-g+\zeta}$ $(\zeta \leqslant g')$. The first method requires integrations in order to reduce from n to n'. The second method requires no integrations but the equations obtained depend on $g-\zeta$ parameters.

If the Goursat system is closed and if the unimportant quantities with valence $> g$ are dropped, after the reduction to a system of genus ζ only the sections of the remaining quantities with the $X_{n-g+\zeta}$ are used and of these sections only those with a valence $\leqslant \zeta$. This implies that in the original system all quantities with a valence $> \zeta$ can be dropped and that therefore

$$v_{\max} \leqslant \zeta. \tag{11.8}$$

If $\zeta = 1$ for the Cartan system C^x_λ, we have $s_1 = 0$ and consequently the system

$$B^\lambda_b\, \partial_\lambda f = 0 \tag{11.9}$$

is complete. Then $g = r$ and the problem reduces to the determination of all integral-X_r's of an X_r-forming E_r-field. Using the method just described we start from a sufficiently general arbitrary $X_{n-r_1-1} = X_{n-r}$ through $X_{\zeta-1} = X_0 = \overset{}{\underset{0}{\xi^\kappa}}$, that is, an X_{n-r} whose tangent E_{n-r} in $\underset{0}{\xi^\kappa}$ has no direction in common with the local E_r of the field, and an arbitrary system of ∞^{r-1} X_{n-r+1}'s containing this X_{n-r} and depending on $r-1$ parameters. Then in each of these X_{n-r+1}'s the integral curves of an E_1-field have to be determined. But this process is just the same as the process indicated by Mayer (cf. III, § 16). Hence, Mayer's method of integration of a complete system is a special case of Cartan's method.‡ From this point of view Mayer's method loses its artificial appearance and comes in quite naturally as was predicted in III, § 16.

† Because of this fact Cartan has called ζ the *genre vrai* of the system: 1901. 1, p. 291.

‡ E. Cartan, 1901. 1, p. 294.

12. The invariant σ of a scalar-free Cartan system

If the E_r-field determined by the Cartan system C_λ^x $(x = \mathrm{r}+1,\ldots,\mathrm{n})$ is X_ν-enveloping (cf. III, § 1) the equations

$$C_\lambda^x d\xi^\lambda = 0 \quad (x = \mathrm{r}+1,\ldots,\mathrm{n}) \tag{12.1}$$

can be written in such a way that the number of differentials occurring in these equations is $n-\nu$. Conversely, if the equations can be written with $n-\nu$ differentials but not with a smaller number of them, the E_r-field is X_ν-enveloping. In this case and only in this case the q-vector

$$w_{\lambda_1\ldots\lambda_q} = C_{[\lambda_1}^{\mathrm{r}+1}\ldots C_{\lambda_q]}^{\mathrm{n}} \quad (q = n-r) \tag{12.2}$$

is a divisor of a non-vanishing alternating product of $n-\nu$ gradient vectors and accordingly there exists a system of $\sigma = n-\nu-q$ functions $\overset{1}{f},\ldots,\overset{r-\nu}{f}$ such that

$$w_{[\lambda_1\ldots\lambda_q}\overset{1}{f}_{\lambda_{q+1}}\cdots\overset{r-\nu}{f}_{\lambda_{n-\nu}]} \quad (q = n-r) \tag{12.3}$$

is a *non-vanishing* gradient product to within a scalar factor.†

From $\nu \geqslant g$ it follows that (cf. VIII, § 10)

$$\sigma \leqslant r-g = r'-g'. \tag{12.4}$$

Unlike ν and g the integer σ is invariant for changes of the number of the variables in which the equations (12.1) are expressed.

Integral-X_m's with $m > g$ cannot be determined directly by the methods described in VIII, §§ 5–9. This implies that the same holds for the invariant σ. A necessary and sufficient condition that (12.3) be a non-vanishing gradient product to within a scalar factor is that $w_{\lambda_1\ldots\lambda_q}$ is a divisor of

$$(\partial_{[\mu}w_{\lambda_1\ldots\lambda_q})\overset{1}{f}_{\lambda_{q+1}}\cdots\overset{r-\nu}{f}_{\lambda_{n-\nu}]}. \tag{12.5}$$

But this condition is equivalent to the condition that

$$C_{[\omega\mu}^{\cdot\cdot x}C_{\lambda_1}^{\mathrm{r}+1}\ldots C_{\lambda_q}^{\mathrm{n}}\overset{1}{f}_{\lambda_{q+1}}\cdots\overset{r-\nu}{f}_{\lambda_{n-\nu}]} = 0 \quad (x = \mathrm{r}+1,\ldots,\mathrm{n}). \tag{12.6}$$

Now we consider the Goursat system

$$C_{[\omega\mu}^{\cdot\cdot x}C_{\lambda_1}^{\mathrm{r}+1}\ldots C_{\lambda_q]}^{\mathrm{n}} \quad (x = \mathrm{r}+1,\ldots,\mathrm{n}). \tag{12.7}$$

Generally this system is not closed. If a normal system of integral-X_m's of this system has been found, this means that $n-m$ functions are known whose gradients multiplied with $w_{\lambda_1\ldots\lambda_q}$ form a gradient product to within a scalar factor. From this point of view we see that the maximum possible value of m is $n-\sigma$. But it is doubtful whether these integral-$X_{n-\sigma}$'s can be obtained by the method of Cartan-Kähler or

† J. M. Thomas, 1933. 3, has called σ the 'species' of the Cartan system. This invariant is not to be confounded with another invariant introduced by Cartan, 1901. 1, p. 288, and called *espèce*, this latter invariant being equal to s_g+1.

whether the process stops at $m = g+q$. In other words, if G is the genus of (12.7) we have to decide whether $G \leqslant g+q$ or $G > g+q$ and in this latter case perhaps even $G = n-\sigma$. If an integral-E_m with the coordinates $v^{\kappa_1 \dots \kappa_m}$ of the Goursat system is known, the section of this E_m with the E_{n-q} of $w_{\lambda_1 \dots \lambda_q}$ is in general an E_{m-q} determined by the $(m-q)$-vector

$$C_{\lambda_1}^{\mathrm{r}+1} \dots C_{\lambda_q}^{\mathrm{n}} v^{\lambda_1 \dots \lambda_m} = {}'v^{\lambda_{q+1} \dots \lambda_m}. \tag{12.8}$$

According to (12.7) we have for this $(m-q)$-vector

$$\begin{aligned} C_{\lambda_1}^{x}\, {}'v^{\lambda_1 \dots \lambda_{m-q}} &= 0 \\ C_{\lambda_1 \lambda_2}^{\cdot\,\cdot\,x}\, {}'v^{\lambda_1 \dots \lambda_{m-q}} &= 0 \end{aligned} \qquad (x = \mathrm{r}+1, \dots, \mathrm{n}) \tag{12.9}$$

and these equations express the fact that the E_{m-q} is an integral-E_{m-q} of the Cartan system C_{λ}^{x}.

Now let E_g in $\overset{}{\underset{0}{\xi}}{}^{\kappa}$ be regular and the last element of a regular chain of the Cartan system. Then there exists a normal system of integral-X_g's containing an X_g through $\underset{0}{\xi}{}^{\kappa}$ tangent to the given E_g. If

$$\overset{1}{\phi} = \text{const.}, \quad \dots, \quad \overset{n-g}{\phi} = \text{const.} \tag{12.10}$$

are the equations of these X_g's the q-vector $w_{\lambda_1 \dots \lambda_q}$ is a divisor of the gradient product

$$\overset{1}{\phi}_{[\lambda_1} \dots \overset{n-g}{\phi}_{\lambda_{n-g}]} \quad (\phi_\lambda \overset{\text{def}}{=} \partial_\lambda \phi). \tag{12.11}$$

Hence among the ϕ_λ there always exist $n-g-q$ gradient vectors whose product with $w_{\lambda_1 \dots \lambda_q}$ is a gradient product to within a scalar factor. By interchanging indices we can always make $\overset{1}{\phi}_\lambda, \dots, \overset{n-g-q}{\phi}_\lambda$ form such a set of gradient vectors. Then we have

$$C_{[\omega\mu}^{\cdot\,\cdot\,x} C_{\lambda_1}^{\mathrm{r}+1} \dots C_{\lambda_q}^{\mathrm{n}} \overset{1}{\phi}_{\lambda_{q+1}} \dots \overset{r-g}{\phi}_{\lambda_{n-g}]} = 0, \tag{12.12}$$

and this means that the equations

$$\overset{1}{\phi} = \text{const.}, \quad \dots, \quad \overset{r-g}{\phi} = \text{const.} \tag{12.13}$$

represent a system of integral-X_{q+g}'s of the Goursat system. In $\underset{0}{\xi}{}^{\kappa}$, the tangent E_{q+g} of the X_{q+g} passing through $\underset{0}{\xi}{}^{\kappa}$ is an integral-E_{q+g} containing the integral-E_g from which we started. If now $G > q+g$ the E_{q+g} is contained in at least one integral-E_{q+g+1} of the Goursat system, determined by a covariant $(r-g-1)$-vector of the form

$$\phi_{\lambda_1 \dots \lambda_{r-g-1}} = \overset{1}{\phi}_{[\lambda_1} \dots \overset{r-g}{\phi}_{\lambda_{r-g}]} v^{\lambda_{r-g}}. \tag{12.14}$$

Hence

$$C_{[\lambda_1}^{\mathrm{r}+1} \dots C_{\lambda_q}^{\mathrm{n}} \phi_{\lambda_{q+1} \dots \lambda_{n-g-1}]} \qquad (12.15$$

represents an integral-E_{g+1} in $\underset{0}{\xi^\kappa}$ containing the integral-E_g. But since this is impossible we have $G \leqslant q+g$. This proves that the Goursat system (12.7) cannot be used to determine σ by the methods described in VIII, §§ 5–9.

There is still another way to reduce the determination of σ to the integration of a Goursat system. We consider the vector manifold $\mathfrak{N}_{n+q}$ with the null form

$$w_{[\lambda_1 \ldots \lambda_q} w_{\lambda]} = 0 \tag{12.16}$$

and the parametric form

$$\begin{aligned} w_\lambda &= \lambda_x C_\lambda^x \\ \xi^\kappa &= \xi^\kappa, \end{aligned} \quad (x = \mathrm{r}+1,\ldots,\mathrm{n}), \tag{12.17}$$

with the $n+q$ parameters ξ^κ, λ_x. The vector $U_{\mathfrak{b}}$ ($\mathfrak{b} = 1,\ldots,n,\mathrm{r}+1,\ldots,\mathrm{n}$) of this $\mathfrak{N}_{n+q}$ (cf. VII, § 3) in the X_{n+q} of the parameters has the components

$$\begin{aligned} U_\lambda &= \lambda_x C_\lambda^x \\ U_y &= 0 \end{aligned} \quad (x, y = \mathrm{r}+1,\ldots,\mathrm{n}), \tag{12.18}$$

and its rotation $U_{\mathfrak{cb}}$ the components (cf. VII (3.14))

$$\begin{aligned} U_{\mu\lambda} &= 2(\partial_{[\mu} w_{|\rho|})\partial_{\lambda]} \xi^\rho = 2\partial_{[\mu} w_{\lambda]} = \lambda_x C_{\mu\lambda}^{\cdot\cdot x} \\ U_{\mu y} &= (\partial_\mu w_\rho)\partial_y \xi^\rho - (\partial_y w_\rho)\partial_\mu \xi^\rho = -C_\mu^y \end{aligned} \quad (x, y = \mathrm{r}+1,\ldots,\mathrm{n}). \tag{12.19}$$

Consequently the matrix of $U_{\mathfrak{cb}}$ has the form

$$\begin{Vmatrix} \lambda_x C_{\mu\lambda}^{\cdot\cdot x} & -C_\mu^y \\ C_\lambda^x & 0 \end{Vmatrix} \begin{matrix} \updownarrow n \\ \updownarrow q \end{matrix} \quad \overset{\longleftarrow n \longrightarrow \longleftarrow q \longrightarrow}{} \quad (x, y = \mathrm{r}+1,\ldots,\mathrm{n}). \tag{12.20}$$

For the rank $2\bar{\rho}$ of this matrix we have (cf. VII, § 3)

$$2\bar{\rho} = 2\rho + 2(n+q-n) = 2\rho + 2q, \tag{12.21}$$

2ρ being the rotation class of the $\mathfrak{N}_{n+q}$ (cf. VII, § 3). Now we consider the $\mathfrak{N}_{n+q+1}$ with the null form

$$w_{[\lambda_1 \ldots \lambda_q} \overset{1}{f}_\lambda w_{\mu]} = 0; \quad \overset{1}{f}_\lambda \overset{\mathrm{def}}{=} \partial_\lambda \overset{1}{f} \tag{12.22}$$

and the parametric form

$$\begin{aligned} w_\lambda &= \lambda_x C_\lambda^x + \lambda_{\mathrm{r}} C_\lambda^{\mathrm{r}}, \quad C_\lambda^{\mathrm{r}} \overset{\mathrm{def}}{=} \overset{1}{f}_\lambda \\ \xi^\kappa &= \xi^\kappa, \end{aligned} \quad (x = \mathrm{r}+1,\ldots,\mathrm{n}), \tag{12.23}$$

with the $n+q+1$ parameters ξ^κ, λ_x, λ_{r}. The matrix of the bivector of this $\mathfrak{N}_{n+q+1}$ in the X_{n+q+1} of the parameters has the form

$$\overset{\longleftarrow n \longrightarrow \longleftarrow q \longrightarrow \longleftarrow 1 \longrightarrow}{\begin{Vmatrix} \lambda_x C_{\mu\lambda}^{\cdot\cdot x} & -C_\mu^y & -\overset{1}{f}_\mu \\ C_\lambda^x & 0 & 0 \\ \overset{1}{f}_\lambda & 0 & 0 \end{Vmatrix}} \quad (x, y = \mathrm{r}+1,\ldots,\mathrm{n}) \tag{12.24}$$

and consequently for the rank $2\bar{\rho}'$ of this matrix we have

$$\begin{aligned} 2\bar{\rho} \leqslant 2\bar{\rho}' &\leqslant 2\bar{\rho}+2, \\ 2\bar{\rho}' &= 2\rho'+2q+2, \end{aligned} \tag{12.25}$$

$2\rho'$ being the rotation class of $\mathfrak{N}_{n+q+1}$. From this it follows that the rotation class of $\mathfrak{N}_{n+q}$ exceeds the rotation class of $\mathfrak{N}_{n+q+1}$ by 2 if and only if

$$2\bar{\rho}' = 2\bar{\rho}. \tag{12.26}$$

Continuing in this way we prove that the matrix

$$\overset{\longleftarrow n \longrightarrow \longleftarrow q \longrightarrow \longleftarrow \qquad \sigma \qquad \longrightarrow}{\left\| \begin{array}{ccccc} \lambda_x C^{\cdot\cdot x}_{\mu\lambda} & -C^y_\mu & -\overset{1}{f}_\mu & \dots & -\overset{\sigma}{f}_\mu \\ C^x_\lambda & 0 & 0 & & 0 \\ \overset{1}{f}_\lambda & 0 & . & & . \\ . & . & . & & . \\ \overset{\sigma}{f}_\lambda & 0 & . & & 0 \end{array} \right\|} \qquad (x, y = \mathrm{r}+1, \dots, \mathrm{n}) \tag{12.27}$$

must have the rank $2\bar{\rho}+2\sigma-2\rho = 2q+2\sigma$ because, according to our suppositions, the rotation class of the $\mathfrak{N}_{n+q+\sigma}$ with the null form

$$w_{[\lambda_1 \dots \lambda_q} \overset{1}{f}_{\mu_1} \dots \overset{\sigma}{f}_{\mu_\sigma} w_{\mu]} = 0 \tag{12.28}$$

has to vanish. Since the rank of (12.20) is $2\rho+2q$, it follows that the rank of (12.27) is at least $2\rho+2q$, i.e. that

$$\sigma \geqslant \rho† \tag{12.29}$$

or

$$\nu \leqslant r-\rho. \tag{12.30}$$

Since the $\mathfrak{N}_{n+q}$ is homogeneous the class of $U_{\mathfrak{b}}$ is even. Accordingly since the rank of (12.27) is $2\bar{\rho}+2\sigma-2\rho = 2q+2\sigma$, the set $\overset{1}{f}, \dots, \overset{\sigma}{f}$, looked upon as functions of the ξ^κ and the λ_x has the index 2ρ or $2\rho-1$ with respect to $U_{\mathfrak{b}}$ (cf. IV, § 4). Hence the problem is to find the smallest possible number m of functions with index 2ρ or $2\rho-1$ with respect to $U_{\mathfrak{b}}$ and independent of the λ_x. If we use the notation $\overset{2\tau}{U}$ for the 2τ-vector $U_{[\mathfrak{c}_1 \mathfrak{b}_1} \dots U_{\mathfrak{c}_\tau \mathfrak{b}_\tau]}$ (cf. IV, § 2) the condition that (12.27) with $\sigma = m$ has the rank $2q+2m$ takes the form

$$\begin{aligned} &(a) \qquad \overset{2q}{U} \overset{\bar{1}}{f} \dots \overset{\bar{m}}{f} \neq 0, \\ &(b) \qquad \overset{2q+2}{U} \overset{\bar{1}}{f} \dots \overset{\bar{m}}{f} = 0. \end{aligned} \tag{12.31}$$

Only the values $m < r-1$ have to be considered because (12.31 b) is

† J. M. Thomas, 1933. 4.

satisfied by every set of $r-1$ functions. In fact (12.3) is an $(n-1)$-vector for $\sigma = r-1$ and every $(n-1)$-vector is a gradient product to within a scalar factor. If $v^{\mathfrak{a}_1\ldots\mathfrak{a}_{n+q-m}}$ has the $(n+q-m)$-direction of the m-vector $\overset{1}{f}_{[\mathfrak{b}_1}\ldots\overset{m}{f}_{\mathfrak{b}_m]}$ in the X_{n+q} of ξ^κ, λ_x, the condition that the functions $\overset{1}{f},\ldots,\overset{m}{f}$ are independent of the λ_x is equivalent to the condition that $\underset{\mathrm{r}+1}{e}^{[\mathfrak{a}_1}\ldots\underset{\mathrm{n}}{e}^{\mathfrak{a}_q]}$ is a divisor of $v^{\mathfrak{a}_1\ldots\mathfrak{a}_{n+q-m}}$. The conditions (12.31) take the form

$$\begin{aligned} \overset{2q}{U}_{\mathfrak{b}_1\ldots\mathfrak{b}_{2q}}\, v^{\mathfrak{b}_1\ldots\mathfrak{b}_{n+q-m}} &\neq 0, \\ \overset{2q+2}{U}_{\mathfrak{b}_1\ldots\mathfrak{b}_{2q+2}}\, v^{\mathfrak{b}_1\ldots\dot{\mathfrak{b}}_{n+q-m}} &= 0. \end{aligned} \tag{12.32}$$

Hence we have to determine the integral-X_M's of the Goursat system

$$\overset{2q+2}{U}_{\mathfrak{b}_1\ldots\mathfrak{b}_{2q+2}} \quad (\mathfrak{b}_1,\ldots,\mathfrak{b}_{2q+2} = 1,\ldots, n, \mathrm{r}+1,\ldots,\mathrm{n}) \tag{12.33}$$

in the X_{n+q} of ξ^κ, λ_x, satisfying the additional conditions, for the greatest value of M. Every X_{2q+1} is an integral-X_{2q+1} of this system but when $M = 2q+1$ it follows that $m = n-q-1$ and this value of m is excluded already. If $M > 2q+1$ every normal system of X_M's satisfying the additional conditions determines a set of $n+q-M$ functions of the ξ^κ with the index 2ρ or $2\rho-1$. Hence we have to decide whether the genus G' of the Goursat system is $\leqslant 2q+g$ or $> 2q+g$ and in this latter case perhaps even equal to $n+q-\sigma$. If a general integral-E_M is determined by an M-vector $v^{\mathfrak{a}_1\ldots\mathfrak{a}_M}$ having $\underset{\mathrm{r}+1}{e}^{[\mathfrak{a}_1}\ldots\underset{\mathrm{n}}{e}^{\mathfrak{a}_q]}$ as a divisor, by transvection with $\overset{\mathrm{r}+1}{e}_{[\mathfrak{a}_1}\ldots\overset{\mathrm{n}}{e}_{\mathfrak{a}_q]}$ we get a contravariant $(M-q)$-vector whose components vanish if they have at least one index $\mathrm{r}+1,\ldots,\mathrm{n}$. By transvection of this $(M-q)$-vector with $w_{\lambda_1\ldots\lambda_q}$ we get a contravariant $(M-2q)$-vector representing an integral-E_{M-2q} of the Cartan system. This proves that it is not always possible to determine σ directly by applying the methods described in VIII, §§ 5–9, on the Goursat system, because it is not certain *a priori* that G' is equal to $n+q-\sigma$. Because $G' \leqslant n+q-\sigma$ we always find an upper limit for σ, viz. $\sigma \leqslant n+q-G'$. Now $\sigma \geqslant 1$ and this implies that if G' happens to be equal to $n+q-1$ we are sure that $\sigma = 1$. But also apart from this special case the two Goursat systems (12.7) and (12.33) are by no means useless because in many circumstances they may give a hint how to make a guess at the value of σ.

As an example we take the system

$$C^{\cdot x}_{\lambda} = \overset{x}{e}_\lambda + \underset{x}{\phi}\overset{x\,r}{e}_\lambda \quad (x = r+1,\ldots, n\,;\; r \leqslant n-2) \tag{12.34}$$

with functions $\underset{x}{\phi}$ not solely dependent on $\xi^r,\ldots, \xi^n$. Then

$$q+2 \leqslant n' \leqslant 2q+1 \quad (n' \leqslant n;\; q = n-r). \tag{12.35}$$

Obviously $\sigma = 1$ because by multiplying $w_{\lambda_1\ldots\lambda_q}$ with a suitable vector depending linearly on $\overset{r}{e}_\lambda,\ldots,\overset{n}{e}_\lambda$ we get $\overset{r}{e}_{[\lambda_r}\ldots\overset{n}{e}_{\lambda_n]}$ to within a scalar factor. Accordingly $\nu = n-q-1$. For B_b^κ we may take

$$\begin{aligned} B_1^\kappa &= \underset{1}{e}^\kappa \\ &\cdot\ \cdot\ \cdot\ \cdot\ \cdot \\ B_{r-1}^\kappa &= \underset{r-1}{e}^\kappa \qquad\qquad (x = r+1,\ldots,n). \\ B_r^\kappa &= \underset{r}{e}^\kappa - \overset{x}{\phi}\underset{x}{e}^\kappa \end{aligned} \tag{12.36}$$

The equations for $\underset{1}{v}^\kappa$ are

$$C_\lambda^x \underset{1}{v}^\lambda = 0 \quad (x = r+1,\ldots,n). \tag{12,37}$$

Hence $r_1 = r-1$. The general form of $\underset{1}{v}^\kappa$ is

$$\underset{1}{v}^\kappa = \lambda^b B_b^\kappa \quad (b = 1,\ldots,r). \tag{12.38}$$

Accordingly the equations for $\underset{2}{v}^\kappa$ are

$$\begin{aligned} C_\lambda^x \underset{2}{v}^\lambda &= 0 &\quad (b &= 1,\ldots,r; \\ \lambda^b B_b^\mu \overset{x}{\phi}_\mu \overset{r}{e}_\lambda \underset{2}{v}^\lambda - \lambda^b B_b^\mu \overset{r}{e}_\mu \overset{x}{\phi}_\lambda \underset{2}{v}^\lambda &= 0 & x &= r+1,\ldots,n). \end{aligned} \tag{12.39}$$

Now we have

$$\begin{aligned} &\lambda^b B_b^\mu \overset{x}{\phi}_\mu \overset{r}{e}_\lambda - \lambda^b B_b^\mu \overset{r}{e}_\mu \overset{x}{\phi}_\lambda \\ &= \lambda^b \overset{x}{\phi}_b \overset{r}{e}_\lambda - \lambda^r \overset{y}{\phi}\overset{x}{\phi}_y \overset{r}{e}_\lambda - \lambda^r \overset{x}{\phi}_\lambda \qquad (b = 1,\ldots,r; \\ &= \lambda^b \overset{x}{\phi}_b \overset{r}{e}_\lambda - \lambda^r \overset{x}{\phi}_\lambda - \lambda^r \overset{x}{\phi}_y C_\lambda^y + \lambda^r \overset{x}{\phi}_y \overset{y}{e}_\lambda \qquad x = r+1,\ldots,n), \\ &= \lambda^b \overset{x}{\phi}_b \overset{r}{e}_\lambda - \lambda^r \overset{x}{\phi}_b \overset{b}{e}_\lambda - \lambda^r \overset{x}{\phi}_y C_\lambda^y \end{aligned} \tag{12.40}$$

and consequently the rank of (12.39) is the rank of the matrix of

$$\begin{aligned} C_\lambda^x &= \overset{x}{\phi}\overset{r}{e}_\lambda + \overset{x}{e}_\lambda \quad (b = 1,\ldots,r; \\ \lambda^b \overset{x}{\phi}_b \overset{r}{e}_\lambda &- \lambda^r \overset{x}{\phi}_b \overset{b}{e}_\lambda \qquad x = r+1,\ldots,n). \end{aligned} \tag{12.41}$$

This matrix has the form $(q = n-r)$:

$$\underbrace{\quad}_{r-1}\quad\underbrace{\quad}_{1}\quad\underbrace{\quad}_{q}$$

$$\left\|\begin{array}{cccccccc} 0 & \cdots & \cdots & 0 & \overset{r+1}{\phi} & 1 & \cdots\ \cdots & 0 \\ \vdots & & & \vdots & \vdots & \vdots & \ddots & \vdots \\ \vdots & & & \vdots & \vdots & \vdots & & \vdots \\ 0 & \cdots & \cdots & 0 & \overset{n}{\phi} & 0 & \cdots\ \cdots & 1 \\ -\lambda^r\overset{x}{\phi}_1 & \cdots & \cdots & -\lambda^r\overset{x}{\phi}_{r-1} & \lambda^b\overset{x}{\phi}_b - \lambda^r\overset{x}{\phi}_r & 0 & \cdots\ \cdots & 0 \end{array}\right\| \begin{array}{l} \\ \\ q \\ \\ q \end{array} \tag{12.42}$$

and for $\lambda^r \neq 0$ the same rank as the matrix

$$\begin{array}{c} \\ q\left\{ \begin{array}{c} \\ \\ \\ \\ \end{array} \right. \\ q\left\{ \begin{array}{c} \\ \end{array} \right. \end{array} \begin{array}{c} \overbrace{\hphantom{0\ \cdots\ \cdots\ 0}}^{r-1}\ \overbrace{\hphantom{1\ \cdots\ \cdots\ 0}}^{q} \\ \left\| \begin{array}{cccccccc} 0 & \cdots & \cdots & 0 & 1 & \cdots & \cdots & 0 \\ \vdots & & & \vdots & \vdots & \ddots & & \vdots \\ \vdots & & & \vdots & \vdots & & \ddots & \vdots \\ 0 & \cdots & \cdots & 0 & 0 & \cdots & \cdots & 1 \\ \overset{x}{\phi}_1 & \cdots & \cdots & \overset{x}{\phi}_{r-1} & 0 & \cdots & \cdots & 0 \end{array} \right\| \end{array} \tag{12.43}$$

Now the functional matrix of the $\xi^r, \ldots, \xi^n, \overset{x}{\phi}$ has the form

$$\begin{array}{c} \\ q+1\left\{ \begin{array}{c} \\ \\ \\ \\ \end{array} \right. \\ q\left\{ \begin{array}{c} \\ \end{array} \right. \end{array} \begin{array}{c} \overbrace{\hphantom{0\ \cdots\ \cdots\ 0}}^{r-1}\ \overbrace{\hphantom{1\ \cdots\ \cdots\ 0}}^{q+1} \\ \left\| \begin{array}{cccccccc} 0 & \cdots & \cdots & 0 & 1 & \cdots & \cdots & 0 \\ \vdots & & & \vdots & \vdots & \ddots & & \vdots \\ \vdots & & & \vdots & \vdots & & \ddots & \vdots \\ 0 & \cdots & \cdots & 0 & 0 & \cdots & \cdots & 1 \\ \overset{x}{\phi}_1 & \cdots & \cdots & \overset{x}{\phi}_{r-1} & \overset{x}{\phi}_r & \cdots & \cdots & \overset{x}{\phi}_n \end{array} \right\| \end{array} \tag{12.44}$$

and we know that this matrix has the rank n'. Hence (12.43) has the rank $n'-1$ and from this it follows that

$$r_2 = n-n'+1-2 = n-n'-1 \tag{12.45}$$

and

$$s_1 = s_1' = n'-q-1. \tag{12.46}$$

As a result of (10.43) we have

$$s_1 \leqslant n-q-g = n'-q-g', \tag{12.47}$$

and from (12.46) and (12.47) it follows that

$$g' = 1, \qquad g = n-n'+1. \tag{12.48}$$

Hence, though integral-X_{r-1}'s exist, there are only regular integral-$X_{n-n'+1}$'s. Only if $n' = q+2$, that is, if the $\overset{x}{\phi}$ depend only on ξ^r, ξ^x and *one* other function is it possible to find these integral-X_{r-1}'s by means of the methods of VIII, §§ 5–9.

The first Goursat system (12.7) takes the form

$$\overset{x}{\phi}_{[\lambda_1} \overset{r}{e}_{\lambda_2} \overset{r+1}{e}_{\lambda_3} \cdots \overset{n}{e}_{\lambda_{q+2}]}. \tag{12.49}$$

The variables $\xi^1, \ldots, \xi^{r-1}$ may be chosen in such a way that the $\overset{x}{\phi}$ only depend on the n' variables $\xi^{n-n'+1}, \ldots, \xi^r, \xi^{r+1}, \ldots, \xi^n$. Then the vectors $\underset{1}{e^\kappa}, \ldots, \underset{n-n'}{e^\kappa}, \underset{r}{e^\kappa}, \ldots, \underset{n}{e^\kappa}$ span an integral-$E_{n-n'+q+1}$. If an integral-$E_{n-n'+q+2}$

contains this $E_{n-n'+q+1}$ it is spanned by the vectors $\underset{1}{e}^{\kappa},\dots,\underset{n-n'}{e}^{\kappa},\ \underset{r}{e}^{\kappa},\dots,\underset{n}{e}^{\kappa}$, and a vector v^{κ} with

$$v^1 = 0, \quad \dots, \quad v^{n-n'} = 0, \qquad v^r = 0, \quad \dots, \quad v^n = 0, \tag{12.50}$$

and this vector has to satisfy the equations

$$\overset{x}{\phi}_{[\lambda_1} \overset{r}{e}_{\lambda_2} \dots \overset{n}{e}_{\lambda_{q+2}]} \underset{1}{e}^{[\lambda_1} \dots \underset{n-n'}{e}^{\lambda_{n-n'}} \underset{r}{e}^{\lambda_{n-n'+1}} \dots \underset{n}{e}^{\lambda_{n-n'+q+1}} v^{\lambda_{n-n'+q+2}]} = 0$$
$$(x = r+1,\dots,n) \tag{12.51}$$

equivalent to

$$\overset{x}{\phi}_{n-n'+1} v^{n-n'+1} + \dots + \overset{x}{\phi}_{r-1} v^{r-1} = 0 \quad (x = r+1,\dots,n). \tag{12.52}$$

Since (12.43) has the rank $n'-1$ and since $\overset{x}{\phi}_1 = 0,\dots, \overset{x}{\phi}_{n-n'} = 0$, it follows that the homogeneous system (12.52) of q equations with

$$r-1-n+n' = n'-q-1$$

unknowns has no non-trivial solutions and consequently

$$G \leqslant n-n'+q+1.$$

Using the second Goursat system, the matrix (12.24) takes the form

$$\begin{array}{ccc|c|ccc|ccc||c}
\multicolumn{3}{c}{\longleftarrow r-1 \longrightarrow} & \multicolumn{1}{c}{\leftarrow 1 \rightarrow} & \multicolumn{3}{c}{\longleftarrow q \longrightarrow} & \multicolumn{3}{c}{\longleftarrow q \longrightarrow} & \multicolumn{1}{c}{\leftarrow 1 \rightarrow} \\
0 & \dots & 0 & -\lambda_x \overset{x}{\phi}_1 & 0 & \dots & 0 & 0 & \dots & 0 & -\overset{1}{f}_1 \\
\vdots & & \vdots & \vdots & \vdots & & \vdots & \vdots & & \vdots & \vdots \\
0 & \dots & 0 & -\lambda_x \overset{x}{\phi}_{r-1} & 0 & \dots & 0 & 0 & \dots & 0 & -\overset{1}{f}_{r-1} \\
\lambda_x \overset{x}{\phi}_1 & \dots & \lambda_x \overset{x}{\phi}_{r-1} & 0 & \lambda_x \overset{x}{\phi}_{r+1} & \dots & \lambda_x \overset{x}{\phi}_n & -\overset{r+1}{\phi} & \dots & -\overset{n}{\phi} & -\overset{1}{f}_r \\
0 & \dots & 0 & -\lambda_x \overset{x}{\phi}_{r+1} & 0 & \dots & 0 & -1 & \dots & 0 & -\overset{1}{f}_{r+1} \\
\vdots & & \vdots & \vdots & \vdots & & \vdots & \vdots & & \vdots & \vdots \\
0 & \dots & 0 & -\lambda_x \overset{x}{\phi}_n & 0 & \dots & 0 & 0 & \dots & -1 & -\overset{1}{f}_n \\
0 & \dots & 0 & \overset{r+1}{\phi} & 1 & \dots & 0 & 0 & \dots & 0 & 0 \\
\vdots & & \vdots & \vdots & \vdots & & \vdots & \vdots & & \vdots & \vdots \\
0 & \dots & 0 & \overset{n}{\phi} & 0 & \dots & 1 & 0 & \dots & 0 & 0 \\
\overset{1}{f}_1 & \dots & \overset{1}{f}_{r-1} & \overset{1}{f}_r & \overset{1}{f}_{r+1} & \dots & \overset{1}{f}_n & 0 & \dots & 0 & 0
\end{array}$$
$$(x = r+1,\dots,n) \tag{12.53}$$

and the matrix (12.20) of $U_{\mathfrak{cb}}$ takes the form of the $(n+q)$-rowed matrix contained in (12.53) and indicated by an extra couple of bars. By elementary transformations this matrix can be transformed into

$$\begin{array}{c}
\overleftrightarrow{\;r-1\;}\quad\overleftrightarrow{\;1\;}\quad\overleftrightarrow{\;q\;}\quad\overleftrightarrow{\;q\;}\quad\overleftrightarrow{\;1\;}\\
\left\|\begin{array}{ccccccccccc|c}
0 & \cdots & 0 & -\lambda_x\overset{x}{\phi}_1 & 0 & \cdots & 0 & 0 & \cdots & 0 & & -\overset{1}{f}_1\\
\vdots & & \vdots & \vdots & \vdots & & \vdots & \vdots & & \vdots & & \vdots\\
0 & \cdots & 0 & -\lambda_x\overset{x}{\phi}_{r-1} & 0 & \cdots & 0 & 0 & \cdots & 0 & & -\overset{1}{f}_{r-1}\\
\lambda_x\overset{x}{\phi}_1 & \cdots & \lambda_x\overset{x}{\phi}_{r-1} & 0 & 0 & \cdots & 0 & 0 & \cdots & 0 & & -\Phi\\
0 & \cdots & 0 & 0 & 0 & \cdots & 0 & -1 & \cdots & 0 & & 0\\
\vdots & & \vdots & \vdots & \vdots & & \vdots & \vdots & \ddots & \vdots & & \vdots\\
\vdots & & \vdots & \vdots & \vdots & & \vdots & \vdots & & \vdots & & \vdots\\
0 & \cdots & 0 & 0 & 0 & \cdots & 0 & 0 & \cdots & -1 & & 0\\
0 & \cdots & 0 & 0 & 1 & \cdots & 0 & 0 & \cdots & 0 & & 0\\
\vdots & & \vdots & \vdots & \vdots & \ddots & \vdots & \vdots & & \vdots & & \vdots\\
\vdots & & \vdots & \vdots & \vdots & & \vdots & \vdots & & \vdots & & \vdots\\
0 & \cdots & 0 & 0 & 0 & \cdots & 1 & 0 & \cdots & 0 & & 0\\
\overset{1}{f}_1 & \cdots & \overset{1}{f}_{r-1} & +\Phi & 0 & \cdots & 0 & 0 & \cdots & 0 & & 0
\end{array}\right\|
\end{array}$$

$$\Big(\Phi \overset{\text{def}}{=} \overset{1}{f}_r - \overset{r+1}{\phi}\,\overset{1}{f}_{r+1} - \cdots - \overset{n}{\phi}\,\overset{1}{f}_n;\ x = r+1,\ldots,n\Big). \qquad (12.54)$$

Obviously the $(n+q)$-rowed matrix has rank $2q+2$. Hence $\rho = 1$ as a consequence of (12.21) and this is in accordance with (12.29) and $\sigma = 1$. $\overset{1}{f}$ has to satisfy the condition that the $(n+q+1)$-rowed matrix (12.54) has rank $2q+2$ and this is equivalent to the condition that the matrix

$$\begin{array}{c}
\overleftrightarrow{\;r-1\;}\quad\overleftrightarrow{\;1\;}\quad\overleftrightarrow{\;1\;}\\
\left\|\begin{array}{ccccc}
0 & \cdots & 0 & -\lambda_x\overset{x}{\phi}_1 & -\overset{1}{f}_1\\
\vdots & & \vdots & \vdots & \vdots\\
0 & \cdots & 0 & -\lambda_x\overset{x}{\phi}_{r-1} & -\overset{1}{f}_{r-1}\\
\lambda_x\overset{x}{\phi}_1 & \cdots & \lambda_x\overset{x}{\phi}_{r-1} & 0 & -\Phi\\
\overset{1}{f}_1 & \cdots & \overset{1}{f}_{r-1} & +\Phi & 0
\end{array}\right\|
\end{array}
\qquad (x = r+1,\ldots,n) \qquad (12.55)$$

has rank 2 for general values of the parameters λ_x. For $n' > q+2$ this is the case if and only if all derivatives $\overset{1}{f}_1,\ldots,\overset{1}{f}_{r-1}$ vanish.

Since the bivector $U_{\mathfrak{cb}}$ has rank $2q+2$ the quantity $\overset{2q+2}{I}_{\mathfrak{b}_1\ldots\mathfrak{b}_{2q+2}}$ is a gradient product. Hence the Goursat system consisting of this quantity alone has regular integral-X_{n+q-1}'s and consequently

$$G' = n+q-1.$$

This is the special case, mentioned above, in which σ can be computed by using the second Goursat system.

13. Tests for regular chains of integral elements

A. *Direct method*

We will investigate whether a given integral element $\underset{0}{E_m}$ of a Goursat system contains regular chains with $p+1$ elements ($p = 0,\ldots,m$). If regular chains with $p+1$ elements exist, we know that any chain with $p+1$ elements which is sufficiently close to a regular chain is regular as well. From this it follows that, if regular chains with $p+1$ elements exist, in every neighbourhood of any not necessarily regular chain with $p+1$ integral elements there always exists at least one regular chain with $p+1$ elements. Hence we may restrict ourselves to the neighbourhood of a given not necessarily regular chain

$$\underset{0}{\xi^\kappa} = E_0, \quad \underset{*}{E_1}, \quad \ldots, \quad \underset{*}{E_{m-1}}, \quad \underset{0}{E_m} \tag{13.1}$$

in $\underset{0}{E_m}$ with the coordinates

$$\underset{0}{\xi^\kappa}, \quad \underset{*}{U_1^\kappa}, \quad \underset{*}{U_1^{[\kappa_1}}\underset{*}{U_2^{\kappa_2]}}, \quad \ldots, \quad \underset{*}{U_1^{[\kappa_1}}\ldots\underset{*}{U_m^{\kappa_m]}} = \underset{0}{v^{\kappa_1\ldots\kappa_m}}. \tag{13.2}$$

The coordinate system may be chosen in such a way that $\underset{0}{v^{1\ldots m}} = 1$. $\underset{*}{U_b^\kappa}$ ($b = 1,\ldots,m$) is the contravariant connecting quantity of the last element $\underset{0}{E_m}$ of the chain. By a suitable linear transformation in b it can always be arranged that

$$\begin{array}{llll} \underset{*}{U_1^1} = 1, & & & \\ \underset{*}{U_2^1} = 0, & \underset{*}{U_2^2} = 1, & & \\ \cdot \quad \cdot \quad \cdot & \cdot \quad \cdot \quad \cdot & & \\ \underset{*}{U_m^1} = 0, & \ldots, & \underset{*}{U_m^{m-1}} = 0, & \underset{*}{U_m^m} = 1. \end{array} \tag{13.3}$$

Then for every sufficiently close chain

$$\xi^\kappa, \quad U_1^\kappa, \quad U_1^{[\kappa_1}U_2^{\kappa_2]}, \quad \ldots, \quad U_1^{[\kappa_1}\ldots U_m^{\kappa_m]} = v^{\kappa_1\ldots\kappa_m} \tag{13.4}$$

$v^{1\ldots m}$ is $\neq 0$ and can be taken $= 1$, and without loss of generality it can be assumed that for all these neighbouring chains

$$
\begin{aligned}
&U_{\mathrm{1}}^{1} = 1, \\
&U_{\mathrm{2}}^{1} = 0, \quad U_{\mathrm{2}}^{2} = 1, \\
&\cdot \quad \cdot \quad \cdot \quad \cdot \quad \cdot \quad \cdot \quad \cdot \\
&U_{\mathrm{m}}^{1} = 0, \quad \ldots, \quad U_{\mathrm{m}}^{m-1} = 0, \quad U_{\mathrm{m}}^{m} = 1.
\end{aligned} \tag{13.5}
$$

The first conditions of regularity of a chain beginning with the point $\underset{0}{\xi}^{\kappa}$ are that $\underset{0}{\xi}^{\kappa}$ satisfies the system

$$\overset{\chi_0}{U}(\xi^{\kappa}) = 0 \quad (\chi_0 = 1,\ldots, \overset{0}{N}) \tag{13.6}$$

and that this system is regular in $\underset{0}{\xi}^{\kappa}$. If $\mathfrak{r}_0$ is its dimension, (13.6) represents an $X_{\mathfrak{r}_0}$ in $\mathfrak{N}(\underset{0}{\xi}^{\kappa})$ consisting of all integral-E_0's in $\mathfrak{N}(\underset{0}{\xi}^{\kappa})$. From (13.6) just $n-\mathfrak{r}_0$ of the ξ^{κ} (in this section called the *principal* ξ^{κ} and denoted by ξ^{ζ}) can be solved as functions of the remaining $\mathfrak{r}_0$ (in this section called the *parametrical* ξ^{κ} and denoted by ξ^{α}). The solution represents the most general integral-E_0 in $\mathfrak{N}(\underset{0}{\xi}^{\kappa})$, depending on the $\mathfrak{r}_0$ parameters ξ^{α} and consequently $r_0 = \mathfrak{r}_0$.

Suppose these conditions are satisfied. Then the E_1 with the coordinates $\underset{0}{\xi}^{\kappa}$, $\underset{0}{U}_{\mathrm{1}}^{\kappa}$ in $\mathfrak{N}(\underset{0}{\xi}^{\kappa}, \underset{0}{U}_{\mathrm{1}}^{\kappa})$ is an integral-E_1 if and only if $\underset{0}{\xi}^{\kappa}$ and $\underset{0}{U}_{\mathrm{1}}^{\kappa}$ satisfy the equations

$$\overset{\chi_1}{U}_{\lambda} U_{\mathrm{1}}^{\lambda} = 0 \quad (\chi_1 = 1,\ldots, \overset{1}{N}). \tag{13.7}$$

Among these equations are the equations

$$\overset{\chi_0\ \kappa}{U} e_{\lambda} U_{\mathrm{1}}^{\lambda} = 0 \quad (\chi_0 = 1,\ldots, \overset{0}{N}) \tag{13.8}$$

and consequently, U_{1}^{1} being $= 1$, (13.6) is a sub-system of (13.7). If the rank of (13.7) with respect to U_{1}^{κ} is $n-\mathfrak{r}_1-1$ for $\xi^{\kappa} = \underset{0}{\xi}^{\kappa}$, an $\mathfrak{N}(\underset{0}{\xi}^{\kappa})$ can be chosen so small that this rank is $\geqslant n-\mathfrak{r}_1-1$ everywhere in $\mathfrak{N}(\underset{0}{\xi}^{\kappa})$. Since $\underset{0}{E}_m$ is an integral-E_m we have $\mathfrak{r}_1 \geqslant m-1$ because for $\xi^{\kappa} = \underset{0}{\xi}^{\kappa}$ all vector factors of $\underset{0}{v}^{\kappa_1 \ldots \kappa_m}$ are solutions of (13.7). From (13.7) a system of $n-\mathfrak{r}_1-1$ equations can always be chosen whose rank with respect to U_{1}^{κ} is $n-\mathfrak{r}_1-1$ in $\mathfrak{N}(\underset{0}{\xi}^{\kappa})$. If now the ξ^{ζ} solved from (13.6) are substituted into (13.7) there are only two possible cases:

1. The remaining equations of (13.7) are consequences of the $n-\mathfrak{r}_1-1$ chosen equations if $\mathfrak{N}(\underset{0}{\xi}^{\kappa})$ is chosen sufficiently small. In this case (13.7) is, after the substitution, for each integral-E_0 in $\mathfrak{N}(\underset{0}{\xi}^{\kappa})$, equivalent to a system of $n-\mathfrak{r}_1-1$ linearly independent linear equations in U_{1}^{κ}. After

a suitable interchange of indices just $U_1^{\mathfrak{r}_1+2},\ldots, U_1^n$ (in this section called the *principal* U_1^κ and denoted by $U_1^{\zeta_1}$) can be solved from these equations as functions of the ξ^α and $U_1^2,\ldots, U_1^{\mathfrak{r}_1+1}$ (in this section called the *parametrical* U_1^κ and denoted by $U_1^{\alpha_1}$). Hence every integral-E_0 in $\mathfrak{N}(\underset{0}{\xi^\kappa})$ is contained in precisely $\infty^{\mathfrak{r}_1}$ integral-E_1's and consequently every one of these E_0's is regular. Since the dimension of $H(E_0)$ is $\mathfrak{r}_1+1$ we have $r_1 = \mathfrak{r}_1$.

2. The remaining equations of (13.7) are not for any choice of $\mathfrak{N}(\underset{0}{\xi^\kappa})$ consequences of the $n-\mathfrak{r}_1-1$ chosen equations. Then there exist in every $\mathfrak{N}(\underset{0}{\xi^\kappa})$ integral-E_0's through which pass less than $\infty^{\mathfrak{r}_1}$ integral-E_1's. In this case $\underset{0}{\xi^\kappa}$ is not regular.

In the first case the equations (13.7) have the rank $n-\mathfrak{r}_1-1$ with respect to U_1^κ after the substitution everywhere in $\mathfrak{N}(\underset{0}{\xi^\alpha})$ and consequently they form a system which is regular for $\xi^\alpha = \underset{0}{\xi^\alpha}$ and arbitrary U_1^κ. In the second case they have the rank $n-\mathfrak{r}_1-1$ in $\underset{0}{\xi^\alpha}$ but in every $\mathfrak{N}(\underset{0}{\xi^\alpha})$, since there are points where the rank is $> n-\mathfrak{r}_1-1$, they form a system which is not regular for $\xi^\alpha = \underset{0}{\xi^\alpha}$ and arbitrary U_1^κ. Now since (13.6) is regular in $\underset{0}{\xi^\kappa}$, from the theorem of decomposition of regular systems II.9 it follows that *before* the substitution the system (13.7) is regular for $\xi^\kappa = \underset{0}{\xi^\kappa}$ and arbitrary U_1^κ in case 1 and not regular in case 2. This proves the theorem

THEOREM VIII.9. *An integral element $\underset{0}{E_m}$ of a Goursat system with the coordinates $\underset{0}{\xi^\kappa}$, $\underset{0}{v^{\kappa_1\ldots\kappa_m}}$ contains regular chains of two elements if and only if* (13.6) *is regular in $\underset{0}{\xi^\kappa}$ and* (13.7) *regular for $\xi^\kappa = \underset{0}{\xi^\kappa}$ and arbitrary U_1^κ. If these conditions are satisfied, every vector factor of $\underset{0}{v^{\kappa_1\ldots\kappa_m}}$ forms with $\underset{0}{\xi^\kappa}$ a regular chain.*

Suppose, when the regularity conditions of Theorem VIII.9 are satisfied, that $\underset{0}{\xi^\kappa}$, $\underset{0}{U_1^\kappa}$ is a regular chain in $\underset{0}{E_m}$. Then the E_2 with the coordinates $\underset{0}{\xi^\kappa}$, $\underset{0}{U_1^{[\kappa_1}}\underset{0}{U_2^{\kappa_2]}}$ is an integral-E_2 if and only if $\underset{0}{\xi^\kappa}$, $\underset{0}{U_1^\kappa}$, and $\underset{0}{U_2^\kappa}$ satisfy the equations

$$\overset{\chi_2}{U}_{\lambda_1\lambda_2} U_1^{\lambda_1} U_2^{\lambda_2} = 0 \quad (\chi_2 = 1,\ldots, \overset{2}{N}). \tag{13.9}$$

Among these equations are the equations

$$\begin{aligned} &\overset{\chi_0\kappa_1}{U} e_{[\lambda_1} \overset{\kappa_2}{e}_{\lambda_2]} U_1^{\lambda_1} U_2^{\lambda_2} = 0 \\ &\overset{\chi_1}{U}_{[\lambda_1} \overset{\kappa}{e}_{\lambda_2]} U_1^{\lambda_1} U_2^{\lambda_2} = 0 \end{aligned} \qquad (\chi_0 = 1,\dots, \overset{0}{N};\ \chi_1 = 1,\dots, \overset{1}{N}) \qquad (13.10)$$

and consequently, since U_1^κ and U_2^κ satisfy the conditions (13.5), the systems (13.6) and (13.7) are sub-systems of (13.9) and

$$\overset{\chi_1}{U}_\lambda U_2^\lambda = 0 \quad (\chi_1 = 1,\dots, \overset{1}{N}) \qquad (13.11)$$

is another sub-system. If the rank of (13.9) with respect to U_2^κ is $n-\mathfrak{r}_2-2$ for $\xi^\kappa = \underset{0}{\xi^\kappa}$, $U_1^\kappa = \underset{0}{U_1^\kappa}$, an $\mathfrak{N}(\underset{0}{\xi^\kappa}, \underset{0}{U_1^\kappa})$ can be chosen so small that this rank is $\geqslant n-\mathfrak{r}_2-2$ everywhere in $\mathfrak{N}(\underset{0}{\xi^\kappa}, \underset{0}{U_1^\kappa})$. The value of $\mathfrak{r}_2$ depends on the choice of $\underset{0}{U_1^\kappa}$. Naturally $\mathfrak{r}_2 \geqslant m-2$ because for $\xi^\kappa = \underset{0}{\xi^\kappa}$, $U_1^\kappa = \underset{0}{U_1^\kappa}$ all vector factors of $\underset{0}{v^{\kappa_1\dots\kappa_m}}$ are solutions of (13.9). From the equations (13.9) a system of $n-\mathfrak{r}_2-2$ equations can always be chosen whose rank with respect to U_2^κ is $n-\mathfrak{r}_2-2$ in $\mathfrak{N}(\underset{0}{\xi^\kappa}, \underset{0}{U_1^\kappa})$. If now the ξ^ζ and $U_1^{\zeta_1}$ solved from (13.6) and (13.7) are substituted into (13.9) there are only two possible cases:

1. The remaining equations of (13.9) are consequences of the $n-\mathfrak{r}_2-2$ chosen equations if $\mathfrak{N}(\underset{0}{\xi^\kappa}, \underset{0}{U_1^\kappa})$ is chosen sufficiently small. In this case (13.9) is, after the substitution, for all values of ξ^κ, U_1^κ in $\mathfrak{N}(\underset{0}{\xi^\kappa}, \underset{0}{U_1^\kappa})$, equivalent to a system of $n-\mathfrak{r}_2-2$ linearly independent linear equations in U_2^κ. From these equations just $n-\mathfrak{r}_2-2$ of the U_2^κ can be solved as functions of the other $\mathfrak{r}_2$ and the ξ^α and $U_1^{\alpha_1}$. Now the equations (13.11) occur among (13.9) and this implies that with the change of indices already performed $U_2^{\zeta_1}$ can be solved from the $n-\mathfrak{r}_2-2$ equations as functions of the ξ^α, $U_1^{\alpha_1}$, and $U_2^{\alpha_1}$. Now $n-\mathfrak{r}_2-2 \geqslant n-\mathfrak{r}_1-1$ and consequently the indices $\alpha_1 = 2,\dots, \mathfrak{r}_1+1$ can be interchanged in such a way that just $U_2^{\mathfrak{r}_2+3},\dots, U_2^{\mathfrak{r}_1+1}$ can be solved as functions of the ξ^α, $U_1^{\alpha_1}$ and $U_2^3,\dots, U_2^{\mathfrak{r}_2+2}$. As a final result we get that $U_2^{\mathfrak{r}_2+3},\dots, U_2^n$ (in this section called the *principal* U_2^κ and denoted by $U_2^{\zeta_2}$) are expressed in terms of ξ^α, $U_1^{\alpha_1}$ and $U_2^3,\dots, U_2^{\mathfrak{r}_2+2}$ (in this section called the *parametrical* U_2^κ and denoted by $U_2^{\alpha_2}$). Hence every integral-E_1 in $\mathfrak{N}(\underset{0}{\xi^\kappa}, \underset{0}{U_1^\kappa})$ is contained in precisely $\infty^{\mathfrak{r}_2}$ integral-E_2's and consequently every one of these E_1's is regular. The dimension of $H(E_1)$ being $\mathfrak{r}_2+2$ we have $r_2 = \mathfrak{r}_2$.

2. The remaining equations of (13.9) are not consequences of the $n-\mathfrak{r}_2-2$ chosen equations for any choice of $\mathfrak{N}(\underset{0}{\xi^\kappa}, \underset{0}{U^\kappa_1})$. Then there exist in every $\mathfrak{N}(\underset{0}{\xi^\kappa}, \underset{0}{U^\kappa_1})$ integral-E_1's through which pass less than $\infty^{\mathfrak{r}_2}$ integral-E_2's. In this case $\underset{0}{\xi^\kappa}$, $\underset{0}{U^\kappa_1}$ is not regular.

In the first case the equations (13.9) have the rank $n-\mathfrak{r}_2-2$ with respect to U^κ_2, after the substitution, everywhere in $\mathfrak{N}(\underset{0}{\xi^\alpha}, \underset{0}{U^{\alpha_1}_1})$ and consequently they form a system regular in $\underset{0}{\xi^\alpha}$, $\underset{0}{U^{\alpha_1}_1}$. In the second case they have the rank $n-\mathfrak{r}_2-2$ in $\underset{0}{\xi^\alpha}$, $\underset{0}{U^\alpha_1}$, but in every $\mathfrak{N}(\underset{0}{\xi^\alpha}, \underset{0}{U^{\alpha_1}_1})$, since there are points where the rank is $> n-\mathfrak{r}_2-2$, they form a system which is not regular in $\underset{0}{\xi^\alpha}$, $\underset{0}{U^\alpha_1}$. Now, since (13.7) is regular for $\xi^\kappa = \underset{0}{\xi^\kappa}$ and arbitrary U^κ_1, from the theorem of decomposition of regular systems II.9 it follows that *before* the substitution the system (13.9) is regular for $\xi^\kappa = \underset{0}{\xi^\kappa}$, $U^\kappa_1 = \underset{0}{U^\kappa_1}$ and arbitrary $\underset{2}{U^\kappa}$ in case 1 and not regular in case 2. This proves the theorem

Theorem VIII.10. *An integral element $\underset{0}{E_m}$ of a Goursat system with the coordinates $\underset{0}{\xi^\kappa}$, $\underset{0}{v^{\kappa_1\ldots\kappa_m}}$ contains regular chains of three elements if and only if* (13.6) *is regular in $\underset{0}{\xi^\kappa}$,* (13.7) *regular for $\xi^\kappa = \underset{0}{\xi^\kappa}$ and arbitrary U^κ_1, and* (13.9) *regular for $\xi^\kappa = \underset{0}{\xi^\kappa}$, $U^\kappa_1 = \underset{0}{U^\kappa_1}$ and arbitrary U^κ_2. If these conditions are satisfied every vector factor of $\underset{0}{v^{\kappa_1\ldots\kappa_m}}$ linearly independent of $\underset{0}{U^\kappa_1}$ determines with $\underset{0}{\xi^\kappa}$ and $\underset{0}{U^\kappa_1}$ a regular chain.*

If $m = 2$ the investigation has come to an end. In consequence of the invariance of regularity with respect to the change of ordinary coordinates into supernumerary coordinates the last condition in Theorem VIII.10 can be replaced by the condition that the system

$$\begin{aligned} \overset{\chi_2}{U}_{\lambda_1\lambda_2} v^{\lambda_1\lambda_2} &= 0 \\ v^{[\kappa_1\kappa_2} v^{\lambda_1]\lambda_2} &= 0 \end{aligned} \qquad (\chi_2 = 1,\ldots, \overset{2}{N}) \tag{13.12}$$

be regular in $\underset{0}{\xi^\kappa}$, $\underset{0}{v^{\kappa_1\kappa_2}}$.

Continuing in this way we get the theorem

Theorem VIII.11. *An integral element $\underset{0}{E_m}$ of a Goursat system with the coordinates $\underset{0}{\xi^\kappa}$, $\underset{0}{v^{\kappa_1\ldots\kappa_m}}$ contains regular chains of $p+1$ elements if and* *only if* (13.6) *is regular in* $\underset{0}{\xi}^{\kappa}$ *and if vector factors* $\underset{0}{U}{}^{\kappa}_{1},\ldots,\ \underset{0}{U}{}^{\kappa}_{p-1}$ *of* $\underset{0}{v}{}^{\kappa_1\ldots\kappa_m}$ *exist such that the systems*

$$\overset{\chi_p}{U}_{\lambda_1\ldots\lambda_p} U^{\lambda_1}_{1} \ldots U^{\lambda_p}_{t} = 0 \quad (\chi_t = 1,\ldots,\overset{p}{N};\ t = 1,\ldots,m) \tag{13.13}$$

are regular for $\xi^{\kappa} = \underset{0}{\xi}^{\kappa},\ U^{\kappa}_{1} = \underset{0}{U}{}^{\kappa}_{1},\ldots,\ U^{\kappa}_{t-1} = \underset{0}{U}{}^{\kappa}_{t-1}$ *and arbitrary* U^{κ}_{t} *for every value of* t = 0,..., p. *If these conditions are satisfied every vector factor of* $\underset{0}{v}{}^{\kappa_1\ldots\kappa_m}$ *linearly independent of* $\underset{0}{U}{}^{\kappa}_{1},\ldots,\ \underset{0}{U}{}^{\kappa}_{p-1}$ *determines with* $\underset{0}{\xi}^{\kappa}$, $\underset{0}{U}{}^{\kappa}_{1},\ldots,\ \underset{0}{U}{}^{\kappa}_{p-1}$ *a regular chain.*

If $p = m$ the last condition in Theorem VIII.11 concerning the equations (13.13) with $p = m$ can be replaced by the condition that the system

$$\left.\begin{aligned} &\overset{\chi_m}{U}_{\lambda_1\ldots\lambda_m} v^{\lambda_1\ldots\lambda_m} = 0 \\ &v^{[\kappa_1\ldots\kappa_m} v^{\lambda_1]\ldots\lambda_m} = 0 \end{aligned}\right\} \quad (\chi_m = 1,\ldots,\overset{m}{N}) \tag{13.14}$$

be regular in $\underset{0}{\xi}^{\kappa},\ \underset{0}{v}{}^{\kappa_1\ldots\kappa_m}$.

The geometrical meaning of the non-existence of regular chains of $p+1$ elements in a given integral-$\underset{0}{E}_m$ is the following. In the $(p-1)(n-p+1)$-dimensional manifold of all E_{p-1}'s in the neighbourhood of $\underset{*}{E}_{p-1}$ the points where (13.13) is not regular form a sub-manifold with a dimension $< (p-1)(n-p+1)$. If, and only if, all E_{p-1}'s in $\underset{0}{E}_m$ are contained in this manifold will there exist no regular chains of $p+1$ elements in $\underset{0}{E}_m$.

B. *Indirect method*

There is another method, due to E. Kähler,† starting from a given chain in an integral element $\underset{0}{E}_m$. If this chain does not satisfy the conditions of regularity it has to be replaced by another chain. Characteristic of this method is the use of non-supernumerary coordinates. The method can be used for chains of any length but will be expounded here only for the most important case of chains with $m+1$ elements.

If $\underset{0}{\xi}^{\kappa},\ \underset{0}{v}{}^{\kappa_1\ldots\kappa_m}$ are the coordinates of $\underset{0}{E}_m$ we have

$$\overset{\chi_m}{U}_{\lambda_1\ldots\lambda_m} \underset{0}{v}{}^{\lambda_1\ldots\lambda_m} = 0 \quad (\chi_m = 1,\ldots,\overset{m}{N}). \tag{13.15}$$

Now let $\underset{i}{e}^{\kappa},\ \overset{h}{e}_{\lambda}$ $(h, i = 1,\ldots,n)$ be the measuring vectors of an arbitrary

† 1934. 1, pp. 40 ff.

not necessarily holonomic coordinate system (cf. II, § 6) in $\mathfrak{N}(\overset{}{\underset{0}{\xi^\kappa}})$, chosen in such a way that $\underset{0}{v}^{1\ldots m} = 1$. Then we require the necessary and sufficient conditions that the sections of the E_{n-m+q}'s of the alternating quantities

$$\overset{q+1}{e}_{[\lambda_1}\ldots\overset{m}{e}_{\lambda_m]} \quad (q = 1,\ldots, m) \tag{13.16}$$

with $\underset{0}{E_m}$ form with $\underset{0}{\xi^\kappa}$ a regular chain

$$\underset{0}{\xi^\kappa} = \underset{0}{E_0}, \underset{0}{E_1},\ldots, \underset{0}{E_m}. \tag{13.17}$$

Every chain in $\underset{0}{E_m}$ can be obtained in this way by a suitable choice of the system (h).

Let ξ^κ, $v^{\kappa_1\ldots\kappa_m}$ be an integral-E_m in the neighbourhood of $\underset{0}{E_m}$. Then $v^{1\ldots m} \neq 0$ and without loss of generality we may suppose that $v^{1\ldots m} = 1$. Introducing (cf. VIII, § 8)

$$U_b^h \overset{\text{def}}{=} v^{1\ldots b-1\, h\, b+1\ldots m} \quad (b = 1,\ldots, m;\ h = 1,\ldots, n) \tag{13.18}$$

the

$$U_b^x \quad (b = 1,\ldots, m;\ x = m+1,\ldots, n) \tag{13.19}$$

are non-supernumerary coordinates of E_m and we have (cf. VIII, § 8)

$$\begin{aligned} v^{h_1\ldots h_m} &= m!\, U^{h_1}_{[1}\ldots U^{h_m}_{m]} \quad (h_1,\ldots, h_m = 1,\ldots, n) \\ U_b^a &= \delta_b^a \quad (a, b = 1,\ldots, m). \end{aligned} \tag{13.20}$$

For $\xi^\kappa = \underset{0}{\xi^\kappa}$, $v^{\kappa_1\ldots\kappa_m} = \underset{0}{v}^{\kappa_1\ldots\kappa_m}$ the U_b^h pass into $\underset{0}{U}_b^h$.

The E_q arising from the intersection of E_m with the E_{n-m+q} (13.16) in ξ^κ is determined by ξ^κ and

$$v^{h_1\ldots h_q} \overset{\text{def}}{=} v^{h_1\ldots h_m}\, \overset{q+1}{e}_{[h_{q+1}}\ldots\overset{m}{e}_{h_m]} \quad (h_1,\ldots, h_m = 1,\ldots, n). \tag{13.21}$$

Hence $U_1^x,\ldots,\ U_q^x$ $(x = m+1,\ldots, n)$ can be used as non-supernumerary coordinates of E_q for every value of $q = 1,\ldots, m-1$.

Now we suppose that the chain intersected on $\underset{0}{E_m}$ be regular. Then, if the neighbourhood of $\underset{0}{E_m}$ is chosen sufficiently small, the chains intersected on the E_m's are regular as well. Since the E_q's are integral elements we have

$$\overset{\chi_q}{U}_{i_1\ldots i_q} U_1^{i_1}\ldots U_q^{i_q} = 0 \quad (i_1,\ldots, i_q = 1,\ldots, n;\ \chi_q = 1,\ldots, \overset{q}{N};\ q = 1,\ldots, m) \tag{13.22}$$

and about these equations we know that for a special value of q every set is contained as a sub-set in every one of the sets for higher values of q.

The first set

$$\overset{\chi_0}{U} = 0 \quad (\chi_0 = 1,\ldots, \overset{0}{N}) \tag{13.23}$$

is a system regular of dimension r_0 in $\overset{0}{\xi}{}^\kappa$ and represents an X_{r_0} in X_n consisting of all integral-E_0's in $\mathfrak{N}(\overset{0}{\xi}{}^\kappa)$. Consequently, after a suitable interchange of the indices κ, the variables $\xi^{r_0+1},\ldots, \xi^n$ can be solved from (13.23) as functions of $\xi^1,\ldots, \xi^{r_0}$. The solution represents the most general integral-E_0 in $\mathfrak{N}(\overset{0}{\xi}{}^\kappa)$, depending on r_0 parameters.

The second set

$$\overset{\chi_1}{U}_i U^i_{\mathrm{1}} = 0 \quad (i = 1,\ldots,\mathrm{n};\ \chi_1 = 1,\ldots,\overset{1}{N}) \tag{13.24}$$

contains (13.23), and in this set according to (13.20) the only components of U^h_{1} occurring are U^x_{1} $(x = \mathrm{m}+1,\ldots,\mathrm{n})$. A vector ξ^κ, V^h is contained in $H(E_0)$ if and only if

$$\overset{\chi_1}{U}_i V^i = 0 \quad (i = 1,\ldots,\mathrm{n};\ \chi_1 = 1,\ldots,\overset{1}{N}). \tag{13.25}$$

Hence the equations (13.24) determine only those vectors of $H(E_0)$ satisfying the conditions

$$V^1 = 1, \quad V^2 = 0, \quad \ldots, \quad V^{\mathrm{m}} = 0, \tag{13.26}$$

that are the vectors in the section of $H(E_0)$ with the local E_{n-m+1} spanned by $\underset{1}{e}{}^\kappa, \underset{\mathrm{m}+1}{e}{}^\kappa,\ldots, \underset{\mathrm{n}}{e}{}^\kappa$ whose first component is equal to 1. Now the dimension of $H(E_0)$ is $1+r_1$ and because $\overset{0}{v}{}^{1\ldots\mathrm{m}} = 1$ the local E_{n-m+1} in $\overset{0}{\xi}{}^\kappa$ and $\overset{0}{E}_m$ have just an E_1 in common (cf. I, Ex. 2). Consequently $\overset{0}{E}_m$ and E_{n-m+1} cannot be contained in an E_{n-1} and the same holds for $H(\overset{0}{E}_0)$ and E_{n-m+1}. From this it follows that $H(\overset{0}{E}_0)$ and E_{n-m+1} intersect in an E_{r_1-m+2}. Because of the regularity of E_0 this holds as well for $H(E_0)$ and the local E_{n-m+1} in ξ^κ and this is only possible if the equations (13.24), after substituting the $\xi^{r_0+1},\ldots, \xi^n$ solved from (13.23) as functions of $\xi^1,\ldots, \xi^{r_0}$, reduce to $n-r_1-1$ independent linear equations in U^x_{1}. Hence, after a suitable interchange of indices, $U^{2+\mathrm{r}_1}_{\mathrm{1}},\ldots, U^{\mathrm{n}}_{\mathrm{1}}$ can be solved from them as functions of $\xi^1,\ldots, \xi^{r_0}, U^{\mathrm{m}+1}_{\mathrm{1}},\ldots, U^{1+\mathrm{r}_1}_{\mathrm{1}}$.

The third set

$$\overset{\chi_2}{U}_{i_1 i_2} U^{i_1}_{\mathrm{1}} U^{i_2}_{\mathrm{2}} = 0 \quad (i_1, i_2 = 1,\ldots,\mathrm{n};\ \chi_2 = 1,\ldots,\overset{2}{N}) \tag{13.27}$$

contains (13.23) and (13.24) and in this set the only components of U^h_{2} occurring are U^x_{2} $(x = \mathrm{m}+1,\ldots,\mathrm{n})$. A vector ξ^κ, V^h is contained in $H(E_1)$ if and only if

$$\overset{\chi_2}{U}_{i_1 i_2} U^{i_1}_{\mathrm{1}} V^{i_2} = 0 \quad (i_1, i_2 = 1,\ldots,\mathrm{n};\ \chi_2 = 1,\ldots,\overset{2}{N}). \tag{13.28}$$

Hence the equations (13.27) determine only those vectors of $H(E_1)$ satisfying the equations

$$V^1 = 0, \quad V^2 = 1, \quad V^3 = 0, \quad ..., \quad V^{\mathrm{m}} = 0, \tag{13.29}$$

that are the vectors in the section of $H(E_1)$ with the local E_{n-m+1} spanned by $\underset{2}{e^\kappa}, \underset{\mathrm{m}+1}{e^\kappa},..., \underset{\mathrm{n}}{e^\kappa}$ whose second components are equal to one. Now the dimension of $H(E_1)$ is $2+r_2$ and in the same way as above it can be shown that the section of $H(E_1)$ with the local E_{n-m+1} in ξ^κ is an E_{r_2-m+3}. This is only possible if the equations (13.27), after substituting the $\xi^{r_0+1},..., \xi^n, U_1^{2+\mathrm{r}_1},..., U_1^{\mathrm{n}}$ solved from (13.24) as functions of $\xi^1,..., \xi^{r_0}, U_1^{\mathrm{m}+1},..., U_1^{1+\mathrm{r}_1}$, reduce to $n-r_2-2$ independent linear equations in U_2^x. Hence, just $n-r_2-2$ of the U_2^x can be solved from them as functions of the remaining r_2-m+2 and $\xi^1,..., \xi^{r_0}, U_1^{\mathrm{m}+1},..., U_1^{1+\mathrm{r}_1}$. These $n-r_2-2$ variables can be chosen conveniently. The equations

$$\overset{\chi_1}{U_i} U_2^i = 0 \quad (i = 1,..., \mathrm{n}; \ \chi_1 = 1,..., \overset{1}{N}) \tag{13.30}$$

are contained in (13.27) and consequently $U_2^{2+\mathrm{r}_1},..., U_2^{\mathrm{n}}$ can be solved as functions of $\xi^1,..., \xi^{r_0}, U_1^{\mathrm{m}+1},..., U_1^{1+\mathrm{r}_1}, U_2^{\mathrm{m}+1},..., U_2^{1+\mathrm{r}_1}$. Hence it is possible to interchange the indices $\mathrm{m}+1,..., 1+\mathrm{r}_1$, without disturbing the order of the indices $2+\mathrm{r}_1,..., \mathrm{n}$ already attained, in such a way that $U_2^{3+\mathrm{r}_2},..., U_2^{\mathrm{n}}$ can be expressed in terms of $\xi^1,..., \xi^{r_0}, U_1^{\mathrm{m}+1},..., U_1^{1+\mathrm{r}_1}$ and $U_2^{\mathrm{m}+1},..., U_2^{2+\mathrm{r}_2}$.

This process may be continued. If the variables are divided in the following way:

Parametrical variables	*Principal variables*
$\xi^\alpha \quad (\alpha = 1,..., r_0)$	$\xi^\zeta \quad (\zeta = r_0+1,..., n)$
$U_1^{\alpha_1} \quad (\alpha_1 = \mathrm{m}+1,..., 1+\mathrm{r}_1)$	$U_1^{\zeta_1} \quad (\zeta_1 = 2+\mathrm{r}_1,..., \mathrm{n})$
. . . .	. . . .
$U_{\mathrm{m}}^{\alpha_m} \quad (\alpha_m = \mathrm{m}+1,..., \mathrm{m}+\mathrm{r}_m)$	$U_{\mathrm{m}}^{\zeta_m} \quad (\zeta_m = \mathrm{m}+1+\mathrm{r}_m,..., \mathrm{n})$

(13.31)

the equations (13.22) can be solved step by step in $\mathfrak{N}(\underset{0}{\xi^\kappa}, \underset{0}{U_b^x})$ with respect to the principal variables. In all there are $n-r_0$ equations in ξ^κ and m times a system of $n-q-r_q$ $(q = 1,..., m)$ linear equations to be solved. The solution represents the most general integral-E_m in the neighbourhood of $\underset{0}{E_m}$ with the regular chain intersected on this E_m by (13.16). This general integral-E_m depends on

$$r_0+r_1+...+r_m-\binom{m}{2} \tag{13.32}$$

variables, viz. the parametrical variables. This number can readily be verified. In $\mathfrak{N}(\underset{0}{\xi}^\kappa)$ there are ∞^{r_0} integral-E_0's, every integral-E_0 is contained in ∞^{r_1} integral-E_1's, every integral-E_1 in ∞^{r_2} integral-E_2's, etc. But since every integral-E_2 contains ∞^1 integral-E_1's, every integral-E_3 contains ∞^2 integral-E_2's, etc., the total number has to be diminished by $\binom{m}{2}$.

Conversely we will prove now that the chain intersected by (13.16) on $\underset{0}{E}_m$ is regular if the equations (13.22) can be solved step by step. The following theorem gives the exact formulation:

THEOREM VIII.12. *The sections of the E_{n-m+q}'s of the alternating quantities*

$$\overset{q+1}{e}_{[\lambda_{q+1}}\cdots\overset{m}{e}_{\lambda_m]} \quad (q = 1,\ldots, m) \tag{13.33}$$

with the integral element-$\underset{0}{E}_m$ with the coordinates $\underset{0}{\xi}^\kappa$, $\underset{0}{U}{}^x_b$ with respect to the anholonomic system (h) form with $\underset{0}{\xi}^\kappa$ a regular chain $\underset{0}{E}_0,\ldots, \underset{0}{E}_m$ if and only if the following conditions are satisfied:

(1) *The equations*

$$\overset{\chi_0}{U} = 0 \quad (\chi_0 = 1,\ldots, \overset{0}{N}) \tag{13.34}$$

are in $\underset{0}{\xi}^\kappa$ regular of dimension $\mathfrak{r}_0$ and consequently $n-\mathfrak{r}_0$ of the ξ^κ (the principal ξ^κ) can be solved from (13.34) *as functions of the remaining ones (the parametrical ξ^κ).*

(2) *$n-q-\mathfrak{r}_q$ being the number of linearly independent equations among*

$$\overset{\chi_q}{U}_{i_1\ldots i_q}(\underset{0}{\xi}^\kappa)\underset{0}{U}{}^{i_1}_{\mathrm{1}}\cdots\underset{0}{U}{}^{i_{q-1}}_{\mathrm{q-1}}\,U^{i_q}_{\mathrm{q}} = 0 \quad (i_1,\ldots, i_q = 1,\ldots, \mathrm{n};\ \chi_q = 1,\ldots, \overset{q}{N}), \tag{13.35}$$

there exist among the equations in U^h_{q}

$$\overset{\chi_q}{U}_{i_1\ldots i_q}U^{i_1}_{\mathrm{1}}\cdots U^{i_{q-1}}_{\mathrm{q-1}}\,U^{i_q}_{\mathrm{q}} = 0 \quad (i_1,\ldots, i_q = 1,\ldots, \mathrm{n};\ \chi_q = 1,\ldots, \overset{q}{N})$$
$$(U^a_b = \delta^a_b) \tag{13.36}$$

for every value of $q = 1,\ldots, m$, after substitution of the solutions ξ^κ, $U^h_{\mathrm{1}},\ldots, U^h_{\mathrm{q-1}}$ of all equations with lower values of q, just $n-q-\mathfrak{r}_q$ equations linearly independent with respect to U^h_{q}, and consequently $n-q-\mathfrak{r}_q$ of the U^h_{q} (the principal U^h_{q}) can be solved from these $n-q-\mathfrak{r}_q$ equations as functions of the remaining ones (the parametrical U^h_{q}) and the parametrical ξ^κ, $U^h_{\mathrm{1}},\ldots, U^h_{\mathrm{q-1}}$.

(3) *If the solutions obtained are substituted in the equations remaining these equations are identically satisfied.*

If these conditions are satisfied we have

$$r_0 = \mathfrak{r}_0\,;\; r_{q+1} = \mathfrak{r}_{q+1} \quad (q = 0, \ldots, m-1) \tag{13.37}$$

and the variables ξ^κ, $U^x_{\mathfrak{b}}$ *can (after a suitable interchange of indices) be divided into*

Parametrical variables	*Principal variables*
$\xi^\alpha \quad (\alpha = 1, \ldots, \mathfrak{r}_0)$	$\xi^\zeta \quad (\zeta = \mathfrak{r}_0+1, \ldots, n)$
$U^{\alpha_q}_{\mathfrak{q}} \quad (\alpha_q = \mathrm{m}+1, \ldots, \mathrm{q}+\mathfrak{r}_q)$	$U^{\zeta_q}_{\mathfrak{q}} \quad (\zeta_q = \mathrm{q}+1+\mathfrak{r}_q, \ldots, \mathrm{n}\,;\; q = 1, \ldots, m)$

(13.38)

such that the principal variables can be solved from (13.34, 36) *as functions of the parametrical variables and in the expressions for* $U^{\zeta_q}_{q}$ *only the* ξ^α *and the parametrical variables* $U^{\alpha_t}_{\mathfrak{t}}$ *occur for all values* $t \leqslant q$.

Proof. Since the necessity of the conditions is proved only a proof of the sufficiency is required.

A general E_q $(q < m)$ in the neighbourhood of $\underset{0}{E}_q$ can be determined by the $n+q(n-q)$ non-supernumerary coordinates

$$\xi^\kappa, \quad V^{\mathfrak{x}}_{\mathfrak{b}}, \quad V^{\mathfrak{a}}_{\mathfrak{b}} = \delta^{\mathfrak{a}}_{\mathfrak{b}} \quad (\mathfrak{a}, \mathfrak{b} = 1, \ldots, \mathrm{q};\; \mathfrak{x} = \mathrm{q}+1, \ldots, \mathrm{n}) \tag{13.39}$$

with respect to the system (h). Using these coordinates the most general integral-E_q in the neighbourhood of $\underset{0}{E}_q$ is obtained by taking a solution of

$$\overset{\chi_q}{U}_{i_1 \ldots i_q} V^{i_1}_{1} \ldots V^{i_q}_{\mathfrak{q}} = 0 \quad (i_1, \ldots, i_q = 1, \ldots, \mathrm{n};\; \chi_q = 1, \ldots, \overset{q}{N}) \tag{13.40}$$

satisfying the conditions that $V^x_1, \ldots, V^x_{\mathfrak{q}}$ are sufficiently close to $\underset{0}{U}{}^x_1, \ldots, \underset{0}{U}{}^x_{\mathfrak{q}}$ $(x = \mathrm{m}+1, \ldots, \mathrm{n})$ and that $V^z_1, \ldots, V^z_{\mathfrak{q}}$ $(z = \mathrm{q}+1, \ldots, \mathrm{m})$ are sufficiently small. Now we prove first that the system (13.40) is regular for $\xi^\kappa = \underset{0}{\xi}{}^\kappa$, $V^x_{\mathfrak{b}} = \underset{0}{U}{}^x_{\mathfrak{b}}$, $V^z_{\mathfrak{b}} = 0$ $(\mathfrak{b} = 1, \ldots, \mathrm{q};\; z = \mathrm{q}+1, \ldots, \mathrm{m};\; x = \mathrm{m}+1, \ldots, \mathrm{n})$. According to our conditions the system (13.36) contains an equivalent sub-system of

$$\underset{0}{N}_q = n - \mathfrak{r}_0 + n - \mathfrak{r}_1 - 1 + \ldots + n - \mathfrak{r}_q - q \tag{13.41}$$

equations, minimal regular for $\xi^\kappa = \underset{0}{\xi}{}^\kappa$, $U^x_{\mathfrak{b}} = \underset{0}{U}{}^x_{\mathfrak{b}}$, from which the principal variables up to $U^{\zeta_q}_{q}$ can be solved as functions of the parametrical variables up to $U^{\alpha_q}_{q}$. Hence the *corresponding* equations of (13.40) form a system which is minimal regular for $\xi^\kappa = \underset{0}{\xi}{}^\kappa$, $V^x_{\mathfrak{b}} = \underset{0}{U}{}^x_{\mathfrak{b}}$, $V^z_{\mathfrak{b}} = 0$, and from this system the principal variables

$$\begin{aligned} &\xi^\zeta \quad (\zeta = \mathfrak{r}_0+1, \ldots, n) \\ &V^{\zeta_1}_{1}, \ldots, V^{\zeta_q}_{\mathfrak{q}} \quad (\zeta_1 = 2+\mathfrak{r}_1, \ldots, \mathrm{n};\; \ldots;\; \zeta_q = \mathrm{q}+1+\mathfrak{r}_q, \ldots, \mathrm{n}) \end{aligned} \tag{13.42}$$

can be solved in a neighbourhood of $\xi^\kappa = \underset{0}{\xi^\kappa}$, $V^x_{\mathfrak{b}} = \underset{0}{U^x_{\mathfrak{b}}}$, $V^z_{\mathfrak{b}} = 0$ as functions of the parametrical variables

$$\begin{array}{lll} (a) & \xi^\alpha & (\alpha = 1,\dots,\mathfrak{r}_0), \\ (b) & V^z_1,\dots,V^z_{\mathrm{q}} & (z = \mathrm{q}+1,\dots,\mathrm{m}), \\ (c) & V^{\alpha_1}_1,\dots,V^{\alpha_q}_{\mathrm{q}} & (\alpha_1 = \mathrm{m}+1,\dots,1+\mathfrak{r}_1;\ \dots;\ \alpha_q = \mathrm{m}+1,\dots,\mathrm{q}+\mathfrak{r}_q). \end{array} \tag{13.43}$$

Now, if we can prove that this sub-system of (13.40) is equivalent to (13.40) the regularity of (13.40) is proved. Suppose this were not the case. Then relations between the parametrical variables (13.43) would exist. If all variables (13.43 *b*) are replaced by zero the equations (13.40) represent a manifold with the dimension

$$\underset{0}{D_q} = \mathfrak{r}_0+\mathfrak{r}_1+1-m+\dots+\mathfrak{r}_q+q-m \tag{13.44}$$

in the manifold of all integral-E_q's in the neighbourhood of $\underset{0}{E_q}$, because for these values of the variables (13.43 *b*) according to our conditions no unsatisfied remaining equations exist. But there would exist unsatisfied remaining equations for at least one system of non-vanishing fixed values of these variables. Hence the dimension of the manifold of all integral-E_q's in the neighbourhood of $\underset{0}{E_q}$ which satisfy the equations (13.40) for these values of the variables (13.43 *b*) would be $D_q < \underset{0}{D_q}$. Among these E_q's all E_q's occur that can be obtained by the section of an integral-E_m, in the neighbourhood of $\underset{0}{E_m}$ with the coordinates ξ^κ, $v^{\kappa_1\dots\kappa_m}$, with the local E_{n-m+q} of the E_{n-m+q}-field determined by the vectors

$$\overset{(\mathrm{q}+1)'}{e_\lambda} = \overset{\mathrm{q}+1}{e_\lambda} - V^{\mathrm{q}+1}_{\mathfrak{b}} \overset{\mathfrak{b}}{e_\lambda},\quad \dots,\quad \overset{\mathrm{m}'}{e_\lambda} = \overset{\mathrm{m}}{e_\lambda} - V^{\mathrm{m}}_{\mathfrak{b}} \overset{\mathfrak{b}}{e_\lambda} \quad (\mathfrak{b} = 1,\dots,\mathrm{q}). \tag{13.45}$$

Hence, if

$$\begin{aligned} v^{\kappa_1\dots\kappa_m} &= v^{\kappa_1\dots\kappa_m}(\xi^\alpha, \eta^k) \quad (\alpha = 1,\dots,\mathfrak{r}_0;\ k = \bar{1},\dots,\bar{d}), \\ \xi^\kappa &= f^\kappa(\xi^\alpha) \end{aligned} \tag{13.46}$$

is a parametric form† of the manifold of all integral-E_m's in the neighbourhood of $\underset{0}{E_m}$ with the parameters ξ^α, η^k, the equations

$$\begin{aligned} v^{\kappa_1\dots\kappa_q} &= \overset{(\mathrm{q}+1)'}{e_{\kappa_{q+1}}} \dots \overset{\mathrm{m}'}{e_{\kappa_m}} v^{\kappa_1\dots\kappa_m}(\xi^\alpha, \eta^k) \quad (k = \bar{1},\dots,\bar{d};\ \alpha = 1,\dots,\mathfrak{r}_0), \\ \xi^\kappa &= f^\kappa(\xi^\alpha) \end{aligned} \tag{13.47}$$

constitute a parametric form of the manifold of all these special

† The existence of such a form can be proved readily from the conditions (1, 2, 3) of Theorem VIII.12.

integral-E_q's under consideration. The dimension of this manifold is the rank of the matrix of the derivatives of $v^{\kappa_1 \dots \kappa_q}$, ξ^κ with respect to ξ^α, η^k, and is $\leqslant D_q$. Now we know that for sufficiently small values of the $V^{\mathfrak{z}}_{\mathfrak{b}}$ this rank can have only those values which are equal to or greater than the value for $V^{\mathfrak{z}}_{\mathfrak{b}} = 0$. Hence $D_q \geqslant \underset{0}{D_q}$ and that proves that $D_q = \underset{0}{D_q}$ and that consequently no relations can exist between the parametrical variables.

Now we still have to prove that $\underset{0}{E_q}$ $(q < m)$ is regular, i.e. that $\underset{0}{E_q}$ is contained in as many integral-E_{q+1}'s as every neighbouring E_q. Let a neighbouring E_q be spanned by the vectors $W^h_{\mathfrak{1}}, \dots, W^h_{\mathfrak{q}}$ not necessarily satisfying the condition $W^{\mathfrak{a}}_{\mathfrak{b}} = \delta^{\mathfrak{a}}_{\mathfrak{b}}$ $(\mathfrak{a}, \mathfrak{b} = 1, \dots, \mathrm{q})$. Let

$$'\overset{\chi'_q}{U}_{i_1 \dots i_q} V^{i_1}_{\mathfrak{1}} \dots V^{i_q}_{\mathfrak{q}} = 0 \quad (i_1, \dots, i_q = 1, \dots, \mathrm{n};\ \chi'_q = 1, \dots, \underset{0}{N_q}) \tag{13.48}$$

be the sub-system of (13.40) of $\underset{0}{N_q}$ equations minimal regular of dimension $\underset{0}{D_q}$ in $\xi^\kappa = \underset{0}{\xi^\kappa}$, $V^{\mathfrak{x}}_{\mathfrak{b}} = \underset{0}{U^{\mathfrak{x}}_{\mathfrak{b}}}$, $V^{\mathfrak{z}}_{\mathfrak{b}} = 0$, constructed above. Then, since the equations

$$V^{\mathfrak{a}}_{\mathfrak{b}} = 0 \quad (\mathfrak{a}, \mathfrak{b} = 1, \dots, \mathrm{q}) \tag{13.49}$$

are regular, it follows from Theorem II.10 that the system (13.48) is minimal regular of dimension $\underset{0}{D_q} + q^2$ in $\xi^\kappa = \underset{0}{\xi^\kappa}$, $V^{\mathfrak{a}}_{\mathfrak{b}} = 0$, $V^{\mathfrak{x}}_{\mathfrak{b}} = \underset{0}{U^{\mathfrak{x}}_{\mathfrak{b}}}$, $V^{\mathfrak{z}}_{\mathfrak{b}} = 0$ if the $V^{\mathfrak{a}}_{\mathfrak{b}}$ are looked upon as free variables (cf. the proof of Theorem VIII.6 in VIII, § 8) and this implies that the system

$$'\overset{\chi'_q}{U}_{i_1 \dots i_q} W^{i_1}_{\mathfrak{1}} \dots W^{i_q}_{\mathfrak{q}} = 0 \quad (i_1, \dots, i_q = 1, \dots, \mathrm{n};\ \chi'_q = 1, \dots, \underset{0}{N_q}) \tag{13.50}$$

is minimal regular of dimension $\underset{0}{D_q} + q^2$ in $\xi^\kappa = \underset{0}{\xi^\kappa}$, $W^{\mathfrak{a}}_{\mathfrak{b}} = 0$, $W^{\mathfrak{x}}_{\mathfrak{b}} = \underset{0}{U^{\mathfrak{x}}_{\mathfrak{b}}}$, $W^{\mathfrak{z}}_{\mathfrak{b}} = 0$. In the same way a minimal regular system of $\underset{0}{N_{q+1}}$ equations in $W^h_{\mathfrak{1}}, \dots, W^h_{\mathfrak{q}+1}$ exists for the integral-E_{q+1}'s and this system contains (13.50) as a sub-system. The remaining

$$\underset{0}{N_{q+1}} - \underset{0}{N_q} = n - \mathfrak{r}_{q+1} - q - 1 \tag{13.51}$$

equations are linear in the $W^h_{\mathfrak{q}+1}$ and linearly independent. They determine the $H(E_q)$ for an arbitrary E_q in the neighbourhood of $\underset{0}{E_q}$. Hence the dimension of $H(E_q)$ is $q + 1 + \mathfrak{r}_{q+1}$ and this proves that $\underset{0}{E_q}$ is regular and $r_{q+1} = \mathfrak{r}_{q+1}$ $(q = 0, \dots, m-1)$. The division into parametrical variables and principal variables (13.38) can be obtained as on p. 405.

If the chain intersected by (13.33) is not regular another system $\overset{1'}{e}_\lambda,\ldots,\overset{n'}{e}_\lambda$ has to be taken. For the special Cartan systems dealt with in the next section it is possible to take into consideration at once all possible systems $\overset{1'}{e}_\lambda,\ldots,\overset{n'}{e}_\lambda$.

14. Special Cartan systems†

A special kind of Cartan system occurs if the theory of Cartan-Kähler is applied to the integration of a system of partial differential equations (cf. X, § 1). These systems, called *SC*-systems (*special Cartan systems*) have the form

$$\begin{aligned} &\overset{\chi_0}{u} && (\chi_0 = 1,\ldots,N_0),\\ &\overset{\chi_1}{u}_\lambda && (\chi_1 = 1,\ldots,N_1),\\ &\overset{\chi_2}{u}_{\mu\lambda} && (\chi_2 = 1,\ldots,N_2) \end{aligned} \tag{14.1}$$

satisfying the conditions:

(1) *the system*

$$\overset{\chi_0}{u} = 0 \quad (\chi_0 = 1,\ldots,N_0) \tag{14.2}$$

is regular of dimension r_0 *in the null point* $\underset{0}{\xi}^\kappa$;

(2) *the* $\overset{\chi_1}{u}_\lambda$ *are linearly independent and the gradients* $\partial_\lambda \overset{\chi_0}{u}$ *depend linearly on them at the null points of* (14.2);

(3) *the* $\overset{\chi_2}{u}_{\mu\lambda}$ *are linearly independent and the rotations* $\partial_{[\mu}\overset{\chi_1}{u}_{\lambda]}$ *depend linearly on them and vice versa at the null points of* (14.2);

(4) *a set of m linearly independent covariant vector fields* $\overset{1}{e}_\lambda,\ldots,\overset{m}{e}_\lambda$ (*not necessarily gradients*) *exists, such that*

$$\overset{\chi_2}{u}_{\mu\lambda} = 2\underset{b}{\overset{\chi_2\, b}{p}}_{[\mu}\, e_{\lambda]} \quad (b = 1,\ldots,\mathrm{m};\ \chi_2 = 1,\ldots,N_2). \tag{14.3}$$

The condition (4) means, geometrically, that there exists an E_{n-m}-field such that the sections of the $\overset{\chi_2}{u}_{\mu\lambda}$ with the local E_{n-m} of this field vanish at all points.

Now we need the integral-X_m's through $\underset{0}{\xi}^\kappa$, whose section with $\overset{1}{e}_{[\lambda_1}\ldots\overset{m}{e}_{\lambda_m]}$ does not vanish. The coordinates ξ^κ, $v^{\kappa_1\ldots\kappa_m}$ of the integral-E_m's

† E. Cartan 1904. 1, pp. 159 ff.; E. Kähler 1934. 1, pp. 51 ff. Kähler defines special Goursat systems. The only difference is that among the $\overset{\chi_2}{u}_{\mu\lambda}$ other bivectors with vanishing rotations may occur. The other conditions are the same. We restrict ourselves here to the special Cartan systems because the integration of systems of partial differential equations always leads to such a system (cf. X, § 1).

are the solutions of the equations

$$(a)\qquad \overset{\chi_0}{u} = 0$$

$$(b)\qquad \overset{\chi_1}{u}_{\lambda_1} v^{\lambda_1\ldots\lambda_m} = 0 \qquad (\chi_0 = 1,\ldots, N_0;\ \chi_1 = 1,\ldots, N_1;$$

$$\chi_2 = 1,\ldots, N_2), \quad (14.4)$$

$$(c)\qquad \overset{\chi_2}{u}_{\lambda_1\lambda_2} v^{\lambda_1\ldots\lambda_m} = 0$$

satisfying the conditions

$$v^{\lambda_1\ldots\lambda_m} \overset{1}{e}_{\lambda_1}\ldots\overset{m}{e}_{\lambda_m} \neq 0. \qquad (14.5)$$

We must decide whether there are regular chains of $m+1$ elements in these E_m's.

It is possible that, as a consequence of (14.4a) there are linear relations between the $\overset{\chi_1}{u}_\lambda$ and the $\overset{b}{e}_\lambda$ ($b = 1,\ldots, m$)

$$\underset{\chi_1}{\alpha}\overset{\chi_1}{u}_\lambda + \underset{b}{\beta}\overset{b}{e}_\lambda = 0 \quad (b = 1,\ldots, m;\ \chi_1 = 1,\ldots, N_1) \qquad (14.6)$$

with at least one non-vanishing coefficient $\underset{b}{\beta}$. In that case it follows from (14.4b) that

$$\underset{b}{\beta}\overset{b}{e}_{\lambda_1} v^{\lambda_1\ldots\lambda_m} = 0 \quad (b = 1,\ldots, m), \qquad (14.7)$$

and according to (14.5) this is only possible if

$$\underset{b}{\beta} = 0 \quad (b = 1,\ldots, m). \qquad (14.8)$$

If the system (14.4a, 14.8) has no solutions, no integral-X_m's exist. If this system is not regular at $\underset{0}{\xi}^\kappa$ it can be replaced by a finite number of systems (cf. II, Ex. 10), minimal regular at $\underset{0}{\xi}^\kappa$ or at a point of $\mathfrak{N}(\underset{0}{\xi}^\kappa)$. Each set of scalars thus obtained gives, in combination with its gradients, the vectors among the $\overset{\chi_1}{u}_\lambda$ linearly independent of these gradients at the null points of the set, and the bivectors (14.3) an SC-system. If in one of these SC-systems there exists a linear relation between the $\overset{b}{e}_\lambda$ and its $\overset{\chi_1}{u}_\lambda$ at the null points of the scalar equations, this system can be dealt with in the same way, etc. Finally, we either arrive at the conclusion that there are no integral X_m's or we get a finite number of SC-systems such that in each of them no linear relation between the $\overset{b}{e}_\lambda$ and the $\overset{\chi_1}{u}_\lambda$ exists at the null points of its scalar equations. From this we see that we may assume that the SC-system satisfies the four conditions already mentioned and the fifth condition

(5) *the* $\overset{\chi_1}{u}_\lambda$ *and* $\overset{b}{e}_\lambda$ *are linearly independent at* $\underset{0}{\xi}^\kappa$ *and therefore in an* $\mathfrak{N}(\underset{0}{\xi}^\kappa)$.

A Cartan system satisfying these five conditions will be called an RSC-system (*reduced special Cartan system*).

It is convenient to choose an anholonomic system (cf. II, § 6) $\overset{h}{e}_\lambda$ $(h = 1,\dots, \mathrm{n})$ in $\mathfrak{N}(\underset{0}{\xi}^\kappa)$ in such a way that the RSC-system takes the form

$$\begin{aligned} &\overset{\chi_0}{u} \quad (\chi_0 = 1,\dots, N_0),\\ &\overset{\mathfrak{x}}{e}_\lambda \quad (\mathfrak{x} = \mathrm{r}+1,\dots,\mathrm{n}),\\ &\overset{\chi}{p}_{b[\mu}\overset{b}{e}_{\lambda]} \quad (\chi = 1,\dots, P;\ P \leqslant n-r;\ b = 1,\dots,\mathrm{m};\ m \leqslant r). \end{aligned} \tag{14.9}$$

Now let $\underset{0}{E}_m$ be an integral-E_m in $\underset{0}{\xi}^\kappa$ satisfying the condition (14.5). Then we first investigate whether possibly the alternating quantities

$$\overset{\mathrm{q}+1}{e}_{[\lambda_{q+1}}\cdots\overset{\mathrm{m}}{e}_{\lambda_m]} \quad (q = 1,\dots,\mathrm{m}) \tag{14.10}$$

determine a regular chain in $\underset{0}{E}_m$ (cf. VIII, § 13, indirect method B). As before we introduce the coordinates $\underset{0}{\xi}^\kappa$, $\underset{0}{U}{}^h_b$, $\underset{0}{U}{}^a_b = \delta^a_b$ for $\underset{0}{E}_m$, and ξ^κ, U^h_b, $U^a_b = \delta^a_b$ for all neighbouring E_m's. The first set of equations

$$\overset{\chi_0}{u} = 0 \quad (\chi_0 = 1,\dots, N_0) \tag{14.11}$$

is regular in $\underset{0}{\xi}^\kappa$ and represents an X_{r_0} in $\mathfrak{N}(\underset{0}{\xi}^\kappa)$. The second set is here

$$\left.\begin{aligned} \overset{\chi_0}{u} &= 0\\ U^{\mathfrak{x}}_1 &= 0 \end{aligned}\right. \quad (\chi_0 = 1,\dots, N_0;\ \mathfrak{x} = \mathrm{r}+1,\dots,\mathrm{n}), \tag{14.12}$$

and consequently we have

$$r_1 = r-1. \tag{14.13}$$

The third set is

$$\begin{aligned} &(a) & \overset{\chi_0}{u} &= 0 & &(\chi_0 = 1,\dots, N_0;\ \mathfrak{x} = \mathrm{r}+1,\dots,\mathrm{n};\\ &(b) & U^{\mathfrak{x}}_1 = 0,\ \ U^{\mathfrak{x}}_2 &= 0 & &\chi = 1,\dots, P;\ b = 1,\dots,\mathrm{m};\\ &(c) & (\overset{\chi}{p}_{bi_1}\overset{b}{e}_{i_2} - \overset{\chi}{p}_{bi_2}\overset{b}{e}_{i_1})U^{i_1}_1 U^{i_2}_2 &= 0 & &i_1, i_2 = 1,\dots,\mathrm{n}). \end{aligned} \tag{14.14}$$

By using (14.14b) the equations (14.14c) can be put into the simpler form

$$\overset{\chi}{p}_{21} - \overset{\chi}{p}_{12} + \overset{\chi}{p}_{2\mathfrak{m}}U^{\mathfrak{m}}_1 - \overset{\chi}{p}_{1\mathfrak{m}}U^{\mathfrak{m}}_2 = 0 \quad (\chi = 1,\dots, P;\ \mathfrak{m} = \mathrm{m}+1,\dots,\mathrm{r}). \tag{14.15}$$

Continuing in this way we find at last for the equations of the last set, *containing all former sets:*

$$\begin{aligned} &\overset{\chi_0}{u} = 0 && (\chi_0 = 1,\ldots,N_0;\ b,c = 1,\ldots,\mathrm{m};\ b < c; \\ &U^{\mathfrak{x}}_{c} = 0 && \quad \mathfrak{x} = \mathrm{r}+1,\ldots,\mathrm{n};\ \chi = 1,\ldots,P; \\ &\overset{\chi}{p}_{[cb]} + \overset{\chi}{p}_{[c|\mathfrak{m}|} U^{\mathfrak{m}}_{b]} = 0 && \quad \mathfrak{m} = \mathrm{m}+1,\ldots,\mathrm{r}). \end{aligned} \tag{14.16}$$

The equations not containing $U^{x}_{\mathrm{q}+1},\ldots, U^{x}_{\mathrm{m}}$ $(x = \mathrm{m}+1,\ldots,\mathrm{n})$ together form the $(q+1)$th set. The equations of this set necessary for the determination of the U^{x}_{q} are

$$\begin{aligned} &U^{\mathfrak{x}}_{\mathrm{q}} = 0 && (\mathfrak{b} = 1,\ldots,\mathrm{q}-1;\ \mathfrak{m} = \mathrm{m}+1,\ldots,\mathrm{r}; \\ &\overset{\chi}{p}_{\mathfrak{b}\mathfrak{m}} U^{\mathfrak{m}}_{\mathrm{q}} = \overset{\chi}{p}_{\mathrm{q}\mathfrak{b}} - \overset{\chi}{p}_{\mathfrak{b}\mathrm{q}} + \overset{\chi}{p}_{\mathrm{q}\mathfrak{m}} U^{\mathfrak{m}}_{\mathfrak{b}} && \quad \mathfrak{x} = \mathrm{r}+1,\ldots,\mathrm{n};\ \chi = 1,\ldots,P). \end{aligned} \tag{14.17}$$

It is convenient to denote the $\mathfrak{m}$-rank of the system $\overset{\chi}{p}_{\mathfrak{b}\mathfrak{m}}$ $(\mathfrak{b} = 1,\ldots,\mathrm{q})$ for $\xi^\kappa = \underset{0}{\xi}{}^\kappa$ and for every choice of q by

$$\sigma_1 + \ldots + \sigma_q. \tag{14.18}$$

Then the number of linearly independent equations of (14.17) is

$$n - r + \sigma_1 + \ldots + \sigma_{q-1} \tag{14.19}$$

and the total number of linearly independent equations for the determination of the U^{x}_{b} for all values of $b = 1,\ldots,\mathrm{m}$ is for $\xi^\kappa = \underset{0}{\xi}{}^\kappa$ equal to

$$N_0 \overset{\text{def}}{=} m(n-r) + (m-1)\sigma_1 + (m-2)\sigma_2 + \ldots + \sigma_{m-1}. \tag{14.20}$$

If now N is the total number of independent equations in $\mathfrak{N}(\underset{0}{\xi}{}^\kappa)$ among (14.16), we have

$$N \geqslant n - r_0 + m(n-r) + (m-1)\sigma_1 + (m-2)\sigma_2 + \ldots + \sigma_{m-1} \tag{14.21}$$

and, because of Theorem VIII.12, the chain determined by (14.10) is regular if and only if in (14.21) the equality sign holds. If the sign $>$ holds this can be due to the unfavourable situation of the vectors $\overset{1}{e}_\lambda,\ldots, \overset{\mathrm{m}}{e}_\lambda$. Then we have to choose another set of linearly independent vectors $\overset{h'}{e}_\lambda$:

$$\begin{aligned} &\overset{a'}{e}_\lambda = \overset{-1}{P}{}^{a'}_{a} \overset{a}{e}_\lambda, \quad \overset{a}{e}_\lambda = P^{a}_{a'} \overset{a'}{e}_\lambda \quad (a = 1,\ldots,\mathrm{m};\ a' = 1',\ldots,\mathrm{m}'), \\ &\overset{x'}{e}_\lambda = \delta^{x'}_{x} \overset{x}{e}_\lambda \quad (x = \mathrm{m}+1,\ldots,\mathrm{n};\ x' = (\mathrm{m}+1)',\ldots,\mathrm{n}'). \end{aligned} \tag{14.22}$$

The U^{x}_{b} and the $\overset{\chi}{p}_{cb}$ transform in the following way

$$\begin{aligned} &U^{x'}_{b'} = \delta^{x'}_{x} P^{b}_{b'} U^{x}_{b} && (b,c = 1,\ldots,\mathrm{m};\ x = \mathrm{m}+1,\ldots,\mathrm{n};\ b',c' = 1',\ldots,\mathrm{m}'; \\ &\overset{\chi}{p}_{c'b'} = P^{c}_{c'} P^{b}_{b'} \overset{\chi}{p}_{cb} && \quad x' = (\mathrm{m}+1)',\ldots,\mathrm{n}';\ \chi = 1,\ldots,P;\ \mathfrak{m} = \mathrm{m}+1,\ldots,\mathrm{r}; \\ &\overset{\chi}{p}_{c'\mathfrak{m}'} = P^{c}_{c'} \overset{\chi}{p}_{c\mathfrak{m}} \delta^{\mathfrak{m}}_{\mathfrak{m}'} && \quad \mathfrak{m}' = (\mathrm{m}+1)',\ldots,\mathrm{r}'). \end{aligned} \tag{14.23}$$

and consequently the equations (14.16) change into

$$
\begin{array}{lll}
(a) & \overset{\chi_0}{u} = 0 & (b,c = 1,\ldots,m;\ b',c' = 1',\ldots,m'; \\
(b) & U^{\mathfrak{x}'}_{b'} = 0 & \mathfrak{m} = m+1,\ldots,r;\ \mathfrak{m}' = (m+1)',\ldots,r' \\
(c) & \overset{\chi}{p}_{[c'b']}+\delta^{\mathfrak{m}}_{\mathfrak{m}'}\overset{\chi}{p}_{c\mathfrak{m}}P^{c}_{[c'}U^{\mathfrak{m}'}_{b']} = 0 & \mathfrak{x}' = (r+1)',\ldots,n';\ \chi = 1,\ldots,P).
\end{array}
\tag{14.24}
$$

Hence the equations necessary for the determination of the $U^{x'}_{q'}$ are (cf. (14.17))

$$U^{\mathfrak{x}'}_{q'} = 0,$$

$$\delta^{\mathfrak{m}}_{\mathfrak{m}'}\overset{\chi}{p}_{b\mathfrak{m}}U^{\mathfrak{m}'}_{q'}P^{b}_{\mathfrak{b}'} = \overset{\chi}{p}_{q'\mathfrak{b}'}-\overset{\chi}{p}_{\mathfrak{b}'q'}+\overset{\chi}{p}_{q'\mathfrak{m}'}U^{\mathfrak{m}'}_{\mathfrak{b}'}$$

$$(b = 1,\ldots,m;\ \mathfrak{b}' = 1',\ldots,(q-1)';\ \mathfrak{m} = m+1,\ldots,r;$$
$$\mathfrak{m}' = (m+1)',\ldots,r';\ \mathfrak{x}' = (r+1)',\ldots,n';\ \chi = 1,\ldots,P). \tag{14.25}$$

Now let

$$\sigma'_1+\ldots+\sigma'_q \tag{14.26}$$

be the $\mathfrak{m}$-rank of the system

$$P^{b}_{\mathfrak{b}'}\overset{\chi}{p}_{b\mathfrak{m}} \quad (b = 1,\ldots,m;\ \mathfrak{b}' = 1',\ldots,q';$$
$$\mathfrak{m} = m+1,\ldots,r;\ \chi = 1,\ldots,P) \tag{14.27}$$

for $\xi^\kappa = \underset{0}{\xi^\kappa}$ and for every value of q, looking upon the $P^{b}_{\mathfrak{b}'}$ as parameters, i.e. the maximum value the $\mathfrak{m}$-rank of the system (14.27) can take if the $P^{b}_{\mathfrak{b}'}$ are chosen in a suitable way. Obviously

$$\sigma'_1+\ldots+\sigma'_m = \sigma_1+\ldots+\sigma_m. \tag{14.28}$$

If then N' is the total number of independent equations in $\mathfrak{N}(\underset{0}{\xi^\kappa})$ among (14.24), regular chains exist in every integral-E_m in a sufficiently small neighbourhood of $\underset{0}{E_m}$ if and only if in the relations

$$N' \geqslant N'_0, \quad N'_0 \overset{\text{def}}{=} n-r_0+m(n-r)+(m-1)\sigma'_1+(m-2)\sigma'_2+\ldots+\sigma'_{m-1} \tag{14.29}$$

the equality sign holds.

If there are no regular chains with $m+1$ elements in $\underset{0}{\xi^\kappa}$, it may happen that there are regular chains at other points of the manifold $\overset{\chi_0}{u} = 0$. Now if we substitute $\xi^{r_0+1},\ldots,\xi^n$, solved from (14.24 a) (if necessary after suitable interchange of the indices κ) as functions of $\xi^1,\ldots,\xi^{r_0}$, in (14.24 b,c), the system obtained has a rank N'_0-n+r_0 in $\underset{0}{\xi^\kappa}$ and a rank $\geqslant N'_0-n+r_0$ in $\mathfrak{N}(\underset{0}{\xi^\kappa})$. This system is linear and therefore regular in $\xi^\kappa = \underset{0}{\xi^\kappa}$ for arbitrary values of the $U^{x'}_{b'}$ if and only if $N' = N'_0$. Since the system (14.24 a) is regular in $\underset{0}{\xi^\kappa}$, the whole system

(14.24) is regular in $\underset{0}{\xi}^{\kappa}$ for arbitrary values of the $U_{b'}^{x'}$ if and only if $N' = N'_0$ (cf. II, § 8, Theorem II.9). This implies that the integral-E_m's in the neighbourhood of $\underset{0}{E}_m$ contain regular chains with $m+1$ elements if and only if the system (14.24) is regular in $\underset{0}{\xi}^{\kappa}$ for arbitrary values of $U_{b'}^{x'}$. Hence, if M is the manifold of all points in $\mathfrak{N}(\underset{0}{\xi}^{\kappa})$ where the system (14.24) is *not* regular, there are regular chains with $m+1$ elements in all points of the manifold $\overset{x_0}{u} = 0$ not belonging to M.

Collecting results we get the theorem

THEOREM VIII.13. *An RSC-system of the form* (14.9) *has regular integral-X_m's whose section with $\overset{1}{e}_{[\lambda_1} \dots \overset{m}{e}_{\lambda_m]}$ does not vanish if and only if there exist points of the X_{r_0} with the equations* (14.24 *a*), *where the equations* (14.24) (*with indefinite $P_{b'}^{a}$*) *are regular.*

In the above considerations we have not used the possibility of reducing the Cartan system to a scalar-free system. If this is done the result is even more simple, because in this case regular integral-X_m's exist if and only if there exist points in $\mathfrak{N}(\underset{0}{\xi}^{\kappa})$ where (14.24) is regular.

If there are regular chains with $m+1$ elements in $\underset{0}{\xi}^{\kappa}$, such a chain can be easily constructed by giving the $P_{b'}^{a}$ suitable constant values. Then the general integral-X_m in $\mathfrak{N}(\underset{0}{\xi}^{\kappa})$ can be constructed by means of the method described in VIII, § 9.

Since the ξ^{κ}, U_b^x are $n+m(n-m)$ non-supernumerary coordinates of the E_m, the number of parameters of the general integral-E_m in the neighbourhood of $\underset{0}{\xi}^{\kappa}$ is $n+m(n-m)-N'$. Because of (14.29)

$$n+m(n-m)-N' \leqslant r_0+m(r-m)-(m-1)\sigma'_1-(m-2)\sigma'_2-\dots-\sigma'_{m-1} \tag{14.30}$$

and the equality sign holds if and only if there exist regular chains with $m+1$ elements. This proves the theorem†

THEOREM VIII.14. *The genus* g *for the integral-*X_m*'s of an* RSC*-system of the form* (14.9) *whose section with* $\overset{1}{e}_{[\lambda_1}\cdots\overset{m}{e}_{\lambda_m]}$ *does not vanish, is* $\geqslant m$ *if and only if there exist points on the* X_{r_0} *with the equations* (14.24 a) *in whose neighbourhood the number of parameters on which the general integral-*E_m*, whose section with* $\overset{1}{e}_{[\lambda_1}\cdots\overset{m}{e}_{\lambda_m]}$ *does not vanish, depends is equal to*

$$r_0+m(r-m)-(m-1)\sigma'_1-(m-2)\sigma'_2-\ldots-\sigma'_{m-1}. \qquad (14.31)$$

EXERCISES‡

1. Prove that the system

$$\begin{aligned} r &= R(x,y,z,p,q,s) \\ t &= T(x,y,z,p,q,s) \end{aligned} \quad \left(p=\frac{\partial z}{\partial x},\ q=\frac{\partial z}{\partial y},\ r=\frac{\partial^2 z}{\partial x^2},\ s=\frac{\partial^2 z}{\partial x\partial y},\ t=\frac{\partial^2 z}{\partial y^2}\right) \qquad (1\alpha)$$

is connected with an E_3-field in the X_6 of x, y, z, p, q, s and that the class of this field is 5 or 6 if the matrix

$$\left\|\begin{matrix} YR & R_s & 1 \\ -XT & 1 & T_s \end{matrix}\right\| \quad \left(\begin{aligned} Xf &\overset{\text{def}}{=} \frac{\partial f}{\partial x}+p\frac{\partial f}{\partial z}+s\frac{\partial f}{\partial q}+R\frac{\partial f}{\partial p}; \\ Yf &\overset{\text{def}}{=} \frac{\partial f}{\partial y}+q\frac{\partial f}{\partial z}+s\frac{\partial f}{\partial p}+T\frac{\partial f}{\partial q} \end{aligned}\right) \qquad (1\beta)$$

has rank 1 or 2 respectively. Prove that, if the class is 5, the characteristic X_1's of the E_3-field are determined by the equations

$$\begin{aligned} dz &= p\,dx+q\,dy, & ds &= YR\,dx, \\ dp &= R\,dx+s\,dy, & dy+R_s\,dx &= 0.\S \\ dq &= s\,dx+T\,dy, \end{aligned} \qquad (1\gamma)$$

2. Solve the system (Ex. VIII (1 α)).

3. Prove that the Cartan system

$$\begin{array}{llll} C_\lambda^{r+1} : \overline{1}, & & & \\ \cdot\ \cdot\ \cdot\ \cdot\ \cdot & & & \\ C_\lambda^{n-t} : \overline{q-t} \quad (q=n-r), & & & \\ C_\lambda^{n-t+1} : \overline{q-t+1}-\xi^{q-t+2}\overline{n}, & & C_{\mu\lambda}^{\cdot\cdot\,n-t+1} : -\overline{q-t+2}\,\overline{n}, & \\ \cdot\ \cdot\ \cdot\ \cdot\ \cdot\ \cdot\ \cdot\ \cdot & & \cdot\ \cdot\ \cdot\ \cdot\ \cdot\ \cdot\ \cdot & \\ C_\lambda^{n} : \overline{q}-\xi^{q+1}\overline{n}, & & C_{\mu\lambda}^{\cdot\cdot\,n} : -\overline{q+1}\,\overline{n} & \end{array} \qquad (3\alpha)$$

has a genus $g=r-1$ and determine the integral-X_{r-1}'s.

4. Prove that the equation

$$F(x,y,z,p,q,r,s,t)=0 \qquad (4\alpha)$$

† Cf. Cartan 1904. 1, p. 162.

‡ Cf. the suggestions at the end of the book.

§ Goursat 1922, 1, p. 276.

is connected with an E_4-field in an X_7 in the X_8 of x, y, z, p, q, r, s, t and that the genus of the corresponding Cartan system is 2. Determine the non-regular integral-E_1's.†

5. The only one-to-one contact transformations of the one-dimensional elements of order n in an X_2 are the extended C_1-transformations of the elements of order 1.

6. If the Goursat system

$$\begin{array}{ll} \overset{\chi_0}{u} & (\chi_0 = 1,\dots,N_0), \\ \overset{\chi_1}{u}_{\lambda_1} & (\chi_1 = 1,\dots,N_1), \\ \cdot\;\cdot\;\cdot & \cdot\;\cdot\;\cdot\;\cdot \\ \overset{\chi_\sigma}{u}_{\lambda_1\dots\lambda_\sigma} & (\chi_\sigma = 1,\dots,N_\sigma) \end{array} \tag{6α}$$

is closed and if K is the λ_1-rank of the quantities (6α), all quantities of the system can be expressed in terms of K and not less than K variables and their gradients. K is the generalization of the class K of a covariant q-vector defined in V, § 2.

7. All alternating quantities that can be written as a sum of terms each containing at least one quantity of the closed Goursat system (VIII, Ex. (6α)) as a factor form the *ring* of the system. If among the equations, linear in v^κ, expressing that the quantities

$$v^{\lambda_1}\overset{\chi_\rho}{u}_{\lambda_1\dots\lambda_\rho} \quad (\rho = 1,\dots,\sigma;\ \chi_\rho = 1,\dots,N_\rho) \tag{7α}$$

belong to the ring of the system, there are just n' linear independent ones, the Goursat system is equivalent (= having the same integral-X_m's for all values of m) to a system containing only those quantities which are expressible in terms of n' variables and their gradients. n' is the invariant occurring in VIII, § 10, and the generalization of the similarity class k of a covariant q-vector, defined in V, § 2.‡

† Cartan 1946. 1, p. 81.

‡ Cf. Cartan 1946. 1, p. 52. Kähler 1934. 1 uses the term *Differentialideal* and Cartan 1946. 1 the term *anneau*. The 'class' of Cartan is our similarity class.

IX

THEORY OF $\mathfrak{S}_d^m$-FIELDS†

1. Introduction

AN E_m through the contact point in the local E_n of ξ^κ can be given by one of its connecting quantities B_b^κ or C_λ^x or by the pseudo m-vector $\lfloor v^{\kappa_1\ldots\kappa_m}\rfloor$, $v^{\kappa_1\ldots\kappa_m}$ being defined by

$$v^{\kappa_1\ldots\kappa_m} = B_1^{[\kappa_1}\ldots B_m^{\kappa_m]} \tag{1.1}$$

and satisfying the conditions

$$v^{[\kappa_1\ldots\kappa_m}\, v^{\lambda_1]\ldots\lambda_m} = 0. \tag{1.2}$$

The $v^{\kappa_1\ldots\kappa_m}$ can be looked upon as projective coordinates (*Grassmannian* coordinates) in an $\left\{\binom{n}{m}-1\right\}$-dimensional flat space $\mathfrak{P}^m(\xi^\kappa)$ and the equation (1.2) represents an $m(n-m)$-dimensional manifold $\mathfrak{S}^m(\xi^\kappa)$ in this $\mathfrak{P}^m(\xi^\kappa)$ whose points are in one-to-one correspondence to the E_m's under consideration. In this $\mathfrak{S}^m$ the $v^{\kappa_1\ldots\kappa_m}$ are supernumerary coordinates with $\epsilon_1 = \binom{n}{m}-m(n-m)-1$; $\epsilon_2 = 1$ and the B_b^κ and C_λ^x are supernumerary coordinates with $\epsilon_1 = 0$, $\epsilon_2 = m^2$, and $\epsilon_1 = 0$, $\epsilon_2 = (n-m)^2$ respectively (cf. II, §§ 9 and 10). An X_d in this $\mathfrak{S}^m$ will be called an $\mathfrak{S}_d^m$ (cf. VII, § 1).

If an $\mathfrak{S}_d^m$ is given in each point of an X_p in X_n we get an $\mathfrak{S}_d^m$-*field* with *field dimension* p. A Goursat system defines an $\mathfrak{S}_d^m$-field for every value of m for which the equations VIII (5.2) are compatible. Since the equations VIII (5.2) are all linear in $v^{\kappa_1\ldots\kappa_m}$ except VIII (5.2c) these $\mathfrak{S}_d^m$-fields are of a special kind. We call them *quasi-linear*. In this chapter we consider general $\mathfrak{S}_d^m$-fields.

Every X_m in X_n whose tangent-E_m at every point belongs to the $\mathfrak{S}_d^m$-field is said to be an *integral-X_m of the $\mathfrak{S}_d^m$-field*. The problem to be investigated is the determination of the integral-X_m's of a given $\mathfrak{S}_d^m$-field. This problem is a generalization of the problem of the determination of the integral-X_m's of a Goursat system solved in Chapter VIII for the case of regular integral-X_m's.

If an $\mathfrak{S}_d^m$-field has a field dimension $M \leqslant n$ every integral-X_m is contained in the field region X_M. Hence the only E_m's of the $\mathfrak{S}_d^m$-field that need to be considered are the E_m's at points of this X_M contained in the tangent-E_M at these points. They constitute an $\mathfrak{S}_{d'}^m$-field in X_M

† Cf. v. d. Kulk 1941. 1; 1942. 2; 1943. 7, 8; 1945. 1.

with a field dimension M. Hence the determination of the integral-X_m's of an $\mathfrak{S}_d^m$-field with a field dimension $< n$ can always be reduced to the determination of the integral-X_m's of an $\mathfrak{S}_d^m$-field with a field dimension n with, in general, lower values of n and d. For this reason we restrict ourselves to $\mathfrak{S}_d^m$-fields with field dimension n.

2. The parametric form of an $\mathfrak{S}_d^m$-field

When dealing with the quasi-linear $\mathfrak{S}_d^m$-fields of Chapter VIII we always used the null form. For investigations concerning general $\mathfrak{S}_d^m$-fields it is more convenient to use a parametric form. Using the B_b^κ we get the parametric form

$$\begin{aligned} B_b^\kappa &= B_b^\kappa(\xi^\nu, \eta^k) \quad (k = \bar{1}, \ldots, \bar{d};\ b = 1, \ldots, \mathrm{m}), \\ \xi^\kappa &= \xi^\kappa \end{aligned} \tag{2.1}$$

and there is another parametric form using the C_λ^x,

$$\begin{aligned} C_\lambda^x &= C_\lambda^x(\xi^\nu, \eta^k) \quad (k = \bar{1}, \ldots, \bar{d};\ x = \mathrm{m}+1, \ldots, \mathrm{n}), \\ \xi^\kappa &= \xi^\kappa \end{aligned} \tag{2.2}$$

with the parameters ξ^κ and η^k. Both parametric forms are supposed to be minimal regular in an $\mathfrak{N}(\overset{}{\underset{0}{\xi^\nu}}, \underset{0}{\eta^k})$ (cf. II, § 4). A necessary and sufficient condition that (2.1) be minimal regular is that the B_b^κ be analytic in $\mathfrak{N}(\underset{0}{\xi^\nu}, \underset{0}{\eta^k})$ and that the i-rank of $\partial_i B_b^\kappa$ ($\partial_i \overset{\text{def}}{=} \partial/\partial\eta^i$) be d. If this condition is satisfied (2.1) represents an X_{n+d} in the $n(m+1)$-dimensional manifold of ξ^κ, B_b^κ. But since the B_b^κ are supernumerary coordinates, this does not yet imply that (2.1) represents an X_{n+d} in the $\{n+m(n-m)\}$-dimensional manifold of all elements E_m in X_n. A necessary and sufficient condition that this will be the case is that the E_m's with the coordinates ξ^κ, η^k and ξ^κ, $\eta^k+d\eta^k$ coincide if and only if $d\eta^k = 0$. Hence, from $B_b^\lambda C_\lambda^x = 0$ it follows that the equation

$$(B_b^\lambda + dB_b^\lambda)C_\lambda^x = d\eta^j(\partial_j B_b^\lambda)C_\lambda^x = 0 \quad (b = 1, \ldots, \mathrm{m};\ x = \mathrm{m}+1, \ldots, \mathrm{n}; \ j = \bar{1}, \ldots, \bar{d};\ \lambda = 1, \ldots, n) \tag{2.3}$$

has to be satisfied only if $d\eta^j = 0$. This proves *that* (2.1) (and in the same way (2.2)) *represent an $\mathfrak{S}_d^m$-field if and only if B_b^κ or C_λ^x respectively are analytic in $\mathfrak{N}(\underset{0}{\xi^\kappa}, \underset{0}{\eta^k})$ and if the j-rank of the quantity*

$$T_{jb}{}^{\cdot x} \overset{\text{def}}{=} -(\partial_j B_b^\lambda)C_\lambda^x = B_b^\lambda \partial_j C_\lambda^x \quad (j = \bar{1}, \ldots, \bar{d};\ b = 1, \ldots, \mathrm{m}; \ x = \mathrm{m}+1, \ldots, \mathrm{n}) \tag{2.4}$$

is equal to d.

We denote the manifold of ξ^κ, η^k by $'X_{n+d}$ and in order to distinguish the objects in $'X_{n+d}$ from the objects in X_n the former will always be denoted by a letter with an accent to the left. Besides coordinate transformations in X_n and linear transformations with analytic coefficients in b and x we allow transformations of the parameters η^k of the form

$$\eta^{k'} = \eta^{k'}(\xi^\kappa, \eta^k) \quad (k = \bar{1},..., \bar{d};\ k' = \bar{1}',..., \bar{d}') \tag{2.5}$$

with functions $\eta^{k'}$ analytic in an $\mathfrak{N}(\underset{0}{\xi^\kappa}, \underset{0}{\eta^k})$ and with a determinant $|\partial_i \eta^{k'}|$ which does not vanish in that region. Together with the transformations of the ξ^κ, (2.5) constitutes all allowable coordinate transformations in $'X_{n+d}$.

3. The adjoint $'E_{m+d}$-field

For the coordinates ξ^κ, η^k in the $'X_{n+d}$ we also use the notation X^A $(A = 1,..., n;\ \bar{1},..., \bar{d})$:

$$X^\kappa \overset{\text{def}}{=} \xi^\kappa, \quad X^k \overset{\text{def}}{=} \eta^k \quad (k = \bar{1},..., \bar{d}). \tag{3.1}$$

Now we consider the quantity $'C_B^x$ $(x = \mathrm{m}+1,..., \mathrm{n};\ B = 1,..., n, \bar{1},..., \bar{d})$, defined by

$$'C_\lambda^x \overset{\text{def}}{=} C_\lambda^x, \quad 'C_i^x \overset{\text{def}}{=} 0 \quad (x = \mathrm{m}+1,..., \mathrm{n};\ i = \bar{1},..., \bar{d}). \tag{3.2}$$

Obviously this definition is invariant for all allowable transformations of coordinates ξ^κ, indices x, and parameters η^k. The $'C_\lambda^x$ are analytic in an $\mathfrak{N}(\underset{0}{\xi^\kappa}, \underset{0}{\eta^k})$ and the B-rank of $'C_B^x$ is equal to the λ-rank of C_λ^x, viz. $n-m$. Consequently $'C_B^x$ is a covariant connecting quantity of an $'E_{m+d}$-field in the $'X_{n+d}$. This $'E_{m+d}$-field will be said to be *adjoint to the* $\mathfrak{S}_d^m$*-field.* Evidently its contravariant connecting quantity $'B_Q^A$ $(A = 1,..., n, \bar{1},..., \bar{d};\ Q = 1,..., \mathrm{m}, \bar{1},..., \bar{d})$ has the components

$$\begin{aligned} 'B_b^\kappa &= B_b^\kappa, & 'B_b^k &= 0 \\ 'B_i^\kappa &= 0, & 'B_i^k &= \delta_i^k \end{aligned} \qquad (b = 1,..., \mathrm{m};\ k, i = \bar{1},..., \bar{d}). \tag{3.3}$$

In every point of $'X_{n+d}$ there is one $'E_{m+d}$ fixed by $'C_B^x$ or $'B_Q^A$. Now every point of $'X_{n+d}$ represents an E_m of the $\mathfrak{S}_d^m$-field. Hence there is a one-to-one correspondence between the E_m's of the $\mathfrak{S}_d^m$-field and the $'E_{m+d}$'s of the $'E_{m+d}$-field in $'X_{n+d}$ and this implies that every geometrical property of the $\mathfrak{S}_d^m$-field corresponds to a geometrical property of the $'E_{m+d}$-field and vice versa.

4. Complete integrability of an $\mathfrak{S}_d^m$-field

Let

$$\xi^\kappa = f^\kappa(z^a) \quad (a = 1,..., \mathrm{m}) \tag{4.1}$$

be a parametric form of an integral-X_m of the $\mathfrak{S}_d^m$-field (2.1), which is minimal regular in an $\mathfrak{N}(\underset{0}{z^a})$. The tangent E_m in any point of X_m is spanned by the m vectors

$$\partial_b f^\kappa, \quad \partial_b \overset{\text{def}}{=} \frac{\partial}{\partial z^b} \quad (b = 1,\ldots, \mathrm{m}). \tag{4.2}$$

Since this E_m belongs to the $\mathfrak{S}_d^m$-field its coordinates η^k depend only on the parameters z^a and, therefore, relations of the form

$$\eta^k = g^k(z^a) \quad (a = 1,\ldots, \mathrm{m};\ k = \bar{1},\ldots, \bar{d}) \tag{4.3}$$

have to exist. Substituting (4.1) and (4.3) into (2.2) we get the covariant connecting quantity C_λ^x of this E_m as a function of the z^a. Because the transvection of C_λ^x and $\partial_b f^\lambda$ is zero, the necessary and sufficient condition that the X_m be an integral-X_m is that the relations

$$(\partial_b f^\lambda) C_\lambda^x(f^\nu, g^k) = 0 \quad (b = 1,\ldots, \mathrm{m};\ x = \mathrm{m}+1,\ldots, \mathrm{n};\ k = \bar{1},\ldots, \bar{d}) \tag{4.4}$$

are identically satisfied in the z^a.

Now we gather the equations (4.1) and (4.3) into the equation

$$X^A = F^A(z^a) \quad (A = 1,\ldots, n, \bar{1},\ldots, \bar{d};\ a = 1,\ldots, \mathrm{m}) \tag{4.5}$$

with

$$F^\kappa \overset{\text{def}}{=} f^\kappa, \quad F^k \overset{\text{def}}{=} g^k \quad (k = \bar{1},\ldots, \bar{d}). \tag{4.6}$$

(4.5) is a minimal regular parametric form of an $'X_m$ in $'X_{n+d}$ whose points are in one-to-one correspondence with the tangent E_m's of the given integral-X_m. The contravariant connecting quantity of this tangent E_m is $\partial_b F^\kappa$. According to (3.2) and (4.6) the equation (4.4) takes the form

$$(\partial_b F^B)\, 'C_B^x = 0 \quad (b = 1,\ldots, \mathrm{m};\ x = \mathrm{m}+1,\ldots, \mathrm{n};\ B = 1,\ldots, n, \bar{1},\ldots, \bar{d}) \tag{4.7}$$

and this equation expresses the fact that the $'X_m$ in $'X_{n+d}$ is an integral-$'X_m$ of the $'E_{m+d}$-field adjoint to the $\mathfrak{S}_d^m$-field. But this integral-$'X_m$ is not an arbitrary one. If in each point X^A of $'X_{n+d}$ we consider the $'E_d$ spanned by the contravariant measuring vectors $'\underset{i}{e}{}^A$ $(i = \bar{1},\ldots, \bar{d})$ we get an $'E_d$-field in $'X_{n+d}$ and this $'E_d$-field is invariant with all allowable transformations. Because $'B_i^A \overset{*}{=} '\underset{i}{e}{}^A$, the local $'E_d$ is always contained in the local $'E_{m+d}$ of the $'E_{m+d}$-field. Obviously the $'E_d$-field is $'X_d$-forming. If $'X_{n+d}$ is reduced with respect to this normal system of ∞^n $'X_d$'s, the $'E_{m+d}$-field becomes the $\mathfrak{S}_d^m$-field in X_n. Since the quantity $\partial_b f^\kappa$ occurring in (4.2) has the b-rank m, the local $'E_d$ of the $'E_d$-field has nowhere a direction in common with the tangent $'E_m$ of the integral-$'X_m$. Conversely, by each integral-$'X_m$ of the $'E_{m+d}$-field whose tangent $'E_m$'s have nowhere a direction in common with the local $'E_d$ of the invariant $'E_d$-field, an integral-X_m of the $\mathfrak{S}_d^m$-field is uniquely determined. We collect results in the theorem

THEOREM IX.1. *Every integral-X_m of an $\mathfrak{S}_d^m$-field in an X_n determines uniquely and is determined uniquely by an integral-$'X_m$ of the adjoint $'E_{m+d}$-field in an $'X_{n+d}$ whose tangent $'E_m$'s have nowhere a direction in common with the local $'E_d$ of the invariant $'E_d$-field in this $'X_{n+d}$.*

An $\mathfrak{S}_d^m$-field is said to be *completely integrable* if each E_m of the field is tangent to at least one integral-X_m of the field. Obviously every $\mathfrak{S}_d^1$-field is completely integrable. The following theorem is an immediate consequence of the theorem IX.1:

THEOREM IX.2. *An $\mathfrak{S}_d^m$-field is completely integrable if and only if each point of the $'X_{n+d}$ of the adjoint $'E_{m+d}$-field lies on at least one integral-$'X_m$ of this latter field, whose tangent $'E_m$'s have nowhere a direction in common with the local $'E_d$ of the invariant $'E_d$-field.*

From these theorems we see that the determination of the integral-X_m's of an $\mathfrak{S}_d^m$-field can be brought back to the determination of the integral-$'X_m$'s of a scalar-free Cartan system, consisting of $n-m$ vectors $'C_B^x$ in an $'X_{n+d}$ and their rotations

$$'C_{\dot{C}\dot{B}}^{\ \ x} \overset{\text{def}}{=} 2\partial_{[C}\,'C_{B]}^x, \quad \partial_C \overset{\text{def}}{=} \partial/\partial X^C \quad (x = \mathrm{m}+1,\dots,\mathrm{n}; \; B, C = 1,\dots,n,\bar{1},\dots,\bar{d}). \tag{4.8}$$

We will prove that this system can be replaced by an *RSC*-system (cf. VIII, § 14). The rotations $'C_{\dot{C}\dot{B}}^{\ \ x}$ of the $'C_B^x$ have the components

$$\begin{aligned} 'C_{\mu\lambda}^{\cdot\cdot x} &= 2\partial_{[\mu}C_{\lambda]}^x = C_{\mu\lambda}^{\cdot\cdot x} \\ 'C_{j\lambda}^{\cdot\cdot x} &= \partial_j C_\lambda^x \qquad (x = \mathrm{m}+1,\dots,\mathrm{n};\; i,j = \bar{1},\dots,\bar{d}) \\ 'C_{ji}^{\cdot\cdot x} &= 0 \end{aligned} \tag{4.9}$$

and the sections of these rotations with the $'E_{m+d}$

$$'D_{\dot{R}\dot{Q}}^{\ \ x} \overset{\text{def}}{=} {'B_R^C}\,{'B_Q^B}\,{'C_{\dot{C}\dot{B}}^{\ \ x}} \quad (x = \mathrm{m}+1,\dots,\mathrm{n};\; B, C = 1,\dots,n,\bar{1},\dots,\bar{d};\; Q, R = 1,\dots,\mathrm{m},\bar{1},\dots,\bar{d}) \tag{4.10}$$

have the components

$$\begin{aligned} &(a) \quad 'D_{\dot{c}\dot{b}}^{\ \ x} = D_{\dot{c}\dot{b}}^{\ \ x}, \quad D_{\dot{c}\dot{b}}^{\ \ x} \overset{\text{def}}{=} 2B_c^\mu B_b^\lambda \bar{\partial}_{[\mu} C_{\lambda]}^x \\ &(b) \quad 'D_{j\dot{b}}^{\ \ x} = B_b^\lambda \partial_j C_\lambda^x = T_{j\dot{b}}^{\ \ x} \\ &(c) \quad 'D_{ji}^{\cdot\cdot x} = 0 \quad (b, c = 1,\dots,\mathrm{m};\; x = \mathrm{m}+1,\dots,\mathrm{n};\; i,j = \bar{1},\dots,\bar{d}; \\ &\qquad \bar{\partial}_\mu \overset{\text{def}}{=} \frac{\partial}{\partial \xi^\mu}, \text{ the } \eta^k \text{ being treated as constants}) \end{aligned} \tag{4.11}$$

according to (2.4). Now from (4.10) it follows that

$$'C_{\dot{C}\dot{B}}^{\ \ x} \equiv {'D_{\dot{C}\dot{B}}^{\ \ x}} \;(\mathrm{mod}\; 'C_B^x) \quad (x = \mathrm{m}+1,\dots,\mathrm{n};\; B, C = 1,\dots,n,\bar{1},\dots,\bar{d}), \tag{4.12}$$

where the $'D_{\dot{C}\dot{B}}^{\ \ x}$ $(x = \mathrm{m}+1,\ldots,\mathrm{n})$ are any $n-m$ bivectors whose sections with the $'E_{m+d}$ are equal to the $'D_{\dot{R}\dot{Q}}^{\ \ x}$. Such bivectors can be found by taking $m+d$ arbitrary covariant vectors $'i_B^P$ $(P = 1,\ldots,\mathrm{m}, \bar{1},\ldots,\bar{d})$ satisfying the conditions $'i_B^P{}'B_Q^B = \delta_Q^P$ (cf. I, § 9). Then the bivectors required are

$$'D_{\dot{C}\dot{B}}^{\ \ x} \overset{\text{def}}{=} {}'D_{\dot{R}\dot{Q}}^{\ \ x}{}'i_C^R{}'i_B^Q \quad (x = \mathrm{m}+1,\ldots,\mathrm{n};\ B,C = 1,\ldots,n,\bar{1},\ldots,\bar{d};\ Q,R = 1,\ldots,\mathrm{m},\bar{1},\ldots,\bar{d}). \tag{4.13}$$

According to (4.12) the rotations $'C_{\dot{C}\dot{B}}^{\ \ x}$ can be replaced by the $'D_{\dot{C}\dot{B}}^{\ \ x}$ and according to (4.11) we have

$$'D_{\dot{C}\dot{B}}^{\ \ x} = (D_{\dot{c}\dot{b}}^{\ \ \cdot x}{}'i_{[C}^c + 2T_{jb}^{\ \ \cdot x}{}'i_{[C}^j){}'i_{B]}^b \quad (b,c = 1,\ldots,\mathrm{m};\ x = \mathrm{m}+1,\ldots,\mathrm{n};\ B,C = 1,\ldots,n,\bar{1},\ldots,\bar{d};\ j = \bar{1},\ldots,\bar{d}). \tag{4.14}$$

The $'i_B^b$ and $'C_B^x$ are linearly independent. Hence, if the $n-m$ bivectors $'D_{\dot{C}\dot{B}}^{\ \ x}$ are replaced by the maximum number of linearly independent ones among them, the Cartan system satisfies the five conditions for *RSC*-systems of VIII, § 14.

From the considerations of VIII, § 5, it follows that the conditions of Theorem IX.2 can only be satisfied if there exists in every point of the region of the $'X_{n+d}$ under consideration at least one integral-$'E_m$ of the $'E_{m+d}$-field having no direction in common with the local $'E_d$. But this latter condition is only necessary and not sufficient. If it is satisfied the $\mathfrak{S}_d^m$-field is said to be *preferred.*

To obtain a form of this necessary condition in terms of the quantities B_b^κ and C_λ^x, in any point $'X^A$ of $'X_{n+d}$ we consider an $'E_m$ contained in the local $'E_{m+d}$ and having no direction in common with the local $'E_d$. Every vector in this $'E_m$ has to be linearly independent of the d measuring vectors $'\underset{i}{e}{}^A$ $(i = \bar{1},\ldots,\bar{d})$, that is, of the vectors $'B_i^A$ $(i = \bar{1},\ldots,\bar{d})$ (cf. IX (3.3)). Hence the $'E_m$ can always be spanned by m vectors of the form

$$'B_b^A + Z_b^i{}'B_i^A \quad (b = 1,\ldots,\mathrm{m};\ i = \bar{1},\ldots,\bar{d};\ A = 1,\ldots,n,\bar{1},\ldots,\bar{d}). \tag{4.15}$$

This $'E_m$ is an integral-$'E_m$ if and only if (cf. VIII, § 2)

$$'C_{\dot{C}\dot{B}}^{\ \ x}('B_c^C + Z_c^j{}'B_j^C)('B_b^B + Z_b^i{}'B_i^B) = 0 \quad (b,c = 1,\ldots,\mathrm{m};\ x = \mathrm{m}+1,\ldots,\mathrm{n};\ i,j = \bar{1},\ldots,\bar{d};\ B,C = 1,\ldots,n,\bar{1},\ldots,\bar{d}). \tag{4.16}$$

From this and (4.10) and (4.11) we get the equations

$$D_{\dot{c}\dot{b}}^{\ \ \cdot x} + 2Z_{[c}^i T_{|i|\dot{b}]}^{\ \ \ \ x} = 0 \quad (b,c = 1,\ldots,\mathrm{m};\ x = \mathrm{m}+1,\ldots,\mathrm{n};\ i = \bar{1},\ldots,\bar{d}). \tag{4.17}$$

The only difference between $D_{\dot{c}\dot{b}}^{\ \ \cdot x}$ and the quantity $D_{\dot{c}\dot{b}}^{\ \ \cdot x}$ in III, § 2, is that here the B_b^κ and C_λ^x depend on the ξ^κ and the parameters η^k. Conversely, if (4.17) holds, the $'E_m$ spanned by the vectors (4.15) is an integral-$'E_m$ having no direction in common with the local $'E_d$. Hence *an* $\mathfrak{S}_d^m$*-field given by its parametric form* (2.1) *or* (2.2) *is preferred if and only if the equations* (4.17) *with the md unknown functions* Z_c^i *have at least one solution.*

That an $\mathfrak{S}_d^m$-field can be preferred without being completely integrable can be seen from the following example. Consider the $\mathfrak{S}_1^2$-field in X_4 with the parametric form

$$B_1^\kappa = \underset{1}{e}^\kappa + \eta \underset{4}{e}^\kappa, \quad B_2^\kappa = \underset{2}{e}^\kappa + \phi\eta \underset{3}{e}^\kappa \quad (\kappa = 1,\dots,4), \tag{4.18}$$

ϕ being an arbitrary function of the ξ^κ and η the only parameter. Then

$$C_\lambda^3 = \overset{3}{e}_\lambda - \phi\eta\overset{2}{e}_\lambda, \quad C_\lambda^4 = \overset{4}{e}_\lambda - \eta\overset{1}{e}_\lambda \quad (\lambda = 1,\dots,4) \tag{4.19}$$

is another parametric form and we have according to (4.11 a) and (2.4)

$$\begin{aligned}
D_{\dot{1}\dot{2}}{}^{3} &= -2(\underset{1}{e}^\mu + \eta\underset{4}{e}^\mu)(\underset{2}{e}^\lambda + \phi\eta\underset{3}{e}^\lambda)(\partial_{[\mu}\phi)\eta\overset{2}{e}_{\lambda]} = -\eta\partial_1\phi - \eta^2\partial_4\phi \\
D_{\dot{1}\dot{2}}{}^{4} &= 0 \\
T_{\bar{1}1}^{\cdot\cdot 3} &= -(\underset{1}{e}^\lambda + \eta\underset{4}{e}^\lambda)\phi\overset{2}{e}_\lambda = 0 \\
T_{\bar{1}1}^{\cdot\cdot 4} &= -(\underset{1}{e}^\lambda + \eta\underset{4}{e}^\lambda)\overset{1}{e}_\lambda = -1 \qquad\qquad (\lambda, \mu = 1,\dots,4), \\
T_{\bar{1}2}^{\cdot\cdot 3} &= -(\underset{2}{e}^\lambda + \phi\eta\underset{3}{e}^\lambda)\phi\overset{2}{e}_\lambda = -\phi \\
T_{\bar{1}2}^{\cdot\cdot 4} &= -(\underset{2}{e}^\lambda + \phi\eta\underset{3}{e}^\lambda)\overset{1}{e}_\lambda = 0
\end{aligned} \tag{4.20}$$

and consequently

$$\begin{aligned}
D_{\dot{1}\dot{2}}{}^{3} + Z_1^{\bar{1}}T_{\bar{1}2}^{\cdot\cdot 3} - Z_2^{\bar{1}}T_{\bar{1}1}^{\cdot\cdot 3} &= -\eta\partial_1\phi - \eta^2\partial_4\phi - \phi Z_1^{\bar{1}} = 0, \\
D_{\dot{1}\dot{2}}{}^{4} + Z_1^{\bar{1}}T_{\bar{1}2}^{\cdot\cdot 4} - Z_2^{\bar{1}}T_{\bar{1}1}^{\cdot\cdot 4} &= Z_2^{\bar{1}} = 0.
\end{aligned} \tag{4.21}$$

Since these equations have solutions the $\mathfrak{S}_1^2$-field is preferred. But if, for instance, ϕ is a function of ξ^1 and ξ^2 without being a product of a function of ξ^1 with a function of ξ^2 the only integral-X_2's are

$$\xi^3 = \text{const.}, \quad \xi^4 = \text{const.} \tag{4.22}$$

This can be proved as follows. From (4.18) it follows that $B_{[1}^1 B_{2]}^2 \neq 0$. Hence ξ^1 and ξ^2 can be used as coordinates in every integral-X_2. Now let

$$\xi^3 = f(\xi^1, \xi^2), \quad \xi^4 = g(\xi^1, \xi^2) \tag{4.23}$$

be the parametric form of an integral-X_2. The tangent E_2 is spanned by the vectors

$$\underset{1}{e^\kappa}+(\partial_1 f)\underset{3}{e^\kappa}+(\partial_1 g)\underset{4}{e^\kappa}, \qquad \underset{2}{e^\kappa}+(\partial_2 f)\underset{3}{e^\kappa}+(\partial_2 g)\underset{4}{e^\kappa} \quad (\kappa = 1,\ldots,4) \tag{4.24}$$

and since this E_2 is an integral-E_2 it has also to be spanned by the vectors (4.18) for some value of η. Hence

$$\partial_1 f = 0, \quad \partial_1 g = \eta, \quad \partial_2 f = \phi\eta, \quad \partial_2 g = 0. \tag{4.25}$$

Consequently f depends only on ξ^2 and g only on ξ^1 and either ϕ is a product of a function of ξ^1 and a function of ξ^2 or $\eta = 0$ and $f = \text{const.}$, $g = \text{const.}$

5. Some special cases of complete integrability

In a few special cases the additional conditions for complete integrability can easily be derived. We prove the following theorem (cf. V, § 6):

THEOREM IX.3. *A preferred $\mathfrak{S}_d^m$-field is completely integrable if the system $'C_B^x$ in the auxiliary $'X_{n+d}$ belongs to one of the cases* A, B, *or* C *of Grynaeus.*†

PROOF. According to (4.11), (4.17) can be written in the form

$$'D_{\dot{c}\dot{b}}^{\;\;x} = -2Z^i_{[c}\, 'D_{|\dot{i}|\dot{b}]}^{\;\;x} \quad (b, c = 1,\ldots,\mathrm{m};\ x = \mathrm{m}+1,\ldots,\mathrm{n};\ i = \bar{1},\ldots,\bar{d}) \tag{5.1}$$

or, if we introduce the d covariant vectors $'Z^i_Q$ in $'X_{n+d}$,

$$\begin{aligned} &(a) \qquad 'Z^i_b \overset{\text{def}}{=} Z^i_b \\ &(b) \qquad 'Z^i_j \overset{\text{def}}{=} -\delta^i_j \end{aligned} \quad (b = 1,\ldots,\mathrm{m};\ i,j = \bar{1},\ldots,\bar{d}) \tag{5.2}$$

in the form

$$'D_{\dot{R}\dot{Q}}^{\;\;x} = -2\,'Z^i_{[R}\, 'D_{|\dot{i}|\dot{Q}]}^{\;\;x} \quad (x = \mathrm{m}+1,\ldots,\mathrm{n};\ Q, R = 1,\ldots,\mathrm{m},\bar{1},\ldots,\bar{d};\ i = \bar{1},\ldots,\bar{d}). \tag{5.3}$$

Now we assume that $'C_B^x$ belongs to one of the cases A, B, or C of Grynaeus:

Case A

All rotations of the $'C_B^x$ vanish by proper choice of $'C_B^x$. Consequently $\partial_j C^x_\lambda = 0$ and this means that the C^x_λ depend only on the ξ^κ. Hence $d = 0$. Because $D_{\dot{c}\dot{b}}^{\;\;x} = 0$, the system

$$B^\lambda_b\, \partial_\lambda f = 0 \quad (b = 1,\ldots,\mathrm{m}) \tag{5.4}$$

is complete and this means that the E_m-field in X_n is X_m-forming. This proves the theorem for the case A.

† Cf. v. d. Kulk 1945. 1, ch. i.

Case B

The $'C_B^x$ can be chosen in such a way that the rotations of all vectors $'C_B^{\mathrm{m}+1},\ldots,\, 'C_B^{\mathrm{n}-1}$ vanish and that $'C_B^{\mathrm{n}}$ is of a class $2\tau+1 \geqslant 3$. Hence

$$\begin{aligned} &\partial_{[\mu}\, C_{\lambda]}^{\mathrm{m}+1} = 0, \quad \partial_j\, C_\lambda^{\mathrm{m}+1} = 0 \\ &\quad \cdot \quad \cdot \quad \cdot \quad \cdot \quad \cdot \quad \cdot \quad \cdot \quad \cdot \quad \cdot \qquad (j = \bar{1},\ldots,\bar{d}) \\ &\partial_{[\mu}\, C_{\lambda]}^{\mathrm{n}-1} = 0, \quad \partial_j\, C_\lambda^{\mathrm{n}-1} = 0 \end{aligned} \tag{5.5}$$

and the only vector depending on the η^k is C_λ^{n}. The only equation remaining from (5.3) is

$$'D_{\dot{R}\dot{Q}}{}^{\mathrm{n}} = -2\,'Z^i_{[R}\,'D_{|\dot{i}|\dot{Q}]}{}^{\mathrm{n}} \quad (i = \bar{1},\ldots,\bar{d};\ Q, R = 1,\ldots,\mathrm{m},\bar{1},\ldots,\bar{d}) \tag{5.6}$$

and the rank of the bivector $'D_{\dot{R}\dot{Q}}{}^{\mathrm{n}}$ has to be $2\tau \geqslant 2$. Now, since the i-rank of $T_{\dot{i}\dot{b}}{}^{\mathrm{n}}$ is d, according to (4.11 b, c) the i-rank of $'D_{\dot{i}\dot{Q}}{}^{\mathrm{n}}$ is also d. From this and (5.2) it follows that the $2d$ vectors $'Z^i_Q$, $'D_{\dot{i}\dot{Q}}{}^{\mathrm{n}}$ ($i = \bar{1},\ldots,\bar{d}$) are linearly independent and that consequently the rank of $'D_{\dot{R}\dot{Q}}{}^{\mathrm{n}}$ is $2d$. Hence $\tau = d$ and this implies that d cannot be zero.

The field of the E_{m+1}'s in X_n determined by the set of gradient vectors $C_\lambda^{\mathrm{m}+1},\ldots,\, C_\lambda^{\mathrm{n}-1}$ is X_{m+1}-forming and the E_m's of the $\mathfrak{S}_d^m$-field in each point are contained in the local E_{m+1} of this field. In each local E_{m+1} the E_m's of the $\mathfrak{S}_d^m$-field depend on the d parameters η^k. The field of the $'E_{m+d+1}$'s in $'X_{n+d}$ determined by the set of gradient vectors $'C_B^{\mathrm{m}+1},\ldots,\, 'C_B^{\mathrm{n}-1}$ is $'X_{m+d+1}$-forming and the $'E_{m+d}$ of the $'E_{m+d}$-field in each point is contained in the local $'E_{m+d+1}$ of this $'E_{m+d+1}$-field. $'C_B^{\mathrm{n}}$ has a section of class $2\tau+1 = 2d+1$ in each of these $'X_{m+d+1}$'s. Hence this section is $'X_m$-enveloping (cf. VI, § 1) and each of the enveloped $'X_m$'s is an integral-$'X_m$ of the $'E_{m+d}$-field in $'X_{m+d+1}$. Moreover, we know that there exists an integral-$'X_m$ through every integral-$'E_m$ in this $'E_{m+d}$-field (cf. VIII, § 9). Now, since the $\mathfrak{S}_d^m$-field is preferred, there exists in every point of $'X_{n+d}$ at least one integral-$'E_m$ of the $'E_{m+d}$-field in $'X_{n+d}$ having no direction in common with the local $'E_d$. If $\underset{1}{v}{}^A$ and $\underset{2}{v}{}^A$ are any two vectors in this integral-$'E_m$ we have

$$\begin{aligned} &(a) \qquad 'C_B^x\, \underset{1}{v}{}^B = 0, \quad 'C_B^x\, \underset{2}{v}{}^B = 0 \qquad (x = \mathrm{m}+1,\ldots,\mathrm{n}; \\ &(b) \quad 'C_{\dot{C}\dot{B}}{}^x\, \underset{1}{v}{}^C \underset{2}{v}{}^B = 0 \qquad\qquad B, C = 1,\ldots,n,\bar{1},\ldots,\bar{d}). \end{aligned} \tag{5.7}$$

From (5.7 a) it follows that this integral-$'E_m$ is an $'E_m$ of $'X_{m+d+1}$ and from (5.7 b) it follows for $x = \mathrm{n}$ that this $'E_m$ is an integral-$'E_m$ of the $'E_{m+d}$-field in $'X_{m+d+1}$. This proves that there exists through every point of $'X_{n+d}$ at least one integral-$'X_m$ whose tangent $'X_m$ in this point, and consequently in a sufficiently small neighbourhood of this point, has no direction in common with the local $'E_d$.

Case C

In case C we have the following normal form for $'C_B^x$ (cf. V, § 6):

$$'C_B^y = \partial_B f^y + h^y \partial_B f, \quad 'C_B^{\mathrm{n}} = \partial_B f^{\mathrm{n}} + f^{\mathrm{n}-1}\partial_B f$$
$$(y = \mathrm{m}+1,\dots,\mathrm{n}-1;\ B = 1,\dots,n,\bar{1},\dots,\bar{d}) \quad (5.8)$$

and the similarity class k of $'C_B^x$ is $n-m+2$. We remark first that this case cannot occur for $d = 0$. Because in that case $'C_B^x$ reduces to C_λ^x and, the E_m-field being completely integrable (as a consequence of the preference and $d = 0$), $'C_B^x$ could not have the class $n-m+2$. Now k is the C-rank of the system $'C_C^x$, $'C_{\dot{C}\dot{B}}{}^{x}\,'B_Q^B$ and accordingly $k-n+m$ is the R-rank of $'D_{\dot{R}\dot{Q}}{}^{x}$ (cf. V, § 2). Hence the R-rank of $'D_{\dot{R}\dot{Q}}{}^{x}$ is 2 and this means that $'D_{\dot{R}\dot{Q}}{}^{x}$ can be written in the form

$$'D_{\dot{R}\dot{Q}}{}^{x} = 2\,'U_{[R}\,'V_{Q]}\,'P^x \quad (x = \mathrm{m}+1,\dots,\mathrm{n};\ Q,R = 1,\dots,\mathrm{m},\bar{1},\dots,\bar{d}). \quad (5.9)$$

Since $'D_{\dot{j}\dot{i}}{}^{x}$ is zero, $'V_Q$ can always be chosen in such a way that $'V_i = 0$. Then $'D_{\dot{i}\dot{b}}{}^{x}$ takes the form

$$'D_{\dot{i}\dot{b}}{}^{x} = 'U_i\,'V_b\,'P^x \quad (b = 1,\dots,\mathrm{m};\ x = \mathrm{m}+1,\dots,\mathrm{n};\ i = \bar{1},\dots,\bar{d}). \quad (5.10)$$

Now $'U_i\,'V_b\,'P^x$ has the i-rank 1 or 0 and we have seen that $'D_{\dot{i}\dot{b}}{}^{x}$ has the i-rank d. Since the case $d = 0$ is already excluded, it follows that $d = 1$ and that the $'E_{m+d}$-field in the $'X_{n+d}$ is an $'E_{m+1}$-field in an $'X_{n+1}$. The characteristics of this field have the dimension $n+1-k = m-1$. If the $'X_{n+1}$ is reduced with respect to these characteristics to an $''X_{n-m+2}$, the $'E_{m+1}$-field is reduced to an $''E_2$-field. Each point of the $''X_{n-m+2}$ lies on at least one integral-$''X_1$ of the $''E_2$-field and consequently every point of the $'X_{n+1}$ lies on at least one integral-$'X_m$ of the $'E_{m+1}$-field. The only thing to prove is that this integral-$'X_m$ can always be chosen in such a way that its tangent $'E_m$'s have nowhere a direction in common with the local $'E_1$ of the invariant $'E_1$-field. This local $'E_1$ in any point has the direction of the vector $'\underset{\bar{1}}{e}{}^A$ and is contained in the local $'E_{m+1}$ of the field. Now according to (3.2)

$$'\underset{\bar{1}}{e}{}^B\,'C_B^x = 'C_{\bar{1}}^x = 0 \quad (x = \mathrm{m}+1,\dots,\mathrm{n};\ B = 1,\dots,n,\bar{1},\dots,\bar{d}) \quad (5.11)$$

and according to (3.2) and (4.9) the components of

$$\begin{aligned} '\underset{\bar{1}}{e}{}^C\,'C_{\dot{C}\dot{B}}{}^{x}B_Q^B &= 'C_{\dot{\bar{1}}\dot{B}}{}^{x}B_Q^B \\ &= (\partial_{\bar{1}}C_\lambda^x)\underset{b}{B_Q^\lambda} \\ &= 'D_{\dot{\bar{1}}\dot{b}}{}^{x}e_Q \end{aligned} \quad \begin{aligned} &(x = \mathrm{m}+1,\dots,\mathrm{n};\ B,C = 1,\dots,n,\bar{1},\dots,\bar{d}; \\ &\quad b = 1,\dots,\mathrm{m};\ Q = 1,\dots,\mathrm{m},\bar{1},\dots,\bar{d}) \end{aligned}$$
$$(5.12)$$

cannot all vanish. Hence the local $'E_1$ does not lie in the $(m-1)$-direction of the reduction and consequently this $'E_1$ is reduced to an $''E_1$ in the resulting $''E_2$. Now it is always possible to choose in the $''E_2$ in the point considered, a direction not coinciding with the local $''E_1$ and from this direction we get an integral-$''X_1$ of the $''E_2$-field, corresponding to an integral-$'X_m$ of the $'E_{m+1}$-field whose tangent $'E_m$ has in this particular point, and therefore in a sufficiently small neighbourhood, no direction in common with the local $'E_d$.

Theorem IX.3 contains only conditions for the adjoint $'E_{m+d}$-field. It is interesting to express these conditions in terms of the $\mathfrak{S}_d^m$-field. This leads to the following three theorems.

THEOREM IX.4. *A preferred $\mathfrak{S}_d^m$-field is completely integrable if $d = 0$. (Case I.)*†

PROOF. Since $d = 0$ the C_λ^x depend only on the ξ^κ. Consequently $\partial_j C_\lambda^x = 0$ and the condition for the preference takes the form $D_{\dot{c}\dot{b}}{}^x = 0$. The $\mathfrak{S}_d^m$-field is an X_m-forming E_m-field in X_n and the system $'C_B^x$ belongs to the case A of Grynaeus.

THEOREM IX.5. *A preferred $\mathfrak{S}_d^m$-field with $d \geqslant 2$ is completely integrable if in each point ξ^κ all E_m's belonging to $\mathfrak{S}_d^m(\xi^\kappa)$ are contained in the same E_{m+1}. These E_{m+1}'s together constitute a completely integrable E_{m+1}-field in X_n. (Case II.)*†

PROOF. The x can be transformed in such a way that the $\mathfrak{S}_d^m$-field is given by the equations

$$\begin{aligned} &(a) \quad C_\lambda^y = C_\lambda^y(\xi^\kappa) \\ &(b) \quad C_\lambda^{\mathrm{n}} = C_\lambda^{\mathrm{n}}(\xi^\kappa, \eta^k) \end{aligned} \qquad (y = \mathrm{m}+1,\dots,\mathrm{n}-1;\ k = \bar{1},\dots,\bar{d}) \qquad (5.13)$$

and the E_{m+1}-field by the equations (5.13 a). Then from (2.4) it follows that $T_{j\dot{b}}{}^y = 0$ $(y = \mathrm{m}+1,\dots,\mathrm{n}-1)$. Since the $\mathfrak{S}_d^m$-field is preferred (5.3) holds, hence

$$'D_{\dot{R}\dot{Q}}{}^y = 0 \quad (y = \mathrm{m}+1,\dots,\mathrm{n}-1;\ Q, R = 1,\dots,\mathrm{m},\bar{1},\dots,\bar{d}) \quad (5.14)$$

and this implies that the x-rank of $'D_{\dot{R}\dot{Q}}{}^x$ is 1. The similarity class k of the $'E_{m+d}$-field is $n-m+$the Q-rank of $'D_{\dot{R}\dot{Q}}{}^x$, that is, of $'D_{\dot{R}\dot{Q}}{}^{\mathrm{n}}$. Now, according to (5.3) and (4.11 b), we have

$$'D_{\dot{R}\dot{Q}}{}^{\mathrm{n}} = -2\,'Z^i_{[R}\,'D_{|i|\dot{Q}]}{}^{\mathrm{n}} = -2\,'Z^i_{[R}\overset{b}{e}_{Q]}\,T_{i\dot{b}}{}^{\mathrm{n}}$$
$$(b = 1,\dots,\mathrm{m};\ i = \bar{1},\dots,\bar{d};\ Q, R = 1,\dots,\mathrm{m},\bar{1},\dots,\bar{d}) \quad (5.15)$$

† Cf. v. d. Kulk 1945. 1, ch. i.

and we know that $T_{i\dot{b}}^{\cdot\cdot\mathrm{n}}$ has the i-rank d, $T_{i\dot{b}}^{\cdot\cdot y}$ ($y = \mathrm{m}+1,\ldots,\mathrm{n}-1$) being zero. Hence, according to (5.2b) the $2d$ vectors $'Z_Q^i$, $\overset{b}{e}_Q T_{\bar{i}\dot{b}}^{\cdot\cdot\mathrm{n}}$ ($i = \bar{1},\ldots,\bar{d}$) are linearly independent and the Q-rank of $'D_{\dot{R}\dot{Q}}^{\cdot\cdot\mathrm{n}}$ is $2d$. From this and (V, 2.17) it follows that $k = n-m+2d \geqslant n-m+4$ and that consequently the system $'C_B^x$ belongs to the case B of Grynaeus.

In order to formulate the last theorem of integrability of this section, at a point ξ^κ we consider the set of all E_m's belonging to $\mathfrak{S}_d^m(\xi^\kappa)$. The E_1's in these E_m's form a cone $\mathfrak{C}(\xi^\kappa)$ in the local E_n of ξ^κ. If d_c is the dimension of this cone, the tangent E_{d_c} of $\mathfrak{C}(\xi^\kappa)$ is the same in all points of one of the constituting E_1's but in general not the same in all points of one of the constituting E_m's. If the tangent E_{d_c} is the same in all points of a general constituting E_m, the cone $\mathfrak{C}(\xi^\kappa)$ is said to be *stationary*. Now we prove the theorem

THEOREM IX.6. *A preferred $\mathfrak{S}_d^m$-field with $d = 1$ is completely integrable if in each point ξ^κ the cone $\mathfrak{C}(\xi^\kappa)$ is stationary.* (*Case* III.)†

PROOF. Obviously $d_c \geqslant m$. We will first prove that $d_c = m+1$ if $d = 1$. Every vector contained in an E_m of $\mathfrak{S}_1^m$ has the form

$$v^\kappa = p^b B_b^\kappa(\xi^\kappa, \eta) \quad (b = 1,\ldots,\mathrm{m}). \tag{5.16}$$

If the ξ^κ are looked upon as constants this equation is a parametric form of $\mathfrak{C}(\xi^\kappa)$ with the $m+1$ parameters p^b, η. In a point where this parametric form is minimal regular the vectors

$$\begin{aligned} \partial v^\kappa/\partial p^b &= B_b^\kappa \\ \partial v^\kappa/\partial\eta &= p^b \partial_{\bar{1}} B_b^\kappa \end{aligned} \quad (b = 1,\ldots,\mathrm{m}) \tag{5.17}$$

have to be linearly independent. Hence we must choose p^b in such a way that

$$p^b(\partial_{\bar{1}} B_b^\kappa) C_\kappa^x = -p^b\, 'D_{\bar{1}b}^{\cdot\cdot x} \neq 0$$
$$(b = 1,\ldots,\mathrm{m};\ x = \mathrm{m}+1,\ldots,\mathrm{n}). \tag{5.18}$$

Now we know that $'D_{\bar{1}b}^{\cdot\cdot x} \neq 0$. Hence p^b can always be chosen in such a way that (5.18) is satisfied and this proves that $\mathfrak{C}(\xi^\kappa)$ has the dimension $m+1$.

If $\mathfrak{C}(\xi^\kappa)$ is stationary and $d = 1$ the E_{m+1} spanned by the $m+1$ vectors (5.17) is independent of the choice of p^a. Hence there must exist a vector $P^\kappa = P^\kappa(\xi^\kappa, \eta)$ independent of the p^a and such that the E_{m+1} is spanned by the B_b^κ ($b = 1,\ldots,\mathrm{m}$) and P^κ. The vector $p^b\partial_{\bar{1}} B_b^\kappa$ depends linearly on these $m+1$ vectors and consequently, according to (2.4),

$$C_\lambda^x P^\lambda :: p^b C_\lambda^x \partial_{\bar{1}} B_b^\lambda = -\, p^b T_{\bar{1}b}^{\cdot\cdot x} \quad (b = 1,\ldots,\mathrm{m};\ x = \mathrm{m}+1,\ldots,\mathrm{n}) \tag{5.19}$$

† Cf. v. d. Kulk 1945. 1, ch. i.

for each choice of p^b. Hence $T_{\bar{1}b}^{\cdot\cdot x}$ can be written in the form

$$T_{\bar{1}b}^{\cdot\cdot x} = q_b P^\lambda C_\lambda^x \quad (b = 1,\dots,\mathrm{m};\ x = \mathrm{m}+1,\dots,\mathrm{n}) \tag{5.20}$$

the q_b being functions of the ξ^κ and η. As $T_{\bar{1}b}^{\cdot\cdot x}$ does not vanish, neither all $P^\lambda C_\lambda^x$ nor all q_b vanish. Conversely, it is readily proved that $\mathfrak{C}(\xi^\kappa)$ is stationary if (5.20) holds.

Now we consider the set of $n-m$ covariant vectors $'C_B^x$ ($x = \mathrm{m}+1$, ..., n) in $'X_{n+d}$. The equations (5.3) take the form

$$'D_{\dot{R}\dot{Q}}^{\ \ x} = -2\,'Z_{[R}^{\bar{1}}\,'D_{|\bar{1}|Q]}^{\cdot\cdot\ x} = -2\,'Z_{[R}^{\bar{1}}\,'Q_{Q]}\,P^\lambda C_\lambda^x$$
$$(x = \mathrm{m}+1,\dots,\mathrm{n};\ Q, R = 1,\dots,\mathrm{m},\bar{1},\dots,\bar{d}) \tag{5.21}$$

with

$$'Z_b^{\bar{1}} \overset{\text{def}}{=} Z_b^{\bar{1}}, \quad 'Q_b \overset{\text{def}}{=} q_b \quad (b = 1,\dots,\mathrm{m}).$$
$$'Z_{\bar{1}}^{\bar{1}} \overset{\text{def}}{=} 1, \quad 'Q_{\bar{1}} = 0 \tag{5.22}$$

From (5.21) we see that the R-rank of $'D_{\dot{R}\dot{Q}}^{\ \ x}$ is 2. Hence $k = n-m+2$ and consequently the system $'C_\lambda^x$ belongs to the case B or to the case C of Grynaeus. It is easily proved that it belongs to the case B if $\mathfrak{C}(\xi^\kappa)$ is an E_{m+1} and if all these E_{m+1}'s together constitute a completely integrable E_{m+1}-field (Case III 1) and to the case C in the other case (Case III 2).

Here is a summary of the relations between the cases dealt with in the theorems IX 4, 5, 6 and the cases A, B, C, and D of Grynaeus:

$\mathfrak{S}_d^m$-*field*	*Adjoint* $'E_{m+d}$-*field*
I	A
II	B with $\tau = d \geqslant 2$
III 1	B with $\tau = d = 1$
III 2	C with $d \neq 0$
all other cases	either B with $\tau \neq d$ or C with $d = 0$ or D

(5.23)

If an $'E_{m+d}$-field in an $'X_{n+d}$ is given by the covariant connecting quantity $'C_B^x$, one may require the necessary and sufficient conditions that this $'E_{m+d}$-field be the adjoint field of an $\mathfrak{S}_d^m$-field in some X_n. Obviously a necessary condition is that the $'E_{m+d}$-field is $'X_d$-enveloping. Choosing the coordinates in $'X_{n+d}$ such that the normal system of enveloped $'X_d$'s has the equations

$$\xi^1 = \text{const.}, \quad \dots, \quad \xi^n = \text{const.} \tag{5.24}$$

and that η^k ($k = \bar{1},\dots,\bar{d}$) are the other coordinates, we have

$$'C_i^x = 0 \quad (i = \bar{1},\dots,\bar{d};\ x = \mathrm{m}+1,\dots,\mathrm{n}). \tag{5.25}$$

Writing

$$C_\lambda^x \overset{\text{def}}{=} {'C_\lambda^x} \quad (x = \mathrm{m}+1,\dots,\mathrm{n}) \tag{5.26}$$

C_λ^x can be looked upon as the covariant connecting quantity of an E_m

in the X_n of the ξ^κ depending on the parameters η^k. The necessary and sufficient condition that the field C_λ^x represents an $\mathfrak{S}_d^m$-field is that $B_b^\lambda \partial_j C_\lambda^x$ has the j-rank d, B_b^κ being the contravariant connecting quantity belonging to C_λ^x. According to (4.11)

$$'D_{j\dot{b}}^{\ \ x} = B_b^\lambda \partial_j C_\lambda^x \quad (b = 1,..., \mathrm{m};\ x = \mathrm{m}+1,..., \mathrm{n};\ j = \bar{1},..., \bar{d}). \tag{5.27}$$

Hence, if $'U_i^A = \underset{i}{'e^A}$ is the contravariant connecting quantity of the tangent $'E_d$'s of the $'X_d$'s this condition is equivalent to the condition that the i-rank of the quantity

$$'U_i^C B_Q^B\, 'C_{\dot{C}\dot{B}}^{\ \ x} \quad (x = \mathrm{m}+1,..., \mathrm{n};\ i = \bar{1},..., \bar{d};\ B, C = 1,..., n, \bar{1},..., \bar{d}) \tag{5.28}$$

is equal to d. Now suppose this i-rank were $< d$. Then there would exist a non-zero vector v^i satisfying the equation

$$v^i\, 'U_i^C B_Q^B\, 'C_{\dot{C}\dot{B}}^{\ \ x} = 0 \quad (x = \mathrm{m}+1,..., \mathrm{n};\ i = \bar{1},..., \bar{d};\ B, C = 1,..., n, \bar{1},..., \bar{d}) \tag{5.29}$$

and this would imply that the non-zero vector $v^i\, 'U_i^C$ in the local $'E_d$ would lie in the characteristics of the $'E_{m+d}$-field. Hence the geometrical form of the necessary and sufficient condition is that the $'E_{m+d}$-field has a normal system of ∞^n integral-$'E_d$'s having no $'X_p$'s ($p \geqslant 1$) in common with the characteristics of the field.

6. The induced $\mathfrak{S}_{d_p}^p$-field†

If an $\mathfrak{S}_d^m$-field is given, all E_p's through the contact points ($p \leqslant m$) contained in the E_m's of the field constitute an $\mathfrak{S}_{d_p}^p$-field. Obviously $d_0 = 0$ and $d_m = d$. This field we call the *induced $\mathfrak{S}_{d_p}^p$-field* of the given $\mathfrak{S}_d^m$-field. Writing $U_\mathfrak{b}^\kappa$ ($\mathfrak{b} = \dot{1},..., \dot{p}$) for the connecting quantity of an E_p in a point ξ^κ the components of a p-vector in E_p are

$$v^{\kappa_1 \dots \kappa_p} = U_{[\dot{1}}^{\kappa_1} \dots U_{\dot{p}]}^{\kappa_p}. \tag{6.1}$$

The $v^{\kappa_1 \dots \kappa_p}$ are projective coordinates in $\mathfrak{P}^p(\xi^\kappa)$ and supernumerary coordinates in $\mathfrak{S}^p$ with $\epsilon_1 = \binom{n}{p} - p(n-p) - 1$, $\epsilon_2 = 1$. The $U_\mathfrak{b}^\kappa$ are supernumerary coordinates in $\mathfrak{S}^p$ with $\epsilon_1 = 0$, $\epsilon_2 = p^2$ (cf. IX, § 1). The E_p's through the contact point in ξ^κ are the points of $\mathfrak{S}^p$ and the E_p's of $\mathfrak{S}_{d_p}^p$ are the points of an X_{d_p} in this $\mathfrak{S}^p$.

The equations (6.1) constitute a parametric form of $\mathfrak{S}^p(\xi^\kappa)$. The tangent $P_{p(n-p)}$ of $\mathfrak{S}^p(\xi^\kappa)$ in $\mathfrak{P}^p(\xi^\kappa)$ is spanned by the np points of $\mathfrak{P}^p(\xi^\kappa)$

† Cf. v. d. Kulk 1942. 2; 1945. 1, ch. ii.

with the coordinates

$$\frac{\partial v^{\kappa_1 \ldots \kappa_p}}{\partial U_{\mathfrak{b}}^{\lambda}} = pA_{\lambda}^{[\kappa_1} U_{\dot{2}}^{\kappa_2} \ldots U_{\dot{p}}^{\kappa_p]} \delta_{\dot{1}]}^{\mathfrak{b}} \quad (\mathfrak{b} = \dot{1},\ldots,\dot{p}). \tag{6.2}$$

Among them there are just $p(n-p)+1$ linearly independent ones.

In order to determine the dimension d_p we establish a parametric form for $\mathfrak{S}_{d_p}^p(\xi^\kappa)$. Since $B_b^\kappa(\xi^\nu, \eta^k)$ is the connecting quantity of an E_m of $\mathfrak{S}_d^m$ and since E_p is contained in E_m, relations of the form

$$U_{\mathfrak{b}}^{\kappa} = U_{\mathfrak{b}}^{a} B_a^\kappa(\xi^\nu, \eta^k) \quad (\mathfrak{b} = \dot{1},\ldots,\dot{p};\ a = 1,\ldots,\mathrm{m};\ k = \bar{1},\ldots,\bar{d}) \tag{6.3}$$

exist and $U_{\mathfrak{b}}^a$ can be looked upon as the connecting quantity of the E_p in E_m. Consequently we get a parametric form of $\mathfrak{S}_{d_p}^p(\xi^\kappa)$ if the values (6.3) are substituted into (6.1), and in this parametric form the ξ^κ have to be looked upon as constants and the $U_{\mathfrak{b}}^a$ and η^k as $pm+d$ independent parameters. The tangent P_{d_p} of $\mathfrak{S}_{d_p}^p(\xi^\kappa)$ in $\mathfrak{P}^p$ in any point $U_{\mathfrak{b}}^a$, η^k contains the $d+mp$ points (= p-vectors) with the coordinates

$$\begin{aligned} &(a) \quad \frac{\partial v^{\kappa_1 \ldots \kappa_p}}{\partial \eta^i} = p(U_{\mathfrak{b}}^b \partial_i B_b^{[\kappa_1}) U_{\dot{2}}^{\kappa_2} \ldots U_{\dot{p}}^{\kappa_p]} \delta_{\dot{1}]}^{\mathfrak{b}} \quad (\mathfrak{b} = \dot{1},\ldots,\dot{p}; \\ &(b) \quad \frac{\partial v^{\kappa_1 \ldots \kappa_p}}{\partial U_{\mathfrak{b}}^a} = pB_a^{[\kappa_1} U_{\dot{2}}^{\kappa_2} \ldots U_{\dot{p}}^{\kappa_p]} \delta_{\dot{1}]}^{\mathfrak{b}} \qquad a, b = 1,\ldots,\mathrm{m};\ i = \bar{1},\ldots,\bar{d}). \end{aligned} \tag{6.4}$$

Conversely, in every general point of $\mathfrak{S}_{d_p}^p(\xi^\kappa)$ the space with the smallest dimension containing all points (6.4) coincides with the tangent P_{d_p}. Hence we have to determine the number of linearly independent p-vectors among (6.4). If every E_m of the $\mathfrak{S}_d^m$-field is rigged by introducing an E_{n-m} with the connecting quantities C_y^κ, B_λ^x dependent on the ξ^κ and η^k (cf. I, § 9), in consequence of (I (9.33)), that is

$$A_\lambda^\kappa = B_b^\kappa B_\lambda^b + C_y^\kappa C_\lambda^y \quad (b = 1,\ldots,\mathrm{m};\ y = \mathrm{m}+1,\ldots,\mathrm{n}), \tag{6.5}$$

and (2.4) we get from (6.4)

$$\frac{\partial v^{\kappa_1 \ldots \kappa_p}}{\partial \eta^i} = p(U_{\mathfrak{b}}^b \partial_i B_b^\lambda) B_\lambda^a B_a^{[\kappa_1} U_{\dot{2}}^{\kappa_2} \ldots U_{\dot{p}}^{\kappa_p]} \delta_{\dot{1}]}^{\mathfrak{b}} - pU_{\mathfrak{b}}^b T_{ib}^{\cdot\cdot y} C_y^{[\kappa_1} U_{\dot{2}}^{\kappa_2} \ldots U_{\dot{p}}^{\kappa_p]} \delta_{\dot{1}]}^{\mathfrak{b}}$$

$$(a, b = 1,\ldots,\mathrm{m};\ y = \mathrm{m}+1,\ldots,\mathrm{n};\ i = \bar{1},\ldots,\bar{d};\ \mathfrak{b} = \dot{1},\ldots,\dot{p}). \tag{6.6}$$

Since the first terms of the right-hand sides of (6.6) are linearly dependent on the right-hand sides of (6.4b) the $d+mp$ points (6.4) can be replaced by

$$\begin{aligned} &(a) \quad U_{\mathfrak{b}}^b T_{ib}^{\cdot\cdot y} C_y^{[\kappa_1} U_{\dot{2}}^{\kappa_2} \ldots U_{\dot{p}}^{\kappa_p]} \delta_{\dot{1}]}^{\mathfrak{b}} \quad (b = 1,\ldots,\mathrm{m};\ y = \mathrm{m}+1,\ldots,\mathrm{n}; \\ &(b) \quad B_a^{[\kappa_1} U_{\dot{2}}^{\kappa_2} \ldots U_{\dot{p}}^{\kappa_p]} \delta_{\dot{1}]}^{\mathfrak{b}} \qquad i = \bar{1},\ldots,\bar{d};\ \mathfrak{b} = \dot{1},\ldots,\dot{p}). \end{aligned} \tag{6.7}$$

Now the B_b^κ and C_y^κ are n linearly independent vectors and consequently the number of independent p-vectors among (6.7) is the sum of these numbers for (6.7 a) and (6.7 b) separately. The points (6.7 b) span the tangent $P_{p(m-p)}$ of the manifold of all E_p's in E_m, and from this it follows that the number of linearly independent vectors among (6.7 b) is $p(m-p)+1$. Because the $p(n-m)$ vectors

$$C_y^{[\kappa_1} U_{\dot{2}}^{\kappa_2} \ldots U_{\dot{p}}^{\kappa_p]} \delta_{\dot{1}]}^{\mathfrak{b}} \quad (y = \mathrm{m}+1,\ldots,\mathrm{n};\ \mathfrak{b} = \dot{1},\ldots,\dot{p}) \tag{6.8}$$

are linearly independent the number of linearly independent p-vectors among (6.7 a) is just the i-rank of the quantity

$$U_{\mathfrak{b}}^b T_{i b}^{\cdot\cdot x} \quad (b = 1,\ldots,\mathrm{m};\ x = \mathrm{m}+1,\ldots,\mathrm{n};\ i = \bar{1},\ldots,\bar{d};\ \mathfrak{b} = \dot{1},\ldots,\dot{p}). \tag{6.9}$$

Denoting this i-rank by $d-\tau_p$, the maximum number of linearly independent p-vectors among (6.7) is $p(m-p)+1+d-\tau_p$ and consequently

$$d_p = p(m-p)+d-\tau_p \tag{6.10}$$

in every region of the variables ξ^κ, η^k, $U_{\mathfrak{b}}^a$ where the i-rank of (6.9) is constant. Notice that $\tau_0 = d$ and $\tau_m = 0$.

An E_m of the $\mathfrak{S}_d^m$-field is determined by the parameters ξ^κ and η^k, and an E_p in such an E_m by the parameters ξ^κ, η^k, and $U_{\mathfrak{b}}^a$. The quantity $T_{i b}^{\cdot\cdot x}$ depends on ξ^κ and η^k and consequently the quantity (6.9) depends on ξ^κ, η^k, and $U_{\mathfrak{b}}^a$. Now the three elements ξ^κ, E_p, and E_m are said to form an *ordinary triplet* if the i-rank of $U_{\mathfrak{b}}^b T_{i b}^{\cdot\cdot x}$ has the same value for this triplet as for all neighbouring triplets. From this it follows that a triplet is ordinary if it is sufficiently close to an ordinary triplet and that in every neighbourhood of every extraordinary triplet there exists at least one ordinary triplet. All ordinary triplets have the same i-rank and all extraordinary ones lower i-ranks.

In order to obtain a geometrical interpretation of the arithmetic invariant τ_p of the $\mathfrak{S}_d^m$-field we consider a fixed E_p of $\mathfrak{S}_{d_p}^p(\xi^\kappa)$ and ask for all E_m's of $\mathfrak{S}_d^m(\xi^\kappa)$ containing this E_p and forming with ξ^κ and E_p an ordinary triplet. Let $U_{\mathfrak{b}}^a$ be the connecting quantity of E_p in a variable E_m of $\mathfrak{S}_d^m(\xi^\kappa)$ containing E_p. Then we have

$$U_{\mathfrak{b}}^\kappa = U_{\mathfrak{b}}^b B_b^\kappa(\xi^\nu, \eta^k) \quad (b = 1,\ldots,\mathrm{m};\ \mathfrak{b} = \dot{1},\ldots,\dot{p};\ k = \bar{1},\ldots,\bar{d}), \tag{6.11}$$

and in this equation $U_{\mathfrak{b}}^\kappa$ is the fixed connecting quantity of E_p in the local E_n in ξ^κ whilst $U_{\mathfrak{b}}^b$ is the varying connecting quantity of E_p with respect to the varying E_m and the B_b^κ are known functions of ξ^κ and

η^k. Hence to determine all possible E_m's of $\mathfrak{S}_d^m(\xi^\kappa)$ through E_p we have to solve the np equations

$$U_{\mathfrak{b}}^b B_b^\kappa(\xi^\nu, \eta^k) = U_{\mathfrak{b}}^\kappa = \text{constants} \quad (b = 1,\dots,\text{m};\ \mathfrak{b} = \dot{1},\dots,\dot{\text{p}};\ k = \bar{1},\dots,\bar{d}) \tag{6.12}$$

in which the ξ^ν have to be looked upon as constants and the η^k, $U_{\mathfrak{b}}^b$ as $d+mp$ unknowns. The functional matrix of this system has the form

$$\| \; B_b^\kappa B_{\mathfrak{b}}^{\mathfrak{c}} \quad U_{\mathfrak{b}}^b(\partial_i B_b^\lambda) B_\lambda^c B_c^\kappa - U_{\mathfrak{b}}^b T_{ib}^{\cdot\cdot y} C_y^\kappa \; \|$$

$$(b, c = 1,\dots,\text{m};\ y = \text{m}+1,\dots,\text{n};\ i = \bar{1},\dots,\bar{d};\ \mathfrak{b}, \mathfrak{c} = \dot{1},\dots,\dot{\text{p}}). \tag{6.13}$$

Since the i-rank of $U_{\mathfrak{b}}^b T_{ib}^{\cdot\cdot y} C_y^\kappa$ is $d - \tau_p$ the η^k can be interchanged in such a way that the $U_{\mathfrak{b}}^b T_{i'b}^{\cdot\cdot y} C_y^\kappa$ ($i' = \overline{\tau_p + 1},\dots,\bar{d}$) are linearly independent. Now the B_b^κ and C_y^κ are linearly independent, and from this it follows that the derivatives with respect to the $\eta^{k'}$ ($k' = \overline{\tau_p + 1},\dots,\bar{d}$) and the derivatives with respect to the $U_{\mathfrak{b}}^b$ are all linearly independent of each other, whereas the remaining derivatives can be expressed linearly in them. This implies that the $U_{\mathfrak{b}}^b$ and the $\eta^{k'}$ can be solved from (6.12) as functions of the $\eta^{\bar{1}},\dots, \eta^{\bar{\tau}_p}$. Hence the number of E_m's of $\mathfrak{S}_d^m(\xi^\kappa)$ containing E_p is just ∞^{τ_p}. Now that this is known the formula (6.10) gets an intuitive meaning. The number of E_m's in $\mathfrak{S}_d^m(\xi^\kappa)$ is ∞^d and the number of E_p's in every E_m is $\infty^{p(m-p)}$. Hence, if every E_p were contained in only one E_m the total number of E_p's would be $\infty^{p(m-p)+d}$. But since every E_p is contained in ∞^{τ_p} E_m's the real number of E_p's contained in all E_m's of $\mathfrak{S}_d^m(\xi^\kappa)$ is $\infty^{p(m-p)+d-\tau_p}$.

In the local E_n in ξ^κ we now consider the cone consisting of all ∞^{τ_p} E_m's of $\mathfrak{S}_d^m(\xi^\kappa)$ containing a given E_p. This cone will be denoted by $\mathfrak{C}(E_p)$. Now we consider an E_1 of $\mathfrak{C}(E_p)$ not contained in E_p. Then this E_1 and E_p span an E_{p+1} belonging to $\mathfrak{S}_{d_{p+1}}^{p+1}$ and consequently contained in $\infty^{\tau_{p+1}}$ of the ∞^{τ_p} E_m's containing E_p. From this it follows that the E_1 is contained in these $\infty^{\tau_{p+1}}$ E_m's. The number of E_m's of $\mathfrak{S}_d^m$ containing E_p is ∞^{τ_p}. Hence the number of E_1's contained in these E_m's would be $\infty^{m-1+\tau_p}$ if every E_1 were contained in only one E_m. But since every E_1 is contained in $\infty^{\tau_{p+1}}$ E_m's the real number of E_1's is $\infty^{m-1+\tau_p-\tau_{p+1}}$ and the dimension of the cone is $m+\tau_p-\tau_{p+1}$. Here is an exact proof. Consider an ordinary triplet ξ^κ, E_p, E_m. Then the number of E_m's of $\mathfrak{S}_d^m(\xi^\kappa)$ containing E_p is ∞^{τ_p}. If the ξ^κ are looked upon as constants the η^k of these E_m's depend on τ_p parameters

$$\eta^k = f^k(\zeta^{i'}) \quad (k = \bar{1},\dots,\bar{d};\ i' = 1',\dots,\tau_p'). \tag{6.14}$$

These E_m's satisfy the equations

$$U_{\mathfrak{b}}^{b} B_{b}^{\kappa}(\xi^{\kappa}, f^{k}) = U_{\mathfrak{b}}^{\kappa} = \text{constants} \quad (b = 1,\ldots,\mathrm{m};\ \mathfrak{b} = \dot{1},\ldots,\dot{\mathrm{p}};\ k = \bar{1},\ldots,\bar{d}) \tag{6.15}$$

in which the $U_{\mathfrak{b}}^{b}$ have to be considered as functions of the $\zeta^{i'}$. By differentiation we get

$$(\partial_{i'} U_{\mathfrak{b}}^{b}) B_{b}^{\kappa} + U_{\mathfrak{b}}^{b}(\partial_{j} B_{b}^{\kappa}) \partial_{i'} f^{j} = 0$$
$$(b = 1,\ldots,\mathrm{m};\ \mathfrak{b} = \dot{1},\ldots,\dot{\mathrm{p}};\ j = \bar{1},\ldots,\bar{d};\ i' = 1',\ldots,\tau_p') \tag{6.16}$$

and by transvection with C_{κ}^{x}

$$U_{\mathfrak{b}}^{b} T_{j\dot{b}}{}^{x} \partial_{i'} f^{j} = 0 \quad (b = 1,\ldots,\mathrm{m};\ \mathfrak{b} = \dot{1},\ldots,\dot{\mathrm{p}};\ x = \mathrm{m}+1,\ldots,\mathrm{n};$$
$$j = \bar{1},\ldots,\bar{d};\ i' = 1',\ldots,\tau_p'). \tag{6.17}$$

As we know, the j-rank of $U_{\mathfrak{b}}^{b}\, T_{j\dot{b}}{}^{x}$ is $d-\tau_p$ and this implies that the support of the j-domain is an E_{τ_p}. Now the τ_p vectors $\partial_{i'} f^{j}$ ($i' = 1',\ldots, \tau_p'$) are linearly independent and span the tangent E_{τ_p} of the manifold of all E_m's concerned in the X_d of the parameters η^k and (6.17) expresses the fact that these vectors all lie in the E_{τ_p} first mentioned. *Hence the support of the j-domain of* $U_{\mathfrak{b}}^{b}\, T_{j\dot{b}}{}^{x}$ *is the tangent* E_{τ_p} *of the* X_{τ_p} *in the* X_d *of the* η^k *representing all* E_m*'s of* $\mathfrak{S}_d^m$ *containing the* E_p *of the ordinary triplet fixed by* ξ^κ, η^k, *and* $U_{\mathfrak{b}}^{a}$. Now consider the $\mathfrak{C}(E_p)$ consisting of all ∞^{τ_p} E_m's containing E_p and a vector v^κ on this cone not lying in E_p. Since this vector lies in one of the E_m's we have for v^κ the parametric form

$$v^{\kappa} = p^{b} B_{b}^{\kappa}(\xi^{\kappa}, f^{k}) \quad (b = 1,\ldots,\mathrm{m};\ k = \bar{1},\ldots,\bar{d}) \tag{6.18}$$

with the τ_p+m parameters p^b, $\zeta^{i'}$. The dimension of $\mathfrak{C}(E_p)$ is the number of linearly independent vectors among the τ_p+m vectors

$$\partial v^{\kappa}/\partial p^{b} = B_{b}^{\kappa},$$
$$\partial v^{\kappa}/\partial \zeta^{i'} = p^{b}(\partial_{j} B_{b}^{\kappa}) B_{\lambda}^{c} B_{c}^{\kappa}\, \partial_{i'} f^{j} + p^{b} T_{j\dot{b}}{}^{x} C_{x}^{\kappa}\, \partial_{i'} f^{j}$$
$$(b = 1,\ldots,\mathrm{m};\ j = \bar{1},\ldots,\bar{d};\ i' = 1',\ldots,\tau_p') \tag{6.19}$$

and this number equals m plus the number of linearly independent vectors among the τ_p vectors

$$p^{b} T_{j\dot{b}}{}^{x} C_{x}^{\kappa}\, \partial_{i'} f^{j} \quad (b = 1,\ldots,\mathrm{m};\ x = \mathrm{m}+1,\ldots,\mathrm{n};\ j = \bar{1},\ldots,\bar{d};$$
$$i' = 1',\ldots,\tau_p';\ \kappa = 1,\ldots,n). \tag{6.20}$$

Since C_{x}^{κ} has rank $n-m$ this number is the same as the number of linearly independent vectors among the τ_p vectors

$$p^{b} T_{j\dot{b}}{}^{x} \partial_{i'} f^{j} \quad (b = 1,\ldots,\mathrm{m};\ j = \bar{1},\ldots,\bar{d};\ i' = 1',\ldots,\tau_p';\ x = \mathrm{m}+1,\ldots,\mathrm{n}). \tag{6.21}$$

If this number is λ the support of the i'-domain has the dimension $\tau_p-\lambda$. Now we know that the τ_p contravariant vectors $\partial_{i'} f^{j}$ span the support E_{τ_p} of the j-region of $U_{\mathfrak{b}}^b\,T_{j\dot{b}}{}^x$. Hence $\tau_p-\lambda$ is also the dimension of the support of the j-domain of the system

$$U_{\mathfrak{b}}^b\,T_{j\dot{b}}{}^x,\quad p^b T_{j\dot{b}}{}^x\quad(\mathfrak{b}=\dot{1},...,\dot{p}).\tag{6.22}$$

If now ξ^κ, B_b^κ, and $U_{\mathfrak{b}}^b$, p^b determine an ordinary triplet ξ^κ, E_{p+1}, E_m, we know that the dimension of this support is τ_{p+1} and from this it follows that

$$\tau_p-\lambda=\tau_{p+1}\tag{6.23}$$

and that consequently the dimension of $\mathfrak{C}(E_p)$ is $m+\tau_p-\tau_{p+1}$. We collect results in the theorem

THEOREM IX.7. *If ξ^κ, E_p, E_m and ξ^κ, E_{p+1}, E_m are ordinary triplets and if $E_p\subset E_{p+1}$, the cone $\mathfrak{C}(E_p)$ has the dimension $m+\tau_p-\tau_{p+1}$.*

From this it follows immediately that if E_p and E_{p+1} satisfy the conditions of Theorem IX.7 there exist $\infty^{\rho_{p+1}}\,E_{p+1}$'s of $\mathfrak{S}_{d_{p+1}}^{p+1}$ containing E_p and forming ordinary triplets with ξ^κ and E_m, ρ_{p+1} being defined by

$$\rho_{p+1}\overset{\text{def}}{=} m-p-1+\tau_p-\tau_{p+1}\quad(0\leqslant p\leqslant m-1).\tag{6.24}$$

7. The stationary $\mathfrak{S}_{d_p}^p(\xi^\kappa)$. The principal theorem of integrability of $\mathfrak{S}_d^m$-fields

$\mathfrak{S}_{d_p}^p(\xi^\kappa)$ and $\mathfrak{S}_{d_{p+1}}^{p+1}(\xi^\kappa)$ consist of all E_p's and E_{p+1}'s respectively contained in the $\infty^d\,E_m$'s of $\mathfrak{S}_d^m(\xi^\kappa)$. Consequently $\mathfrak{S}_{d_p}^p(\xi^\kappa)$ consists of all E_p's contained in the $\infty^{d_{p+1}}\,E_{p+1}$'s of $\mathfrak{S}_{d_{p+1}}^{p+1}(\xi^\kappa)$. Now every E_p of $\mathfrak{S}_{d_p}^p(\xi^\kappa)$ is a point in $\mathfrak{P}^p(\xi^\kappa)$ and all E_p's lying in a given E_{p+1} are the points of a flat p-dimensional space P_p in $\mathfrak{P}^p(\xi^\kappa)$. Hence $\mathfrak{S}_{d_p}^p(\xi^\kappa)$ consists of $\infty^{d_{p+1}}\,P_p$'s. Now we consider one of these P_p's and construct in $p+1$ linearly independent points of it the tangent P_{d_p} of $\mathfrak{S}_{d_p}^p(\xi^\kappa)$. In general these $p+1$ P_{d_p}'s will not coincide and their junction, viz. the flat space in $\mathfrak{P}^p(\xi^\kappa)$ of smallest dimension containing them all (cf. I, § 2), has a dimension $\geqslant d_p$. Let this junction be called $J(P_p)$. It is readily proved that the tangent P_{d_p} in every point of P_p is contained in $J(P_p)$ and that, therefore, $J(P_p)$ depends only on the choice of P_p and not on the choice of the $p+1$ points. The tangent P_{d_p} in any point of P_p is also contained in the tangent $P_{p(n-p)}$ of $\mathfrak{S}^p(\xi^\kappa)$ in that point and consequently also in the section of $J(P_p)$ with this tangent $P_{p(n-p)}$.

If for each point of each of the $\infty^{d_{p+1}}\,P_p$'s of $\mathfrak{S}_{d_p}^p(\xi^\kappa)$ the tangent P_{d_p} of $\mathfrak{S}_{d_p}^p(\xi^\kappa)$ coincides with the section of $J(P_p)$ with the tangent $P_{p(n-p)}$ of $\mathfrak{S}^p(\xi^\kappa)$, $\mathfrak{S}_{d_p}^p(\xi^\kappa)$ is said to be stationary.†

---

† It is understood that in this definition we restrict ourselves to those spaces P_p and those points in P_p for whose corresponding elements E_{p+1} and E_p there exists an E_m of $\mathfrak{S}_d^m(\xi^\kappa)$ containing E_{p+1} and such that ξ^κ, E_p, E_m is an ordinary triplet.

The following summary may be useful:

	$\mathfrak{P}^p(\xi^\kappa)$ $\supset$	$\mathfrak{S}^p(\xi^\kappa)$ $\supset$	$\mathfrak{S}^p_{d_p}(\xi^\kappa)$ $\supset$	P_p
represents: . .	all p-vectors at ξ^κ to within a scalar factor	all E_p's at ξ^κ	all E_p's at ξ^κ in $\mathfrak{S}^p_{d_p}(\xi^\kappa)$	the E_p's in a definite E_{p+1} of $\mathfrak{S}^{p+1}_{d_{p+1}}(\xi^\kappa)$
dimension: . .	$\binom{n}{p}-1$	$p(n-p)$	d_p	p
the tangent space is a:	$P_{\binom{n}{p}-1}$ $\supset$	$P_{p(n-p)}$ $\supset$	P_{d_p} $\supset$	P_p

$J(P_p)$ = junction of all P_{d_p}'s belonging to the points of P_p.
Always: $P_{d_p} \subset$ section of $J(P_p)$ and $P_{p(n-p)}$.
In the stationary case: P_{d_p} = section of $J(P_p)$ and $P_{p(n-p)}$.

If we take $p = 0$ the cone $\mathfrak{C}(E_0)$ is the same as the cone $\mathfrak{C}(\xi^\kappa)$ defined in IX, § 5. $\mathfrak{C}(E_0)$ consists of all ∞^{d_1} E_1's of $\mathfrak{S}^1_{d_1}$ and each E_1 is a point of $\mathfrak{P}^1(\xi^\kappa)$. The ∞^1 E_1's lying in an E_2 of $\mathfrak{S}^2_{d_2}$ are the points of a P_1 in $\mathfrak{P}^1(\xi^\kappa)$ and consequently the image of $\mathfrak{C}(E_0)$ consists of ∞^{d_2} P_1's. According to our definition $\mathfrak{S}^1_{d_1}$ is stationary if its tangent space in any point of any P_1 is the section of the junction of all tangent spaces in all points of P_1 with the tangent space of $\mathfrak{S}^1(\xi^\kappa)$. But since $\mathfrak{S}^1(\xi^\kappa)$ is identical with $\mathfrak{P}^1(\xi^\kappa)$ this means that the tangent spaces in all points of P_1 are the same and from this it follows that the tangent space of $\mathfrak{C}(E_0)$ is the same for all points of any E_2 of $\mathfrak{S}^2_{d_2}(\xi^\kappa)$ and consequently for all points of any E_m of $\mathfrak{S}^m_d(\xi^\kappa)$. Hence the definition of stationarity of $\mathfrak{S}^p_{d_p}(\xi^\kappa)$ coincides for $p = 1$ with the definition of stationariness of $\mathfrak{C}(\xi^\kappa)$ given in IX, § 5.

Now the following theorem can be formulated:

THEOREM IX.8. (*Principal theorem of integrability of $\mathfrak{S}^m_d$-fields.*)† *If an $\mathfrak{S}^m_d$-field given in an $\mathfrak{N}(\underset{0}{\xi^\kappa}, \underset{0}{\eta^k})$ is preferred and if its induced $\mathfrak{S}^p_{d_p}(\xi^\kappa)$'s are stationary in all points of $\mathfrak{N}(\underset{0}{\xi^\kappa}, \underset{0}{\eta^k})$ for each value of $p = 1,..., m-1$, there exists a region in $\mathfrak{N}(\underset{0}{\xi^\kappa}, \underset{0}{\eta^k})$ where the field is completely integrable.*

This theorem will be proved in the next section.

In order to obtain an algebraic test for a stationary $\mathfrak{S}^p_{d_p}(\xi^\kappa)$ we consider an ordinary triplet ξ^κ, E_p, E_m and an E_{p+1} containing E_p and belonging to $\mathfrak{S}^{p+1}_{d_{p+1}}(\xi^\kappa)$. Then each E_p in E_{p+1} which is sufficiently close to E_p forms with ξ^κ and E_m an ordinary triplet. In E_{p+1} we choose $p+1$ of these E_p's having no E_1 in common. Their images in $\mathfrak{P}^p(\xi^\kappa)$ are $p+1$ linearly independent points $Q_1,..., Q_{p+1}$. Every set of p of these E_p's have an E_1 in common. We denote the vector of E_m in the section

† Cf. v. d. Kulk 1942. 2; 1945. 1, ch. ii.

of the E_p's corresponding to $Q_1, \ldots, Q_{\epsilon-1}, Q_{\epsilon+1}, \ldots, Q_{p+1}$ by W_ϵ^a. These $p+1$ vectors are linearly independent and the contravariant p-vector

$$W_{[1}^{\kappa_1} \ldots W_p^{\kappa_p} \delta_{p+1]}^{\epsilon}; \quad W_\epsilon^\kappa \overset{\text{def}}{=} W_\epsilon^b B_b^\kappa \quad (\epsilon = 1, \ldots, p+1; \; b = 1, \ldots, m) \quad (7.1)$$

lies in the E_p corresponding to Q_ϵ ($\epsilon = 1, \ldots, p+1$). Accordingly the tangent P_{d_p} of $\mathfrak{S}_{d_p}^p(\xi^\kappa)$ in Q_ϵ is spanned by the $d+mp$ points of $\mathfrak{P}^p(\xi)$

$$\begin{aligned} &(a) \quad W_\eta^b T_{\cdot ib}^{\cdot\cdot y} C_y^{[\kappa_1} W_{[2}^{\kappa_2} \ldots W_p^{\kappa_p]} \delta_1^\eta \delta_{p+1]}^\epsilon \quad (b = 1, \ldots, m; \; y = m+1, \ldots, n; \\ &(b) \quad B_b^{[\kappa_1} W_{[2}^{\kappa_2} \ldots W_p^{\kappa_1]} \delta_1^\eta \delta_{p+1]}^\epsilon \qquad\qquad i = \bar{1}, \ldots, \bar{d}; \; \epsilon, \eta = 1, \ldots, p+1), \end{aligned} \quad (7.2)$$

ϵ being fixed (cf. (6.7)). The junction $J(P_p)$ of these $p+1$ tangent P_{d_p}'s is spanned by all points (7.2), ϵ taking all values $1, \ldots, p+1$. Hence an arbitrary point of $J(P_p)$ has the coordinates

$$(\lambda_\epsilon^i W_\eta^b T_{\cdot ib}^{\cdot\cdot y} C_y^{[\kappa_1} + \lambda_{\epsilon\eta}^b B_b^{[\kappa_1}) W_{[2}^{\kappa_2} \ldots W_p^{\kappa_p]} \delta_1^\eta \delta_{p+1]}^\epsilon$$
$$(b = 1, \ldots, m; \; y = m+1, \ldots, n; \; i = \bar{1}, \ldots, \bar{d}; \; \epsilon, \eta = 1, \ldots, p+1). \quad (7.3)$$

Now in an arbitrary point of P_p we construct the tangent $P_{p(n-p)}$ of $\mathfrak{S}^p(\xi^\kappa)$. Since the points $Q_1, \ldots, Q_{p+1}$ are chosen at random we may suppose that Q_{p+1} is this point. Using (6.2) and splitting up A into B and C according to (6.5) we see that the tangent $P_{p(n-p)}$ is spanned by the points of $\mathfrak{P}^p(\xi^\kappa)$

$$\begin{aligned} &C_y^{[\kappa_1} W_{[2}^{\kappa_2} \ldots W_p^{\kappa_p]} \delta_{1]}^\beta \\ &B_b^{[\kappa_1} W_{[2}^{\kappa_2} \ldots W_p^{\kappa_p]} \delta_{1]}^\beta \end{aligned} \quad (\beta = 1, \ldots, p; \; b = 1, \ldots, m; \; y = m+1, \ldots, n). \quad (7.4)$$

Consequently an arbitrary point of this tangent $P_{p(n-p)}$ has the coordinates

$$(\mu_\beta^y C_y^{[\kappa_1} + \mu_\beta^b B_b^{[\kappa_1}) W_{[2}^{\kappa_2} \ldots W_p^{\kappa_p]} \delta_{1]}^\beta \quad (\beta = 1, \ldots, p; \; b = 1, \ldots, m;$$
$$y = m+1, \ldots, n). \quad (7.5)$$

Every point of the section of $J(P_p)$ with the tangent $P_{p(n-p)}$ in Q_{p+1} can be expressed either in the form (7.3) or in the form (7.5). Hence, since $C_\kappa^x W_\epsilon^\kappa$ ($\epsilon = 1, \ldots, p+1$) are zero we get for the points of this section from (7.3) and (7.5) by transvection with $C_{\kappa_1}^x$

$$\lambda_\epsilon^i W_\eta^b T_{\cdot ib}^{\cdot\cdot x} W_{[2}^{\kappa_2} \ldots W_p^{\kappa_p} \delta_1^\eta \delta_{p+1]}^\epsilon = \mu_\beta^x W_{[2}^{\kappa_2} \ldots W_p^{\kappa_p} \delta_{1]}^\beta \quad (b = 1, \ldots, m;$$
$$x = m+1, \ldots, n; \; i = \bar{1}, \ldots, \bar{d}; \; \epsilon, \eta = 1, \ldots, p+1; \; \beta = 1, \ldots, p) \quad (7.6)$$

or

$$-T_{\cdot ib}^{\cdot\cdot x} \lambda_{[1}^i W_{p+1}^b W_2^{\kappa_2} \ldots W_{p]}^{\kappa_p} = \mu_{[1}^x W_2^{\kappa_2} \ldots W_{p]}^{\kappa_p}$$
$$(b = 1, \ldots, m; \; x = m+1, \ldots, n; \; i = \bar{1}, \ldots, \bar{d}). \quad (7.7)$$

Since the W_ϵ^κ ($\epsilon = 1,\ldots,p+1$) are linearly independent, (7.7) is equivalent to

$$\begin{aligned}
&(a) \qquad \lambda^i_{[\beta} W^b_{\gamma]} T_{\cdot i b}^{\cdot\cdot x} = 0 \qquad && (b = 1,\ldots,m;\ x = m+1,\ldots,n;\\
&(b) \qquad \frac{2}{p+1}\lambda^i_{[p+1} W^b_{\beta]} T_{\cdot i b}^{\cdot\cdot x} = \mu^x_\beta && i = \bar{1},\ldots,\bar{d};\ \beta,\gamma = 1,\ldots,p). \qquad (7.8)
\end{aligned}$$

Now these equations express the fact that the first term of (7.3) equals the first term of (7.5). Hence the second terms have to be equal as well:

$$\lambda^b_{\epsilon\eta} B_b^{[\kappa_1} W_{[2}^{\kappa_2}\ldots W_p^{\kappa_p]}\delta^\epsilon_1 \delta^\eta_{p+1]} = \mu^b_\beta B_b^{[\kappa_1} W_{[2}^{\kappa_2}\ldots W_p^{\kappa_p]}\delta^\beta_{1]}$$
$$(b = 1,\ldots,m;\ \epsilon,\eta = 1,\ldots,p+1;\ \beta = 1,\ldots,p). \qquad (7.9)$$

(7.8) and (7.9) are the necessary and sufficient conditions that a point with the parameters λ^i_β, $\lambda^b_{\epsilon\eta}$, μ^b_β, μ^x_β is a point of the section of $J(P_p)$ and the tangent $P_{p(n-p)}$ of $\mathfrak{S}^p$. Now the tangent P_{d_p} of $\mathfrak{S}^p_{d_p}(\xi^\kappa)$ in Q_{p+1} is contained in $J(P_p)$ and in $P_{n(n-p)}$. Hence in order to find the necessary and sufficient conditions that P_{d_p} coincides with the section of $J(P_p)$ and $P_{p(n-p)}$ we have only to establish the necessary and sufficient conditions that this section is contained in P_{d_p}. According to (6.7) P_{d_p} is spanned by the points

$$\begin{aligned}
&W^b_\beta T_{\cdot i b}^{\cdot\cdot y} C_y^{[\kappa_1} W_{[2}^{\kappa_2}\ldots W_p^{\kappa_p]}\delta^\beta_{1]} \qquad && (b = 1,\ldots,m;\ y = m+1,\ldots,n;\\
&B_b^{[\kappa_1} W_{[2}^{\kappa_2}\ldots W_p^{\kappa_p]}\delta^\beta_{1]} && i = \bar{1},\ldots,\bar{d};\ \beta = 1,\ldots,p). \qquad (7.10)
\end{aligned}$$

Accordingly an arbitrary point of P_{d_p} has the coordinates

$$(\nu^i W^b_\beta T_{\cdot i b}^{\cdot\cdot y} C_y^{[\kappa_1} + \nu^b_\beta B_b^{[\kappa_1}) W_{[2}^{\kappa_2}\ldots W_p^{\kappa_p]}\delta^\beta_{1]}$$
$$(b = 1,\ldots,m;\ y = m+1,\ldots,n;\ i = \bar{1},\ldots,\bar{d};\ \beta = 1,\ldots,p). \qquad (7.11)$$

A point of $P_{p(n-p)}$ is contained in P_{d_p} if and only if (7.5) equals (7.11). Transvecting with $C^x_{\kappa_1}$ we get

$$\nu^i W^b_\beta T_{\cdot i b}^{\cdot\cdot x} = \mu^x_\beta \quad (b = 1,\ldots,m;\ x = m+1,\ldots,n;\ i = \bar{1},\ldots,\bar{d};$$
$$\beta = 1,\ldots,p) \qquad (7.12)$$

as conditions that the first term of (7.5) equals the first term of (7.11). The second terms can always be made equal to each other, for instance, by taking $\nu^b_\beta = \mu^b_\beta$. Consequently a point of $P_{p(n-p)}$ with the parameters μ^y_β, μ^b_β is contained in P_{d_p} if and only if the equations (7.12) with the ν^i as unknowns are compatible. If the point of $P_{p(n-p)}$ is a point of the section of $P_{p(n-p)}$ with $J(P_p)$, (7.8) holds and consequently (7.12) takes the form

$$\lambda^i_\beta W^b_{p+1} T_{\cdot i b}^{\cdot\cdot x} = \sigma^i W^b_\beta T_{\cdot i b}^{\cdot\cdot x} \quad (b = 1,\ldots,m;\ x = m+1,\ldots,n;$$
$$i = \bar{1},\ldots,\bar{d};\ \beta = 1,\ldots,p) \qquad (7.13)$$

with $\sigma^i = \lambda^i_{p+1} - (p+1)\nu^i$. Hence the section of $J(P_p)$ and $P_{p(n-p)}$ is contained in P_{d_p} if and only if the equations (7.13) with the d unknowns σ^i are compatible as a consequence of (7.8 a). Now every vector in the neighbourhood of W^b_{p+1} forms with $W^b_1, \ldots, W^b_p$ a set of $p+1$ vectors such that each set of p of them spans an E_p forming with ξ^κ and E_m an ordinary triplet. Hence, if W^b_{p+1} is replaced by any vector in a sufficiently small neighbourhood of W^b_{p+1}, (7.13) has to be compatible as a consequence of (7.8 a) as well. But that means that the section of $J(P_p)$ and $P_{p(n-p)}$ is contained in P_{d_p} if and only if the equations

$$\lambda^i_\beta T_{i b}^{\cdot\cdot x} = \sigma^i_b W^a_\beta T_{i a}^{\cdot\cdot x} \quad (a, b = 1,\ldots, \mathrm{m};\ x = \mathrm{m}+1,\ldots, \mathrm{n};\ i = \bar{1},\ldots, \bar{d};\ \beta = 1,\ldots, p) \qquad (7.14)$$

with the md unknowns σ^i_b are compatible as a consequence of (7.8 a). W^b_β is a special form of the contravariant connecting quantity of the E_p we started from in E_m. Since $U^b_{\mathfrak{b}}$ is the general form of this connecting quantity, relations of the form

$$W^b_\beta = P^{\mathfrak{b}}_\beta U^b_{\mathfrak{b}} \quad (\mathrm{Det}(P^{\mathfrak{b}}_\beta) \neq 0;\ b = 1,\ldots, \mathrm{m};\ \beta = 1,\ldots, p;\ \mathfrak{b} = \dot{1},\ldots, \dot{p}) \qquad (7.15)$$

exist. Hence, writing

$$\lambda^i_{\mathfrak{b}} = \overset{-1}{P}{}^\beta_{\mathfrak{b}} \lambda^i_\beta \quad (i = \bar{1},\ldots, \bar{d};\ \beta = 1,\ldots, p;\ \mathfrak{b} = \dot{1},\ldots, \dot{p}), \qquad (7.16)$$

(7.8 a) is equivalent to

$$\lambda^i_{[\mathfrak{c}} U^b_{\mathfrak{b}]} T_{i b}^{\cdot\cdot x} = 0 \quad (b = 1,\ldots, \mathrm{m};\ x = \mathrm{m}+1,\ldots, \mathrm{n};\ i = \bar{1},\ldots, \bar{d};\ \mathfrak{b}, \mathfrak{c} = \dot{1},\ldots, \dot{p}) \qquad (7.17)$$

and (7.14) equivalent to

$$\lambda^i_{\mathfrak{b}} T_{i b}^{\cdot\cdot x} = \sigma^i_b U^c_{\mathfrak{b}} T_{i c}^{\cdot\cdot x} \quad (b, c = 1,\ldots, \mathrm{m};\ x = \mathrm{m}+1,\ldots, \mathrm{n};\ i = \bar{1},\ldots, \bar{d};\ \mathfrak{b} = \dot{1},\ldots, \dot{p}). \qquad (7.18)$$

(7.18) expresses the fact that the $\mathfrak{b}x$-domain of $\lambda^i_{\mathfrak{b}} T_{i b}^{\cdot\cdot x}$ is contained in the $\mathfrak{b}x$-domain of $U^c_{\mathfrak{b}} T_{i c}^{\cdot\cdot x}$. This proves the theorem

THEOREM IX.9. *$\mathfrak{S}^p_{d_p}(\xi^\kappa)$ is stationary if and only if for each ordinary triplet determined by ξ^κ, η^k, $U^a_{\mathfrak{b}}$ and each solution of* (7.17) *the equations* (7.18) *have solutions σ^i_b.*

8. Proof of the principal theorem of integrability†

A chain of elements

$$\xi^\kappa = E_0 \subset E_1 \subset \ldots \subset E_{m-1} \subset E_m, \quad E_m \in \mathfrak{S}^m_d\text{-field} \qquad (8.1)$$

† Cf. v. d. Kulk 1943. 7; 1945. 1, ch. ii.

is said to be *ordinary* if each triplet ξ^κ, E_p, E_m $(1 \leqslant p \leqslant m-1)$ is ordinary. From this it follows that every chain whose elements are sufficiently close to the corresponding elements of an ordinary chain is ordinary as well. In order to prove that if an $\mathfrak{S}_d^m$-field be given ordinary chains always exist, we consider the manifold of the $n+d+m^2$ variables ξ^κ, η^k, $U_{\dot{1}}^a, \ldots, U_{\dot{m}}^a$. In this manifold a region $\mathfrak{R}_0$ exists where $T_{ib}^{\cdot\cdot x}$ has the maximum rank and where the determinant of $U_{\mathfrak{b}}^a$ ($a = 1, \ldots, \mathrm{m}$; $\mathfrak{b} = \dot{1}, \ldots, \dot{\mathrm{m}}$) does not vanish. In $\mathfrak{R}_0$ a region $\mathfrak{R}_1$ always exists where the i-rank of $U_{\dot{1}}^b T_{ib}^{\cdot\cdot x}$ is constant, in $\mathfrak{R}_1$ a region $\mathfrak{R}_2$ where the i-rank of the system $U_{\dot{1}}^b T_{ib}^{\cdot\cdot x}$, $U_{\dot{2}}^b T_{ib}^{\cdot\cdot x}$ is constant, etc. At last we get a region $\mathfrak{R}_{m-1}$ where the i-ranks of all systems

$$\begin{array}{l} T_{ib}^{\cdot\cdot x}, \\ U_{\dot{1}}^b T_{ib}^{\cdot\cdot x}, \\ \quad \cdot \quad \cdot \quad \cdot \\ U_{\dot{1}}^b T_{ib}^{\cdot\cdot x}, \quad \ldots, \quad U_{\dot{\mathrm{m}}-\dot{1}}^b T_{ib}^{\cdot\cdot x} \end{array}$$
$$(b = 1, \ldots, \mathrm{m};\ x = \mathrm{m}+1, \ldots, \mathrm{n};\ i = \bar{1}, \ldots, \bar{d}) \quad (8.2)$$

are constant. Then the chain consisting of ξ^κ, the E_1 of $U_{\dot{1}}^a$, the E_2 of $U_{\dot{1}}^a$ and $U_{\dot{2}}^a$, etc., and the E_m with the coordinates ξ^κ, η^k is ordinary. Obviously in every neighbourhood of every extraordinary chain there always exists at least one ordinary chain.

Starting from this ordinary chain and supposing the $\mathfrak{S}_d^m$-field to be preferred with stationary $\mathfrak{S}_{d_p}^p(\xi^\kappa)$'s $(p = 1, \ldots, m-1)$, we will construct a chain

$$X^A = {}'E_0 \subset {}'E_1 \subset \ldots \subset {}'E_m \quad (8.3)$$

of integral elements of the field ${}'C_B^x$ in the ${}'X_{n+d}$ of ξ^κ and η^k (cf. IX, § 3) such that the reduction of ${}'E_p$ $(p = 1, \ldots, m)$ in ${}'E_{n+d}$ with respect to the invariant ${}'E_d$ is E_p. If ${}'U_{\mathfrak{b}}^A$ ($\mathfrak{b} = \dot{1}, \ldots, \dot{\mathrm{p}}$) is the connecting quantity of an ${}'E_p$ and if ${}'U_{\mathfrak{b}}^Q$ is defined by

$$'U_{\mathfrak{b}}^A = {}'U_{\mathfrak{b}}^Q\, {}'B_Q^A \quad (\mathfrak{b} = \dot{1}, \ldots, \dot{\mathrm{p}};\ A = 1, \ldots, n, \bar{1}, \ldots, \bar{d};$$
$$Q = 1, \ldots, \mathrm{m}, \bar{1}, \ldots, \bar{d}), \quad (8.4)$$

the necessary and sufficient condition that this ${}'E_p$ is an integral-${}'E_p$ of ${}'C_B^x$ is

$$'D_{RQ}^{\cdot\cdot x}\, {}'U_{\mathfrak{c}}^R\, {}'U_{\mathfrak{b}}^Q = 0 \quad (Q, R = 1, \ldots, \mathrm{m}, \bar{1}, \ldots, \bar{d};$$
$$\mathfrak{b}, \mathfrak{c} = \dot{1}, \ldots, \dot{\mathrm{p}}). \quad (8.5)$$

Now take ${}'U_{\dot{1}}^P$ according to the conditions

$$'U_{\dot{1}}^a = U_{\dot{1}}^a, \quad {}'U_{\dot{1}}^k = \text{arbitrary} \quad (a = 1, \ldots, \mathrm{m};\ k = \bar{1}, \ldots, \bar{d}), \quad (8.6)$$

then ${}'U_{\dot{1}}^P$ determines an integral-${}'E_1$ of ${}'C_B^x$ and its reduction with respect to the invariant $'E_d$ is E_1. Now suppose we have already found an integral-$'E_p$ whose reduction is E_p. Then the coordinates X^A, $'U^P_{\mathfrak{b}}$ of this $'E_p$ can always be chosen in such a way that

$$'U^a_{\mathfrak{b}} = U^a_{\mathfrak{b}} \quad (\mathfrak{b} = \dot{1},\ldots,\dot{p};\ a = 1,\ldots,m). \tag{8.7}$$

Since the $\mathfrak{S}_d^m$-field is preferred we have the relation (5.6), that is,

$$'D_{\dot{R}\dot{Q}}{}^x = -2\,'Z^i_{[R}\,'D_{|\dot{i}|\dot{Q}]}{}^x \quad (x = m+1,\ldots,n;\ i = \bar{1},\ldots,\bar{d};$$
$$Q, R = 1,\ldots,m,\bar{1},\ldots,\bar{d}) \tag{8.8}$$

and on account of these the relation (8.5) takes the form

$$'Z^i_R\,'D_{\dot{i}\dot{Q}}{}^x\,'U^R_{[\mathfrak{c}}\,'U^Q_{\mathfrak{b}]} = 0 \quad (x = m+1,\ldots,n;\ i = \bar{1},\ldots,\bar{d};\ \mathfrak{b},\mathfrak{c} = \dot{1},\ldots,\dot{p};$$
$$Q, R = 1,\ldots,m,\bar{1},\ldots,\bar{d}) \tag{8.9}$$

or, according to (5.2), (4.11), and (8.7),

$$T_{\dot{i}\dot{b}}{}^x \lambda^i_{[\mathfrak{c}}\, U^b_{\mathfrak{b}]} = 0 \quad (b = 1,\ldots,m;\ x = m+1,\ldots,n;$$
$$i = \bar{1},\ldots,\bar{d};\ \mathfrak{b},\mathfrak{c} = \dot{1},\ldots,\dot{p}), \tag{8.10}$$

where $\lambda^i_{\mathfrak{c}}$ is defined by

$$\lambda^i_{\mathfrak{c}} \overset{\text{def}}{=} {}'U^i_{\mathfrak{c}} - Z^i_c\, U^c_{\mathfrak{c}} \quad (c = 1,\ldots,m;\ i = \bar{1},\ldots,\bar{d};\ \mathfrak{c} = \dot{1},\ldots,\dot{p}). \tag{8.11}$$

Now let $'U^P$ be a vector spanning with $'E_p$ an $'E_{p+1}$. Then the necessary and sufficient condition that this $'E_{p+1}$ is an integral-$'E_{p+1}$ is

$$'D_{\dot{R}\dot{Q}}{}^x\,'U^R_{\mathfrak{c}}\,'U^Q = 0 \quad (x = m+1,\ldots,n;$$
$$Q, R = 1,\ldots,m,\bar{1},\ldots,\bar{d};\ \mathfrak{c} = \dot{1},\ldots,\dot{\ }). \tag{8.12}$$

According to (8.8) this relation takes the form

$$2\,'Z^i_{[R}\,'D_{|\dot{i}|\dot{Q}]}{}^x\,'U^R_{\mathfrak{c}}\,'U^Q = -2\,'Z^i_{[c}\,'D_{|\dot{i}|\dot{b}]}{}^x\,'U^b_{\mathfrak{c}}\,'U^c +$$
$$+\,'Z^i_j\,'D_{\dot{i}\dot{b}}{}^x\,'U^j_{\mathfrak{c}}\,'U^b - {}'Z^i_j\,'D_{\dot{i}\dot{b}}{}^x\,'U^b_{\mathfrak{c}}\,'U^j = 0$$
$$(b, c = 1,\ldots,m;\ x = m+1,\ldots,n;\ i,j = \bar{1},\ldots,\bar{d};$$
$$\mathfrak{c} = \dot{1},\ldots,\dot{p};\ Q, R = 1,\ldots,m,\bar{1},\ldots,\bar{d}) \tag{8.13}$$

or, according to (5.2), (4.11), and (8.7),

$$Z^i_c\, T_{\dot{i}\dot{b}}{}^x U^b_{\mathfrak{c}}\,'U^c - Z^i_c\, T_{\dot{i}\dot{b}}{}^x U^c_{\mathfrak{c}}\,'U^b + T_{\dot{i}\dot{b}}{}^x\,'U^i_{\mathfrak{c}}\,'U^b - T_{\dot{i}\dot{b}}{}^x\, U^b_{\mathfrak{c}}\,'U^i$$
$$= (-'U^i + Z^i_c\,'U^c) T_{\dot{i}\dot{b}}{}^x U^b_{\mathfrak{c}} + \lambda^i_{\mathfrak{c}}\,'U^b T_{\dot{i}\dot{b}}{}^x = 0$$
$$(b, c = 1,\ldots,m;\ x = m+1,\ldots,n;\ i,j = \bar{1},\ldots,\bar{d};\ \mathfrak{c} = \dot{1},\ldots,\dot{p}). \tag{8.14}$$

The triplet ξ^κ, E_p, E_m is ordinary and $\mathfrak{S}^p_{d_p}(\xi^\kappa)$ stationary. Further, the equations (8.10) are identical with (7.17). Hence the $\lambda^i_{\mathfrak{b}}$ satisfy the equations (7.17), and consequently values σ^i_b satisfying (7.18) exist. By substitution of (7.18) in (8.14) we get

$$('U^i - Z^i_c\,'U^c) U^b_{\mathfrak{c}}\, T_{\dot{i}\dot{b}}{}^x - \sigma^i_c\, U^b_{\mathfrak{c}}\, T_{\dot{i}\dot{b}}{}^x\,'U^c = \{'U^i - (Z^i_c + \sigma^i_c)'U^c\} U^b_{\mathfrak{c}}\, T_{\dot{i}\dot{b}}{}^x = 0$$
$$(b, c = 1,\ldots,m;\ x = m+1,\ldots,n;\ i = \bar{1},\ldots,\bar{d};\ \mathfrak{c} = \dot{1},\ldots,\dot{p}). \tag{8.15}$$

In order to satisfy this equation we may choose the vector $'U^P$ as follows:

$$'U^a = U^a, \quad 'U^k = (Z_b^k + \sigma_b^k) U^b$$
$$(a, b = 1, \ldots, \mathrm{m};\ k = \bar{1}, \ldots, \bar{d}), \qquad (8.16)$$

U^a being an arbitrary vector in E_{p+1} not contained in E_p. Then the reduction of the $'E_{p+1}$ spanned by $'E_p$ and $'U^P$ is E_{p+1}, and since the conditions (8.12) are satisfied this $'E_{p+1}$ is an integral-$'E_{p+1}$. Continuing in this way the chain (8.3) can be constructed.

Now we have only to prove that the chain (8.3) obtained in this way is regular. Since the quantity $U_{\mathfrak{b}}^b T_{\cdot i b}^{\cdot\cdot x}$ has the i-rank $d - \tau_p$ (cf. IX, § 6), (8.15) is equivalent to a system of $d - \tau_p$ linearly independent equations for the $'U^P$. Consequently $H('E_p)$ determined by (8.15) is $(m + \tau_p)$-dimensional. Hence, denoting this dimension by $p + 1 + 'r_{p+1}$ we have

$$'r_{p+1} = m - p - 1 + \tau_p. \qquad (8.17)$$

Notice that this formula is only valid if the $\mathfrak{S}_d^m$-field is preferred and the $\mathfrak{S}_{d_p}^p(\xi^\kappa)$ are stationary. Now τ_p has the same value for all ordinary chains in the neighbourhood of (8.1). Hence $'r_{p+1}$ has the same value for all integral-$'E_p$'s whose reductions belong to an ordinary chain in the neighbourhood of (8.1). Moreover, each integral-$'E_p$ of a chain in the neighbourhood of the chain (8.3) has a reduction in the neighbourhood of $'E_p$ which consequently belongs to an ordinary chain. From this it follows that $'r_{p+1}$ has the same value for all integral-$'E_p$'s in the neighbourhood of the $'E_p$ of the chain (8.3) and that consequently $'E_p$ is regular. Since this reasoning holds for all values of p, the chain (8.3) is regular and according to the theorem of integrability VIII.4 there exists at least one integral-$'X_m$ in $'X_{n+d}$ tangent to the last element $'E_m$ of the chain in the point X^A of this element. But since $'E_m$ has no direction in common with the local invariant $'E_d$ the same holds for the tangent $'E_m$'s of $'X_m$ in the neighbourhood of X^A. Hence, according to Theorem IX.1 there exists an integral-X_m of the $\mathfrak{S}_d^m$-field tangent to the last element of the chain (8.1). This proves the theorem

THEOREM IX.10. *Each last element E_m of an ordinary chain of a preferred $\mathfrak{S}_d^m$-field whose $\mathfrak{S}_{d_p}^p(\xi^\kappa)$'s are stationary in each point ξ^κ of the region considered and for all values of $p = 1, \ldots, m-1$ is tangent to at least one integral-X_m of the field.*

Now, as we have proved, ordinary chains always exist and since E_m is the last element of an ordinary chain, every E_m in a sufficiently small neighbourhood is also the last element of a regular chain. This proves the chief theorem of integrability IX.8 announced in the preceding section.

That the preference of an $\mathfrak{S}_d^m$-field together with the stationariness of its $\mathfrak{S}_{d_p}^p(\xi^\kappa)$'s constitute conditions which are sufficient but not necessary for the complete integrability of the field will be shown by the following example. The $\mathfrak{S}_d^m$-field with the parametric forms

$$\begin{aligned} B_b^\kappa &= B_b^\kappa(\eta^k) \\ C_\lambda^x &= C_\lambda^x(\eta^k) \end{aligned} \quad (b = 1,\ldots, \mathrm{m};\ k = \bar{1},\ldots,\bar{d}) \tag{8.18}$$

has the property that the B_b^κ and C_λ^x are independent of the ξ^κ. Hence the field is completely integrable. The functions B_b^κ can be chosen arbitrarily and we may choose them in such a way that $\mathfrak{S}_{d_p}^p(\overset{0}{\xi}{}^\kappa)$ is not stationary for any value of p. Then the $\mathfrak{S}_{d_p}^p(\xi^\kappa)$'s are not stationary for any point ξ^κ of an $\mathfrak{N}(\overset{0}{\xi}{}^\kappa)$.

Now we will prove that the three theorems of integrability IX.4, 5, 6 are special cases of the principal theorem of integrability IX.8. In the case of Theorem IX.4 this is trivial because $d = 0$ and $T_{\cdot ib}^{\cdot\cdot x} = 0$. If the $\mathfrak{S}_d^m$-field satisfies the conditions of IX.5 or IX.6 the cone $\mathfrak{C}(\xi^\kappa)$ is $(m+1)$-dimensional and stationary. Every vector contained in an E_m of $\mathfrak{S}_d^m(\xi^\kappa)$ has the form

$$v^\kappa = p^b B_b^\kappa(\xi^\nu, \eta^k) \quad (b = 1,\ldots, \mathrm{m};\ k = \bar{1},\ldots,\bar{d}) \tag{8.19}$$

and this equation is a parametric form of $\mathfrak{C}(\xi^\kappa)$ if the ξ^κ are looked upon as constants. The tangent E_{m+1} contains the vectors

$$\begin{aligned} \partial v^\kappa/\partial p^b &= B_b^\kappa \\ \partial v^\kappa/\partial \eta^i &= p^b \partial_i B_b^\kappa \end{aligned} \quad (b = 1,\ldots, \mathrm{m};\ i = \bar{1},\ldots,\bar{d}) \tag{8.20}$$

and has to be independent of the choice of the p^a. Hence there exists a vector P^κ, independent of the p^a, such that the tangent E_{m+1} is spanned by B_b^κ $(b = 1,\ldots,\mathrm{m})$ and P^κ. The vectors $p^b \partial_i B_b^\kappa$ have to depend linearly on these $m+1$ vectors and consequently according to (2.4)

$$C_\lambda^x P^\lambda :: p^b C_\lambda^x \partial_i B_b^\lambda = -p^b T_{\cdot ib}^{\cdot\cdot x} \quad (b = 1,\ldots,\mathrm{m};\ x = \mathrm{m}+1,\ldots,\mathrm{n};\ i = \bar{1},\ldots,\bar{d}) \tag{8.21}$$

for every value of i. Hence $T_{\cdot ib}^{\cdot\cdot x}$ can be written in the form

$$T_{\cdot ib}^{\cdot\cdot x} = \phi_{ib} P^\lambda C_\lambda^x, \tag{8.22}$$

where $P^\lambda C_\lambda^x$ cannot vanish. The i-rank ϕ_{ib} is d and the i-rank of $U_{\mathfrak{b}}^b T_{\cdot ib}^{\cdot\cdot x}$ is equal to the i-rank of $U_{\mathfrak{b}}^b \phi_{ib}$. Now we know that a triplet defined by ξ^κ, η^k, $U_{\mathfrak{b}}^b$ $(\mathfrak{b} = \dot{1},\ldots,\dot{\mathrm{p}})$ is ordinary if and only if the i-rank of $U_{\mathfrak{b}}^b T_{\cdot ib}^{\cdot\cdot x}$ has the maximum possible value. The maximum possible value of the i-rank of $U_{\mathfrak{b}}^b \phi_{ib}$ is p for $p \leqslant d$ and d for $p \geqslant d$. In consequence of (8.22) the equations (7.17) and (7.18) take the form

$$\lambda^i_{[\mathfrak{c}} U^b_{\mathfrak{b}]} \phi_{ib} = 0 \qquad (b,c = 1,\dots,\mathrm{m};\ x = \mathrm{m}+1,\dots,\mathrm{n}; \tag{8.23}$$

$$\lambda^i_{\mathfrak{b}} \phi_{ib} = \sigma^i_b U^c_{\mathfrak{b}} \phi_{ic} \qquad i = \bar{1},\dots,\bar{d};\ \mathfrak{b},\mathfrak{c} = \dot{1},\dots,\dot{\mathrm{p}}) \tag{8.24}$$

and we have to prove that for all solutions $\lambda^i_{\mathfrak{b}}$ of (8.23) there are solutions σ^i_b of (8.24). If $p \leqslant d$ the $\mathfrak{b}$-rank of $U^b_{\mathfrak{b}} \phi_{ib}$ is p and consequently (8.24) always has solutions σ^i_b. If $p > d$ the $\mathfrak{b}$-rank of $U^b_{\mathfrak{b}} \phi_{ib}$ is d. As a consequence of (8.23) the vectors $\lambda^i_{\mathfrak{b}}$ $(i = \bar{1},\dots,\bar{d})$ are linearly dependent on the d linearly independent vectors $U^b_{\mathfrak{b}} \phi_{ib}$ $(i = \bar{1},\dots,\bar{d})$ and accordingly there exist relations of the form

$$\lambda^i_{\mathfrak{b}} = \lambda^{ij} U^b_{\mathfrak{b}} \phi_{jb} \quad (b = 1,\dots,\mathrm{m};\ i,j = \bar{1},\dots,\bar{d};\ \mathfrak{b} = \dot{1},\dots,\dot{\mathrm{p}}). \tag{8.25}$$

Transvecting with ϕ_{ib} we get

$$\lambda^i_{\mathfrak{b}} \phi_{ib} = \lambda^{ij} \phi_{ib} U^c_{\mathfrak{b}} \phi_{jc} \quad (b,c = 1,\dots,\mathrm{m};\ i,j = \bar{1},\dots,\bar{d};\ \mathfrak{b} = \dot{1},\dots,\dot{\mathrm{p}}) \tag{8.26}$$

and from this it follows that

$$\sigma^i_b = \lambda^{ji} \phi_{jb} \quad (b = 1,\dots,\mathrm{m};\ i,j = \bar{1},\dots,\bar{d}) \tag{8.27}$$

are solutions of (8.24).

9. The connexion between Goursat systems and $\mathfrak{S}_d^m$-fields

If a scalar-free Goursat system (VIII (5.3)) be given, the equations VIII (5.2) determine an $\mathfrak{S}^m_{d_m}$-field for each value of m. These $\mathfrak{S}^m_{d_m}$-fields are said to be the *connected fields* of the Goursat system. The equations of a connected field are all linear except for the equation VIII (5.2 c) expressing the fact that $v^{\kappa_1\dots\kappa_m}$ is simple. A system of equations in $v^{\kappa_1\dots\kappa_m}$ with this property will be called *quasi-linear* (cf. IX, § 1). Since every E_p in an integral-E_m of the Goursat system is an integral-E_p, the induced $\mathfrak{S}^p_{\delta_p}$-field of the connected $\mathfrak{S}^m_{d_m}$-field contains only integral-E_p's. Hence *the induced $\mathfrak{S}^p_{\delta_p}$-field of the connected $\mathfrak{S}^m_{d_m}$-field of a Goursat system is contained in the connected $\mathfrak{S}^p_{d_p}$-field.*

From the theory of Goursat systems we know that the number of integral-E_{p+1}'s containing a given integral-E_p is $\infty^{r_{p+1}}$ if the E_p is regular and even more if the E_p is not regular and that $r_{p+1} > -1$ for $p < g$. Hence for $p < m$ and $m \leqslant g$ every integral-E_p is contained in at least one integral-E_m and this implies that every E_p of the connected $\mathfrak{S}^p_{d_p}$-field is contained in the induced $\mathfrak{S}^p_{\delta_p}$-field of the connected $\mathfrak{S}^m_{d_m}$-field. Hence the connected $\mathfrak{S}^p_{d_p}$-field and the induced $\mathfrak{S}^p_{\delta_p}$-field are always identical if $p < m$ and $m \leqslant g$. But if $m > g$ and $p < m$, but $p \geqslant g$, no regular integral-E_p is contained in an integral-E_{p+1} and consequently in an integral-E_m and this implies that E_p's of the connected $\mathfrak{S}^p_{d_p}$-field exist which are not contained in the induced $\mathfrak{S}_{\delta_p}^p$-field of the connected $\mathfrak{S}_{d_m}^m$-field. Collecting results we have the theorem

THEOREM IX.11. *The connected $\mathfrak{S}_{d_p}^p$-field of a scalar-free Goursat system of genus g coincides with the induced $\mathfrak{S}_{\delta_p}^p$-field of the connected $\mathfrak{S}_{d_m}^m$-field for all values of $p = 1,\ldots, m-1$ if and only if $m \leqslant g$. If $m > g$ the connected $\mathfrak{S}_{d_p}^p$-field contains the induced $\mathfrak{S}_{\delta_p}^p$-field but at least for $p \geqslant g$ there exist E_p's of the $\mathfrak{S}_{d_p}^p$-field not contained in the $\mathfrak{S}_{\delta_p}^p$-field and the equations of this latter field in $v^{\kappa_1\ldots\kappa_p}$ are not necessarily quasi-linear.*

The following theorem is a direct consequence of this theorem and the theorem of integrability of Cartan-Kähler VIII.4.

THEOREM IX.12. *The connected $\mathfrak{S}_{d_m}^m$-field of a scalar-free Goursat system with genus g is completely integrable if for all values $p = 1,\ldots, m-1$ the connected $\mathfrak{S}_{d_p}^p$-field coincides with the induced $\mathfrak{S}_{\delta_p}^p$-field of the $\mathfrak{S}_{d_m}^m$-field and this is the case if and only if $m \leqslant g$.*

The condition of Theorem IX.12 is sufficient but not necessary for the complete integrability of the connected $\mathfrak{S}_{d_m}^m$-field, as is to be seen from the following example. For the Goursat system

$$\begin{gathered} \overset{4}{e}_\lambda \\ \overset{1}{e}_{[\mu}\overset{2}{e}_{\lambda]}, \quad \overset{1}{e}_{[\mu}\overset{3}{e}_{\lambda]} \end{gathered} \tag{9.1}$$

in X_4 we have $g = 1$ but the connected $\mathfrak{S}_0^2$-field is ξ^κ, $\underset{2}{e}^{[\kappa_1}\underset{3}{e}^{\kappa_2]}$ and this field is completely integrable.

We have proved Theorem IX.12 here starting from the theory of Goursat systems. But it is also possible to give a proof using only the theory of $\mathfrak{S}_d^m$-fields. To this end we prove first the following theorem

THEOREM IX.13.† *An $\mathfrak{S}_d^m$-field is completely integrable in an $\mathfrak{N}(\underset{0}{\xi}^\kappa)$ if it satisfies the conditions:*

(1) *the induced $\mathfrak{S}_{d_p}^p$-fields have for all values of $p = 1,\ldots, m-1$ the quasi-linear form*

$$\begin{aligned} &(a) \qquad \overset{\theta_p}{R}_{\lambda_1\ldots\lambda_p} v^{\lambda_1\ldots\lambda_p} = 0 \\ &(b) \qquad v^{[\kappa_1\ldots\kappa_p} v^{\lambda_1]\ldots\lambda_p} = 0 \end{aligned} \qquad (\theta_p = 1,\ldots, \overset{p}{N}) \tag{9.2}$$

† Cf. v. d. Kulk 1945. 1, ch. iii.

regular in an $\mathfrak{N}(\overset{}{\underset{0}{\xi^\kappa}}, \underset{0}{v^{\kappa_1\ldots\kappa_p}})$; $\underset{0}{\xi^\kappa}, \underset{0}{v^{\kappa_1\ldots\kappa_p}}$ *being an element of a given chain* $\underset{0}{\xi^\kappa} = \underset{0}{E_0}, \ldots, \underset{0}{E_m}$, *whose last element* $\underset{0}{\xi^\kappa}, \underset{0}{v^{\kappa_1\ldots\kappa_m}}$ *belongs to the field;*

(2) *the induced* $\mathfrak{S}_{d_{p+1}}^{p+1}(\xi^\kappa)$ *consists for all values of* $p = 1, \ldots, m-1$ *only of* E_{p+1}*'s satisfying the equations*

$$(\partial_\mu \overset{\theta_p}{R}_{\lambda_1\ldots\lambda_p}) v^{\mu\lambda_1\ldots\lambda_p} = 0. \tag{9.3}$$

PROOF. We will prove that the $\mathfrak{S}_d^m$-field is preferred and that its induced $\mathfrak{S}_{d_p}^p(\xi^\kappa)$'s are stationary for all values of $p = 1, \ldots, m-1$ in an $\mathfrak{N}(\underset{0}{\xi^\kappa})$. The tangent P_{d_p} in an arbitrary point of $\mathfrak{S}_{d_p}^p(\xi^\kappa)$, if it exists, lies in the flat space $R^p(\xi^\kappa)$ in $\mathfrak{P}^p(\xi^\kappa)$ defined by (9.2 a). Now let P_p be one of the $\infty^{d_{p+1}}$ flat spaces constituting $\mathfrak{S}_{d_p}^p(\xi^\kappa)$ (cf. IX, § 6). Then $J(P_p)$, if it exists, also lies in $R^p(\xi^\kappa)$ and consequently the section of $J(P_p)$ with the tangent $P_{p(n-p)}$ of $\mathfrak{S}^p(\xi^\kappa)$ lies in the section of $R^p(\xi^\kappa)$ with this tangent $P_{p(n-p)}$. But since (9.2) is regular in an $\mathfrak{N}(\underset{0}{\xi^\kappa}, \underset{0}{v^{\kappa_1\ldots\kappa_p}})$ this latter section is the tangent P_{d_p} itself. Hence this tangent P_{d_p} coincides with the section of $J(P_p)$ with the tangent $P_{p(n-p)}$ of $\mathfrak{S}^p(\xi^\kappa)$ and this means that $\mathfrak{S}_{d_p}^p(\xi^\kappa)$ is stationary in an $\mathfrak{N}(\underset{0}{\xi^\kappa})$.

In order to prove the preference of the $\mathfrak{S}_d^m$-field we need another form of the criterion for preferred fields. Writing

$$v^{\kappa_1\ldots\kappa_m} = B_1^{[\kappa_1}\ldots B_{\mathrm{m}}^{\kappa_m]} = B_{[1}^{\kappa_1}\ldots B_{\mathrm{m}]}^{\kappa_m}, \tag{9.4}$$

where the B_b^κ are functions of ξ^κ and η^k, we get by differentiation with respect to ξ^κ, leaving the η^k constant,

$$\bar\partial_\mu v^{\mu\kappa_2\ldots\kappa_m} = (\bar\partial_\mu B_{[1}^\mu) B_2^{\kappa_2}\ldots B_{\mathrm{m}]}^{\kappa_m} + (m-1) B_{[1}^\mu (\bar\partial_{|\mu|} B_2^{\kappa_2}) B_3^{\kappa_3}\ldots B_{\mathrm{m}]}^{\kappa_m}. \tag{9.5}$$

Now (4.17) expresses the fact that the $\frac{1}{2}m(m-1)$ vectors

$$B_{[c}^\mu \bar\partial_\mu B_{b]}^\kappa + Z_{[c}^i \partial_{|i|} B_{b]}^\kappa \quad (b, c = 1, \ldots, \mathrm{m};\ i = \bar 1, \ldots, \bar d) \tag{9.6}$$

are all contained in E_m. Hence, if (4.17) holds, that is, if the $\mathfrak{S}_d^m$-field is preferred, the vectors (9.6) have the form $p_{cb}^a B_a^\kappa$ and (9.5) can be written in the form

$$\bar\partial_\mu v^{\mu\kappa_2\ldots\kappa_m} = (\bar\partial_\mu B_{[1}^\mu) B_2^{\kappa_2}\ldots B_{\mathrm{m}]}^{\kappa_m} + (m-1) p_{[12}^a B_{|a|}^{\kappa_2} B_3^{\kappa_3}\ldots B_{\mathrm{m}]}^{\kappa_m} -$$
$$-(m-1) Z_{[1}^i (\partial_{|i|} B_2^{\kappa_2}) B_3^{\kappa_3}\ldots B_{\mathrm{m}]}^{\kappa_m} \quad (a = 1, \ldots, \mathrm{m};\ i = \bar 1, \ldots, \bar d). \tag{9.7}$$

Conversely (4.17) follows from (9.7) by transvecting with $C_{\kappa_2}^x$ and using (9.5). Hence (9.7) is a necessary and sufficient condition that the $\mathfrak{S}_d^m$-field (9.4) is preferred.

If instead of the η^k the supernumerary coordinates ζ^ω ($\omega = \bar 1, \ldots, \bar s$;

$s > d$) are used, connected with the η^k by the equation

$$\eta^k = f^k(\xi^\kappa, \zeta^\omega) \quad (k = \bar{1},..., \bar{d};\ \omega = \bar{1},..., \bar{s}), \tag{9.8}$$

we have

$$\begin{aligned} \bar{\partial}'_\mu v^{\mu\kappa_2...\kappa_m} &= \bar{\partial}_\mu v^{\mu\kappa_2...\kappa_m} + (\bar{\partial}'_\mu f^i)\partial_i v^{\mu\kappa_2...\kappa_m} \\ &= \bar{\partial}_\mu v^{\mu\kappa_2...\kappa_m} + (\bar{\partial}'_\mu f^i)\{(\partial_i B^\mu_{[1})B^{\kappa_2}_2 ... B^{\kappa_m}_{m]} + \\ &\quad + (m-1)B^\mu_{[1}(\partial_{|i|} B^{[\kappa_2}_2)B^{\kappa_3}_3 ... B^{\kappa_m]}_{m]}\} \quad (i = \bar{1},..., \bar{d}), \end{aligned} \tag{9.9}$$

$\bar{\partial}'_\mu$ symbolizing the differentiation with respect to the ξ^μ leaving the ζ^ω constant, and the conditions (9.7) take the form

$$\begin{aligned} \bar{\partial}'_\mu v^{\mu\kappa_2...\kappa_m} &= (\bar{\partial}_\mu B^\mu_{[1})B^{\kappa_2}_2 ... B^{\kappa_m}_{m]} + (m-1)p^a_{[12} B^{[\kappa_2}_{|a|} B^{\kappa_3}_3 ... B^{\kappa_m]}_{m]} - \\ &- (m-1)Z^i_{[1}(\partial_{|i|} B^{[\kappa_2}_2)B^{\kappa_3}_3 ... B^{\kappa_m]}_{m]} + \\ &+ (\bar{\partial}'_\mu f^i)\{(\partial_i B^\mu_{[1})B^{[\kappa_2}_2 ... B^{\kappa_m]}_{m]} + (m-1)B^\mu_{[1}(\partial_{|i|} B^{[\kappa_2}_2)B^{\kappa_3}_3 ... B^{\kappa_m]}_{m]}\} \\ &(a = 1,..., \mathrm{m};\ i = \bar{1},..., \bar{d}). \end{aligned} \tag{9.10}$$

In order to obtain a geometrical interpretation of these conditions we consider all the E_{m-1}'s lying in the E_m of the $\mathfrak{S}_d^m$-field with the coordinates ξ^κ, ζ^ω. In $\mathfrak{P}^{m-1}(\xi^\kappa)$ these E_{m-1}'s correspond to the points of a P_{m-1} belonging to the d_{m-1}-dimensional manifold $\mathfrak{S}^{m-1}_{d_{m-1}}(\xi^\kappa)$. For the determination of $J(P_{m-1})$ we have to choose m points $Q_1,..., Q_\mathrm{m}$ of this P_{m-1} corresponding to m E_{m-1}'s in the E_m having no direction in common and each forming with ξ^κ and E_m an ordinary triplet. This choice is always possible if E_m is the third element of at least one ordinary triplet ξ^κ, E_{m-1}, E_m (cf. IX, § 6). In that case the B^κ_b can always be chosen in such a way that the vector B^κ_ϵ for each value of $\epsilon = 1,..., \mathrm{m}$ lies in the section of the $m-1$ E_{m-1}'s corresponding to the points $Q_1,..., Q_{\epsilon-1}, Q_{\epsilon+1},..., Q_\mathrm{m}$. Then Q_ϵ corresponds for each value of $\epsilon = 1,..., \mathrm{m}$ to the E_{m-1} spanned by the vectors $B^\kappa_1,..., B^\kappa_{\epsilon-1}, B^\kappa_{\epsilon+1},..., B^\kappa_\mathrm{m}$. The connecting quantity $U^\kappa_\mathfrak{b}$ of the E_{m-1} corresponding to Q_ϵ is

$$U^\kappa_\mathfrak{b} = B^\kappa_\mathfrak{b} \quad (\mathfrak{b} = 1,..., \epsilon-1, \epsilon+1,..., \mathrm{m};\ \kappa = 1,..., n) \tag{9.11}$$

and for the $U^b_\mathfrak{b}$ we have

$$U^b_\mathfrak{b} = \delta^b_\mathfrak{b} \quad (\mathfrak{b} = 1,..., \epsilon-1, \epsilon+1,..., \mathrm{m};\ b = 1,..., \mathrm{m}). \tag{9.12}$$

Accordingly the tangent $P_{d_{m-1}}$ of $\mathfrak{S}^{m-1}_{d_{m-1}}(\xi^\kappa)$ in Q_ϵ contains the $d+m(m-1)$ points (= $(m-1)$-vectors) with the coordinates

$$\begin{aligned} (a) \quad & \delta^\mathfrak{b}_b(\partial_i B^{[\kappa_1}_b)B^{\kappa_2}_{[2} ... B^{\kappa_{\epsilon-1}}_{\epsilon-1} B^{\kappa_\epsilon}_{\epsilon+1} ... B^{\kappa_{m-1}]}_\mathrm{m} \delta^\mathfrak{b}_{1]} \\ &= (\partial_i B^{[\kappa_1}_{[1})B^{\kappa_2}_2 ... B^{\kappa_{\epsilon-1}}_{\epsilon-1} B^{\kappa_\epsilon}_{\epsilon+1} ... B^{\kappa_{m-1}]}_{\mathrm{m}]} \\ &= (-1)^{m-\epsilon} m(\partial_i B^{[\kappa_1}_{[1})B^{\kappa_2}_2 ... B^{\kappa_{m-1}]}_{\mathrm{m}-1} \delta^\epsilon_{\mathrm{m}]}; \\ (b) \quad & B^{[\kappa_1}_a B^{\kappa_2}_{[2} ... B^{\kappa_{\epsilon-1}}_{\epsilon-1} B^{\kappa_\epsilon}_{\epsilon+1} ... B^{\kappa_{m-1}]}_\mathrm{m} \delta^\mathfrak{b}_{1]} \\ &= (-1)^{m-\epsilon} m B^{[\kappa_1}_a B^{\kappa_2}_{[2} ... B^{\kappa_{m-1}]}_{\mathrm{m}-1} \delta^\epsilon_\mathrm{m} \delta^b_{1]} \\ &(a, b = 1,..., \mathrm{m};\ \mathfrak{b} = 1,..., \epsilon-1, \epsilon+1,..., \mathrm{m}). \end{aligned} \tag{9.13}$$

Since $J(P_{m-1})$ is the junction of the m $P_{d_{m-1}}$'s in $Q_1,\dots, Q_m$, it contains all points (9.13), a, b, and ϵ taking all values 1,..., m. Now in the right-hand sides of (9.10) the first and the second term represent the coordinates of a point of P_{m-1}. The third term arises from (9.13a) by transvection with $(-1)^{\epsilon-1}(m-1/m)Z^i_\epsilon$ (ϵ is now a running index!) and consequently represents the coordinates of a point of $J(P_{m-1})$. The fourth term represents the coordinates of a point of P_{m-1}. The fifth term arises from (9.13a) by transvection with $(-1)^{\epsilon-1}(m-1/m)B^\mu_\epsilon$ and consequently represents the coordinates of a point of $J(P_{m-1})$. Hence the right-hand side of (9.9) represents a point in $J(P_{m-1})$, and in consequence of the form of the fourth and fifth term of (9.10) the same holds for the right-hand side of (9.5).

Conversely, if $\bar\partial'_\mu v^{\mu\kappa_2\dots\kappa_m}$ represents a point of $J(P_{m-1})$ the same holds for $\bar\partial_\mu v^{\mu\kappa_2\dots\kappa_m}$ and according to (9.5) and (9.13) we have an equation of the form

$$(\bar\partial_\mu B^\mu_{[1})B^{\kappa_2}_2\dots B^{\kappa_m}_{m]}+(m-1)B^\mu_{[1}(\bar\partial_{|\mu|}B^{[\kappa_2}_2)B^{\kappa_3}_3\dots B^{\kappa_m]}_{m]}$$
$$= \alpha^i_{[m}(\partial_{|i|}B^{[\kappa_2}_1)\dots B^{\kappa_m]}_{m-1]}+\beta^a_{[m1}B^{[\kappa_2}_{|a|}B^{\kappa_3}_2\dots B^{\kappa_m]}_{m-1]}$$
$$(a = 1,\dots, m;\ i = \bar1,\dots,\bar d). \quad (9.14)$$

From this equation we get by transvection with $C^x_{\kappa_2}$

$$(m-1)C^x_{\kappa_2}B^\mu_{[1}(\bar\partial_{|\mu|}B^{\kappa_2}_2)B^{[\kappa_3}_3\dots B^{\kappa_m]}_{m]} = \alpha^i_{[m}C^x_{|\kappa_2|}(\partial_{|i|}B^{\kappa_2}_1)B^{[\kappa_3}_2\dots B^{\kappa_m]}_{m-1]}$$
$$(x = m+1,\dots, n;\ i = \bar1,\dots,\bar d), \quad (9.15)$$

or, using (2.4) and (4.11),

$$-(m-1)D_{[i2}{}^x B^{[\kappa_3}_3\dots B^{\kappa_m]}_{m]}+2\alpha^i_{[m}T_{|i|1}{}^x B^{[\kappa_3}_2\dots B^{\kappa_m]}_{m-1]} = 0$$
$$(x = m+1,\dots, n;\ i = \bar1,\dots,\bar d). \quad (9.16)$$

Since $B^\kappa_1,\dots, B^\kappa_m$ are linearly independent, (9.16) is equivalent to an equation of the form (4.17), and this means that (4.17) has at least one solution and that consequently the $\mathfrak{S}_d^m$-field is preferred. Hence we have the theorem

THEOREM IX.14.† *An $\mathfrak{S}_d^m$-field with the (eventually supernumerary) parametric form*

$$v^{\kappa_1\dots\kappa_m} = v^{\kappa_1\dots\kappa_m}(\xi^\kappa, \zeta^\omega) \quad (\omega = \bar1,\dots,\bar s;\ s \geqslant d) \quad (9.17)$$

is preferred if and only if for the third element of each ordinary triplet ξ^κ, E_{m-1}, E_m the point in $\mathfrak{P}^{m-1}(\xi^\kappa)$ with the coordinates $\bar\partial'_\mu v^{\mu\kappa_2\dots\kappa_m}$ is contained in $J(P_{m-1})$, P_{m-1} being the flat space in $\mathfrak{P}^{m-1}(\xi^\kappa)$ corresponding to all E_{m-1}'s in E_m.

† Cf. v. d. Kulk 1945. 1, ch. iii.

The preference of an $\mathfrak{S}_d^m$-field satisfying the conditions of Theorem IX.13 can now be proved by induction. Since an $\mathfrak{S}_{d_1}^1$-field is always completely integrable the induced $\mathfrak{S}_{d_1}^1$-field is preferred. Now suppose the induced $\mathfrak{S}_{d_p}^p$-field to be preferred. Then the preference of the induced $\mathfrak{S}_{d_{p+1}}^{p+1}$-field has to be proved. The manifold $\mathfrak{S}_{d_p}^p(\xi^\kappa)$ in $\mathfrak{P}^p(\xi^\kappa)$ can be determined by the parametric form

$$v^{\kappa_1\dots\kappa_p} = U_{\mathrm{i}}^{[\kappa_1}\dots U_{\dot{\mathrm{p}}}^{\kappa_p]}, \quad U_{\mathfrak{b}}^\kappa = U_{\mathfrak{b}}^b B_b^\kappa \quad (b = 1,\dots,\mathrm{m};\ \mathfrak{b} = \dot{1},\dots,\dot{\mathrm{p}}) \tag{9.18}$$

with the supernumerary coordinates ξ^κ, η^k, $U_{\mathfrak{b}}^a$ (cf. IX, § 6) and in an $\mathfrak{N}(\underset{0}{\xi^\kappa}, \underset{0}{v^{\kappa_1\dots\kappa_p}})$ also by the equations (9.2). The manifold $\mathfrak{S}_{d_{p+1}}^{p+1}(\xi^\kappa)$ can be determined by the parametric form

$$v^{\kappa_1\dots\kappa_{p+1}} = U^{[\kappa_1} U_{\mathrm{i}}^{\kappa_2}\dots U_{\dot{\mathrm{p}}}^{\kappa_{p+1}]} = U^{[\kappa_1} v^{\kappa_2\dots\kappa_{p+1}]}, \quad U^\kappa = U^b B_b^\kappa$$

$$(b = 1,\dots,\mathrm{m}) \tag{9.19}$$

with the supernumerary coordinates ξ^κ, η^k, $U_{\mathfrak{b}}^a$, U^a. Now we choose a chain $\xi^\kappa = E_0, E_1,\dots, E_m$ in the neighbourhood of the chain $\underset{0}{\xi^\kappa} = \underset{0}{E_0}$, $\underset{0}{E_1},\dots, \underset{0}{E_m}$ such that ξ^κ, E_{p-1}, E_p forms an ordinary triplet for each value of p. That this is always possible can be proved as follows. First we take an ordinary chain ξ^κ, $E_1,\dots, E_m$ in the neighbourhood considered. Then by slightly changing ξ^κ, E_1, E_2 we can always arrange that these elements form an ordinary triplet and that the whole chain remains ordinary. After that, by slightly changing ξ^κ, E_1, E_2, and E_3 we can always arrange that ξ^κ, E_1, E_2 and ξ^κ, E_2, E_3 form ordinary triplets and that the whole chain remains ordinary. Continuing in this way we get the chain required. The $U_{\mathfrak{b}}^\kappa$, U^κ in E_{p+1} we choose in such a way that all E_p's spanned by p of these $p+1$ vectors are sufficiently close to $\underset{0}{E_p}$. Since these E_p's belong to $\mathfrak{S}_{d_p}^p(\xi^\kappa)$ they satisfy the equations (9.2) and from this it follows that according to (9.2 a)

$$\overset{\theta_p}{R}_{\lambda_1\dots\lambda_p} v^{\mu\lambda_1\dots\lambda_p} = 0 \quad (\theta_p = 1,\dots,\overset{p}{N}) \tag{9.20}$$

in an $\mathfrak{N}(\underset{0}{\xi^\kappa}, \underset{0}{v^{\kappa_1\dots\kappa_{p+1}}})$. Differentiating (9.20) with respect to ξ^κ and looking upon η^k, $U_{\mathfrak{b}}^a$, and U^a as constants (symbol $\overline{\partial}'_\mu$) we get

$$(\partial_\mu \overset{\theta_p}{R}_{\lambda_1\dots\lambda_p}) v^{\mu\lambda_1\dots\lambda_p} + \overset{\theta_p}{R}_{\lambda_1\dots\lambda_p} \overline{\partial}'_\mu v^{\mu\lambda_1\dots\lambda_p} = 0 \quad (\theta_p = 1,\dots,\overset{p}{N}), \tag{9.21}$$

and from this and (9.3) it follows that

$$\overset{\theta_p}{R}_{\lambda_1\dots\lambda_p} \overline{\partial}'_\mu v^{\mu\lambda_1\dots\lambda_p} = 0 \quad (\theta_p = 1,\dots,\overset{p}{N}) \tag{9.22}$$

expressing the fact that the point $\overline{\partial}'_\mu v^{\mu\lambda_1\dots\lambda_p}$ in $\mathfrak{P}^p(\xi^\kappa)$ lies in the flat space $R^p(\xi^\kappa)$ defined by (9.2 a). But we have to prove that this point lies in $J(P_p)$. If $Q_1,\ldots, Q_{p+1}$ are $p+1$ linearly independent points of P_p corresponding to the E_p's mentioned above belonging to ordinary triplets, $J(P_p)$ is the junction of the $p+1$ tangent P_{d_p}'s of $\mathfrak{S}^p_{d_p}(\xi^\kappa)$. But in the case under consideration each of these P_{d_p}'s is the section of $R^p(\xi^\kappa)$ and the tangent $P_{p(n-p)}$ of $\mathfrak{S}^p(\xi^\kappa)$ in the same point. Hence $J(P_p)$ is the section of $R^p(\xi^\kappa)$ and the junction $L(P_p)$ of these $p+1$ $P_{p(n-p)}$'s. Accordingly we have only to prove that $\bar{\partial}_\mu v^{\mu\kappa_1\ldots\kappa_p}$ is a point of $L(P_p)$. Now from (9.19) it follows that

$$\begin{aligned}(p+1)\bar{\partial}'_\mu v^{\mu\kappa_1\ldots\kappa_p} &= (p+1)\bar{\partial}'_\mu U^{[\mu}v^{\kappa_1\ldots\kappa_p]}\\ &= (\bar{\partial}'_\mu U^\mu)v^{\kappa_1\ldots\kappa_p}+U^\mu\bar{\partial}'_\mu v^{\kappa_1\ldots\kappa_p}-p(\bar{\partial}'_\mu U^{[\kappa_1})v^{|\mu|\kappa_2\ldots\kappa_p]}-\\ &\qquad\qquad -pU^{[\kappa_1}\bar{\partial}'_\mu v^{|\mu|\kappa_2\ldots\kappa_p]}\\ &= \{(\bar{\partial}'_\mu U^\mu)U^{[\kappa_1}_{\dot{1}}\ldots U^{\kappa_p]}_{\dot{p}}+pU^\mu(\bar{\partial}'_\mu U^{[\kappa_1}_{\dot{1}})U^{\kappa_2}_{\dot{2}}\ldots U^{\kappa_p]}_{\dot{p}}-\\ &\quad -p(U^\mu_{[\dot{1}}\bar{\partial}'_{|\mu|}U^{[\kappa_1})U^{\kappa_2}_{\dot{2}}\ldots U^{\kappa_p]}_{\dot{p}]}\}-pU^{[\kappa_1}\bar{\partial}'_\mu v^{|\mu|\kappa_2\ldots\kappa_p]}. \qquad (9.23)\end{aligned}$$

Since the terms in { } depend linearly on the vectors (6.2), these terms represent a point in the tangent $P_{p(n-p)}$ of $\mathfrak{S}^p(\xi^\kappa)$ in the point with the coordinates (9.18). Because this $P_{p(n-p)}$ is contained in $L(P_p)$ we have only to prove that the last term of the right-hand side of (9.23) represents a point of $L(P_p)$. Since the $\mathfrak{S}^p_{d_p}$-field is preferred and since the E_p with the coordinates (9.18) is the third element of an ordinary triplet ξ^κ, E_{p-1}, E_p of the $\mathfrak{S}^p_{d_p}$-field the point $\bar{\partial}_\mu v^{\mu\kappa_2\ldots\kappa_p}$ is contained in $J(P_{p-1})$, P_{p-1} being the flat space in $\mathfrak{P}^{p-1}(\xi^\kappa)$ corresponding to all the E_{p-1}'s in E_p. Hence this point is also contained in $L(P_{p-1})$. Now we prove *that if $u^{\kappa_2\ldots\kappa_p}$ is a point of $L(P_{p-1})$, $U^{[\kappa_1}u^{\kappa_2\ldots\kappa_m]}$ is always a point of $L(P_p)$.* For that purpose we choose p linearly independent points $Q'_1,\ldots, Q'_{\mathrm{p}}$ in P_{p-1} and choose the $U^\kappa_{\mathfrak{b}}$ ($\mathfrak{b} = \dot{1},\ldots, \dot{p}$) in such a way that the E_{p-1} corresponding to Q'_ϵ is spanned by $U^\kappa_{\dot{1}},\ldots, U^\kappa_{\dot{\epsilon}-\dot{1}}, U^\kappa_{\dot{\epsilon}+\dot{1}},\ldots, U^\kappa_{\dot{p}}$ for all values of $\epsilon = 1,\ldots, \mathrm{p}$. Then the tangent $P_{(p-1)(n-p+1)}$ of $\mathfrak{S}^{p-1}(\xi^\kappa)$ in Q'_ϵ is spanned by the points with the coordinates (cf. (6.2))

$$A^{[\kappa_2}_\lambda U^{\kappa_3}_{[\dot{3}}\ldots U^{\kappa_p]}_{\dot{p}}\delta^{\mathfrak{a}}_{\dot{2}}\delta^{\epsilon}_{\dot{1}]} \quad (\mathfrak{a} = \dot{1},\ldots, \dot{p}), \qquad (9.24)$$

ϵ having a fixed value, and $L(P_{p-1})$ is spanned by all the points (9.24), ϵ taking all values $\dot{1},\ldots, \dot{p}$. Now consider the point Q_ϵ in P_p corresponding to the p-vector spanned by $U^\kappa_{\dot{1}},\ldots, U^\kappa_{\dot{\epsilon}-\dot{1}}, U^\kappa_{\dot{\epsilon}+\dot{1}},\ldots, U^\kappa_{\dot{p}}, U^\kappa$. The tangent $P_{p(n-p)}$ of $\mathfrak{S}^p(\xi^\kappa)$ in Q_ϵ is spanned by the vectors with the coordinates

$$A^{[\kappa_2}_\lambda U^{\kappa_3}_{[\dot{3}}\ldots U^{\kappa_p}_{\dot{p}}U^{\kappa_1]}\delta^{\mathfrak{a}}_{\dot{2}}\delta^{\epsilon}_{\dot{1}]}; \qquad A^{[\kappa_1}_\lambda U^{\kappa_2}_{[\dot{2}}\ldots U^{\kappa_p]}_{\dot{p}}\delta^{\epsilon}_{\dot{1}]} \quad (\mathfrak{a} = \dot{1},\ldots, \dot{p}), \qquad (9.25)$$

ϵ having a fixed value. If $u^{\kappa_2...\kappa_p}$ is a point of $L(P_{p-1})$, then $u^{\kappa_2...\kappa_p}$ depends linearly on the $(p-1)$-vectors (9.24) ($\epsilon = \dot{1},..., \dot{p}$). Hence $U^{[\kappa_1}u^{\kappa_2...\kappa_p]}$ depends linearly on the p-vectors (9.25) ($\epsilon = \dot{1},..., \dot{p}$) and consequently $U^{[\kappa_1}u^{\kappa_2...\kappa_p]}$ is a point contained in the junction of the tangent $P_{p(n-p)}$'s in the point $Q_{\dot{1}},..., Q_{\dot{p}}$ and this junction is contained in $L(P_p)$. Hence $U^{[\kappa_1}u^{\kappa_2...\kappa_p]}$ is a point of $L(P_p)$. That finishes the proof of Theorem IX.13.

Since the conditions of Theorem IX.13 are satisfied by every connected $\mathfrak{S}_d^m$-field of a Goursat system, this theorem is a generalization of the theorem of integrability of Cartan-Kähler VIII.4 (or IX.12). The difference is that the connected $\mathfrak{S}_{d_m}^m$-field of a Goursat system is quasi-linear, whereas the $\mathfrak{S}_d^m$-field of (IX.13), though its induced fields are all quasi-linear for $p < m$, need not be quasi-linear itself.

In Chapter VIII we proved the theorem of integrability of Cartan-Kähler VIII.4 by using the theorem of Cauchy-Kowalewski III.4. In this chapter we proved the generalization IX.13 by using the theorem of integrability of Cartan VIII.3. From this we see that it is possible to prove Cartan-Kähler's theorem VIII.4 only by using Cartan's theorem VIII.3.

10. Relations between the arithmetic invariants d_p, τ_p, ρ_p, and σ_p of an $\mathfrak{S}_d^m$-field†

Consider an ordinary chain of an $\mathfrak{S}_d^m$-field

$$\xi^\kappa = E_0 \subset E_1 \subset ... \subset E_m, \quad E_m \in \mathfrak{S}_d^m\text{-field.} \tag{10.1}$$

Then for the cones $\mathfrak{C}(E_0),..., \mathfrak{C}(E_{m-1})$ the relations

$$E_n \supset \mathfrak{C}(E_0) \supset \mathfrak{C}(E_1) \supset ... \supset \mathfrak{C}(E_{m-1}) \supset E_m \tag{10.2}$$

hold as follows immediately from the definition of these cones. We have the relations (6.10) and (6.24), viz.

$$d_p = p(m-p)+d-\tau_p \quad (0 \leqslant p \leqslant m), \tag{10.3}$$

$$\rho_{p+1} = m-p-1+\tau_p-\tau_{p+1} \quad (0 \leqslant p \leqslant m-1), \tag{10.4}$$

and according to Theorem IX.7 and (10.4) the dimension of $\mathfrak{C}(E_p)$ is

$$m+\tau_p-\tau_{p+1} = p+1+\rho_{p+1} \quad (0 \leqslant p \leqslant m-1). \tag{10.5}$$

As a consequence of (10.2) and (10.5) we have

$$n \geqslant 1+\rho_1 \geqslant 2+\rho_2 \geqslant ... \geqslant m+\rho_m \geqslant m. \tag{10.6}$$

Hence, if we define

$$\sigma_p \overset{\text{def}}{=} \rho_p-\rho_{p+1}-1 \quad (p = 1,..., m-1), \tag{10.7}$$

† Cf. v. d. Kulk 1945. 1, ch. iv.

the inequalities (10.6) except for the first and the last one can be written in the form

$$\sigma_1 \geqslant 0, \quad ..., \quad \sigma_{m-1} \geqslant 0. \tag{10.8}$$

It follows from (10.3) and (10.5) that

$$d_p - d_{p+1} = p - \rho_{p+1} \quad (0 \leqslant p \leqslant m-1). \tag{10.9}$$

By summation we get

$$d_p = \rho_1 + ... + \rho_p - 1 - 2 - ... - (p-1) \tag{10.10}$$

and according to (10.6) and (10.10)

$$d_p \geqslant p\rho_p \quad (1 \leqslant p \leqslant m-1). \tag{10.11}$$

If in these relations the equality sign holds for $p = h$ it holds for $p < h$ and the first h cones $\mathfrak{C}(E_0),..., \mathfrak{C}(E_{h-1})$ coincide. Substituting (10.11) into (10.9) we get

$$\frac{d_p}{p} - \frac{d_{p+1}}{p+1} - 1 \geqslant 0. \tag{10.12}$$

11. Initial conditions for integral-X_m's of an $\mathfrak{S}_d^m$-field†

As in the case of a Goursat system the integral-X_m's tangent to a given integral-E_m can be uniquely determined by certain initial conditions. The following theorem holds:

THEOREM IX.15. (*First theorem of uniqueness.*)† *If*

$$\underset{0}{\xi^\kappa} = \underset{0}{E_0} \subset \underset{0}{E_1} \subset ... \subset \underset{0}{E_m}, \quad \underset{0}{E_m} \in \mathfrak{S}_d^m\text{-field} \tag{11.1}$$

is an ordinary chain of a preferred $\mathfrak{S}_d^m$-field whose induced $\mathfrak{S}_{d_p}^p(\xi^\kappa)$ is stationary in an $\mathfrak{N}(\underset{0}{\xi^\kappa})$ for each value of $p = 1,..., m-1$ and if an integral-X_{m-1} of the induced $\mathfrak{S}_{d_{m-1}}^{m-1}$-field is given tangent to $\underset{0}{E_{m-1}}$ in $\underset{0}{\xi^\kappa}$ and an $X_{n-\rho_m}$ containing X_{m-1} and such that the section of its tangent $E_{n-\rho_m}$ in $\underset{0}{\xi^\kappa}$ and the tangent $E_{m+\rho_m}$ of $\mathfrak{C}(\underset{0}{E_{m-1}})$ along $\underset{0}{E_m}$ coincides with $\underset{0}{E_m}$, there is one and only one integral-X_m of the $\mathfrak{S}_d^m$-field, containing X_{m-1}, contained in $X_{n-\rho_m}$ and tangent to $\underset{0}{E_m}$ in $\underset{0}{\xi^\kappa}$.

After a suitable choice of an $'X_{n+d-\rho_m}$ in $'X_{n+d}$ the proof of this theorem can be given by applying the first theorem of uniqueness VIII.5 to the adjoint $'E_{m+d}$-field.

By repeated application of the first theorem of uniqueness IX.15 the following theorem can be proved:

† Cf. v. d. Kulk 1945. 1, ch. iv.

THEOREM IX.16. (*Second theorem of uniqueness.*) *Let* (11.1) *be an ordinary chain of a preferred* $\mathfrak{S}_d^m$*-field whose induced* $\mathfrak{S}_{d_p}^p(\xi^\kappa)$ *is stationary in an* $\mathfrak{N}(\underset{0}{\xi^\kappa})$ *for each value of* $p = 1,\dots, m-1$. *Let*

$$X_{n-\rho_1} \subset X_{n-\rho_2} \subset \dots \subset X_{n-\rho_m} \tag{11.2}$$

be a set of manifolds through $\underset{0}{\xi^\kappa}$, *subject to the condition that the section of the tangent* $E_{n-\rho_p}$ $(p = 1,\dots,m)$ *of* $X_{n-\rho_p}$ *in* $\underset{0}{\xi^\kappa}$ *with the tangent* $E_{p+\rho_p}$ *of* $\mathfrak{C}(\underset{0}{E}_{p-1})$ *along* $\underset{0}{E}_p$ *coincides with* $\underset{0}{E}_p$. *Then there is one and only one set of manifolds*

$$X_1 \subset X_2 \subset \dots \subset X_m \tag{11.3}$$

through $\underset{0}{\xi^\kappa}$ *satisfying the following conditions*:

(1) X_p $(p = 1,\dots,m)$ *is an integral-*X_p *of the induced* $\mathfrak{S}_{d_p}^p$*-field*;
(2) X_p *is contained in* $X_{n-\rho_p}$;
(3) X_p *is tangent to* $\underset{0}{E}_p$ *in* $\underset{0}{\xi^\kappa}$.

As in the case of the Goursat system it may be asked whether it is possible to obtain *every* integral-X_m tangent to the last element of an ordinary chain. The answer to this question may be formulated in the theorem

THEOREM IX.17. (*Third theorem of uniqueness.*)† *Let* (11.1) *be an ordinary chain of a preferred* $\mathfrak{S}_d^m$*-field whose induced* $\mathfrak{S}_{d_p}^p(\xi^\kappa)$ *is stationary in an* $\mathfrak{N}(\underset{0}{\xi^\kappa})$ *for each value of* $p = 1,\dots, m-1$. *Let the coordinate system be chosen in such a way that* $\underset{0}{\xi^\kappa} = 0$ *and that* $\underset{0}{E}_p$ $(p = 1,\dots,m)$ *is spanned by the measuring vectors*

$$\underset{1}{e^\kappa},\dots, \underset{p}{e^\kappa} \tag{11.4}$$

and that the tangent $E_{p+\rho_p}$ $(p = 1,\dots,m)$ *of* $\mathfrak{C}(\underset{0}{E}_{q-1})$ *along* $\underset{0}{E}_p$ *is spanned by the measuring vectors*

$$\underset{1}{e^\kappa},\dots, \underset{p+\rho_p}{e^\kappa} \tag{11.5}$$

Then there is always one and only one integral-X_m *of the* $\mathfrak{S}_d^m$*-field with equations of the form*

$$\begin{aligned} \xi^{m+1} &= f^{m+1}(\xi^1,\dots,\xi^m), \\ &\cdot\quad\cdot\quad\cdot\quad\cdot\quad\cdot\quad\cdot\quad\cdot \\ \xi^n &= f^n(\xi^1,\dots,\xi^m) \end{aligned} \tag{11.6}$$

† Cf. v. d. Kulk 1945. 1, ch. iv.

satisfying the initial conditions

$$\left.\begin{array}{l} f^{m+1}(\xi^1,\ldots,\xi^m) = \phi^{m+1}(\xi^1,\ldots,\xi^m) \\ \cdot\quad\cdot\quad\cdot\quad\cdot\quad\cdot\quad\cdot\quad\cdot\quad\cdot\quad\cdot \\ f^{m+\rho_m}(\xi^1,\ldots,\xi^m) = \phi^{m+\rho_m}(\xi^1,\ldots,\xi^m) \end{array}\right\} (\rho_m \textit{ equations}),$$

$$\left.\begin{array}{l} f^{m+\rho_m+1}(\xi^1,\ldots,\xi^{m-1},\underset{0}{\xi^m}) = \phi^{m+\rho_m+1}(\xi^1,\ldots,\xi^{m-1}) \\ \cdot\quad\cdot\quad\cdot\quad\cdot\quad\cdot\quad\cdot\quad\cdot\quad\cdot\quad\cdot\quad\cdot\quad\cdot \\ f^{m-1+\rho_{m-1}}(\xi^1,\ldots,\xi^{m-1},\underset{0}{\xi^m}) = \phi^{m-1+\rho_{m-1}}(\xi^1,\ldots,\xi^{m-1}) \end{array}\right\} (\sigma_{m-1} \textit{ equations}),$$

$$\cdot\quad\cdot\quad\cdot\quad\cdot\quad\cdot\quad\cdot\quad\cdot\quad\cdot\quad\cdot\quad\cdot\quad\cdot\quad\cdot$$

$$\left.\begin{array}{l} f^{3+\rho_2}(\xi^1,\underset{0}{\xi^2},\ldots,\underset{0}{\xi^m}) = \phi^{3+\rho_2}(\xi^1) \\ \cdot\quad\cdot\quad\cdot\quad\cdot\quad\cdot\quad\cdot\quad\cdot\quad\cdot\quad\cdot \\ f^{1+\rho_1}(\xi^1,\underset{0}{\xi^2},\ldots,\underset{0}{\xi^m}) = \phi^{1+\rho_1}(\xi^1) \end{array}\right\} (\sigma_1 \textit{ equations}),$$

$$\left.\begin{array}{l} f^{2+\rho_1}(\underset{0}{\xi^1},\ldots,\underset{0}{\xi^m}) = \phi^{2+\rho_1} \\ \cdot\quad\cdot\quad\cdot\quad\cdot\quad\cdot\quad\cdot\quad\cdot \\ f^{n}(\underset{0}{\xi^1},\ldots,\underset{0}{\xi^m}) = \phi^{n} \end{array}\right\} (n-\rho_1-1 \textit{ equations}), \tag{11.7}$$

in which $\phi^{m+1},\ldots,\phi^{1+\rho_1}$ *are arbitrarily given functions in* $\mathfrak{N}(\underset{0}{\xi^\kappa})$ *and* $\phi^{2+\rho_1},\ldots,\phi^n$ *arbitrarily given constants, satisfying the conditions that the values of* $\phi^{m+1},\ldots,\phi^n$ *and their first derivatives are sufficiently small in* $\mathfrak{N}(\underset{0}{\xi^\kappa})$. *Every integral-*$X_m$ *of the* $\mathfrak{S}_d^m$*-field through a point* $\underset{*}{\xi^\kappa}$ *in* $\mathfrak{N}(\underset{0}{\xi^\kappa})$ *having in* $\underset{*}{\xi^\kappa}$ *a tangent* E_m *with the coordinates* $\underset{*}{\xi^\kappa}$, $\underset{*}{v^{\kappa_1\ldots\kappa_m}}$ *contained in a sufficiently small* $\mathfrak{N}(\underset{0}{\xi^\kappa},\underset{0}{v^{\kappa_1\ldots\kappa_m}})$ *has equations of the form* (11.6) *whose right-hand sides are uniquely determined by initial conditions of the form* (11.7).

This theorem can be deduced from the second theorem of uniqueness IX.16 in the same way as Theorem VIII.8 was deduced from Theorem VIII.7. The general integral-X_m formed by means of this theorem is not always the most profitable one, there may exist a general integral-X_m depending on fewer functions or functions of fewer variables (cf. VIII, § 9).

As an example of the third theorem of uniqueness IX.17 we consider case C of IX, § 5. For this case we have $d = 1$ and the i-rank of $U_{\mathfrak{b}}^{b} T_{\dot{i}\dot{b}}^{\;\;x}$ is 1 or 0. For each ordinary triplet this i-rank must have the maximum value. Consequently $\tau_p = 0$ $(p = 1,\ldots,m)$ for all ordinary triplets. According to (6.24) we find $\rho_{p+1} = m-p-1$ $(p = 1,\ldots, m-1)$ and $\rho_1 = d_1 = m$. Hence

$$\sigma_1 = 1, \quad \sigma_p = 0, \quad \rho_m = 0 \quad (p = 2,\ldots,m-1) \tag{11.8}$$

and this proves that the general integral-X_m of an $\mathfrak{S}_d^m$-field of this kind depends on one arbitrary function of one variable and $n-m-1$ arbitrary constants.

According to Theorem IX.1 there is one-to-one correspondence between the integral-X_m's of the $\mathfrak{S}_d^m$-field and the integral-$'X_m$'s of the adjoint $'E_{m+d}$-field whose tangent $'E_m$'s have no direction in common with the local $'E_d$ of the invariant $'E_d$-field. According to the third theorem of uniqueness of Goursat systems VIII.8 a general integral-$'X_m$ of the adjoint $'E_{m+d}$-field and consequently also a general integral-X_m of the $\mathfrak{S}_d^m$-field exists depending on

$$\begin{aligned} &'r_m \text{ functions of } m \text{ variables,} \\ &'s_{m-1} \text{ functions of } m-1 \text{ variables,} \\ &\cdots\cdots\cdots\cdots \\ &'s_1 \text{ functions of } 1 \text{ variable,} \\ &n-m \text{ constants.} \end{aligned} \tag{11.9}$$

Now from the third theorem of uniqueness of the $\mathfrak{S}_d^m$-field we see that a general integral-X_m of this field exists depending on

$$\begin{aligned} &\rho_m \text{ functions of } m \text{ variables,} \\ &\sigma_{m-1} \text{ functions of } m-1 \text{ variables,} \\ &\cdots\cdots\cdots\cdots \\ &\sigma_1 \text{ functions of } 1 \text{ variable,} \\ &n-\rho_1-1 \text{ constants} \end{aligned} \tag{11.10}$$

and it has to be asked which of these general integral-X_m's is most advantageous. According to (6.24) and (8.17) respectively we have

$$\left.\begin{aligned} \rho_p &= m-p+\tau_{p-1}-\tau_p \\ 'r_p &= m-p+\tau_{p-1} \end{aligned}\right\} \quad (p = 1,\ldots,m) \tag{11.11}$$

and from this it follows that

$$\begin{aligned} 'r_m &= \rho_m \\ 's_{m-1} &= \sigma_{m-1}+'r_m \\ 's_p &= \sigma_p+'s_{p+1} \\ n-m &= n-\rho_1-1+'s_1 \end{aligned} \qquad (p = 1,\ldots,m-2). \tag{11.12}$$

Since the numbers $'s_1,\ldots, 's_m$ are $\geqslant 0$ this leads to the relations

$$\begin{aligned} 'r_m &= \rho_m, \\ 's_{m-1} &\geqslant \sigma_{m-1}, \\ &\cdots\cdots \\ 's_1 &\geqslant \sigma_1, \\ n-m &\geqslant n-\rho_1-1, \end{aligned} \tag{11.13}$$

from which we see that in the case when the $\mathfrak{S}_d^m$-field is preferred and its induced $\mathfrak{S}_{d_p}^p(\xi^\kappa)$ is stationary for each point ξ^κ and each value of $p = 1,..., m-1$ it is not advantageous to use the integral-$'X_m$'s of the adjoint $'E_{m+d}$-field as given by Cartan's theorem.

12. The null form of an $\mathfrak{S}_d^m$-field†

In the preceding sections the $\mathfrak{S}_d^m$-field was given by its parametric forms (2.1, 2). But an $\mathfrak{S}_d^m$-field in an $\mathfrak{N}(\underset{0}{\xi^\kappa})$ can also be given by the system of equations

$$\begin{aligned} &(a) \qquad F^\Omega(\xi^\kappa, v^{\kappa_1\ldots\kappa_m}) = 0 \\ &(b) \qquad v^{[\kappa_1\ldots\kappa_m} v^{\lambda_1]\ldots\lambda_m} = 0 \end{aligned} \qquad (\Omega = \overline{d+1},..., \overline{m(n-m)}) \tag{12.1}$$

with functions F^Ω analytic in an $\mathfrak{N}(\underset{0}{\xi^\kappa}, \underset{0}{v^{\kappa_1\ldots\kappa_m}})$ and homogeneous in the $v^{\kappa_1\ldots\kappa_m}$ if the condition is satisfied that for $\xi^\kappa = \underset{0}{\xi^\kappa}$ (12.1) is regular of dimension $d+1$ in $\underset{0}{v^{\kappa_1\ldots\kappa_m}}$. (12.1) is called a *null form* of the $\mathfrak{S}_d^m$-field. We prove the theorem

THEOREM IX.18. *The system* (12.1) *is for* $\xi^\kappa = \underset{0}{\xi^\kappa}$ *regular of dimension* $d+1$ *in* $\underset{0}{v^{\kappa_1\ldots\kappa_m}}$ *if and only if the quantities*

$$\partial_\lambda^\kappa F^\Omega \overset{\text{def}}{=} \frac{\partial F^\Omega}{\partial v^{\lambda\lambda_2\ldots\lambda_m}} v^{\kappa\lambda_2\ldots\lambda_m} \quad (\Omega = \overline{d+1},..., \overline{m(n-m)}) \tag{12.2}$$

are linearly independent for $\xi^\kappa = \underset{0}{\xi^\kappa}$.

PROOF. The system (12.1 b) is regular of dimension $m(n-m)+1$ in all its null points (cf. II, § 9). Hence this system contains an equivalent sub-system of the form

$$\Phi^A(v^{\kappa_1\ldots\kappa_m}) = 0 \quad \left(A = \overline{m(n-m)+1},..., \overline{\binom{n}{m}-1}\right) \tag{12.3}$$

minimal regular of dimension $m(n-m)+1$ and constituting together with (12.1 a) a system of $\binom{n}{m}-d-1$ equations in the $n+\binom{n}{m}$ variables $\xi^\kappa, v^{\kappa_1\ldots\kappa_m}$. In order to prove that for $\xi^\kappa = \underset{0}{\xi^\kappa}$ (12.1) is regular of dimension $d+1$ in $\underset{0}{v^{\kappa_1\ldots\kappa_m}}$ we have only to prove that for $\xi^\kappa = \underset{0}{\xi^\kappa}$ the system (12.1 a, 12.3) is minimal regular of dimension $d+1$ in $\underset{0}{v^{\kappa_1\ldots\kappa_m}}$, i.e. that the

† Cf. v. d. Kulk 1943. 7; 1945. 1, ch. iv.

$\binom{n}{m}-d-1$ differentials dF^Ω, $d\Phi^\Lambda$ are linearly independent or that the matrix

$$\left\| \frac{\partial F^\Omega}{\partial v^{\lambda_1\ldots\lambda_m}} \quad \frac{\partial \Phi^\Lambda}{\partial v^{\lambda_1\ldots\lambda_m}} \right\|$$

$$\left(\Omega = \overline{d+1},\ldots,\overline{m(n-m)};\ \Lambda = \overline{m(n-m)+1},\ldots,\overline{\binom{n}{m}-1}\right) \tag{12.4}$$

has the rank $\binom{n}{m}-d-1$ in $\underset{0}{\xi}^\kappa$, $\underset{0}{v}^{\kappa_1\ldots\kappa_m}$. Now the equations

$$\frac{\partial \Phi^\Lambda}{\partial v^{\lambda_1\ldots\lambda_m}} X^{\lambda_1\ldots\lambda_m} = 0 \quad \left(\Lambda = \overline{m(n-m)+1},\ldots,\overline{\binom{n}{m}-1}\right) \tag{12.5}$$

define the tangent $P_{m(n-m)}$ of $\mathfrak{S}^m(\xi^\kappa)$ in $\mathfrak{P}^m(\xi^\kappa)$. But, writing

$$v^{\kappa_1\ldots\kappa_m} = B^{[\kappa_1}_{1}\ldots B^{\kappa_m]}_{\mathrm{m}}$$

we know that this $P_{m(n-m)}$ is spanned by the points (= m-vectors) with the coordinates

$$A^{[\kappa_1}_{\lambda} B^{\kappa_2}_{[2}\ldots B^{\kappa_m]}_{\mathrm{m}} \delta^a_{1]} \quad (a = 1,\ldots,\mathrm{m}). \tag{12.6}$$

Because of $\delta^a_b = B^\kappa_b B^a_\kappa$ (cf. (6.5)) the tangent $P_{m(n-m)}$ is also spanned by the points

$$A^{[\kappa_1}_{\lambda} B^{\kappa_2}_{[2}\ldots B^{\kappa_m]}_{\mathrm{m}} B^\kappa_{1]} = A^{[\kappa_1}_{\lambda} v^{|\kappa|\kappa_2\ldots\kappa_m]}. \tag{12.7}$$

Since the $\partial\Phi^\Lambda/\partial v^{\lambda_1\ldots\lambda_m}$ are linearly independent, a necessary and sufficient condition that (12.4) has the rank $\binom{n}{m}-d-1$ is that there are no relations of the form

$$\lambda_\Omega \frac{\partial F^\Omega}{\partial v^{\lambda_1\ldots\lambda_m}} X^{\lambda_1\ldots\lambda_m} = 0 \quad (\Omega = \overline{d+1},\ldots,\overline{m(n-m)}) \tag{12.8}$$

valid for all solutions of (12.5). Since the general solution of (12.5) is linearly dependent on the m-vectors (12.7), this means that no relations of the form

$$\lambda_\Omega \frac{\partial F^\Omega}{\partial v^{\lambda\lambda_2\ldots\lambda_m}} v^{\kappa\lambda_2\ldots\lambda_m} = 0 \quad (\Omega = \overline{d+1},\ldots,\overline{m(n-m)}) \tag{12.9}$$

exist and this implies that the $\partial^\kappa_\lambda F^\Omega$ defined in (12.2) are linearly independent. This proves the theorem.

In view of the linear independence of the $\partial^\kappa_\lambda F^\Omega$, the equations

$$X^\kappa_\lambda \partial^\lambda_\kappa F^\Omega = 0 \quad (\Omega = \overline{d+1},\ldots,\overline{m(n-m)}) \tag{12.10}$$

with the n^2 unknowns X^κ_λ possess $d+m^2+n^2-mn$ linearly independent solutions. It is easily proved that the

$$d+m^2+m(n-m)+(n-m)^2 = d+m^2+n^2-mn$$

quantities

$$\begin{matrix} T_{\cdot ib}^{\cdot\cdot y}\, B_\lambda^b\, C_y^\kappa \\ B_b^\kappa\, B_\lambda^a \\ B_b^\kappa\, C_\lambda^x \\ C_y^\kappa\, C_\lambda^x \end{matrix} \qquad (a, b = 1,\dots,\mathrm{m};\ x, y = \mathrm{m}+1,\dots,\mathrm{n}) \qquad (12.11)$$

constitute a system of linearly independent solutions of (12.10). By means of these solutions every property of an $\mathfrak{S}_d^m$-field, formulated with respect to the parametric form, can be formulated with respect to a null form. If (12.1) is regular in its null point ξ^κ, $v^{\kappa_1\dots\kappa_m}$ it can be proved that the tangent P_d of $\mathfrak{S}_d^m(\xi^\kappa)$ in $\mathfrak{P}^m(\xi^\kappa)$ consists of all points with the coordinates

$$X_\lambda^{[\kappa_1}\, v^{|\lambda|\kappa_2\dots\kappa_m]}, \qquad (12.12)$$

where X_λ^κ is an arbitrary solution of (12.10). It can also be proved that an $\mathfrak{S}_d^m$-field given by its null form (12.1) is *preferred* if and only if for each null point ξ^κ, $v^{\kappa_1\dots\kappa_m}$ in which (12.1) is regular, the linear equations

$$v^{\mu\kappa_2\dots\kappa_m}(\bar{\partial}_\mu F^\Omega + mU_{\mu\lambda}^\kappa\, \partial_\kappa^\lambda F^\Omega) = 0 \quad (\bar{\partial}_\mu = \partial_\mu \text{ with constant } v^{\kappa_1\dots\kappa_m}) \qquad (12.13)$$

with the $\frac{1}{2}n^2(n+1)$ unknowns $U_{\mu\lambda}^\kappa$ $(U_{\mu\lambda}^\kappa = U_{\lambda\mu}^\kappa)$ are compatible (cf. the corresponding formulation on p. 424).

Let

$$\xi^\kappa = E_0 \subset E_p \subset E_m, \quad E_m \in \mathfrak{S}_d^m\text{-field} \qquad (12.14)$$

be a triplet of an $\mathfrak{S}_d^m$-field with the null form (12.1), regular in the null point E_m with the coordinates ξ^κ, $v^{\kappa_1\dots\kappa_m}$. Let ξ^κ, $v^{\kappa_1\dots\kappa_p}$ be the coordinates of E_p. Then it can readily be proved that all points in $\mathfrak{P}^p(\xi^\kappa)$ with the coordinates

$$X_\lambda^{[\kappa_1}\, v^{|\lambda|\kappa_2\dots\kappa_p]}, \qquad (12.15)$$

where X_λ^κ are arbitrary solutions of (12.10), constitute a $P_{p(m-p)+d-\tau_p}$ if $d-\tau_p$ is the i-rank of $U_b^b\, T_{\cdot jb}^{\cdot\cdot x}$ evaluated for the triplet (12.14). If the triplet is extraordinary the dimension $p(m-p)+d-\tau_p$ is $< d_p$. Hence (12.14) is ordinary if and only if this dimension has the maximum value d_p. This property enables us to evaluate d_p if the $\mathfrak{S}_d^m$-field is given by its null form. It can be proved that for each ordinary triplet (12.14) the $P_{p(m-p)+d-\tau_p}$ coincides with the tangent P_{d_p} of $\mathfrak{S}_{d_p}^p(\xi^\kappa)$ in $\mathfrak{P}^p(\xi^\kappa)$ at the point corresponding to E_p.

In order to formulate Theorem IX.9 with respect to the null form we consider the three following systems of linear equations

$$v^{\mu\kappa_2\dots\kappa_m}\, X_{\mu\lambda}^\kappa\, \partial_\kappa^\lambda F^\Omega = 0 \quad (\Omega = \overline{d+1},\dots,\overline{m(n-m)}) \qquad (12.16)$$

with the n^3 unknowns $X_{\mu\lambda}^\kappa$,

$$v^{\mu\kappa_2\dots\kappa_m}\, Y_{\mu\lambda}^\kappa\, v^{\lambda\lambda_2\dots\lambda_m} = 0 \qquad (12.17)$$

with the n^3 unknowns $Y^{\kappa}_{\mu\lambda}$, and

$$v^{\mu\kappa_2\ldots\kappa_p} Z^{\kappa}_{\mu\lambda}\, \partial^{\lambda}_{\kappa} F^{\Omega} = 0;\ Z^{\kappa}_{[\mu\lambda]} = 0 \quad (\Omega = \overline{d+1},\ldots,\overline{m(n-m)}) \tag{12.18}$$

with the n^3 unknowns $Z^{\kappa}_{\mu\lambda}$. Then the theorem corresponding to Theorem IX.9 is

THEOREM IX.19.† *The induced $\mathfrak{S}^p_{d_p}(\xi^\kappa)$ of an $\mathfrak{S}^m_d$-field with the null form* (12.1) *is stationary if and only if for each ordinary triplet, in whose E_m the system* (12.1) *is regular, each solution $Z^{\kappa}_{\mu\lambda}$ of* (12.18) *can be written as the sum of a solution $X^{\kappa}_{\mu\lambda}$ of* (12.16) *and a solution $Y^{\kappa}_{\mu\lambda}$ of* (12.17).

The rule given on p. 459 and Theorem IX.19 enable us to test whether an $\mathfrak{S}^m_d$-field given by its null form satisfies the conditions of the chief theorem of integrability IX.8.

From the results collected in this section it follows that the theorems for an $\mathfrak{S}^m_d$-field given by a null form are rather more complicated than the corresponding theorems for an $\mathfrak{S}^m_d$-field given by a parametric form.

An $\mathfrak{S}^m_d$-field given by a parametric form (2.2) is connected with the system of partial differential equations (4.4) with the $n+d$ unknown functions f^λ, g^k in the m variables z^a. In order to obtain the differential equations connected with an $\mathfrak{S}^m_d$-field given by a null form (12.1), we consider a normal system of ∞^{n-m} X_m's with the equations

$$f^x(\xi^\kappa) = \text{const.} \quad (x = \mathrm{m}+1,\ldots,\mathrm{n}). \tag{12.19}$$

For these X_m's to be integral-X_m's of the $\mathfrak{S}^m_d$-field the $f^x(\xi^\kappa)$ have to satisfy the equations

$$F^{\Omega}(\xi^\kappa, E^{\kappa_1\ldots\kappa_n}(\partial_{\kappa_{m+1}} f^{\mathrm{m}+1})\ldots(\partial_{\kappa_n} f^{\mathrm{n}})) = 0 \quad (\Omega = \overline{d+1},\ldots,\overline{m(n-m)}). \tag{12.20}$$

This system of partial differential equations with the $n-m$ unknown functions f^x in the n variables ξ^κ is the system required.

EXERCISES‡

1. If an $\mathfrak{S}^m_d$-field is preferred and $\dfrac{m+d}{1+d}-1 < p \leqslant \dfrac{m+d}{1+d}$, through every point of X_n there exists at least one integral-X_p of the induced $\mathfrak{S}^p_{d_p}$-field, tangent to an arbitrarily given E_m of $\mathfrak{S}^m_d(\xi^\kappa)$. (For $d = 0$ this is Theorem IX.4.)

2. A preferred $\mathfrak{S}^m_1$-field with a non-stationary $\mathfrak{C}(\xi^\kappa)$ possesses at most ∞^{n-m+1} integral-X_m's.

3. If $m > g$ the $\mathfrak{S}^m_d$-field connected with a Goursat system is not only not completely integrable but also in general not preferred. Give an example.§

† Cf. v. d. Kulk 1945. 1, ch. iv.

‡ Cf. the suggestions at the end of the book.

§ Cf. v. d. Kulk 1945. 1, p. 39.

X

SOLUTION OF SYSTEMS OF DIFFERENTIAL EQUATIONS†

1. Reduction of a system of partial differential equations to a Cartan system

It is well known that every system of partial differential equations of arbitrary order can be reduced to the form

$$F^{\omega}(\xi^{\kappa}, \partial_{\beta}\xi^{\zeta}) = 0 \quad (\omega = 1,..., N;\ \beta = 1,..., m;\ \zeta = m+1,..., n), \tag{1.1}$$

containing only the independent variables ξ^{α} $(\alpha = 1,..., m)$, the unknown variables ξ^{ζ} $(\zeta = m+1,..., n)$, and their first derivatives. If the $p^{\zeta}_{\beta} \overset{\text{def}}{=} \partial_{\beta}\xi^{\zeta}$ are considered as non-supernumerary coordinates of an E_m in E_n, the equations

$$F^{\omega}(\xi^{\kappa}, p^{\zeta}_{\beta}) = 0 \quad (\omega = 1,..., N;\ \beta = 1,..., m;\ \zeta = m+1,..., n) \tag{1.2}$$

represent an $\mathfrak{S}^{m}_{d}$-field in X_n. The integral-X_m's of this field, whose sections with $\overset{1}{e}_{[\lambda_1} \cdots \overset{m}{e}_{\lambda_m]}$ do not vanish, can be written in the form

$$\xi^{\zeta} = f^{\zeta}(\xi^{\alpha}) \quad (\alpha = 1,..., m;\ \zeta = m+1,..., n) \tag{1.3}$$

and are in one-to-one correspondence to the solutions of (1.1). As was proved in IX, § 4, the determination of these integral-X_m's can always be brought back to the determination of the integral-X_m's of a scalar-free RSC-system in an X_{n+d}. It is often more convenient to use the Cartan system in the $X_{n+m(n-m)}$ of the variables ξ^{κ}, p^{ζ}_{β}, consisting of the scalars

$$F^{\omega}(\xi^{\kappa}, p^{\zeta}_{\beta}) \quad (\omega = 1,..., N;\ \beta = 1,..., m;\ \zeta = m+1,..., n) \tag{1.4}$$

and the $n-m$ covariant vectors with the components

$$-p^{\zeta}_{\beta},\quad \delta^{\zeta}_{\eta},\quad 0 \quad (\beta = 1,..., m;\ \zeta, \eta = m+1,..., n) \tag{1.5}$$

with respect to the variables ξ^{α}, ξ^{ζ}, p^{ζ}_{β}, corresponding to the Pfaffian

$$d\xi^{\zeta} - p^{\zeta}_{\beta}\, d\xi^{\beta} \quad (\beta = 1,..., m;\ \zeta = m+1,..., n). \tag{1.6}$$

The integral-X_m's of this Cartan system, whose equations can be written in the form

$$\begin{aligned} \xi^{\zeta} &= f^{\zeta}(\xi^{\alpha}) \\ p^{\zeta}_{\beta} &= f^{\zeta}_{\beta}(\xi^{\alpha}) \end{aligned} \quad (\alpha, \beta = 1,..., m;\ \zeta = m+1,..., n) \tag{1.7}$$

are in one-to-one correspondence to the solutions of (1.1). This means geometrically that we have only to consider those integral-X_m's in the

† General references: Cartan 1904. 1, 1946. 1; Kähler 1934. 1.

$X_{n+m(n-m)}$ that have no direction in common with the normal system of ∞^m $X_{(m+1)(n-m)}$'s with the equations $\xi^\alpha =$ const.

We will show that the Cartan system can be replaced by a finite number of *RSC*-systems. In the neighbourhood of every arbitrarily chosen set of values $\underset{0}{\xi^\kappa}$, $\underset{0}{p^\zeta_\beta}$ the set of equations

$$F^\omega(\xi^\kappa, p^\zeta_\beta) = 0 \quad (\beta = 1,\ldots, m;\ \zeta = m+1,\ldots, n;\ \omega = 1,\ldots, N) \tag{1.8}$$

can be replaced by a finite number of sets, each minimal regular in a point of this neighbourhood (cf. II, Ex. 10). If the rank of one of these sets with respect to the p^ζ_β is $R < N$, just $N-R$ of the variables ξ^κ can be expressed in terms of the others. By means of these solutions the number of variables can be diminished. In this way we get a finite number of Cartan systems. Each of them can be written in the form (1.4, 6) with suitable values of n and N and each satisfies the conditions that its equations (1.8) are minimal regular and that their rank with respect to the p^ζ_β is equal to N. We consider one of these systems. Its closed system consists of

(1) the N scalars

$$F^\omega(\xi^\kappa, p^\zeta_\beta) \quad (\beta = 1,\ldots, m;\ \zeta = m+1,\ldots, n;\ \omega = 1,\ldots, N); \tag{1.9}$$

(2) the gradients of these scalars and the $n-m$ vectors (1.5). If we write ζ^X $(X = \bar{1},\ldots, \overline{m(n-m)})$ for the p and

$$\begin{aligned} \overset{\kappa}{e}_I,\ \overset{X}{e}_I\ \ (X &= \bar{1},\ldots, \overline{m(n-m)}; \\ I &= 1,\ldots, n, \bar{1},\ldots, \overline{m(n-m)}) \end{aligned} \tag{1.10}$$

for the covariant measuring vectors in the $X_{n+m(n-m)}$ of ξ^κ, ζ^X, the gradient vectors and the vectors (1.5) take the form

$$\begin{aligned} &(a) \quad (\partial_\lambda F^\omega)\overset{\lambda}{e}_I + (\partial_Y F^\omega)\overset{Y}{e}_I \\ &(b) \quad -p^\zeta_\beta \overset{\beta}{e}_I + \overset{\zeta}{e}_I \\ &\quad (\omega = 1,\ldots, N;\ \beta = 1,\ldots, m;\ \zeta = m+1,\ldots, n; \\ &\quad Y = \bar{1},\ldots, \overline{m(n-m)};\ I = 1,\ldots, n, \bar{1},\ldots, \overline{m(n-m)}); \end{aligned} \tag{1.11}$$

(3) the rotations of the vectors (1.11 *b*). According to (1.11 *b*) these bivectors have the form

$$P^\zeta_{\beta[J} \overset{\beta}{e}_{I]} \quad (\beta = 1,\ldots, m;\ \zeta = m+1,\ldots, n; \quad I, J = 1,\ldots, n, \bar{1},\ldots, \overline{m(n-m)}). \tag{1.12}$$

If these bivectors are not linearly independent they can be replaced by $n-m' < n-m$ linearly independent ones among them and by a suitable interchange of the indices ζ it can be arranged that these are

$$P^{\zeta'}_{\beta[J} \overset{\beta}{e}_{I]} \quad (\zeta' = m'+1,\ldots,n;\ \beta = 1,\ldots,m;$$
$$I, J = 1,\ldots,n, \bar{1},\ldots,\overline{m(n-m)}). \quad (1.13)$$

Since the system (1.8) is minimal regular in $\underset{0}{\xi}^{\kappa}$, $\underset{0}{p}^{\zeta}_{\beta}$ the differentials dF^{ω} are linearly independent. Now $\partial_Y F^{\omega}$ has rank N and this implies that the $N+n-m$ vectors (1.11) are linearly independent and that consequently the second condition of VIII, § 14, is satisfied. The third condition of VIII, § 14, is satisfied because of the linear independence of the bivectors (1.13). From the form of (1.13) it follows that the fourth condition of VIII, § 14, is also satisfied. Hence the Cartan system is an SC-system. Since the rank of $\partial_Y F^{\omega}$ is N the vectors (1.11) and the $\overset{\beta}{e}_I$ are linearly independent and this implies that the fifth condition of VIII, § 14, is also satisfied and that accordingly the Cartan system is an RSC-system. We see that all RSC-systems derived in this way have the property that the vectors $\overset{\beta}{e}_I$ are gradient vectors.

The methods developed in VIII, §§ 13, 14 enable us to decide whether an integral-E_m of the RSC-system exists, which is the last element of a regular chain. If these integral-E_m's exist, the general integral-X_m can be obtained by the methods developed in VIII, § 9. If there are no integral-E_m's of this kind, i.e. if m exceeds the genus g of the RSC-system, no regular integral-X_m's exist. But it is possible that non-regular integral-X_m's exist. These can be obtained by the process of *prolongation*. This process will be described in the following section for a general Goursat system and in § 3 for SC-systems.

2. Prolongation of a Goursat system

In order to find the integral-X_m's of a Goursat system for some definite value of $m > g$, the Goursat system has to be replaced by another Goursat system with a genus $\geqslant m$ from whose integral-X_m's the integral-X_m's of the original system can be deduced.

Such a new system can be derived in the following way. We start from an element $\underset{0}{E}_m$ in $\underset{0}{\xi}^{\kappa}$ with the coordinates

$$\underset{0}{\xi}^{\kappa}, \quad \underset{0}{v}^{\kappa_1\ldots\kappa_m} \overset{\text{def}}{=} \underset{1}{e}^{[\kappa_1}\ldots\underset{m}{e}^{\kappa_m]} \tag{2.1}$$

and consider all E_m's in a sufficiently small neighbourhood of $\underset{0}{E}_m$. Then $v^{1...m} \neq 0$ for each of these elements and consequently the ξ^κ and B^ζ_β ($\beta = 1,..., m$; $\zeta = m+1,..., n$) defined by (II. (9.4), $p \to m$) are non-supernumerary coordinates in the manifold of these E_m's. The integral-E_m's of the given closed Goursat system

$$\begin{aligned} &\overset{\chi_0}{u} \quad (\chi_0 = 1,..., N_0), \\ &\overset{\chi_1}{u}_\lambda \quad (\chi_1 = 1,..., N_1), \\ &\cdot \quad \cdot \quad \cdot \quad \cdot \quad \cdot \quad \cdot \quad \cdot \\ &\overset{\chi_m}{u}_{\lambda_1...\lambda_m} \quad (\chi_m = 1,..., N_m) \end{aligned} \tag{2.2}$$

in this manifold are given by the equations

$$\begin{aligned} &\overset{\chi_0}{u} = 0 \quad (\chi_0 = 1,..., N_0), \\ &\overset{\chi_1}{u}_\kappa B^\kappa_\beta = 0 \quad (\chi_1 = 1,..., N_1), \\ &\cdot \quad \cdot \quad \cdot \quad \cdot \quad \cdot \quad \cdot \quad \cdot \quad \cdot \quad \cdot \quad \cdot \quad \cdot \\ &\overset{\chi_m}{u}_{\kappa_1...\kappa_m} B^{\kappa_1}_{\beta_1}...B^{\kappa_m}_{\beta_m} = 0 \quad (\chi_m = 1,..., N_m) \\ &(\beta, \beta_1,..., \beta_m = 1,..., m;\ B^\alpha_\beta = \delta^\alpha_\beta). \end{aligned} \tag{2.3}$$

Every linear element $d\xi^\kappa$ in ξ^κ in the E_m with the coordinates ξ^κ, B^ζ_β satisfies the conditions

$$d\xi^\zeta - B^\zeta_\beta d\xi^\beta = 0 \quad (\beta = 1,..., m;\ \zeta = m+1,..., n). \tag{2.4}$$

Let X_m be any integral-X_m of the Goursat system. Then the ξ^β can be used as coordinates in this X_m and in all its points B^κ_β can be looked upon as the contravariant connecting quantity of the X_m. (2.4) expresses the fact that $d\xi^\kappa$ is a linear element of X_m. Now we look upon the ξ^κ, B^ζ_β as coordinates in the $X_{n+m(n-m)}$ of all E_m's in the neighbourhood of $\underset{0}{E}_m$. In the $X_{n+m(n-m)}$ the equations (2.3) single out all integral-E_m's of the Goursat system, and among them the ∞^m integral-E_m's tangent to the integral-X_m form an X_m in $X_{n+m(n-m)}$ whose linear elements $d\xi^\kappa$, dB^ζ_β satisfy the equations (2.4).

Hence this X_m in $X_{n+m(n-m)}$ is an integral-X_m of the Cartan system in the $n+m(n-m)$ variables ξ^κ, B^ζ_β consisting of the scalars

$$\overset{\chi_0}{u}, \quad \overset{\chi_1}{u}_\kappa B^\kappa_\beta, \quad ..., \quad \overset{\chi_m}{u}_{\kappa_1...\kappa_m} B^{\kappa_1}_{\beta_1}...B^{\kappa_m}_{\beta_m}$$

$$(\beta, \beta_1,..., \beta_m = 1,..., m;\ \chi_0 = 1,..., N_0;\ ...;\ \chi_m = 1,..., N_m), \tag{2.5}$$

the gradients of these scalars, the $n-m$ vectors $\overset{\zeta}{w}_B$ with the components

$$\overset{\zeta}{w}_B\colon \quad -B^{\zeta}_{\beta},\ \delta^{\zeta}_{\eta},\ 0 \quad (\beta = 1,\dots,m;\ \zeta,\eta = m+1,\dots,n;$$
$$B = 1,\dots,n,\bar{1},\dots,\overline{m(n-m)}) \quad (2.6)$$

belonging to the coordinates ξ^{β}, ξ^{ζ}, B^{ζ}_{β} and the rotations of these vectors. If we write X^A ($A = 1,\dots,n,\bar{1},\dots,\overline{m(n-m)}$) for the coordinates ξ^{κ}, B^{ζ}_{β} of the $X_{n+m(n-m)}$:

$$X^{\kappa} \overset{\text{def}}{=} \xi^{\kappa}$$
$$X^{\overline{\beta+(\zeta-m-1)m}} \overset{\text{def}}{=} B^{\zeta}_{\beta} \quad (\beta = 1,\dots,m;\ \zeta = m+1,\dots,n), \quad (2.7)$$

the vectors (2.6) are

$$\overset{\zeta}{w}_B = -\sum_{\beta} X^{\overline{\beta+(\zeta-m-1)m}}\overset{\beta}{e}_B + \overset{\zeta}{e}_B \quad (\beta = 1,\dots,m;\ \zeta = m+1,\dots,n;$$
$$B = 1,\dots,n,\bar{1},\dots,\overline{m(n-m)}) \quad (2.8)$$

and the rotations of these vectors are

$$\overset{\zeta}{W}_{CB} = -2\sum \overset{\overline{\beta+(\zeta-m-1)m}}{e}_{[C}\overset{\beta}{e}_{B]} \quad (\beta = 1,\dots,m;\ \zeta = m+1,\dots,n;$$
$$B, C = 1,\dots,n,\bar{1},\dots,\overline{m(n-m)}). \quad (2.9)$$

If the system (2.3) is regular or semi-regular in $\overset{}{\underset{0}{X^A}}$ it can be replaced by its minimal regular equivalent system. If it is irregular it can be replaced by a finite number of systems, each minimal regular in a point of $\mathfrak{N}(\underset{0}{X^A})$.† Each of these systems gives in combination with (2.4) a Cartan system and each integral-X_m of the Goursat system corresponds to an integral-X_m of one of these Cartan systems. In each of these Cartan systems the gradients of the scalars are linearly independent and the vectors $\overset{\zeta}{w}_B$ can be replaced by a number of them, which are linearly independent of each other and of the gradients. In the same way the rotations of the remaining ones can be replaced by a number of them which are linearly independent of each other. When this has been done the Cartan systems are all SC-systems and the $\overset{\beta}{e}_B$ are gradient vectors in all these systems.

If an integral-X_m of one of the Cartan systems has been found, this

† Cf. II, Ex. 9.

X_m represents a system of ∞^m E_m's in the X_n and these E_m's are all integral-E_m's of the Goursat system because they satisfy (2.3). If from the $(m+1)(n-m)$ equations of this integral-X_m the ξ^ζ, B^ζ_β ($\beta = 1,\ldots,m$; $\zeta = m+1,\ldots,n$) can be solved as functions of the ξ^α ($\alpha = 1,\ldots,m$), these solutions represent an integral-X_m of the Goursat system. But this is the case if and only if the X_m in the $X_{n+m(n-m)}$ nowhere has a direction in common with the normal system of ∞^m $X_{(m+1)(n-m)}$'s with the equations $\xi^\alpha = \text{const}$. Hence there is a one-to-one correspondence between the integral-X_m's of the Goursat system and the integral-X_m's with this special property of all SC-systems. This proves the theorem

THEOREM X.1. *Each integral-X_m of a Goursat system in X_n corresponds to one and only one integral-X_m of one of a finite number of SC-systems in the auxiliary $X_{n+m(n-m)}$ of the ξ^κ, B^ζ_β, whose tangent E_m nowhere has a direction in common with the tangent $E_{(m+1)(n-m)}$ of the normal system of $X_{(m+1)(n-m)}$'s with the equations $\xi^\alpha = \text{const.}$, and vice versa.*

There is still another way to connect a given Goursat system with a finite number of Cartan systems. For the sake of simplicity we assume that the Goursat system is scalar free. If this were not the case, the scalars could be got rid of first by reducing the number of coordinates. Then the B^ζ_β can be solved from the equations (2.3), algebraically in the B^ζ_β, as functions of the ξ^κ and a certain number of parameters. It may happen that there exists a finite number of sets of solutions. Each set can be written in the parametric form

$$B^\zeta_\beta = B^\zeta_\beta(\xi^\kappa, \eta^k) \quad (\beta = 1,\ldots,m;\ \zeta = m+1,\ldots,n;\ k = \bar{1},\ldots,\bar{d}) \tag{2.10}$$

with d parameters η^k belonging to this set of solutions which are minimal regular in $\underset{0}{\xi}{}^\kappa$, $\underset{0}{\eta}{}^k$. (2.10) represents an $\mathfrak{S}^m_d$-field whose E_m's all lie in the neighbourhood of $\underset{0}{E}_m$. As we have proved in IX, § 4, the determination of the integral-X_m's of this $\mathfrak{S}^m_d$-field can be brought back to the determination of certain integral-X_m's of a scalar-free RSC-system in an X_{n+d}. Hence we have the theorem

THEOREM X.2. *Each integral-X_m of a Goursat system in X_n corresponds to one and only one integral-X_m of one of a finite number of scalar-free RSC-systems, each in an auxiliary X_{n+d}, whose tangent E_m nowhere has a direction in common with the tangent E_d of the normal system of X_d's with the equations $\xi^\kappa = \text{const.}$, and vice versa.*

3. Prolongation of a special Cartan system

As we have seen in VIII, § 14, every SC-system can be replaced by a finite number of RSC-systems. Let

$$
\begin{aligned}
&(a) \quad F^{\omega}(\xi^{\kappa}) \quad (\omega = r_0+1,\dots,n),\\
&(b) \quad \overset{\mathfrak{x}}{e}_{\lambda} \quad (\mathfrak{x} = \mathrm{r}+1,\dots,\mathrm{n}),\\
&(c) \quad \overset{\chi}{p}_{b[\mu}\overset{b}{e}_{\lambda]} \quad (b = 1,\dots,\mathrm{m};\ \chi = 1,\dots,P;\ P \leqslant n-r;\ r \geqslant m)
\end{aligned}
\tag{3.1}
$$

be a given RSC-system. Let the set of equations

$$F^{\omega}(\xi^{\kappa}) = 0 \tag{3.2}$$

be minimal regular in $\underset{0}{\xi}^{\kappa}$. If the RSC-system arises from a system of partial differential equations the $\overset{b}{e}_{\lambda}$ can be chosen as gradient vectors. Every E_m in the E_r of the $\overset{\mathfrak{x}}{e}_{\lambda}$ with $v^{1\dots\mathrm{m}} \neq 0$ is the section of the $\overset{\mathfrak{x}}{e}_{\lambda}$ and $r-m$ vectors of the form

$$\overset{\mathfrak{m}}{e}_{\lambda} - B^{\mathfrak{m}}_{b}\overset{b}{e}_{\lambda} \quad (\mathfrak{m} = \mathrm{m}+1,\dots,\mathrm{r};\ b = 1,\dots,\mathrm{m}). \tag{3.3}$$

It is spanned by the m vectors

$$\underset{b}{e}^{\kappa} + B^{\mathfrak{m}}_{b}\underset{\mathfrak{m}}{e}^{\kappa} \quad (\mathfrak{m} = \mathrm{m}+1,\dots,\mathrm{r};\ b = 1,\dots,\mathrm{m}). \tag{3.4}$$

The $B^{\mathfrak{m}}_{b}$ are non-supernumerary coordinates of the E_m's in the E_r of the $\overset{\mathfrak{x}}{e}_{\lambda}$. In order that the E_m should be an integral-E_m it is necessary and sufficient that

$$\overset{\chi}{p}_{[cb]} + \overset{\chi}{p}_{[c|\mathfrak{m}|}B^{\mathfrak{m}}_{b]} = 0 \quad (b, c = 1,\dots,\mathrm{m};\ \mathfrak{m} = \mathrm{m}+1,\dots,\mathrm{r};\ \chi = 1,\dots,P). \tag{3.5}$$

(3.5) is equivalent to a system of relations between the ξ^{κ}

$$F^{\phi}(\xi^{\kappa}) = 0 \quad (\phi = r_0'+1,\dots,r_0) \tag{3.6}$$

and equations of the form

$$B^{\mathfrak{m}}_{b} = f^{\mathfrak{m}}_{b}(\xi^{\kappa}, \eta^{k}) \quad (b = 1,\dots,\mathrm{m};\ \mathfrak{m} = \mathrm{m}+1,\dots,\mathrm{r};\ k = \bar{1},\dots,\bar{d}), \tag{3.7}$$

which are linear in the d non-supernumerary parameters η^{k}. The ξ^{κ}, η^{k} are non-supernumerary coordinates of the integral-E_m's with $v^{1\dots\mathrm{m}} \neq 0$.

If we write X^{A} $(A = 1,\dots,n,\bar{1},\dots,\bar{d})$ for ξ^{κ}, η^{k}, in the X_{n+d} of the X^{A} we get the Cartan system consisting of the scalars

$$
\begin{aligned}
&F^{\omega}(\xi^{\kappa}) \quad (\omega = r_0+1,\dots,n),\\
&F^{\phi}(\xi^{\kappa}) \quad (\phi = r_0'+1,\dots,r_0),
\end{aligned}
\tag{3.8}
$$

the covariant vectors of X_{n+d} with the components

$$
\begin{array}{lll}
(a) & \partial_B F^\omega: & \partial_\lambda F^\omega,\ 0 \quad (\omega = r_0+1,\dots,n);\\
(b) & \partial_B F^\phi: & \partial_\lambda F^\phi,\ 0 \quad (\phi = r'_0+1,\dots,n);\\
(c) & \overset{\mathfrak{x}}{e}_B: & \overset{\mathfrak{x}}{e}_\lambda,\ 0 \quad (\mathfrak{x} = \mathrm{r}+1,\dots,\mathrm{n}); \qquad (3.9)\\
(d) & \overset{\mathfrak{m}}{e}_B - f^{\mathfrak{m}}_b(\xi^\kappa, \eta^k)\overset{b}{e}_B: & \overset{\mathfrak{m}}{e}_\lambda - f^{\mathfrak{m}}_b(\xi^\kappa, \eta^k)\overset{b}{e}_\lambda,\ 0
\end{array}
$$

$$(b = 1,\dots,\mathrm{m};\ \mathfrak{m} = \mathrm{m}+1,\dots,\mathrm{r};\ k = \bar{1},\dots,\bar{d};\ B = 1,\dots,n,\bar{1},\dots,\bar{d}),$$

and the rotations of the vectors (3.9 *c*) and (3.9 *d*). Now the rotations of the $\overset{\mathfrak{x}}{e}_\lambda$ are linearly dependent on the bivectors (3.1 *c*) mod $\overset{\mathfrak{x}}{e}_\lambda$ and the $B^{\mathfrak{m}}_b$ satisfy the equation (3.5), expressing the vanishing of the sections of the bivectors (3.1 *c*) mod $\overset{\mathfrak{x}}{e}_\lambda$ with the E_m of the vectors $\overset{\mathfrak{x}}{e}_\lambda$ and (3.3). Hence the rotations of the $\overset{\mathfrak{x}}{e}_B$ are zero mod (3.9 *c*, *d*) and can be dropped. The rotations of (3.9 *d*) can be expressed in terms of the $n+d$ linearly independent vectors

$$
\begin{array}{lllll}
(a) & \overset{a}{e}_B: & \overset{a}{e}_\lambda, & 0 & (a = 1,\dots,\mathrm{m});\\
(b) & \overset{\mathfrak{m}}{e}_B: & \overset{\mathfrak{m}}{e}_\lambda, & 0 & (\mathfrak{m} = \mathrm{m}+1,\dots,\mathrm{r}); \qquad (3.10)\\
(c) & \overset{\mathfrak{x}}{e}_B: & \overset{\mathfrak{x}}{e}_\lambda, & 0 & (\mathfrak{x} = \mathrm{r}+1,\dots,\mathrm{n});\\
(d) & \overset{k}{e}_B: & 0, & \delta^k_i & (i,k = \bar{1},\dots,\bar{d};\ B = 1,\dots,n,\bar{1},\dots,\bar{d}).
\end{array}
$$

Now in these rotations all terms that are zero mod (3.9 *c*, *d*) can be dropped. According to (3.9 *d*) the rotations of the vectors (3.9 *d*) do not contain terms of the form $d_{ij}\overset{i}{e}_{[C}\overset{j}{e}_{B]}$. Hence only terms containing at least one factor $\overset{b}{e}_B$ remain, i.e. the rotations of (3.9 *d*) can be replaced by bivectors of the form $\overset{\mathfrak{m}}{P}_{[C|b|}\overset{b}{e}_{B]}$. If the set of equations

$$F^\omega(\xi^\kappa) = 0, \quad F^\phi(\xi^\kappa) = 0 \quad (\omega = r_0+1,\dots,n;\ \phi = r'_0+1,\dots,r_0) \qquad (3.11)$$

is not regular in $\overset{0}{\xi}{}^\kappa$ it has to be replaced by a finite number of sets, each of which is regular in a point of $\mathfrak{N}(\overset{0}{\xi}{}^\kappa)$. To each of them we get a Cartan system and in each of these systems the vectors and bivectors have to be replaced by the minimum number of linearly independent ones among them. Then each Cartan system is an *SC*-system and each integral-X_m of the original *RSC*-system corresponds to one and only one integral-X_m of one of the *SC*-systems, nowhere having a direction in common with the E_{n-m+d} of the $\overset{a}{e}_B$.

It is sometimes convenient to use a *partial prolongation* instead of this total prolongation. Then we do not add all $r-m$ vectors (3.9 *d*) but only $r-m_1$, $m_1 > m$, linear combinations of them. The prolonged system then consists of the scalars

$$\begin{aligned} &F^{\omega}(\xi^{\kappa}) \quad (\omega = r_0+1,\dots,n), \\ &F^{\phi}(\xi^{\kappa}) \quad (\phi = r'_0+1,\dots,r_0), \end{aligned} \tag{3.12}$$

the covariant vectors

$$\begin{aligned}
&(a) \quad \partial_B F^{\omega} \quad (\omega = r_0+1,\dots,n),\\
&(b) \quad \partial_B F^{\phi} \quad (\phi = r'_0+1,\dots,r_0),\\
&(c) \quad \overset{\mathfrak{x}}{e}_B \qquad (\mathfrak{x} = \mathrm{r}+1,\dots,\mathrm{n};\ \mathfrak{b} = 1,\dots,\mathrm{m};\ \mathfrak{m} = \mathrm{m}+1,\dots,\mathrm{r}), \qquad (3.13)\\
&(d) \quad H^{\mathfrak{a}}_{\mathfrak{m}}(\overset{\mathfrak{m}}{e}_B - f^{\mathfrak{m}}_{\mathfrak{b}}(\xi^{\kappa},\eta^{k})\overset{\mathfrak{b}}{e}_B) \quad (\mathfrak{a} = \overline{\mathrm{m}_1+1,\dots,\mathrm{r}};\ k = \bar{1},\dots,\bar{d};\\
&\qquad\qquad B = 1,\dots,n,\bar{1},\dots,\bar{d}),
\end{aligned}$$

and the rotations of (3.13 *c*, *d*). The $H^{\mathfrak{a}}_{\mathfrak{m}}$ are functions of ξ^{κ}, η^{k}. In general the rotations of (3.13 *c*) cannot be dropped. In the way described above we get a finite number of Cartan systems, but these systems need not be special. Every integral-X_m of the original *RSC*-system with $v^{1\dots m} \neq 0$ corresponds to one and only one integral-X_m of one of these Cartan systems nowhere having a direction in common with the E_{n-m+d} of the $\overset{a}{e}_B$, and vice versa.

The total prolongation is the adjoint system (cf. IX, § 3) of the $\mathfrak{S}^m_d$-field consisting of all integral-E_m's with $v^{1\dots m} \neq 0$ of the *RSC*-system and the partial prolongation is the adjoint system of an $\mathfrak{S}^{m_1}_{d_1}$-field, $m_1 > m$, containing the $\mathfrak{S}^m_d$-field.

In many cases the partial prolongation is more profitable than the total one, as we shall see in the following sections.

If the original system has a genus $< m$ it may be possible that some of the prolonged systems have a genus $\geqslant m$. Then for these systems the regular integral-X_m's can be obtained and these furnish a part of the integral-X_m's of the original system. With the remaining systems we may proceed in the same way and look for total or partial prolongations with a genus $\geqslant m$, etc. Some prolonged systems may have no integral-E_m's at all. These systems drop out. Now we may ask whether this process always comes to an end, and, after a finite number of prolongations, enables us either to determine all integral-X_m's of the original system or to conclude that there are no integral-X_m's at all. The answer is not so easy to formulate. Although it is highly probable that, by using only total prolongations, we always come to an end after a finite number of steps, the proof has never been given. Cartan has proved in a very ingenious way† that, if a special Cartan system be given, it is always possible to choose total or partial prolongations in such a way that the process is finite. This beautiful but rather complicated proof will be shown in the next three sections. In general we shall follow the line of thought of Cartan. Only for the construction of the normalized forms we introduce sets of auxiliary polynomials in order to make more clear what is really done.

4. The solution of an *RSC*-system reduced to the solution of a finite number of *PNRSC*-systems with $\overset{\Omega}{\mathbf{\Pi}}_{bc}(u^a) = 0$.

We start from an *RSC*-system

$$\begin{aligned}
&(a) \qquad F^{\omega} && (\omega = 1,\ldots, n-r_0),\\
&(b) \qquad \overset{\mathfrak{x}}{e}_{\lambda} && (\mathfrak{x} = \mathrm{r}+1,\ldots,\mathrm{n};\; r \leqslant r_0), && (4.1)\\
&(c) \qquad \overset{\chi}{u}_{\mu\lambda} = \overset{\chi}{p}_{b[\mu}\overset{b}{e}_{\lambda]} && (b = 1,\ldots,\mathrm{m};\; \chi = 1,\ldots,P;\\
& && \qquad P \leqslant n-r;\; m \leqslant r).
\end{aligned}$$

The $\overset{b}{e}_{\lambda}$, $\overset{\mathfrak{x}}{e}_{\lambda}$ are $m+n-r$ measuring vectors of an anholonomic system (h) (cf. II, § 6). The gradients of the F^{ω} are linearly dependent on the $\overset{\mathfrak{x}}{e}_{\lambda}$. The $\partial_{[\mu}\overset{\mathfrak{x}}{e}_{\lambda]}$ are linearly dependent on the $\overset{\chi}{u}_{\mu\lambda} \bmod \overset{\mathfrak{x}}{e}_{\lambda}$ *and vice versa.*

We look for the integral-X_m's for which $v^{1\ldots\mathrm{m}} \neq 0$. It may be noticed that in the cases mentioned above, where the *RSC*-system is derived from a system of partial differential equations or arises from a process of prolongation, the $\overset{b}{e}_{\lambda}$ can be chosen as gradient vectors.

The $\overset{\chi}{p}_{b\mu}$ can always be written in the form

$$\overset{\chi}{p}_{b\mu} = \overset{\chi}{p}_{bc}\overset{c}{e}_{\mu} + \overset{\chi}{p}_{b\mathfrak{m}}\overset{\mathfrak{m}}{e}_{\mu} + \overset{\chi}{p}_{b\mathfrak{x}}\overset{\mathfrak{x}}{e}_{\mu} \qquad (4.2)$$

and from this it follows that in consequence of (4.1 *b*) the $\overset{\chi}{u}_{\mu\lambda}$ can always be replaced by the quantities

$$\overset{\chi}{\psi}_{\mu\lambda} = \overset{\chi}{p}_{cb}\overset{c}{e}_{[\mu}\overset{b}{e}_{\lambda]} + \overset{\chi}{p}_{b\mathfrak{m}}\overset{b}{e}_{[\mu}\overset{\mathfrak{m}}{e}_{\lambda]}. \qquad (4.3)$$

Without loss of generality we may assume that $\overset{\chi}{p}_{cb}$ is alternating in bc.

As in VIII, § 14, we denote the $\mathfrak{m}$-rank of the system

$$\overset{\chi}{p}_{\mathfrak{b}\mathfrak{m}} \quad (\mathfrak{b} = 1,\ldots,\mathrm{q};\; \mathfrak{m} = \mathrm{m}+1,\ldots,\mathrm{r};\; \chi = 1,\ldots,P) \qquad (4.4)$$

by

$$\sigma_1 + \ldots + \sigma_q \qquad (4.5)$$

† 1904. 1.

and the maximum $\mathfrak{m}$-rank of the system

$$P^b_{\mathfrak{b}'}\overset{\chi}{p}_{b\mathfrak{m}} \quad (\mathfrak{b}' = 1',\dots,q';\ b = 1,\dots,m;\ \mathfrak{m} = m+1,\dots,r;\ \chi = 1,\dots,P) \tag{4.6}$$

for an arbitrary choice of the $P^b_{\mathfrak{b}'}$ by

$$\sigma'_1+\dots+\sigma'_q \tag{4.7}$$

for every value of q from $1,\dots, m$. By a suitable choice of the $\overset{b}{e}_\lambda$ we can always make

$$\sigma'_1+\dots+\sigma'_q = \sigma_1+\dots+\sigma_q \tag{4.8}$$

for every value of q. Then among the vectors $\overset{\chi}{p}_{1\mathfrak{m}}$ there occur just σ'_1 linearly independent ones and by a suitable interchange of the indices χ it can always be arranged that these are just

$$\overset{1}{p}_{1\mathfrak{m}},\ \dots,\ \overset{\sigma'_1}{p}_{1\mathfrak{m}} \quad (\mathfrak{m} = m+1,\dots,r). \tag{4.9}$$

Now among the $2P$ vectors

$$\overset{\chi}{p}_{1\mathfrak{m}},\ \overset{\chi}{p}_{1\mathfrak{m}}+\alpha\overset{\chi}{p}_{2\mathfrak{m}} \quad (\mathfrak{m} = m+1,\dots,r;\ \chi = 1,\dots,P) \tag{4.10}$$

there occur just $\sigma'_1+\sigma'_2$ linearly independent ones for $\alpha \neq 0$. Hence among the P vectors

$$\overset{\chi}{p}_{1\mathfrak{m}}+\alpha\overset{\chi}{p}_{2\mathfrak{m}} \quad (\mathfrak{m} = m+1,\dots,r;\ \chi = 1,\dots,P) \tag{4.11}$$

there occur just σ'_2 vectors which are linearly independent of each other and of (4.9). The $\mathfrak{m}$-rank of (4.11) is σ'_1 for $\alpha = 0$ and consequently $\geqslant \sigma'_1$ for $\alpha \neq 0$ and sufficiently small. Now, according to the definition of σ'_1, this rank is $\leqslant \sigma'_1$. Hence the rank is σ'_1 and α can be chosen $\neq 0$ and so small that the vectors

$$\overset{1}{p}_{1\mathfrak{m}}+\alpha\overset{1}{p}_{2\mathfrak{m}},\ \dots,\ \overset{\sigma'_1}{p}_{1\mathfrak{m}}+\alpha\overset{\sigma'_1}{p}_{2\mathfrak{m}} \quad (\mathfrak{m} = m+1,\dots,r) \tag{4.12}$$

are linearly independent and that all vectors (4.11) depend linearly on them. This means that the σ'_2 vectors among (4.11) linearly independent of each other and of (4.9) can be chosen from (4.12), and from this it follows, because of $\sigma'_2 \leqslant \sigma'_1$, that the indices $1,\dots, \sigma'_1$ can be interchanged in such a way that these vectors are just

$$\overset{1}{p}_{1\mathfrak{m}}+\alpha\overset{1}{p}_{2\mathfrak{m}},\ \dots,\ \overset{\sigma'_2}{p}_{1\mathfrak{m}}+\alpha\overset{\sigma'_2}{p}_{2\mathfrak{m}} \quad (\mathfrak{m} = m+1,\dots,r). \tag{4.13}$$

Hence

$$\begin{matrix} \overset{1}{p}_{1\mathfrak{m}}, & \dots, & \overset{\sigma'_1}{p}_{1\mathfrak{m}}, \\ \overset{1}{p}_{2\mathfrak{m}}, & \dots, & \overset{\sigma'_2}{p}_{2\mathfrak{m}} \end{matrix} \tag{4.14}$$

are linearly independent. Continuing in this way it can be proved that the $\overset{b}{e}_\lambda$ can always be chosen in such a way that the $\sigma'_1+\ldots+\sigma'_m$ vectors

$$\begin{matrix} \overset{1}{p}_{1\mathfrak{m}}, & \ldots, & \overset{\sigma'_1}{p}_{1\mathfrak{m}} \\ \overset{1}{p}_{2\mathfrak{m}}, & \ldots, & \overset{\sigma'_2}{p}_{2\mathfrak{m}} \\ \cdot & \cdot & \cdot \\ \overset{1}{p}_{m\mathfrak{m}}, & \ldots, & \overset{\sigma'_m}{p}_{m\mathfrak{m}} \end{matrix} \quad (\sigma'_1 \geqslant \sigma'_2 \geqslant \ldots \geqslant \sigma'_m) \tag{4.15}$$

are linearly independent and that all other vectors $\overset{\chi}{p}_{b\mathfrak{m}}$ ($\chi = 1,\ldots, P$; $b = 1,\ldots, m$) depend linearly on them. If the $\overset{b}{e}_\lambda$ happen to be gradient vectors the choice can always be effected in such a way that this property does not get lost.

An *RSC*-system will be called *preferred*, or briefly a *PRSC*-system, if in every point of X_{r_0} there exists at least one integral-E_m with coordinates $v^{\kappa_1\ldots\kappa_m}$ satisfying the condition that $v^{1\ldots m} \neq 0$. We prove

THEOREM X.3. *If a non-preferred RSC-system is given, there exists a definite process leading either to a finite number of PRSC-systems, having together the same integral-X_m's as the given system, or to the conclusion that the given system has no integral-X_m's.*

PROOF. Let ξ^κ, U^x_b ($b = 1,\ldots, m$; $x = m+1,\ldots, n$) be the non-supernumerary coordinates of an integral-E_m of the non-preferred system (4.1):

$$\begin{aligned} F^\omega(\xi^\kappa) &= 0 \quad (\omega = 1,\ldots, n-r_0;\ b, c = 1,\ldots, m; \\ U^{\mathfrak{x}}_b &= 0 \qquad\quad \mathfrak{m} = m+1,\ldots, r;\ \mathfrak{x} = r+1,\ldots, n; \\ 2\overset{\chi}{p}_{cb}+\overset{\chi}{p}_{c\mathfrak{m}}\, U^{\mathfrak{m}}_b-\overset{\chi}{p}_{b\mathfrak{m}}\, U^{\mathfrak{m}}_c &= 0 \qquad\qquad\qquad\qquad \chi = 1,\ldots, P). \end{aligned} \tag{4.16}$$

Since the system is not preferred these equations cannot be satisfied in every point of X_{r_0}. Consequently by elimination of the U^x_b we get a number of equations of the form

$$F^{\mathfrak{a}}(\xi^\kappa) = 0 \quad (\mathfrak{a} = n-r_0+1,\ldots, n-r_0+\tau). \tag{4.17}$$

Hence we get a new Cartan system

$$\begin{aligned} &F^\omega, \quad F^{\mathfrak{a}} && (\omega = 1,\ldots, n-r_0;\ \mathfrak{a} = n-r_0+1,\ldots, n-r_0+\tau), \\ &\partial_\lambda F^{\mathfrak{a}}, \quad \overset{\mathfrak{x}}{e}_\lambda && (\mathfrak{x} = r+1,\ldots, n), \\ &\overset{\chi}{p}_{b[\mu}\, \overset{b}{e}_{\lambda]} && (b = 1,\ldots, m;\ \chi = 1,\ldots, P). \end{aligned} \tag{4.18}$$

If the system $F^\omega = 0$, $F^{\mathfrak{a}} = 0$ has no solutions, (4.1) has no integral-X_m's. In the other case this system can always be replaced by a finite number of systems, each minimal regular in a point of $\mathfrak{N}(\overset{0}{\xi^\kappa})$, and from them a finite number of RSC-systems can be derived, each with a value of r_0 smaller than the original r_0 and having together the same integral-X_m's as (4.1). If the systems obtained in this way are not preferred, the process has to be repeated. After a finite number of steps we obtain either a contradiction or a finite number of $PRSC$-systems. The whole process leading from a non-preferred RSC-system (4.1) to a finite number of equivalent $PRSC$-systems will be called the *cutting off* of (4.1).

For a $PRSC$-system we prove the theorem

THEOREM X.4. *If* (4.1) *is a PRSC-system, the measuring vectors* $\overset{\mathfrak{m}}{e}_\lambda$ ($\mathfrak{m} = \mathrm{m}+1,\dots,\mathrm{r}$) *can always be chosen in such a way that*

$$\overset{\chi}{p}_{bc} = 0 \quad (b, c = 1,\dots,\mathrm{m};\ \chi = 1,\dots,P). \tag{4.19}$$

If this is done the $\overset{\chi}{p}_{b\mathfrak{m}}$ *satisfy the congruences*

$$\partial_{[\mu}(\overset{\mathfrak{m}}{e}_{\lambda]}\overset{\chi}{p}_{b\mathfrak{m}}) \equiv 0 \ (\mathrm{mod}\, \overset{a}{e}_\lambda, \overset{\mathfrak{m}}{e}_\lambda \overset{\chi}{p}_{b\mathfrak{m}}, \overset{\mathfrak{x}}{e}_\lambda)$$
$$(a, b = 1,\dots,\mathrm{m};\ \mathfrak{m} = \mathrm{m}+1,\dots,\mathrm{r};\ \mathfrak{x} = \mathrm{r}+1,\dots,\mathrm{n};\ \chi = 1,\dots,P). \tag{4.20}$$

PROOF. Since (4.1) is preferred, there exists in every point of X_{r_0} an integral-E_m ξ^κ, $v^{\kappa_1\dots\kappa_m}$ with $v^{1\dots\mathrm{m}} \neq 0$. This E_m is the section of the $n-r$ vectors $\overset{\mathfrak{x}}{e}_\lambda$ and $r-m$ other covariant vectors linearly independent of the $\overset{\mathfrak{x}}{e}_\lambda$ and $\overset{a}{e}_\lambda$. Hence these $r-m$ vectors can be chosen as the (anholonomic) measuring vectors $\overset{\mathfrak{m}}{e}_\lambda$. Then E_m is the section of the $n-m$ vectors $\overset{\mathfrak{m}}{e}_\lambda$, $\overset{\mathfrak{x}}{e}_\lambda$ and the $\overset{\chi}{u}_{\mu\lambda}$ are zero mod $\overset{\mathfrak{m}}{e}_\lambda$, $\overset{\mathfrak{x}}{e}_\lambda$, and the same holds for the $\overset{\chi}{\psi}_{\mu\lambda}$ in (4.3). Hence

$$\overset{\chi}{p}_{bc}\overset{b}{e}_{[\mu}\overset{c}{e}_{\lambda]} + \overset{\chi}{p}_{b\mathfrak{m}}\overset{b}{e}_{[\mu}\overset{\mathfrak{m}}{e}_{\lambda]} \equiv 0 \ (\mathrm{mod}\, \overset{\mathfrak{m}}{e}_\lambda, \overset{\mathfrak{x}}{e}_\lambda)$$
$$(b, c = 1,\dots,\mathrm{m};\ \mathfrak{m} = \mathrm{m}+1,\dots,\mathrm{r};\ \mathfrak{x} = \mathrm{r}+1,\dots,\mathrm{n};\ \chi = 1,\dots,P) \tag{4.21}$$

and consequently

$$\overset{\chi}{p}_{bc}\overset{b}{e}_{[\mu}\overset{c}{e}_{\lambda]} = 0 \quad (b, c = 1,\dots,\mathrm{m};\ \chi = 1,\dots,P) \tag{4.22}$$

equivalent to (4.19). According to (4.19) it follows from (4.3) that

$$\partial_{[\nu}\overset{\chi}{\psi}_{\mu\lambda]} \equiv \overset{b}{e}_{[\mu}\partial_{\nu}(\overset{\mathfrak{m}}{e}_{\lambda]}\overset{\chi}{p}_{b\mathfrak{m}}) \ (\mathrm{mod}\, \overset{\mathfrak{m}}{e}_\lambda \overset{\chi}{p}_{b\mathfrak{m}})$$
$$(b = 1,\dots,\mathrm{m};\ \mathfrak{m} = \mathrm{m}+1,\dots,\mathrm{r};\ \chi = 1,\dots,P). \tag{4.23}$$

Now $\overset{\chi}{\psi}_{\mu\lambda}$ is zero mod $\overset{\chi}{u}_{\mu\lambda}$, $\overset{\mathfrak{x}}{e}_\lambda$ and $\partial_{[\mu}\overset{\mathfrak{x}}{e}_{\lambda]}$ is zero mod $\overset{\chi}{u}_{\mu\lambda}$. Hence $\partial_{[\nu}\overset{\chi}{\psi}_{\mu\lambda]}$

is zero mod $\overset{\chi}{u}_{\mu\lambda}, \overset{\mathfrak{x}}{e}_{\lambda}$. But $\overset{\chi}{u}_{\mu\lambda}$ is zero mod $\overset{\mathfrak{x}}{e}_{\lambda}, \overset{\chi}{\psi}_{\mu\lambda}$ and according to (4.19) $\overset{\chi}{\psi}_{\mu\lambda}$ is zero mod $\overset{\mathfrak{m}}{e}_{\lambda}\overset{\chi}{p}_{b\mathfrak{m}}$. Hence $\partial_{[\nu}\overset{\chi}{\psi}_{\mu\lambda]}$ is zero mod $\overset{\mathfrak{x}}{e}_{\lambda}, \overset{\mathfrak{m}}{e}_{\lambda}\overset{\chi}{p}_{b\mathfrak{m}}$. Consequently, according to (4.23)

$$\overset{b}{e}_{[\mu}\,\partial_{\nu}(\overset{\mathfrak{m}}{e}_{\lambda]}\overset{\chi}{p}_{b\mathfrak{m}}) \equiv 0 \quad (\mathrm{mod}\, \overset{\mathfrak{x}}{e}_{\lambda}, \overset{\mathfrak{m}}{e}_{\lambda}\overset{\chi}{p}_{b\mathfrak{m}}) \tag{4.24}$$

and (4.20) follows immediately from this.

In order to get a normalized form for a not necessarily preferred *RSC*-system (4.1) we multiply the $\overset{\chi}{\psi}_{\mu\lambda}$ with P arbitrary polynomials $f_{\chi}(u^a)$ ($\chi = 1,\dots, P$) in the auxiliary variables u^a ($a = 1,\dots, \mathrm{m}$). Then we can form the bivector polynomials†

$$\boldsymbol{\Psi}_{\mu\lambda}(u^a) \overset{\mathrm{def}}{=} \overset{\chi}{\psi}_{\mu\lambda} f_{\chi}(u^a) = \overset{b}{e}_{[\mu}\overset{c}{e}_{\lambda]}\boldsymbol{\Pi}_{bc}(u^a) + \overset{b}{e}_{[\mu}\overset{\mathfrak{m}}{e}_{\lambda]}\boldsymbol{\Pi}_{b\mathfrak{m}}(u^a), \tag{4.25}$$

where

$$(a)\quad \boldsymbol{\Pi}_{bc} \overset{\mathrm{def}}{=} \overset{\chi}{p}_{bc}\, f_{\chi}(u^a), \qquad (b)\quad \boldsymbol{\Pi}_{b\mathfrak{m}} \overset{\mathrm{def}}{=} \overset{\chi}{p}_{b\mathfrak{m}}\, f_{\chi}(u^a). \tag{4.26}$$

If $\psi_{\mu\lambda}^{\alpha_1\dots\alpha_\mathrm{m}}$ is the coefficient of $(u^1)^{\alpha_1}\dots(u^{\mathrm{m}})^{\alpha_\mathrm{m}}$ in $\boldsymbol{\Psi}_{\mu\lambda}$, according to (4.25) this term depends linearly on the $\overset{\chi}{\psi}_{\mu\lambda}$. It is always possible to construct T bivector polynomials

$$\overset{\Omega}{\boldsymbol{\Psi}}_{\mu\lambda}(u^a) \quad (\Omega = 1,\dots, T) \tag{4.27}$$

such that conversely every bivector $\overset{\chi}{\psi}_{\mu\lambda}$ depends linearly on the coefficients of these bivector polynomials. In that case (4.1) is equivalent to the system

$$\begin{aligned}
&(a)\quad F^{\omega},\\
&(b)\quad \overset{\mathfrak{x}}{e}_{\lambda},\\
&(c)\quad \overset{\Omega}{\boldsymbol{\Psi}}_{\mu\lambda}(u^a) \overset{\mathrm{def}}{=} \overset{b}{e}_{[\mu}\overset{c}{e}_{\lambda]}\overset{\Omega}{\boldsymbol{\Pi}}_{bc}(u^a) + \overset{b}{e}_{[\mu}\overset{\mathfrak{m}}{e}_{\lambda]}\overset{\Omega}{\boldsymbol{\Pi}}_{b\mathfrak{m}}(u^a) \quad (a,b,c = 1,\dots,\mathrm{m};\\
&\qquad\qquad \mathfrak{m} = \mathrm{m}+1,\dots,\mathrm{r};\ \mathfrak{x} = \mathrm{r}+1,\dots,\mathrm{n};\ \Omega = 1,\dots, T).
\end{aligned} \tag{4.28}$$

This form of the system will be called *normalized*, or briefly an *NRSC-system*, if the following conditions are satisfied:

A. There exist vector polynomials $\overset{\Omega}{\boldsymbol{\Pi}}_{\mathfrak{m}}(u^a)$ such that

$$\overset{\Omega}{\boldsymbol{\Pi}}_{b\mathfrak{m}} = \frac{\partial\overset{\Omega}{\boldsymbol{\Pi}}_{\mathfrak{m}}}{\partial u^b} \quad (b = 1,\dots,\mathrm{m};\ \mathfrak{m} = \mathrm{m}+1,\dots,\mathrm{r};\ \Omega = 1,\dots, T). \tag{4.29}$$

B. The bivector polynomial $\overset{\Omega}{\boldsymbol{\Pi}}_{bc}(u^a)$ is homogeneous of a degree $n_{\Omega} \geqslant 0$ ($\Omega = 1,\dots, T$) in the u^a.

† We denote all quantities whose components are polynomials in u^a by a kernel letter in heavy greek capitals.

C. The vector polynomial $\overset{\Omega}{\mathbf{\Pi}}_{\mathfrak{m}}(u^a)$ is homogeneous of degree $n_\Omega + 1$ in the u^a.

D. There exist numbers h_Ω $(0 \leqslant h_\Omega \leqslant m)$, such that all vector coefficients of the vector polynomials

$$\overset{\Omega}{\mathbf{\Pi}}_{\mathfrak{m}}(u^1, \ldots, u^{h_\Omega}, 0, \ldots, 0) \tag{4.30}$$

with $h_\Omega \geqslant 1$, considered as vectors in the E_{r-m} of the index $\mathfrak{m}$ are $\neq 0$ and linearly independent. We call these vector coefficients *parametrical*.†

E. The remaining vector coefficients of the $\overset{\Omega}{\mathbf{\Pi}}_{\mathfrak{m}}$, called *principal*, are linearly dependent on the parametrical vector coefficients.

If the total number of coefficients of a homogeneous polynomial of degree N in p variables is denoted by $\phi(N,p)$, we have

$$\phi(N,p) = \frac{(N+p-1)!}{N!(p-1)!} \quad (p \geqslant 1) \tag{4.31}$$

and consequently, if we define $\phi(N,p) = 0$ for $p \leqslant 0$, the total number of parametrical vector coefficients is

$$\sum_{\Omega=1}^{\Omega=T} \phi(n_\Omega + 1, h_\Omega). \tag{4.32}$$

According to the condition (D) this number is equal to the $\mathfrak{m}$-rank of the vector coefficients of the $\overset{\Omega}{\mathbf{\Pi}}_{\mathfrak{m}}$. But, since (4.28) is equivalent to (4.1), this $\mathfrak{m}$-rank is also the $\mathfrak{m}$-rank of the $\overset{\chi}{p}_{b\mathfrak{m}}$, hence

$$\sigma_1' + \ldots + \sigma_m' = \sum_{\Omega=1}^{\Omega=T} \phi(n_\Omega + 1, h_\Omega). \tag{4.33}$$

In consequence of (4.26 b) and (4.29) we have

$$\partial_b \overset{\Omega}{\mathbf{\Pi}}_{\mathfrak{m}} = \overset{\chi}{p}_{b\mathfrak{m}} \overset{\Omega}{f}_\chi(u^a) \quad (b = 1, \ldots, \mathrm{m};\ \mathfrak{m} = \mathrm{m}+1, \ldots, \mathrm{r};$$
$$\chi = 1, \ldots, P;\ \Omega = 1, \ldots, T) \tag{4.34}$$

and accordingly

$$\partial_{\mathfrak{b}} \overset{\Omega}{\mathbf{\Pi}}_{\mathfrak{m}} = \overset{\chi}{p}_{\mathfrak{b}\mathfrak{m}} \overset{\Omega}{f}_\chi(u^a) \quad (\mathfrak{b} = 1, \ldots, \mathrm{q};\ \mathfrak{m} = \mathrm{m}+1, \ldots, \mathrm{r};$$
$$\chi = 1, \ldots, P;\ \Omega = 1, \ldots, T). \tag{4.35}$$

Accordingly the $\mathfrak{m}$-domain of $\partial_{\mathfrak{b}} \overset{\Omega}{\mathbf{\Pi}}_{\mathfrak{m}}$ is contained in the $\mathfrak{m}$-domain of $\overset{\chi}{p}_{\mathfrak{b}\mathfrak{m}}$. Since the quantities (4.27) are equivalent to the $\overset{\chi}{\psi}_{\mu\lambda}$, every $\overset{\chi}{\psi}_{\mu\lambda}$

† Cartan, 1904. 1, uses the terms principal and non-principal in just the opposite way.

depends linearly on the $\overset{\Omega}{\mathbf{\Psi}}_{\mu\lambda}$, hence

$$\overset{\chi}{p}_{bc}\overset{b}{e}_{[j}\overset{c}{e}_{i]}+\overset{b}{e}_{[j}\overset{\mathfrak{m}}{e}_{i]}\overset{\chi}{p}_{b\mathfrak{m}} \equiv 0 \ (\text{mod coeff. } \overset{\Omega}{\mathbf{\Psi}}_{ji}(u^a))$$
$$(a,b,c = 1,\dots,\mathrm{m};\ \mathfrak{m} = \mathrm{m}+1,\dots,\mathrm{r};\ \mathfrak{x} = \mathrm{r}+1,\dots,\mathrm{n};$$
$$i,j = 1,\dots,\mathrm{n};\ \chi = 1,\dots,P;\ \Omega = 1,\dots,T) \qquad (4.36)$$

and $$\overset{\chi}{p}_{b\mathfrak{m}} \equiv 0 \ (\text{mod coeff. } \partial_b \overset{\Omega}{\mathbf{\Pi}}_{\mathfrak{m}}) \quad (b = 1,\dots,\mathrm{m};\ \mathfrak{m} = \mathrm{m}+1,\dots,\mathrm{r};$$
$$\chi = 1,\dots,P;\ \Omega = 1,\dots,T), \qquad (4.37)$$

which proves that every $\overset{\chi}{p}_{b\mathfrak{m}}$ $(\chi = 1,\dots,P)$ depends linearly on the coefficients of the T polynomials $\partial_b \overset{\Omega}{\mathbf{\Pi}}_{\mathfrak{m}}$. Therefore the $\mathfrak{m}$-domain of $\overset{\chi}{p}_{\mathfrak{b}\mathfrak{m}}$ is contained in the $\mathfrak{m}$-domain of the coefficients of $\partial_{\mathfrak{b}} \overset{\Omega}{\mathbf{\Pi}}_{\mathfrak{m}}$ and this has as a consequence that both domains coincide. From this we see that the $\mathfrak{m}$-rank of the coefficients of the $\partial_{\mathfrak{b}} \overset{\Omega}{\mathbf{\Pi}}_{\mathfrak{m}}$ $(\mathfrak{b} = 1,\dots,\mathrm{q})$ is $\leqslant \sigma'_1+\dots+\sigma'_q$. The parametrical vector coefficients of the $\overset{\Omega}{\mathbf{\Pi}}_{\mathfrak{m}}$ occurring in the $\partial_{\mathfrak{b}} \overset{\Omega}{\mathbf{\Pi}}_{\mathfrak{m}}$ $(\mathfrak{b} = 1,\dots,\mathrm{q};\ \Omega = 1,\dots,T)$, being linearly independent, their number is consequently $\leqslant \sigma'_1+\dots+\sigma'_q$. For a fixed value of Ω the number of these parametrical vector coefficients is equal to the number of terms in $\overset{\Omega}{\mathbf{\Pi}}_{\mathfrak{m}}(u^1,\dots,u^{\mathrm{h}_\Omega},0,\dots,0)$, containing at least one of the variables $u^1,\dots,u^{\mathrm{q}}$. Hence for $q \geqslant h_\Omega$ the number of parametrical vector coefficients of $\overset{\Omega}{\mathbf{\Pi}}_{\mathfrak{m}}$ is equal to $\phi(n_\Omega+1,h_\Omega)$ and for $q < h_\Omega$ this number is equal to $\phi(n_\Omega+1,h_\Omega)-\phi(n_\Omega+1,h_\Omega-q)$. Consequently the number of parametrical vector coefficients of the $\overset{\Omega}{\mathbf{\Pi}}_{\mathfrak{m}}$ occurring in the $\partial_{\mathfrak{b}} \overset{\Omega}{\mathbf{\Pi}}_{\mathfrak{m}}$ $(\mathfrak{b} = 1,\dots,\mathrm{q};$ $\Omega = 1,\dots,T)$ is equal to $\phi(n_\Omega+1,h_\Omega)-\phi(n_\Omega+1, h_\Omega-q)$. Summation over Ω gives

$$\sum_{\Omega=1}^{\Omega=T} \{\phi(n_\Omega+1,h_\Omega)-\phi(n_\Omega+1,h_\Omega-q)\} \leqslant \sigma'_1+\dots+\sigma'_q \qquad (4.38)$$

and, according to (4.33),

$$\sigma'_{q+1}+\dots+\sigma'_m \leqslant \sum_{\Omega=1}^{\Omega=T} \phi(n_\Omega+1,h_\Omega-q). \qquad (4.39)$$

Summation of (4.39) over q from 0 to $m-1$ gives

$$\sigma'_1+2\sigma'_2+\dots+m\sigma'_m \leqslant \sum_{\Omega=1}^{\Omega=T} \sum_{q=0}^{q=m-1} \phi(n_\Omega+1,h_\Omega-q)$$
$$= \sum_{\Omega=1}^{\Omega=T} \{\phi(n_\Omega+1,h_\Omega)+\dots+\phi(n_\Omega+1,1)\} = \sum_{\Omega=1}^{\Omega=T} \phi(n_\Omega+2,h_\Omega). \qquad (4.40)$$

Now we can prove the theorem:

THEOREM X.5. *Every RSC-system can be replaced by an NRSC-system.*

PROOF. Let (4.1) be an RSC-system and let the $\overset{b}{e}_\lambda$ be chosen in such a way that the vectors (4.15) are linearly independent. If then we choose

$$\overset{\chi}{\mathbf{\Pi}}_{\mathfrak{m}} \overset{\text{def}}{=} \overset{\chi}{p}_{b\mathfrak{m}} u^b, \quad \overset{\chi}{\mathbf{\Pi}}_{bc} \overset{\text{def}}{=} \overset{\chi}{p}_{bc} \quad (b, c = 1,\dots,\mathrm{m}; \; \mathfrak{m} = \mathrm{m}+1,\dots,\mathrm{r};\; \chi = 1,\dots, P), \tag{4.41}$$

we have

$$\overset{\chi}{\mathbf{\Psi}}_{\mu\lambda} = \overset{\chi}{\mathbf{\Pi}}_{bc} \overset{b}{e}_{[\mu} \overset{c}{e}_{\lambda]} + \overset{b}{e}_{[\mu} \overset{\mathfrak{m}}{e}_{\lambda]} \partial_b \overset{\chi}{\mathbf{\Pi}}_{\mathfrak{m}} \quad (b, c = 1,\dots,\mathrm{m};\; \mathfrak{m} = \mathrm{m}+1,\dots,\mathrm{r};\; \chi = 1,\dots, P) \tag{4.42}$$

and the conditions (B) and (C) are satisfied with $T = P$ and $n_\chi = 0$. If now we choose $h_\chi = i$ for $\sigma'_{i+1} < \chi \leqslant \sigma'_i$ and $h_\chi = 0$ for $\chi > \sigma'_1$, $h_\chi = m$ for $\chi \leqslant \sigma'_m$, the parametrical vector coefficients are

$$\begin{array}{l} \overset{1}{p}_{1\mathfrak{m}}, \;\dots,\; \overset{\sigma'_m}{p}_{1\mathfrak{m}},\; \overset{\sigma'_m+1}{p}_{1\mathfrak{m}},\;\dots,\; \overset{\sigma'_{m-1}}{p}_{1\mathfrak{m}},\; \overset{\sigma'_{m-1}+1}{p}_{1\mathfrak{m}},\;\dots,\; \overset{\sigma'_{m-2}}{p}_{1\mathfrak{m}},\;\dots,\; \overset{\sigma'_2+1}{p}_{1\mathfrak{m}},\;\dots,\; \overset{\sigma'_1}{p}_{1\mathfrak{m}}, \\ \overset{1}{p}_{2\mathfrak{m}},\;\dots,\; \overset{\sigma'_m}{p}_{2\mathfrak{m}},\;\dots,\; \overset{\sigma'_3+1}{p}_{2\mathfrak{m}},\;\dots,\; \overset{\sigma'_2}{p}_{2\mathfrak{m}}, \\ \cdot\;\cdot\;\cdot\;\cdot\;\cdot\;\cdot\;\cdot\;\cdot\;\cdot\;\cdot\;\cdot\;\cdot\;\cdot \\ \overset{1}{p}_{\mathrm{m}\mathfrak{m}},\;\dots,\; \overset{\sigma'_m}{p}_{\mathrm{m}\mathfrak{m}} \quad (\mathfrak{m} = \mathrm{m}+1,\dots,\mathrm{r}) \end{array} \tag{4.43}$$

and, according to our choice of the $\overset{b}{e}_\lambda$ these $\sigma'_1+\dots+\sigma'_m$ vectors are linearly independent. Hence the condition (D) is satisfied. Since there are no more than $\sigma'_1+\dots+\sigma'_m$ linearly independent vectors among the $\overset{\chi}{p}_{b\mathfrak{m}}$ $(b = 1,\dots,\mathrm{m};\; \chi = 1,\dots, P)$ every one of these vectors depends linearly on the vectors (4.43). Hence the condition (E) is satisfied and the system obtained is normalized.

From this we see that the property of being normalized is not a geometrical property of a Cartan system but only a property of its form.

For $NPRSC$-systems (normalized preferred RSC-systems) a theorem can be proved, analogous to the theorem X.4 for $PRSC$-systems:

THEOREM X.6. *If* (4.28) *is an NPRSC-system, the measuring vectors* $\overset{\mathfrak{m}}{e}_\lambda$ $(\mathfrak{m} = \mathrm{m}+1,\dots,\mathrm{r})$ *can always be chosen in such a way that the polynomials* $\overset{\Omega}{\mathbf{\Pi}}_{bc}(u^a)$ *vanish identically. After this transformation of the* $\overset{\mathfrak{m}}{e}_\lambda$ *the vector polynomials* $\overset{\Omega}{\mathbf{\Pi}}_{\mathfrak{m}}$ *can be chosen in such a way that the values of the numbers* n_Ω, h_Ω $(\Omega = 1,\dots, T)$ *remain unchanged.*

PROOF. Since the system is preferred it is possible to choose $r-m$ vectors $\overset{\mathfrak{m}'}{e}_\lambda$ ($\mathfrak{m}' = (\mathrm{m}+1)',\ldots,\mathrm{r}'$) in such a way that the section of the $n-m$ vectors $\overset{\mathfrak{m}'}{e}_\lambda$, $\overset{\mathfrak{x}}{e}_\lambda$ is an integral-E_m with $v^{1\ldots\mathrm{m}} \neq 0$. Let

$$\overset{\mathfrak{m}}{e}_\lambda = S^{\mathfrak{m}}_{\mathfrak{m}'}\overset{\mathfrak{m}'}{e}_\lambda + S^{\mathfrak{m}}_{b}\overset{b}{e}_\lambda + S^{\mathfrak{m}}_{\mathfrak{x}}\overset{\mathfrak{x}}{e}_\lambda, \quad \mathrm{Det}\,(S^{\mathfrak{m}}_{\mathfrak{m}'}) \neq 0$$
$$(b = 1,\ldots,\mathrm{m};\ \mathfrak{m} = \mathrm{m}+1,\ldots,\mathrm{r};$$
$$\mathfrak{x} = \mathrm{r}+1,\ldots,\mathrm{n};\ \mathfrak{m}' = (\mathrm{m}+1)',\ldots,\mathrm{r}'). \tag{4.44}$$

Substitution of (4.44) in (4.28 c) gives

$$\overset{\Omega}{\mathbf{\Psi}}_{\mu\lambda}(u^a) \equiv \overset{b}{e}_{[\mu}\overset{c}{e}_{\lambda]}\overset{\Omega}{\mathbf{\Pi}}{}'_{bc} + \overset{b}{e}_{[\mu}\overset{\mathfrak{m}'}{e}_{\lambda]}\overset{\Omega}{\mathbf{\Pi}}{}'_{b\mathfrak{m}'} \ (\mathrm{mod}\,\overset{\mathfrak{x}}{e}_\lambda)$$
$$(b,c = 1,\ldots,\mathrm{m};\ \mathfrak{m}' = (\mathrm{m}+1)',\ldots,\mathrm{r}';$$
$$\mathfrak{x} = \mathrm{r}+1,\ldots,\mathrm{n};\ \Omega = 1,\ldots,T), \tag{4.45}$$

where

$$(a)\qquad \overset{\Omega}{\mathbf{\Pi}}{}'_{bc} \overset{\mathrm{def}}{=} \overset{\Omega}{\mathbf{\Pi}}_{bc} + \overset{\Omega}{\mathbf{\Pi}}_{[b|\mathfrak{m}|}\, S^{\mathfrak{m}}_{c]},$$

$$(b)\qquad \overset{\Omega}{\mathbf{\Pi}}{}'_{b\mathfrak{m}'} \overset{\mathrm{def}}{=} S^{\mathfrak{m}}_{\mathfrak{m}'}\overset{\Omega}{\mathbf{\Pi}}_{b\mathfrak{m}} = \frac{\partial\overset{\Omega}{\mathbf{\Pi}}{}'_{\mathfrak{m}'}}{\partial u^b}, \tag{4.46}$$

$$(c)\qquad \overset{\Omega}{\mathbf{\Pi}}{}'_{\mathfrak{m}'} \overset{\mathrm{def}}{=} S^{\mathfrak{m}}_{\mathfrak{m}'}\overset{\Omega}{\mathbf{\Pi}}_{\mathfrak{m}}$$

$$(b,c = 1,\ldots,\mathrm{m};\ \mathfrak{m} = \mathrm{m}+1,\ldots,\mathrm{r};\ \mathfrak{m}' = (\mathrm{m}+1)',\ldots,\mathrm{r}';\ \Omega = 1,\ldots,T).$$

Now we have to show that $\overset{\Omega}{\mathbf{\Pi}}{}'_{bc} = 0$. Since $\overset{\mathfrak{m}'}{e}_\lambda$, $\overset{\mathfrak{x}}{e}_\lambda$ define an integral-E_m, we know that $\overset{\Omega}{\mathbf{\Psi}}_{\mu\lambda}(u^a)$ is zero mod $\overset{\mathfrak{m}'}{e}_\lambda$, $\overset{\mathfrak{x}}{e}_\lambda$ and this has as a consequence that

$$\overset{b}{e}_{[\mu}\overset{c}{e}_{\lambda]}\overset{\Omega}{\mathbf{\Pi}}{}'_{bc} \equiv 0 \ (\mathrm{mod}\,\overset{\mathfrak{m}'}{e}_\lambda, \overset{\mathfrak{x}}{e}_\lambda) \quad (b,c = 1,\ldots,\mathrm{m};\ \mathfrak{m}' = (\mathrm{m}+1)',\ldots,\mathrm{r}';$$
$$\mathfrak{x} = \mathrm{r}+1,\ldots,\mathrm{n};\ \Omega = 1,\ldots,T). \tag{4.47}$$

But, according to the linear independence of the $\overset{b}{e}_\lambda$, $\overset{\mathfrak{m}'}{e}_\lambda$, $\overset{\mathfrak{x}}{e}_\lambda$ this proves that $\overset{\Omega}{\mathbf{\Pi}}{}'_{bc} = 0$. Hence, according to (4.45) and (4.46 b) the $\overset{\Omega}{\mathbf{\Psi}}_{\mu\lambda}$ can be replaced by the bivector polynomials

$$\overset{\Omega}{\mathbf{\Psi}}{}'_{\mu\lambda}(u^a) \overset{\mathrm{def}}{=} \overset{b}{e}_{[\mu}\overset{\mathfrak{m}'}{e}_{\lambda]}\frac{\partial\overset{\Omega}{\mathbf{\Pi}}{}'_{\mathfrak{m}'}}{\partial u^b}. \tag{4.48}$$

The new polynomials $\overset{\Omega}{\mathbf{\Pi}}{}'_{\mathfrak{m}'}$ are defined by (4.46 c). If we choose the old values for the h_Ω, it follows from (4.46 c) that the new parametrical vector coefficients can be formed from the old ones by transvection with $S^{\mathfrak{m}}_{\mathfrak{m}'}$. Since the determinant of $S^{\mathfrak{m}}_{\mathfrak{m}'}$ is $\neq 0$, these new parametrical vector coefficients are linearly independent. In the same way we see that the principal vector coefficients transform with $S^{\mathfrak{m}}_{\mathfrak{m}'}$. This proves that the system arising from (4.28) by replacing the $\overset{\Omega}{\Psi}_{\mu\lambda}(u^a)$ by the $\overset{\Omega}{\Psi}{}'_{\mu\lambda}(u^a)$ is normalized and has the same values of n_Ω, h_Ω.

The following theorem holds for *NRSC*-systems:

THEOREM X.7. *If a non-preferred NRSC-system* (4.28) *is given, the process of cutting off leads either to a finite number of PNRSC-systems having together the same integral-X_m's as the given system or to the conclusion that the given system has no integral-X_m's at all. One bivector polynomial with the same values of the n and h or one or more bivector polynomials with a lower value of the h correspond in each of the PNRSC-systems obtained to each bivector polynomial* (4.28 *c*).

PROOF. By the process of cutting off we get a system of the form (cf. (4.18))

$$\begin{aligned}
&(a) && F^{\omega}, \quad F^{\mathfrak{a}}, \\
&(b) && \partial_\lambda F^{\mathfrak{a}}, \quad \overset{\mathfrak{x}}{e}_\lambda, \qquad (4.49)\\
&(c) && \overset{\Omega}{\Psi}_{\mu\lambda}(u^a) = \overset{b}{e}_{[\mu} \overset{c}{e}_{\lambda]} \overset{\Omega}{\Pi}_{bc} + \overset{b}{e}_{[\mu} \overset{\mathfrak{m}}{e}_{\lambda]} \overset{\Omega}{\Pi}_{b\mathfrak{m}}, \quad \overset{\Omega}{\Pi}_{b\mathfrak{m}} = \frac{\partial \overset{\Omega}{\Pi}_{\mathfrak{m}}}{\partial u^b}
\end{aligned}$$

$$(b, c = 1,\ldots, \mathrm{m};\ \mathfrak{m} = \mathrm{m}+1,\ldots, \mathrm{r};\ \omega = 1,\ldots, n-r_0;$$
$$\mathfrak{a} = n-r_0+1,\ldots, n-r_0+\tau;\ \mathfrak{x} = \mathrm{r}+1,\ldots, \mathrm{n};\ \Omega = 1,\ldots, T).$$

By the process of reduction it can always be arranged that the vectors $\overset{b}{e}_\lambda$ are linearly independent of the vectors (4.49 *b*). But it is still possible that some of the vectors $\overset{\mathfrak{m}}{e}_\lambda$ depend linearly on the other vectors $\overset{\mathfrak{m}}{e}_\lambda$, the $\overset{b}{e}_\lambda$, and the vectors (4.49 *b*). Then, after a suitable interchange of the indices m+1,..., r, relations of the form

$$\overset{\mathfrak{m}}{e}_\lambda = Z^{\mathfrak{m}}_{\overline{\mathfrak{m}}} \overset{\overline{\mathfrak{m}}}{e}_\lambda + Z^{\mathfrak{m}}_{\mathfrak{x}} \overset{\mathfrak{x}}{e}_\lambda + Z^{\mathfrak{m}}_{\mathfrak{a}} \partial_\lambda F^{\mathfrak{a}} + Z^{\mathfrak{m}}_{b} \overset{b}{e}_\lambda$$
$$(b = 1,\ldots, \mathrm{m};\ \mathfrak{m} = \mathrm{m}+1,\ldots, \mathrm{r};\ \mathfrak{x} = \mathrm{r}+1,\ldots, \mathrm{n};$$
$$\overline{\mathfrak{m}} = \overline{\mathrm{m}+1},\ldots, \bar{\mathrm{r}};\ \bar{r} < r;\ \mathfrak{a} = n-r_0+1,\ldots, n-r_0+\tau) \qquad (4.50)$$

exist. By substitution of (4.50) into (4.49 *c*) we get

$$\overset{\Omega}{\Psi}_{\mu\lambda}(u^a) \equiv \overset{b}{e}_{[\mu} \overset{c}{e}_{\lambda]} {}'\overset{\Omega}{\Pi}_{bc} + \overset{b}{e}_{[\mu} \overset{\overline{\mathfrak{m}}}{e}_{\lambda]} {}'\overset{\Omega}{\Pi}_{b\overline{\mathfrak{m}}} \pmod{\overset{\mathfrak{x}}{e}_\lambda, \partial_\lambda F^{\mathfrak{a}}}$$
$$(b, c = 1,\ldots, \mathrm{m};\ \overline{\mathfrak{m}} = \overline{\mathrm{m}+1},\ldots, \bar{\mathrm{r}};\ \mathfrak{x} = \mathrm{r}+1,\ldots, \mathrm{n};$$
$$\mathfrak{a} = n-r_0+1,\ldots, n-r_0+\tau;\ \Omega = 1,\ldots, T), \qquad (4.51)$$

where

$$\begin{aligned}
&(a) && {}'\overset{\Omega}{\mathbf{\Pi}}_{bc} \overset{\text{def}}{=} \overset{\Omega}{\mathbf{\Pi}}_{bc} + Z^{\mathfrak{m}}_{[c} \overset{\Omega}{\mathbf{\Pi}}_{b]\mathfrak{m}}, \\
&(b) && {}'\overset{\Omega}{\mathbf{\Pi}}_{b\overline{\mathfrak{m}}} \overset{\text{def}}{=} \partial_b \, {}'\overset{\Omega}{\mathbf{\Pi}}_{\overline{\mathfrak{m}}}, \qquad (4.52) \\
&(c) && {}'\overset{\Omega}{\mathbf{\Pi}}_{\overline{\mathfrak{m}}} \overset{\text{def}}{=} Z^{\mathfrak{m}}_{\overline{\mathfrak{m}}} \overset{\Omega}{\mathbf{\Pi}}_{\mathfrak{m}}
\end{aligned}$$

$$(b, c = 1,\ldots, \mathrm{m};\ \mathfrak{m} = \mathrm{m}+1,\ldots, \mathrm{r};\ \overline{\mathfrak{m}} = \overline{\mathrm{m}+1},\ldots, \overline{\mathrm{r}};\ \Omega = 1,\ldots, T).$$

Accordingly the system (4.49) can be replaced by

$$\begin{aligned}
&(a) && F^{\omega}, \quad F^{\mathfrak{a}}, \\
&(b) && \partial_\lambda F^{\mathfrak{a}}, \quad \overset{\mathfrak{x}}{e}_\lambda, \\
&(c) && {}'\overset{\Omega}{\mathbf{\Psi}}_{\mu\lambda}(u^a) \overset{\text{def}}{=} \overset{b}{e}_{[\mu} \overset{c}{e}_{\lambda]} \, {}'\overset{\Omega}{\mathbf{\Pi}}_{bc} + \overset{b}{e}_{[\mu} \overset{\overline{\mathfrak{m}}}{e}_{\lambda]} \, {}'\overset{\Omega}{\mathbf{\Pi}}_{b\overline{\mathfrak{m}}}
\end{aligned}$$

$$(b, c = 1,\ldots, \mathrm{m};\ \overline{\mathfrak{m}} = \overline{\mathrm{m}+1},\ldots, \overline{\mathrm{r}};\ \mathfrak{x} = \mathrm{r}+1,\ldots, \mathrm{n};$$

$$\mathfrak{a} = n - r_0 + 1,\ldots, n - r_0 + \tau;\ \Omega = 1,\ldots, T). \qquad (4.53)$$

If we take for the ${}'\overset{\Omega}{\mathbf{\Pi}}_{\overline{\mathfrak{m}}}$'s the same h_Ω's as for the $\overset{\Omega}{\mathbf{\Pi}}_{\mathfrak{m}}$'s it follows from (4.52 c) that the parametrical vector coefficients of ${}'\overset{\Omega}{\mathbf{\Pi}}_{\overline{\mathfrak{m}}}$ can be obtained from those of $\overset{\Omega}{\mathbf{\Pi}}_{\mathfrak{m}}$ by transvection with $Z^{\mathfrak{m}}_{\overline{\mathfrak{m}}}$. The same holds for the principal vector coefficients of ${}'\overset{\Omega}{\mathbf{\Pi}}_{\overline{\mathfrak{m}}}$ and $\overset{\Omega}{\mathbf{\Pi}}_{\mathfrak{m}}$. From this it follows that the principal vector coefficients of ${}'\overset{\Omega}{\mathbf{\Pi}}_{\overline{\mathfrak{m}}}$ depend linearly on the parametrical ones. This proves that the conditions (B), (C), and (E) are satisfied. The parametrical vector coefficients of $\overset{\Omega}{\mathbf{\Pi}}_{\mathfrak{m}}$ are linearly independent but it may happen that this independence gets lost by transvection with $Z^{\mathfrak{m}}_{\overline{\mathfrak{m}}}$. If the independence is not lost, the condition (D) is satisfied and the system (4.53) is really an *NRSC*-system with the same values of n_Ω and h_Ω as the system (4.49) and with a lower value of r_0. If the independence gets lost, there must be linear relations between the parametrical vector coefficients of the ${}'\overset{\Omega}{\mathbf{\Pi}}_{\overline{\mathfrak{m}}}$'s. We consider first the case where one such relation exists that contains parametrical vector coefficients of, for instance, ${}'\overset{1}{\mathbf{\Pi}}_{\overline{\mathfrak{m}}}$. The parametrical vector coefficients of ${}'\overset{1}{\mathbf{\Pi}}_{\overline{\mathfrak{m}}}$ are the vector coefficients of the vector polynomial

$${}'\overset{1}{\mathbf{\Pi}}_{\overline{\mathfrak{m}}}(u^1,\ldots, u^{\mathrm{h}_1}, 0,\ldots, 0) \quad (\overline{\mathfrak{m}} = \overline{\mathrm{m}+1},\ldots, \overline{\mathrm{r}}). \qquad (4.54)$$

Now there are two cases:

I. The linear relation contains the coefficient of $(u^{\mathrm{h}_1})^{n_1+1}$, denoted by $p_{\overline{\mathfrak{m}}}$, of (4.54).

II. The relation does not contain this coefficient.

In case I the coefficient $p_{\overline{\mathfrak{m}}}$ can be written as a linear combination of the other parametrical vector coefficients of the $'\overset{\Omega}{\mathbf{\Pi}}_{\overline{\mathfrak{m}}}$'s. Now we try to replace $'\overset{1}{\mathbf{\Psi}}_{\mu\lambda}(u^a)$ in (4.53 c) by a number of bivector polynomials such that, with a suitable choice of the corresponding values h, the new parametrical vector coefficients are the same as the old ones, except $p_{\overline{\mathfrak{m}}}$, and $p_{\overline{\mathfrak{m}}}$ becomes principal.

For these new bivector polynomials we choose all coefficients of $'\overset{1}{\mathbf{\Psi}}_{\mu\lambda}(u^a)$. These coefficients can be considered as derivatives of order n_1 of $'\overset{1}{\mathbf{\Psi}}_{\mu\lambda}(u^a)$ with respect to the u^a. If we denote this differentiation by

$$D^{(n_1)} = \partial_{b_1}\partial_{b_2}\dots\partial_{b_{n_1}} \quad (b_1,\dots,b_{n_1} = 1,\dots,\mathrm{m}) \tag{4.55}$$

we have

$$D^{(n_1)}\,'\overset{1}{\mathbf{\Psi}}_{\mu\lambda} = \overset{b}{e}_{[\mu}\overset{c}{e}_{\lambda]}\,D^{(n_1)}\,'\overset{1}{\mathbf{\Pi}}_{bc} + \overset{b}{e}_{[\mu}\overset{\overline{\mathfrak{m}}}{e}_{\lambda]}\,\partial_b\,D^{(n_1)}\,'\overset{1}{\mathbf{\Pi}}_{\overline{\mathfrak{m}}}$$
$$(b,c = 1,\dots,\mathrm{m};\ \overline{\mathfrak{m}} = \overline{\mathrm{m}+1},\dots,\bar{\mathrm{r}}). \tag{4.56}$$

If in (4.53) we replace $'\overset{1}{\mathbf{\Psi}}_{\mu\lambda}(u^a)$ by the coefficients (4.56), we get an equivalent system. We show that this system can be put in a normalized form. For that purpose we notice that (4.56) can be written in the form

$$D^{(n_1)}\,'\overset{1}{\mathbf{\Psi}}_{\mu\lambda} = \overset{b}{e}_{[\mu}\overset{c}{e}_{\lambda]}\,D^{(n_1)}\,'\overset{1}{\mathbf{\Pi}}_{bc} + \overset{b}{e}_{[\mu}\overset{\mathfrak{m}}{e}_{\lambda]}\,\frac{\partial\,'\overset{1}{\mathbf{\Pi}}{}^{(n_1)}_{\overline{\mathfrak{m}}}}{\partial u^b}$$
$$(b,c = 1,\dots,\mathrm{m};\ \overline{\mathfrak{m}} = \overline{\mathrm{m}+1},\dots,\bar{\mathrm{r}}), \tag{4.57}$$

where

$$'\overset{1}{\mathbf{\Pi}}{}^{(n_1)}_{\overline{\mathfrak{m}}} \overset{\text{def}}{=} u^b\partial_b\,D^{(n_1)}\,'\overset{1}{\mathbf{\Pi}}_{\overline{\mathfrak{m}}} \quad (b = 1,\dots,\mathrm{m};\ \overline{\mathfrak{m}} = \overline{\mathrm{m}+1},\dots,\bar{\mathrm{r}}). \tag{4.58}$$

Since $\partial_b D^{(n_1)}$ is a differential operator of order $1+n_1$ and $'\overset{1}{\mathbf{\Pi}}_{\overline{\mathfrak{m}}}$ is of degree $1+n_1$, $'\mathbf{\Pi}^{(n_1)}_{\overline{\mathfrak{m}}}$ is of degree 1 in the u^b. Hence the bivectors (4.56) satisfy the conditions (B) and (C) with $n = 0$. Now for each of the bivector polynomials (4.56) the h has to be chosen in a suitable way. If $D^{(n_1)} = \partial_{b_1}\dots\partial_{b_{n_1}}$ contains only differentiations with respect to $u^1,\dots,u^{\mathrm{h}_1}$, we choose $h = h_1 - 1$. If $D^{(n_1)}$ contains at least one of the differentiations with respect to $u^{\mathrm{h}_1+1},\dots,u^{\mathrm{m}}$, we choose $h = 0$. Then the chosen values of h are in fact all $< h_1$. Now we show that the new system satisfies the conditions (D) and (E). According to our choice of the h's the parametrical vector coefficients in (4.58) can be written

$$\partial_{\mathfrak{b}}\,D^{(n_1)}\,'\overset{1}{\mathbf{\Pi}}_{\overline{\mathfrak{m}}} = \partial_{\mathfrak{b}}\,\partial_{b_1}\dots\partial_{b_{n_1}}\,'\overset{1}{\mathbf{\Pi}}_{\overline{\mathfrak{m}}}$$
$$(b_1,\dots,b_{n_1} = 1,\dots,\mathrm{h}_1;\ \mathfrak{b} = 1,\dots,\mathrm{h}_1 - 1). \tag{4.59}$$

From this it follows that each parametrical vector coefficient in (4.58) is, to within a scalar factor, a vector coefficient of the polynomial $'\overset{1}{\mathbf{\Pi}}_{\overline{\mathfrak{m}}}(u^1,\ldots,u^{\mathrm{h}_1},0,\ldots,0)$. Conversely every vector coefficient of this polynomial that is not the vector coefficient of $(u^{\mathrm{h}_1})^{n_1+1}$ can, except for a scalar factor, be written in the form (4.59). This means that in fact the new parametrical vector coefficients of (4.58) are the same as the old ones, except $p_{\overline{\mathfrak{m}}}$, and that $p_{\overline{\mathfrak{m}}}$ is now principal. The other vector coefficients of (4.58) are all principal, according to our choice of the h's. Hence the new principal vector coefficients are the old ones and $p_{\overline{\mathfrak{m}}}$. The old principal vector coefficients can be expressed linearly in the new parametrical ones and $p_{\overline{\mathfrak{m}}}$. But $p_{\overline{\mathfrak{m}}}$ can be expressed linearly in the new parametrical ones. Hence the condition (E) is satisfied. If no linear relations between the new parametrical vector coefficients exist, the condition (D) is satisfied. In that case the new system is normalized and $'\overset{1}{\mathbf{\Psi}}_{\mu\lambda}(u^a)$ is replaced by a finite number of bivector polynomials with $n = 0$ and *lower* h-values ($h = h_1 - 1$ or 0). If the new parametrical vector coefficients are not linearly independent, the process can be repeated till at last we arrive at a finite number of systems with linearly independent parametrical vector coefficients and lower values of the h's or at a contradiction.

The case II can be reduced to the case I. The linear relation may contain certain parametrical vector coefficients of $'\overset{1}{\mathbf{\Pi}}_{\overline{\mathfrak{m}}}$, but $p_{\overline{\mathfrak{m}}}$ does not occur. The parametrical vector coefficients of $'\overset{1}{\mathbf{\Pi}}_{\overline{\mathfrak{m}}}$ are the vector coefficients of $'\overset{1}{\mathbf{\Pi}}_{\overline{\mathfrak{m}}}(u^1,\ldots,u^{\mathrm{h}_1},0,\ldots,0)$. If we write

$$'\overset{1}{\mathbf{\Pi}}_{\overline{\mathfrak{m}}}(u^1,\ldots,u^{\mathrm{h}_1},0,\ldots,0) = p_{\overline{\mathfrak{m}}i_0\ldots i_{n_1}} u^{i_0}\ldots u^{i_{n_1}}$$
$$(\overline{\mathfrak{m}} = \overline{\mathrm{m}+1},\ldots,\overline{\mathrm{r}};\ i_0,\ldots,i_{n_1} = 1,\ldots,\mathrm{h}_1) \qquad (4.60)$$

the terms of the linear relation containing parametrical vector coefficients of $'\overset{1}{\mathbf{\Pi}}_{\overline{\mathfrak{m}}}$ with coefficients can be written

$$\phi_{\overline{\mathfrak{m}}} \overset{\text{def}}{=} A^{i_0\ldots i_{n_1}} p_{\overline{\mathfrak{m}}i_0\ldots i_{n_1}} \quad (\mathfrak{m} = \overline{\mathrm{m}+1},\ldots,\overline{\mathrm{r}};\ i_0,\ldots,i_{n_1} = 1,\ldots,\mathrm{h}_1) \quad (4.61)$$

and among these terms there is not one with $p_{\overline{\mathfrak{m}}} = p_{\overline{\mathfrak{m}}\mathrm{h}_1\ldots\mathrm{h}_1}$, hence $A^{\mathrm{h}_1\ldots\mathrm{h}_1} = 0$. In order to derive from the given linear relation another relation containing $p_{\overline{\mathfrak{m}}}$, we transform the u^a in the following way

$$u^i = Q^i_{i'} u^{i'}, \quad u^{i'} = \overset{-1}{Q}{}^{i'}_i u^i, \quad \mathrm{Det}(Q^i_{i'}) \neq 0,$$
$$u^{\mathrm{h}_1+1} = u^{(\mathrm{h}_1+1)'}, \quad \ldots, \quad u^{\mathrm{m}} = u^{\mathrm{m}'}$$
$$(i = 1,\ldots,\mathrm{h}_1;\ i' = 1',\ldots,\mathrm{h}_1'). \qquad (4.62)$$

The $Q^i_{i'}$ are arbitrary and can be taken as constant. With the transformation (4.62) the $p_{\overline{\mathfrak{m}}i_0\ldots i_{n_1}}$ ($\overline{\mathfrak{m}} = \overline{\mathrm{m}+1},\ldots,\bar{\mathrm{r}}$) behave like the components of a tensor of valence n_1+1. Since $\phi_{\overline{\mathfrak{m}}}$ is a definite vector, $A^{i_0\ldots i_{n_1}}$ is a contravariant tensor of valence n_1+1, whose components are not all zero. From this it follows that the transformation (4.62) can be chosen in such a way that $A^{\mathrm{h}'_1\ldots\mathrm{h}'_1} \neq 0$. Then after the transformation $\phi_{\overline{\mathfrak{m}}}$ contains in fact a term with $p_{\overline{\mathfrak{m}}\mathrm{h}'_1\ldots\mathrm{h}'_1}$. But it is not yet certain that the system remains normalized with the same values of the n's and h's if (4.62) is applied! We will prove that this invariance exists if we transform the measuring vectors $\overset{a}{e}_\lambda$ simultaneously in the same way as the u^a. Let

$$u^a = Q^a_{a'} u^{a'}, \quad u^{a'} = \overset{-1}{Q}{}^{a'}_a u^a, \quad \mathrm{Det}(Q^a_{a'}) \neq 0,$$

$$\overset{a}{e}_\lambda = Q^a_{a'} \overset{a'}{e}_\lambda, \quad \overset{a'}{e}_\lambda = \overset{-1}{Q}{}^{a'}_a \overset{a}{e}_\lambda$$

$$(a = 1,\ldots,\mathrm{m};\ a' = 1',\ldots,\mathrm{m}') \tag{4.63}$$

be such a transformation. Then we have

$$''\overset{\Omega}{\mathbf{\Psi}}_{\mu\lambda}(u^{a'}) \overset{\mathrm{def}}{=} {}'\overset{\Omega}{\mathbf{\Psi}}_{\mu\lambda}(Q^a_{a'} u^{a'}) = \overset{b'}{e}_{[\mu} \overset{c'}{e}_{\lambda]} {}''\overset{\Omega}{\mathbf{\Pi}}_{b'c'} + \overset{b'}{e}_{[\mu} \overset{\overline{\mathfrak{m}}}{e}_{\lambda]} \frac{\partial {}''\overset{\Omega}{\mathbf{\Pi}}_{\overline{\mathfrak{m}}}}{\partial u^{b'}}$$

$$(a = 1,\ldots,\mathrm{m};\ b',c' = 1',\ldots,\mathrm{m}';\ \overline{\mathfrak{m}} = \overline{\mathrm{m}+1},\ldots,\bar{\mathrm{r}};\ \Omega = 1,\ldots,T), \tag{4.64}$$

where

$$(a) \quad {}''\overset{\Omega}{\mathbf{\Pi}}_{b'c'}(u^{a'}) = Q^b_{b'} Q^c_{c'} {}'\overset{\Omega}{\mathbf{\Pi}}_{bc}(Q^a_{a'} u^{a'}), \qquad (b) \quad {}''\overset{\Omega}{\mathbf{\Pi}}_{\overline{\mathfrak{m}}}(u^{a'}) = {}'\overset{\Omega}{\mathbf{\Pi}}_{\overline{\mathfrak{m}}}(Q^a_{a'} u^{a'})$$

$$(a,b,c = 1,\ldots,\mathrm{m};\ a',b',c' = 1',\ldots,\mathrm{m}';\ \overline{\mathfrak{m}} = \overline{\mathrm{m}+1},\ldots,\bar{\mathrm{r}};\ \Omega = 1,\ldots,T). \tag{4.65}$$

If we replace (4.53 *c*) by (4.64) we see that the new system satisfies the conditions (B) and (C) with the same values of the $\overset{\Omega}{n}$. Now we take for ${}''\overset{\Omega}{\mathbf{\Pi}}_{\overline{\mathfrak{m}}}$ the same h-values as for ${}'\overset{\Omega}{\mathbf{\Pi}}_{\overline{\mathfrak{m}}}$. Then the new parametrical vector coefficients are the coefficients of ${}''\overset{\Omega}{\mathbf{\Pi}}_{\overline{\mathfrak{m}}}(u^{1'},\ldots,u^{\mathrm{h}'_\Omega}, 0,\ldots,0)$. For $Q^a_{a'} = \delta^a_{a'}$ these vector coefficients are identical with the old ones and, therefore, are linearly independent. They remain independent if $Q^a_{a'}$ is chosen in a sufficiently small neighbourhood of $\delta^a_{a'}$. Hence the new system satisfies the condition (D). From (4.65 *b*) it follows that every vector coefficient of ${}''\overset{\Omega}{\mathbf{\Pi}}_{\overline{\mathfrak{m}}}$ can be expressed linearly in the vector coefficients of ${}'\overset{\Omega}{\mathbf{\Pi}}_{\overline{\mathfrak{m}}}$ and vice versa. Hence the $\overline{\mathfrak{m}}$-domain and the $\overline{\mathfrak{m}}$-rank of the coefficients of ${}''\overset{\Omega}{\mathbf{\Pi}}_{\overline{\mathfrak{m}}}$ and ${}'\overset{\Omega}{\mathbf{\Pi}}_{\overline{\mathfrak{m}}}$ are the same. Consequently the $\overline{\mathfrak{m}}$-rank of the vector coefficients of $''\overset{\Omega}{\mathbf{\Pi}}_{\overline{\mathfrak{m}}}$ is equal to the number of parametrical vector coefficients of $'\overset{\Omega}{\mathbf{\Pi}}_{\overline{\mathfrak{m}}}$ and, from the fact that the h-values are the same, it is also equal to the number of parametrical vector coefficients of $''\overset{\Omega}{\mathbf{\Pi}}_{\overline{\mathfrak{m}}}$. Hence all new principal vector coefficients can be expressed linearly in the new parametrical ones and this means that the condition (E) is satisfied. This completes the proof of Theorem X.7.

The transformations of Cartan systems are collected in the following diagram:

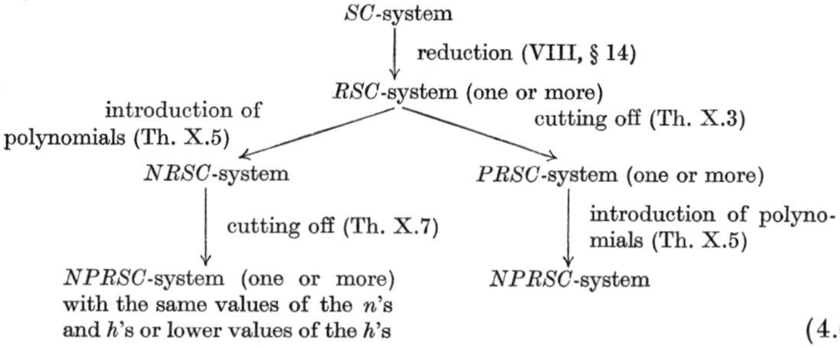

(4.66)

In order to get a clear insight into the meaning of the preceding theorems we will denote the number of vector polynomials of an *NRSC*-system (4.28), for which h_Ω has a given value z, by ν_z. Then ν_z is defined for $z = 0, 1, \ldots, m$. If the *NRSC*-system (4.28) is not preferred, by using Theorems X.6, 7 one or more *PNRSC*-systems can be constructed, having together the same integral-X_m's as (4.28) and satisfying the conditions that $\overset{\Omega}{\mathbf{\Pi}}_{bc} = 0$ and that for each new system every bivector polynomial of (4.28) corresponds either to one bivector polynomial of this new system with the same values of the n's and h's or to more bivector polynomials with lower values of the h's. From this it follows that for each new system there exists an integer p, such that the bivector polynomials with $h_\Omega = p+1, \ldots, m$ of the old system correspond each to one bivector polynomial of the new system with the same value of h_Ω and that there exists in the old system at least one vector polynomial with $h_\Omega = p$, corresponding to more than one vector polynomial of the new system with lower h-values. Consequently the new system cannot contain more bivector polynomials with $h \geqslant p$ than the old one. Hence, denoting the ν-values of the new system by ν'_z $(z = 0, 1, \ldots, m)$, Theorems X.6, 7 express the fact *that for each PNRSC-system obtained in this way either*

$$\nu'_0 = \nu_0 \quad \ldots, \quad \nu'_m = \nu_m \tag{4.67}$$

or $$\nu'_p < \nu_p, \quad \nu'_{p+1} = \nu_{p+1}, \quad \ldots, \quad \nu'_m = \nu_m \quad (p \geqslant 1) \tag{4.68}$$
holds.

Gathering all results together we see that the solution of every *SC*-system can be reduced to the solution of one or more *PNRSC*-systems (4.28), satisfying the condition that $\overset{\Omega}{\mathbf{\Pi}}_{bc}(u^a) = 0$. During this process all numbers $\nu_0, \nu_1, \ldots, \nu_m$ either remain unchanged or they change according to (4.68).

5. The integral-E_m's of a *PNRSC*-system with $\overset{\Omega}{\mathbf{\Pi}}_{bc}(u^a) = 0$

Each integral-E_m of an *NRSC*-system (4.28) is contained in the section of the $n-r$ measuring vectors $\overset{\mathfrak{x}}{e}_\lambda$. In this section we consider an E_m, not necessarily integral-E_m, with $v^{1\ldots m} \neq 0$. If w_λ is an arbitrary vector, the sections of w_λ, $\overset{b}{e}_\lambda$ with this E_m are linearly dependent and consequently m numbers λ_b exist such that the E_{n-1} of $w_\lambda + \overset{b}{e}_\lambda \lambda_b$ contains the E_m. These numbers are uniquely determined by $\overset{b}{e}_\lambda$, w_λ and the E_m. In this way for every vector coefficient of the vector polynomial $\overset{\mathfrak{m}}{e}_\lambda \overset{\Omega}{\mathbf{\Pi}}_{\mathfrak{m}}(u^a)$ such a set of m numbers λ_b can be found. If now we write

$$\overset{\Omega}{\mathbf{\Pi}}_{\mathfrak{m}}(u^a) = \overset{\Omega}{\pi}_{\mathfrak{m}b_0 b_1 \ldots b_{n_\Omega}} u^{b_0} u^{b_1} \ldots u^{b_{n_\Omega}}$$
$$(b_0, b_1, \ldots, b_{n_\Omega} = 1, \ldots, \mathrm{m};\ \mathfrak{m} = \mathrm{m}+1, \ldots, \mathrm{r};\ \Omega = 1, \ldots, T), \tag{5.1}$$

for every vector coefficient $\overset{\mathfrak{m}}{e}_\lambda \overset{\Omega}{\pi}_{\mathfrak{m}b_0 b_1 \ldots b_{n_\Omega}}$ there exist m numbers $\overset{\Omega}{\lambda}_{bb_0 b_1 \ldots b_{n_\Omega}}$ which are uniquely determined by the choice of the E_m and are such that the E_m is contained in each of the E_{n-1}'s of the vectors

$$\overset{\Omega}{\theta}_{\lambda b_0 b_1 \ldots b_{n_\Omega}} \overset{\text{def}}{=} \overset{\mathfrak{m}}{e}_\lambda \overset{\Omega}{\pi}_{\mathfrak{m}b_0 b_1 \ldots b_{n_\Omega}} + \overset{b}{e}_\lambda \overset{\Omega}{\lambda}_{bb_0 b_1 \ldots b_{n_\Omega}}$$
$$(b_0, b_1, \ldots, b_{n_\Omega} = 1, \ldots, \mathrm{m};\ \mathfrak{m} = \mathrm{m}+1, \ldots, \mathrm{r};\ \Omega = 1, \ldots, T). \tag{5.2}$$

Transvection of (5.2) with $u^{b_0} u^{b_1} \ldots u^{b_{n_\Omega}}$ gives

$$\overset{\Omega}{\mathbf{\Theta}}_\lambda(u^a) = \overset{\mathfrak{m}}{e}_\lambda \overset{\Omega}{\mathbf{\Pi}}_{\mathfrak{m}}(u^a) + \overset{b}{e}_\lambda \overset{\Omega}{\mathbf{\Lambda}}_b(u^a)$$
$$(a, b = 1, \ldots, \mathrm{m};\ \mathfrak{m} = \mathrm{m}+1, \ldots, \mathrm{r};\ \Omega = 1, \ldots, T), \tag{5.3}$$

where
$$\overset{\Omega}{\mathbf{\Theta}}_\lambda(u^a) \overset{\text{def}}{=} \overset{\Omega}{\theta}_{\lambda b_0 b_1 \ldots b_{n_\Omega}} u^{b_0} u^{b_1} \ldots u^{b_{n_\Omega}},$$
$$\overset{\Omega}{\mathbf{\Lambda}}_b(u^a) \overset{\text{def}}{=} \overset{\Omega}{\lambda}_{bb_0 b_1 \ldots b_{n_\Omega}} u^{b_0} u^{b_1} \ldots u^{b_{n_\Omega}}$$
$$(a, b, b_0, \ldots, b_{n_\Omega} = 1, \ldots, \mathrm{m};\ \Omega = 1, \ldots, T). \tag{5.4}$$

$\overset{\Omega}{\mathbf{\Theta}}_\lambda(u^a)$ and $\overset{\Omega}{\mathbf{\Lambda}}_b(u^a)$ are homogeneous of degree $n_\Omega + 1$ in the u^a. From this we see that *every* E_m *with* $v^{1\ldots\mathrm{m}} \neq 0$ *in the section of the* $\overset{*}{e}_\lambda$ *uniquely determines a set of* T *vector polynomials* $\overset{\Omega}{\mathbf{\Lambda}}_b(u^a)$ *such that the* E_m *is contained in the section of the* $\overset{*}{e}_\lambda$ *and the vector coefficients of the* $\overset{\Omega}{\mathbf{\Theta}}_\lambda(u^a)$ *given by* (5.3).

The vector coefficients of the polynomials $\overset{\Omega}{\mathbf{\Lambda}}_b(u^a)$ satisfy certain conditions. We know that the principal vector coefficients of the $\overset{\Omega}{\mathbf{\Pi}}_{\mathfrak{m}}(u^a)$ depend linearly on the parametrical vector coefficients. Consequently there are certain linear relations between the vector coefficients of the $\overset{\Omega}{\mathbf{\Pi}}_{\mathfrak{m}}(u^a)$. Let

$$\underset{\Omega}{A}{}^{b_0 b_1 \ldots b_{n_\Omega}} \overset{\Omega}{\pi}_{\mathfrak{m} b_0 b_1 \ldots b_{n_\Omega}} = 0 \quad (b_0, b_1, \ldots, b_{n_\Omega} = 1, \ldots, \mathrm{m}; \quad \mathfrak{m} = \mathrm{m}+1, \ldots, \mathrm{r};\ \Omega = 1, \ldots, T) \tag{5.5}$$

be such a relation. Then from (5.2) and (5.5) we get

$$\underset{\Omega}{A}{}^{b_0 b_1 \ldots b_{n_\Omega}} \overset{\Omega}{\theta}_{\lambda b_0 b_1 \ldots b_{n_\Omega}} = \overset{b}{e}_\lambda \underset{\Omega}{A}{}^{b_0 b_1 \ldots b_{n_\Omega}} \overset{\Omega}{\lambda}_{b b_0 b_1 \ldots b_{n_\Omega}}. \tag{5.6}$$

If the vector (5.6) were $\neq 0$, the E_m would have to be contained in the E_{n-1} and from this it would follow that $v^{1\ldots\mathrm{m}} = 0$, in contradiction with our assumption. Consequently

$$\begin{aligned} &(a) \qquad \underset{\Omega}{A}{}^{b_0 b_1 \ldots b_{n_\Omega}} \overset{\Omega}{\theta}_{\lambda b_0 b_1 \ldots b_{n_\Omega}} = 0, \\ &(b) \qquad \underset{\Omega}{A}{}^{b_0 b_1 \ldots b_{n_\Omega}} \overset{\Omega}{\lambda}_{b b_0 b_1 \ldots b_{n_\Omega}} = 0. \end{aligned} \tag{5.7}$$

Notice that (5.7 a) and (5.7 b) are equivalent in consequence of (5.6). Hence we may conclude that the vector coefficient of $\overset{\Omega}{\mathbf{\Lambda}}_b$ (running index b) and also the vector coefficients of the $\overset{\Omega}{\mathbf{\Theta}}_\lambda$ (running index λ) satisfy the same linear relations as the vector coefficients of the $\overset{\Omega}{\mathbf{\Pi}}_{\mathfrak{m}}$ (running index $\mathfrak{m}$).

Now let us suppose that a set of vector polynomials $\overset{\Omega}{\mathbf{\Lambda}}_b$ be given such that their vector coefficients satisfy the same linear relations as the vector coefficients of the vector polynomials $\overset{\Omega}{\mathbf{\Pi}}_{\mathfrak{m}}$. Then the vector coefficients of the vector polynomials $\overset{\Omega}{\mathbf{\Theta}}_\lambda$, defined by (5.3) satisfy the same linear relations. Since the principal vector coefficients of the $\overset{\Omega}{\mathbf{\Pi}}_{\mathfrak{m}}$ are linearly dependent on the parametrical ones, every vector coefficient of the $\overset{\Omega}{\mathbf{\Pi}}_{\mathfrak{m}}(u^1, \ldots, u^{\mathrm{m}})$ can be expressed linearly in the vector coefficients of the vector polynomials $\overset{\Omega}{\mathbf{\Pi}}_{\mathfrak{m}}(u^1,\ldots,u^{h_\Omega},0,\ldots,0)$. Accordingly every vector coefficient of the $\overset{\Omega}{\mathbf{\Theta}}_\lambda(u^1,\ldots,u^{\mathrm{m}})$ can be expressed linearly in the vector coefficients of the vector polynomials $\overset{\Omega}{\mathbf{\Theta}}_\lambda(u^1,\ldots,u^{h_\Omega},0,\ldots,0)$. From this it follows that the section of the $\overset{x}{e}_\lambda$ and the vector coefficients of the $\overset{\Omega}{\mathbf{\Theta}}_\lambda(u^1,\ldots,u^{\mathrm{m}})$ coincides with the section of the $\overset{x}{e}_\lambda$ and the vector coefficients of the $\overset{\Omega}{\mathbf{\Theta}}_\lambda(u^1,\ldots,u^{h_\Omega},0,\ldots,0)$. Because the vector coefficients of the $\overset{\Omega}{\mathbf{\Pi}}_{\mathfrak{m}}(u^1,\ldots,u^{h_\Omega},0,\ldots,0)$ are parametrical and thus linearly independent, it follows from (5.3) and the independence of $\overset{b}{e}_\lambda$, $\overset{\mathfrak{m}}{e}_\lambda$, $\overset{x}{e}_\lambda$, that the $\overset{b}{e}_\lambda$, $\overset{x}{e}_\lambda$ and the vector coefficients of the vector polynomials $\overset{\Omega}{\mathbf{\Theta}}_\lambda(u^1,\ldots,u^{h_\Omega},0,\ldots,0)$ are linearly independent. Consequently the section of the m vectors $\overset{b}{e}_\lambda$ with the E_s spanned by the $\overset{x}{e}_\lambda$ and the vector coefficients of the vector polynomials $\overset{\Omega}{\mathbf{\Theta}}_\lambda(u^1,\ldots,u^{h_\Omega},0,\ldots,0)$ are linearly independent. Hence $s \geqslant m$. $n-s$ is the sum of the number $n-r$ of vectors $\overset{x}{e}_\lambda$ and the number of vector coefficients of the vector polynomials $\overset{\Omega}{\mathbf{\Theta}}_\lambda(u^1,\ldots,u^{h_\Omega},0,\ldots,0)$. But since this latter number is equal to $\sigma'_1+\ldots+\sigma'_m$ (cf. (4.33)) we have

$$s = r-\sigma', \quad \sigma' \overset{\text{def}}{=} \sigma'_1+\ldots+\sigma'_m. \tag{5.8}$$

From $s \geqslant m$ it follows that

$$\sigma' = \sigma'_1+\ldots+\sigma'_m \leqslant r-m, \tag{5.9}$$

which inequality is also a consequence of the fact that all parametrical vector coefficients of the $\overset{\Omega}{\mathbf{\Pi}}_{\mathfrak{m}}$ are contained in the E_{r-m} of the index $\mathfrak{m} = \mathrm{m}+1,\ldots,\mathrm{r}$. $E_{r-\sigma'}$ really contains E_m's with $v^{1\ldots\mathrm{m}} \neq 0$. Collecting results we have the theorem

THEOREM X.8. *If an E_m with $v^{1\ldots\mathrm{m}} \neq 0$ in the section of the $n-r$ vectors $\overset{x}{e}_\lambda$ of an NRSC-system is given, there exists a set of uniquely determined homogeneous vector polynomials $\overset{\Omega}{\mathbf{\Lambda}}_b(u^a)$ of degree $n_\Omega+1$ ($\Omega = 1,\ldots,T$) such that the E_m is contained in the section of the vector polynomials $\overset{\Omega}{\mathbf{\Theta}}_\lambda(u^a)$, defined by* (5.3). *This section is an $E_{r-\sigma'}$. The vector coefficients of the vector polynomials $\overset{\Omega}{\mathbf{\Lambda}}_b$ and also those of the vector polynomials $\overset{\Omega}{\mathbf{\Theta}}_\lambda$ satisfy the same linear relations as the vector coefficients of the vector polynomials $\overset{\Omega}{\mathbf{\Pi}}_{\mathfrak{m}}$.*

Conversely, each set of vector polynomials $\overset{\Omega}{\mathbf{\Lambda}}_b(u^a)$, *whose vector coefficients satisfy the same linear relations as the vector coefficients of the* $\overset{\Omega}{\mathbf{\Pi}}_{\mathfrak{m}}$, *uniquely determines a set of vector polynomials* $\overset{\Omega}{\mathbf{\Theta}}_\lambda(u^a)$, *whose vector coefficients also satisfy the same linear relations. Besides the section of the vectors* $\overset{x}{e}_\lambda$ *and the vector coefficients of the vector polynomials* $\overset{\Omega}{\mathbf{\Theta}}_\lambda(u^a)$ *is an* $E_{r-\sigma'}$ *containing at least one* E_m *with* $v^{1\dots\mathrm{m}} \neq 0$.

Now we suppose that (4.28) is a *PNRSC*-system with $\overset{\Omega}{\mathbf{\Pi}}_{bc} = 0$ and we require the supplementary conditions to be imposed on the vector polynomials $\overset{\Omega}{\mathbf{\Lambda}}_b(u^a)$ in order that at least one of the E_m's of the second part of Theorem X.8 is an integral-E_m of this system. By solving the $\overset{\mathfrak{m}}{e}_\lambda \overset{\Omega}{\mathbf{\Pi}}_{\mathfrak{m}}$ from (5.3) and substituting the solutions in (4.28c) we get in consideration of (4.29) and $\overset{\Omega}{\mathbf{\Pi}}_{bc} = 0$

$$\overset{\Omega}{\mathbf{\Psi}}_{\mu\lambda} = \overset{b}{e}_{[\mu}\, \partial_{|b|} \overset{\Omega}{\mathbf{\Theta}}_{\lambda]} - \overset{b}{e}_{[\mu} \overset{c}{e}_{\lambda]}\, \partial_b \overset{\Omega}{\mathbf{\Lambda}}_c$$
$$(b, c = 1,\dots,\mathrm{m};\ \Omega = 1,\dots, T). \quad (5.10)$$

Since the vector coefficients of $\partial_b \overset{\Omega}{\mathbf{\Theta}}_\lambda$ are, to within scalar factors, equal to the vector coefficients of $\overset{\Omega}{\mathbf{\Theta}}_\lambda(u^a)$, it follows from (5.10) that

$$\overset{\Omega}{\mathbf{\Psi}}_{\mu\lambda} \equiv -\overset{b}{e}_{[\mu} \overset{c}{e}_{\lambda]}\, \partial_b \overset{\Omega}{\mathbf{\Lambda}}_c \ \ (\mathrm{mod\,coeff.}\ \overset{\Omega}{\mathbf{\Theta}}_\lambda(u^a))$$
$$(a, b, c = 1,\dots,\mathrm{m};\ \Omega = 1,\dots, T). \quad (5.11)$$

The right-hand sides of these congruences may be considered as the sections of the bivector polynomials $\overset{\Omega}{\mathbf{\Psi}}_{\mu\lambda}$ with the section $E_{r-\sigma'}$ of the $\overset{x}{e}_\lambda$ and the vector coefficients of the $\overset{\Omega}{\mathbf{\Theta}}_\lambda$. Now, if possible, take for the E_m an *integral-*E_m with $v^{1\dots\mathrm{m}} \neq 0$ in this $E_{r-\sigma'}$. Then the sections of the bivector polynomials $\overset{\Omega}{\mathbf{\Psi}}_{\mu\lambda}$ with this E_m have to be zero and from this it follows that the sections of the right-hand sides of (5.11) with the E_m have to be zero. But, since $v^{1\dots\mathrm{m}} \neq 0$ this means that

$$\partial_{[b} \overset{\Omega}{\mathbf{\Lambda}}_{c]} = 0 \quad (b, c = 1,\dots,\mathrm{m};\ \Omega = 1,\dots, T), \quad (5.12)$$

identically in the u^a. Consequently a set of T uniquely determined polynomials $\overset{\Omega}{\mathbf{\Lambda}}(u^a)$ exists, which is homogeneous of degree $n_\Omega + 2$ in the u^a, such that

$$\overset{\Omega}{\mathbf{\Lambda}}_b = \partial_b \overset{\Omega}{\mathbf{\Lambda}}. \quad (5.13)$$

If the $\overset{\Omega}{\mathbf{\Lambda}}_b$ are known the $\overset{\Omega}{\mathbf{\Lambda}}$ are uniquely determined according to Euler's formula. Conversely, if (5.13) holds identically in the u^a, the right-hand sides of (5.11) are zero and consequently the sections of the $\overset{\Omega}{\mathbf{\Psi}}_{\mu\lambda}(u^a)$ with the $E_{r-\sigma'}$ are zero and this $E_{r-\sigma'}$ is an integral-$E_{r-\sigma'}$. From this it follows that in this $E_{r-\sigma'}$ there exist $\infty^{m(r-m-\sigma')}$ integral-E_m's with $v^{1...\mathrm{m}} \neq 0$. This proves the theorem

THEOREM X.9. *Every integral-E_m with $v^{1...\mathrm{m}} \neq 0$ of the PNRSC-system (4.28) with $\overset{\Omega}{\mathbf{\Pi}}_{bc} = 0$ uniquely determines a set of T polynomials $\overset{\Omega}{\mathbf{\Lambda}}(u^a)$ such that the E_m is contained in the section of the $\overset{*}{\mathrm{e}}_\lambda$ and the vector coefficients of T vector polynomials $\overset{\Omega}{\mathbf{\Theta}}_\lambda(u^a)$, defined by the equations* (5.3) *in which the $\overset{\Omega}{\mathbf{\Lambda}}_b$ are given by the relations* (5.13). *The $\overset{\Omega}{\mathbf{\Lambda}}(u^a)$ satisfy the conditions:*

I. *The $\overset{\Omega}{\mathbf{\Lambda}}(u^a)$ are homogeneous of degree $n_\Omega + 2$ in the u^a;*

II. *The vector coefficients of the vector polynomials $\partial_b \overset{\Omega}{\mathbf{\Lambda}}$ (running index b) satisfy the same linear relations as the vector coefficients of the vector polynomials $\overset{\Omega}{\mathbf{\Pi}}_{\mathfrak{m}}$ (running index $\mathfrak{m}$).*

Conversely, if T polynomials $\overset{\Omega}{\mathbf{\Lambda}}(u^a)$ are given, satisfying the conditions I *and* II, *the section of the $\overset{*}{\mathrm{e}}_\lambda$ and the vector coefficients of the vector polynomials $\overset{\Omega}{\mathbf{\Theta}}_\lambda(u^a)$ defined by* (5.3) *is an integral-$E_{r-\sigma'}$* $(r-\sigma' \geqslant m)$ *containing $\infty^{m(r-m-\sigma')}$ integral-E_m's with $v^{1...\mathrm{m}} \neq 0$ and every integral-E_m with $v^{1...\mathrm{m}} \neq 0$ is contained in one and only one of these integral-$E_{r-\sigma'}$'s.*

For a further investigation of the integral-E_m's of the *PNRSC*-system (4.28) we have to study the polynomials $\overset{\Omega}{\mathbf{\Lambda}}(u^a)$ satisfying the conditions I and II. Since the relations mentioned in the condition II are linear homogeneous, it is always possible by means of the solution of linear homogeneous algebraical equations to decide whether the polynomials $\overset{\Omega}{\mathbf{\Lambda}}(u^a)$ exist or not and, in the first case, to determine these polynomials. If no polynomials $\overset{\Omega}{\mathbf{\Lambda}}(u^a)$ exist, the system (4.28) does not possess integral-E_m's with $v^{1...\mathrm{m}} \neq 0$ and accordingly no integral-X_m's of the kind required.

If polynomials $\overset{\Omega}{\mathbf{\Lambda}}(u^a)$ exist we wish to decide which coefficients of the $\overset{\Omega}{\mathbf{\Lambda}}(u^a)$ can be chosen arbitrarily according to the conditions I and II. We prove the theorem

THEOREM X.10. *In order that a set of T polynomials $\overset{\Omega}{\mathbf{\Lambda}}(u^a)$, homogeneous of degree $n_\Omega+2$, satisfies the conditions* I *and* II *of Theorem* X.9, *it is necessary and sufficient that their coefficients satisfy a definite system of homogeneous linear relations. By means of these relations it is possible to write all coefficients of the $\overset{\Omega}{\mathbf{\Lambda}}(u^a)$ as homogeneous linear expressions of the coefficients of those polynomials $\overset{\Omega}{\mathbf{\Lambda}}(u^1,..., u^{h_\Omega}, 0,..., 0)$ for which $h_\Omega \geqslant 1$.*

PROOF. According to the condition II the vector coefficients of the vector polynomials

$$\overset{\Omega}{\mathbf{\Lambda}}_b(u^1,..., u^{\mathrm{m}}) = \frac{\partial \overset{\Omega}{\mathbf{\Lambda}}}{\partial u^b} \quad (b = 1,..., \mathrm{m};\ \Omega = 1,..., N) \tag{5.14}$$

satisfy the same h.l.† relations as the vector coefficients of the vector polynomials $\overset{\Omega}{\mathbf{\Pi}}_{\mathrm{m}}$. Let this latter system of h.l. relations be symbolized by $P(\mathbf{\Pi}_{\mathrm{m}}) = 0$. Then the system of h.l. relations between the vector coefficients of the $\overset{\Omega}{\mathbf{\Lambda}}_b$ can be symbolized by $P(\mathbf{\Lambda}_b) = 0$. Hence we have the same h.l. relations for each of the components

$$P(\mathbf{\Lambda}_1) = 0, \quad ..., \quad P(\mathbf{\Lambda}_{\mathrm{m}}) = 0. \tag{5.15}$$

Now the coefficients of the polynomials $\overset{\Omega}{\mathbf{\Lambda}}_1,..., \overset{\Omega}{\mathbf{\Lambda}}_{\mathrm{m}}$ are to within scalar factors coefficients of the polynomials $\overset{\Omega}{\mathbf{\Lambda}}$. Hence the equations (5.15) together form a system of h.l. relations between the coefficients of the polynomials $\overset{\Omega}{\mathbf{\Lambda}}$. We call this system S.

By means of the h.l. relations $P(\mathbf{\Pi}_{\mathrm{m}}) = 0$ all vector coefficients of the vector polynomials $\overset{\Omega}{\mathbf{\Pi}}_{\mathrm{m}}$ can be expressed h.l. in the vector coefficients of the vector polynomials $\overset{\Omega}{\mathbf{\Pi}}_{\mathrm{m}}(u^1,..., u^{h_\Omega}, 0,..., 0)$ with $h_\Omega \geqslant 1$.‡ Hence for every *fixed* value β of b ($\beta = 1,..., \mathrm{m}$) the coefficients of the polynomials (not vector polynomials!) $\overset{\Omega}{\mathbf{\Lambda}}_\beta$ can be expressed h.l. in the coefficients of the polynomials $\overset{\Omega}{\mathbf{\Lambda}}_\beta(u^1,..., u^{h_\Omega}, 0,..., 0)$ with $h_\Omega \geqslant 1$.‡ From this it follows that by means of the relations S the coefficients of the mT polynomials $\overset{\Omega}{\mathbf{\Lambda}}_b(u^1,..., u^{\mathrm{m}})$ and consequently those of the T polynomials $\overset{\Omega}{\mathbf{\Lambda}}(u^1,..., u^{\mathrm{h}})$ can be expressed h.l. in the coefficients of the polynomials $\overset{\Omega}{\mathbf{\Lambda}}_b(u^1,..., u^{h_\Omega}, 0,..., 0)$ with $h_\Omega \geqslant 1$ and $b = 1,..., \mathrm{m}$. Hence the

† In the following pages h.l. = homogeneous linear(ly).

‡ For $h_\Omega = 0$ we have $\overset{\Omega}{\mathbf{\Pi}}_{\mathrm{m}}(0,..., 0) = 0$ and $\overset{\Omega}{\mathbf{\Lambda}}_b(0,..., 0) = 0$.

only thing to prove is, that by means of S these latter coefficients can be expressed h.l. in the coefficients of those polynomials

$$\overset{\Omega}{\mathbf{\Lambda}}(u^1,\ldots,u^{h_\Omega},0,\ldots,0) \quad (\Omega = 1,\ldots,T) \tag{5.16}$$

for which $h_\Omega \geqslant 1$.

We show first that by means of S the coefficients of the polynomials $\overset{\Omega}{\mathbf{\Lambda}}_1(u^1,\ldots,u^{h_\Omega},0,\ldots,0)$ with $h_\Omega \geqslant 1$ can be expressed h.l. in the coefficients of the polynomials (5.16). Because of

$$\overset{\Omega}{\mathbf{\Lambda}}_1(u^a) = \frac{\partial \overset{\Omega}{\mathbf{\Lambda}}}{\partial u^1} \quad (\Omega = 1,\ldots,T,\ a = 1,\ldots,\mathrm{m}) \tag{5.17}$$

all coefficients of $\overset{\Omega}{\mathbf{\Lambda}}_1(u^1,\ldots,u^{h_\Omega},0,\ldots,0)$ are for every value of Ω to within scalar factors equal to certain coefficients of the polynomials (5.16).

Now we suppose that it has been proved that by means of S the coefficients of the polynomials $\overset{\Omega}{\mathbf{\Lambda}}_b(u^1,\ldots,u^{h_\Omega},0,\ldots,0)$ with $h_\Omega \geqslant 1$ for $b = 1,\ldots,\mathrm{q}$ can be expressed h.l. in the coefficients of the polynomials (5.16). Then we will prove that by means of S the coefficients of the polynomials $\overset{\Omega}{\mathbf{\Lambda}}_{\mathrm{q}+1}(u^1,\ldots,u^{h_\Omega},0,\ldots,0)$ with $h_\Omega \geqslant 1$ can be expressed h.l. in the coefficients of the polynomials (5.16). If for some definite value of Ω ($\Omega = 1,\ldots,T$) we have $h_\Omega \geqslant q+1$, the coefficients of $\overset{\Omega}{\mathbf{\Lambda}}_{\mathrm{q}+1}(u^1,\ldots,u^{h_\Omega},0,\ldots,0)$ are equal to certain coefficients of (5.16) to within scalar factors. Hence we have only to consider values of Ω for which $h_\Omega < q+1$. Now let $a(u^1)^{\alpha_1}\ldots(u^{h_\Omega})^{\alpha_{h_\Omega}}$ be a term of $\overset{\Omega}{\mathbf{\Lambda}}_{\mathrm{q}+1}(u^1,\ldots,u^{h_\Omega},0,\ldots,0)$, for such a value of Ω. Then, according to $h_\Omega < q+1$, $a(u^1)^{\alpha_1}\ldots(u^{h_\Omega})^{\alpha_{h_\Omega}}u^{\mathrm{q}+1}$ is a term of $\overset{\Omega}{\mathbf{\Lambda}}(u^1,\ldots,u^{\mathrm{m}})$ for this special value of Ω. Now $\overset{\Omega}{\mathbf{\Lambda}}$ has degree $n_\Omega+2$, hence $\alpha_1+\ldots+\alpha_{h_\Omega} \geqslant 1$ and consequently at least one of the α's has to be > 0. Suppose $\alpha_\beta > 0$ $(\beta \leqslant h_\Omega)$. Then the term

$$\alpha_\beta\, a(u^1)^{\alpha_1}\ldots(u^{\beta-1})^{\alpha_{\beta-1}}(u^\beta)^{\alpha_\beta-1}(u^{\beta+1})^{\alpha_{\beta+1}}\ldots(u^{h_\Omega})^{\alpha_{h_\Omega}}u^{\mathrm{q}+1} \tag{5.18}$$

occurs in $\overset{\Omega}{\mathbf{\Lambda}}_\beta(u^1,\ldots,u^{\mathrm{m}})$.

Because of the relations $P(\mathbf{\Lambda}_\beta) = 0$ all coefficients of $\overset{\Omega}{\mathbf{\Lambda}}_\beta(u^1,\ldots,u^{\mathrm{m}})$, and consequently also (5.18), can be expressed h.l. in the coefficients of the polynomials $\overset{\Omega}{\mathbf{\Lambda}}_\beta(u^1,\ldots,u^{h_\Omega},0,\ldots,0)$ by means of S. Now $\beta \leqslant h_\Omega \leqslant q$ and we know already that all coefficients of these polynomials can be expressed h.l. in the coefficients of the polynomials (5.16) by means of S. Hence by means of S it is possible to express (5.18) h.l. in the coefficients of the polynomials (5.16). This proves that by means of S the coefficients of the polynomials $\overset{\Omega}{\mathbf{\Lambda}}_{q+1}(u^1,\dots,u^{h_\Omega},0,\dots,0)$ with $h_\Omega \geqslant 1$ can be expressed h.l. in the coefficients of the polynomials (5.16). Continuing in this way we see that the same holds for the coefficients of all polynomials $\overset{\Omega}{\mathbf{\Lambda}}_b(u^1,\dots,u^{h_\Omega},0,\dots,0)$ with $h_\Omega \geqslant 1$. This completes the proof of Theorem X.10.

Now we have to consider two cases:

(α) from the relations S no relations between the coefficients of the T polynomials (5.16) can be derived;

(β) from the relations S one or more h.l. relations between the coefficients of the T polynomials (5.16) can be derived.

In case (α) the coefficients of (5.16) can be chosen *arbitrarily* and from them the other coefficients of the T polynomials $\overset{\Omega}{\mathbf{\Lambda}}(u^1,\dots,u^m)$ can be determined uniquely by means of the relations S.

In case (β) the coefficients of (5.16) cannot be chosen arbitrarily. We prove the theorem

THEOREM X.11. *If for a PNRSC-system the case* (α) *holds, that is, if the coefficients of the T polynomials* (5.16) *can be chosen arbitrarily and from them, by means of the relations S, the coefficients of the T polynomials* $\overset{\Omega}{\mathbf{\Lambda}}(u^1,\dots,u^m)$, *satisfying the conditions* I *and* II *of Theorem* X.9 *can be uniquely determined, the genus of the PNRSC-system is* $\geqslant m$.

PROOF. The coefficients of the polynomials (5.16) can be chosen arbitrarily. Their number is

$$M \overset{\text{def}}{=} \sum_{\Omega=1}^{\Omega=T} \phi(n_\Omega+2, h_\Omega) \tag{5.19}$$

and the other coefficients of the polynomials $\overset{\Omega}{\mathbf{\Lambda}}(u^1,\dots,u^m)$ depend h.l. on them. If we denote the arbitrarily chosen coefficients by λ^ζ $(\zeta = 1,\dots,M)$, the other coefficients can be considered as depending on the M non-supernumerary coordinates λ^ζ.

In consequence of (5.3) the T vector polynomials $\overset{\Omega}{\mathbf{\Theta}}_\lambda(u^a)$ depend also on the non-supernumerary coordinates λ^ζ. In consequence of Theorem X.9 the section of the $\overset{x}{e}_\lambda$ and the vector coefficients of the $\overset{\Omega}{\mathbf{\Theta}}_\lambda(u^a)$ is an integral-$E_{r-\sigma'}$. Hence in every point ξ^κ this $E_{r-\sigma'}$ depends on the λ^ζ. But it is not yet certain that the λ^ζ are non-supernumerary coordinates of $E_{r-\sigma'}$. In fact the $E_{r-\sigma'}$ is uniquely determined by the $\overset{\Omega}{\mathbf{\Theta}}_\lambda(u^a)$ but we do not yet know if the $\overset{\Omega}{\mathbf{\Theta}}_\lambda(u^a)$ are uniquely determined by the

$E_{r-\sigma'}$. Now every $E_{r-\sigma'}$ contains $\infty^{m(r-m-\sigma')}$ E_m's with $v^{1\ldots m} \neq 0$ and these are all integral-E_m's. Let p^ψ ($\psi = 1, \ldots, m(r-m-\sigma')$) be non-supernumerary coordinates of an E_m with $v^{1\ldots m} \neq 0$ in $E_{r-\sigma'}$. Then all integral-E_m's with $v^{1\ldots m} \neq 0$ in a definitely chosen point ξ^κ depend on the $M+m(r-m-\sigma')$ coordinates λ^ζ, p^ψ but it is not yet certain that these coordinates are non-supernumerary.

The chosen point ξ^κ, where integral-E_m's with $v^{1\ldots m} \neq 0$ exist, is a point of X_{r_0} and depends on r_0 coordinates, say $\xi^1, \ldots, \xi^{r_0}$. Hence *all* integral-E_m's with $v^{1\ldots m} \neq 0$ of the *PNRSC*-system depend on $r_0+M+m(r-m-\sigma')$ coordinates $\xi^1, \ldots, \xi^{r_0}, \lambda^\zeta, p^\psi$. We will prove that these coordinates are non-supernumerary, that is, that $\xi^1, \ldots, \xi^{r_0}, \lambda^\zeta, p^\psi$ are uniquely determined by the integral-E_m. If E_m is given, $\xi^1, \ldots, \xi^{r_0}$ are uniquely determined. Since E_m is an integral-E_m, the polynomials $\overset{\Omega}{\mathbf{\Lambda}}(u^a)$, and consequently also the λ^ζ, are uniquely determined according to Theorem X.9. The p^ψ are the non-supernumerary coordinates of the E_m in $E_{r-\sigma'}$ and are accordingly uniquely determined. Hence the

$$R \overset{\text{def}}{=} r_0+M+m(r-m-\sigma') \tag{5.20}$$

coordinates $\xi^1, \ldots, \xi^{r_0}, \lambda^\zeta, p^\psi$ are non-supernumerary coordinates of all integral-E_m's with $v^{1\ldots m} \neq 0$. Notice that (cf. VIII, § 14)

$$R = n+m(n-m)-N'. \tag{5.21}$$

Now, according to (4.40) and (5.19)

$$\begin{aligned} R &\geqslant r_0+\sigma_1'+2\sigma_2'+\ldots+m\sigma_m'+m(r-m-\sigma') \\ &= r_0+m(r-m)-(m-1)\sigma_1'-(m-2)\sigma_2'-\ldots-\sigma_{m-1}' \end{aligned} \tag{5.22}$$

or
$$N' \leqslant n-r_0+m(n-r)+(m-1)\sigma_1'+(m-2)\sigma_2'+\ldots+\sigma_{m-1}'. \tag{5.23}$$

Consequently in (VIII (14.29)) the equality sign must hold and from this it follows that $g \geqslant m$ (cf. VIII, § 14).

6. Prolongation of a *PNRSC*-system

According to Theorem X.9 every integral-E_m with $v^{1\ldots m} \neq 0$ is contained in an integral-$E_{r-\sigma'}$ which is the section of the $\overset{x}{e}_\lambda$ and the vector coefficients of the vector polynomials $\overset{\Omega}{\mathbf{\Theta}}_\lambda(u^a)$. According to (5.3) and (5.13) the $\overset{\Omega}{\mathbf{\Theta}}_\lambda(u^a)$ are determined by the polynomials $\overset{\Omega}{\mathbf{\Lambda}}(u^a)$. The $\overset{\Omega}{\mathbf{\Lambda}}(u^a)$ have to satisfy the conditions I and II, and from Theorem X.10 we see that it is necessary that the $\overset{\Omega}{\mathbf{\Lambda}}(u^a)$ satisfy the h.l. conditions S. This means that a certain number d of the coefficients of the $\overset{\Omega}{\mathbf{\Lambda}}(u^a)$ can be chosen arbitrarily and that the other ones are then uniquely determined. Denoting these d coefficients by λ^i ($i = \bar{1},\ldots,\bar{d}$) the $\overset{\Omega}{\boldsymbol{\Theta}}_\lambda(u^a)$ and therefore the integral-$E_{r-\sigma'}$'s in a point ξ^κ depend on d independent coordinate λ^i. In the case (α) the coefficients of the polynomials (5.16) can be chosen for the λ^i. Then the λ^i coincide with the λ^ζ in the proof of Theorem X.11 and $d = M$. In the case (β) some of the coefficients of the polynomials (5.16) can be chosen for the λ^i. But in that case also it can be proved (in the same way as in the proof of Theorem X.11) that the λ^i are non-supernumerary coordinates. In every point ξ^κ there are ∞^d integral-$E_{r-\sigma'}$'s forming together an $\mathfrak{S}_d^{r-\sigma'}$-field over X_{r_0}.

The adjoint Cartan system of this field is a prolongation of the *PNRSC*-system (cf. X, § 3). This prolongation is total if $r-\sigma' = m$ and partial if $r-\sigma' > m$.

Since the integral-$E_{r-\sigma'}$ is the section of the $\overset{\mathfrak{x}}{e}_\lambda$ and the vector coefficients of the $\overset{\Omega}{\boldsymbol{\Theta}}_\lambda(u^a)$, the $\mathfrak{S}_d^{r-\sigma'}$-field is given by the equations

$$F^\omega(\xi^\kappa) = 0 \quad (\omega = r_0+1,\ldots,n) \tag{6.1}$$

and the vectors

$$\begin{aligned}
&(a) \qquad \overset{\mathfrak{x}}{e}_\lambda \quad (\mathfrak{x} = \mathrm{r}+1,\ldots,\mathrm{n}),\\
&(b) \qquad \overset{\Omega}{\boldsymbol{\Theta}}_\lambda(u^a) = \overset{\mathfrak{m}}{e}_\lambda \overset{\Omega}{\boldsymbol{\Pi}}_{\mathfrak{m}}(u^a) + \overset{b}{e}_\lambda \frac{\partial \overset{\Omega}{\boldsymbol{\Lambda}}}{\partial u^b}
\end{aligned}$$

$$(a, b = 1,\ldots,\mathrm{m};\ \mathfrak{m} = \mathrm{m}+1,\ldots,\mathrm{r};\ \Omega = 1,\ldots,T), \tag{6.2}$$

containing the parameters λ^i only in the $\overset{\Omega}{\boldsymbol{\Lambda}}$.

According to IX, § 3, we get the adjoint Cartan system by considering the variables ξ^κ, λ^i as the coordinates X^A ($A = 1,\ldots,n,\bar{1},\ldots,\bar{d}$) of an $'X_{n+d}$. Then we get in this $'X_{n+d}$ the Cartan system

$$\begin{aligned}
&(a) \qquad 'F^\omega(X^A) \overset{\text{def}}{=} F^\omega(\xi^\kappa)\\
&(b) \qquad '\overset{\mathfrak{x}}{e}_B \quad \begin{cases} '\overset{\mathfrak{x}}{e}_\lambda = \overset{\mathfrak{x}}{e}_\lambda \\ '\overset{\mathfrak{x}}{e}_i = 0 \end{cases}\\
&(c) \qquad '\overset{\Omega}{\boldsymbol{\Theta}}_B(u^a) \quad \begin{cases} '\overset{\Omega}{\boldsymbol{\Theta}}_\lambda(u^a) = \overset{\Omega}{\boldsymbol{\Theta}}_\lambda(u^a) \\ '\overset{\Omega}{\boldsymbol{\Theta}}_i(u^a) = 0 \end{cases}
\end{aligned} \tag{6.3}$$

$$(\omega = r_0+1,\ldots,n;\ A, B = 1,\ldots,n,\bar{1},\ldots,\bar{d};$$
$$\mathfrak{x} = \mathrm{r}+1,\ldots,\mathrm{n};\ i = \bar{1},\ldots,\bar{d}).$$

From (6.3 *c*) we see that

$$
\begin{gathered}
'\overset{\Omega}{\mathbf{\Theta}}_B(u^a) = {}'\overset{\mathfrak{m}}{e}_B \overset{\Omega}{\mathbf{\Pi}}_{\mathfrak{m}}(u^a) + {}'\overset{b}{e}_B \frac{\partial \overset{\Omega}{\mathbf{\Lambda}}}{\partial u^b} \\
'\overset{\mathfrak{m}}{e}_i = 0, \quad '\overset{b}{e}_i = 0 \\
'\overset{\mathfrak{m}}{e}_\lambda = \overset{\mathfrak{m}}{e}_\lambda, \quad '\overset{b}{e}_\lambda = \overset{b}{e}_\lambda
\end{gathered}
\tag{6.4}
$$

$$(a,b = 1,\dots,\mathrm{m};\ \mathfrak{m} = \mathrm{m}+1,\dots,\mathrm{r};\ i = \bar{1},\dots,\bar{d};\ B = 1,\dots,n,\bar{1},\dots,\bar{d};\ \Omega = 1,\dots,T).$$

The system (6.3) is a partial prolongation of the given *PNRSC*-system. Because it is the adjoint system of an $\mathfrak{S}_d^{r-\sigma'}$-field it is clear that it is an *SC*-system. We will prove that it is an *NRSC*-system. The only non-vanishing components of the rotations $2\partial_{[C}\,'\overset{\mathfrak{x}}{e}_{B]}$ are $2\partial_{[\mu}\overset{\mathfrak{x}}{e}_{\lambda]}$ because $'\overset{\mathfrak{x}}{e}_i = 0$ and the $\overset{\mathfrak{x}}{e}_\lambda$ do not depend on the λ^i. Since the vectors (6.2) span an integral-$E_{r-\sigma'}$, the $\partial_{[\mu}\overset{\mathfrak{x}}{e}_{\lambda]}$ are zero mod $\overset{\mathfrak{x}}{e}_\lambda$, coeff. $\overset{\Omega}{\mathbf{\Theta}}_\lambda$.† Hence the $\partial_{[C}\,'\overset{\mathfrak{x}}{e}_{B]}$ are zero mod $'\overset{\mathfrak{x}}{e}_B$, coeff. $'\overset{\Omega}{\mathbf{\Theta}}_B$ and as a result these rotations can be dropped. The rotations of (6.4) are

$$2\partial_{[C}\,'\overset{\Omega}{\mathbf{\Theta}}_{B]} = 2\,'\overset{\mu}{e}_C\,'\overset{\lambda}{e}_B\,\partial_{[\mu}\overset{\Omega}{\mathbf{\Theta}}_{\lambda]} + 2\,'\overset{i}{e}_{[C}\,'\overset{\lambda}{e}_{B]}\,\partial_i\overset{\Omega}{\mathbf{\Theta}}_\lambda, \quad \partial_i = \frac{\partial}{\partial\lambda^i}, \quad '\overset{A}{e}_B \overset{\text{def}}{=} \delta^A_B$$

$$(i = \bar{1},\dots,\bar{d};\ A,B,C = 1,\dots,n,\bar{1},\dots,\bar{d};\ \Omega = 1,\dots,T). \tag{6.5}$$

The $\overset{\Omega}{\mathbf{\Pi}}_{\mathfrak{m}}$ do not depend on the λ^i, hence

$$\partial_i\overset{\Omega}{\mathbf{\Theta}}_\lambda = \overset{b}{e}_\lambda\,\partial_i\,\partial_b\overset{\Omega}{\mathbf{\Lambda}} \quad (b = 1,\dots,\mathrm{m};\ i = \bar{1},\dots,\bar{d};\ \Omega = 1,\dots,T). \tag{6.6}$$

As we have seen in X, § 4, the bivector polynomials $\overset{\Omega}{\mathbf{\Psi}}_{\mu\lambda}(u^a)$ of the given *PNRSC*-system are zero mod $\overset{\mathfrak{x}}{e}_\lambda$, $\partial_{[\mu}\overset{\mathfrak{x}}{e}_{\lambda]}$. Accordingly the $\partial_{[\nu}\overset{\Omega}{\mathbf{\Psi}}_{\mu\lambda]}$ are also zero mod $\overset{\mathfrak{x}}{e}_\lambda$, $\partial_{[\mu}\overset{\mathfrak{x}}{e}_{\lambda]}$. Now the $\partial_{[\mu}\overset{\mathfrak{x}}{e}_{\lambda]}$ are zero mod $\overset{\mathfrak{x}}{e}_\lambda$, coeff. $\overset{\Omega}{\mathbf{\Psi}}_{\mu\lambda}(u^a)$. Hence

$$\partial_{[\nu}\overset{\Omega}{\mathbf{\Psi}}_{\mu\lambda]} \equiv 0 \ (\text{mod}\ \overset{\mathfrak{x}}{e}_\lambda,\ \text{coeff.}\ \overset{\Omega}{\mathbf{\Psi}}_{\mu\lambda}(u^a))$$

$$(a = 1,\dots,\mathrm{m};\ \mathfrak{x} = \mathrm{r}+1,\dots,\mathrm{n};\ \Omega = 1,\dots,T). \tag{6.7}$$

According to Theorem X.6 we may suppose that $\overset{\Omega}{\mathbf{\Pi}}_{bc}(u^a) = 0$, identically in the u^a. Then we have, according to (4.28 *c*) and (4.29)

$$\overset{\Omega}{\mathbf{\Psi}}_{\mu\lambda} = \overset{b}{e}_{[\mu}\overset{\mathfrak{m}}{e}_{\lambda]}\,\partial_b\overset{\Omega}{\mathbf{\Pi}}_{\mathfrak{m}} \quad (b = 1,\dots,\mathrm{m};\ \mathfrak{m} = \mathrm{m}+1,\dots,\mathrm{r};\ \Omega = 1,\dots,T). \tag{6.8}$$

† We write coeff. to make clear that here we mean modulus $\overset{\mathfrak{x}}{e}_\lambda$ and modulus the coefficients of $\overset{\Omega}{\mathbf{\Theta}}_\lambda$.

Now from (6.2b) we get by differentiation

$$\partial_b \overset{\Omega}{\mathbf{\Theta}}_\lambda = \overset{\mathfrak{m}}{e}_\lambda \partial_b \overset{\Omega}{\mathbf{\Pi}}_{\mathfrak{m}} + \overset{c}{e}_\lambda \partial_b \partial_c \overset{\Omega}{\mathbf{\Lambda}}$$

$$(b, c = 1,\ldots,\mathrm{m};\ \mathfrak{m} = \mathrm{m}+1,\ldots,\mathrm{r};\ \Omega = 1,\ldots,T). \tag{6.9}$$

Substituting (6.9) into (6.8) we get

$$\overset{\Omega}{\mathbf{\Psi}}_{\mu\lambda} = \overset{b}{e}_{[\mu} \partial_{|b|} \overset{\Omega}{\mathbf{\Theta}}_{\lambda]} \quad (b = 1,\ldots,\mathrm{m};\ \Omega = 1,\ldots,T). \tag{6.10}$$

Substituting (6.10) into (6.7) we get

$$(\partial_{[\nu} \overset{b}{e}_{\mu})\partial_{|b|} \overset{\Omega}{\mathbf{\Theta}}_{\lambda]} + \overset{b}{e}_{[\mu} \partial_{|b|} \partial_\nu \overset{\Omega}{\mathbf{\Theta}}_{\lambda]} \equiv 0 \ \ (\mathrm{mod}\, \overset{\mathfrak{x}}{e}_\lambda,\ \mathrm{coeff.} \overset{\Omega}{\mathbf{\Psi}}_{\mu\lambda}(u^a))$$

$$(a, b = 1,\ldots,\mathrm{m};\ \mathfrak{x} = \mathrm{r}+1,\ldots,\mathrm{n};\ \Omega = 1,\ldots,T). \tag{6.11}$$

According to (6.10) $\overset{\Omega}{\mathbf{\Psi}}_{\mu\lambda}$ is zero mod $\partial_b \overset{\Omega}{\mathbf{\Theta}}_\lambda$. But the vector coefficients of the vector polynomials $\partial_b \overset{\Omega}{\mathbf{\Theta}}_\lambda$ ($b = 1,\ldots,\mathrm{m}$; $\Omega = 1,\ldots,T$), are to within scalar factors vector coefficients of the vector polynomials $\overset{\Omega}{\mathbf{\Theta}}_\lambda$ ($\Omega = 1,\ldots,T$). Hence the $\partial_b \overset{\Omega}{\mathbf{\Theta}}_\lambda$ and consequently the $\overset{\Omega}{\mathbf{\Psi}}_{\mu\lambda}(u^a)$ also are zero mod the vector coefficients of the $\overset{\Omega}{\mathbf{\Theta}}_\lambda(u^a)$. From this and (6.11) it follows that

$$\overset{b}{e}_{[\mu} \partial_{|b|} \partial_\nu \overset{\Omega}{\mathbf{\Theta}}_{\lambda]} \equiv 0 \ \ (\mathrm{mod}\, \overset{\mathfrak{x}}{e}_\lambda,\ \mathrm{coeff.} \overset{\Omega}{\mathbf{\Theta}}_\lambda(u^a)) \quad (a, b = 1,\ldots,\mathrm{m};$$

$$\mathfrak{x} = \mathrm{r}+1,\ldots,\mathrm{n};\ \Omega = 1,\ldots,T). \tag{6.12}$$

Since the $\overset{b}{e}_\lambda$ are linearly independent of the $\overset{\mathfrak{x}}{e}_\lambda$ and the vector coefficients of the $\overset{\Omega}{\mathbf{\Theta}}_\lambda(u^a)$, it follows from (6.12) that

$$\partial_b \partial_{[\mu} \overset{\Omega}{\mathbf{\Theta}}_{\lambda]} \equiv 0 \ \ (\mathrm{mod}\, \overset{b}{e}_\lambda, \overset{\mathfrak{x}}{e}_\lambda,\ \mathrm{coeff.} \overset{\Omega}{\mathbf{\Theta}}_\lambda(u^a)) \quad (a, b = 1,\ldots,\mathrm{m};$$

$$\mathfrak{x} = \mathrm{r}+1,\ldots,\mathrm{n};\ \Omega = 1,\ldots,T). \tag{6.13}$$

Hence relations of the form

$$2\partial_{[\mu} \overset{\Omega}{\mathbf{\Theta}}_{\lambda]} \equiv \overset{b}{e}_{[\mu} \overset{\Omega}{\mathbf{\Gamma}}_{|b|\lambda]} \ \ (\mathrm{mod}\, \overset{\mathfrak{x}}{e}_\lambda,\ \mathrm{coeff.} \overset{\Omega}{\mathbf{\Theta}}_\lambda(u^a)) \quad (a, b = 1,\ldots,\mathrm{m};$$

$$\mathfrak{x} = \mathrm{r}+1,\ldots,\mathrm{n};\ \Omega = 1,\ldots,T) \tag{6.14}$$

exist, where the $\overset{\Omega}{\mathbf{\Gamma}}_{b\lambda}$ are polynomials homogeneous of degree $n_\Omega + 1$ in the u^a.

According to Theorem X.8 the vector coefficients of the $\overset{\Omega}{\mathbf{\Theta}}_\lambda(u^a)$ satisfy the same h.l. relations as the vector coefficients of the $\overset{\Omega}{\mathbf{\Pi}}_{\mathfrak{m}}(u^a)$. Consequently the vector coefficients of the $\overset{\Omega}{\mathbf{\Theta}}_\lambda(u^a)$ can be expressed h.l. in the vector coefficients of the vector polynomials $\overset{\Omega}{\mathbf{\Theta}}_\lambda(u^1,\ldots,u^{\mathrm{h}_\Omega}, 0,\ldots,0)$

with $h_\Omega \geqslant 1$, and the number of these latter vector coefficients is equal to the number of the vector coefficients of the $\overset{\Omega}{\mathbf{\Pi}}_{\mathrm{m}}(u^1,\ldots, u^{h_\Omega}, 0,\ldots, 0)$, that is, equal to σ' (cf. (4.33)). Now denote the σ' vector coefficients of the $\overset{\Omega}{\mathbf{\Theta}}_\lambda(u^1,\ldots, u^{h_\Omega}, 0,\ldots, 0)$ $(\Omega = 1,\ldots, T)$ by $\overset{1}{w}_\lambda,\ldots, \overset{\sigma'}{w}_\lambda$. Then all vector coefficients of the $\overset{\Omega}{\mathbf{\Theta}}_\lambda(u^a)$ can be expressed h.l. in $\overset{1}{w}_\lambda,\ldots, \overset{\sigma'}{w}_\lambda$. Hence the section of the $\overset{\mathfrak{x}}{e}_\lambda$ and $\overset{1}{w}_\lambda,\ldots, \overset{\sigma'}{w}_\lambda$ is identical with the section of the $\overset{\mathfrak{x}}{e}_\lambda$ and the vector coefficients of the $\overset{\Omega}{\mathbf{\Theta}}_\lambda(u^a)$. But this section is an $E_{r-\sigma'}$ whose section with $\overset{1}{e}_{[\lambda_1}\ldots\overset{\mathrm{m}}{e}_{\lambda_m]}$ does not vanish. Consequently the $n-r+m+\sigma'$ vectors $\overset{b}{e}_\lambda$, $\overset{\mathfrak{x}}{e}_\lambda$, $\overset{1}{w}_\lambda,\ldots, \overset{\sigma'}{w}_\lambda$ are linearly independent and the vectors $\overset{1}{w}_\lambda,\ldots, \overset{\sigma'}{w}_\lambda$ can be chosen as the measuring vectors $\overset{\mathfrak{a}}{e}_\lambda$ $(\mathfrak{a} = \mathrm{m}+1,\ldots, \mathrm{m}+\sigma')$. Let the remaining vectors $\overset{\mathfrak{m}}{e}_\lambda$ be written $\overset{\mathfrak{p}}{e}_\lambda$ $(\mathfrak{p} = \mathrm{m}+\sigma'+1,\ldots, \mathrm{r})$. When this has been done each vector can be expressed linearly in the vectors $\overset{b}{e}_\lambda$, $\overset{\mathfrak{a}}{e}_\lambda$, $\overset{\mathfrak{p}}{e}_\lambda$, $\overset{\mathfrak{x}}{e}_\lambda$. Using this possibility the $\overset{\Omega}{\mathbf{\Gamma}}_{b\lambda}$ may be written in the form

$$\overset{\Omega}{\mathbf{\Gamma}}_{b\lambda} \equiv \overset{c}{e}_\lambda \overset{\Omega}{\mathbf{\Gamma}}_{bc} + \overset{\mathfrak{p}}{e}_\lambda \overset{\Omega}{\mathbf{\Gamma}}_{b\mathfrak{p}} \pmod{\overset{\mathfrak{a}}{e}_\lambda, \overset{\mathfrak{x}}{e}_\lambda}$$
$$(b, c = 1,\ldots, \mathrm{m};\ \mathfrak{a} = \mathrm{m}+1,\ldots, \mathrm{m}+\sigma';\ \mathfrak{p} = \mathrm{m}+\sigma'+1,\ldots, \mathrm{r};$$
$$\mathfrak{x} = \mathrm{r}+1,\ldots, \mathrm{n};\ \Omega = 1,\ldots, T). \qquad (6.15)$$

Since all vector coefficients of the $\overset{\Omega}{\mathbf{\Theta}}_\lambda(u^a)$ are linearly dependent on the $\overset{\mathfrak{a}}{e}_\lambda$, the equations (6.12) and (6.14) can be written in the form

$$\overset{b}{e}_{[\mu}\, \partial_{|b|}\, \partial_\nu \overset{\Omega}{\mathbf{\Theta}}_{\lambda]} \equiv 0 \pmod{\overset{\mathfrak{a}}{e}_\lambda, \overset{\mathfrak{x}}{e}_\lambda}, \qquad (6.16)$$

and

$$2\partial_{[\mu} \overset{\Omega}{\mathbf{\Theta}}_{\lambda]} \equiv \overset{b}{e}_{[\mu} \overset{c}{e}_{\lambda]} \overset{\Omega}{\mathbf{\Gamma}}_{bc} + \overset{b}{e}_{[\mu} \overset{\mathfrak{p}}{e}_{\lambda]} \overset{\Omega}{\mathbf{\Gamma}}_{b\mathfrak{p}} \pmod{\overset{\mathfrak{a}}{e}_\lambda, \overset{\mathfrak{x}}{e}_\lambda}$$
$$(b, c = 1,\ldots, \mathrm{m};\ \mathfrak{a} = \mathrm{m}+1,\ldots, \mathrm{m}+\sigma';\ \mathfrak{p} = \mathrm{m}+\sigma'+1,\ldots, \mathrm{r};$$
$$\mathfrak{x} = \mathrm{r}+1,\ldots, \mathrm{n};\ \Omega = 1,\ldots, T). \qquad (6.17)$$

If (6.17) is substituted into (6.16), we get

$$\overset{b}{e}_{[\mu} \overset{a}{e}_\nu \overset{c}{e}_{\lambda]}\, \partial_b \overset{\Omega}{\mathbf{\Gamma}}_{ac} + \overset{b}{e}_{[\mu} \overset{c}{e}_\nu \overset{\mathfrak{p}}{e}_{\lambda]}\, \partial_b \overset{\Omega}{\mathbf{\Gamma}}_{c\mathfrak{p}} \equiv 0 \pmod{\overset{\mathfrak{a}}{e}_\lambda, \overset{\mathfrak{x}}{e}_\lambda}$$
$$(a, b, c = 1,\ldots, \mathrm{m};\ \mathfrak{a} = \mathrm{m}+1,\ldots, \mathrm{m}+\sigma';\ \mathfrak{p} = \mathrm{m}+\sigma'+1,\ldots, \mathrm{r};$$
$$\mathfrak{x} = \mathrm{r}+1,\ldots, \mathrm{n};\ \Omega = 1,\ldots, T), \qquad (6.18)$$

but this is only possible if

$$\partial_{[b} \overset{\Omega}{\mathbf{\Gamma}}_{ac]} = 0 \quad (a, b, c = 1,\ldots, \mathrm{m};\ \mathfrak{p} = \mathrm{m}+\sigma'+1,\ldots, \mathrm{r};$$
$$\partial_{[b} \overset{\Omega}{\mathbf{\Gamma}}_{c]\mathfrak{p}} = 0 \qquad \Omega = 1,\ldots, T). \qquad (6.19)$$

Hence relations of the form

$$\overset{\Omega}{\mathbf{\Gamma}}_{b\mathfrak{p}}(u^a) = \partial_b \overset{\Omega}{\mathbf{\Gamma}}_{\mathfrak{p}}(u^a) \quad (a,b = 1,\ldots,\mathrm{m};\ \mathfrak{p} = \mathrm{m}+\sigma'+1,\ldots,\mathrm{r};\ \Omega = 1,\ldots,T) \quad (6.20)$$

exist, where the $\overset{\Omega}{\mathbf{\Gamma}}_{\mathfrak{p}}(u^a)$ are vector polynomials homogeneous of degree $n_\Omega+2$ in the u^a. Substituting (6.20) into (6.17) we get

$$2\partial_{[\mu}\overset{\Omega}{\mathbf{\Theta}}_{\lambda]} \equiv \overset{b}{e}_{[\mu}\overset{c}{e}_{\lambda]}\overset{\Omega}{\mathbf{\Gamma}}_{cb} + \overset{b}{e}_{[\mu}\overset{\mathfrak{p}}{e}_{\lambda]}\partial_b\overset{\Omega}{\mathbf{\Gamma}}_{\mathfrak{p}} \ (\mathrm{mod}\, \overset{\mathfrak{a}}{e}_\lambda, \overset{\mathfrak{x}}{e}_\lambda)$$

$$(b,c = 1,\ldots,\mathrm{m};\ \mathfrak{a} = \mathrm{m}+1,\ldots,\mathrm{m}+\sigma';\ \mathfrak{p} = \mathrm{m}+\sigma'+1,\ldots,\mathrm{r};\ \mathfrak{x} = \mathrm{r}+1,\ldots,\mathrm{n};\ \Omega = 1,\ldots,T). \quad (6.21)$$

Substituting (6.21) into (6.5) we get on account of (6.6),

$$2\partial_{[C}{}'\overset{\Omega}{\mathbf{\Theta}}_{B]} \equiv {}'\overset{c}{e}_{[C}{}'\overset{b}{e}_{B]}\overset{\Omega}{\mathbf{\Gamma}}_{cb} + {}'\overset{b}{e}_{[C}{}'\overset{\mathfrak{p}}{e}_{B]}\partial_b\overset{\Omega}{\mathbf{\Gamma}}_{\mathfrak{p}} + 2\,{}'\overset{i}{e}_{[C}{}'\overset{b}{e}_{B]}\partial_b\partial_i\overset{\Omega}{\mathbf{\Lambda}} \ (\mathrm{mod}\, {}'\overset{\mathfrak{a}}{e}_B, {}'\overset{\mathfrak{x}}{e}_B)$$

$$(b,c = 1,\ldots,\mathrm{m};\ \mathfrak{a} = \mathrm{m}+1,\ldots,\mathrm{m}+\sigma';\ \mathfrak{p} = \mathrm{m}+\sigma',\ldots,\mathrm{m}+\mathrm{r};\ \mathfrak{x} = \mathrm{r}+1,\ldots,\mathrm{n};\ i = \bar{1},\ldots,\bar{d};\ \Omega = 1,\ldots,T) \quad (6.22)$$

with

$$\begin{array}{lll} {}'\overset{b}{e}_B: & \overset{b}{e}_\lambda, & 0 \\ {}'\overset{\mathfrak{a}}{e}_B: & \overset{\mathfrak{a}}{e}_\lambda, & 0 \\ {}'\overset{\mathfrak{p}}{e}_B: & \overset{\mathfrak{p}}{e}_\lambda, & 0 \\ {}'\overset{\mathfrak{x}}{e}_B: & \overset{\mathfrak{x}}{e}_\lambda, & 0 \\ {}'\overset{i}{e}_C: & 0, & \delta^i_j \end{array} \quad \begin{array}{l} (b = 1,\ldots,\mathrm{m};\ \mathfrak{a} = \mathrm{m}+1,\ldots,\mathrm{m}+\sigma'; \\ \mathfrak{p} = \mathrm{m}+\sigma'+1,\ldots,\mathrm{r};\ \mathfrak{x} = \mathrm{r}+1,\ldots,\mathrm{n}; \\ i,j = \bar{1},\ldots,\bar{d};\ B = 1,\ldots,n,\bar{1},\ldots,\bar{d}). \end{array} \quad (6.23)$$

Now, if we write

$$\begin{aligned} {}'\overset{\Omega}{\mathbf{\Gamma}}_{\mathfrak{p}} &\overset{\text{def}}{=} \overset{\Omega}{\mathbf{\Gamma}}_{\mathfrak{p}} \\ {}'\overset{\Omega}{\mathbf{\Gamma}}_i &\overset{\text{def}}{=} -2\partial_i\overset{\Omega}{\mathbf{\Lambda}} \end{aligned} \quad (\mathfrak{p} = \mathrm{m}+\sigma'+1,\ldots,\mathrm{r};\ i = \bar{1},\ldots,\bar{d};\ \Omega = 1,\ldots,T), \quad (6.24)$$

(6.22) can be written in the form

$$2\partial_{[C}{}'\overset{\Omega}{\mathbf{\Theta}}_{B]} \equiv {}'\overset{c}{e}_{[C}{}'\overset{b}{e}_{B]}\overset{\Omega}{\mathbf{\Gamma}}_{cb} + {}'\overset{b}{e}_{[C}{}'\overset{\epsilon}{e}_{B]}\partial_b{}'\overset{\Omega}{\mathbf{\Gamma}}_\epsilon \ (\mathrm{mod}\, {}'\overset{\mathfrak{a}}{e}_B, {}'\overset{\mathfrak{x}}{e}_B)$$

$$(b,c = 1,\ldots,\mathrm{m};\ \mathfrak{a} = \mathrm{m}+1,\ldots,\mathrm{m}+\sigma';\ \mathfrak{x} = \mathrm{r}+1,\ldots,\mathrm{n};\ \epsilon = \mathrm{m}+\sigma'+1,\ldots,\mathrm{r},\ \bar{1},\ldots,\bar{d};\ B,C = 1,\ldots,n,\bar{1},\ldots,\bar{d};\ \Omega = 1,\ldots,T). \quad (6.25)$$

$\overset{\Omega}{\mathbf{\Gamma}}_{cb}$ and ${}'\overset{\Omega}{\mathbf{\Gamma}}_\epsilon$ are homogeneous of degree $n_\Omega+1$ and $n_\Omega+2$ respectively in the u^a. The vector coefficients of the $\overset{\Omega}{\mathbf{\Theta}}_\lambda(u^a)$ depend linearly on the $\overset{\mathfrak{a}}{e}_\lambda$ and conversely the $\overset{\mathfrak{a}}{e}_\lambda$ occur among the $\overset{\Omega}{\mathbf{\Theta}}_\lambda(u^a)$. Hence the $\overset{\Omega}{\mathbf{\Theta}}_\lambda(u^a)$

in (6.2 *b*) can be replaced by the $\overset{\mathfrak{a}}{e}_\lambda$ and the $'\overset{\Omega}{\mathbf{\Theta}}_B(u^a)$ in (6.3 *c*) by the $'\overset{\mathfrak{a}}{e}_B$. Then the prolonged system (6.3) takes the form

$$\begin{aligned}
&'F^\omega(X^A) \\
&'\overset{\mathfrak{x}}{e}_B \\
&'\overset{\mathfrak{a}}{e}_B \\
\Xi_{CB} &\overset{\text{def}}{=} \overset{c}{e}_{[C}\overset{b}{e}_{B]}\overset{\Omega}{\mathbf{\Gamma}}_{cb}+\overset{b}{e}_{[C}\overset{\epsilon}{e}_{B]}\,\partial_b\,'\overset{\Omega}{\mathbf{\Gamma}}_\epsilon
\end{aligned}$$

$(\omega = 1,\dots, n-r_0;\ A, B, C = 1,\dots, n, \bar{1},\dots, \bar{d};\ b, c = 1,\dots, \mathrm{m};\ \mathfrak{a} = \mathrm{m}+1,\dots, \mathrm{m}+\sigma';\ \mathfrak{x} = \mathrm{r}+1,\dots,\mathrm{n};\ \epsilon = \mathrm{m}+\sigma'+1,\dots, \mathrm{r}, \bar{1},\dots, \bar{d};\ \Omega = 1,\dots, T)$ (6.26)

and from this form we see that it is an *RSC*-system. To prove that it is an *NRSC*-system, we remark that the conditions (A), (B), and (C) of X, § 4, are satisfied. ($'\overset{\Omega}{\mathbf{\Gamma}}_\epsilon$ takes the place of $\overset{\Omega}{\mathbf{\Pi}}_{\mathfrak{m}}$ and the degrees in (B) and (C) are $n_\Omega+1$ and $n_\Omega+2$ respectively.) In order to show that the condition (E) is satisfied we will prove that the vector coefficients of the vector polynomials $'\overset{\Omega}{\mathbf{\Gamma}}_\epsilon(u^a)$ satisfy the same system S of h.l. relations as the coefficients of the polynomials $\overset{\Omega}{\mathbf{\Lambda}}(u^a)$ (cf. Theorem X.10). If the h.l. relations between the vector coefficients of the $\overset{\Omega}{\mathbf{\Pi}}_{\mathfrak{m}}$ are symbolized by $P(\mathbf{\Pi}_{\mathfrak{m}}) = 0$ as in § 5, the h.l. relations S are (cf. (5.15))

$$P(\mathbf{\Lambda}_1) = 0,\quad \dots,\quad P(\mathbf{\Lambda}_{\mathrm{m}}) = 0;\quad \overset{\Omega}{\mathbf{\Lambda}}_b = \partial_b\overset{\Omega}{\mathbf{\Lambda}}$$
$$(b = 1,\dots, \mathrm{m};\ \Omega = 1,\dots, T). \tag{6.27}$$

Accordingly we have to prove that

$$P(\partial_1\,'\mathbf{\Gamma}_\epsilon) = 0,\quad \dots,\quad P(\partial_{\mathrm{m}}\,'\mathbf{\Gamma}_\epsilon) = 0\quad (\epsilon = \mathrm{m}+\sigma'+1,\dots, \mathrm{r}, \bar{1},\dots, \bar{d}). \tag{6.28}$$

A relation from $P(\mathbf{\Pi}_{\mathfrak{m}}) = 0$ has the form (5.5). According to Theorem X.8 this same relation holds for the vector coefficients of the vector polynomials $\overset{\Omega}{\mathbf{\Theta}}_\lambda$ and for the vector coefficients of the vector polynomials $\overset{\Omega}{\mathbf{\Lambda}}_b$ (cf. (5.7)). Writing

$$\partial_b\,'\overset{\Omega}{\mathbf{\Gamma}}_\epsilon = \overset{\Omega}{\gamma}_{\epsilon b b_0\dots b_{n_\Omega}} u^{b_0}\dots u^{b_{n_\Omega}}$$
$$(b, b_0,\dots, b_{n_\Omega} = 1,\dots, \mathrm{m};\ \epsilon = \mathrm{m}+\sigma'+1,\dots, \mathrm{r}, \bar{1},\dots, \bar{d};\ \Omega = 1,\dots, T) \tag{6.29}$$

we have to prove that (cf. (5.7))

$$\underset{\Omega}{A}^{b_0\dots b_{n_\Omega}}\overset{\Omega}{\gamma}_{\epsilon b b_0\dots b_{n_\Omega}} = 0\quad (b_0,\dots, b_{n_\Omega} = 1,\dots, \mathrm{m};$$
$$\epsilon = \mathrm{m}+\sigma'+1,\dots, \mathrm{r}, \bar{1},\dots, \bar{d};\ \Omega = 1,\dots, T). \tag{6.30}$$

If we write (5.7 a) in the form

$$\underset{\Omega}{A}^{b_0\ldots b_{n\Omega}}\,{}'\overset{\Omega}{\theta}_{Bb_0\ldots b_{n\Omega}}=0 \quad (b_0,\ldots,b_{n\Omega}=1,\ldots,\mathrm{m};$$
$$B=1,\ldots,n,\bar{1},\ldots,\bar{d};\ \Omega=1,\ldots,T), \quad (6.31)$$

where

$${}'\overset{\Omega}{\theta}_{\mu b_0\ldots b_{n\Omega}}\overset{\text{def}}{=}\overset{\Omega}{\theta}_{\mu b_0\ldots b_{n\Omega}} \quad (b_0,\ldots,b_{n\Omega}=1,\ldots,\mathrm{m};\ i=\bar{1},\ldots,\bar{d};$$
$${}'\overset{\Omega}{\theta}_{ib_0\ldots b_{n\Omega}}\overset{\text{def}}{=}0 \qquad \Omega=1,\ldots,T), \quad (6.32)$$

we get by differentiation of (6.31)

$$\underset{\Omega}{A}^{b_0\ldots b_{n\Omega}}\,\partial_{[C}\,{}'\overset{\Omega}{\theta}_{B]b_0\ldots b_{n\Omega}}+(\partial_{[C}\underset{|\Omega|}{A}^{b_0\ldots b_{n\Omega}})\,{}'\overset{\Omega}{\theta}_{B]b_0\ldots b_{n\Omega}}=0$$
$$(b_0,\ldots,b_{n\Omega}=1,\ldots,\mathrm{m};\ B,C=1,\ldots,n,\bar{1},\ldots,\bar{d};\ \Omega=1,\ldots,T). \quad (6.33)$$

Now the ${}'\overset{\Omega}{\theta}_{Bb_0\ldots b_{n\Omega}}$ are zero mod ${}'\overset{\mathfrak{a}}{e}_B$. Hence

$$\underset{\Omega}{A}^{b_0\ldots b_{n\Omega}}\,\partial_{[C}\,{}'\overset{\Omega}{\theta}_{B]b_0\ldots b_{n\Omega}}\equiv 0 \ (\mathrm{mod}\ {}'\overset{\mathfrak{a}}{e}_B) \quad (b_0,\ldots,b_{n\Omega}=1,\ldots,\mathrm{m};$$
$$B,C=1,\ldots,n,\bar{1},\ldots,\bar{d};\ \mathfrak{a}=\mathrm{m}+1,\ldots,\mathrm{m}+\sigma';\ \Omega=1,\ldots,T). \quad (6.34)$$

Using (6.25) we immediately get (6.30).

Since the ${}'\overset{\Omega}{\mathbf{\Gamma}}_\epsilon(u^a)$ satisfy the h.l. relations S, by means of S all vector coefficients of these vector polynomials can be expressed linearly in the vector coefficients of the polynomials ${}'\overset{\Omega}{\mathbf{\Gamma}}_\epsilon(u^1,\ldots,u^{\mathrm{h}_\Omega},0,\ldots,0)$ with $h_\Omega\geqslant 1$ (cf. Theorem X.10). Hence, if we take for the vector polynomials ${}'\overset{\Omega}{\mathbf{\Gamma}}_\epsilon(u^a)$ the same values of the h's as for the vector polynomials $\overset{\Omega}{\mathbf{\Pi}}_{\mathfrak{m}}(u^a)$, the principal vector coefficients of the ${}'\overset{\Omega}{\mathbf{\Gamma}}_\epsilon(u^a)$ can be expressed h.l. in the parametrical vector coefficients and this means that the condition (E) is satisfied for the prolonged system.

In order to prove that the condition (D) is also satisfied we suppose first that the original *PNRSC*-system is in the case (α). Then the coefficients of the polynomials $\overset{\Omega}{\mathbf{\Lambda}}(u^1,\ldots,u^{\mathrm{h}_\Omega},0,\ldots,0)$ can be chosen arbitrarily and the other coefficients can be determined from them uniquely by means of the relations S. In this case for the λ^i just *all* M coefficients of the $\overset{\Omega}{\mathbf{\Lambda}}(u^1,\ldots,u^{\mathrm{h}_\Omega},0,\ldots,0)$ with $h_\Omega\geqslant 1$ can be chosen and we have $d=M$. According to (6.24) the ${}'\overset{\Omega}{\mathbf{\Gamma}}_\epsilon(u^1,\ldots,u^{\mathrm{h}_\Omega},0,\ldots,0)$ consist of

$${}'\overset{\Omega}{\mathbf{\Gamma}}_{\mathfrak{p}}(u^1,\ldots,u^{\mathrm{h}_\Omega},0,\ldots,0) \quad (\mathfrak{p}=\mathrm{m}+\sigma'+1,\ldots,\mathrm{r};\ i=\bar{1},\ldots,\bar{d};$$
$$-2(\partial_i\overset{\Omega}{\mathbf{\Lambda}})(u^1,\ldots,u^{\mathrm{h}_\Omega},0,\ldots,0) \qquad \Omega=1,\ldots,T), \quad (6.35)$$

and, according to the definition of the λ_i, the coefficients of the $\partial_i \overset{\Omega}{\mathbf{\Lambda}}(u^1,\ldots,u^{\mathrm{h}_\Omega},0,\ldots,0)$ are all *1* or *0*. Hence the vector coefficients of the vector polynomials $'\overset{\Omega}{\mathbf{\Gamma}}_\epsilon(u^1,\ldots,u^{\mathrm{h}_\Omega},0,\ldots,0)$ can be written in the order

$$\begin{array}{l} \overset{(1)}{\gamma}_{\mathfrak{p}},\ -2,\ 0,\ldots,\ 0 \\ \overset{(2)}{\gamma}_{\mathfrak{p}},\ 0,\ -2,\ 0,\ldots,\ 0 \\ \cdot\quad\cdot\quad\cdot\quad\cdot\quad\cdot\quad\cdot \\ \overset{(M)}{\gamma}_{\mathfrak{p}},\ 0,\ldots,\ -2 \end{array} \quad (\mathfrak{p} = \mathrm{m}+\sigma'+1,\ldots,\mathrm{r}). \tag{6.36}$$

Besides (6.36) there are no other parametrical vector coefficients of $'\overset{\Omega}{\mathbf{\Gamma}}_\epsilon(u^a)$. From (6.36) we see that they are linearly independent. Hence the condition (D) is satisfied and the prolonged system is an *NRSC*-system *with the same values of the h*'s as the original *PNRSC*-system.

If the original system is in the case (β), the coefficients of the polynomials $\overset{\Omega}{\mathbf{\Lambda}}(u^1,\ldots,u^{\mathrm{h}_\Omega},0,\ldots,0)$ cannot be chosen arbitrarily because S establishes h.l. relations between them. But then, as we have proved, the *same* h.l. relations exist between the vector coefficients of the vector polynomials $'\overset{\Omega}{\mathbf{\Gamma}}_\epsilon(u^1,\ldots,u^{\mathrm{h}_\Omega},0,\ldots,0)$ and this means that h.l. relations exist between the parametrical vector coefficients of the prolonged system (6.26). Using the process described in the proof of Theorem X.7 the relations can be used successively to replace all bivector polynomials of (6.26) by bivector polynomials with lower h-values, and in that way an *NRSC*-system *with lower values of the h*'s can be constructed.

Collecting results we have the theorem

THEOREM X.12. *Every PNRSC-system can be prolonged to an NRSC-system. If the ν-values of the original system are $\nu_1,\ldots,\nu_m$ and those of the prolonged system $\nu_1',\ldots,\nu_m'$, there are two possibilities, either*

$$\nu_1' = \nu_1, \quad \ldots, \quad \nu_m' = \nu_m \tag{6.37}$$

or

$$\nu_p' < \nu_p, \quad \nu_{p+1}' = \nu_{p+1}, \quad \ldots, \quad \nu_m' = \nu_m \quad (p \geqslant 1). \tag{6.38}$$

If (6.37) *holds the genus g of the original system is* $\geqslant m$.

Next to the methods developed in VIII, § 13, this theorem gives another method of deciding whether a given *PNRSC*-system has a genus $\geqslant m$.

7. Proof of Cartan's theorem of prolongation

By means of Theorems X.7 and X.12 it is now possible to prove Cartan's theorem of prolongation. Let an arbitrary system of partial differential equations of the first order be given. An *SC*-system can be constructed from this system (cf. X, § 1). This *SC*-system can be replaced by a finite number of *RSC*-systems (cf. VIII, § 14) and each *RSC*-system by an *NRSC*-system (cf. X, § 4). According to Theorem X.7 from each *NRSC*-system a finite number of *PNRSC*-systems can be deduced, having together the same integral-X_m's as the original *NRSC*-system. The ν-values of all these systems are either the same as the ν-values of the original *NRSC*-system or 'more profitable', that is, there exists a number $p \geqslant 1$ such that $\nu'_p < \nu_p$, $\nu'_{p+1} = \nu_{p+1}, \ldots, \nu'_m = \nu_m$. Every *PNRSC*-system can be prolonged and each of the prolonged systems has either the same ν-values as the system from which it was derived or more profitable ν-values. In the first case the process stops because this latter system has a genus $\geqslant m$ and can be dealt with by the methods of VIII, § 9. The only remaining *NRSC*-systems all have more profitable ν-values than the *PNRSC*-systems from which they arise. They can be handled in the same way, that is, *PNRSC*-systems can be formed with the same or with more profitable ν-values and these systems can be prolonged. The only thing to prove is that this process comes to an end.

In order to prove this we write $S_1 \sim S_2$ if the systems S_1 and S_2 have the same ν-values, and $S_1 < S_2$ if S_1 is more profitable than S_2. Obviously the symbols $\sim$, $<$, $>$ are transitive. Now we suppose that after $k-1$ prolongations we have obtained N *PNRSC*-systems. One of them, $\sim$ or $>$ than all others we denote by $S^{(k)}$. Prolongation of these systems and dropping of all systems with unchanged ν-values leads to $N' \leqslant N$ *NRSC*-systems $< S^{(k)}$. By making these systems preferred the number of systems may increase but all systems remain $< S^{(k)}$. If $S^{(k+1)}$ is a system of the set obtained, $\sim$ or $>$ all others, we have $S^{(k+1)} < S^{(k)}$. Continuing in this way we get a series

$$S^{(k)} > S^{(k+1)} > S^{(k+2)} > \ldots \tag{7.1}$$

consisting of the most unprofitable systems of each set. Now in this series the value of ν_m cannot decrease infinitely, hence, after a finite number of steps all following systems have the same value of ν_m. Thereafter ν_{m-1} can either remain constant or decrease. Now we can proceed till ν_{m-1} remains constant, etc. At last all ν's have got constant values and the process stops. Hence the number of prolongations is finite.

There is only one point where this proof is not absolutely rigorous. Starting from an *NRSC*-system in the form (4.28) we have supposed that the following conditions were satisfied:

(α) $\overset{b}{e}_\lambda$, $\overset{\mathfrak{x}}{e}_\lambda$, $\overset{\mathfrak{m}}{e}_\lambda$ are linearly independent;

(β) the parametrical vector coefficients of the vector polynomials $\overset{\Omega}{\boldsymbol{\Pi}}_{\mathfrak{m}}(u^a)$ are linearly independent;

(γ) the principal vector coefficients can be expressed h.l. in the parametrical ones.

There may, however, be points ξ^κ of X_{r_0} where these conditions are not all satisfied. These points are the null-points of a finite number of minimal regular systems of equations of the form

$$F^{\mathfrak{a}}(\xi^\kappa) = 0 \quad (\mathfrak{a} = r'_0+1,\dots, n;\ r'_0 < r_0). \tag{7.2}$$

Let these points be called *extraordinary* and each integral-X_m of (4.28), containing only extraordinary points an *extraordinary integral*-X_m. In the proof of Cartan's theorem of prolongation these extraordinary integral-X_m's are not considered. The extraordinary integral-X_m's belonging to (7.2) constitute the integral-X_m's of the non-normalized *SC*-system

$$\begin{aligned}
&F^{\mathfrak{a}} && (\mathfrak{a} = r'_0+1,\dots, n;\\
&\partial_\lambda F^{\mathfrak{a}},\ \overset{\mathfrak{x}}{e}_\lambda && \mathfrak{x} = \mathrm{r}+1,\dots,\mathrm{n};\\
&\overset{\Omega}{\boldsymbol{\Psi}}_{\mu\lambda}(u^a) && a = 1,\dots,\mathrm{m};\ \Omega = 1,\dots, T).
\end{aligned} \tag{7.3}$$

If for the points (7.2) the condition (γ) is satisfied but not the conditions (α) and/or (β), by the process of cutting-off the system (7.3) can be replaced by a finite number of *NRSC*-systems from which it can be proved that they possess the same ν-values or more advantageous ones. Hence this case does not disturb the finiteness of the whole process. If, however, in all points (7.2) the condition (γ) is not satisfied it is not yet certain that the system (7.3) can always be replaced by *NRSC*-systems with the same or more advantageous ν-values. Of course the system (7.3) can be treated in the ordinary way and, as we have proved, this is a finite process. But during this process new extraordinary points may arise leading to new *SC*-systems that have to be treated in the same way, etc. Though it is highly probable that the whole process will remain finite, the proof is not given. We would have to prove, either that for every *SC*-system (7.3) a process of cutting-off can be found such that only *NRSC*-systems with the same or lower ν-values arise, or that the intrusion of new extraordinary points cannot go on infinitely.

In the proof of the theorem of prolongation of Cartan it was necessary to make use of partial prolongations. This is due to the fact that a total prolongation, unlike a partial one, cannot always be chosen in such a way that the prolonged system has the same or more profitable ν-values than the original one. Moreover, the partial prolongation can always be chosen in such a way that the prolonged system is really an *NRSC*-system. But if these two conditions have to be satisfied, it is not always possible to choose the partial prolongation 'most economical', that is, such that the $E_{r'}$-field defined by the prolonged system has the smallest possible value of r'.

Now we will investigate the effect of a total prolongation for the case $m = 2$. We start from a given $\mathfrak{S}^2_d$-field in X_n. The adjoint Cartan system defines an $'E_{2+d}$-field in an $'X_{n+d}$. Let X^A be a point of $'X_{n+d}$ where this field possesses integral-$'E_2$'s forming together a cone $\mathfrak{C}(X^A)$. The X^A are coordinates of a certain E_2 of the $\mathfrak{S}^2_d$-field in a point ξ^κ and the E_2 is contained in the cone $\mathfrak{C}(\xi^\kappa)$. We require the relations between the cones $\mathfrak{C}(\xi^\kappa)$ and $\mathfrak{C}(X^A)$. We may expect that the cone $\mathfrak{C}(X^A)$ is 'more flat' than the cone $\mathfrak{C}(\xi^\kappa)$. It is possible to define a number measuring the 'flatness' of the cone $\mathfrak{C}(\xi^\kappa)$. If t is the dimension of $\mathfrak{C}(\xi^\kappa)$ we consider the tangent E_t's of the cone in the ∞^1 E_1's of E_2. Then there exists a finite number of these E_1's where the tangent E_t's each have at least an E_1 in common with any arbitrarily chosen general E_{n-t}. This number $N(E_2)$ depends on the choice of E_2 and is an arithmetical invariant of E_2. If $N(E_2) = 0$ for every choice of E_2 on $\mathfrak{C}(\xi^\kappa)$, the cone $\mathfrak{C}(\xi^\kappa)$ is stationary (cf. IX, § 5). In the same way an invariant $'N('E_2)$ can be formed for the $'E_2$'s of $\mathfrak{C}(X^A)$. If $'N('E_2) = 0$ for every choice of $'E_2$ on $\mathfrak{C}(X^A)$ the cone $\mathfrak{C}(X^A)$ is flat. This is a consequence of the fact that the cone $\mathfrak{C}(X^A)$ belongs to an *SC*-system. Now it can be proved that

$$'N('E_2) \leqslant N(E_2)-1, \tag{7.4}$$

and this includes the case where the cone becomes flat after a finite number of prolongations. If we denote the number of integral-E_2's containing an arbitrarily given E_1 of $\mathfrak{C}(\xi^\kappa)$ by ∞^ρ, this property can be used to give a rigorous proof of the theorem of prolongation for the cases $\rho = 0$ and $\rho = 1$. But it does not seem to be possible to use it in the general case.

There is still another interesting property of the cone $\mathfrak{C}(X^A)$. If $'t$ is the dimension of $\mathfrak{C}(X^A)$, the integral-$'E_2$'s on $\mathfrak{C}(X^A)$ are contained in ∞^μ $'E_{'t-\mu}$'s, where μ is an arithmetical invariant intimately connected with the invariant $'N$. Hence, if the points of $'X_{n+d}$ where $\mathfrak{C}(X^A)$

exists form an $'X_{'r_0}$, the integral-$'E_2$'s of the $'E_{2+d}$-field form an $'\mathfrak{S}_{\mu}^{'t-\mu}$-field in $'X_{n+d}$ defined over an $'X_{'r_0}$. The adjoint Cartan system of this field is a partial prolongation of the adjoint Cartan system of the $\mathfrak{S}_d^2$-field and it defines an $''E_{''r}$-field with $''r = 't$. This partial prolongation is 'most economical' in the sense defined above. In fact, consider any $'\mathfrak{S}_{\delta_1}^{m_1}$-field whose $'E_{m_1}$'s contain all integral-$'E_2$'s of the $'E_{2+d}$-field. Then in every point X^A of $X_{'r_0}$ the cone $\mathfrak{C}(X^A)$ is contained in the cone formed by the $\infty^{\delta_1}\,'E_{m_1}$'s of $'\mathfrak{S}_{\delta_1}^{m_1}(X^A)$. Since $\mathfrak{C}(X^A)$ has dimension $'t$, it follows that $'t \leqslant m_1+\delta_1$. The adjoint Cartan system of the $'\mathfrak{S}_{\delta_1}^{m_1}$-field is a partial prolongation of the adjoint Cartan system of the $\mathfrak{S}_d^2$-field and it defines an $''E_{m_1+\delta_1}$-field. Because $m_1+\delta_1 \geqslant 't$ this partial prolongation cannot be more economical than the one described above.

Now we may try to construct a process of prolongation such that each system has a lower value of r than the preceding one. Starting from a Cartan system whose integral-E_2's occur only in the points of an X_{r_0}, we get by section with this X_{r_0} a PC-system with the same or a lower value of r. The integral-E_2's of a PC-system form in every point ξ^κ a t-dimensional cone $\mathfrak{C}(\xi^\kappa)$ in the E_r of the E_r-field of the system. Hence $t \leqslant r$. If $t = r$ in every point, the cone fills the whole E_r. In that case each integral-E_1 is contained in at least one integral-E_2 and consequently the genus is $\geqslant 2$. Accordingly we only have to consider the case where $t < r$. The total prolongation of the PC-system defines an $E_{'r}$-field. If ∞^d is the total number of integral-E_2's on $\mathfrak{C}(\xi^\kappa)$, we have $'r = 2+d$. It may happen that $2+d < r$. Then the new Cartan system has a lower r-value. But if $2+d \geqslant r$ total prolongation does not yield any profit and we have to look for a suitable partial prolongation. If the original Cartan system is a PSC-system such a partial prolongation can always be found. In that case $\mathfrak{C}(\xi^\kappa)$ consists of $\infty^\mu\, E_{t-\mu}$'s and each integral-E_2 is contained in one of these $E_{t-\mu}$'s. The Cartan system belonging to the $\mathfrak{S}_\mu^{t-\mu}$-field of the $E_{t-\mu}$'s is a partial prolongation of the original PSC-system and represents an $E_{'r}$-field with

$$'r = t-\mu+\mu = t < r.$$

Unfortunately the prolonged system is not necessarily an SC-system and consequently the process cannot be continued.†

Now we will look for a partial prolongation if the original system is not a PSC-system but only a PC-system with $2+d \geqslant r$, $t < r$. For a partial prolongation we need an $\mathfrak{S}_{d_1}^{m_1}(\xi^\kappa)$ with $m_1+d_1 < r$ such that

† E. Cartan, 1946. 1, gives another method of partial prolongation which always leads to an SC-system with a lower value of r. By means of this method he gets another proof of the theorem of prolongation for the special case $m = 2$.

each of the ∞^d integral-E_2's in ξ^κ is contained in at least one of the E_{m_1}'s of $\mathfrak{S}^{m_1}_{d_1}(\xi^\kappa)$. If the sections of the rotations of the PC-system with the local E_r are denoted by $D_{\dot{\mathfrak{c}}\dot{\mathfrak{b}}}{}^{\mathfrak{x}}$ ($\mathfrak{b}, \mathfrak{c} = 1,\ldots, \mathrm{r}$; $\mathfrak{x} = \mathrm{r}+1,\ldots,\mathrm{n}$) and the coordinates of the E_2's in E_r by $U^{\mathfrak{c}\mathfrak{b}}$, the ∞^d integral-E_2's are the solutions of the $n-r$ equations

$$D_{\dot{\mathfrak{c}}\dot{\mathfrak{b}}}{}^{\mathfrak{x}}\, U^{\mathfrak{c}\mathfrak{b}} = 0 \quad (\mathfrak{b}, \mathfrak{c} = 1,\ldots, \mathrm{r};\ \mathfrak{x} = \mathrm{r}+1,\ldots,\mathrm{n}). \tag{7.5}$$

If the $U^{\mathfrak{c}\mathfrak{b}}$ are looked upon as line coordinates in a flat $(r-1)$-dimensional projective space P_{r-1}, each equation (7.5) represents a linear complex in P_{r-1}. Hence the $\mathfrak{S}^{m}_{d_1}(\xi^\kappa)$ required can always be constructed if the following theorem holds:

THEOREM X.13. *If the section of a finite number of linear complexes in a P_{r-1} consists of ∞^d P_1's ($d \geqslant r-2$), and if these lines do not fill the whole P_{r-1}, there exist ∞^{d_1} P_{m_1-1}'s such that $d_1+m_1 < r$ and that each of the ∞^d P_1's is contained in at least one P_{m_1-1}.*

This theorem has not yet been proved. If the proof can be given, it opens the possibility of a new proof of the theorem of prolongation for the case $m = 2$. It is highly probable that this proof can be generalized for higher values of m.

8. The theory of Riquier†

Riquier has proved that, by means of differentiations and algebraic operations only, it is possible to decide whether a given system of a finite number of partial differential equations has solutions and to determine the degree of freedom of the general solution.

Just like the theory of Cartan, the theory of Riquier consists of two parts. In the first part the existence theorem of the solutions of a special kind of systems of partial differential equations, viz. the *passive orthonomic systems*, is proved. In the second part a method of prolongation is developed by means of which every system can be replaced by a finite number of passive orthonomic systems.

In contradistinction to the existence theorem of Cartan, Riquier's existence theorem is rather difficult to prove and, in consequence of the uninvariant treatment of the variables, it lacks the symmetry and elegance of Cartan's theorem. But this is fully compensated for by the fact that Riquier's process of prolongation is much simpler than the prolongation of Cartan.

† Cf. Riquier 1910. 1; Janet 1929. 1; J. M. Thomas 1929. 2; 1931. 2; 1933. 5; 1934. 3; 1934. 4; 1937. 5.

In order to formulate the existence theorem of Riquier we denote the independent variables by ξ^κ and the unknowns by u^k ($k = 1,\ldots,N$). Now we consider an arrangement of the ξ^κ, the u^k, and the derivatives, obtained by joining to each of these quantities a definite set of p integers, called *cotes*. If $c_1^\kappa,\ldots, c_p^\kappa$ are the cotes of the ξ^κ and $c_1^k,\ldots, c_p^k$ the cotes of the u^k, the cotes of the derivative

$$\frac{\partial^{a_1+\ldots+a_n}}{(\partial\xi^1)^{a_1}\ldots(\partial\xi^n)^{a_n}}u^k \tag{8.1}$$

are chosen equal to

$$c_1^k+a_\lambda c_1^\lambda, \quad \ldots, \quad c_p^k+a_\lambda c_p^\lambda. \tag{8.2}$$

Riquier always takes $c_1^\kappa = 1$. Such an arrangement will be called a *Riquier arrangement*. If $D'u^h$ and $D''u^k$ symbolize two derivatives with the cotes $c'_1,\ldots, c'_p$ and $c''_1,\ldots, c''_p$ we will write

$$\begin{array}{llllll} (a) & D'u^h \sim D''u^k & \text{if} & c'_1 = c''_1, & \ldots, & c'_p = c''_p, \\ (b) & D'u^h < D''u^k & \text{if} & c'_1 = c''_1, & \ldots, & c'_q = c''_q;\quad c'_{q+1} < c''_{q+1}, \\ (c) & D'u^h > D''u^k & \text{if} & c'_1 = c''_1, & \ldots, & c'_q = c''_q,\quad c'_{q+1} > c''_{q+1}, \end{array} \tag{8.3}$$

where q is a number $< p$. The relation $\gtrless$ is transitive. The arrangement is said to be *complete* if the relation (8.3 a) implies that the two derivatives are identical. It can be proved that every incomplete arrangement can be extended to a complete one.

By solving a given system of equations with respect to certain derivatives we get an equivalent system of equations whose left-hand sides each consist of only one of these derivatives and whose right-hand sides are functions of ξ^κ, u^k, and a finite number of other derivatives. When this has been done all derivatives occurring in the left-hand sides and all derivatives of them are called *principal* and all others *parametrical*.

If the system obtained in this way satisfies the two conditions,

(A) the right-hand sides are analytic functions and the derivatives constituting the left-hand sides are distinct;

(B) it is possible to find a complete Riquier arrangement such that in each equation the derivative in the left-hand side is $>$ than all derivatives in the right-hand side,

the system is called *orthonomic*. It is easily proved that a way can be given to determine all principal derivatives at a point $\underset{0}{\xi^\kappa}$ if the system is orthonomic and if all parametrical derivatives at $\underset{0}{\xi^\kappa}$ are given. Using this property it is possible to develop the unknowns u^k into power series in $\xi^\kappa - \overset{0}{\xi}{}^\kappa$. The convergence of these series can be proved by a refinement of the method of majorants of Cauchy.

Now it may happen that a principal derivative in $\overset{0}{\xi}{}^\kappa$ can be determined in another way than that mentioned above and that this new way does not lead to the same result. In that case the power series obtained do not represent a solution. In order to exclude this possibility Riquier introduces a finite number of conditions of integrability, to be satisfied identically in the ξ^κ, the u^k, and the parametrical derivatives. An orthonomic system satisfying these conditions is called a *passive orthonomic system*. For such a system the above convergent power series for the u^k really constitute a solution for the system. Hence

Every passive orthonomic system has solutions and every solution is uniquely determined by giving arbitrary values for the u^k and the parametrical derivatives in a point $\overset{0}{\xi}{}^\kappa$.

This is Riquier's existence theorem.

Now it can be proved that every system of a finite number of partial differential equations can be replaced by an equivalent orthonomic system. If this system is not passive the integrability conditions in ξ^κ, u^k, and the parametrical derivatives are not identically satisfied. If these conditions are incompatible the system has no solutions. If they are compatible they can be used to express some of the parametrical derivatives in terms of the ξ^κ and other parametrical derivatives $<$ with respect to the solved ones. Of course there can be more than one solution. If the equations obtained in this way are added to the equations of the system we get one or more orthonomic systems. If one or more of these systems are not passive the process can be repeated, etc. After a finite number of steps we either arrive at a contradiction or at a finite number of passive orthonomic systems. The finiteness of the process is an immediate consequence of the fact that a sequence of derivatives of one unknown, satisfying the condition that no derivative of the sequence can arise from differentiation of one of the preceding ones, is necessarily finite. This is Riquier's theorem of prolongation. As we see the *proof* of the finiteness of the process of prolongation is much simpler than the corresponding proof in Cartan's theory.

We note that Riquier considers derivatives of order higher than one, whereas Cartan restricts himself to derivatives of order one. Riquier determines all derivatives of the u^k in a definite point $\overset{0}{\xi}{}^\kappa$. Hence it can be said that Riquier uses a neighbourhood of arbitrarily high order in a single point and Cartan neighbourhoods of order one in successive points.

We may ask what remains of the theorems of Cartan and Riquier if the functions occurring in the differential equations are no longer analytic but only functions with a sufficient number of continuous derivatives (eventually satisfying some Lipschitz conditions). The theory of functional determinants is fully developed for these functions but the existence theorem of Cauchy-Kowalewski has not yet been proved for them. If this proof were given Cartan's theorem could be established for these more general functions, as the proof of this theorem requires only the theory of functional determinants and the existence theorem of Cauchy-Kowalewski. But Riquier's theorem, because it needs in addition a refined method of majorants, could not yet be proved.

Now it is remarkable that at least for $m = 2$ the existence theorem of Riquier can be brought back to the theorem of Cartan. Every passive orthonomic system can be transformed into a passive orthonomic system of order one. This system represents an $\mathfrak{S}_d^2$-field, and by using the properties of an orthonomic system it is possible to decompose the set of conditions of integrability expressing the passivity of the system into two sets, expressing the preference of the $\mathfrak{S}_d^2$-field and the stationarity of $\mathfrak{C}(\xi^\kappa)$ respectively. Hence the $\mathfrak{S}_d^2$-field satisfies the conditions of Theorem IX.10 and consequently the adjoint system of the $\mathfrak{S}_d^2$-field is an RSC-system with a genus $\geqslant 2$. Hence it is possible, at least for $m = 2$, to connect each passive orthonomic system with an RSC-system with a genus $\geqslant 2$ such that each solution of the passive orthonomic system determines a regular integral-X_2 of the RSC-system and conversely. However, we must notice that the initial conditions are not the same in both cases. If ξ^1 and ξ^2 are the independent variables, the parametrical derivatives are the coefficients of the power series of a finite number N_1 of functions of ξ^1, ξ^2, a finite number N_2 of functions of ξ^1, a finite number N_3 of functions of ξ^2, and a finite number N_4 of constants, and this means that the general solution of Riquier depends on these $N_1+N_2+N_3$ functions and N_4 constants, to be chosen arbitrarily. But the general solution of Cartan depends on N_1 arbitrary functions of ξ^1, ξ^2, N_5 arbitrary functions of ξ^1, or the same number of arbitrary functions of ξ^2, and N_6 constants.

It is highly probable that the reduction of the existence theorem of Riquier to the theorem of Cartan is also possible for $m > 2$, but this has not yet been proved. The presumption is equivalent to the presumption that every passive orthonomic system can be transformed into a regular system in the sense of König.† If this presumption, already proved for $m = 2$, is true, not only Cartan's theorem but also Riquier's theorem (with modified initial conditions) can be proved for all classes of functions for which the existence theorem of Cauchy-Kowalewski holds.

† Cf. J. M. Thomas 1933. 5.

TABLE OF OPERATIONS

Quadrature	O_0	III.6
Ordinary differential equation of order r	O_r	III.6
One homogeneous linear partial differential equation of first order:		
one solution	O_{n-1}	III.6
all solutions	$O_{n-1},\ldots, O_1$	III.6
an $(m+1)$th solution if m independent solutions are known	O_{n-1-m}	III.6
all solutions if m independent solutions are known	$O_{n-1-m},\ldots, O_1$	III.6
the last solution if $n-2$ independent solutions and an integrating factor are known	O_0	III.9
One non-homogeneous linear partial differential equation of first order:		
one solution	O_n	III.7
one solution if $n-1$ independent solutions of the reduced equation are known	O_0	III.7
all solutions	$O_{n-1},\ldots, O_1, O_0$	III.7
Complete system of p homogeneous linear partial differential equations of first order:		
one solution	O_{n-p}	III.16
all solutions	$O_{n-p},\ldots, O_1$	III.16
an $(m+1)$th solution if m independent solutions are known	O_{n-p-m}	III.16
all solutions if m independent solutions are known	$O_{n-p-m},\ldots, O_1$	III.16
the last solution if $n-p-1$ independent solutions and an integrating factor are known	O_0	III.17
all solutions if some solutions and some admitted infinitesimal transformations are known	See III, § 18	
Complete system of p non-homogeneous linear partial differential equations of first order:		
one solution	O_{n+1-p}	III.14, 16
one solution if $n-p$ independent solutions of the reduced system are known	O_0	III.14
all solutions	$O_{n-p},\ldots, O_1, O_0$	III.14, 16

Systems S_1', S_2', S_3', S_4' of a Pfaffian:

S_1': $\overset{2\rho}{I}\overset{\;}{f} = 0$	$O_{2\rho},\ldots, O_2, O_0$	IV.3
S_4' for $K = 2\rho+1$: $\overset{2\rho+1}{I}\overset{\;}{f} = 0$	$O_{2\rho+1},\ldots, O_2, O_0$	IV.3
for $K = 2\rho$: $\overset{2\rho-1}{I}\overset{\;}{f} = 0$	$O_{2\rho-1},\ldots, O_1$	IV.3
$S_1' = S_2'$ for $K = 2\rho$ if $2\rho-1$ solutions of $S_3' = S_4'$ are known	No integrations	IV.3
Function with index 2 with respect to w_λ	O_{K-1}	IV.4
,, ,, 1 with respect to w_λ $(K > 2)$	O_K	IV.4
,, ,, 1 with respect to w_λ $(K = 2)$	O_1	IV.4
,, ,, 1 with respect to w_λ $(K = 1)$	O_0	IV.4
Conjugate set of $n-m$ functions	$O_{K-1}, O_{K-3},\ldots, O_{K+1-2(n-m)}$	IV.4
Semi-conjugate set of $n-m$ functions	$O_K, O_{K-2},\ldots, O_{K+2-2(n-m)}$	IV.4
or for $\Big\{\ K > 2(n-m)$	$O_{K-1}, O_{K-3},\ldots, O_{K+3-2(n-m)}, O_{K+2-2(n-m)}$	IV.4
$K = 2(n-m)$	$O_{K-1}, O_{K-3},\ldots, O_1$	IV.4
$K = 2(n-m)-1$	$O_{K-1}, O_{K-3},\ldots, O_0$	IV.4
Conjugate set of $\frac{1}{2}K$ functions (K even)	$O_{K-1}, O_{K-3},\ldots, O_1$	IV.4
Set of S functions with index κ:		
for $2K-2n+2S \geqslant \kappa$	$O_{2n-2S+\kappa-K-1},$ $O_{2n-2S+\kappa-K-3},\ldots, O_{K-\kappa+1}$	IV.4
for $2K-2n+2S \leqslant \kappa+1$, κ even	$O_{K-1}, O_{K-3},\ldots, O_{K-\kappa+1}$	IV.4
for $2K-2n+2S \leqslant \kappa+1$, $\Big\{\ K > \kappa+1$	$O_{K-1}, O_{K-3},\ldots, O_{K-\kappa+2}, O_{K-\kappa+1}$	IV.4
κ odd $\quad K = \kappa+1$	$O_{K-1}, O_{K-3},\ldots, O_1$	IV.4
$K = \kappa$	$O_{K-1}, O_{K-3},\ldots, O_0$	IV.4
Canonical form of w_λ:		
for $K = 2\rho+1$	$O_{K-1}, O_{K-3},\ldots, O_1$	IV.5
for $K = 2\rho$	$O_{K-1}, O_{K-3},\ldots, O_0$	IV.5
Systems S_1', S_2', S_3', S_4' of a system of Pfaffians:		
S_1'	$O_{c_1}, O_{c_1-1},\ldots, O_2, O_0$	V.3
$S_2' = S_4'$ in case I	$O_K, O_{K-1},\ldots, O_2, O_0$	V.3
$S_1' = S_2'$ in case II if $K-1$ solutions of $S_3' = S_4'$ are known	No integrations	V.4
System $v^{\mu\kappa_2\ldots\kappa_p}\partial_\mu f = 0$ ($v^{\kappa_1\ldots\kappa_p}$ simple) if a t-vector $u_{\lambda_1\ldots\lambda_t}$ $(1 \leqslant t \leqslant n-p)$ of class K is known, absolutely invariant with respect to $\lfloor v^{\kappa_1\ldots\kappa_p}\rfloor$:		
$t < n-p$	$O_K,\ldots, O_1, O_{n-p-K},\ldots, O_1$	V.5
$t = n-p$ $(K = n-p)$	$O_{n-p},\ldots, O_2, O_0$	III.18, V.5

To determine a C_2-transformation $\xi^\kappa, w_\lambda \to '\xi^\kappa, 'w_\lambda$ with $'\xi^{\mathfrak{a}} = '\phi^{\mathfrak{a}}$ or $'w_{\mathfrak{b}} = '\psi_{\mathfrak{b}}$ $(\mathfrak{a}, \mathfrak{b} = 1, \ldots, \tau < n)$ if $'\phi^{\mathfrak{a}}$ or $'\psi_{\mathfrak{b}}$ respectively are given	$O_{2n-2\tau}, O_{2n-2\tau-2}, \ldots, O_0$	VI.9
To determine a C_3-transformation $\xi^\kappa, w_\lambda \to '\xi^\kappa, 'w_\lambda$ with $'\xi^{\mathfrak{a}} = '\phi^{\mathfrak{a}}$ or $'w_{\mathfrak{b}} = '\psi_{\mathfrak{b}}$ $(\mathfrak{a}, \mathfrak{b} = 1, \ldots, \tau < n)$ if τ functions $'\phi^{\mathfrak{a}}$ or $'\psi_{\mathfrak{b}}$ homogeneous of degree 0 or 1 respectively in the w_λ are given	$O_{2n-2\tau-1}, O_{2n-2\tau-3}, \ldots, O_1$	VI.9
Complete solution of a system of $2n-m$ partial differential equations of first order in n variables in involution:		
non-homogeneous case:		
Method of Jacobi-Mayer	$O_{2(m-n)}, O_{2(m-n-1)}, \ldots, O_2, O_0$	VII.6
Generalized method of Cauchy	$O_{2(m-n)}, O_{2(m-n)-1}, \ldots, O_1, O_0$	VII.6
$2n-m_1$ solutions of (6.28) are known, constituting a $(2n-m_1)$-dimensional function group of rank $2\rho_1$	$O_{2(m_1-n+\rho_1)}, O_{2(m_1-n+\rho_1-1)}, \ldots, O_2, O_0$	VII.6
homogeneous case:		
Method of Jacobi-Mayer	$O_{2(m-n)-1}, O_{2(m-n-1)-1}, \ldots, O_1, O_0$	VII.6
$2n-m_1$ solutions of (6.40) are known, constituting a $(2n-m_1)$-dimensional homogeneous function group of class K_1:		
if $K_1 = 2\rho_1+1$	$O_{2(m_1-n+\rho_1)}, O_{2(m_1-n+\rho_1-1)}, \ldots, O_2, O_0$	VII.6
if $K_1 = 2\rho_1$ and if all groups from G_σ on are of odd class for $\sigma > 1$	$O_{2(m_1-n+\rho_1)-1}, O_{2(m_1-n+\rho_1-1)-1}, \ldots, O_{2(m_1-n+\rho_1-\sigma)+3}, O_{2(m_1-n+\rho_1-\sigma)}, O_{2(m_1-n+\rho_1-\sigma)-2}, \ldots, O_2, O_0$	VII.6
for $\sigma = 1$	$O_{2(m_1-n+\rho_1)}, O_{2(m_1-n+\rho_1-1)}, \ldots, O_2, O_0$	

SUGGESTIONS FOR THE SOLUTION OF EXERCISES

I.1. If the $(n-2)$-vector is contra(co)variant, use a corresponding co(contra)-variant 2-vector.

I.2. Suppose the E_p and the E_q had an E_s $(s > r)$ in common. Then $u^{\kappa_1 \dots \kappa_p}$ and $v^{\kappa_1 \dots \kappa_q}$ could be written as products containing a simple s-vector $w^{\kappa_1 \dots \kappa_s}$ and it would follow that the n-vector $u^{[\kappa_1 \dots \kappa_p} v^{\lambda_1 \dots \lambda_{q-r}]1 \dots r}$ was $\neq 0$. Thus the junction of E_p and E_q is E_n and this leads to a contradiction.

I.3. Write $P^{\kappa\lambda}$ in the form

$$P^{\kappa\lambda} = \underset{1}{e^{\kappa}} \underset{1}{v^{\lambda}} + \dots + \underset{n}{e^{\kappa}} \underset{n}{v^{\lambda}}. \tag{3γ}$$

I.4.

$$nn!\, A^{[1}_{\kappa} A^{[1}_{\lambda} P^{22} \dots P^{n]n]} P^{\kappa\nu} = nn!\, P^{[1|\nu|} A^{[1}_{\lambda} P^{22} \dots P^{n]n]} = n\Delta E^{1 \dots n} E^{\nu[2 \dots n} A^{1]}_{\lambda} = \Delta A^{\nu}_{\lambda}. \tag{4β}$$

I.5. Choose the coordinate system in such a way that

$$v^{\kappa\lambda} = 2\underset{1}{e^{[\kappa}} \underset{2}{e^{\lambda]}} + \dots + 2\underset{n-1}{e^{[\kappa}} \underset{n}{e^{\lambda]}}. \tag{5β}$$

I.6. Choose the coordinate system in such a way that

$$v^{\kappa\lambda} = 2\underset{1}{e^{[\kappa}} \underset{2}{e^{\lambda]}} + \dots + 2\underset{2\rho-1}{e^{[\kappa}} \underset{2\rho}{e^{\lambda]}}. \tag{6β}$$

I.7. From Ex. I.6 it follows that all 2ρ-rowed sub-determinants of the matrix of $v^{\kappa\lambda}$ can be expressed as products of two Pfaffian aggregates. If all 2ρ-rowed main sub-determinants vanish, all Pfaffian aggregates of order 2ρ vanish and consequently also all 2ρ-rowed sub-determinants.

I.8. If we write $u_\lambda = P_{0\lambda}$ and $v_\lambda = P_{\lambda 0}$ we have

$$\begin{aligned}
\begin{vmatrix} P_{\lambda\kappa} & P_{0\kappa} \\ P_{\lambda 0} & 0 \end{vmatrix} &= (n+1)!\, P_{[0[0} P_{11} \dots P_{n]n]} \\
&= (n+1)!\, P_{0[0} P_{|1|1} \dots P_{|n|n]} \\
&= n!\, P_{00} P_{1[1} \dots P_{|n|n]} - \\
&\quad - n!\, P_{01} P_{1[0} P_{|2|2} \dots P_{|n|n]} - \\
&\quad \cdot \quad \cdot \quad \cdot \quad \cdot \quad \cdot \quad \cdot \quad \cdot \quad \cdot \\
&\quad - n!\, P_{0n} P_{1[1} \dots P_{|n-1|n-1} P_{|n|0]} \\
&= - n!\, u_1 P_{[1|0|} P_{2|2|} \dots P_{n]n} - \\
&\quad \cdot \quad \cdot \quad \cdot \quad \cdot \quad \cdot \quad \cdot \quad \cdot \quad \cdot \\
&\quad - n!\, u_n P_{[1|1|} \dots P_{n-1|n-1|} P_{n]0} \\
&= - n!\, u_1 v_{[1} P_{2|2|} \dots P_{n]n} - \\
&\quad \cdot \quad \cdot \quad \cdot \quad \cdot \quad \cdot \quad \cdot \quad \cdot \quad \cdot \\
&\quad - n!\, u_n P_{[1|1|} \dots P_{n-1|n-1|} v_{n]} \\
&= - n!\, u_\lambda v_\kappa A^{\lambda}_{1} A^{\kappa}_{[1} P_{2|2|} \dots P_{n]n} \\
&\quad \cdot \quad \cdot \quad \cdot \quad \cdot \quad \cdot \quad \cdot \quad \cdot \quad \cdot \\
&\quad - n!\, u_\lambda v_\kappa A^{\lambda}_{n} A^{\kappa}_{[n} P_{1|1|} \dots P_{n-1]n-1} \\
&= - \Delta u_\lambda v_\kappa \overset{-1}{P}{}^{\kappa\lambda}.
\end{aligned} \tag{8β}$$

I.9. If we write $\overset{1}{u}_\lambda = w_{\lambda,n+1} = -w_{n+1,\lambda},\ldots, \overset{\sigma}{u}_\lambda = w_{\lambda,n+\sigma} = -w_{n+\sigma,\lambda}$ and 2τ for the rank of (9 α), a 2τ-rowed sub-determinant, $2\tau \leqslant n+\sigma$, takes the form (cf. Ex. I.6)

$$(2\tau)!\, w_{[\gamma_1[\beta_1}\ldots w_{\gamma_{2\tau}]\beta_{2\tau}]} = \left(\frac{(2\tau)!}{2^\tau \tau!}\right)^2 w_{[\gamma_1\gamma_2}\ldots w_{\gamma_{2\tau-1}\gamma_{2\tau}]}\, w_{[\beta_1\beta_2}\ldots w_{\beta_{2\tau-1}\beta_{2\tau}]} \tag{9β}$$

with indices $\beta_1,\ldots, \beta_{2\tau}, \gamma_1,\ldots, \gamma_{2\tau}$ definitely chosen from $1,\ldots, n+\sigma$. Hence, if the sub-determinant is non-vanishing, a certain number $\tau-\omega$ of the indices γ have values from $n+1,\ldots, n+\sigma$ and the other $\tau+\omega$ have values from $1,\ldots, n$. It is necessary that

$$\begin{aligned} 0 \leqslant \tau-\omega \leqslant \sigma, \\ \tau \leqslant \tau+\omega \leqslant n. \end{aligned} \tag{9γ}$$

Accordingly $w_{[\gamma_1\gamma_2}\ldots w_{\gamma_{2\tau-1}\gamma_{2\tau}]}$ can be written in the form

$$w_{[\mu_1\lambda_1}\ldots w_{\mu_\omega\lambda_\omega} w_{\mu_{\omega+1}\mathfrak{b}_1}\ldots w_{\mu_\tau\mathfrak{b}_{\tau-\omega}]}, \tag{9δ}$$

where $\mu_1, \lambda_1,\ldots, \mu_\omega, \lambda_\omega, \mu_{\omega+1},\ldots, \mu_\tau$ are definitely chosen from $1,\ldots, n$ and $\mathfrak{b}_1,\ldots, \mathfrak{b}_{\tau-\omega}$ from $n+1,\ldots, n+\sigma$.

According to our suppositions and Theorem I.4 the rank of the matrix

$$\left\|\begin{matrix} w_{\mu\lambda} & w_{\mu\mathfrak{b}_1} & \ldots & w_{\mu\mathfrak{b}_{\tau-\omega}} \\ w_{\mathfrak{b}_1\lambda} & 0 & \ldots & 0 \\ \vdots & \vdots & & \vdots \\ w_{\mathfrak{b}_{\tau-\omega}\lambda} & 0 & \ldots & 0 \end{matrix}\right\| \tag{9ε}$$

for any choice of $\mathfrak{b}_1,\ldots, \mathfrak{b}_{\tau-\omega}$ has at most the value $2\rho+2\tau-2\omega-\kappa_{\tau-\omega}$. Hence, if (9 δ) does not vanish, we must have

$$\begin{aligned} 2\omega &\leqslant 2\rho-\kappa_{\tau-\omega}, \\ 0 &\leqslant \tau-\omega \leqslant \sigma, \\ \tau &\leqslant \tau+\omega \leqslant n. \end{aligned} \tag{9ζ}$$

It is always possible to choose $\mathfrak{b}_1,\ldots, \mathfrak{b}_{\tau-\omega}$ in such a way that the rank of (9 ε) is just $2\rho+2\tau-2\omega-\kappa_{\tau-\omega}$. Hence, among the expressions (9 δ) for any value ω, satisfying (9 ζ), there must be at least one that is not zero. All expressions with values of ω not satisfying (9 ζ) are necessarily zero.

II.1. Use the second basis theorem.

II.2. $x^2 = 0,\ y = 0;\ x = 0.$

II.3. Use a minimal regular sub-system and prove that the parts of it belonging to (3 α a) and (3 α a, b) are equivalent sub-systems of (3 α a) and (3 α a, b) respectively.

II.8.

$$\begin{aligned} 2\underset{L}{\overset{[1}{D}}\underset{L}{\overset{2]}{D}}u^\kappa &= 2\underset{[1}{v^\omega}\partial_\omega(\underset{2]}{v^\mu}\partial_\mu u^\kappa - u^\mu\partial_\mu \underset{2]}{v^\kappa}) - (\underset{[2}{v^\omega}\partial_\omega u^\mu - u^\omega\partial_\omega \underset{[2}{v^\mu})\partial_\mu \underset{1]}{v^\kappa} \\ &= 2(\underset{[1}{v^\omega}\partial_{|\omega|}\underset{2]}{v^\mu})\partial_\mu u^\kappa - u^\omega\partial_\omega \underset{[1}{v^\mu}\partial_{|\mu|}\underset{2]}{v^\kappa} \\ &= \underset{3}{v^\mu}\partial_\mu u^\kappa - u^\mu\partial_\mu \underset{3}{v^\kappa} = \underset{L}{\overset{3}{D}}u^\kappa. \end{aligned} \tag{8β}$$

II.9. Let

$$\xi^\kappa = f^\kappa(\eta^{\mathfrak{a}}) \quad (\mathfrak{a} = 1,\ldots, \mathrm{p}) \tag{9α}$$

be a parametric form of X_p, minimal regular in $\underset{0}{\eta}^{\mathfrak{a}}$, satisfying the condition

$$\underset{0}{\xi}^\kappa = f^\kappa(\underset{0}{\eta}^{\mathfrak{a}}) \quad (\mathfrak{a} = 1,\ldots, \mathrm{p}) \tag{9β}$$

and $$F^{\omega}(\xi^{\kappa}) = 0 \quad (\omega = \mathrm{q}+1,\ldots,\mathrm{n}) \tag{9γ}$$
a null form of X_q, minimal regular in $\underset{0}{\xi^{\kappa}}$. Then the function
$$G^{\mathrm{q}+1}(\eta^{\mathfrak{a}}) \overset{\text{def}}{=} F^{\mathrm{q}+1}(f^{\kappa}(\eta^{\mathfrak{a}})) \quad (\mathfrak{a} = 1,\ldots,\mathrm{p}) \tag{9δ}$$
is either identically zero or analytic in $\underset{0}{\eta^{\mathfrak{a}}}$ and, in the latter case, according to a well-known theorem of the theory of functions of several variables, its null points are $\underset{0}{\eta^{\mathfrak{a}}}$ and the points of a finite number of X_{p-1}'s. It is possible but not necessary that $\underset{0}{\eta^{\mathfrak{a}}}$ is a point of one or more of the X_{p-1}'s.† Let
$$\eta^{\mathfrak{a}} = \phi^{\mathfrak{a}}(\zeta^{\mathfrak{b}}) \quad (\mathfrak{a} = 1,\ldots,\mathrm{p};\ \mathfrak{b} = 1',\ldots,(\mathrm{p}-1)') \tag{9ϵ}$$
be a parametric form of one of these X_{p-1}'s, minimal regular in all points of an $\mathfrak{N}(\underset{0}{\zeta^{\mathfrak{b}}})$ except perhaps the point $\underset{0}{\zeta^{\mathfrak{b}}}$ itself, with
$$\underset{0}{\eta^{\mathfrak{a}}} = \phi^{\mathfrak{a}}(\underset{0}{\zeta^{\mathfrak{b}}}) \tag{9ζ}$$
and with functions $\phi^{\mathfrak{a}}$ analytic in $\underset{0}{\zeta^{\mathfrak{b}}}$. The function
$$H^{\mathrm{q}+2}(\zeta^{\mathfrak{b}}) \overset{\text{def}}{=} F^{\mathrm{q}+2}\{f^{\kappa}(\phi^{\mathfrak{a}}(\zeta^{\mathfrak{b}}))\} \tag{9η}$$
is either identically zero or analytic in $\underset{0}{\zeta^{\mathfrak{b}}}$. In the latter case its null points are $\underset{0}{\zeta^{\mathfrak{b}}}$ and the points of a finite number of X_{p-2}'s in the X_{p-1}. Continuing in this way till all functions F^{ω} are used, we get the proof.

II.10. Every one of the equations (10α) represents a finite number of X_{n-1}'s plus $\underset{0}{\xi^{\kappa}}$. We get all null points by forming the intersection of every set of N X_{n-1}'s, each belonging to a different equation (10α) in all possible combinations. According to (II, Ex. 9) each intersection consists of a finite number of X_s's ($s = 0, 1,\ldots, n-1$). The minimal regular null forms of all X_s's of all intersections have together the same null points as (10α).

III.1. Use the inequality $\mu \geqslant p_{\omega}$.

III.2. Take the canonical form $v^{\kappa} = \underset{1}{e^{\kappa}}$. Then the conditions for $\mathfrak{P}_{\lambda}^{\kappa}$ are (cf. (8.1) and (8.2))
$$\partial_1 \mathfrak{P}_{\lambda}^{\kappa} = 0, \qquad \mathfrak{P}_1^{\kappa} A_{\lambda}^{\mu} - \mathfrak{P}_{\lambda}^{\mu} \underset{1}{e^{\kappa}} + \mathfrak{k}\mathfrak{P}_{\lambda}^{\kappa} \underset{1}{e^{\mu}} = 0. \tag{2δ}$$
Hence, for $\lambda = \mu = 2$, $$\mathfrak{P}_1^{\kappa} = \mathfrak{P}_2^2 \underset{1}{e^{\kappa}} \tag{2ϵ}$$
and thus $$\mathfrak{k}\mathfrak{P}_{\lambda}^{\kappa} \underset{1}{e^{\mu}} + (\mathfrak{P}_2^2 A_{\lambda}^{\mu} - \mathfrak{P}_{\lambda}^{\mu}) \underset{1}{e^{\kappa}} = 0. \tag{2ζ}$$
Accordingly we have for $\mathfrak{k} = 0$ the form
$$\mathfrak{P}_{\lambda}^{\kappa} = pA_{\lambda}^{\kappa}, \quad \underset{L}{D}p = 0, \tag{2η}$$
and for $\mathfrak{k} \neq 0$ and $\mu = 1$ it follows that
$$\mathfrak{k}\mathfrak{P}_{\lambda}^{\kappa} + (\mathfrak{P}_2^2 \overset{1}{e_{\lambda}} - \mathfrak{P}_{\lambda}^{1}) \underset{1}{e^{\kappa}} = 0 \tag{2θ}$$
and this means that $\mathfrak{P}_{\lambda}^{\kappa}$ can be written in the form
$$\mathfrak{P}_{\lambda}^{\kappa} = \mathfrak{v}_{\lambda} \underset{1}{e^{\kappa}}. \tag{2ι}$$

† Cf. Behnke and Thullen 1934. 2, p. 59. An X_{p-1} is an *analytisches Flächenstück*, cf. pp. 24, 25. If $\underset{0}{\eta^{\mathfrak{a}}}$ does not lie on one of the X_{p-1}'s, it is an *unwesentlicher Randpunkt* of this X_{p-1}. If the point $\underset{0}{\eta^{\mathfrak{a}}}$ is added to the X_{p-1} we get an *ergänztes analytisches Flächenstück*.

By substitution in (2ζ) we get

$$(\mathfrak{k}-1)\mathfrak{v}_\lambda = 0 \qquad (2\kappa)$$

and this is only possible if $\mathfrak{k} = 1$. From (2ι) we get $\mathfrak{P}_2^2 = 0$, hence, according to (2ϵ) and (2ι),

$$\mathfrak{v}_1 = 0. \qquad (2\lambda)$$

III.3. Take the canonical form $v^\kappa = e^\kappa$. Then the conditions for $\mathfrak{P}^{\kappa\lambda}$ are (cf. (8.1) and (8.2))

$$\begin{array}{ll} (a) & \partial_1 \mathfrak{P}^{\kappa\lambda} = 0, \\ (b) & -\mathfrak{P}^{\mu\lambda} \underset{1}{e^\kappa} - \mathfrak{P}^{\kappa\mu} \underset{1}{e^\lambda} + \mathfrak{k}\mathfrak{P}^{\kappa\lambda} \underset{1}{e^\mu} = 0. \end{array} \qquad (3\delta)$$

The left-hand side of $(3\delta b)$ vanishes identically if $\kappa, \lambda, \mu \neq 1$. Hence we have only to consider the cases where one or more of these coefficients are 1. This gives the equations

$$\begin{array}{ll} -\mathfrak{P}^{11}-\mathfrak{P}^{11}+\mathfrak{k}\mathfrak{P}^{11} = 0, & \\ -\mathfrak{P}^{\zeta 1}+\mathfrak{k}\mathfrak{P}^{\zeta 1} = 0, & \mathfrak{k}\mathfrak{P}^{\zeta\eta} = 0 \\ -\mathfrak{P}^{1\zeta}+\mathfrak{k}\mathfrak{P}^{1\zeta} = 0, & -\mathfrak{P}^{\zeta\eta} = 0 \\ -\mathfrak{P}^{\zeta 1}-\mathfrak{P}^{1\zeta} = 0, & -\mathfrak{P}^{\zeta\eta} = 0 \end{array} \quad (\zeta, \eta = 2,\ldots, n). \qquad (3\epsilon)$$

Hence the only possibilities are

$$\begin{array}{l} \mathfrak{k} = 2, \quad \mathfrak{P}^{1\zeta} = \mathfrak{P}^{\zeta 1} = 0, \quad \mathfrak{P}^{\zeta\eta} = 0; \\ \mathfrak{k} = 1, \quad \mathfrak{P}^{11} = 0, \quad \mathfrak{P}^{\zeta\eta} = 0, \quad \mathfrak{P}^{1\zeta} = -\mathfrak{P}^{\zeta 1}. \end{array} \qquad (3\zeta)$$

III.4. Use the identity $W_{[\mu\lambda} w_{\nu]} = 0$ and prove that the rotation of $(w_\nu \xi^\nu)^{-1} w_\lambda$ vanishes.

III.5. The abbreviated auxiliary system is

$$\begin{array}{l} \dfrac{\partial f}{\partial \eta^0} = E_\zeta \eta^\zeta \dfrac{\partial f}{\partial \eta^3} + F_\zeta \eta^\zeta \dfrac{\partial f}{\partial \eta^4} \\ E_\zeta \overset{\text{def}}{=} \eta^1 A_\zeta + \eta^2 C_\zeta, \quad F_\zeta \overset{\text{def}}{=} \eta^1 B_\zeta + \eta^2 D_\zeta \end{array} \quad (\zeta = 3, 4). \qquad (5\beta)$$

The adjoint system is

$$\begin{array}{l} \dfrac{d\eta^3}{d\eta^0} = E_\zeta \eta^\zeta \\ \dfrac{d\eta^4}{d\eta^0} = F_\zeta \eta^\zeta \end{array} \quad (\zeta = 3, 4) \qquad (5\gamma)$$

and this system has the general solution

$$\begin{array}{l} \eta^3 = C_1 E_4 e^{\alpha_1 \eta^0} + (\alpha_2 - F_4) C_2 e^{\alpha_2 \eta^0}, \\ \eta^4 = (\alpha_1 - E_3) C_1 e^{\alpha_1 \eta^0} + C_3 F_3 e^{\alpha_2 \eta^0} \end{array} \qquad (5\delta)$$

with two arbitrary constants, α_1 and α_2 being the solutions of

$$\begin{vmatrix} E_3 - \alpha & E_4 \\ F_3 & F_4 - \alpha \end{vmatrix} = 0. \qquad (5\epsilon)$$

From this we get the principal solutions of (5β) with respect to $\eta^0 = 0$

$$\begin{array}{l} \overset{1}{f} = \dfrac{\alpha_2 \eta^3 - E_\zeta \eta^\zeta}{\alpha_2 - \alpha_1} e^{-\alpha_1 \eta^0} + \dfrac{\alpha_1 \eta^3 - E_\zeta \eta^\zeta}{\alpha_1 - \alpha_2} e^{-\alpha_2 \eta^0}, \\ \overset{2}{f} = \dfrac{\alpha_2 \eta^4 - F_\zeta \eta^\zeta}{\alpha_2 - \alpha_1} e^{-\alpha_1 \eta^0} + \dfrac{\alpha_1 \eta^4 - F_\zeta \eta^\zeta}{\alpha_1 - \alpha_2} e^{-\alpha_2 \eta^0}, \end{array} \qquad (5\zeta)$$

reducing to η^3 and η^4 respectively for $\eta^0 = 0$. Now in these solutions $\alpha_1, \alpha_2, E_\zeta, F_\zeta$ are homogeneous of order 1 in η^1, η^2. Hence $\overset{1}{f}$ and $\overset{2}{f}$ can be written as functions of $\eta^0\eta^1, \eta^0\eta^2, \eta^3$, and η^4, that is, of $\xi^1-\underset{0}{\xi^1}, \xi^2-\underset{0}{\xi^2}, \xi^3$, and ξ^4, and represent then the principal solutions with respect to $\xi^1 = \underset{0}{\xi^1}, \xi^2 = \underset{0}{\xi^2}$ of (5 α).

III.6. In order to obtain the integral functions passing into x and y respectively for $x = x_0$, $y = y_0$ we use the transformation

$$\begin{aligned} A &\overset{\text{def}}{=} x_0+\zeta\xi = x, \\ B &\overset{\text{def}}{=} y_0+\zeta\eta = y. \end{aligned} \tag{6β}$$

Then the expressions (6 α) take the form

$$\begin{aligned} (Bv-Au)\,du &= (u^2+B^2)(\zeta\,d\xi+\xi\,d\zeta)+(uv+AB)(\zeta\,d\eta+\eta\,d\zeta), \\ (Au-Bv)\,dv &= (uv+AB)(\zeta\,d\xi+\xi\,d\zeta)+(v^2+A^2)(\zeta\,d\eta+\eta\,d\zeta) \end{aligned} \tag{6γ}$$

and the abbreviated auxiliary system is

$$\begin{aligned} \frac{du}{d\zeta} &= \frac{u^2\xi+B^2\xi+uv\eta+AB\eta}{Bv-Au}, \\ \frac{dv}{d\zeta} &= \frac{uv\xi+AB\xi+v^2\eta+A^2\eta}{Au-Bv}, \end{aligned} \tag{6δ}$$

in which x_0, y_0, ξ, and η are to be considered as constants. From these equations we easily get

$$\frac{duv}{d\zeta} = B\xi+A\eta = y_0\xi+x_0\eta+2\xi\eta\zeta \tag{6ε}$$

and

$$A\frac{du}{d\zeta}+B\frac{dv}{d\zeta} = -u\xi-v\eta = -u\frac{dA}{d\zeta}-v\frac{dB}{d\zeta} \tag{6ζ}$$

or

$$\frac{d}{d\zeta}(Au+Bv) = 0. \tag{6η}$$

Integration gives

$$uv = (y_0\xi+x_0\eta)\zeta+\xi\eta\zeta^2+C_1, \qquad Au+Bv = C_2. \tag{6θ}$$

The constants have to be chosen in such a way that $u = x$, $v = y$ for $\zeta = 0$:

$$C_1 = x_0 y_0, \qquad C_2 = x_0^2+y_0^2. \tag{6ι}$$

Hence the solutions of the abbreviated auxiliary system satisfying the initial conditions are the solutions of the algebraical equations

$$uv = (y_0\xi+x_0\eta)\zeta+\xi\eta\zeta^2+x_0 y_0, \qquad Au+Bv = x_0^2+y_0^2. \tag{6κ}$$

Consequently the solutions of (6 α) required are the solutions of the algebraical equations

$$uv = xy, \qquad ux+vy = x_0^2+y_0^2. \tag{6λ}$$

III.7. From Theorem III.12 it follows that the coordinate system (κ) can be chosen in such a way that

$$v^{\kappa_1\ldots\kappa_p} :: \underset{1}{e}^{[\kappa_1}\ldots\underset{p}{e}^{\kappa_p]}. \tag{7α}$$

Hence, if $\mathfrak{a}$ is a scalar density of weight $+1$ having the value 1 with respect to (κ), there is a scalar density $\underset{0}{\mathfrak{p}}$ such that

$$\underset{0}{\mathfrak{p}}v^{\kappa_1\ldots\kappa_p} = \mathfrak{a}\underset{1}{e}^{[\kappa_1}\ldots\underset{p}{e}^{\kappa_p]}. \tag{7β}$$

Obviously this scalar density is a solution of (17.15). Now we know that (17.20) has at least one solution, for instance, $\log \underset{0}{\mathfrak{p}}$. Accordingly we have

$$\underset{b}{v}^{\mu}\partial_{\mu}(\log \mathfrak{p} - \log \underset{0}{\mathfrak{p}}) = 0 \quad (b = 1,..., \mathrm{p}). \tag{7γ}$$

But since this system is complete, it has p independent solutions and this proves that (17.20) is complete.

IV.1. If (1β) is written out we get n terms of the form

$$\bar{p}_1\bar{\xi}^1\bar{p}_2\bar{\xi}^2...\bar{p}_{n-1}\bar{\xi}^{n-1}(\bar{\xi}^0+p_n\bar{\xi}^n)\overset{\bar{1}}{f}\overset{\bar{2}}{f}$$
$$= \bar{\xi}^0\bar{p}_1\bar{\xi}^1...\bar{p}_{n-1}\bar{\xi}^{n-1}\bar{p}_n\bar{\xi}^n\left(\frac{\partial \overset{1}{f}}{\partial p_n}\frac{\partial \overset{2}{f}}{\partial \xi^n}-\frac{\partial \overset{2}{f}}{\partial p_n}\frac{\partial \overset{1}{f}}{\partial \xi^n}-\frac{\partial \overset{1}{f}}{\partial p_n}p_n\frac{\partial \overset{2}{f}}{\partial \xi^0}+\frac{\partial \overset{2}{f}}{\partial p_n}p_n\frac{\partial \overset{1}{f}}{\partial \xi^0}\right). \tag{1δ}$$

Addition gives (1γ).

IV.3. If $\epsilon = 0$ we have

$$\overset{2\rho-2}{I}u = 0 \tag{3β}$$

and this means that the reduction number of u_λ with respect to the bivector $\overset{2}{I}_{\mu\lambda}$ is $\geqslant 4$ which is impossible (cf. I, § 10).

If $\epsilon = 1$ we have

$$\overset{2\rho-2}{I}wu = 0. \tag{3γ}$$

If u_λ and w_λ are linearly independent, this means that the reduction number of the system u_λ, w_λ with respect to the bivector $\overset{2}{I}_{\mu\lambda}$ is four. But this is only possible if the reduction number of w_λ is two, that is, if w_λ is lying in the domain of $\overset{2\rho}{I}$ But this is impossible for $\epsilon = 1$. Hence $u_\lambda :: w_\lambda$.

IV.4. If $\epsilon = 1$ we have

$$\overset{2\rho}{I} = \overset{2\rho-1}{I}u = \overset{2\rho-2}{I}wu. \tag{4β}$$

But this is impossible because w cannot be a divisor of $\overset{2\rho}{I}$.

If $\epsilon = 0$ we have

$$\overset{2\rho-1}{I} = \overset{2\rho-2}{I}u \tag{4γ}$$

and accordingly

$$\overset{2\rho-2}{I}(u-w) = 0. \tag{4δ}$$

But this would imply that the reduction number of $u_\lambda - w_\lambda$ was $\geqslant 4$, which is impossible (cf. I, § 10). Hence $u_\lambda = w_\lambda$.

IV.5. It is evident that the conditions (5β) are necessary. (5α) expresses the fact that f reduces the class of the section of w_λ with the $X_{2\rho+\epsilon-S}$'s with the equations

$$\overset{1}{f} = \text{const.}, \quad ..., \quad \overset{S}{f} = \text{const.} \tag{5γ}$$

in the $X_{2\rho+\epsilon}$ of the canonical variables of w_λ to $2\rho+\epsilon-2S-2$ and has accordingly $2\rho+\epsilon-S-1$ independent solutions including $\overset{1}{f},..., \overset{S}{f}$. Now ($5\beta$) is equivalent to a system of $S+1$ equations in the $2\rho+\epsilon$ canonical variables. Hence, the only thing to prove is that the equations (5β) are linearly independent. If a relation

$$\alpha_0 \overset{2\rho+\epsilon-1}{I} + \overset{2\rho+\epsilon-2}{I}(\alpha_1\overset{1}{f}+...+\alpha_S\overset{\bar{S}}{f}) \tag{5δ}$$

exists with $\alpha_0 \neq 0$, according to Ex. 4 we have $\epsilon = 0$ and

$$\frac{\alpha_1}{\alpha_0}\overset{1}{f}_\lambda + \dots + \frac{\alpha_S}{\alpha_0}\overset{S}{f}_\lambda = w_\lambda \tag{5ϵ}$$

which would imply that the class of w_λ was at most $2S$. But in that case the equation (5α) does not exist. If $\alpha_0 = 0$, according to Ex. 3 we have $\epsilon = 1$ and

$$\alpha_1 \overset{1}{f}_\lambda + \dots + \alpha_S \overset{S}{f}_\lambda :: w_\lambda, \tag{5ζ}$$

which would imply that the class of w_λ was at most $2S-1$. Also in that case the equation (5α) does not exist.

IV.6. f must have index 1 or 2 and the systems $\overset{1}{f}, f, \dots, \overset{S}{f}, f$ must all have index 3 or 4. This is just what (6β) expresses. That proves that the condition (6β) is necessary.

(6α) expresses that f reduces the class of the section of w_λ with the $X_{2\rho+\epsilon-S}$'s with the equations

$$\overset{1}{f} = \text{const.}, \quad \dots, \quad \overset{S}{f} = \text{const.} \tag{6γ}$$

in the $X_{2\rho+\epsilon}$ of the canonical variables of w_λ to $2\rho+\epsilon-2S-1$. This section has the class $2\rho+\epsilon-2S+1$. (6α) has $2\rho+\epsilon-2S$ independent solutions. Now the first equation of (6β) expresses that f is a function of the canonical variables and the other S equations are equivalent to a system of S equations in the canonical variables. Hence the only thing to prove is that the last S equations of (6β) are linearly independent. But this can be proved as in Ex. 5.

IV.7. If the index of every function f were 2 the following equations would hold:

$$\text{for } \epsilon = 1: \quad \begin{aligned} &(a) \quad \overset{2\rho}{I}\overset{\bar 1}{f} = 0, \quad \dots, \quad \overset{2\rho}{I}\overset{\bar S}{f} = 0, \\ &(b) \quad \overset{2\rho-2S+2}{I}\ \overset{\bar 1}{f}\dots\overset{\bar S}{f} \neq 0, \\ &(c) \quad \overset{2\rho-2S+3}{I}\ \overset{\bar 1}{f}\dots\overset{\bar S}{f} = 0; \end{aligned} \tag{7α}$$

$$\text{for } \epsilon = 0: \quad \begin{aligned} &(a) \quad \overset{2\rho-1}{I}\ \overset{\bar 1}{f} = 0, \quad \dots, \quad \overset{2\rho-1}{I}\ \overset{\bar S}{f} = 0, \\ &(b) \quad \overset{2\rho-2S+1}{I}\ \overset{\bar 1}{f}\dots\overset{\bar S}{f} \neq 0, \\ &(c) \quad \overset{2\rho-2S+2}{I}\ \overset{\bar 1}{f}\dots\overset{\bar S}{f} = 0. \end{aligned} \tag{7β}$$

If w_λ is written in the canonical form

$$\begin{aligned} \epsilon = 1: \quad w_\lambda &= \overset{1}{e}_\lambda + \xi^2 \overset{3}{e}_\lambda + \dots + \xi^{2\rho}\overset{2\rho+1}{e}_\lambda, \\ \epsilon = 0: \quad w_\lambda &= \xi^1 \overset{2}{e}_\lambda + \dots + \xi^{2\rho-1}\overset{2\rho}{e}_\lambda, \end{aligned} \tag{7γ}$$

(7αa) and (7βa) are equivalent to

$$\begin{aligned} &\epsilon = 1: \quad \partial_1 \overset{\mathfrak{a}}{f} = 0; \\ &\epsilon = 0: \quad \xi^1 \partial_1 \overset{\mathfrak{a}}{f} + \xi^3 \partial_3 \overset{\mathfrak{a}}{f} + \dots + \xi^{2\rho-1}\partial_{2\rho-1}\overset{\mathfrak{a}}{f} = 0 \quad (\mathfrak{a} = 1, \dots, S). \end{aligned} \tag{7δ}$$

If $\epsilon = 1$ neither in $\overset{2\rho-2S+2}{I}$ nor in the $\partial_\lambda \overset{\mathfrak{a}}{f}$, the vector $\overset{1}{e}_\lambda$ occurs. Hence from (7αb) it follows that

$$\overset{2\rho-2S+3}{I}\ \overset{\bar 1}{f}\dots\overset{\bar S}{f} = \overset{2\rho-2S+2}{I}\ w\overset{\bar 1}{f}\dots\overset{\bar S}{f} \neq 0 \tag{7ϵ}$$

and this contradicts (7αc).

If $\epsilon = 0$ ($7\beta a$) expresses the fact that the $\overset{a}{f}$ are homogeneous of degree zero in $\xi^1, \xi^3, \ldots, \xi^{2\rho-1}$:

$$v^\mu \partial_\mu \overset{a}{f} = 0, \quad v^\mu \overset{\text{def}}{=} \xi^1 \underset{1}{e^\mu} + \xi^3 \underset{3}{e^\mu} + \ldots + \xi^{2\rho-1} \underset{2\rho-1}{e^\mu}. \tag{7ζ}$$

Now we have

$$v^\mu W_{\mu\lambda} = 2v^\mu (\overset{1}{e}_{[\mu} \overset{2}{e}_{\lambda]} + \ldots + \overset{2\rho-1}{e}_{[\mu} \overset{2\rho}{e}_{\lambda]}) = \xi^1 \overset{2}{e}_\lambda + \ldots + \xi^{2\rho-1} \overset{2\rho}{e}_\lambda = w_\lambda \tag{7η}$$

and accordingly

$$v^{\mu_1} \overset{2\tau}{I}_{[\mu_1 \ldots \mu_{2\tau}} \overset{1}{f}_{\mu_{2\tau+1}} \ldots \overset{S}{f}_{\mu_{2\tau+S}]} = \frac{2\tau}{2\tau + S} \overset{2\tau-1}{I}_{[\mu_2 \ldots \mu_{2\tau}} \overset{1}{f}_{\mu_{2\tau+1}} \ldots \overset{S}{f}_{\mu_{2\tau+S}]}. \tag{7θ}$$

If we take $\tau = \rho - S + 1$ it follows that ($7\beta b$) and ($7\beta c$) are in contradiction.

IV.8. We give the proof for $\rho = 2$. If

$$w_\lambda = \overset{1}{e}_\lambda + \xi^2 \overset{3}{e}_\lambda + \xi^4 \overset{5}{e}_\lambda, \tag{8β}$$

we have for the two functions of index 2

$$\begin{array}{l} \overset{1}{f}_1 = 0, \quad \overset{1}{f}_6 = 0, \quad \ldots, \quad \overset{1}{f}_n = 0, \\ \overset{2}{f}_1 = 0, \quad \overset{2}{f}_6 = 0, \quad \ldots, \quad \overset{2}{f}_n = 0. \end{array} \tag{8γ}$$

Now
$$f = \frac{\overset{3}{I} \overset{1}{\overline{f}} \overset{2}{\overline{f}}}{\overset{5}{I}} = \overset{1}{f}_4 \overset{2}{f}_5 - \overset{1}{f}_5 \overset{2}{f}_4 + \overset{1}{f}_2 \overset{2}{f}_3 - \overset{1}{f}_3 \overset{2}{f}_2, \tag{8δ}$$

hence
$$f_1 = 0, \quad f_6 = 0, \quad \ldots, \quad f_n = 0 \tag{8ϵ}$$

and this proves that f is either zero or a function of index 2.

IV.9. The proof is similar to the proof of Ex. IV, 8.

IV.10, 11. Write w_λ in a canonical form.

V.1, 2. Use the methods developed in V, § 6.

V.3. First assume that $z = 1$. Let

$$u = \overline{1} \ldots \overline{v-t}(\overline{v-t+1} + \xi^{v-t+2}\overline{v+2}) \ldots (\bar{v} + \xi^{v+1}\overline{v+2}) \quad (1 \leqslant t \leqslant v) \tag{3ϵ}$$

($\overline{1}$ symbolizes ξ^1, etc.)

be a normal form of u. Then we may write

$$w = u \overset{v+1}{w} \ldots \overset{q}{w}, \tag{3ζ}$$

$\overset{v+1}{w}, \ldots, \overset{q}{w}$ being vectors not containing the measuring vectors $\overline{1}, \ldots, \overline{v-t}$. Then, since u is a divisor of $\overset{(1)}{w}$, the rotations of the factors of u have to vanish mod $\overline{1}, \ldots, \overline{v-t}, \overline{v-t+1} + \xi^{v-t+2}\overline{v+2}, \ldots, \bar{v} + \xi^{v+1}\overline{v+2}, \overset{v+1}{w}, \ldots, \overset{q}{w}$ (cf. III, § 11). Writing out these congruences the only one not identically satisfied is

$$\overline{v+1}\,\overline{v+2} \equiv 0 \pmod{\overset{v+1}{w}, \ldots, \overset{q}{w}} \tag{3η}$$

and this congruence shows that $\overset{v+1}{w}, \ldots, \overset{q}{w}$ can be chosen in such a way that

$$\overset{v+1}{w} = \overline{v+1} + \zeta \overline{v+2}. \tag{3θ}$$

If ζ only depended on $\xi^1, \ldots, \xi^{v+2}$, the $(v+1)$-vector $u \overset{v+1}{w}$ would have a class

$\leqslant v+2$ and accordingly be in case A. But this contradicts the assumption that w does not possess $v+1$ gradient factors. Hence ζ can be chosen as a new $(v+3)$th variable instead of ξ^{v+3} and then $\overset{v+1}{w}$ takes the form

$$\overset{v+1}{w} = \overline{v+1} + \xi^{v+3}\overline{v+2}. \tag{3ι}$$

But from this we see that $u\,\overset{v+1}{w}$ is in the special case C I.

Now returning to general values of z, we first prove that the quantity $\overset{(z-1)}{w}_{\lambda_1\ldots\lambda_{s_1}}$ belonging to $S_{(z-1)}$ has a divisor $\overset{1}{u}_{\lambda_1\ldots\lambda_{v+1}}$ of class $v+3$, such that $\overset{1}{u}_{\lambda_1\ldots\lambda_{v+1}}\, d\xi^{\lambda_1} = 0$ is a special system, then that the quantity $\overset{(z-2)}{w}_{\lambda_1\ldots\lambda_{s_2}}$ belonging to $S_{(z-2)}$ has a divisor $\overset{2}{u}_{\lambda_1\ldots\lambda_{v+2}}$ of class $v+4$, such that $\overset{2}{u}_{\lambda_1\ldots\lambda_{v+2}}\, d\xi^{\lambda_1} = 0$ is a special system, etc.

V.4. The system S' is

$$\partial_n f = 0, \qquad \phi^1\partial_1 f + \ldots + \phi^{n-2}\partial_{n-2} f - \partial_{n-1} f = 0. \tag{4β}$$

The coefficients of all equations that have to be added in order to get the derived systems have constant coefficients. From this it follows that all invariants μ are $\leqslant 1$.

VI.2. If we write

$$X^x \overset{\text{def}}{=} \frac{\partial F^x}{\partial w_\lambda}\frac{\partial}{\partial \xi^\lambda} - \frac{\partial F^x}{\partial \xi^\lambda}\frac{\partial}{\partial w_\lambda} \quad (x = \mathrm{m}+1,\ldots, 2\mathrm{n}), \tag{2β}$$

the Jacobian identity

$$(F^y,(F^x,f)) + (F^x,(f,F^y)) + (f,(F^y,F^x)) = 0 \quad (x,y = \mathrm{m}+1,\ldots,2\mathrm{n}) \tag{2γ}$$

takes the form

$$(X^y X^x)f = X^y X^x f - X^x X^y f = ((F^y,F^x),f) \quad (x,y = \mathrm{m}+1,\ldots,2\mathrm{n}). \tag{2δ}$$

Now the equations

$$((F^y,F^x),f) = 0 \quad (x,y = \mathrm{m}+1,\ldots,2\mathrm{n}) \tag{2ϵ}$$

are a consequence of (2α) if and only if the (F^y,F^x) are functions of the F^x.

VI.3. Going back to the notations of VI, § 2, we have to prove that the transformations in ξ^κ $(\kappa = 1,\ldots,n = 2\rho+1)$, leaving invariant the Pfaffian $d\xi^1 + \xi^2 d\xi^3 + \ldots + \xi^{n-1} d\xi^n$, and the transformations in ξ^κ $(\kappa = 1,\ldots,n = 2\rho)$, leaving invariant the Pfaffian $\xi^1 d\xi^2 + \ldots + \xi^{n-1} d\xi^n$, except for an additive gradient, leave the infinitesimal volume in the X_n invariant. But this is evident, because the transformations leave the n-vector $\overset{n}{I}$ invariant.

Here is another proof for infinitesimal transformations. In the notation of VI, § 3, an infinitesimal transformation $X^A \to X^A + v^A\,dt$ transforms an infinitesimal volume dV into $dV(1+\partial_B v^B\,dt)$. For $\epsilon = 1$ we have (cf. (8.28))

$$v^0 = -w_\lambda \frac{\partial F}{\partial w_\lambda} + F, \qquad \frac{\partial F}{\partial \xi^0} = 0, \qquad v^\kappa = \frac{\partial F}{\partial w_\kappa}, \qquad v^{(\lambda)} = -\frac{\partial F}{\partial \xi^\lambda}, \tag{3α}$$

hence

$$\partial_B v^B = -w_\lambda \frac{\partial^2 F}{\partial \xi^0 \partial w_\lambda} + \frac{\partial F}{\partial \xi^0} + \frac{\partial^2 F}{\partial \xi^\lambda \partial w_\lambda} - \frac{\partial^2 F}{\partial w_\lambda \partial \xi^\lambda} = 0. \tag{3β}$$

For $\epsilon = 0$ we have (cf. (8.26))

$$v^\kappa = \frac{\partial G}{\partial w_\kappa}, \qquad v^{(\lambda)} = -\frac{\partial G}{\partial \xi^\lambda}, \tag{3γ}$$

hence

$$\partial_B v^B = \frac{\partial^2 G}{\partial \xi^\lambda \partial w_\lambda} - \frac{\partial^2 G}{\partial w_\lambda \partial \xi^\lambda} = 0. \tag{3δ}$$

VI.4. From the identity of Jacobi it follows that

$$(X_1 X_2 - X_2 X_1) f = (F_1, (F_2, f)) - (F_2, (F_1, f)) = ((F_1, F_2), f). \tag{4γ}$$

VI.5. From (5α) it follows that

$$\delta' \xi^\kappa = (F, '\xi^\kappa)\, dt, \qquad \delta' w_\lambda = (F, 'w_\lambda)\, dt. \tag{5γ}$$

If the transformation $\xi^\kappa, w_\lambda \to '\xi^\kappa, 'w_\lambda$ is a C_2-transformation, the bracket expressions are invariant, hence

$$(F, '\xi^\kappa) = (F, '\xi^\kappa)', \qquad (F, 'w_\lambda) = (F, 'w_\lambda)'. \tag{5δ}$$

Every C_1-transformation is equivalent to a C_3-transformation followed by a C_1-transformation of the form

$$'w_\lambda = \sigma(\xi^\kappa, w_\lambda) w_\lambda, \qquad '\xi^\kappa = \xi^\kappa. \tag{5ϵ}$$

Since the bracket expressions are invariant with C_3-transformations, we may assume that the transformation $\xi^\kappa, w_\lambda \to '\xi^\kappa, 'w_\lambda$ has the form (5ε). Now, according to (10.10),

$$\begin{aligned}(\sigma F, '\xi^\kappa)' &= \frac{1}{\sigma}(\sigma F, '\xi^\kappa) - (\sigma F)'\Big('\xi^\kappa, \frac{1}{\sigma}\Big) + ('\xi^\kappa)'\Big(\sigma F, \frac{1}{\sigma}\Big) \\ &= \frac{1}{\sigma}(\sigma F, '\xi^\kappa) + \sigma F\Big(\frac{1}{\sigma}, '\xi^\kappa\Big) = (F, '\xi^\kappa)\end{aligned} \tag{5ζ}$$

and

$$\begin{aligned}(\sigma F, 'w_\lambda)' &= \frac{1}{\sigma}(\sigma F, 'w_\lambda) - (\sigma F)'\Big('w_\lambda, \frac{1}{\sigma}\Big) + ('w_\lambda)'\Big(\sigma F, \frac{1}{\sigma}\Big) \\ &= (F, 'w_\lambda) + 'w_\lambda\Big(\sigma F, \frac{1}{\sigma}\Big).\end{aligned}$$

VI.6. In consequence of the identity of Mayer (IV, Ex. 2) we have

$$\begin{aligned} X_1 X_2 f - X_2 X_1 f &= [F_1, [F_2, f]] + [F_1, F_2 f_0] - [F_2, [F_1, f]] - [F_2, F_1 f_0] + \\ &\quad + F_1[F_{20}, f] + F_1[F_2, f_0] - F_2[F_{10}, f] - F_2[F_1, f_0] + \\ &\quad + F_1 F_{20} f_0 + F_1 F_2 f_{00} - F_2 F_{10} f_0 - F_2 F_1 f_{00} \\ &= [[F_1, F_2], f] - F_{10}[F_2, f] - F_{20}[f, F_1] - f_0[F_1, F_2] + \\ &\quad + F_2[F_1, f_0] + f_0[F_1, F_2] - F_1[F_2, f_0] - f_0[F_2, F_1] + F_1[F_{20}, f] + \\ &\quad + F_1[F_2, f_0] - F_2[F_{10}, f] - F_2[F_1, f_0] + F_1 F_{20} f_0 - F_2 F_{10} f_0 \\ &= [[F_1, F_2]], f] + [F_1 F_2] f_0 + [F_1 F_{20} - F_2 F_{10}, f] + \\ &\quad + (F_1 F_{20} - F_2 F_{10}) f_0 \\ &= [F, f] + F f_0. \end{aligned} \tag{6ϵ}$$

VI.7. From (7β) it can be deduced that

$$['\xi^0, '\xi^\kappa] = 0, \qquad ['\xi^0, 'w_\lambda] = \sigma' w_\lambda, \qquad ['\xi^\mu, '\xi^\kappa] = 0, \qquad ['w_\lambda, '\xi^\kappa] = \sigma \delta^\kappa_\lambda. \tag{7γ}$$

Substituting these expressions in

$$[F, G] = \frac{\partial F}{\partial' \xi^\mu} \frac{\partial F}{\partial' \xi^\kappa} ['\xi^\mu, '\xi^\kappa] + \ldots \tag{7δ}$$

we get (7α). Here is another proof.† For $[F, G]$ we have (cf. IV, Ex. 8)

$$[F, G] = \frac{\overset{2\rho-1}{I} \,\overline{F}\,\overline{G}}{\overset{2\rho+1}{I}}. \tag{7ϵ}$$

† Cf. Cartan 1899. 4, p. 322.

Now according to IV (7.4)

$$\overset{2\rho-1}{'I} = \sigma^{\rho}\overset{2\rho-1}{I}, \qquad \overset{2\rho+1}{'I} = \sigma^{\rho+1}\overset{2\rho}{I}, \tag{7ζ}$$

hence

$$[F, G]' = \frac{\overset{2\rho-1}{'I}\,\overline{F}\,\overline{G}}{\overset{2\rho+1}{'I}} = \sigma^{-1}[F, G]. \tag{7η}$$

VI.8. Use the identity of Mayer (IV, Ex. 2) and the identities (Ex. 7γ).

VI.9. Using the identities (Ex. 7α) and (Ex. 8α) we have

$$\begin{aligned}[F,f]+F\frac{\partial f}{\partial \xi^0} &= \sigma[F,f]'+F\frac{\partial f}{\partial '\xi^0}\frac{\partial '\xi^0}{\partial \xi^0}+F\frac{\partial f}{\partial '\xi^\kappa}\frac{\partial '\xi^\kappa}{\partial \xi^0}+F\frac{\partial f}{\partial 'w_\lambda}\frac{\partial 'w_\lambda}{\partial \xi^0}\\ &= \sigma[F,f]'+F\frac{\partial f}{\partial '\xi^0}\left(\sigma+\frac{1}{\sigma}[\sigma,'\xi^0]\right)+F\frac{\partial f}{\partial '\xi^\kappa}\frac{1}{\sigma}[\sigma,'\xi^\kappa]+F\frac{\partial f}{\partial 'w_\lambda}\frac{1}{\sigma}[\sigma,'w_\lambda]\\ &= \sigma[F,f]'+\sigma F\frac{\partial f}{\partial '\xi^0}+F[\sigma,f]'\\ &= [\sigma F,f]'+\sigma F\frac{\partial f}{\partial '\xi^0}.\end{aligned}$$

VII.1. If we write

$$F^{10} \overset{\text{def}}{=} \xi^1\xi^2-w_4 w_5 = 0, \qquad F^{11} \overset{\text{def}}{=} \xi^3\xi^4-w_6 w_1 = 0, \qquad F^{12} \overset{\text{def}}{=} \xi^5\xi^6-w_2 w_3 = 0, \tag{1β}$$

we have

$$\begin{aligned} K^{11,12} &= \xi^4 w_2-\xi^5 w_1, & K^{10} &= -2w_4 w_5,\\ K^{12,10} &= \xi^6 w_4-\xi^1 w_3, & K^{11} &= -2w_6 w_1,\\ K^{10,11} &= \xi^2 w_6-\xi^3 w_5, & K^{12} &= -2w_2 w_3,\end{aligned} \tag{1γ}$$

hence $K = 3$. If $w_1,\dots, w_6, \xi^2, \xi^4, \xi^6$ are taken as parameters, the matrix of U_b, U_{cb} is

$$\left.\begin{array}{ccc|ccc|ccc|c}
0 & -\frac{w_6}{\xi^4} & \frac{w_4}{\xi^2} & 0 & \frac{w_5}{\xi^2} & 0 & -\frac{w_4 w_5}{\xi^2\xi^2} & 0 & 0 & \frac{w_3 w_6}{\xi^4}\\
\frac{w_6}{\xi^4} & 0 & -\frac{w_2}{\xi^6} & 0 & 0 & \frac{w_1}{\xi^4} & 0 & -\frac{w_6 w_1}{\xi^4\xi^4} & 0 & \frac{w_5 w_2}{\xi^6}\\
-\frac{w_4}{\xi^2} & \frac{w_2}{\xi^6} & 0 & \frac{w_3}{\xi^6} & 0 & 0 & 0 & 0 & -\frac{w_2 w_3}{\xi^6\xi^6} & \frac{w_1 w_4}{\xi^2}\\
\hline
0 & 0 & -\frac{w_3}{\xi^6} & 0 & 0 & 0 & 1 & 0 & 0 & \frac{w_5 w_3}{\xi^6}\\
-\frac{w_5}{\xi^2} & 0 & 0 & 0 & 0 & 0 & 0 & 1 & 0 & \frac{w_1 w_5}{\xi^2}\\
0 & -\frac{w_1}{\xi^4} & 0 & 0 & 0 & 0 & 0 & 0 & 1 & \frac{w_3 w_1}{\xi^4}\\
\hline
\frac{w_4 w_5}{\xi^2\xi^2} & 0 & 0 & -1 & 0 & 0 & 0 & 0 & 0 & -\frac{w_1 w_4 w_5}{\xi^2\xi^2}+w_2\\
0 & \frac{w_6 w_1}{\xi^4\xi^4} & 0 & 0 & -1 & 0 & 0 & 0 & 0 & -\frac{w_3 w_6 w_1}{\xi^4\xi^4}+w\\
0 & 0 & \frac{w_2 w_3}{\xi^6\xi^6} & 0 & 0 & -1 & 0 & 0 & 0 & -\frac{w_5 w_2 w_3}{\xi^6\xi^6}+w_6\\
\hline
-\frac{w_3 w_6}{\xi^4} & -\frac{w_5 w_2}{\xi^6} & -\frac{w_1 w_4}{\xi^2} & -\frac{w_5 w_3}{\xi^6} & -\frac{w_1 w_5}{\xi^2} & -\frac{w_3 w_1}{\xi^4} & \frac{w_1 w_4 w_5}{\xi^2\xi^2}-w_2 & \frac{w_3 w_6 w_1}{\xi^4\xi^4}-w_4 & \frac{w_5 w_2 w_3}{\xi^6\xi^6}-w_6 & 0
\end{array}\right. \tag{1δ}$$

Hence $\overline{K} = 9$. If we add the equations

$$F^7 \stackrel{\text{def}}{=} \xi^4 w_2 - \xi^5 w_1 = 0, \qquad F^8 \stackrel{\text{def}}{=} \xi^6 w_4 - \xi^1 w_3 = 0, \qquad F^9 \stackrel{\text{def}}{=} \xi^2 w_6 - \xi^3 w_5 = 0, \tag{1ϵ}$$

the solution of the system $(1\beta, 1\epsilon)$ is

$$\begin{aligned} w_1 &= \pm\xi^4, & w_2 &= \pm\xi^5, & w_3 &= \pm\xi^6, \\ w_4 &= \pm\xi^1, & w_5 &= \pm\xi^2, & w_6 &= \pm\xi^3 \end{aligned} \tag{1ζ}$$

and consequently the solution of (1α) is

$$f = \pm\xi^4\xi^1 \pm \xi^6\xi^3 \pm \xi^2\xi^5 + \text{const.} \tag{1η}$$

In the parametric space the equations

$$\xi^2 = \pm w_5, \quad \xi^4 = \pm w_1, \quad \xi^6 = \pm w_3 \tag{1θ}$$

determine an X_3. The system $(1\alpha, \epsilon)$ is in involution and its class is $K' = 1$. Accordingly the section of U_b with this X_3 must have the class $\overline{K}' = 1$ and this implies that the system of three functions $\xi^2 \mp w_5$, $\xi^4 \mp w_1$, $\xi^6 \mp w_3$ diminishes the class of U_b by 8. Now a system of three functions in a region of constant class cannot have an index > 6. Hence the points of X_3 must be extraordinary points of the field U_b. Indeed in the points of X_3 the matrix (1δ) takes the form

$$\left(\begin{array}{ccc|ccc|ccc|c}
0 & \mp\frac{w_6}{w_1} & \pm\frac{w_4}{w_5} & 0 & \pm 1 & 0 & -\frac{w_4}{w_5} & 0 & 0 & \pm\frac{w_3 w_6}{w_1} \\
\pm\frac{w_6}{w_1} & 0 & \mp\frac{w_2}{w_3} & 0 & 0 & \pm 1 & 0 & -\frac{w_6}{w_1} & 0 & \pm\frac{w_5 w_2}{w_3} \\
\mp\frac{w_4}{w_5} & \pm\frac{w_2}{w_3} & 0 & \pm 1 & 0 & 0 & 0 & 0 & -\frac{w_2}{w_3} & \pm\frac{w_1 w_4}{w_5} \\
\hline
0 & 0 & \mp 1 & 0 & 0 & 0 & 1 & 0 & 0 & \pm w_5 \\
\pm 1 & 0 & 0 & 0 & 0 & 0 & 0 & 1 & 0 & \pm w_1 \\
0 & \mp 1 & 0 & 0 & 0 & 0 & 0 & 0 & 1 & \pm w_3 \\
\hline
\frac{w_4}{w_5} & 0 & 0 & -1 & 0 & 0 & 0 & 0 & 0 & -\frac{w_1 w_4}{w_5} + w_2 \\
0 & \frac{w_6}{w_1} & 0 & 0 & -1 & 0 & 0 & 0 & 0 & -\frac{w_3 w_6}{w_1} + w_4 \\
0 & 0 & \frac{w_2}{w_3} & 0 & 0 & -1 & 0 & 0 & 0 & -\frac{w_5 w_2}{w_3} + w_6 \\
\hline
\mp\frac{w_3 w_6}{w_1} & \mp\frac{w_5 w_2}{w_3} & \mp\frac{w_1 w_4}{w_5} & \mp w_5 & \mp w_1 & \mp w_3 & \frac{w_1 w_4}{w_5} - w_2 & \frac{w_3 w_6}{w_1} - w_4 & \frac{w_5 w_2}{w} - w_6 & 0
\end{array}\right) \tag{1ι}$$

Hence the rank of U_{cb} is 6 and $\overline{K} = 7$ in these points.

VII.2.

$$\begin{aligned} \overline{K} - \overline{K}' &= K + 2(m-n) - K' - 2(m'-n) \\ &= K - K' + 2(m-m') > 2(m-m'). \end{aligned} \tag{2α}$$

Now a system of $m-m'$ functions in a region of constant class cannot have an index $> 2(m-m')$. Hence the points of $X_{m'}$ have to be points of diminished class.

VIII.1. A solution of (1 α) can be written in the form

$$z = \psi(x,y), \qquad p = \frac{\partial\psi}{\partial x}, \qquad q = \frac{\partial\psi}{\partial y}, \qquad s = \frac{\partial^2\psi}{\partial x\partial y} \tag{1δ}$$

and represents an integral-X_2 of the Cartan system

$$p\,dx+q\,dy-dz = 0, \qquad R\,dx+s\,dy-dp = 0, \qquad s\,dx+T\,dy-dq = 0, \tag{1ε}$$

satisfying the condition that its tangent E_2 has nowhere a direction in common with the tangent E_4 of the X_4's with the equations $x =$ const., $y =$ const. The vectors corresponding to (1 ε) and their rotations are

$$\begin{aligned} &C^4_\lambda\colon\ p\bar{x}+q\bar{y}-\bar{z}; \qquad && C_{\mu\lambda}^{\cdot\cdot 4}\colon\ \bar{p}\bar{x}+\bar{q}\bar{y};\\ &C^5_\lambda\colon\ R\bar{x}+s\bar{y}-\bar{p}; && C_{\mu\lambda}^{\cdot\cdot 5}\colon\ \bar{R}\bar{x}+\bar{s}\bar{y};\\ &C^6_\lambda\colon\ s\bar{x}+T\bar{y}-\bar{q}; && C_{\mu\lambda}^{\cdot\cdot 6}\colon\ \bar{s}\bar{x}+\bar{T}\bar{y}. \end{aligned} \tag{1ζ}$$

The sections $D_{cb}^{\cdot\cdot x}$ of the rotations with the local E_3 can be found by writing the $C_{\mu\lambda}^{\cdot\cdot x}$ mod C^x_λ in x, y, and s:

$$\begin{aligned} &(a) \qquad && D_{cb}^{\cdot\cdot 4}\colon\ s\bar{y}\bar{x}+s\bar{x}\bar{y} = 0,\\ &(b) && D_{cb}^{\cdot\cdot 5}\colon\ YR\bar{y}\bar{x}+R_s\bar{s}\bar{x}+\bar{s}\bar{y},\\ &(c) && D_{cb}^{\cdot\cdot 6}\colon\ -XT\bar{y}\bar{x}+\bar{s}\bar{x}+T_s\bar{s}\bar{y}. \end{aligned} \tag{1η}$$

An E_2 is an integral-E_2 if it lies in the local E_3 and if its sections with the bivectors (1 η b, c) vanish. Now each of these bivectors represents an E_1 in E_3. The two E_1's have the same direction if and only if the matrix (1 β) has rank *1*. In that case every E_2 containing this E_1 is an integral-E_2. If the rank is *2* the E_2 of the two E_1's is an integral-E_2. k is the sum of *3* and the c-rank of $D_{cb}^{\cdot\cdot x}$ (cf. V, § 6, p. 195), hence $k = 6$ if the rank of (1 β) is *2* and $k = 5$ in the other case. $D_{cb}^{\cdot\cdot 5}$ mod C^x_λ can be written in the form

$$(\bar{s}-YR\bar{x})(\bar{y}+R_s\bar{x}). \tag{1θ}$$

From this it follows that, if $k = 1$, the characteristics are determined by the equations (1 γ).

VIII.2. (*a*) $k = 5$. The characteristics can be found by the integration of (Ex. VIII, 1 (1 γ)). This requires five operations $O_5,\ldots, O_1$. Every integral-X_2 consists of ∞^1 characteristics. Hence, if the section of the X_2 defined by a solution of (Ex. VIII, 1 (1 α)) with the xz-plane is given by the equations

$$z_0 = f(x_0), \qquad y_0 = 0 \tag{2α}$$

with x_0 as parameter, the values of p_0, q_0, and s_0 on this curve can be found as functions of x_0 from the equations

$$\begin{aligned} &(a) \qquad && \frac{df}{dx_0} = p_0,\\ &(b) && \frac{dp_0}{dx_0} = R\Big(x_0, 0, f(x_0), \frac{df}{dx_0}, q_0, s_0\Big),\\ &(c) && \frac{dq_0}{dx_0} = s_0. \end{aligned} \tag{2β}$$

If q_0 is solved from (2 β b) as a function of x_0 and s_0 and substituted into (2 β c), we get an ordinary differential equation of the first order for s_0 whose solution can be found by an operation O_1 and depends on an arbitrary constant. The integral-X_2's required are constituted by the characteristics through all points $x_0, y_0, z_0, p_0, q_0, s_0$.

(*b*) $k = 6$; $R_s T_s = 1$. An integral-E_2 having no direction in common with the tangent-E_4 of the X_4's, $x =$ const., $y =$ const., can be given by the three equations (Ex. VIII, 1 (1 ϵ)) and a fourth equation of the form

$$\alpha\, dx + \beta\, dy - ds = 0. \tag{2γ}$$

The E_2 is then spanned by the three vectors C^x_λ and the vector C^3_λ

$$C^3_\lambda:\ \alpha\bar{x} + \beta\bar{y} - \bar{s}. \tag{2δ}$$

In order that E_2 may be an integral-E_2 it is necessary and sufficient that its sections with the rotations of C^5_λ and C^6_λ vanish. This means that (Ex. VIII, 1 (1 η *b*, *c*)) have to vanish if $\bar{s}$ is replaced by $\alpha\bar{x}+\beta\bar{y}$. This gives for α and β the equations

$$-YR - \beta R_s + \alpha = 0, \qquad -XT - \beta + \alpha T_s = 0. \tag{2ϵ}$$

If (Ex. VIII, 1 (1 β)) has rank *1*, (2 ϵ) has ∞^1 solutions, giving ∞^1 integral-E_2's filling up the whole E_3. This is the case (*a*). If the rank is *2* and if $R_s T_s = 1$, the equations (2 δ) are in contradiction and the equations (Ex. VIII, 1 (1 α)) have no solutions.

(*c*) $k = 6$; $R_s T_s \neq 1$; $Y\alpha - X\beta + \alpha_s\beta - \beta_s\alpha = 0$. The α and β can be solved from (2 ϵ) and consequently there exists an integral-E_2 in every point, given by the system of four equations

$$\begin{aligned} p\,dx + q\,dy - dz &= 0, & R\,dx + s\,dy - dp &= 0, \\ s\,dx + T\,dy - dq &= 0, & \alpha\,dx + \beta\,dy - ds &= 0. \end{aligned} \tag{2ζ}$$

The sections of the E_2 with the rotations (Ex. VIII, 1 (1 ζ)) vanish. In order that the system (2 ζ) may be complete it is necessary and sufficient that the section with the rotation of the vector $\alpha\bar{x}+\beta\bar{y}-\bar{s}$,

$$\begin{aligned} \bar{\alpha}\bar{x} + \bar{\beta}\bar{y} = {} & \alpha_y \bar{y}\bar{x} + \alpha_z \bar{z}\bar{x} + \alpha_p \bar{p}\bar{x} + \alpha_q \bar{q}\bar{x} + \alpha_s \bar{s}\bar{x} + \\ & + \beta_x \bar{x}\bar{y} + \beta_z \bar{z}\bar{y} + \beta_p \bar{p}\bar{y} + \beta_q \bar{q}\bar{y} + \beta_s \bar{s}\bar{y}, \end{aligned} \tag{2η}$$

also vanishes and this means that this bivector vanishes mod C^x_λ, $\alpha\bar{x}+\beta\bar{y}-s$. This gives the equations

$$Y\alpha - X\beta + \alpha_s\beta - \beta_s\alpha = 0, \tag{2θ}$$

where
$$\alpha = \frac{YR - R_s XT}{1 - R_s T_s}, \qquad \beta = \frac{XT + T_s YR}{1 - R_s T_s}. \tag{2ι}$$

Since this condition is satisfied the integration of the complete system (2 ζ) can be effected by means of four operations O_4, O_3, O_2, O_1.

(*d*) $k = 6$; $R_s T_s \neq 1$; $Y\alpha - X\beta + \alpha_s\beta - \beta_s\alpha \neq 0$. In this case the system (Ex. VIII, 1 (1 α)) has no solutions.

VIII.3. From (3 α) we get the following form for the contravariant connecting quantity B^κ_b of the E_r-field:

$$\begin{aligned} B^\kappa_1 &= \underset{q+1}{e^\kappa}, \\ &\ \cdot\quad \cdot\quad \cdot\quad \cdot\quad \cdot \\ B^\kappa_{r-1} &= \underset{n-1}{e^\kappa}, \\ B^\kappa_r &= \xi^{q-t+2} \underset{q-t+1}{e^\kappa} + \ldots + \xi^{q+1} \underset{q}{e^\kappa} + \underset{n}{e^\kappa}. \end{aligned} \tag{3β}$$

Hence the general form of a vector $\underset{1}{v^\kappa}$ in an integral-E_1 is

$$\underset{1}{v^\kappa} = \xi^{q-t+2} \underset{q-t+1}{e^\kappa} + \ldots + \xi^{q+1} \underset{q}{e^\kappa} + \overset{q+1}{\alpha} \underset{q+1}{e^\kappa} + \ldots + \overset{n-1}{\alpha} \underset{n-1}{e^\kappa} + \underset{n}{e^\kappa}. \tag{3γ}$$

Transvecting this vector with $C_{\mu\lambda}^{\cdot\cdot x}$ we get

$$\begin{aligned} C_{\mu\lambda}^{\cdot\cdot n-t+1}\underset{1}{v}{}^{\lambda}&: \quad -\overline{q-t+2}+\xi^{q-t+3}\overline{n};\\ &\cdots\\ C_{\mu\lambda}^{\cdot\cdot n-1}\underset{1}{v}{}^{\lambda}&: \quad -\overline{q}+\xi^{q+1}\overline{n};\\ C_{\mu\lambda}^{\cdot\cdot n}\underset{1}{v}{}^{\lambda}&: \quad -\overline{q+1}+\overset{q+1}{\alpha}\,\overline{n}. \end{aligned} \qquad (3\delta)$$

Hence the general form of a vector $\underset{2}{v}{}^{\kappa}$ in involution with $\underset{1}{v}{}^{\kappa}$ is

$$\underset{2}{v}{}^{\kappa} = \xi^{q-t+2}\underset{q-t+1}{e^{\kappa}}+\dots+\xi^{q+1}\underset{q}{e^{\kappa}}+\overset{q+1}{\alpha}\underset{q+1}{e^{\kappa}}+\overset{q+2}{\beta}\underset{q+2}{e^{\kappa}}+\dots+\overset{n-1}{\beta}\underset{n-1}{e^{\kappa}}+\underset{n}{e^{\kappa}}. \qquad (3\epsilon)$$

From this it follows that just $r-1$ independent integral-E_1's can be constructed that are mutually in involution. Hence $g = r-1$.

The equations

$$\begin{aligned} d\xi^1 = 0, \quad \dots, \quad d\xi^{q-t} &= 0,\\ \frac{d\xi^{q-t+1}}{d\xi^n} &= \xi^{q-t+2},\\ &\cdots\\ \frac{d\xi^q}{d\xi^n} &= \xi^{q+1} \end{aligned} \qquad (3\zeta)$$

have the general solution

$$\begin{aligned} \xi^1 = \text{const.}, \quad \dots, \quad \xi^{q-t} &= \text{const.},\\ \xi^{q-t+1} &= f(\xi^n),\\ \xi^{q-t+2} &= f'(\xi^n),\\ &\cdots\\ \xi^{q+1} &= f^{(t)}(\xi^n), \end{aligned} \qquad (3\eta)$$

depending on one arbitrary function of one variable and $q-t$ arbitrary constants and representing an integral-X_{r-1}. From (3γ) and (3ϵ) it follows that $s_0 = n-r$, $s_1 = 1$, $s_2 = 0$, ..., $s_g = 0$.

VIII.4. A solution of (4α)

$$z = f(x,y), \quad p = \frac{\partial f}{\partial x}, \quad q = \frac{\partial f}{\partial y}, \quad r = \frac{\partial^2 f}{\partial x^2}, \quad s = \frac{\partial^2 f}{\partial x \partial y}, \quad t = \frac{\partial^2 f}{\partial y^2} \qquad (4\beta)$$

represents an integral-X_2 of the Cartan system

$$\begin{aligned} &(a) \quad F = 0,\\ &(b) \quad (F_x+pF_z+rF_p+sF_q)\,dx+(F_y+qF_z+sF_p+tF_q)\,dy+\\ &\qquad\qquad +F_r\,dr+F_s\,ds+F_t\,dt = 0,\\ &(c) \quad dr-p\,dx-q\,dy = 0,\\ &(d) \quad dp-r\,dx-s\,dy = 0,\\ &(e) \quad dq-s\,dx-t\,dy = 0 \end{aligned} \qquad (4\gamma)$$

in the X_8 of x, y, z, p, q, r, s, and t. The only non-vanishing rotations are

$$\bar{x}\bar{r}+\bar{y}\bar{s}, \qquad \bar{x}\bar{s}+\bar{y}\bar{t}. \qquad (4\delta)$$

Because there is one scalar equation we have $r_0 = 7$. The equations $(4\gamma\, b, c, d, e)$ represent an E_4-field in an X_7 in X_8. Hence $r_1 = 3$, and $s_0 = 3$. The points satisfying the six equations

$$\begin{gathered} F = 0, \\ F_x+pF_z+rF_p+sF_q = 0, \\ F_y+qF_z+sF_p+tF_q = 0, \\ F_r = 0, \quad F_s = 0, \quad F_t = 0 \end{gathered} \tag{4ϵ}$$

form a non-regular integral manifold. If $\delta x, \delta y, \delta z, \delta p, \delta q, \delta r, \delta s, \delta t$ represent an integral-E_1, the directions of $H(E_1)$ satisfy the equations ($4\gamma b, c, d, e$) and

$$\delta x dr - \delta r dx + \delta y ds - \delta s dy = 0, \qquad \delta x ds - \delta s dx + \delta y dt - \delta t dy = 0. \tag{4ζ}$$

From this it follows that for a general choice of the integral-E_1 the dimension of $H(E_1)$ is 2, hence $r_2 = 0$, $s_1 = 2$, and

$$s_0 + s_1 = r_0 - 2. \tag{4η}$$

Accordingly $g = 2$. The integral-E_1's satisfying the condition that the rank of

$$\left\| \begin{matrix} F_x+pF_z+rF_p+sF_q & F_y+qF_z+sF_p+tF_q & F_r & F_s & F_t \\ -\delta z & -\delta s & \delta x & \delta y & 0 \\ -\delta s & -\delta t & 0 & \delta x & \delta y \end{matrix} \right\| \tag{4θ}$$

is 2 are non-regular. For them $H(E_1)$ has the dimension 3 and

$$F_t \delta x^2 - F_s \delta x \delta y + F_r \delta y^2 = 0. \tag{4ι}$$

Now we look only for integral-X_2's whose tangent E_2's nowhere have a direction in common with the tangent E_6's of the X_6's $x =$ const., $y =$ const. On these X_2's no relation between x and y can exist and, because of (4ι), if such an X_2 is a non-regular integral-X_2, then for every point of X_2 we have $F_r = 0$, $F_s = 0$, $F_t = 0$ and consequently, according to ($4\gamma b$),

$$F_x+pF_z+rF_p+sF_q = 0, \qquad F_y+qF_z+sF_p+tF_q = 0. \tag{4κ}$$

Hence, each non-regular integral-X_2 on which no relation between x and y exists is necessarily contained in the integral manifold (4ϵ). The non-regular integral-E_1's on a regular integral-X_2 are the E_1's satisfying (4ι). They form on each regular integral-X_2 two systems of curves.†

VIII.5. If p_λ stands for $d^\lambda y/dx^\lambda$ ($\lambda = 1,..., n$), two elements of order n: x, y, p_λ and $x+dx, y+dy, p_\lambda+dp_\lambda$ are *joined*, if there exists a curve containing (up to the order n) both elements (cf. VI, § 3). The necessary and sufficient conditions are

$$dy - p_1 dx = 0, \quad dp_1 - p_2 dx = 0, \quad ..., \quad dp_{n-1} - p_n dx = 0. \tag{5α}$$

A contact transformation is a transformation $x, y, p_\lambda \rightarrow 'x, 'y, 'p_\lambda$ leaving joined situation invariant. Hence such a transformation can be considered as a point transformation in the X_{n+2} of x, y, p_λ, transforming the E_2-field determined by (5α) into the E_2-field

$$d'y - 'p_1 d'x = 0, \quad d'p_1 - 'p_2 d'x = 0, \quad ..., \quad d'p_{n-1} - 'p_n d'x = 0. \tag{5β}$$

This transformation is an extended C_1-transformation of the elements of order 1 if and only if

$$d'y - 'p_1 d'x = \sigma(dy - p_1 dx) \tag{5γ}$$

and if $'x, 'y, 'p_1$ are functions of x, y, p_1. This latter condition is a consequence of (5γ). From (5γ) it follows that $'y$ and consequently also $'p_1$ is a function of $'x$, y, and x. Accordingly p_1 is a function of $'x$, y, and x,

$$p_1 = \psi(x, y, 'x) \tag{5δ}$$

† These curves are 'characteristics' in the sense of Cartan, cf. 1946. 1, p. 82. He calls every $X_{m'}$ in a regular integral-X_m whose tangent $E_{m'}$'s are nowhere regular a characteristic, cf. 1946. 1, p. 79.

and $\partial\psi/\partial x$ cannot vanish because a relation between x, y, and p_1 cannot exist. Hence $'x$ can be solved as a function of x, y, and p:

$$'x = F(x, y, p). \tag{5ϵ}$$

By substitution we get $'y$ and $'p$ as functions of x, y, and p.

In order to prove that a relation of the form (5γ) holds, we show that the E_{n+1}-field represented by $dy - p_1\,dx = 0$ is in an invariant way connected with the E_2-field (5α). The E_2-field is spanned by the two contravariant vectors of X_{n+2}

$$\begin{aligned} &B_1^\kappa\colon\quad \bar{x} + p_1\,\bar{y} + p_2\,\bar{p}_1 + \dots + p_n\,\bar{p}_{n-1};\\ &B_2^\kappa\colon\quad \bar{p}_n. \end{aligned} \tag{5ζ}$$

From these two vectors the invariant

$$B_3^\kappa = B_{12}^\kappa = B_{[1}^\mu\,\partial_{|\mu|}\,B_{2]}^\kappa\colon\quad \bar{p}_{n-1} \tag{5η}$$

can be derived. The vectors B_1^κ, B_2^κ, B_3^κ span an E_3-field, connected in an invariant way with the E_2-field. In the same way an E_4-field spanned by B_1^κ, B_2^κ, B_3^κ, $B_4^\kappa = B_{13}^\kappa$ can be constructed. Continuing in this way we get at last an E_{n+1}-field spanned by B_1^κ, $\bar{p}_n, \dots, \bar{p}_1$ and this E_{n+1}-field is represented by $dy - p_1\,dx = 0$.

VIII.6. The equations

$$v^{\lambda_1}\overset{\chi_\rho}{u}_{\lambda_1\dots\lambda_\rho} = 0 \quad (\rho = 1, \dots, \sigma;\ \chi_\rho = 1, \dots, N_\rho) \tag{6β}$$

have $n-K$ linearly independent solutions. Since the system is closed, two solutions $\underset{1}{v}{}^\kappa$, $\underset{2}{v}{}^\kappa$ satisfy the relations

$$2(\underset{[1}{v}{}^\mu\partial_\mu\underset{2]}{v}{}^{\lambda_1})\overset{\chi_\rho}{u}_{\lambda_1\dots\lambda_\rho} = -2\underset{[1}{v}{}^\mu\underset{2]}{v}{}^{\lambda_1}\partial_\mu\overset{\chi_\rho}{u}_{\lambda_1\dots\lambda_\rho} = \underset{[1}{v}{}^\mu\underset{2]}{v}{}^{\lambda_1}(\partial_{\lambda_2}\overset{\chi_\rho}{u}_{\lambda_1\mu\lambda_3\dots\lambda_\rho} + \dots + \partial_{\lambda_\rho}\overset{\chi_\rho}{u}_{\lambda_1\dots\lambda_{\rho-1}\mu}) = 0$$

$$(\rho = 1, \dots, \sigma;\ \chi_\rho = 1, \dots, N_\rho). \tag{6γ}$$

Hence the E_{n-K}-field determined by the solutions is X_{n-K}-forming. Now we choose the coordinate system in such a way that $\underset{K+1}{e}{}^\kappa, \dots, \underset{n}{e}{}^\kappa$ are solutions of (6β). Then the $\overset{\chi_\sigma}{u}_{\lambda_1\dots\lambda_\sigma}$ can be expressed in terms of $\overset{1}{e}_\lambda, \dots, \overset{K}{e}_\lambda$ and we will show that the coefficients in these expressions do not depend on $\xi^{K+1}, \dots, \xi^n$. The rotations of

$$\overset{\chi_1}{u}_\lambda = \overset{\chi_1}{u}_1\overset{1}{e}_\lambda + \dots + \overset{\chi_1}{u}_K\overset{K}{e}_\lambda \quad (\chi_1 = 1, \dots, N_1) \tag{6δ}$$

are

$$\overset{\bar{\chi}}{u}_1\,\bar{1} + \dots + \overset{\bar{\chi}}{u}_K\,\bar{K} \quad (\chi_1 = 1, \dots, N_1)$$

and we know that in this expression the $\overset{K+1}{e}_\lambda, \dots, \overset{n}{e}_\lambda$ do not occur. Hence the coefficients $\overset{\chi_1}{u}_1, \dots, \overset{\chi_1}{u}_K$ cannot depend on $\xi^{K+1}, \dots, \xi^n$. In the same way it is proved that all coefficients of the $\overset{\chi_\rho}{u}_{\lambda_1\dots\lambda_\rho}(\rho = 2, \dots, \sigma)$ depend only on $\xi^1, \dots, \xi^K$.

VIII.7. If $\underset{1}{v}{}^\kappa$ and $\underset{2}{v}{}^\kappa$ are solutions of the n' equations, it can be proved that $\underset{[1}{v}{}^\mu\partial_\mu\underset{2]}{v}{}^\kappa$ is a solution as well. In the proof the property of the Goursat system of being closed is used. Hence the $E_{n-n'}$-field determined by the solutions is $X_{n-n'}$-forming. Now we choose the coordinate system in such a way that $\underset{n'+1}{e}{}^\kappa, \dots, \underset{n}{e}{}^\kappa$ are solutions. Then the only not necessarily vanishing components of the $\overset{\chi_1}{u}_\lambda$ are $\overset{\chi_1}{u}_{\mathfrak{b}}$ ($\mathfrak{b} = 1, \dots, n'$). The $\overset{\chi_\tau}{u}_{\lambda_1\dots\lambda_\tau}(\tau = 1, \dots, \sigma)$ can be replaced by the quantities

$$\overset{\chi_\tau}{u}_{\lambda_1\dots\lambda_\tau} - \tau\overset{n}{e}_{[\lambda_1}\underset{|n|}{e}{}^\mu\overset{\chi_\tau}{u}_{|\mu|\lambda_2\dots\lambda_\tau]} \tag{7β}$$

whose transvections with $\underset{n}{e}^{\lambda_1}$ vanish. Continuing in this way we get at last an equivalent system whose quantities have only non-vanishing components with indices from 1 to n'. For the sake of simplicity we denote these quantities by $\overset{\chi_\tau}{u}_{\lambda_1\ldots\lambda_\tau}$ $(\tau = 1,\ldots,\sigma)$. We may suppose that the $\overset{\chi_\tau}{u}_{\lambda_1\ldots\lambda_\tau}$ are linearly independent for every value of τ.

Now we introduce instead of the $\overset{\chi_1}{u}_{\mathfrak{b}}$, quantities of the form

$$\overset{\chi_1}{v}_{\mathfrak{b}} = \overset{\chi_1}{\underset{\omega_1}{P}}\overset{\omega_1}{u}_{\mathfrak{b}} \quad (\mathfrak{b} = 1,\ldots,n';\ \chi_1,\omega_1 = 1,\ldots,N_1) \qquad (7\gamma)$$

and try to determine the $\overset{\chi_1}{\underset{\omega_1}{P}}$ in such a way that $\partial_{\mathfrak{y}}\overset{\chi_1}{v}_{\mathfrak{b}} = 0$ $(\mathfrak{y} = n'+1,\ldots,n)$. Necessary and sufficient conditions are

$$(\partial_{\mathfrak{y}}\overset{\chi_1}{\underset{\omega_1}{P}})\overset{\omega_1}{u}_{\mathfrak{b}} + \overset{\chi_1}{\underset{\omega_1}{P}}\partial_{\mathfrak{y}}\overset{\omega_1}{u}_{\mathfrak{b}} = 0 \quad (\mathfrak{b} = 1,\ldots,n';\ \mathfrak{y} = n'+1,\ldots,n;\ \chi_1,\omega_1 = 1,\ldots,N_1). \qquad (7\delta)$$

Since the system is closed, we know that equations of the form

$$\partial_{\mathfrak{y}}\overset{\omega_1}{u}_{\mathfrak{b}} = 2\partial_{[\mathfrak{y}}\overset{\omega_1}{u}_{\mathfrak{b}]} = 2\underset{\mathfrak{y}}{e}^{\mu}\partial_{[\mu}\overset{\omega_1}{u}_{\mathfrak{b}]} = 2\overset{\omega_1}{\underset{\theta_1}{Q}}_{[\mathfrak{y}}\overset{\theta_1}{u}_{\mathfrak{b}]} = \overset{\omega_1}{\underset{\theta_1}{Q}}_{\mathfrak{y}}\overset{\theta_1}{u}_{\mathfrak{b}}$$

$$(\mathfrak{b} = 1,\ldots,n';\ \mathfrak{y} = n'+1,\ldots,n;\ \omega_1,\theta_1 = 1,\ldots,N_1) \qquad (7\epsilon)$$

exist, because the $\overset{\chi_2}{u}_{\mu\lambda}$ only have non-vanishing components with indices from 1 to n'. Substituting this in (7δ) we get

$$\partial_{\mathfrak{y}}\overset{\chi_1}{\underset{\omega_1}{P}} + \overset{\chi_1}{\underset{\theta_1}{P}}\overset{\theta_1}{\underset{\omega_1}{Q}}_{\mathfrak{y}} = 0 \quad (\mathfrak{y} = n'+1,\ldots,n;\ \chi_1,\omega_1,\theta_1 = 1,\ldots,N_1). \qquad (7\zeta)$$

The conditions of integrability of this system are

$$-\overset{\chi_1}{\underset{\eta_1}{P}}\overset{\eta_1}{\underset{\theta_1}{Q}}_{[\mathfrak{x}}\overset{\theta_1}{\underset{\omega_1}{Q}}_{\mathfrak{y}]} + \overset{\chi_1}{\underset{\eta_1}{P}}\partial_{[\mathfrak{x}}\overset{\eta_1}{\underset{\omega_1}{Q}}_{\mathfrak{y}]} = 0 \quad (\mathfrak{x},\mathfrak{y} = n'+1,\ldots,n;\ \chi_1,\omega_1,\theta_1,\eta_1 = 1,\ldots,N_1). \qquad (7\eta)$$

Now from (7ϵ) we get

$$\partial_{[\mathfrak{x}}\overset{\eta_1}{\underset{\omega_1}{Q}}_{\mathfrak{y}]} + \overset{\eta_1}{\underset{\theta_1}{Q}}_{[\mathfrak{y}}\overset{\theta_1}{\underset{\omega_1}{Q}}_{\mathfrak{x}]} = 0 \quad (\mathfrak{x},\mathfrak{y} = n'+1,\ldots,n;\ \omega_1,\theta_1,\eta_1 = 1,\ldots,N_1). \qquad (7\theta)$$

Hence the conditions of integrability are satisfied.

Let us suppose now that the $\overset{\chi_1}{u}_{\mathfrak{b}},\ldots,\overset{\chi_{\tau-1}}{u}_{\mathfrak{b}_1\ldots\mathfrak{b}_{\tau-1}}$ are already replaced by the quantities $\overset{\chi_1}{v}_{\mathfrak{b}},\ldots,\overset{\chi_{\tau-1}}{v}_{\mathfrak{b}_1\ldots\mathfrak{b}_{\tau-1}}$ not depending on ξ^n. Then we try to replace the $\overset{\chi_\tau}{u}_{\mathfrak{b}\ldots\mathfrak{b}_\tau}$ by quantities of the form

$$\overset{\chi_\tau}{v}_{\mathfrak{b}_1\ldots\mathfrak{b}_\tau} = \overset{\chi_\tau}{\underset{\omega_\tau}{P}}\overset{\omega_\tau}{u}_{\mathfrak{b}_1\ldots\mathfrak{b}_\tau} + \overset{\chi_\tau}{\underset{\omega_{\tau-1}}{P}}_{[\mathfrak{b}_1}\overset{\omega_{\tau-1}}{v}_{\mathfrak{b}_2\ldots\mathfrak{b}_\tau]} + \cdots + \overset{\chi_\tau}{\underset{\omega_1}{P}}_{[\mathfrak{b}_1\ldots\mathfrak{b}_{\tau-1}}\overset{\omega_1}{v}_{\mathfrak{b}_\tau]}$$

$$(\mathfrak{b}_1,\ldots,\mathfrak{b}_\tau = 1,\ldots,n';\ \chi_\tau = 1,\ldots,N_\tau;\ \omega_\rho = 1,\ldots,N_\rho;\ \rho = 1,\ldots,\tau), \qquad (7\iota)$$

independent of the ξ^n. Necessary and sufficient conditions are

$$(\partial_n\overset{\chi_\tau}{\underset{\omega_\tau}{P}})\overset{\omega_\tau}{u}_{\mathfrak{b}_1\ldots\mathfrak{b}_\tau} + \overset{\chi_\tau}{\underset{\omega_\tau}{P}}\partial_n\overset{\omega_\tau}{u}_{\mathfrak{b}_1\ldots\mathfrak{b}_\tau} + (\partial_n\overset{\chi_\tau}{\underset{\omega_{\tau-1}}{P}}_{[\mathfrak{b}_1})\overset{\omega_{\tau-1}}{v}_{\mathfrak{b}_2\ldots\mathfrak{b}_\tau]} + \cdots + (\partial_n\overset{\chi_\tau}{\underset{\omega_1}{P}}_{[\mathfrak{b}_1\ldots\mathfrak{b}_{\tau-1}})\overset{\omega_1}{v}_{\mathfrak{b}_\tau]}$$

$$(\mathfrak{b}_1,\ldots,\mathfrak{b}_\tau = 1,\ldots,n';\ \chi_\tau = 1,\ldots,N_\tau;\ \omega_\rho = 1,\ldots,N_\rho;\ \rho = 1,\ldots,\tau). \qquad (7\kappa)$$

Since the system is closed, we know that equations of the form

$$\partial_n\overset{\omega_\tau}{u}_{\mathfrak{b}_1\ldots\mathfrak{b}_\tau} = (\tau+1)\underset{n}{e}^{\mu}\partial_{[\mu}\overset{\omega_\tau}{u}_{\mathfrak{b}_1\ldots\mathfrak{b}_\tau]} = \overset{\omega_\tau}{\underset{\theta_\tau}{Q}}\overset{\theta_\tau}{u}_{\mathfrak{b}_1\ldots\mathfrak{b}_\tau} + \overset{\omega_\tau}{\underset{\theta_{\tau-1}}{Q}}_{[\mathfrak{b}_1}\overset{\theta_{\tau-1}}{v}_{\mathfrak{b}_2\ldots\mathfrak{b}_\tau]} + \cdots + \overset{\omega_\tau}{\underset{\theta_1}{Q}}_{[\mathfrak{b}_1\ldots\mathfrak{b}_{\tau-1}}\overset{\theta_1}{v}_{\mathfrak{b}_\tau]}$$

$$(\mathfrak{b}_1,\ldots,\mathfrak{b}_\tau = 1,\ldots,n';\ \omega_\tau = 1,\ldots,N_\tau;\ \theta_\rho = 1,\ldots,N_\rho;\ \rho = 1,\ldots,\tau). \qquad (7\lambda)$$

exist. Substituting this in (7κ) we get

$$(\partial_n \overset{\chi_\tau}{\underset{\omega_\tau}{P}} + \overset{\chi_\tau\theta_\tau\omega_\tau}{\underset{\theta_\tau\omega_\tau}{PQ}}) u_{\mathfrak{b}_1\ldots\mathfrak{b}_\tau} + (\partial_n \overset{\chi_\tau}{\underset{\omega_{\tau-1}}{P}}{}_{[\mathfrak{b}_1} + \overset{\chi_\tau}{\underset{\theta_\tau}{P}}\, \overset{\theta_\tau}{\underset{\omega_{\tau-1}}{Q}}{}_{[\mathfrak{b}_1})\, \overset{\omega_{\tau-1}}{v}{}_{\mathfrak{b}_2\ldots\mathfrak{b}_\tau]} + \ldots + (\partial_n \overset{\chi_\tau}{\underset{\omega_1}{P}}{}_{[\mathfrak{b}_1\ldots\mathfrak{b}_{\tau-1}} + \overset{\chi_\tau\theta_\tau}{\underset{\theta_\tau\omega_1}{PQ}}{}_{[\mathfrak{b}_1\ldots\mathfrak{b}_{\tau-1}})\, \overset{\omega_1}{v}{}_{\mathfrak{b}_\tau]}$$

$$(\mathfrak{b}_1, \ldots, \mathfrak{b}_\tau = 1, \ldots, n'; \; \chi_\tau, \theta_\tau = 1, \ldots, N_\tau; \; \omega_\rho = 1, \ldots, N_\rho; \; \rho = 1, \ldots, \tau). \qquad (7\mu)$$

Hence we may choose for $\overset{\chi_\tau}{\underset{\omega_\tau}{P}}, \ldots, \overset{\chi_\tau}{\underset{\omega_1}{P}}{}_{\mathfrak{b}_1\ldots\mathfrak{b}_{\tau-1}}$ solutions of the differential equations

$$\begin{aligned} \partial_n \overset{\chi_\tau}{\underset{\omega_\tau}{P}} + \overset{\chi_\tau\theta_\tau}{\underset{\theta_\tau\omega_\tau}{PQ}} &= 0, \\ \partial_n \overset{\chi_\tau}{\underset{\omega_{\tau-1}}{P}}{}_{\mathfrak{b}_1} + \overset{\chi_\tau}{\underset{\theta_\tau}{P}}\, \overset{\theta_\tau}{\underset{\omega_{\tau-1}}{Q}}{}_{\mathfrak{b}_1} &= 0, \\ \cdot \quad \cdot \quad \cdot \quad \cdot \quad \cdot \quad \cdot \quad \cdot \quad \cdot \quad & \cdot \quad \cdot \\ \partial_n \overset{\chi_\tau}{\underset{\omega_1}{P}}{}_{\mathfrak{b}_1\ldots\mathfrak{b}_{\tau-1}} + \overset{\chi_\tau\theta_\tau}{\underset{\theta_\tau\omega_1}{PQ}}{}_{\mathfrak{b}_1\ldots\mathfrak{b}_{\tau-1}} &= 0 \end{aligned}$$

$$(\mathfrak{b}_1, \ldots, \mathfrak{b}_{\tau-1} = 1, \ldots, n'; \; \chi_\tau, \theta_\tau = 1, \ldots, N_\tau; \; \omega_\rho = 1, \ldots, N_\rho; \; \rho = 1, \ldots, \tau). \qquad (7\nu)$$

If we take the initial conditions

$$P^{\chi_\tau}_{\omega_\tau} = \delta^{\chi_\tau}_{\omega_\tau}, \quad P^{\chi_\tau}_{\omega_\rho} = 0 \quad (\rho = 1, \ldots, \tau - 1) \qquad (7o)$$

for $\xi^\kappa = \underset{0}{\xi^\kappa}$, the $\overset{\chi_\tau}{v}{}_{b_1\ldots b_\tau}$ are linearly independent. Continuing in this way we get a system whose quantities are independent of ξ^n. With the variables $\xi^{n'+1}, \ldots, \xi^{n-1}$ we can proceed in the same way.

IX.1. Consider the adjoint $'E_{m+d}$-field. In every point X^A there exists an integral-$'E_m$. Hence an $'E_m$-field of integral-$'E_m$'s can be formed. If the $'E_{m+d}$ is fixed by $n-m$ covariant vectors, the sections of the rotations of these vectors with $'E_m$ are zero. The $'E_m$ can be fixed by these $n-m$ vectors and d other vectors, whose sections with the $'E_m$ necessarily vanish. Now consider an $'E_q$ in $'E_m$. Then $H('E_q)$ can be fixed by qd covariant vectors. Consequently $q+1+r_{q+1} \geqslant m-qd$ or $r_{q+1} \geqslant m+d-(q+1)(1+d)$. From this it follows that $r_{q+1} \geqslant 0$ for $q+1 \leqslant (m+d)/(1+d)$ and that the genus of the $'E_m$-field is $\geqslant p$. Hence there exists an integral-$'X_p$ of the $'E_m$-field through every point X^A. This $'X_p$ corresponds to an integral-X_p of the induced $\mathfrak{S}^p_{d_p}$-field, tangent to an E_m of $\mathfrak{S}^m_d(\xi^\kappa)$.

IX.2. Since $\mathfrak{C}(\xi^\kappa)$ is not stationary, the rank of $T_{\bar{1}b}{}^{\cdot\cdot x}$ is $\geqslant 2$. Consequently the equations (cf. IX (4.17))

$$D_{cb}^{\cdot\cdot x} + Z^{\bar{1}}_{[c}\, T_{|\bar{1}|b]}^{\cdot\cdot x} = 0 \quad (b, c = 1, \ldots, \mathrm{m}; \; x = \mathrm{m}+1, \ldots, \mathrm{n}), \qquad (2\alpha)$$

expressing the preference of the $\mathfrak{S}^m_1$-field, possess at most one solution $Z^{\bar{1}}_c$. Hence for a preferred $\mathfrak{S}^m_1$-field with a non-stationary $\mathfrak{C}(\xi^\kappa)$ the quantities $Z^{\bar{1}}_c$ can be uniquely determined by (2α), and this means that in each point X^A of $'X_{n+1}$ the adjoint $'E_{m+1}$-field in $'X_{n+1}$ possesses a uniquely determined integral-$'E_m$ having no direction in common with the invariant $'E_1$. The integral-$'X_m$'s of the $'E_{m+1}$-field, having no direction in common with the invariant $'E_1$, are therefore also integral-$'X_m$'s of a uniquely determined $'E_m$-field in $'X_{n+1}$. Their number is therefore ∞^{n-m+1} if this $'E_m$-field is completely integrable and less in the other case.

IX.3. Consider the Cartan system in X_5

$$C^4_\lambda: \; \bar{3} - (\xi^1\xi^3 + \xi^5)\bar{2}; \qquad C^5_\lambda: \; \bar{4} - \xi^5\bar{1}; \qquad C_{\mu\lambda}^{\cdot\cdot 4}: \; \xi^1\overline{2}\,\overline{3} - \xi^3\overline{1}\,\overline{2} + \overline{2}\,\overline{5}; \qquad C_{\mu\lambda}^{\cdot\cdot 5}: \; \overline{1}\,\overline{5}. \qquad (3\alpha)$$

If u^κ and v^κ span an integral-E_2 we have

$$\begin{aligned}
&(a) \quad u^3-(\xi^1\xi^3+\xi^5)u^2 = 0, \quad \xi^5 u^1 - u^4 = 0,\\
&(b) \quad v^3-(\xi^1\xi^3+\xi^5)v^2 = 0, \quad \xi^5 v^1 - v^4 = 0,\\
&(c) \quad \xi^1(u^2v^3-u^3v^2)-\xi^3(u^1v^2-u^2v^1)+u^2v^5-u^5v^2 = 0,\\
&(d) \quad u^1v^5-u^5v^1 = 0.
\end{aligned} \tag{3β}$$

As a consequence of ($3\beta d$) the E_2 contains a vector whose first and fifth components vanish. Let this be v^κ. Hence $v^4 = 0$. Since the vector $v^\kappa \neq 0$ we may choose $v^2 = 1$, $v^3 = \xi^1\xi^3+\xi^5$. Since $v^2 \neq 0$ we may choose $u^2 = 0$. Hence $u^3 = 0$. Since the vector $u^\kappa \neq 0$ we may choose $u^1 = 1$, $u^4 = \xi^5$, $u^5 = -\xi^3$. From this it follows that there is at most one integral-E_2 in every point and that consequently the integral-E_2's form an $\mathfrak{S}_0^2$-field, i.e. an E_2-field. Because the vector

$$u^\mu \partial_\mu v^\kappa - v^\mu \partial_\mu u^\kappa = (\xi^1\xi^3+\xi^5)\underset{5}{e}^\kappa \tag{3γ}$$

is linearly independent of u^κ and v^κ the field is not completely integrable. In consequence of Theorem IX.4 it cannot be preferred.

BIBLIOGRAPHY

1814. 1. J. F. Pfaff, 'Methodus generalis, aequationes differentiarum partialium, nec non aequationes differentiales vulgares, utrasque primi ordinis, inter quotcunque variabiles, complete integrandi.' *Abh. kgl. Akad. d. Wiss. Berlin* (1814–15), 76–136.

1872. 1. A. Mayer, 'Ueber unbeschränkt integrabele Systeme von linearen totalen Differentialgleichungen, und die simultane Integration partieller Differentialgleichungen.' *Math. Ann.* **5** (1872), 448–70.

1874. 1. S. v. Kowalewski, *Zur Theorie der partiellen Differentialgleichungen* (Dissertation). Berlin.

1875. 1. S. Lie, 'Begründung einer Invariantentheorie der Berührungstransformationen.' *Math. Ann.* **8** (1875), 215–303.

1876. 1. S. Lie, 'Allgemeine Theorie der partiellen Differentialgleichungen erster Ordnung, I.' *Math. Ann.* **9** (1876), 245–96.

1877. 1. S. Lie, 'Allgemeine Theorie der partiellen Differentialgleichungen erster Ordnung, II.' *Math. Ann.* **11** (1877), 464–557.

1890. 1. S. Lie, *Theorie der Transformationsgruppen*, II. B. G. Teubner, Leipzig.

1890. 2. A. R. Forsyth, *Theory of Differential Equations*. Cambridge. German translation by H. Maser, Leipzig, 1893.

1893. 1. F. Klein, *Einleitung in die höhere Geometrie*, I. Göttingen.

1899. 1. E. Cartan, 'Sur certaines expressions différentielles et le problème de Pfaff.' *Ann. Éc. Norm. Sup.* (3) **16** (1899), 239–332.

1900. 1. E. v. Weber, *Vorlesungen über das Pfaffsche Problem.* B. G. Teubner, Leipzig.

1901. 1. E. Cartan, 'Sur l'intégration des systèmes aux différentielles totales.' *Ann. Éc. Norm. Sup.* (3) **18** (1901), 241–311.

1902. 1. K. Zorawski, 'Sur les propriétés d'une certaine intégrale multiple qui généralisent deux théorèmes de la théorie des tourbillons.' *Prace matematyczno-fizyczne*, **13** (1902), 107–63.

1904. 1. E. Cartan, 'Sur la structure des groupes infinis de transformations.' *Ann. Éc. Norm. Sup.* (3) **21** (1904), 153–216.

1908. 1. Th. de Donder, 'Sur le multiplicateur de Jacobi généralisé.' *Bull. Acad. Roy. Belg.* (1908), 795–811.

1910. 1. C. Riquier, *Les Systèmes d'équations aux dérivées partielles.* Paris, Gauthier Villars.

1915. 1. E. Goursat, *Cours d'analyse mathématique*, I. Paris, Gauthier Villars.

1917. 1. E. T. Whittaker, *A Treatise on Analytical Dynamics.* Cambridge University Press.

1918. 1. E. Goursat, *Cours d'analyse mathématique*, II. Paris, Gauthier Villars.

1921. 1. E. Goursat, *Leçons sur l'intégration des équations aux dérivées partielles du premier ordre.* Paris, Hermann.

1922. 1. E. Goursat, *Leçons sur le problème de Pfaff.* Paris, Hermann.

1922. 2. E. Cartan, *Leçons sur les invariants intégraux.* Paris, Hermann.

1924. 1. R. Courant and D. Hilbert, *Methoden der mathematischen Physik I.* Berlin, Springer.

1925. 1. J. W. Alexander, 'On the Decomposition of Tensors'. *Ann. of Math.* 227 (25/26), 421–3.

1927. 1. O. Veblen, *Invariants of Quadratic Differential Forms*. Cambridge Tracts No. 24. Cambridge University Press.

1927. 2. Th. de Donder, *Théorie des invariants intégraux*. Paris, Gauthier Villars.

1928. 1. L. H. Rice, 'Couche Ranks in the General Matrix.' *Journ. of Math. and Phys. Mass.* **7** (1928), 93–6.

1928. 2. E. Grynaeus, 'Sur les systèmes de Pfaff.' *Bull. Soc. Math. de France*, **56** (1928), 74–97.

1929. 1. M. Janet, *Leçons sur les systèmes d'équations aux dérivées partielles*. Paris, Gauthier Villars.

1929. 2. J. M. Thomas, 'Riquier's Existence Theorem.' *Ann. of Math.* **30** (1929), 285–310.

1930. 1. J. A. Schouten and E. R. v. Kampen, 'Zur Einbettungs- und Krümmungstheorie nichtholonomer Gebilde.' *Math. Zeitschr.* **103** (1930), 752–83.

1931. 1. W. Slebodzinski, 'Sur les équations de Hamilton.' *Bull. Acad. Roy. de Belg.* (5) **17** (1931), 864–70.

1931. 2. J. M. Thomas, 'Matrices of Integers ordering Derivatives.' *Trans. Amer. Math. Soc.* **33** (1931), 398–410.

1932. 1. F. Engel and K. Faber, *Die Lie'sche Theorie der partiellen Differentialgleichungen erster Ordnung*. B. G. Teubner, Leipzig.

1932. 2. O. Veblen and J. H. C. Whitehead, *The Foundations of Differential Geometry*. Cambridge Tracts No. 29. Cambridge University Press.

1933. 1. L. P. Eisenhart. *Continuous Groups of Transformations*. Princeton University Press.

1933. 2. J. A. Schouten and E. R. v. Kampen, 'Beiträge zur Theorie der Deformation.' *Abh. Math. Phys. Warschau*, **41** (1933), 1–19.

1933. 3. J. M. Thomas, 'Pfaffian Systems of Species One.' *Trans. Amer. Math. Soc.* **35** (1933), 356–71.

1933. 4. J. M. Thomas, 'A Lower Limit for the Species of a Pfaffian System.' *Proc. Nat. Ac. of Sc.* **19** (1933), 913–14.

1933. 5. J. M. Thomas, 'Regular Differential Systems of the First Order.' *Proc. Nat. Ac. of Sc.* **69** (1933), 451–3.

1934. 1. E. Kähler, *Einführung in die Theorie der Systeme von Differentialgleichungen*. B. G. Teubner, Leipzig.

1934. 2. H. Behnke and P. Thullen, 'Theorie der Funktionen von mehreren komplexen Veränderlichen.' *Erg. d. Math. u. i. Grenzgeb.* iii. 3. Berlin, Springer.

1934. 3. J. M. Thomas, 'Riquier's Existence Theorem.' *Ann. of Math.* **35** (1934), 306–11.

1934. 4. J. M. Thomas, 'An Existence Theorem for Generalized Pfaffian Systems.' *Bull. Amer. Math. Soc.* **40** (1934), 309–15.

1935. 1. J. A. Schouten and D. J. Struik, *Einführung in die neueren Methoden der Differentialgeometrie*. Groningen, Noordhoff.

1935. 2. J. A. Schouten and D. v. Dantzig, 'Was ist Geometrie?' *Abh. Semin. f. Vektor- und Tensoranalysis, Moskau* (1935), 16–48.

1935. 3. C. Burstin, 'Beiträge zum Problem von Pfaff und zur Theorie der Pfaffschen Aggregate.' *Rec. Math. Moscou*, **41** (1935), 582–618.

1936. 1. J. A. Schouten and J. Haantjes, 'On the Theory of the Geometric Object.' *Proc. Lond. Math. Soc.* (2) **42** (1937), 356–76.

1937. 1. J. van Weyssenhoff, 'Duale Grössen, Grossrotation, Grossdivergenz und die Stokes-Gaussischen Sätze in allgemeinen Räumen.' *Ann. Soc. Pol. de Math.* **16** (1937), 127–44.

1937. 2, 3, 4. J. A. Schouten, 'Zur Differentialgeometrie der Gruppe der Berührungstransformationen I, II, III.' *Proc. Kon. Akad. v. Wet. Amsterdam,* **40** (1937), 100–7, 236–45, 470–9.

1937. 5. J. M. Thomas, *Differential Systems.* Amer. Math. Soc. Publ., vol. xxi.

1938. 1. J. A. Schouten, 'Ueber die geometrische Deutung von gewöhnlichen p-Vektoren und W-p-Vektoren und den korrespondierenden Dichten.' *Proc. Kon. Akad. v. Wet. Amsterdam,* **41** (1938), 709–16.

1938. 2. J. A. Schouten, 'Über die Beziehungen zwischen den geometrischen Grössen in einer X_n und in einer in der X_n eingebetteten X_m.' *Proc. Kon. Akad. v. Wet. Amsterdam,* **41** (1938), 568–75.

1938. 3. J. A. Schouten, 'Zur Differentialgeometrie der Gruppe der Berührungstransformationen IV.' *Proc. Kon. Akad. v. Wet. Amsterdam,* **41** (1938), 576–84.

1940. 1. J. A. Schouten and D. v. Dantzig, 'On Ordinary Quantities and W-quantities.' *Comp. Mathem.* **7** (1940), 447–74.

1940. 2, 3, 4, 5. J. A. Schouten and W. v. d. Kulk, 'Beiträge zur Theorie der Systeme Pfaffscher Gleichungen I, II, III, IV.' *Proc. Kon. Akad. v. Wet. Amsterdam,* **43** (1940), 19–31, 179–88, 453–62, 674–86.

1941. 1. W. v. d. Kulk, *Eine Verallgemeinerung eines Theorems aus der Theorie der Pfaffschen Gleichungen für den einfachsten Fall* $m = 2$.

1942. 1. J. A. Schouten and W. v. d. Kulk, 'Beiträge zur Theorie der Systeme Pfaffscher Gleichungen V.' *Proc. Kon. Akad. v. Wet. Amsterdam,* **45** (1942), 624–9.

1942. 2. W. v. d. Kulk, 'Zur Theorie der verallgemeinerten Pfaffschen Gleichungen.' *Proc. Kon. Akad. v. Wet. Amsterdam,* **45** (1942), 26–31.

1943. 1, 2, 3, 4, 5, 6. J. A. Schouten and W. v. d. Kulk, 'Bijdragen tot de theorie der systemen van Pfaffsche vergelijkingen VI–XI.' *Versl. Kon. Akad. v. Wet. Amsterdam,* **52** (1943), 17–22, 138–45, 197–200, 415–20, 571–4, 646–53.

1943. 7. W. v. d. Kulk, 'Bijdragen tot de theorie van het $\mathfrak{S}_a^m$-veld.' *Versl. Kon. Akad. v. Wet. Amsterdam,* **52** (1943), 575–83.

1943. 8. W. v. d. Kulk, 'Bijdrage tot de theorie van het $\mathfrak{S}_a^m$-veld.' *Versl. Kon. Akad. v. Wet. Amsterdam,* **52** (1943), 662–8.

1945. 1. W. v. d. Kulk, *The Theory of Integrability of* $\mathfrak{S}_a^m$*-fields.* Dissertation Leiden.

1946. 1. E. Cartan, *Les Systèmes différentiels extérieurs et leurs applications géométriques.* Exposés de géométrie XIV. Paris, Hermann.

INDEX

CHELSEA

SCIENTIFIC

BOOKS

GEOMETRY AND THE IMAGINATION

By D. HILBERT and S. COHN-VOSSEN

Translated from the German by P. NEMENYI.

"A fascinating tour of the 20th century mathematical zoo. . . . Anyone who would like to see proof of the fact that a sphere with a hole can always be bent (no matter how small the hole), learn the theorems about Klein's bottle—a bottle with no edges, no inside, and no outside—and meet other strange creatures of modern geometry will be delighted with Hilbert and Cohn-Vossen's book."
—*Scientific American.*

"Should provided stimulus and inspiration to every student and teacher of geometry."—*Nature.*

"A mathematical classic. . . . The purpose is to make the reader *see* and *feel* the proofs. . . . readers can penetrate into higher mathematics with . . . pleasure instead of the usual laborious study."
—*American Scientist.*

"Students, particularly, would benefit very much by reading this book . . . they will experience the sensation of being taken into the friendly confidence of a great mathematician and being shown the real significance of things."—*Science Progress.*

"A person with a minimum of formal training can follow the reasoning. . . . an important [book]."
—*The Mathematics Teacher.*

—1952. 358 pp. 6x9. 8284-0087-3. **$7.50**

GESAMMELTE ABHANDLUNGEN (Collected Papers)

By D. HILBERT

Volume I (Number Theory) contains Hilbert's papers on Number Theory, including his long paper on Algebraic Numbers. Volume II (Algebra, Invariant Theory, Geometry) covers not only the topics indicated in the sub-title but also papers on Diophantine Equations. Volume III carries the sub-title: Analysis, Foundation of Mathematics, Physics, and Miscellaneous Papers.

—1932/33/35-66. 1,457 pp. 6x9. 8284-0195-0.

Three vol. set. **$27.50**

PRINCIPLES OF MATHEMATICAL LOGIC

By D. HILBERT and W. ACKERMANN

"As a text the book has become a classic . . . the best introduction for the student who seriously wants to master the technique. Some of the features which give it this status are as follows:

"The first feature is its extraordinary lucidity. A second is the intuitive approach, with the introduction of formalization only after a full discussion of motivation. Again, the argument is rigorous and exact . . . A fourth feature is the emphasis on general extra-formal principles . . . Finally, the work is relatively free from bias . . . All together, the book still bears the stamp of the genius of one of the great mathematicians of modern times."—*Bulletin of the A.M.S.*

—1959. xii + 172 pp. 6x9. 8284-0069-5. **$3.95**

SQUARING THE CIRCLE, and other Monographs

By HOBSON, HUDSON, SINGH, and KEMPE

FOUR VOLUMES IN ONE.

SQUARING THE CIRCLE, by *Hobson.* A fascinating account of one of the three famous problems of antiquity, its significance, its history, the mathematical work it inspired in modern times, and its eventual solution in the closing years of the last century.

RULER AND COMPASSES, by *Hudson.* "An analytical and geometrical investigation of how far Euclidean constructions can take us. It is as thoroughgoing as it is constructive."—*Sci. Monthly.*

THE THEORY AND CONSTRUCTION OF NON-DIFFERENTIABLE FUNCTIONS, by *Singh.* I. Functions Defined by Series. II. Functions Defined Geometrically. III. Functions Defined Arithmetically. IV. Properties of Non-Differentiable Functions.

HOW TO DRAW A STRAIGHT LINE, by *Kempe.* An intriguing monograph on linkages. Describes, among other things, a linkage that will trisect any angle.

"Intriguing, meaty."—*Scientific American.*

—388 pp. 4½x7½. 8284-0095-4. Four vols. in one. **$4.95**

SPHERICAL AND ELLIPSOIDAL HARMONICS

By E. W. HOBSON

"A comprehensive treatise . . . and the standard reference in its field."—*Bulletin of the A. M. S.*

—1931-65. xi + 500 pp. 5⅜x8. 8284-0104-7. **$7.50**

ELASTOKINETIK: Die Methoden zur Angenäherten Lösung von Eigenwertproblemen in der Elastokinetik

By K. HOHENEMSER

—(Erg. der Math.) 1932-49. 89 pp. 5½x8½. 8284-0055-5. **$2.75**

ERGODENTHEORIE, *by E. HOPF.* *See* BEHNKE

RULER AND COMPASSES, *by H. P. HUDSON.* See HOBSON

PHYSIKALISCH-MATHEMATISCHE MONOGRAPHIEN

By W. v. IGNATOWSKY, et al.

THREE VOLUMES IN ONE.

Of the many well-known monographs in the series published by the Steklov Institute of the Academy of Sciences of the U.S.S.R., only a few were originally published in a language other than Russian. Two of the French-language works have been reprinted and are listed elsewhere in this catalogue: Gunther's book on *Stieltjes Integrals* and Lappo-Danilevski's three-volume work on *Systems of Differential Equations.*

CONTENTS: 1. *Untersuchungen einiger Integrale mit Besselschen Funktionen und ihre Anwendung auf Beugungserscheinungen,* by Ignatowsky. 2. *Kreisscheibenkondensator,* by Ignatowsky. 3. *Table of a Special Function,* by Bursian and Fock.

—1932-66. 16 + 232 pp. 6¼x9¼. 8284-0201-9. Three vols. in one. **$5.50**

GESAMMELTE WERKE

By C. G. J. JACOBI

The collected mathematical works of the celebrated mathematician. [Volume 8 of the collected works is Jacobi's *Vorlesungen über Dynamik*, also available as a separate volume (see below).]

—1881/1891-1968. 4,032 pp. 6½x9¼. Eight vol. set.

VORLESUNGEN UEBER DYNAMIK

By C. G. J. JACOBI

—1884-67. viii+300 pp. 6½x9¼. **In prep.**

A TREATISE ON THE LINE COMPLEX

By C. M. JESSOP

"The best introduction to the subject."—*Virgil Snyder.*

—1903-68. xv + 364 pp. 5⅜x8. 8284-0223-X. **Prob. $7.95**

THE CALCULUS OF FINITE DIFFERENCES

By CHARLES JORDAN

"... destined to remain the classic treatment of the subject . . . for many years to come."—*Harry C. Carver, Founder and formerly Editor of the* ANNALS OF MATHEMATICAL STATISTICS.

—3rd ed. 1965. xxi + 655 pp. 5⅜x8. 8284-0033-4. **$7.50**

THEORIE DER ORTHOGONALREIHEN

By S. KACZMARZ and H. STEINHAUS

The theory of general orthogonal functions. *Monografje Matematyczne*, Vol. VI.

—1935-51. viii + 294 pp. 6x9. 8284-0083-0. **$4.95**

KAHLER, "System von . . . ," see Blaschke

DIFFERENTIALGLEICHUNGEN: LOESUNGSMETHODEN UND LOESUNGEN

By E. KAMKE

Everything possible that can be of use when one has a given differential equation to solve, or when one wishes to investigate that solution thoroughly.

PART A: General Methods of Solution and the Properties of the Solutions.

PART B: Boundary and Characteristic Value Problems.

PART C: Dictionary of some 1600 Equations in Lexicographical Order, with solution, techniques for solving, and references.

"A reference work of outstanding importance which should be in every mathematical library." —*Mathematical Gazette.*

—3rd ed. 1944. 692 pp. 6x9. 8284-0044-X.

DIFFERENTIALGLEICHUNGEN, *by KAEHLER.* See BLASCHKE

HOW TO DRAW A STRAIGHT LINE, *by KEMPE.* See HOBSON

ASYMPTOTISCHE GESETZE DER WAHRSCHEINLICHKEITSRECHNUNG

By A. A. KHINTCHINE

—1933-48. 82 pp. 5½x8½. 8284-0036-9. Paper **$2.00**

WERKE

By L. KRONECKER

Will be issued in five volumes; Volume III, originally published in two parts, will be issued as a single volume.

—6 vols. in 5. 1895/97/99/1929/30/31-68. 2,530 pp. 6½x8½.
Five vol. set. **Prob. $59.50**

GROUP THEORY

By A. KUROSH

Translated from the second Russian edition and with added notes by PROFESSOR K. A. HIRSCH.

Partial Contents: PART ONE: The Elements of Group Theory. Chap. I. Definition. II. Subgroups (Systems, Cyclic Groups, Ascending Sequences of Groups). III. Normal Subgroups. IV. Endomorphisms and Automorphisms. Groups with Operators. V. Series of Subgroups. Direct Products. Defining Relations, etc. PART TWO: Abelian Groups. VI. Foundations of the Theory of Abelian Groups (Finite Abelian Groups, Rings of Endomorphisms, Abelian Groups with Operators). VII. Primary and Mixed Abelian Groups. VIII. Torsion-Free Abelian Groups. Editor's Notes. Bibliography.

Vol. II. PART THREE: Group-Theoretical Constructions. IX. Free Products and Free Groups (Free Products with Amalgamated Subgroup, Fully Invariant Subgroups). X. Finitely Generated Groups. XI. Direct Products. Lattices (Modular, Complete Modular, etc.). XII. Extensions of Groups (of Abelian Groups, of Non-commutative Groups, Cohomology Groups). PART FOUR: Solvable and Nilpotent Groups. XIII. Finiteness Conditions, Sylow Subgroups, etc. XIV. Solvable Groups (Solvable and Generalized Solvable Groups, Local Theorems). XV. Nilpotent Groups (Generalized, Complete, Locally Nilpotent Torsion-Free, etc.). Editor's Notes. Bibliography.

—Vol. I. 2nd ed. 1959. 271 pp. 6x9. 8284-0107-1. **$6.00**
—Vol. II. 2nd ed. 1960. 308 pp. 6x9. 8284-0109-8. **$6.00**
—Vol. III. Approx. 200 pp. 6x9. **In prep.**

LECTURES ON GENERAL ALGEBRA

By A. G. KUROSH

Translated from the Russian by PROFESSOR K. A. HIRSCH, with a special preface for this edition by PROFESSOR KUROSH.

Partial Contents: CHAP. I. Relations. II. Groups and Rings (Groupoids, Semigroups, Groups, Rings, Fields, . . . , Gaussian rings, Dedekind rings). III. Universal Algebras. Groups with Multioperators (. . . Free universal algebras, Free products of groups). IV. Lattices (Complete lattices, Modular lattice, Schmidt-Ore Theorem, . . . , Distributive lattices). V. Operator Groups and Rings. Modules. Linear Algebras (. . . Free modules, Vector spaces over fields, Rings of linear transformations, . . . , Derivations, Differential rings). VI. Ordered and Topological Groups and Rings. Rings with a Valuation. BIBLIOGRAPHY.

—1965. 335 pp. 6x9. 8284-0168-3. **$6.95**

DIFFERENTIAL AND INTEGRAL CALCULUS,

By E. LANDAU

A masterpiece of rigor and clarity.

"And what a book it is! The marks of Landau's thoroughness and elegance, and of his undoubted authority, impress themselves on the reader at every turn, from the opening of the preface . . . to the closing of the final chapter.

"It is a book that all analysts . . . should possess . . . to see how a master of his craft like Landau presented the calculus when he was at the height of his power and reputation."

—*Mathematical Gazette.*

—3rd ed. 1965. 372 pp. 6x9. 8284-0078-4. **$6.95**

HANDBUCH DER LEHRE VON DER VERTEILUNG DER PRIMZAHLEN

By E. LANDAU

TWO VOLUMES IN ONE.

To Landau's monumental work on prime-number theory there has been added, in this edition, two of Landau's papers and an up-to-date guide to the work: an Appendix by Prof. Paul T. Bateman.

—2nd ed. 1953. 1,028 pp. 5⅜x8. 8284-0096-2.
Two vols. in one. **$16.50**

VORLESUNGEN UEBER ZAHLENTHEORIE

By E. LANDAU

The various sections of this important work (Additive, Analytic, Geometric, and Algebraic Number Theory) can be read independently of one another.

—Vol. I, Pt. 2. *(Additive Number Theory) xii + 180 pp. Vol. II. (Analytical Number Theory and Geometrical Number Theory) viii + 308 pp. Vol. III. (Algebraic Number Theory and Fermat's Last Theorem) viii + 341 pp. 5¼x8¼. *(Vol. I, Pt. 1 is issued as **Elementare Zahlentheorie** (in German) or as **Elementary Number Theory** (in English).) 8284-0032-6.

Three vols. in one. **$16.50**

GRUNDLAGEN DER ANALYSIS

By E. LANDAU

The student who wishes to study mathematical German will find Landau's famous *Grundlagen der Analysis* ideally suited to his needs.

Only a few score of German words will enable him to read the entire book with only an occasional glance at the Vocabulary! [A COMPLETE German-English vocabulary, prepared with the novice especially in mind, has been appended to the book.]

—4th ed. 1965. 173 pp. 5½x8½. 8284-0024-5. Cloth **$3.95**
8284-0141-1. Paper **$1.95**

FOUNDATIONS OF ANALYSIS

By E. LANDAU

"Certainly no clearer treatment of the foundations of the number system can be offered. . . . One can only be thankful to the author for this fundamental piece of exposition, which is alive with his vitality and genius."—***J. F. Ritt, Amer. Math. Monthly.***

—2nd ed. 1960. xiv + 136 pp. 6x9. 8284-0079-2. **$3.95**

Mémoires sur la Théorie des SYSTÈMES DES ÉQUATIONS DIFFÉRENTIELLES LINÉAIRES, Vols. I, II, III

By J. A. LAPPO-DANILEVSKIĬ

THREE VOLUMES IN ONE.

A reprint, in one volume, of Volumes 6, 7, and 8 of the monographs of the Steklov Institute of Mathematics in Moscow.

"The theory of [systems of linear differential equations] is treated with elegance and generality by the author, and his contributions constitute an important addition to the field of differential equations."—*Applied Mechanics Reviews.*

—1934/5/6-53. 689 pp. 5⅜x8. 8284-0094-6.
Three vols. in one. **$12.50**

TOPOLOGY

By S. LEFSCHETZ

CONTENTS: I. Elementary Combinatorial Theory of Complexes. II. Topological Invariance of Homology Characters. III. Manifolds and their Duality Theorems. IV. Intersections of Chains on a Manifold. V. Product Complexes. VI. Transformations of Manifolds, their Coincidences, Fixed Points. VII. Infinite Complexes. VIII. Applications to Analytical and Algebraic Varieties.

—2nd ed. 1930-66. 410 pp. 5⅜x8. 8284-0116-0. **$6.00**

ELEMENTS OF ALGEBRA

By HOWARD LEVI

"This book is addressed to beginning students of mathematics. . . . The level of the book, however, is so unusually high, mathematically as well as pedagogically, that it merits the attention of professional mathematicians (as well as of professional pedagogues) interested in the wider dissemination of their subject among cultured people . . . **a closer approximation to the right way to teach mathematics to beginners than anything else now in existence."**—*Bulletin of the A. M. S.*

—4th ed. 1962. 189 pp. 5⅜x8. 8284-0103-9. **$3.95**

VORLESUNGEN UEBER DIFFERENTIALGLEICHUNGEN MIT BEKANNTEN INFINITESIMALEN TRANSFORMATIONEN

By S. LIE

Edited by G. Scheffers. A textbook on the integration of ordinary and partial differential equations in which the Lie theory for solving such equations is expounded.

—1891-1967. xiv + 568 pp. 6x9. 8284-0206-X. **$12.50**

THEORIE DER TRANSFORMATIONSGRUPPEN

By S. LIE

—Reprint of 1st ed. 1888; 1890; 1893. Three vol. set. **Tent.**

THE DEVELOPMENT OF MATHEMATICS IN CHINA AND JAPAN

By Y. MIKAMI

"Filled with valuable information. Mikami's [account of the mathematicians he knew personally] is an attractive features."

—*Scientific American.*

—1913-62. x + 347 pp. 5⅜x8. 8284-0149-7. **$4.95**

GESAMMELTE ABHANDLUNGEN

By H. MINKOWSKI

TWO VOLUMES IN ONE.

Minkowski's Collected Works are issued under the editorship of David Hilbert, with the assistance of Andreas Speiser and Hermann Weyl.

—1911-67. 871 pp. 6x9. 8284-0208-6. Two vols. in one. **$17.50**

GEOMETRIE DER ZAHLEN

By H. MINKOWSKI

—1896-53. viii + 256 pp. 5⅜x8. 8284-0093-8. **$4.95**

DIOPHANTISCHE APPROXIMATIONEN

By H. MINKOWSKI

—1907-57. viii + 235 pp. 5⅜x8. 8284-0118-7. **$4.95**

FERMAT'S LAST THEOREM, *by L. J. MORDELL.* See KLEIN

INVERSIVE GEOMETRY

By F. MORLEY and F. V. MORLEY

—1937-54. xi + 273 pp. 5⅜x8. 8284-0101-2. **$3.95**

INTRODUCTION TO NUMBER THEORY

By T. NAGELL

A special feature of Nagell's well-known text is the rather extensive treatment of Diophantine equations of second and higher degree. A large number of non-routine problems are given.

—2nd ed. 1964. 309 pp. 5⅜x8. 8284-0163-2. **$5.50**

LEHRBUCH DER KOMBINATORIK

By E. NETTO

A standard work on the fascinating subject of Combinatory Analysis.

—2nd ed. 1927-58. viii + 348 pp. 5⅜x8. 8284-0123-3. **$6.00**

THE THEORY OF SUBSTITUTIONS

By E. NETTO

—2nd ed. (C.r. of 1st ed.) 1964. 304 pp. 5⅜x8. 8284-0165-9. **$4.95**

EIGHT-PLACE TABLES OF TRIGONOMETRIC FUNCTIONS

By J. PETERS

Eight-place tables of natural trigonometric functions for every second of arc, with an appendix on the computation to twenty decimal places.

MAIN TABLE: The values of sine, cosine, tangent, and cotangent are given to 8 decimal places for every second of arc, from 0°0′0″ to 90°0′0″. For example, it can be read off directly from the table (without interpolation) that the value of Cos 89°19′33″ is 0.11622293.

TABLE II (*Supplementary Table*): 21-Place Tables of Sine and Cosine for every 10′ from 0°0′ to 90°0′.

TABLE III (*Supplementary Table*): 21-Place Tables of Sine and Cosine and their Differences, for every second from 0′0″ to 10′0″.

Several other supplementary tables are given.

"Peters' table is considered to be the standard (i.e., the best) 8-place trigonometric table."

—*Mathematics of Computation*

—1968. xii + 956 pp. 8x11. 8284-0174-8.
Regular edition **$22.00**
8284-0185-3. Thumb-indexed **$25.00**

METHODS FOR GEOMETRICAL CONSTRUCTION, *by J. PETERSEN*. See BALL

IRRATIONALZAHLEN

By O. PERRON

—2nd ed. 1939-51. 207 pp. 5⅜x8. 8284-0047-4. Cloth **$3.75**
8284-0113-6. Paper **$1.50**

DIE LEHRE VON DEN KETTENBRUECHEN

By O. PERRON

Both the Arithmetic Theory and the Analytic Theory are treated fully.

"An indispensable work . . . Perron remains the best guide for the novice. The style is simple and precise and presents no difficulties."

—*Mathematical Gazette.*

—2nd ed. 1929-50. xii + 524 pp. 5⅜x8. 8284-0073-3. **$6.95**

THÉORIE DES FONCTIONS ALGÉBRIQUES DE DEUX VARIABLES INDÉPENDANTES

By E. PICARD and G. SIMART

TWO VOLUMES IN ONE.

—1897/1906-69. 796 pp. Two vols. in one. **In prep.**

SUBHARMONIC FUNCTIONS

By T. RADO

TWO VOLUMES IN ONE: *Subharmonic Functions* and *The Problem of Plateau*, both by Tibor Rado.

—1937/33-70. 172 pp. 5½x8½. Two vols. in one. **In prep.**

COLLECTED PAPERS

By S. RAMANUJAN

Ramanujan's papers on Number Theory are edited by G. H. Hardy, P. V. Seshu Aiyar, and B. M. Wilson.

—1927-63. xxxvi + 355 pp. 6x9. 8284-0159-4. **$6.95**

RAMANUJAN, *by G. H. HARDY. See* HARDY

EINFUEHRUNG IN DIE KOMBINATORISCHE TOPOLOGIE

By K. REIDEMEISTER

—1932-50. 221 pp. 5½x8¼. 8284-0076-8. **$3.95**

KNOTENTHEORIE

By K. REIDEMEISTER

—1932-48. 78 pp. 5½x8½. 8284-0040-7. **$2.25**

ON THE HYPOTHESES . . . , *by B. RIEMANN.*
See CLIFFORD. *See also* WEYL

FOURIER SERIES

By W. ROGOSINSKI

Translated by H. COHN. Designed for beginners with no more background than a year of calculus, this text covers, nevertheless, an amazing amount of ground. It is suitable for self-study courses as well as classroom use.

"The field covered is extensive and the treatment is thoroughly modern in outlook . . . An admirable guide to the theory."—*Mathematical Gazette.*

—2nd ed. 1959. vi + 176 pp. 4½x6½. 8284-0067-9.
Cloth **$3.00**
8284-0178-0. Paper **$1.39**

ANALYTIC GEOMETRY OF THREE DIMENSIONS

By G. SALMON

A rich and detailed treatment by the author of *Conic Sections, Higher Plane Curves,* etc.

Partial Contents: Chap. I. Coordinates. III. Plane and Line. IV-VI. Quadrics. VIII. Foci and Focal Surfaces. IX. Invariants and Covariants of Systems of Quadrics. XI. General Theory of Surfaces. XII. Curves and Developables (Projective properties, non-projective properties, . . .).

Vol. II. Chap. XIII. Partial Differential Equations of Families of Surfaces. XIII (a). Complexes, Congruences, Ruled Surfaces. XIII (b). Triply Orthogonal Systems of Surfaces, Normal Congruences of Curves. XIV. The Wave Surface, The Centro-surface, etc. XV. Surfaces of Third Degree. XVI. Surfaces of Fourth Degree. XVII. General Theory of Surfaces. XVIII. Reciprocal Surfaces.

—Vol. I. 7th ed. 1927-58. xxiv + 470 pp. 5x8.
8284-0122-5. **$4.95**

—Vol. II. 5th ed. 1928-65. xvi + 334 pp. 5x8. 8284-0196-9.
$4.95

CHAPTER HEADINGS: I. n-Dimensional Projective Space. II. General Projective Coordinates. III. Hyperplane Coordinates. The Duality Principle. IV. The Cross Ratio. V. Projectivities. VI. Linear Projectivities of P_n onto Itself. VII. Correlations. VIII. Hypersurfaces of the Second Order. IX. Projective Classification of Hypersurfaces of the Second Order. X. Projective Properties of Hypersurfaces of the Second Order. XI. The Affine Classification of Hypersurfaces of the Second Order. XII. The Metric Classification of Hypersurfaces of the Second Order.

—1961. 208 pp. 6x9. 8284-0126-8. **$4.95**

VORLESUNGEN UEBER DIE ALGEBRA DER LOGIK

By E. SCHRÖDER

One of the classics of logic.

The present edition includes, as an addendum to the third volume, the complete text of the short two-volume work *Abriss der Algebra der Logik.*

—2nd ed. 1966. (1st ed.: 1890-1905; 1909/10.) 2,192 pp. 6x9. 5 vols. in 3. 8284-0171-3. Three vol. set. **$35.00**

AN INTRODUCTION TO THE OPERATIONS WITH SERIES

By I. J. SCHWATT

Many useful methods for operations on series, methods for expansions of functions, methods for the summation of many types of series, and a wealth of explicit results are contained in this book. The only prerequisite is knowledge of the Calculus.

—1924-62. x + 287 pp. 5⅜x8. 8284-0158-6. **$4.95**

PROJECTIVE METHODS IN PLANE ANALYTICAL GEOMETRY

By C. A. SCOTT

The original title of the present work, as it appeared in the first and second editions, was "An Introductory Account of Certain Modern Ideas and Methods in Plane Analytic Geometry." The title has been changed to the present more concise and more descriptive form, and the corrections indicated in the second edition have been incorporated into the text.

CHAPTER HEADINGS: I. Point and Line Coordinates. II. Infinity. Transformation of Coordinates. III. Figures Determined by Four Elements. IV. The Principle of Duality. V. Descriptive Properties of Curves. VI. Metric Properties of Curves; Line at Infinity. VII. Metric Properties of Curves; Circular Points. VIII. Unicursal (Rational) Curves. Tracing of Curves. IX. Cross-Ratio, Homography, and Involution. X. Projection and Linear Transformation. XI. Theory of Correspondence. XII. The Absolute. XIII. Invariants and Covariants.

—3rd ed. 1923-61. xii + 290 pp. 5⅜x8. 8284-0146-2. **$3.95**

LEHRBUCH DER TOPOLOGIE

By H. SEIFERT and W. THRELFALL

This famous book is a modern work on *combinatorial topology* addressed to the student as well as to the specialist. It is almost indispensable to the mathematician who wishes to gain a knowledge of this important field.

"The exposition proceeds by easy stages **with examples and illustrations at every turn.**"

—*Bulletin of the A. M. S.*

—1934-68. vii + 353 pp. 5⅜x8. 8284-0031-8. **$6.00**

TEXTBOOK OF TOPOLOGY

By H. SEIFERT and W. THRELFALL

A translation of the above.

—Approx. 380 pp. 6x9. **In prep.**

FROM DETERMINANT TO TENSOR,
by W. F. SHEPPARD. See KLEIN

HYPOTHESE DU CONTINU

By W. SIERPIŃSKI

An appendix consisting of sixteen research papers now brings this important work up to date. This represents an increase of more than forty percent in the number of pages.

"One sees how deeply this postulate cuts through all phases of the foundations of mathematics, how intimately many fundamental questions of analysis and geometry are connected with it . . . a most excellent addition to our mathematical literature."

—*Bulletin of A. M. S.*

—2nd ed. 1957. xvii + 274 pp. 5⅜x8. 8284-0117-9. **$4.95**

CONGRUENCE OF SETS, and other monographs

By SIERPIŃSKI, KLEIN, RUNGE, and DICKSON

FOUR VOLUMES IN ONE.

ON THE CONGRUENCE OF SETS AND THEIR EQUIVALENCE BY FINITE DECOMPOSITION, by *W. Sierpiński.* 1. Congr. of Sets. 2. Translation of Sets. 3. Equiv. of Sets by Finite Decomposition. 4. D. into Two Parts. . . . 7. Paradoxical D's. . . . 10. The Hausdorff Paradox. 11. Paradox of Banach and Tarski. 12. Banach Measure. The General Problem of Measure. 13. Absolute Measure. 14. Paradox of J. von Neumann.

THE MATHEMATICAL THEORY OF THE TOP, by *F. Klein.* Well-known lectures on the analytical formulas relating to the motion of the top.

GRAPHICAL METHODS, by *C. Runge.*

INTRODUCTION TO THE THEORY OF ALGEBRAIC EQUATIONS, by *L. E. Dickson.* Dickson's earliest (1903) account of the subject, substantially less abstract than his later exposition. *From Dickson's Preface:* "The subject is here presented in the historical order of its development. The First Part (Chaps. I-IV) is devoted to the Lagrange-Cauchy-Abel theory of general algebraic equations. The Second Part (Chaps. V-XI) is devoted to Galois' theory of algebraic equations . . . The aim has been to make the presentation strictly elementary, with practically no dependence upon any branch of mathematics beyond elementary algebra. There occur numerous illustrative examples, as well as sets of elementary exercises."

—1954/1897/1912/1903-1967. 461 pp. 5¼x8. 8284-0209-4.
Four vols. in one. **$6.50**

NON-DIFFERENTIABLE FUNCTIONS, ***by A. N. SINGH.***
See HOBSON

DIOPHANTISCHE GLEICHUNGEN

By T. SKOLEM

—1938-50. ix + 130 pp. 5½x8½. 8284-0075-X. **$3.50**

COLLECTED MATHEMATICAL PAPERS

By H. J. S. SMITH

Something of Smith's stature as a mathematician may be gathered from one of many references to him in Bell's *Development of Mathematics:* "such men as Lagrange, Legendre, Gauss, Eisenstein, Dirichlet, Hermite, H. J. S. Smith, Minkowski, and Siegal."

Smith's famous *Report on the Theory of Numbers* (also published separately; see below) is included in the present work.

—1894-1965. 1,422 pp. 6½x9¼. 8284-0187-X.
Two vol. set. **$29.50**

REPORT ON THE THEORY OF NUMBERS

By H. J. S. SMITH

A little more than half a century after the publication of Gauss's *Disquisitiones,* H. J. S. Smith undertook to present an account of the status of number theory. The result was Smith's now classical *Report.*

Although it is a standard work and referred to frequently, the report has not been conveniently available to the practising mathematician. It was first published, in six parts, in the "Report of the British Association." It was then reprinted in the 1,400-page *Collected Mathematical Papers.* It is now, for the first time, available separately in book form.

—1894-1965. iv + 360 pp. 6½x9¼. 8284-0186-1. **$6.00**

INTERPOLATION

By J. F. STEFFENSEN

"A landmark in the history of the subject.

"Starting from scratch, the author deals with formulae of interpolation, construction of tables, inverse interpolation, summation of formulae, the symbolic calculus, interpolation with several variables, in a clear, elegant and rigorous manner . . . The student . . . will be rewarded by a comprehensive view of the whole field. . . . A classic account which no serious student can afford to neglect."—*Mathematical Gazette.*

—2nd ed. 1950-65. 256 pp. 5⅜x8. 8284-0071-7. **$4.95**